HANDBOOK OF X-RAYS

For Diffraction, Emission, Absorption, and Microscopy

Edited by

EMMETT F. KAELBLE

Monsanto Company
St. Louis, Missouri

McGRAW-HILL BOOK COMPANY

New York San Francisco Toronto London Sydney

HANDBOOK OF X-RAYS

 Library of Congress Catalog Card Number 63-23535

33200

1234567890MP72106987

CONTRIBUTORS

Isidore Adler, Goddard Space Flight Center, Greenbelt, Maryland.

Charles S. Barrett, University of Chicago, Chicago, Illinois.

Stanley F. Bartram, General Electric Company, Cincinnati, Ohio.

Eugene P. Bertin, Radio Corporation of America, Harrison, New Jersey.

Karl E. Beu, Goodyear Atomic Corporation, Piketon, Ohio.

L. S. Birks, U.S. Naval Research Laboratory, Washington, D.C.

Robert H. Bragg, Lockheed Missiles and Space Company, Palo Alto, California.

Victor E. Buhrke, Picker Nuclear Western, Inc., San Francisco, California.

William J. Campbell, U.S. Bureau of Mines, College Park, Maryland.

William T. Cave, Monsanto Company, West Caldwell, New Jersey.

George L. Clark, University of Illinois, Urbana, Illinois.

John F. Croke, Philips Electronic Instruments, Mount Vernon, New York.

Charles G. Dodd, Owens-Illinois Technical Center, Toledo, Ohio.

Arne Engström, Karolinska Institute, Stockholm, Sweden.

Howard T. Evans, Jr., U.S. Geological Survey, Washington, D.C.

Thomas C. Furnas, Jr., Picker X-ray Corporation, Cleveland, Ohio.

J. C. Grosskreutz, Midwest Research Institute, Kansas City, Missouri.

E. L. Gunn, Humble Oil and Refining Company, Baytown, Texas.

J. Read Holland, Sandia Corporation, Albuquerque, New Mexico.

J. E. Holliday, United States Steel Corporation, Monroeville, Pennsylvania.

William D. Johns, Washington University, St. Louis, Missouri.

Emmett F. Kaelble, Monsanto Company, St. Louis, Missouri.

J. Lawrence Katz, Rensselaer Polytechnic Institute, Troy, New York.

J. W. Kemp, formerly of Applied Research Laboratories, Inc., Glendale, California.

William R. Kiley, Philips Electronic Instruments, Mount Vernon, New York.

H. W. King, Imperial College of Science and Technology, London, England.

Paul Kirkpatrick, Stanford University, Stanford, California.

R. F. Kruh, University of Arkansas, Fayetteville, Arkansas.

Maurice C. Lambert, Pacific Northwest Laboratories, Battelle Memorial Institute, Richland, Washington.

T. C. Loomis, Bell Telephone Laboratories, Inc., Murray Hill, New Jersey.

Dan McLachlan, Jr., The Ohio State University, Columbus, Ohio.

Macon H. Miller, General Motors Corporation, Warren, Michigan.

John Moskal, Philips Electronic Instruments, Mount Vernon, New York.

Poen S. Ong, Philips Electronic Instruments, Mount Vernon, New York.

Donald R. Peacor, University of Michigan, Ann Arbor, Michigan.

Sri Raman, Rensselaer Polytechnic Institute, Troy, New York.

T. H. Rogers, The Machlett Laboratories, Inc., Stamford, Connecticut.

Mark R. Rosumny, Picker X-ray Corporation, Cleveland, Ohio.

Merlyn L. Salmon, FLUO-X-SPEC Analytical Laboratory, Denver, Colorado.

Rita Longobucco Samber, formerly of Radio Corporation of America, Harrison, New Jersey.

F. V. Schossberger, I.I.T. Research Institute, Chicago, Illinois.

C. M. Schwartz, Battelle Memorial Institute, Columbus, Ohio.

S. H. Simonsen, The University of Texas, Austin, Texas.

James W. Starbuck, Mallinckrodt Chemical Works, St. Louis, Missouri.

W. O. Statton, E. I. duPont de Nemours and Company, Wilmington, Delaware.

Irving R. Tannenbaum, Chematics Research, Reseda, California.

R. E. Thoma, Oak Ridge National Laboratory, Oak Ridge, Tennessee.

R. A. Van Nordstrand, Sinclair Research, Inc., Tulsa, Oklahoma.

L. F. Vassamillet, Mellon Institute, Pittsburgh, Pennsylvania.

Shirley M. Vincent, Bell Telephone Laboratories, Inc., Murray Hill, New Jersey.

W. R. Whitford, Philips Electronic Instruments, Mount Vernon, New York.

Tibor Zoltai, University of Minnesota, Minneapolis, Minnesota.

PREFACE

The utilization of x-ray methods of analysis is continuing to expand at a rapid rate. Imaginative use of exciting new techniques and vastly improved instrumentation has opened whole new areas of application to the x-ray worker. The possessor of an electron probe microanalyzer can quantitatively analyze a volume as small as a cubic micron. The x-ray spectroscopist can now determine elements as light as boron, and x-ray spectroscopy has taken its place among the techniques useful for trace analysis. Industrial processes can be monitored and controlled by automatic x-ray analyzers.

In all rapidly developing technical fields, much practical information and data tend to remain scattered in published articles, trade journals, and brochures. In this handbook an attempt has been made to provide a single-volume compilation of such information and data for a broad range of x-ray disciplines—diffraction, emission, adsorption, and microscopy. Subjects common to more than one of these disciplines are treated separately in Part 1, "Fundamentals": properties, generation, detection, and measurement of x-rays; geometry of crystals; laboratory design; and health and safety.

Part 3, "Determination of Crystal Structure," deals with a subject about which many volumes have been written. It is meant to fill the need for a concise guide which can be followed by scientists who are not primarily crystallographers. After discussing single crystal film and diffractometer techniques, the various steps in a structure determination are treated, and examples are given.

Primary emphasis throughout the book has been placed on practical, working information and data; theory has been held to the minimum required to explain basic practices. The book is intended to serve as a ready reference for practicing scientists, technicians, and students. It contains not only "hard-to-find-elsewhere" data valuable to specialists but also much basic information to serve as a guide to scientists new to the x-ray field.

It is fitting that the first chapter of this book should be written by Professor George L. Clark. To this distinguished scientist I express my special thanks for his dedicated teaching and for his guidance, encouragement, and friendship through the years. Without these I could not have undertaken this project.

I also wish to publicly thank all of my contributors whose skill, knowledge, and willing hard work made my job, for the most part, a pleasant and rewarding one. My special thanks are also due to Miss Barbara Prinz, Mrs. Sharon Courtney, and Mrs. Toni Long for their skilled secretarial help.

I am especially grateful to my wife, Martha, and to our children, Alan, Lynne, and Steven, for their patience, encouragement, and help throughout these years.

Emmett F. Kaelble

CONTENTS

Part 4. X-ray Emission Spectroscopy

Part 5. X-ray Absorption Methods

Part 6. Microradiography and X-ray Microscopy

Index follows Chapter 48.

HANDBOOK OF X-RAYS

Part 1

FUNDAMENTALS

Chapter 1

PROPERTIES OF X-RAYS

George L. Clark

University of Illinois

1. SOLVING FOR *X*, THE UNKNOWN IN X-RAYS

Even in a handbook such as this, which is primarily concerned with presentation of scientific facts exactly as they are known today, the most illuminating introduction to a discussion of the physical nature of one kind of radiant energy, upon which depend all the theoretical and practical applications, is a very brief historical approach. It must never be forgotten that x-ray scientists of the present and future generations stand upon the shoulders of giants who in the course of nearly 70 years have brought this area of radiation science to its present status.

There is no doubt now that x-rays, or Roentgen rays, have the fundamental characteristics of electromagnetic waves in which periodically variable electric and magnetic fields are perpendicular to each other and to the direction of propagation—hence transverse. Thus they are identical in nature in all respects except wavelength with visible light and all the other types of radiation which constitute the electromagnetic spectrum—ultraviolet, infrared, γ-rays from radioactive atomic disintegrations, microwaves, radio or Hertzian waves, on to the very long waves from alternating-electric-current generators.

The unequivocal establishment of the nature of these rays was not made in Röntgen's experiments following the discovery of "a new kind of ray" on Nov. 8, 1895. In his first communication, with remarkable simplicity, he described his observations of the properties of these rays: they were invisible; moved in straight lines; were unaffected by electric or magnetic fields, hence not electrically charged; passed through matter opaque to ordinary light (since they penetrated through the black cardboard around his cathode-ray tube); were differentially absorbed by matter of different densities or of different atomic weights (the foundation of radiography, microradiography, and microscopy, absorptiometry or absorption photometry (q.v.), and indeed of all the physical, chemical, and biological effects from absorbed radiation); affected the photographic plate as light does; produced fluorescence in certain chemicals, such as the barium platinocyanide screen with which the discovery was made, and in the glass wall of his evacuated tube opposite the cathode; produced electrification or ionization in gases; and were evidently produced by the stoppage of rays (identified by J. J. Thomson in 1897 as electrons) issuing from the cathode in his cathode-ray tube similar to many being used by physicists all over the world.

But along with these definitive characteristics of these rays carefully observed by Röntgen, other crucial experiments designed to establish similarity or differences from ordinary light were clearly demanded. Well established in 1895 were the fundamental optical properties of light: reflection from mirrors; refraction in prisms (change in direction in passing from air into glass, for example) by means of which a beam of white light could be spread out into a rainbow or spectrum of colors; diffraction by narrow slits or ruled gratings, also a method of producing spectra; and polarization, or constraint of the transverse vibrations in all directions to a single one. In spite of the best efforts of this skilled physicist and his contemporaries, no indubitable evidence of any of these four optical phenomena could be found. Hence the designation *X*—unknown—was assigned by the discoverer of Roentgen rays. Among the many theories proposed to account for the apparently unique quality of these rays, which seemed at the same time to be so closely similar to and so greatly different from light, were: vortex rings in the ether; waves with longitudinal vibrations, as in sound waves, instead of transverse as for light.

Inevitably other scientists studying the enigma found the essential experimental conditions to prove that x-rays can be polarized (Barkla, 1905, by scattering from carbon); diffracted by crystals (von Laue, Friedrich, and Knipping, 1912); refracted in prisms and in crystals, reflected by mirrors, and diffracted by ruled gratings (Compton, 1921–1922). Instead of being refracted in passing from a less dense (air) to a more dense medium (a glass prism or a crystal) in the same direction as light so that the index of refraction is always greater than 1, x-rays are deviated in the opposite direction by a very small amount so that the index of refraction is less than 1 by an amount as small as 10^{-6}. Thus total reflection from mirrors is observed only when the beam impinges at a very small grazing angle, a necessary condition understandably missed by Röntgen. Similarly the beam must graze a ruled diffraction grating if a spectrum is to be observed.

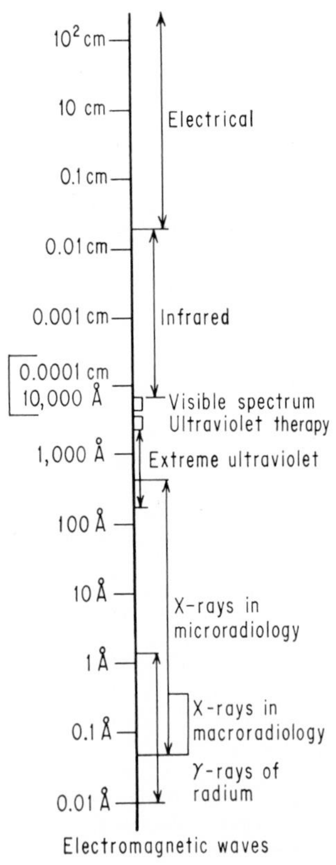

FIG. 1. The electromagnetic spectrum.

From 1895 to 1912, then, there seemed to be no analyzers capable of dispersing an x-ray beam into a spectrum. The spectacular Laue diffraction pattern of a ZnS crystal in 1912 immediately proved the electromagnetic-wave nature of x-rays and the ordered architecture of crystals with atoms lying on families of planes to constitute three-dimensional diffraction gratings, all governed by the simple Bragg law $n\lambda = 2d \sin \theta$ (which must be corrected for refraction in very accurate work), where n is the integer indicating order of the spectrum, λ the wavelength, d the crystal-lattice spacing of one set of planes, and θ the angle of incidence upon this set of planes. Roentgen spectrometry is the science of measuring λ values with a known crystal d; Roentgen diffractometry is the science of determining unknown values of d, and thereby crystal structures, with x-ray beams of known λ. In both cases the experimental measurement is that of angle θ. So in extensive tables, the wavelengths of x-ray emission lines in series (K, L, M, etc.) and absorption edges, characteristic of the chemical elements, afford the necessary information for chemical analyses, exactly as in the case of optical emission spectra, and for derivation of theories of atomic structure to account for the origin of spectra. The range of x-rays in the electromagnetic spectrum (Fig. 1), as excited in x-ray tubes by the bombardment of anode targets by cathode electrons under an accelerating high potential, overlaps the ultraviolet range in the order of 1,000 angstroms (1 Å = 10^{-8} cm) on the long-wavelength side, and the shortest-wavelength limit moves downward as voltages increase; at 1 billion volts, now readily generated, $\lambda = 0.00001 \times 10^{-8}$ cm $= 1 \times 10^{-5}$ Å, even shorter than the presently known range of γ-rays. An average wavelength used in research is 1 Å, or about 1/6,000 the wavelength of yellow light.

In the consideration of Roentgen rays as continuous electromagnetic waves, the fact must not be dismissed that they also appear to be propagated in discontinuous bundles, or quanta in accordance with the laws first enunciated by Planck and extended by Einstein over a half century ago. In diffraction, refraction, polarization, and interference phenomena x-rays, together with all other related radiations, appear to act as waves and λ has a real significance. Beams of corpuscular electrons and neutrons are diffracted so that they too have wavelengths. In other phenomena—such as the appearance of sharp spectral lines; a definite short-wavelength limit λ_0 of the continuous "white" spectrum (defined by $\lambda_0 = hc/eV$, where h is the Planck constant, c the velocity of light and x-rays, e the electronic charge, and V the accelerating voltage); the shift in wavelength of x-rays scattered by electrons in atoms (Compton effect); and the photoelectric effect—the energy seems to be propagated and transferred in quanta (defined by values of $h\nu$, where ν the frequency $= c/\lambda$) called photons. The dual aspect of all the ultimate particles of the universe—photons, electrons, protons, neutrons, and many others—is fundamental though it is obviously impossible to construct a satisfactory model of anything that is both a wave and a particle. The mathematics of the quantum and wave mechanics is adequate to define the atom and all these fundamental ultimate units of matter and energy.

2. X-RAY SPECTRA

As already indicated, the nature of x-rays remained mysterious from their discovery in 1895 until 1912 since there was no method of dispersing the radiation from the target of an x-ray tube into a spectrum such as characterized beams of light after refraction in prisms or diffraction by ruled gratings. By observations of absorption in screens of various elements of beams of x-rays generated at tube targets of known elements, many important facts of *quality* were recognized before wavelengths could be evaluated: increasing absorbability of rays the lower the voltage on the tube (or in other words a clear distinction between "hard" and "soft" rays) and the lower the atomic number of the target. In 1905, Barkla found evidences from absorption measurements of discontinuities in such properties, as if under proper conditions of excitation the energy of emission was distributed in groups instead of continuously. As a matter of fact, he devised the nomenclature used to this day, namely, K, L, M, N, O, P series, by analogy with series in optical spectra. But of course these absorption measurements did not permit resolution of characteristic spectral emission lines or absorption edges. It was the experiment of von Laue in 1912, proving that all crystals are three-dimensional diffraction gratings for x-rays, and the Bragg law, which opened the way for the construction of the crystal spectrometer. The basic principles of the original Bragg spectrometer still prevail in the most modern automatic instruments: a central movable table or goniometer upon which the crystal analyzer can be mounted and rotated to vary the angle of incidence θ; and an ionization chamber, or modern Geiger, proportional, or scintillation counter which can be mounted on a rotating arm the position of which may be read on a scale and thus record the angular 2θ value of any spectral emission line or absorption edge, and by the Bragg law the characteristic wavelength. Of course, a photographic plate or film could also be used as a registration medium. So the spectrometer was put to use by the Braggs, Moseley, Siegbahn, and many others to resolve beams into spectra with emission lines characteristic of the chemical element serving as a target in the x-ray tube. It was soon clearly understood that when a target is bombarded by a stream of electrons in an evacuated bulb, the electrons are stopped by the target atoms and their kinetic energy transformed into x-radiation by a process involving the inner electrons in atoms.

Characteristic Emission Spectra. If the potential on the x-ray tube is sufficiently high the spectrum of the emitted beam will show sharp lines superposed on a continuous background (the general, continuous, or "white" radiation discussed later).

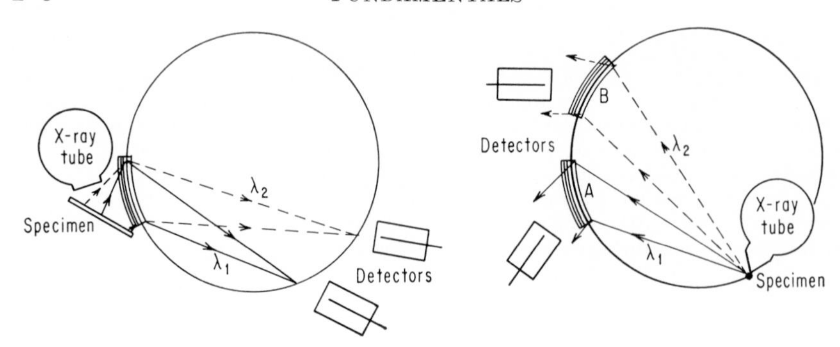

FIG. 2. Design and operation of two types of x-ray fluorescence spectrometers with curved crystal optics to measure two wavelengths. (*After L. S. Birks.*)

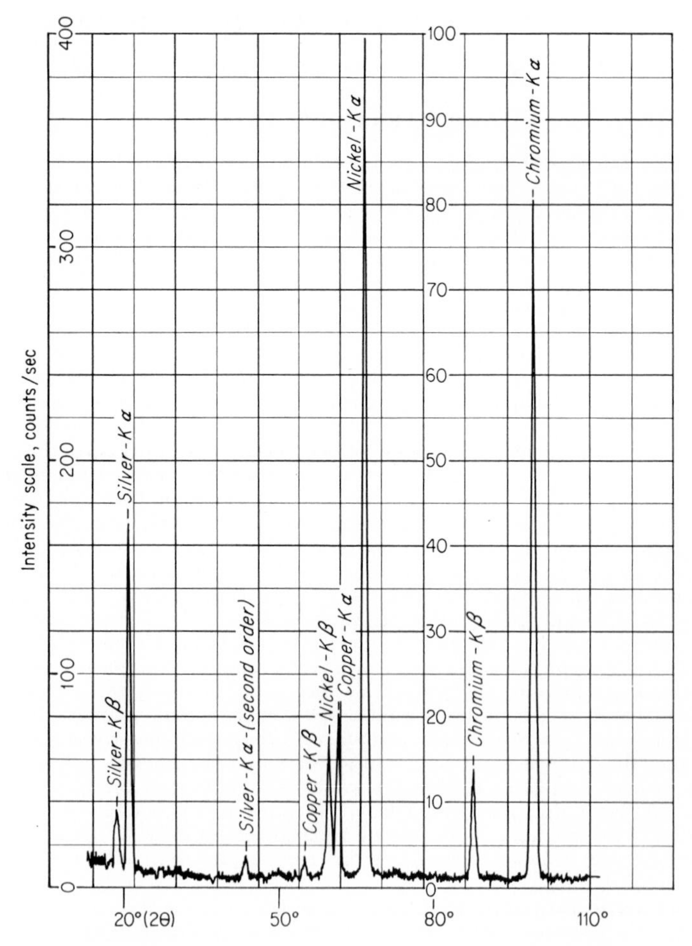

FIG. 3. Typical *K*-emission spectra of silver, copper, nickel, and chromium in an alloy.

These same characteristic x-rays are emitted as secondary fluorescent rays if a beam of primary x-rays with sufficiently short wavelengths falls upon an absorption screen containing the same element as the tube target—a technique almost universally used today for chemical analysis by spectrometry (see Part 4 of this handbook). Figure 2 is a diagram of a fluorescence spectrometer with curved crystal optics for simultaneous registration of two wavelengths. Figure 3 is a part of the *K* spectrum for a Ag-Cu-Ni-Cr alloy; Fig. 4 illustrates the fluorescence analysis of ethyl fluid, containing lead tetraethyl and ethylene dibromide. The characteristic emission lines appear in groups designated as the *K*, *L*, *M*, etc., series, beginning with the most penetrating or shortest-wavelength group. Each of the series of emission lines contains several definite lines of different wavelengths. Probably the most remarkable characteristic

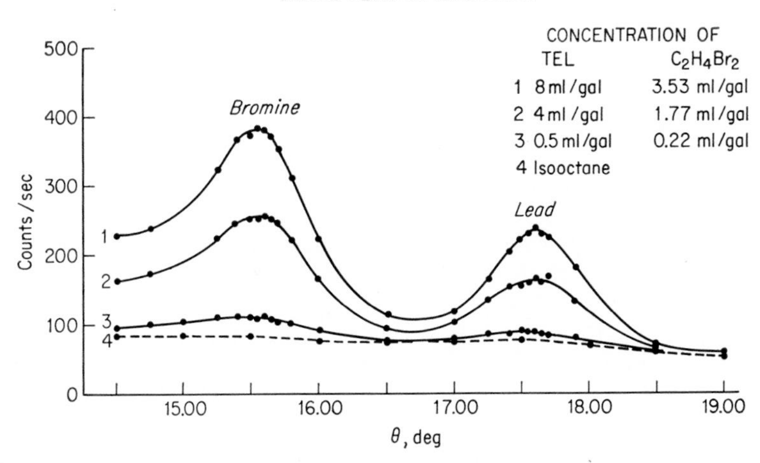

FIG. 4. Chemical analysis by fluorescence spectrometry of ethyl fluid containing lead tetraethyl and ethylene dibromide ($K\alpha$ of Br and $L\alpha_1$ of Pb).

is the uniform simplicity of these spectra. The *K* series of all the elements except the lightest consists of four principal lines: the γ (also designated β_2 and actually a very close doublet), β (really a close doublet β_1 and β_3), and the doublet α_1 and α_2, in the order of increasing wavelengths. The more numerous *L*-series lines (20 odd) are in three groups γ, β, α. At still longer wavelengths *M*- and *N*-series lines have been measured only for heavier elements. Tables 2 to 4, showing wavelengths as they have been measured for the chemical elements, appear on pages 1-14 to 1-19.

Characteristic Absorption Spectra. There are also absorption discontinuities observed in x-ray spectra whenever a beam of x-rays passes through absorbing material. The wavelengths corresponding to these discontinuities, or edges, are also characteristic of each of the chemical elements (see Figs. 5 and 6). All rays with wavelengths shorter than that of a given edge will be absorbed by the element to a markedly greater extent (or have a higher absorption coefficient) than rays with wavelengths longer than this critical value. A single absorption edge is associated with the *K* series, almost entirely independent of the physical or chemical state of the absorbing element, three with the *L*, five with the *M*, seven with the *N*, and five with the *O* series. It is a singular fact that all the lines in the *K*-series emission spectrum are excited simultaneously when the energy conditions permit. Thus the α doublet cannot be made to appear without the shorter γ and β lines. An examination of the wavelength corresponding to the *K* edge discloses the fact that this value is slightly shorter, or is associated with higher energy, than the shortest emission line for the same element. When the voltage on the x-ray tube is adjusted so that $Ve = hc/\lambda_{K_{\text{abs}}}$

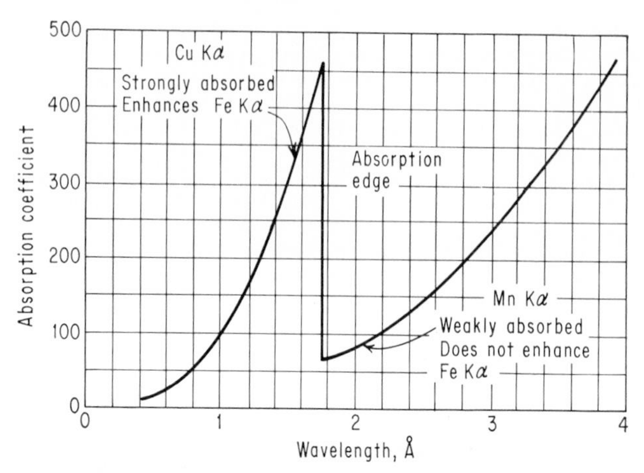

FIG. 5. Plot of mass absorption coefficient of iron against wavelength showing characteristic K edge of Fe at 1.7433 Å and enhancement of intensity for Fe $K\alpha$ by absorbing Cu $K\alpha$ and diminution by absorbing Mn $K\alpha$.

then the entire emission series appears. Thus the energy represented by these terms must be vitally related to definite processes occurring in atoms when electrons in the cathode-ray stream strike them or x-ray photons pass over them in fluorescence excitation. The L series can be generated in three groups, since there are three absorption edges or quantum wavelengths, the M series in five groups, etc. Table 1 gives absorption edges for the elements in Å and kev.

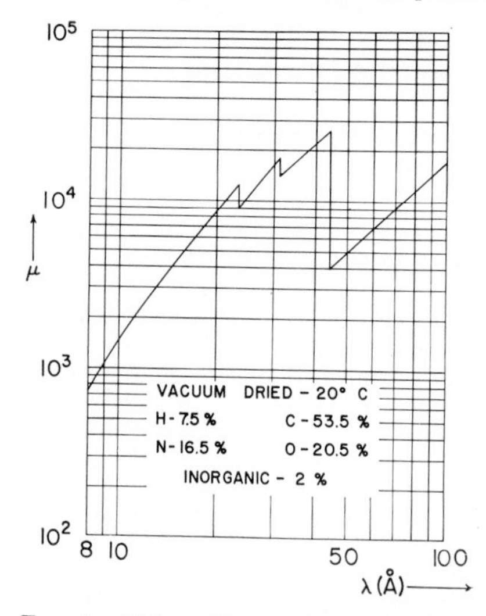

FIG. 6. Extraordinary plot of mass absorption coefficient for erythrocyte from the blood of man, containing H, C, N, and O, against wavelength up to 100 Å showing characteristic absorption edges of the low-atomic-number elements from left to right, respectively, oxygen, nitrogen, carbon (largest drop). (*B. L. Henke.*)

In spectrometers of high resolving power it has been known for several years that the supposedly single, sharp K edge for a given element does display a fine structure over a range of electron volts of energy, depending upon the valence state of the element. While this could be predicted from theory of atomic structure it had nuisance value until lately, when it was found to have immense importance in investigations such as the nature of catalysts. Many industrial laboratories utilize this apparently remote phenomenon to good advantage: MnO_2 and Na_2MnO_4 give quite different Mn K-edge fine structure; the latter adsorbed on silica gel is unchanged, and on carbon gives the MnO_2 fine structure. See Chap. 43 for a complete discussion of fine-structure absorption-edge spectroscopy.

Generalizations from X-ray Spectroscopic Data—the Moseley Law. Moseley, a brilliant British physicist at the age of twenty, was the first to recognize the essential simplicity of the K emission series, for example. He showed that the wavelengths of a given spectral line varied *continuously* step by step in proceeding from one atomic number to the next, and not periodically as is the case for so many atomic properties predicted from the periodic table. He found that if the square root of the reciprocal of the wavelength λ, or of the frequency or wave number (frequency ν = number of vibrations per second = c/λ; wave number $\tilde{\nu}$ = number of vibrations per centimeter = $1/\lambda$), is plotted against atomic number a practically straight line results for any given K or L line, absorption edge, etc. The simplicity of the relationship between spectral line or edge frequency and atomic number, which now we know is the number of external electrons or the net positive charge on the nucleus of atoms, has far-reaching significance. There is a fundamental relationship between all elements from hydrogen to lawrencium (103) in that all are constructed of the same building units in definitely progressing complexity. If x-ray spectral lines are to be ascribed to the innermost electronic levels in atoms, as is indicated by high frequencies and consequently large energy changes, these inner electrons must be essentially the same in number and disposition in all atoms, regardless of the number of electrons in the outer portions or the state of chemical combination. From a practical standpoint the Moseley law has permitted the prediction of characteristic wavelengths of unknown elements, and thereby the positive identification of newly discovered ones such as hafnium, rhenium, and many of the artificially produced species.

Another valuable generalization taken over from optical spectroscopy is the so-called *combination principle* involving sums or differences between the frequencies of various lines or edges [e.g., $\Delta\nu$ $(K - L_{\mathrm{III,II}})$ = the frequencies of the $K\alpha_1$, $K\alpha_2$ doublet]. Such facts as these point at once to the possibility of definite levels of energy in atoms, the differences corresponding to the frequencies of emitted or absorbed radiation, and doublets to a doubling of energy levels.

The Origin of Spectra and Atomic Structure. A brief consideration of the origin of spectra and atomic spectra might begin with the theory and then the fitting of experimental spectral information to the theory. Or the experimental facts can be used to *deduce* an adequate theory. Since x-ray spectrometry played such an essential role in the development of modern theories, the latter has been the order used here. First came the Bohr theory in 1914 with its revolutionary concepts introducing quantum theory, the motions of electrons in orbits around the atomic nucleus like a miniature solar system, the restriction to orbits whose angular momentum multiplied by $2\pi = nh$ in which stationary states the electrons are nonradiating, and emission or absorption of radiation only in the transition from one orbit, or energy level, to another. It is unnecessary here to trace the gradual change from the mechanical Bohr model, because of the introduction of the uncertainty principle and the dropping of determinism from physics, to the present vector or quantum-mechanical model which cannot be pictured in familiar terms of language but only as a mathematical concept. There is basically no change in the interpretation of x-ray spectra. The existence of individual, widely separated spectral series proves that there are a number of electron groups in atoms which differ considerably from each other with respect to orbital energy and the distance between the electrons and the nucleus. Therefore, the K series arises from the transitions from one of the outer groups (L, M, N, etc.) to the innermost (one-quantum, $n = 1$) K level if by ionization a vacancy occurs. For the emission of $K\alpha_1$ the initial state of the atom is the K-ionized state (one electron from the innermost completed shell expelled by impact of an electron or an x-ray photon), and the final state is an L_{III}-ionized state (one electron missing by transition into the K shell). For $K\alpha_2$ similarly the transition is from L_{II} to the single K level. The energies of the various orbits or shells are designated by the $h\nu$ values of the experimentally measured critical absorption edges ($1K$, $3L$, $5M$, etc.), since these are the energies required to lift an electron from its particular orbital out of the atom, thus to produce the characteristic internal ionizations preceding emission processes to return the atom to its normal state. The L-series lines of course result from transitions to the three closely related L energy levels from outer orbitals (there might seem to be 15 possible $L\alpha$ lines from $3L$ and $5M$ level combinations but some are excluded by a quantum theory of selection, as is the transition from L_I to K for a $K\alpha_3$ line). The K-series lines, for example, are not excited separately but appear together only when the kinetic energy E_K of the bombarding electron stream in the x-ray tube is equal to (or greater than) $E_K = Ve = h\nu_{K_{abs}}$. The L-series lines ($L\gamma$, $L\beta$, $L\alpha$) can all be excited if the voltage corresponds to $h\nu_{L_I}$, only those ($L\beta$, $L\alpha$) with wavelengths longer than L_{II} at a lower V, and still fewer ($L\alpha$) if the voltage corresponds to L_{III}. Thus an energy-level diagram can be constructed which will account for all emission lines and absorption edges, and all the nonnuclear electrons can be assigned to orbitals defined by characteristic principal ($K = 1, L = 2, M = 3$, etc.) and subquantum numbers for the multiple levels.

Intensities. It is self-evident that the intensities of spectral lines are measures of the probability of the electronic transitions which result in the emission of monochromatic radiation energy. Thus in the K series the ratios are 15:35:100:50, respectively, for γ, β, α_1, α_2. The ratio $L\alpha_1$:$L\alpha_2$ is 10:1. It is not surprising, therefore, that dependence rests so largely with $K\alpha_1$ and $L\alpha_1$ in quantitative chemical analysis by spectrometry and in diffraction where a known value of λ is required. Under excitation conditions just discussed, $L\alpha_1$ is used for the heavier elements since the voltage required to generate the K series may be inconveniently high and at the same time produce excessive background of general radiation.

Filtration. In diffraction analysis of crystalline structures it is generally necessary to know the value of λ in the Bragg equation since d is the unknown. Obviously a single wavelength $K\alpha_1$ or $L\alpha_1$ is highly desirable but a strictly monochromatic beam can be obtained only by reflection from a suitable crystal at the exact angle for the particular value of λ. Crystal monochromatization results in a very considerable loss of intensity of the primary beam. Recourse is taken then to a filter screen which will effectively absorb the γ and β characteristic rays but transmit the α doublet, a dichromatic beam which is not unduly complex, since the close doublet may be assigned an average wavelength. It is clear from the discussion of emission and absorption that an element is chosen for the absorber whose $\lambda_{K_{abs}}$ lies between $\lambda_{K\beta}$ and $\lambda_{K\alpha_1}$ of the element whose spectrum is used. Thus Zr filters are used for Mo K rays, Ni for Cu, etc. Figure 5 shows the example of the Fe K edge between Cu $K\alpha$ and Mn $K\alpha$ emission lines with consequent effects on the intensity of Fe $K\alpha$.

The Continuous Spectrum. In addition to the characteristic x-rays emitted by targets in stopping cathode rays, governed by the necessary energy conditions, a continuous spectrum is always generated whether or not the voltage is adequate, for example, to generate the K-series spectrum. When such spectral lines do appear they are superposed on the background of continuous, general, or "white" radiation. The outstanding property of the general radiation is that the smooth curve obtained by plotting intensity against wavelength independent of the atomic number of the target has a sharp short-wavelength limit (zero intensity) which depends only upon the voltage applied to the tube according to the Planck-Einstein quantum equation $Ve = h\nu_0 = hc/\lambda_0$ where V is the constant potential, e is the electronic charge, h is the Planck action constant, c the velocity of light, ν_0 the maximum frequency, and λ_0 the minimum wavelength occurring in the spectrum. This law was first applied to the continuous spectrum by Duane and Hunt in 1914, and found to be rigorously true. It is especially valuable in finding the minimum wavelength in any x-ray beam (at 1 billion volts λ_0 is 0.00001 Å) from $\lambda_0 = 12{,}400/V$. Similarly this law was used in the first accurate evaluation of the fundamental constant h, and it is always possible to determine V when the other factors are measured with a spectrometer.

The mechanism of production of noncharacteristic general radiation is by no means as simple and as well understood as the excitation of characteristic rays. Sometimes called bremsstrahlung, the spectrum is emitted as a consequence of the deflection of cathode electrons by the strong fields surrounding the nuclei of atoms in the target. If the electrons are stopped instantaneously at the target, the kinetic energy is transformed into the maximum radiation energy with wavelength λ_0. But there actually is a whole spectrum of longer wavelengths or lower frequencies emitted by electrons which lose only a part of their energy in a single encounter with a nucleus and experience many collisions with target atoms before being brought to rest. Besides being involved in all quantitative determinations of the true intensities of spectrum lines, the general radiation is a prominent factor in radiography, therapy, and other applications involving absorption, and it is employed in the Laue diffraction method of crystal analysis. It is evident that this phenomenon of the short-wave limit is one of the convincing proofs of the fact that x-rays like other rays in the electromagnetic spectrum have the dual character of waves and of quanta or photons.

Types of Excitation. In the foregoing description of excitation of x-rays primary attention has been given to the role of electrons as the ionizing agents for excitation of x-radiation in an x-ray tube, and the control of their kinetic energies by the accelerating potential. It has also been indicated that primary x-ray photons may excite secondary fluorescent x-rays. Thus to generate the K series it is essential that the primary x-ray energy $h\nu_p$ shall be equal to or greater than $h\nu_{K_{\text{abs}}}$ for the secondary rays. Although these may be only 0.1 to 0.01 times as intense as primary rays, there are manifold advantages, especially in the era of very sensitive detectors. With a permanently adjusted high-intensity tube, instead of the task of trying to paste

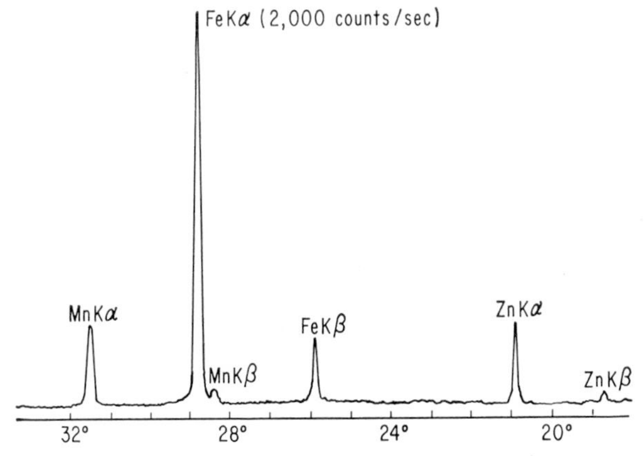

Fig. 7. Primary emission spectrum for a sample of ferrite (Fe, Mn, Zn) made in electron-probe microanalyzer on a sample volume of 1 cu micron. (*P. Duncomb.*)

samples onto targets for electron bombardment, a series of foil screens can be irradiated to produce desired wavelengths. Or the sample for spectrometric analysis (Figs. 3 and 4) is simply placed in the beam and the transmitted or reflected beam analyzed in the spectrometer as described in Part 4 of this handbook. The wavelengths for a given chemical element are, of course, identical whether excited by electrons in primary beams or by x-ray photons in the secondary fluorescent beams. The electron-probe microanalyzer (see Chap. 39) is now about the only survivor of primary-ray spectrometry. Figure 7 is a good example of a probe spectrum for a ferrite (Fe, Mn, Zn) from a sample volume of 1 cu micron.

Because of the extremely simple equipment involved there is a growing interest in radioisotope sources of x-rays. Of course, all radioactive disintegrations which are accompanied by γ-ray emission are of immediate interest since x-rays and γ-rays are identical in nature and have overlapping wavelength ranges. Hence the γ-rays from Co^{60} are indistinguishable from x-rays generated in the appropriate Mev range of high potential. Again the β-emitting isotopes can be used to bombard targets in direct excitation of x-rays in pocket-sized units. The best sources of β particles unaccompained by high-energy γ-rays are H^3 (tritium), Kr^{85}, $Sr^{90} + Y^{90}$, and Pm^{147}. These are combined with a target material which stops the β particles and allows emission of low-energy "bremsstrahlung." More practical is the generation of x-rays in isotopes by a process called *K capture*. In the isotope Fe^{55}, half-life 2.94 years, one of the s electrons in the K shell is captured by the nucleus, thereby transmuting the atom into the next lower atomic species in the periodic table, in this case Mn^{55}. In the process of filling the K vacancy the $K\alpha$ and $K\beta$ rays with a weighted-average wavelength of 2.07 Å are generated. This is a very useful source of radiation for

Table 1. Absorption Edges and Excitation Potentials

At. No.	Element	K edge		L_{I} edge		L_{II} edge		L_{III} edge	
		λ, Å	kev	λ, Å	kev	λ, Å	kev	λ, Å	kev
1	H	918	0.014						
2	He	504	0.025						
3	Li	226.953	0.055						
4	Be	106.9	0.116						
5	B	64.6	0.192						
6	C	43.767	0.283						
7	N	31.052	0.399						
8	O	23.367	0.531						
9	F	18.05	0.687						
10	Ne	14.19	0.874	258	0.048	564	0.022	564	0.022
11	Na	11.48	1.08	225	0.055	365	0.034	365	0.034
12	Mg	9.512	1.303	197	0.063	248	0.050	253	0.049
13	Al	7.951	1.559	143	0.087	170	0.073	172	0.072
14	Si	6.745	1.837	105	0.118	125	0.099	127	0.098
15	P	5.787	2.142	81.0	0.153	96.1	0.129	96.9	0.128
16	S	5.018	2.470	64.2	0.193	75.6	0.164	76.1	0.163
17	Cl	4.397	2.819	52.1	0.238	61.1	0.203	61.4	0.202
18	A	3.871	3.202	43.2	0.287	50.2	0.247	50.6	0.245
19	K	3.437	3.606	36.4	0.341	41.8	0.297	42.2	0.294
20	Ca	3.070	4.037	30.7	0.399	35.2	0.352	35.5	0.349
21	Sc	2.757	4.495	26.8	0.462	30.2	0.411	30.8	0.402
22	Ti	2.497	4.963	23.4	0.530	27.0	0.460	27.3	0.454
23	V	2.269	5.462	20.5	0.604	23.9	0.519	24.2	0.512
24	Cr	2.070	5.987	18.3	0.679	21.3	0.583	21.6	0.574
25	Mn	1.896	6.535	16.3	0.762	19.1	0.650	19.4	0.639
26	Fe	1.743	7.109	14.6	0.849	17.2	0.721	17.5	0.708
27	Co	1.608	7.707	13.3	0.929	15.6	0.794	15.9	0.779
28	Ni	1.488	8.329	12.22	1.015	14.2	0.871	14.5	0.853
29	Cu	1.380	8.978	11.27	1.100	13.0	0.953	13.3	0.933
30	Zn	1.283	9.657	10.33	1.200	11.87	1.045	12.13	1.022
31	Ga	1.196	10.365	9.54	1.30	10.93	1.184	11.10	1.117
32	Ge	1.117	11.100	8.73	1.42	9.94	1.248	10.19	1.217
33	As	1.045	11.860	8.107	1.529	9.124	1.358	9.39	1.32
34	Se	0.980	12.649	7.506	1.651	8.416	1.473	8.67	1.43
35	Br	0.920	13.471	6.97	1.78	7.80	1.59	8.00	1.55
36	Kr	0.866	14.319	6.46	1.92	7.21	1.72	7.43	1.67
37	Rb	0.816	15.197	5.998	2.066	6.643	1.865	6.89	1.80
38	Sr	0.770	16.101	5.583	2.220	6.172	2.008	6.387	1.940
39	Y	0.728	17.032	5.232	2.369	5.755	2.153	5.962	2.079
40	Zr	0.689	17.993	4.867	2.546	5.378	2.304	5.583	2.220
41	Nb	0.653	18.981	4.581	2.705	5.026	2.467	5.223	2.373
42	Mo	0.620	19.996	4.298	2.883	4.718	2.627	4.913	2.523
43	Tc	0.589	21.054	4.060	3.054	4.436	2.795	4.632	2.677
44	Ru	0.561	22.112	3.83	3.24	4.180	2.965	4.369	2.837
45	Rh	0.534	23.217	3.626	3.418	3.942	3.144	4 130	3.001
46	Pd	0.509	24.341	3.428	3.616	3.724	3.328	3.908	3.171
47	Ag	0.486	25.509	3.254	3.809	3.514	3.527	3.698	3.351
48	Cd	0.464	26.704	3.085	4.018	3.326	3.726	3.504	3.537
49	In	0.444	27.920	2.926	4.236	3.147	3.938	3.324	3.728
50	Sn	0.425	29.182	2.777	4.463	2.982	4.156	3.156	3.927
51	Sb	0.407	30.477	2.639	4.695	2.830	4.380	3.000	4.131

Table 1. Absorption Edges and Excitation Potentials *(Continued)*

At. No.	Element	K edge λ, Å	K edge kev	L_I edge λ, Å	L_I edge kev	L_{II} edge λ, Å	L_{II} edge kev	L_{III} edge λ, Å	L_{III} edge kev
52	Te	0.390	31.800	2.511	4.937	2.687	4.611	2.855	4.340
53	I	0.374	33.155	2.389	5.188	2.553	4.855	2.719	4.557
54	Xe	0.359	34.570	2.274	5.451	2.429	5.102	2.592	4.780
55	Cs	0.345	35.949	2.167	5.719	2.314	5.356	2.474	5.010
56	Ba	0.331	37.399	2.068	5.994	2.204	5.622	2.363	5.245
57	La	0.318	38.920	1.973	6.282	2.103	5.893	2.258	5.488
58	Ce	0.307	40.438	1.889	6.559	2.011	6.163	2.164	5.727
59	Pr	0.295	41.986	1.811	6.844	1.924	6.441	2.077	5.967
60	Nd	0.285	43.559	1.735	7.142	1.843	6.725	1.995	6.213
61	Pm	0.274	45.207	1.665	7.448	1.767	7.018	1.918	6.466
62	Sm	0.265	46.833	1.599	7.752	1.703	7.279	1.845	6.719
63	Eu	0.256	48.501	1.536	8.066	1.626	7.621	1.775	6.981
64	Gd	0.247	50.215	1.477	8.391	1.561	7.938	1.710	7.250
65	Tb	0.238	51.984	1.421	8.722	1.501	8.256	1.649	7.517
66	Dy	0.231	53.773	1.365	9.081	1.438	8.619	1.579	7.848
67	Ho	0.223	55.599	1.317	9.408	1.390	8.918	1.535	8.072
68	Er	0.216	57.465	1.268	9.773	1.338	9.260	1.482	8.361
69	Tm	0.209	59.319	1.222	10.141	1.288	9.626	1.433	8.650
70	Yb	0.202	61.282	1.182	10.487	1.243	9.972	1.386	8.941
71	Lu	0.196	63.281	1.140	10.870	1.199	10.341	1.341	9.239
72	Hf	0.190	65.292	1.100	11.271	1.155	10.732	1.297	9.554
73	Ta	0.184	67.379	1.061	11.681	1.114	11.128	1.255	9.874
74	W	0.178	69.479	1.025	12.097	1.075	11.533	1.216	10.196
75	Re	0.173	71.590	0.990	12.524	1.037	11.953	1.177	10.529
76	Os	0.168	73.856	0.956	12.968	1.001	12.380	1.140	10.867
77	Ir	0.163	76.096	0.923	13.427	0.967	12.817	1.106	11.209
78	Pt	0.158	78.352	0.893	13.875	0.934	13.266	1.072	11.556
79	Au	0.153	80.768	0.863	14.354	0.903	13.731	1.040	11.917
80	Hg	0.149	83.046	0.835	14.837	0.872	14.210	1.008	12.3
81	Tl	0.145	85.646	0.808	15.338	0.843	14.695	0.979	12.655
82	Pb	0.141	88.037	0.782	15.858	0.815	15.205	0.950	13.041
83	Bi	0.137	90.420	0.757	16.376	0.789	15.713	0.923	13.422
84	Po	0.133	93.112	0.732	16.935	0.763	16.244	0.897	13.817
85	At	0.130	95.740	0.709	17.490	0.739	16.784	0.872	14.215
86	Rn	0.126	98.418	0.687	18.058	0.715	17.337	0.848	14.618
87	Fr	0.123	101.147	0.665	18.638	0.693	17.904	0.825	15.028
88	Ra	....	....	0.645	19.229	0.671	18.478	0.803	15.439
89	Ac	0.116	106.759	0.625	19.842	0.650	19.078	0.782	15.865
90	Th	0.113	109.741	0.606	20.458	0.630	19.677	0.761	16.293
91	Pa	0.110	112.581	0.588	21.102	0.611	20.311	0.741	16.731
92	U	0.108	115.610	0.569	21.764	0.592	20.938	0.722	17.160
93	Np	0.105	118.619	0.553	22.417	0.574	21.596	0.704	17.614
94	Pu	0.102	121.720	0.537	23.097	0.557	22.262	0.686	18.066
95	Am	0.099	124.816	0.521	23.793	0.540	22.944	0.669	18.525
96	Cm	0.097	128.088	0.506	24.503	0.525	23.640	0.653	18.990
97	Bk	0.094	131.357	0.491	25.230	0.509	24.352	0.637	19.461
98	Cf	0.092	134.683	0.477	25.971	0.494	25.080	0.622	19.938
99	Es	0.090	138.067	0.464	26.729	0.480	25.824	0.607	20.422
100	Fm	0.088	141.510	0.451	27.503	0.466	26.584	0.593	20.912
101	Md								
102	No								

Table 2. *K*-series Diagram Lines

Line		$\alpha_{1,2}$	α_1	α_2	β_1	β_3	β_2	β_4	β_5	($O_{II,III}$)	(L_I)
Approx intensity		150	100	50	15		5	<1	<1	<1	<1
Li	3	230									
Be	4	113									
B	5	67									
C	6	44									
N	7	31.603									
O	8	23.707									
F	9	18.307									
Ne	10	14.615	.....	.....	14.460						
Na	11	11.909	.....	.....	11.574	11.726					
Mg	12	9.889	.....	.....	9.559	9.667					
Al	13	8.339	8.338	8.341	7.960	8.059					
Si	14	7.126	7.125	7.127	6.778						
P	15	6.155	6.154	6.157	5.804						
S	16	5.373	5.372	5.375	5.032						
Cl	17	4.729	4.728	4.731	4.403						
A	18	4.192	4.191	4.194	3.886						
K	19	3.744	3.742	3.745	3.454	.....	.....	.....	3.442		
Ca	20	3.360	3.359	3.362	3.089	.....	.....	.....	3.074		
Sc	21	3.032	3.031	3.034	2.780	.....	.....	.....	2.764		
Ti	22	2.750	2.749	2.753	2.514		.....	.....	2.498		
V	23	2.505	2.503	2.507	2.285		.....	.....	2.270		
Cr	24	2.291	2.290	2.294	2.085		.....	.....	2.071		
Mn	25	2.103	2.102	2.105	1.910		.....	.....	1.897		
Fe	26	1.937	1.936	1.940	1.757		.....	.....	1.745		
Co	27	1.791	1.789	1.793	1.621		.....	.....	1.609		
Ni	28	1.659	1.668	1.661	1.500		1.489	.....	1.489		
Cu	29	1.542	1.540	1.544	1.392	1.393	1.381	.....	1.382		
Zn	30	1.437	1.435	1.439	1.296	.....	1.284	.....	1.285		
Ga	31	1.341	1.340	1.344	1.207	1.208	1.196	.....	1.197		
Ge	32	1.256	1.255	1.258	1.129	1.129	1.117	.....	1.119		
As	33	1.177	1.175	1.179	1.057	1.058	1.045	.....	1.049		
Se	34	1.106	1.105	1.109	0.992	0.993	0.980	.....	0.984		
Br	35	1.041	1.040	1.044	0.933	0.933	0.921	.....	0.926		
Kr	36	0.981	0.980	0.984	0.879	0.879	0.866	0.866	0.871		
Rb	37	0.927	0.926	0.930	0.829	0.830	0.817	0.815	0.822		
Sr	38	0.877	0.875	0.880	0.783	0.784	0.771	0.770	0.776		
Y	39	0.831	0.829	0.833	0.740	0.741	0.728	0.727	0.735		
Zr	40	0.788	0.786	0.791	0.701	0.702	0.690	0.689	0.696		
Nb	41	0.748	0.747	0.751	0.665	0.666	0.654	0.653			
Mo	42	0.710	0.709	0.713	0.632	0.633	0.621	0.620	0.627		
Tc	43	0.676	0.675	0.679	0.601		0.590				
Ru	44	0.644	0.643	0.647	0.572	0.573	0.562	0.561	0.568		
Rh	45	0.614	0.613	0.617	0.546	0.546	0.535	0.534	0.541		
Pd	46	0.587	0.585	0.590	0.521	0.521	0.510	.....	0.517		
Ag	47	0.561	0.559	0.564	0.497	0.498	0.487	0.486	0.493		

Table 2. ***K*-series Diagram Lines** *(Continued)*

Line		$\alpha_{1,2}$	α_1	α_2	β_1	β_3	β_2	β_4	β_5	$(O_{\text{II,III}})$	(L_{I})
Approx intensity		150	100	50	15		5	<1	<1	<1	<1
Cd	48	0.536	0.535	0.539	0.475	0.476	0.465				
In	59	0.514	0.512	0.517	0.455	0.455	0.445	0.444	0.451	0.444	
Sn	50	0.492	0.491	0.495	0.435	0.436	0.426	0.425	0.432	0.425	
Sb	51	0.472	0.470	0.475	0.417	0.418	0.408	0.407	0.414	0.407	
Te	52	0.453	0.451	0.456	0.400	0.401	0.391	.....	.....	0.390	
I	53	0.435	0.433	0.438	0.384	0.385	0.376				
Xe	54	0.418	0.416	0.421	0.369	......	0.360				
Cs	55	0.402	0.401	0.405	0.355	0.355	0.346				
Ba	56	0.387	0.385	0.390	0.341	0.342	0.333	.....	0.338	0.331	
La	57	0.373	0.371	0.376	0.328	0.329	0.320	0.319	0.326	0.319	
Ce	58	0.359	0.357	0.362	0.316	0.317	0.309	0.307	0.313	0.307	
Pr	59	0.346	0.344	0.349	0.305	0.305	0.297				
Nd	60	0.334	0.332	0.337	0.294	0.294	0.287				
Pm	61	0.322	0.321	0.325	0.283						
Sm	62	0.311	0.309	0.314	0.274	0.274	0.267				
Eu	63	0.301	0.299	0.304	0.264	0.265	0.258				
Gd	64	0.291	0.289	0.294	0.255	0.256	0.249				
Tb	65	0.281	0.279	0.284	0.246	0.246	0.239				
Dy	66	0.272	0.270	0.275	0.237	0.238	0.231				
Ho	67	0.263	0.261	0.266							
Er	68	0.255	0.253	0.258	0.222	0.223	0.217				
Tm	69	0.246	0.244	0.250	0.215	0.216					
Yb	70	0.238	0.236	0.241	0.208	0.209	0.203				
Lu	71	0.231	0.229	0.234	0.202	0.203	0.197				
Hf	72	0.224	0.222	0.227	0.195	0.196	0.190				
Ta	73	0.217	0.215	0.220	0.190	0.191	0.185	0.184	0.189	0.184	
W	74	0.211	0.209	0.213	0.184	0.185	0.179	0.179	0.183	0.178	0.216
Re	75	0.204	0.202	0.207	0.179	0.179	0.174	0.174	0.178	0.173	
Os	76	0.198	0.196	0.201	0.173	0.174	0.169	0.168	0.173	0.168	
Ir	77	0.193	0.191	0.196	0.168	0.169	0.164	0.163	0.167	0.163	
Pt	78	0.187	0.186	0.190	0.163	0.164	0.159	0.159	0.162	0.158	
Au	79	0.182	0.180	0.185	0.159	0.160	0.155	0.154	0.158	0.153	0.187
Hg	80	0.177	0.175	0.180	0.154	0.155	0.150	0.150	0.153	0.149	
Tl	81	0.172	0.170	0.175	0.150	0.151	0.146	0.146	0.149	0.145	
Pb	82	0.167	0.165	0.170	0.146	0.147	0.147	0.141	0.145	0.141	
Bi	83	0.162	0.161	0.165	0.142	0.143	0.138	0.138	0.141	0.137	
Po	84	0.158	0.156	0.161	0.138	......	0.133				
At	85										
Rn	86										
Fr	87										
Ra	88										
Ac	89										
Th	90	0.135	0.133	0.138	0.117	0.118	0.114	0.114	0.116	0.113	
Pa	91										
U	92	0.128	0.126	0.131	0.111	0.112	0.108	0.108	0.111	0.107	

Table 3. *L*-series Diagram Lines

Line		α	α_1	α_2	β_1	β_2	β_3	β_4	β_5	β_6	β_7	β_9	β_{10}	β_{15}	β_{17}	γ_1	γ_2	γ_3	γ_4	γ_5	γ_6	γ_8	l	η	s	t
Approx intensity		110	100	10	50	20	6	4	1	<1	<1	<1	<1	<1	<1	10	1	2	<1	<1	<1	<1	3	1	<1	<1
Na	11	.....	.....	.....	.....	.....	.....	.....	.....	.....	.....	.....	.....	.....	.....	.....	.....	.....	.....	.....	.....	.....	410			
Mg	12	.....	.....	.....	.....	.....	.....	.....	.....	.....	.....	.....	.....	.....	.....	.....	.....	.....	.....	.....	.....	.....	260			
Al	13	.....	.....	.....	.....	.....	.....	.....	.....	.....	.....	.....	.....	.....	.....	.....	.....	.....	.....	.....	.....	.....	180			
Si	14																									
P	15																									
S	16																									
Cl	17	.....	.....	.....	.....	.....	.....	.....	.....	.....	.....	.....	.....	.....	.....	.....	.....	.....	.....	.....	.....	.....	67.84	67.25		
A	18	.....	.....	.....	.....	.....	.....	.....	.....	.....	.....	.....	.....	.....	.....	.....	.....	.....	.....	.....	.....	.....	56.212	56.813		
K	19	.....	.....	.....	.....	.....	.....	.....	.....	.....	.....	.....	.....	.....	.....	.....	.....	.....	.....	.....	.....	.....	47.835	47.325		
Ca	20	36.393	.....	.....	36.022	.....	.....	.....	.....	.....	.....	.....	.....	.....	.....	.....	.....	.....	.....	.....	.....	.....	41.042	40.542		
Sc	21	31.393	.....	.....	31.072	.....	.....	.....	.....	.....	.....	.....	.....	.....	.....	.....	.....	.....	.....	.....	.....	.....	35.671	35.200		
Ti	22	27.445	.....	.....	27.074	.....	.....	.....	.....	.....	.....	.....	.....	.....	.....	.....	.....	.....	.....	.....	.....	.....	31.423	30.942		
V	23	24.309	.....	.....	23.898	.....	.....	.....	.....	.....	.....	.....	.....	.....	.....	.....	.....	.....	.....	.....	.....	.....	27.826	27.375		
Cr	24	21.713	.....	.....	21.323	.....	19.429	.....	.....	.....	.....	.....	.....	.....	.....	.....	.....	.....	.....	.....	.....	.....	24.840	24.339		
Mn	25	19.489	.....	.....	19.158	.....	17.575	.....	.....	.....	.....	.....	.....	.....	.....	.....	.....	.....	.....	.....	.....	.....	22.315	21.864		
Fe	26	17.602	.....	.....	17.290	.....	15.742	.....	.....	.....	.....	.....	.....	.....	.....	.....	.....	.....	.....	.....	.....	.....	20.201	19.73		
Co	27	16.000	.....	.....	15.698	.....	14.269	.....	.....	.....	.....	.....	.....	.....	.....	.....	.....	.....	.....	.....	.....	.....	18.358	17.86		
Ni	28	14.595	.....	.....	14.308	.....	13.167	.....	.....	.....	.....	.....	.....	.....	.....	.....	.....	.....	.....	.....	.....	.....	16.693	16.304		
Cu	29	13.357	.....	.....	13.079	.....	12.115	.....	.....	.....	.....	.....	.....	.....	.....	.....	.....	.....	.....	.....	.....	.....	15.297	14.940		
Zn	30	.....	12.282		12.009	.....	11.225	.....	.....	.....	.....	.....	.....	.....	.....	.....	.....	.....	.....	.....	.....	.....	14.081	13.719		
Ga	31	.....	11.313		11.054	.....	.....	.....	.....	.....	.....	.....	.....	.....	.....	.....	.....	.....	.....	.....	.....	.....	12.976	12.620		
Ge	32	.....	10.456		10.194	.....	.....	.....	.....	.....	.....	.....	.....	.....	.....	.....	.....	.....	.....	.....	.....	.....	11.944	11.608		
As	33	.....	9.671		9.414	.....	8.930	.....	.....	.....	.....	.....	.....	.....	.....	.....	.....	.....	.....	.....	.....	.....	11.069	10.732		
Se	34	.....	8.990		8.735	.....	.....	.....	.....	.....	.....	.....	.....	.....	.....	.....	.....	.....	.....	.....	.....	.....	10.293	9.959		
Br	35	.....	8.375		8.126	.....	.....	.....	.....	.....	.....	.....	.....	.....	.....	.....	.....	.....	.....	.....	.....	.....	9.583	9.253		
Kr	36																									
Rb	37	.....	7.318	7.325	7.075	.....	6.788	6.821	.....	6.984	.....	.....	.....	.....	.....	.....	6.045		.....	6.754	.....	.....	8.363	8.042		
Sr	38	.....	6.863	6.870	6.623	.....	6.367	6.403	.....	6.519	.....	.....	.....	.....	.....	.....	5.644		.....	6.297	.....	.....	7.836	7.517		
Y	39	.....	6.449	6.456	6.211	.....	5.983	6.018	.....	6.094	.....	.....	.....	.....	.....	.....	5.283		.....	5.875	.....	.....	7.356	7.040		
Zr	40	.....	6.070	6.077	5.836	5.586	5.632	5.668	.....	5.710	.....	.....	.....	.....	.....	5.384	4.953		.....	5.497	.....	.....	6.918	6.606		

Nb	41	.....	5.725	5.732	5.492	5.238	5.310	5.346	.....	5.361	.....	.....	.....	.....	.....	5.036	4.654		.....	5.151	.....	.....	6.517	6.210		
Mo	42	.....	5.406	5.414	5.176	4.923	5.013	5.048	.....	5.048	.....	.....	.....	.....	.....	4.726	4.380		.....	4.837	.....	.....	6.150	5.847		
Tc	43																									
Ru	44	.....	4.846	4.854	4.620	4.372	4.487	4.523	.....	4.487	.....	.....	.....	.....	.....	4.182	3.897		.....	4.288	.....	.....	5.503	5.204		
Rh	45	.....	4.597	4.605	4.374	4.130	4.253	4.289	.....	4.242	.....	.....	.....	.....	.....	3.944	3.685		.....	4.045	.....	.....	5.217	4.922		
Pd	46	.....	4.368	4.376	4.146	3.909	4.034	4.071	.....	4.016	.....	3.792	3.799	.....	.....	3.725	3.489		.....	3.822	.....	.....	4.952	4.660		
Ag	47	.....	4.154	4.162	3.935	3.703	3.834	3.870	.....	3.808	.....	3.605	3.611	.....	.....	3.523	3.307		.....	3.616	.....	.....	4.707	4.418		
Cd	48	.....	3.956	3.965	3.739	3.514	3.644	3.681	.....	3.614	.....	3.430	3.437	.....	.....	3.336	3.137		.....	3.426	.....	.....	4.480	4.193		
In	49	.....	3.752	3.781	3.555	3.339	3.470	3.507	.....	3.436	.....	3.268	3.274	.....	.....	3.162	2.980		2.926	3.249	.....	.....	4.269	3.983		
Sn	50	.....	3.600	3.609	3.385	3.175	3.306	3.344	.....	3.270	3.155	3.115	3.121	.....	.....	3.001	2.835		2.778	3.085	.....	.....	4.071	3.789		
Sb	51	.....	3.439	3.448	3.226	3.023	3.152	3.190	.....	3.115	3.005	2.973	2.979	.....	.....	2.852	2.695		2.639	2.932	.....	.....	3.888	3.607		
Te	52	.....	3.290	3.299	3.077	2.882	3.009	3.046	.....	2.971	2.863	2.839	2.847	.....	.....	2.712	2.567		2.511	2.790	.....	.....	3.716	3.438		
I	53	.....	3.148	3.157	2.937	2.751	2.874	2.912	.....	2.837	2.730	2.713	2.720	.....	.....	2.582	2.447		2.391	2.657	.....	.....	3.557	3.280		
Xe	54																									
Cs	55	.....	2.892	2.902	2.683	2.511	2.628	2.666	.....	2.593	2.485	2.478	2.492	.....	.....	2.348	2.237	2.233	2.174	2.417	.....	.....	3.267	2.994		
Ba	56	.....	2.776	2.785	2.567	2.404	2.516	2.555	.....	2.482	2.382	2.376	2.387	.....	.....	2.242	2.138	2.134	2.075	2.309	.....	2.222	3.135	2.862		
La	57	.....	2.665	2.674	2.458	2.303	2.410	2.449	.....	2.379	2.275	2.282	2.290	.....	.....	2.141	2.046	2.041	1.983	2.205	.....	.....	3.006	2.740		
Ce	58	.....	2.561	2.570	2.356	2.208	2.311	2.349	.....	2.282	2.180	2.188	2.195	.....	.....	2.048	1.960	1.955	1.899	2.110	.....	2.023	2.892	2.620		
Pr	59	.....	2.463	2.473	2.259	2.119	2.216	2.255	.....	2.190	2.091	2.100	2.107	.....	.....	1.961	1.879	1.874	1.819	2.020	.....	1.936	2.784	2.512		
Nd	60	.....	2.370	2.382	2.166	2.035	2.126	2.166	.....	2.103	2.009	2.016	2.023	.....	.....	1.878	1.801	1.797	1.745	1.935	1.855	.....	2.675	2.409		
Pm	61	.....	2.283	.....	2.081																					
Sm	62	.....	2.199	2.210	1.998	1.882	1.962	2.000	1.779	1.946	1.856	1.862	1.870	.....	.....	1.726	1.659	1.655	1.606	.....	.....	.....	2.482	2.218		
Eu	63	.....	2.120	2.131	1.920	1.812	1.887	1.926	.....	1.875	1.788	1.792	1.800	.....	.....	1.657	1.597	1.591	1.544	1.708	.....	1.632	2.395			
Gd	64	.....	2.046	2.057	1.847	1.746	1.815	1.853	.....	1.807	1.723	.....	1.731	.....	.....	1.592	1.534	1.529	1.485	.....	.....	.....	2.312	2.049		
Tb	65	.....	1.976	1.986	1.777	1.682	1.747	1.785	1.577	1.742	1.659	.....	1.667	.....	.....	1.530	1.477	1.471	1.427	.....	.....	.....	2.234			
Dy	66	.....	1.909	1.920	1.710	1.623	1.681	1.720	.....	1.681	1.599	.....	.....	.....	.....	1.473	1.423	1.417	1.374	1.518	.....	.....	2.158	1.898		
Ho	67	.....	1.845	1.856	1.647	1.567	1.619	1.658	.....	1.622	.....	.....	.....	.....	.....	1.417	1.371	1.364	1.323	1.462	.....	.....	2.086	1.826		
Er	68	.....	1.785	1.796	1.587	1.514	1.561	1.601	.....	1.567	1.494	1.485	1.494	.....	.....	1.364	1.321	1.315	1.276	1.406	.....	.....	2.019	1.757		
Tm	69	.....	1.726	1.738	1.530	1.463	1.505	1.544	.....	1.515	.....	.....	.....	.....	.....	1.316	1.274	1.268	.....	1.355	.....	.....	1.955	1.695		
Yb	70	.....	1.672	1.682	1.476	1.416	1.452	1.491	1.387	1.466	1.395	1.384	1.392	.....	.....	1.268	1.228	1.222	1.185	1.307	1.243	1.250	1.894	1.635	.....	1.831
Lu	71	.....	1.619	1.630	1.424	1.370	1.402	1.441	1.342	1.419	1.350	1.336	1.343	1.372	.....	1.222	1.185	1.179	1.143	1.260	1.198	1.204	1.836	1.478	.....	1.776
Hf	72	.....	1.569	1.580	1.374	1.327	1.353	1.392	1.298	1.374	1.306	1.291	1.299	1.328	1.437	1.179	1.144	1.138	1.103	1.215	1.155	1.161	1.782	1.523	1.663	1.723
Ta	73	.....	1.522	1.533	1.327	1.285	1.307	1.346	1.256	1.331	1.264	1.247	1.254	1.287	.....	1.138	1.105	1.099	1.065	1.173	1.114	1.120	1.728	1.471	1.612	1.672
W	74	.....	1.476	1.487	1.282	1.245	1.263	1.302	1.215	1.290	1.224	1.204	1.212	1.247	1.339	1.098	1.068	1.062	1.028	1.132	1.074	1.081	1.678	1.421		
Re	75	.....	1.433	1.444	1.238	1.206	1.220	1.260	1.177	1.252	1.186	1.165	1.172	1.208	1.293	1.061	1.032	1.026	0.993	1.094	1.037	1.044	1.630	1.374		

Table 3. *L*-series Diagram Lines (*Continued*)

Line		α	α_1	α_2	β_1	β_2	β_3	β_4	β_5	β_6	β_7	β_9	β_{10}	β_{15}	β_{17}	γ_1	γ_2	γ_3	γ_4	γ_5	γ_6	γ_8	l	η	s	t
Approx intensity		110	100	10	50	20	6	4	1	<1	<1	<1	<1	<1	<1	10	1	2	<1	<1	<1	<1	3	1	<1	<1
Os	76	......	1.391	1.402	1.197	1.169	1.179	1.218	1.140	1.213	1.149	1.126	1.133	1.171	.....	1.025	0.998	0.992	0.959	1.057	1.001	1.008	1.585	1.328		
Ir	77	......	1.352	1.363	1.158	1.135	1.141	1.179	1.106	1.179	1.115	1.090	1.097	1.137	.....	0.991	0.966	0.959	0.928	1.022	0.967	0.974	1.541	1.285		
Pt	78	......	1.313	1.325	1.120	1.102	1.104	1.142	1.072	1.143	1.082	1.054	1.062	.....	1.166	0.958	0.934	0.928	0.897	0.988	0.934	0.941	1.499	1.243		
Au	79	......	1.277	1.288	1.083	1.070	1.068	1.106	1.040	1.111	1.050	1.021	1.028	1.072	1.128	0.927	0.905	0.898	0.867	0.956	0.903	0.910	1.460	1.202	1.352	1.414
Hg	80	......	1.242	1.253	1.049	1.040	1.034	1.072	1.010	1.080	1.019	0.986	0.996	1.041	1.090	0.897	0.876	0.869	0.839	0.925	0.873	0.880	1.422	1.164		
Tl	81	......	1.207	1.218	1.015	1.010	1.001	1.039	0.981	1.050	0.990	0.957	0.964	1.012	1.056	0.868	0.848	0.842	0.812	0.895	0.845	0.852	1.385	1.127	1.279	1.342
Pb	82	......	1.175	1.186	0.982	0.983	0.969	1.007	0.953	1.021	0.962	0.927	0.934	0.984	1.022	0.840	0.822	0.815	.....	0.867	0.817	0.824	1.350	1.092	1.244	1.308
Bi	83	......	1.144	1.155	0.952	0.955	0.939	0.977	0.926	0.993	0.935	0.898	0.905	0.957	0.989	0.814	0.796	0.790	0.761	0.840	0.791	0.799	1.317	1.058	1.210	
Po	84	......	1.114	1.126	0.921	0.929	0.908	0.948	0.900	0.967	.....	.....	.....	0.931	.....	0.786	0.771	0.764	.....	.....	0.765	.....	1.283			
At	85																									
Rn	86																									
Fr	87	......	1.030	.....	0.840	0.858	.....	.....	.....	.....	.....	.....	.....	.....	.....	0.716										
Ra	88	......	1.005	1.017	0.814	0.836	0.803	0.841	0.807	0.871	0.817	0.769	0.776	0.838	0.844	0.694	0.682	0.675	0.649	0.717	0.673	0.680	1.167	0.908		
Ac	89																									
Th	90	......	0.956	0.968	0.766	0.794	0.755	0.793	0.765	0.828	0.775	0.723	0.730	.....	.....	0.653	0.642	0.635	0.611	0.675	0.632	0.640	1.115	0.855	1.011	1.080
Pa	91	......	0.933	0.945	0.742	0.774	0.732	0.770	0.746	0.803	0.755	0.701	0.708	.....	.....	0.634	0.624	0.617	0.594	0.655	0.613	.....	1.091	0.830		
U	92	......	0.911	0.923	0.720	0.755	0.710	0.748	0.726	0.789	0.736	0.681	0.687	.....	.....	0.615	0.605	0.598	0.577	0.635	0.595	0.601	1.067	0.806	0.964	1.035
Np	93	......	0.890	0.901	0.698	0.735	.....	.....	.....	.....	.....	.....	.....	.....	.....	0.597										
Pu	94	......	0.868	0.880	0.678	0.719	0.669	0.707	0.691	.....	.....	.....	.....	.....	.....	0.579										
Am	95	......	0.849	0.860	0.658	0.701	.....	.....	.....	.....	.....	.....	.....	.....	.....	0.562										

NOTE: These *L*-spectra tables are incomplete. Additional very weak *L* lines for the heavier elements ($Z > 69$) may be found in Ref. 2, p. 190.

Table 4. *M* and *N* Series

Series		*M*	*M*	*M*	*M*	*M*	Min *M* excitation potential	*N*	*N*
Line		α_1	α_2	β	γ	1		γ^1	γ^3
K	19	.....	.....	......	......	680			
Cu	29	.....	.....	......	......	170			
Ru	44	.....	.....	......	26.85				
Rh	45	.....	.....	......	25.00				
Pd	46								
Ag	47	.....	.....	......	21.80				
Cd	48	.....	.....	......	20.46				
In	49								
Sn	50	.....	.....	......	17.94				
Sb	51	.....	.....	......	16.92				
Te	52	.....	.....	......	15.93				
Ba	56	.....	.....	......	12.700				
La	57	14.88		14.51	12.064				
Ce	58	14.06		13.78	11.534	18.38			
Pr	59	.....	.....	......	10.997				
Nd	60	12.675		Band	10.504				
Pm	61								
Sm	62	Band		Band	9.599				
Eu	63	Band		10.744	9.211	14.22			
Gd	64	Band		10.253	8.844	13.57			
Tb	65	Band		9.792	8.485	12.98			
Dy	66	Band		9.364	8.144	12.43			
Ho	67	Band		8.965	7.865	11.86			
Er	68	Band		8.593	7.545	11.37			
Tm	69	8.460		8.246					
Yb	70	8.139	8.155	7.909	7.023	10.48			
Lu	71	7.840		7.600	6.761	10.07			
Hf	72	7.539	7.546	7.304	6.543	9.69			
Ta	73	7.251	7.258	7.022	6.312	9.32	1.76		
W	74	6.983	6.990	6.756	6.088	8.96	1.84		
Re	75	6.528	.....	6.504	5.887	8.63	1.91		
Os	76	4.490		6.267	5.681	......	1.99		
Ir	77	6.261	6.275	6.037	5.501	8.02	2.07		
Pt	78	6.046	6.057	5.828	5.320	7.74	2.15		
Au	79	5.840	5.854	5.623	5.145	7.47	2.24		
Hg	80	5.666		5.452	......	......	2.32		
Tl	81	5.461	5.472	5.250	4.825	6.97	2.41		
Pb	82	5.285	5.299	5.075	4.674	6.74	2.50		
Bi	83	5.118	5.129	4.909	4.531	6.52	2.60	13.36	
Th	90	4.138	4.151	3.942	3.679	5.24	3.32	9.44	9.40
Pa	91	4.022	4.035	3.827	3.577	5.08			
U	92	3.910	3.924	3.715	3.480	4.95	3.54	8.81	8.76

NOTE: Additional weak *M* lines will be found in Ref. 2, p. 195.

absorption analyses, especially sulfur in gasoline and petroleum. Other K-capture sources are Ni^{59}, Rh^{102}, and Cd^{109}. In other isotopic areas protons and slow neutrons can be used as exciting agents with production of x-rays, β-rays, and γ-rays.

3. X-RAY WAVELENGTH TABLES*

Tables 1 to 4 have been prepared principally for the use of x-ray spectrochemists. Wavelengths are given in angstroms and excitation potentials in kev. Approximate intensities are given relative to the principal member of each series. Care must be taken in the use of x-ray wavelengths greater than about 4 Å since chemical-combination effects become significant at the longer wavelengths (see Chap. 34).

The sources of values presented in these tables are given in Refs. 1 to 12 at the end of this chapter.

The following conversion equations were used: x units to angstroms

$$\lambda_g(\text{in angstroms}) = \lambda_s(\text{in } x \text{ units}) \times 1.00206 \times 10^{-3}$$

angstroms to kev

$$E(\text{in kev}) = 12.4 \div \lambda_g(\text{in angstroms})$$

4. INTERACTION OF X-RAYS WITH MATTER

In the discussion of x-ray spectrometry, it was indicated that absorption of energy in atoms is necessary before there can be emission of characteristic radiation. Thus the characteristic K-absorption wavelength is a measure of the energy required to remove an electron from the K shell completely out of the atom so that a vacancy in the K shell is filled by an outer electron with accompanying emission of photons whose energy is the difference in energies of the two levels involved in the transition. In addition to this characteristic type of absorption there are processes of general absorption of x-rays entirely apart from the specific edge wavelengths for each element. For many years the term absorption has been applied to account for the disappearance of intensity, in a beam traversing matter, without regard to any mechanisms involved. Despite the continued general use of the term "absorption," "attenuation" is a more accurate term. Strictly speaking, therefore, we should speak of "attenuation coefficients" to avoid making a direct implication regarding either the disappearance of the photon or the deposition of energy resulting from an interaction.

Attenuation Coefficients. The attenuation of x-rays or γ-rays in passing through matter follows the exponential equation $I_x = I_0e^{-\mu x}$, or $I_0/I_x = \exp(\mu x)$, or $\log(I_0/I_x) = \mu x$, where I_x is the intensity of radiation of initial intensity I_0, after passage through x cm of homogeneous matter (also expressed as the number of photons N_x and N_0), e is the natural base of logarithms, and μ is a proportionality factor designated the linear attenuation (or absorption) coefficient. One of the most important useful applications of this formula is the expression of attenuation properties in terms of the "half-value layer HVL," or that thickness of the attenuating screen which diminishes the intensity of rays to one-half the initial value: $\frac{1}{2} = \exp(-\mu\,\text{HVL})$, $\text{HVL} = \log 2/\mu = 0.69/\mu$. It is obvious that, since μ must depend upon wavelength, the HVL is widely used to evaluate and compare qualities of x-ray beams as a function of voltage and other factors. When the log I of a monochromatic beam is plotted against the thickness of attenuating material, presupposing no characteristic absorption effects, a straight line holds, the slope of which is an indication of quality or wavelength (Fig. 8). If the beam has a cross section of 1 cm^2 then μ represents the fraction of energy removed per cc of the absorber traversed. Absorption in air of x-rays in all applications is of considerable importance. Figure 9 from National Bureau of Standards data gives the air-absorption correction factor as a function of distance and of voltage, which determines beam quality. Because of a more frequent interest in attenuation per gram instead of per cc, a more useful expression is

* Compiled by J. W. Kemp and reproduced with permission of Applied Research Laboratories, Inc., Glendale, Calif.

$I_x/I_0 = \exp(-\mu/\rho \cdot \rho x)$, where ρ is the density of the attenuating layer and μ/ρ is the *mass absorption coefficient*, which is a simple function of atomic number and of wavelength and is independent of physical state and temperature. The value of μ/ρ for a chemical compound is an additive function of the values for the constituent elements. For a given element, μ/ρ increases with an increase in wavelength of the impinging radiation, with discontinuities appearing at the K, L, M, etc., edges (see Figs. 5 and 6). Extended tables of μ/ρ values for all the elements over a wide range of wavelengths have been prepared from experimental measurement together with sound but empirical methods of calculation (see, for example, J. Leroux, *Advances in X-ray Analysis*, vol. 5, p. 153, Plenum Press, 1962). Figure 10 is a plot of μ/ρ values as functions of λ and of Z over limited ranges. Values of mass absorption coefficients of the elements in the wavelength region from 0.1 to 10 Å are given in Sec. 5 of this chapter.

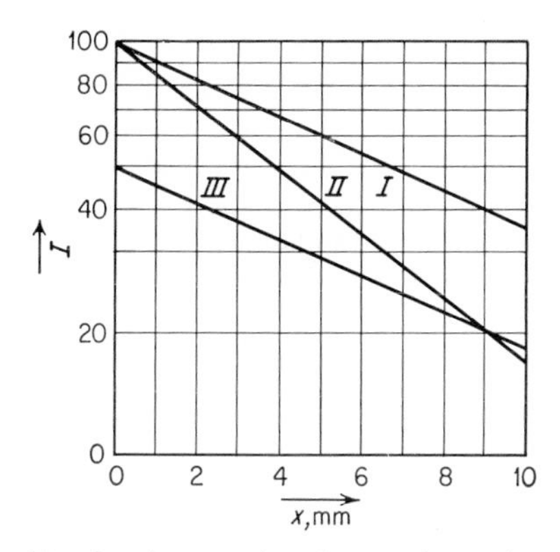

FIG. 8. Attenuation of x-rays in passing through matter with log I plotted against thickness x. The slope indicates quality or wavelength with I and III the same wavelength but different intensities, and I and II the same intensities initially but II longer wavelength.

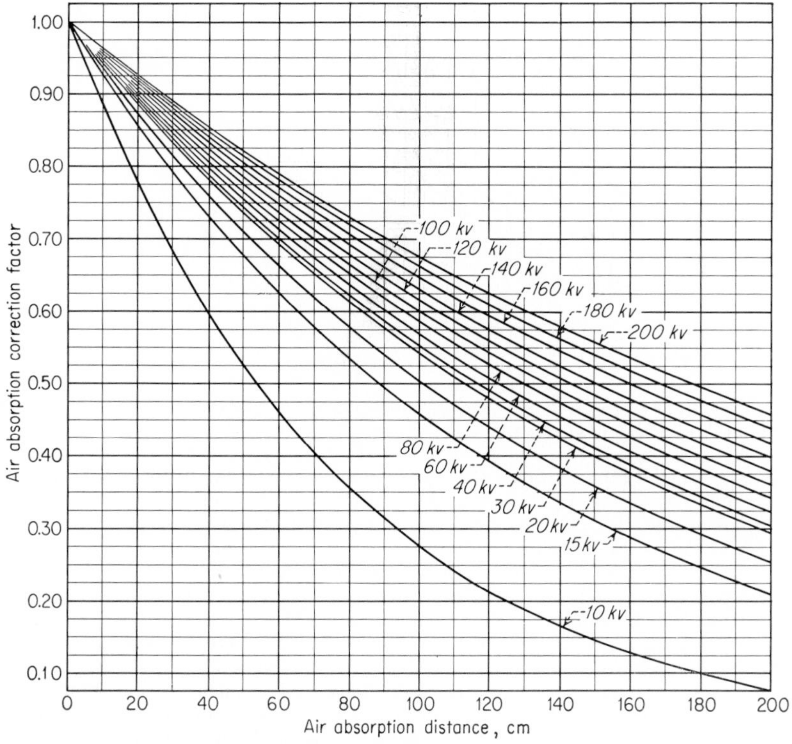

FIG. 9. Air-absorption correction factors as functions of distance and of excitation potentials (wavelengths). (*National Bureau of Standards.*)

Interaction Mechanisms. There are three interaction mechanisms which are responsible for most of the attenuation of x-ray photons: *photoelectric effect, Compton effect,* and *pair production.* In the photoelectric effect, the incident photon transmits its energy directly and completely to an orbital electron of the atom concerned. Part of the photon energy is consumed in supplying the binding energy of the orbital electron and any remainder is given to the electron as kinetic energy of $K_e = h\nu - W$, where $h\nu$ is the photon energy and W the binding energy. So the photon energy must

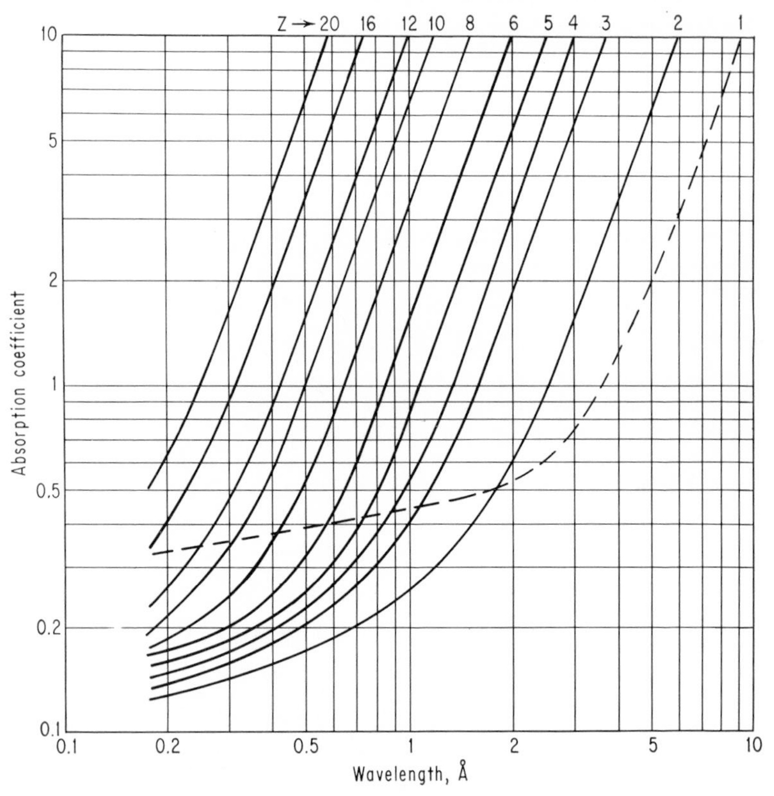

Fig. 10. Mass absorption coefficients as functions of wavelength and of atomic number over limited ranges. (*J. Leroux.*)

be as large as the binding energy for a given shell before electrons in that shell can absorb such photons and be ejected, as has been indicated previously for the production of characteristic fluorescent radiation by electron transitions to fill the vacancy created by the electron removal from its orbital. The Compton effect, or scattering, occurs when an incident photon appears to be deflected or scattered by an electron, much like the collision between billiard balls. The outgoing photon has less energy than the incident photon by an amount which is imparted to the recoiling electron, and moves in a different direction. The Compton-scattering formula is $\Delta\lambda = \lambda - \lambda' = h/mc(1 - \cos\phi)$, where λ is the wavelength of the incident photon and λ' of the scattered photon, ϕ is the angle between directions of these photons, and the constant $h/mc = 0.0242$ Å. Figure 11 is a vectorial picture of the loss of photon energy in Compton scattering from initial $h\nu_0(1)$ with change in ϕ. The lower arrows indicate the corresponding energies imparted to recoil electrons. Photons with $\lambda \gg 0.0242$ Å are not greatly changed by a Compton-scattering event, and hence very little energy is transmittable to the secondary electron (the so-called unmodified scattered radiation), but for $\lambda \ll 0.0242$ for very-high-energy incident photons $\lambda' = 0.0242$ Å at 90°, nearly independent of λ. In pair production the incident photon interacts mainly with the nucleus of an atom, and disappears completely. In its place appear an electron and its positively charged twin, the positron. Obviously the process is impossible at photon energies below that required to create the two particle masses. The Einstein relation $E = mc^2$ allows evaluation of the threshold energy. For an electron $mc^2 = 0.511$ Mev; so for the pair the incident photon must carry at least 1.02 Mev. Electron and positron transfer energy in passing atoms and come to the end of their ranges. At this point the positron joins with any nearby electron, resulting in mutual annihilation and the creation of two photons each of energy equal to 0.511 Mev. The dependence of these phenomena along with others, such as triplet production, is known from theory and experiment.

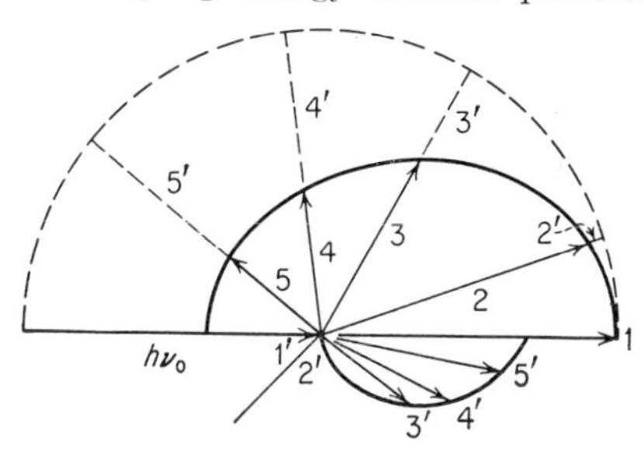

Fig. 11. Vectorial diagram of Compton scattering with energies represented by lengths and directions of full lines and losses by dashed lines, as a function of the angle ϕ between primary beam and scattered beam. Lower arrows indicate corresponding energies imparted to recoil electrons.

From the foregoing complex mechanisms it is evident that the photoelectric or true absorption effect is most important at the lowest energies, pair production at the highest, and the Compton effect predominant in between (say 40 to 400 kv) (see Fig. 12). One interesting consequence is the fact that μ/ρ values for various materials

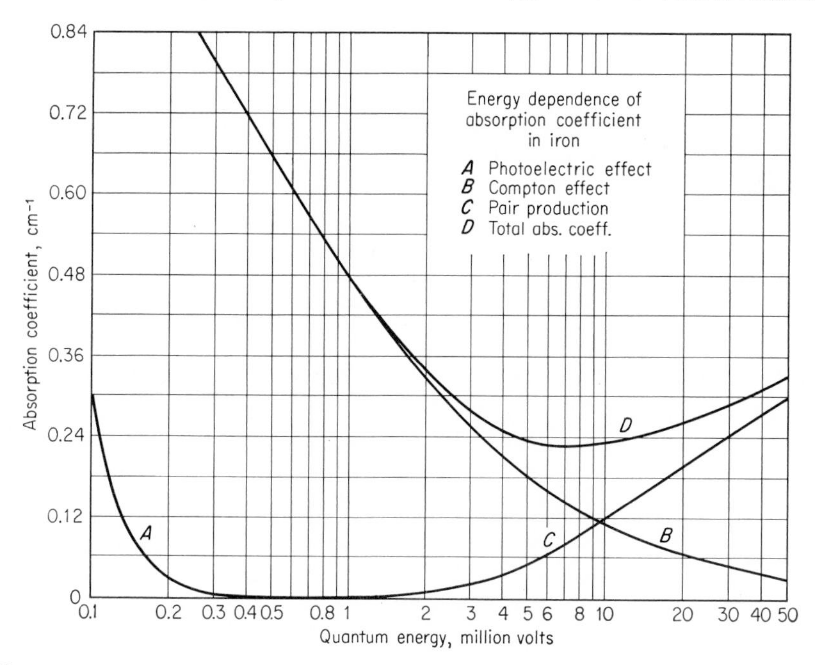

Fig. 12. Interaction mechanisms of x-rays with matter, showing energy dependence of absorption coefficient in iron.

like iron instead of decreasing linearly with log of energy of radiation level off in the range of 1 Mev and thus become essentially independent of wavelength and of thickness of attenuating screen, with resulting absolute sensitivity in radiographs (the least detectable flaw is independent of the metal thickness, aided by the fact that scattering by the Compton effect at these voltages is negligible).

Scattering and Its Uses. From the preceding presentation it would be expected that scattered x-rays whether from crystals or amorphous materials might have primarily nuisance value in the matter of background corrections for intensity measurements of spectral lines and diffraction peaks. However, a distinction is to be made between coherent—Rayleigh or unmodified—and incoherent—Compton or modified—scattering. The former has been used to detect heavy elements in a low-atomic-number matrix. But the ingenious use of scattering can best be illustrated by the analysis of petroleum products for hydrogen and carbon [Dwiggins, *Anal. Chem.*, **33**: 67 (1961); *Encyclopedia of X-rays and Gamma Rays*, p. 113, Reinhold Publishing Corporation, New York, 1963]. Many x-ray spectrometers use tungsten-target tubes and produce a high-intensity coherent scatter peak at the wavelength corresponding to $L\alpha_1$ (the exciting potential is not high enough to generate the K series at 69,300 volts) for substances rich in low-atomic-number elements. An incoherent scatter peak is observed at a wavelength slightly greater than that of the coherent characteristic scatter. The intensities are of the same order of magnitude. But the use of the intensity ratio of coherent to incoherent scatter is remarkably sensitive to changes in carbon-to-hydrogen ratios in the sample. The background near the scatter peaks is produced by scatter of the general or white spectrum from the x-ray tube but varies only very slightly with wavelength. By calibration of ratios with samples of known C-H composition and with suitable corrections for other elements such as sulfur, the accuracy of this method, so valuable in the petroleum industry, for example, is very close to that of the far more laborious and time-consuming microcombustion technique.

Low-angle Scattering. A special case of scattering of x-rays is that at very small angles for various crystalline and noncrystalline materials consisting of small particles or having fairly uniform voids. This effect is often designated Guinier scattering after the discoverer, who derived the theory and equations for the evaluation of the particle sizes and shapes. A detailed presentation appears in Chap. 16.

Crystal Diffraction as Scattering. It is obvious that the diffraction of x-rays by crystals is a special manifestation of coherent scattering of beams and very definite directions as defined by the Bragg law. What appears to be specular reflection of x-rays from the cleavage face of a calcite rhomb, for example, when the beam impinges at a certain exact angle, is actually an extremely complex case of scattering of the beam by atoms and electrons, but by virtue of lattice geometry the secondary scattered beams are in phase and have additive amplitude only in the direction defined by the Bragg law. Thus the final steps in complete single-crystal analysis depend upon the intensities of diffraction interferences from various sets of planes in the crystal. The intensities in turn depend upon scattering factors of the individual atoms and the combination in characteristic geometric relationships in the crystal unit cell. These are defined as follows:

f_0, *the atomic scattering factor*, is the ratio of the amplitude of waves scattered by the atom to that of a free classically scattering electron. If the atom were a point then, of course, $f_0 = Z$, the atomic number or the number of external electrons. However, the atom has a diameter comparable in size with the x-ray wavelengths. Hence the secondary wavelets from the different electrons in the orbitals in space have phase differences so that in certain directions there is a strengthening and in others weakening of radiation. The result is that f_0 is a function of $\sin(\theta/\lambda)$ or, completely expressed,

$$f_0 = \int_0^\infty \frac{U(r) \sin 4\pi r \sin(\theta/\lambda)}{4\pi r \sin(\theta/\lambda)}\, dr$$

where $U(r)$ is the density of electrons between r and $r + dr$. For small values of θ, f_0 becomes equal to Z. Values of f_0 are known with considerable accuracy and are listed in the *International Tables for X-ray Crystallography.* Particularly important are the values for cesium (55) inasmuch as f_0 for elements of higher atomic number can be calculated by multiplying f_0 for Cs by $Z/55$. Values correspond to atoms at rest at absolute zero; hence for ordinary temperature at which the intensities are appreciably weakened on account of thermal oscillations a correction deduced by Debye and Waller must be used: $f_t = f_0 e^{-M}$.

F, the crystal-structure factor, the scattering intensity of a lattice unit cell which contains a single atom, is expressed by $f_0^2 e^{-M}$. If more atoms are present in the cell, as is the actual case, then the phase differences of scattered waves from different atoms must be taken into account. The crystal-structure factor F, a pure number representing a number of electrons, involves the coordinates of atoms in the unit cell. Thus for a cell containing N atoms and with f_n as the atomic scattering factor of the nth atom,

$$F = \sum_{n=1}^{N} f_n \exp 2\pi i(hx_n + ky_n + lz_n)$$

where $i = \sqrt{-1}$ and the coordinates of a given point xyz are expressed as fractional parts of the axial lengths a, b, c. F is a complex quantity, so that the absolute value of $|F|^2$ to which intensity is proportional is expressed as follows:

$$|F(hkl)|^2 = [\Sigma\Sigma f_n \cos 2\pi(hx/a + ky/b + lz/c)]^2 + [\Sigma\Sigma f_n \sin 2\pi(hx/a + ky/b + lz/c)]^2$$

Values of the cosine and sine terms are characteristic of each of the 230 space groups, since they depend upon the equivalent positions in unit cells, and they are listed in *Structure Factor Tables* by Lonsdale. For crystals with a center of symmetry the sine term becomes zero and the calculations are greatly simplified. $F(hkl)$, the crystal-structure factor for any set of planes hkl, becomes the indispensable quantity for the final interpretation of the intensities of diffraction interferences in terms of the actual ultimate crystalline and molecular structures as demonstrated in Part 3 of this handbook. Since basically $F(hkl)$ may be calculated from experimental values of intensity with several correction factors (Lorentz, polarization, etc.), and also calculated from assumed coordinate positions, by the formulas listed above, here lies the test of analysis. Then the $F(hkl)$ values serve as the coefficients in a Fourier series which is designed to determine electron densities at various points and thereby to construct an electron-density contour map of a unit cell in three dimensions or projected upon one plane as a two-dimensional map. Such is the course of the last, the most difficult but fascinating, step in the analysis of the architecture and prevailing motif in crystals.

5. VALUES OF MASS ABSORPTION COEFFICIENTS OF THE ELEMENTS IN THE REGION FROM 0.1 TO 10 Å*

The absorption coefficients in Table 5 were obtained from values in the literature by extrapolation and interpolation. The accuracy decreases as wavelength and atomic number increase. In the region of wavelengths above the L edges, data are scarce, and different sources disagree by as much as a factor of 2. New measurements are needed, especially at longer wavelengths. With the improved methods of measuring intensity now available, it should be possible to make these easily and reliably.

The heavy lines in the table denote the location of the absorption edges.

6. IONIZING PROPERTIES AND DOSIMETRY OF X-RAYS

In concluding the study of the properties of x-rays and their interaction with matter—excitation, absorption, attenuation, scattering, etc.—it is well to remember that the liberation of photons and electrons of irradiated matter may have some irreversible consequences in changing that matter or in the most general sense of

* Reprinted with permission from H. A. Liebhafsky, H. G. Pfeiffer, E. H. Winslow, and P. D. Zemany, *X-ray Absorption and Emission in Analytical Chemistry,* pp. 313–317, John Wiley & Sons, Inc., New York, 1960.

Table 5. Mass

At. No.	Element	0.1	0.15	0.2	0.25	0.3	0.4	0.5	0.6	0.7	0.8	0.9	1.0
		Wavelength, A											
1	H	0.29	0.32	0.34	0.36	0.37	0.38	0.40	0.42	0.43	0.44	0.44	0.45
2	He	0.114	0.124	0.132	0.140	0.146	0.159	0.173	0.186	0.203	0.222	0.241	0.255
3	Li	0.124	0.132	0.143	0.153	0.163	0.180	0.198	0.223	0.254	0.302	0.358	0.428
4	Be	0.131	0.142	0.153	0.162	0.171	0.185	0.210	0.240	0.292	0.362	0.445	0.57
5	B	0.138	0.152	0.164	0.173	0.182	0.198	0.222	0.277	0.355	0.470	0.61	0.76
6	C	0.142	0.155	0.170	0.186	0.204	0.240	0.305	0.41	0.55	0.75	1.05	1.40
7	N	0.144	0.159	0.175	0.195	0.216	0.288	0.395	0.62	0.89	1.25	1.73	2.20
8	O	0.145	0.162	0.181	0.206	0.236	0.345	0.508	0.87	1.25	1.80	2.40	3.20
9	F	0.147	0.165	0.192	0.228	0.270	0.417	0.675	1.20	1.85	2.60	3.40	4.40
10	Ne	0.149	0.169	0.208	0.256	0.319	0.508	0.865	1.55	2.50	3.50	4.75	6.50
11	Na	0.150	0.175	0.228	0.287	0.380	0.630	1.18	2.05	3.25	4.75	6.70	8.80
12	Mg	0.152	0.190	0.251	0.330	0.445	0.78	1.47	2.70	4.30	6.50	9.10	11.7
13	Al	0.155	0.205	0.277	0.380	0.525	0.97	1.82	3.70	5.75	8.80	11.8	15.2
14	Si	0.159	0.215	0.310	0.442	0.615	1.22	2.25	4.65	7.20	11.1	14.2	18.2
15	P	0.165	0.228	0.346	0.510	0.725	1.48	2.80	5.45	8.30	13.3	16.5	21.7
16	S	0.170	0.241	0.392	0.592	0.855	1.78	3.45	6.40	9.6	15.5	19.3	26.0
17	Cl	0.176	0.260	0.433	0.667	1.02	2.13	4.25	7.45	11.3	18.5	22.6	29.7
18	A	0.183	0.278	0.490	0.76	1.21	2.62	5.08	8.60	13.2	21.1	26.4	34.4
19	K	0.191	0.301	0.542	0.86	1.39	3.02	5.75	10.2	15.3	24	30.7	40
20	Ca	0.200	0.327	0.601	0.98	1.63	3.45	6.50	11.5	18.0	26.5	36	48
21	Sc	0.210	0.358	0.667	1.12	1.85	3.95	7.4	13.1	20.2	30	41.0	55
22	Ti	0.221	0.395	0.740	1.26	2.10	4.50	8.4	14.8	22.7	34	47	62.5
23	V	0.231	0.431	0.830	1.42	2.37	5.15	9.6	16.8	25.5	38	54	71.5
24	Cr	0.241	0.480	0.925	1.60	2.68	5.88	10.8	18.9	28.7	42.5	60.3	80.5
25	Mn	0.253	0.528	1.03	1.79	3.05	6.65	12.3	21.4	32.2	47.5	66.6	90
26	Fe	0.265	0.58	1.16	2.02	3.45	7.6	14.1	23.8	36.0	53.2	74	100
27	Co	0.285	0.64	1.28	2.25	3.80	8.35	15.5	26.6	39.8	58.2	80.5	110
28	Ni	0.303	0.71	1.42	2.51	4.15	9.20	17.0	29.6	43.6	64	87.5	121
29	Cu	0.328	0.785	1.57	2.79	4.55	10.1	18.6	32.4	48.5	70	95.5	130
30	Zn	0.350	0.818	1.76	3.07	5.00	11.1	20.6	35.3	53	76.5	106	141
31	Ga	0.378	0.94	1.91	3.36	5.50	12.2	22.3	38.7	59	82	112	152
32	Ge	0.404	1.02	2.06	3.67	6.15	13.3	24.4	42.1	63.5	88	120	163
33	As	0.427	1.12	2.22	4.01	6.45	14.6	26.3	45.1	68.5	94	129	175
34	Se	0.472	1.21	2.41	4.33	7.00	15.8	28.5	48.4	74	101	138	33.2
35	Br	0.502	1.31	2.60	4.70	7.60	17.0	30.8	52.0	79.5	108	149	35.2
36	Kr	0.535	1.41	2.81	5.05	8.30	18.3	33.3	55.5	86	116	26.5	37.5
37	Rb	0.572	1.50	3.03	5.45	9.05	19.7	35.9	59.5	93	125	28.0	40.2
38	Sr	0.61	1.61	3.28	5.82	9.80	21.3	38.7	63	100	22	29.8	43
39	Y	0.65	1.72	3.52	6.20	10.3	22.6	41.3	67.5	108	23.2	32	46
40	Zr	0.69	1.83	3.73	6.60	11.0	24.0	43.5	72	16.8	24.5	33.8	49
41	Nb	0.74	1.93	4.00	7.02	11.7	25.4	46.0	76	17.8	26	36.0	51.8
42	Mo	0.79	2.04	4.29	7.50	12.4	26.9	49.0	81	19.0	27.7	38.4	54.8
43	Tc	0.84	2.15	4.55	7.95	13.1	28.6	50.5	14.2	20.3	29.5	41.0	58
44	Ru	0.89	2.27	4.70	8.4	13.8	30.5	53	15.0	21.6	31.4	43.7	61.2
45	Rh	0.94	2.40	5.01	8.9	14.6	32.3	55.5	15.8	23.0	33.5	46.5	65
46	Pd	1.00	2.53	5.25	9.4	15.5	34.3	58.2	16.6	24.5	35.5	49.5	69
47	Ag	1.05	2.67	5.50	9.9	16.3	36.5	10.0	17.5	26.0	38.0	52.8	72.7
48	Cd	1.10	2.80	5.74	10.3	17.2	38.5	10.7	18.5	27.7	40.2	56.2	76.2
49	In	1.15	2.94	5.98	10.8	17.8	40.6	11.4	19.5	29.5	42.7	60.0	80
50	Sn	1.20	3.07	6.22	11.3	18.7	43.1	12.0	20.5	31	45.5	63.5	84

K

Absorption Coefficients

Wavelength, A (Continued)											
1.5	2.0	2.5	3	4	5	6	7	8	9	10	
0.49	0.52	0.62	0.75	1.25	2.12	3.28	4.85	7.1	10.0	13.7	
0.355	0.715	1.04	1.48	3.55	6.9	11.6	18.1	26.6	37.7	51	
1.02	2.18	3.98	6.6	15.2	28.8	48.8	76	113	157	213	
1.55	3.38	6.2	10.3	22.7	43.7	74	118	174	245	333	
2.31	5.05	9.6	15.8	36.0	69	116	187	285	405	560	
4.2	9.7	14.0	32	74	145	250	390	570	810	1100	
6.9	16.0	30.5	52	123	235	400	620	910	1290	1800	
10.5	24.0	45.5	78	180	350	580	920	1350	1900	2600	
14.2	32	62	102	240	450	760	1190	1750	2450	3300	
19.8	43	90	145	325	630	1040	1580	2350	3200	4300	
25.5	53.5	132	250	520	920	1450	2200	3100	4100	5300	K
32.5	69	185	280	610	1100	1800	2700	3900	5200	340	
41.5	87	235	360	780	1400	2250	3300	280	390	520	
52	112	290	440	950	1700	2800	270	400	550	740	
66	140	330	490	1050	1900	245	380	550	770	1070	
78.5	170	375	590	1250	2200	320	500	730	1040	1400	
95	202	430	680	1400	250	410	620	900	1250	1700	
112	240	485	780	170	300	490	730	1050	1450	1900	
130	280	540	860	205	370	600	910	1300	1800	2350	
150	328	625	950	255	460	730	1100	1550	2100	2800	
172	375	720	145	310	550	880	1320	1850	2520	3300	
195	425	113	175	360	630	1000	1450	2050	2750	3550	
222	485	125	195	400	710	1120	1620	2250	3000	3700	
245	540	136	210	440	760	1200	1720	2350	3200	4100	
277	73	148	232	480	820	1260	1850	2550	3400	4350	
312	80	162	255	510	880	1400	2050	2800	3700	4700	
345	87	177	270	550	960	1500	2200	3000	4000	5200	
44	96	193	295	600	1050	1570	2350	3300	4300	5600	
48.5	101	212	320	660	1150	1750	2550	3500	4600	6000	
53.5	116	227	350	700	1200	1870	2700	3750	4900	6400	L_I
59	126	248	385	760	1300	2020	2950	4050	5400	5500	L_{II}
63	138	267	410	820	1400	2150	3100	4300	4700	4000	L_{III}
69	150	287	440	870	1500	2320	3330	4600	5050	2000	
74	165	311	470	940	1600	2500	3600	3900	1650	2150	
80	180	335	510	1020	1720	2700	2180	1250	1750	2300	
87	192	359	550	1100	1860	2900	2280	1350	1870	2450	
94	207	386	590	1170	2000	3100	950	1440	2000	2620	
102	223	412	640	1260	2150	2600	1020	1540	2150	2800	
109	238	442	690	1380	2320	800	1110	1650	2350	3000	
118	255	478	740	1500	1840	850	1200	1770	2450	3200	
127	271	507	800	1600	1900	910	1300	1900	2600	3400	
136	290	544	860	1700	600	980	1400	2050	2800	3650	
147	310	583	920	1850	650	1030	1510	2200	3000	3900	
158	342	625	960	1530	700	1090	1650	2350	3200	4150	
170	355	670	1050	1050	750	1160	1770	2500	3400	4450	
183	380	720	1140	440	800	1230	1900	2700	3650	4750	
196	405	770	1250	480	850	1350	2050	2900	3900	5100	
210	432	820	1340	510	900	1450	2150	3100	4100	5400	
222	460	880	1120	535	940	1520	2250	3200	4300	5700	
236	495	940	775	560	990	1600	2360	3350	4500	5900	

L_I L_{II} L_{III}

Table 5. Mass Absorption

At. No.	Element	Wavelength, A (Continued)											
		0.1	0.15	0.2	0.25	0.3	0.4	0.5	0.6	0.7	0.8	0.9	1.0
51	Sb	1.25	3.22	6.48	11.8	19.5	45.5	12.8	21.6	33.1	48.5	67	88
52	Te	1.30	3.37	6.76	12.3	20.3	7.4	13.6	22.7	35.2	51.5	70.6	93
53	I	1.36	3.52	7.05	12.9	21.2	7.8	14.3	24	37.5	54.5	74.8	97
54	Xe	1.42	3.68	7.33	13.4	21.9	8.2	15.2	25.2	39.8	58	78.5	101
55	Cs	1.48	3.85	7.65	13.9	22.7	8.6	16.2	26.5	42.0	61.3	82.5	106
56	Ba	1.53	4.03	7.98	14.5	23.1	9.05	17.2	27.9	44.2	64	87	111
57	La	1.60	4.22	8.27	15.0	24.5	9.5	18.1	29.3	46.7	67.2	91	116
58	Ce	1.66	4.37	8.55	15.6	25.2	10.0	19.1	30.9	49.2	70.5	95	122
59	Pr	1.72	4.53	8.88	16.1	4.7	10.5	20.1	32.5	51.6	73.8	100	127
60	Nd	1.80	4.69	9.20	16.7	4.95	11.0	21.1	34.2	54.0	77.2	104	132
61	Pm	1.86	4.86	9.57	17.3	5.20	11.5	22.1	36	56.9	80.7	108	139
62	Sm	1.93	5.03	9.95	17.7	5.45	12.0	23.2	37.7	59.5	84	114	144
63	Eu	2.02	5.20	10.3	18.3	5.71	12.5	24.2	39.8	62.5	87.8	119	150
64	Gd	2.09	5.37	10.5	3.95	6.00	13.2	25.3	41.8	65.5	91.5	125	157
65	Tb	2.18	5.52	10.8	4.15	6.28	13.7	26.6	44.0	69.5	95.5	130	163
66	Dy	2.26	5.70	11.2	4.36	6.57	14.4	27.2	46.2	72	99.5	135	170
67	Ho	2.33	5.87	11.6	4.55	6.90	15.1	28.2	48.6	75	103	141	177
68	Er	2.42	6.03	11.9	4.75	7.2	15.8	30.2	50.8	79	107	147	185
69	Tm	2.50	6.23	12.3	5.02	7.6	16.5	31.4	53.2	82.8	112	152	193
70	Yb	2.58	6.41	12.7	5.27	7.95	17.3	32.7	55.8	87	115	158	201
71	Lu	2.66	6.61	3.07	5.50	8.4	18.2	34.2	58.4	90.5	120	165	210
72	Hf	2.75	6.80	3.22	5.80	8.8	19.0	35.5	61	94.2	124	172	219
73	Ta	2.82	7.02	3.36	6.05	9.2	19.9	37.2	64	99	129	178	229
74	W	2.90	7.24	3.50	6.27	9.7	20.8	38.7	66.5	103	134	185	239
75	Re	2.96	7.45	3.63	6.60	10.2	21.8	40.5	69	106	139	192	213
76	Os	3.03	7.65	3.78	6.9	10.6	22.8	42.2	72	110	144	200	222
77	Ir	3.10	7.86	3.92	7.3	11.1	23.8	44.0	74.5	113	150	208	157
78	Pt	3.17	8.06	4.08	7.6	11.6	25.0	46.0	77.6	117	155	170	163
79	Au	3.23	8.28	4.22	8.0	12.2	26.2	47.5	80.5	122	160	176	170
80	Hg	3.30	2.17	4.38	8.3	12.7	27.4	49.5	83.7	126	165	135	178
81	Tl	3.36	2.24	4.53	8.7	13.3	28.6	51.5	86.6	130	170	140	72
82	Pb	3.41	2.32	4.67	9.2	13.9	30.0	53.5	89.2	135	147	145	75
83	Bi	3.45	2.37	4.81	9.6	14.5	31.3	55.5	92	140	109	150	77
84	Po	3.52	2.43	4.88	10.0	15.2	32.8	57.4	94.5	144	112	58.2	79.5
85	At	3.56	2.49	5.02	10.5	15.7	34.0	59.3	97	149	116	60	82
86	Rn	3.61	2.55	5.14	10.9	16.3	35.4	61	100	135	120	62	84
87	Fr	3.66	2.60	5.21	11.2	17.0	36.7	63	102	88	123	64	87
88	Ra	3.70	2.66	5.28	11.7	17.7	38.3	65	105	91	127	66.5	90
89	Ac	3.75	2.71	5.38	12.1	18.6	39.8	67	107	94	131	68	92
90	Th	3.81	2.76	5.45	12.4	19.5	41.2	69	110	97	52	70	95
91	Pa	3.86	2.80	5.53	12.8	20.1	42.6	71	101	100	53.3	72	98
92	U	3.91	2.85	5.61	13.1	20.9	44.0	83.1	79	103	55	74.4	101
93	Np	3.95	2.90	5.68	13.4	21.7	45.2	85.3	82	106	56.8	76.6	104
94	Pu	4.00	2.95	5.75	13.7	22.5	46.7	87.5	85	51	58.7	78.8	107
95	Am	4.05	3.00	5.81	14.1	23.3	47	89.5	87	52	60.5	81	110
96	Cm	2.50	3.04	5.89	14.5	24.2	49.8	91.5	90	53.5	62.3	83.6	113
97	Bk	2.56	3.08	5.97	14.8	25.0	51.2	84.4	92	55	64.4	86.2	117
98	Cf	2.62	3.12	6.04	15.2	25.8	52.8	65	94	57	66.4	89	121
99	E	2.68	3.16	6.11	15.6	26.6	54.0	67	97	59	68.5	91.6	125
100	Fm	2.74	3.20	6.18	15.9	27.5	55.5	69	46	60	70.5	94.5	128

K L_I L_{II} L_{III}

Coefficients *(Continued)*

Wavelength, A (Continued)											
1.5	2.0	2.5	3	4	5	6	7	8	9	10	
250	525	1000	805	590	1050	1660	2480	3500	4700	6200	
265	557	1070	295	620	1100	1730	2600	3650	4900	6400	
280	590	880	310	650	1160	1810	2700	3700	5100	6700	
296	622	710	340	710	1230	1930	2850	4000	5300	7000	
312	656	215	360	740	1300	2050	3000	4200	5600	7200	
330	690	227	390	790	1370	2150	3150	4400	5800	5400	M_I
347	650	240	415	840	1450	2250	3300	4600	6100	5600	
365	685	252	440	880	1570	2360	3400	4800	4750	5800	
385	540	267	465	920	1600	2470	3650	5000	4950	6000	
405	179	280	485	980	1670	2580	3750	3900	5100	4500	M_{II}
425	187	296	515	1040	1750	2700	3900	3500	5300	3300	M_{III}
446	196	313	535	1080	1830	2810	4100	3600	3900	3400	
470	206	330	555	1120	1900	2910	3300	3700	2900	3500	
440	215	348	575	1170	1980	3020	3370	2700	3000	2800	M_{IV}
465	225	368	610	1230	2090	3200	3440	2800	3100	2170	M_V
365	236	388	635	1300	2200	3400	3530	2200	3200	2270	
390	247	409	665	1350	2280	2500	2800	2260	2500	2380	
136	258	432	690	1410	2350	2570	2300	2330	1890	2490	
142	272	456	720	1480	2500	2650	2390	2400	1970	2500	
148	285	482	750	1540	2600	2740	2480	1950	2050	2600	
156	298	510	780	1600	1980	2060	2570	1580	2130	2700	
162	313	540	825	1660	2050	2100	2650	1660	2210	2800	
168	327	570	855	1720	2210	1520	1900	1740	2290	2900	
176	342	600	890	1800	2280	1660	1350	1820	2370	3020	
184	358	636	925	1900	1750	1700	1400	1900	2450	3130	
193	376	672	970	1980	1300	1740	1460	1980	2560	3250	
200	392	710	1010	1450	1340	1400	1530	2060	2670	3370	
208	410	750	1070	1500	1380	1160	1590	2150	2780	3490	
217	430	795	1130	1550	1430	1200	1650	2250	2900	3600	
225	445	825	1190	1150	1480	1250	1700	2300	2950	3700	
233	460	865	1250	1200	1120	1300	1790	2370	3110	3900	
242	478	900	1310	1250	1150	1360	1880	2440	3270	4100	
252	495	940	1380	920	910	1410	1970	2560	3430	4300	
262	507	980	1050	950	960	1460	2060	2680	3590	4500	
272	532	1020	1080	980	1000	1510	2150	2900	3750	4700	
283	550	1070	1120	1020	1040	1550	2240	3010	3900	4900	
294	572	1110	840	710	1080	1590	2330	3120	4050	5100	
305	592	1160	860	750	1120	1630	2420	3230	4200	5500	
316	615	890	890	620	1160	1660	2510	3450	4350	4300	N_I
328	638	930	920	730	1200	1700	2600	3460	4500	4470	
342	660	725	720	760	1250	1790	2700	3570	4650	4650	
354	683	755	750	790	1300	1890	2790	3690	3600	4820	
367	709	785	780	820	1350	1980	2890	3800	3700	3500	N_{II}
382	733	820	810	850	1400	2080	2980	2900	3850	3650	
395	760	850	610	880	1450	2170	3070	3000	4000	3800	
412	530	880	640	910	1500	2250	3170	3080	3100	3950	
427	420	570	500	950	1560	2330	3270	3180	3200	4100	
443	435	595	515	980	1620	2420	2500	3300	3330	3400	N_{III}
461	452	620	530	1020	1690	2520	2580	3400	3450	3550	
480	470	640	550	1050	1730	2600	2600	2600	3570	3700	
M_I M_{II}	M_{III}	M_{IV} M_V				N_I	N_{II}		N_{III}		

producing damage in the matrix, whether a living cell or an inorganic solid, liquid, or gas. In observing such chemical or biological effects of radiation it is essential that there should be methods to relate the amount of absorbed energy with the change or damage, and that there should be standard units of intensity of radiation flux and of absorbed dose. The importance in radiation therapy is immediately apparent. This general field is the most rapidly advancing perhaps in the entire science, and any kind of adequate treatment would run to great length. Suffice it here to summarize briefly the barest fundamentals of dosimetry, and some of the physical, chemical, and biological effects of radiation.

Dosimetry. The ability of x-rays to ionize gases immediately recognized by Röntgen in 1895 was the basis for the ionization-chamber detector and intensity-measuring device in the Bragg spectrometer, and this phenomenon remains to this day as the simplest and most reliable, especially in the more sensitive Geiger and proportional counters. The first unit, therefore, for expressing intensity and dosage is the ionization produced in 1 cc of air. The intensity of radiation is the energy flowing through a unit area perpendicular to the beam in unit time—in other words the flux; it is measured in ergs/cm^2 sec or watt-sec/cm^2. The word dose now implies specifically the absorbed dose; the dose rate is the amount of energy imparted by ionizing particles per unit time to unit mass of matter, and the absorbed dose is the time integral of dose rate or total amount of energy absorbed by unit mass of matter. Any property or effect of radiation, physical, chemical, or biological, which can be measured and related to an observable change, especially if the relationship is linear, is the basis of a potential dosimeter. At least two dozen dosimeters can be described in 1965. To mention only a few: heat developed upon complete absorption in a block of metal—an absolute method, change in electrical conductivity of solids and liquids, ionization of gases, luminescence of phosphors, blackening of photographic emulsions and reversals, changes in chemical systems such as oxidation of ferrous to ferric salts in solution (the famous Fricke dosimeter), changes of color of dyes and indicators and of activated glass blocks, thermoluminescence, and various lethal effects on biological systems such as fruit-fly eggs. These are all described and compared in the *Encyclopedia of X-rays and Gamma Rays* [George L. Clark (ed.), Reinhold Publishing Corporation, New York, 1963]. As already indicated, the ionization of air involves simply measuring the current which flows between electrodes in the chamber or counter.

Intensity and Dosage Units

1. *roentgen* or *r*: the quantity of x- or γ-rays such that the associated corpuscular emission (the + ions and electrons formed by ionization of gaseous molecules) per 0.001293 g of air produces ions carrying 1 electrostatic unit of quantity of electricity of either sign. This represents a constant energy absorption dose of 83.8 ergs/g in air and 93 ergs/g of water (similar to tissues).
2. *rep*: roentgen equivalent physical, to relate the effects of protons, deuterons, neutrons, and α particles, or the absorption of 93 ergs/g in water.
3. *rad*: inevitably from roentgen and rep, the absorption of 100 ergs/g independent of radiation, now the universally accepted unit.
4. *rem*: roentgen equivalent man, a biological unit which takes into account relative biological effectiveness (RBE), or rads $\times$ RBE; or a quantity of ionizing radiation such that the energy imparted to a biological system per gram of living matter by the ionizing particles has the same biological effectiveness as 1 rad of x- or γ-rays, with an average specific ionization of 100 ion pairs per micron of water (thus 1 rad may be equivalent to 10 or 20 rem for heavier particles producing more than 100 ion pairs).
5. *G*: when absorbed radiation in rads (ergs/g) is converted in radiochemical changes to number of molecules changed per 100 ev of absorbed energy, the *G* value is a quantitative expression of the efficiency of the radiation-induced reaction, with a large value such as for polymerizations indicating chain reactions. *G* for the ferrous-ferric dosimeter is 15.5, or 1.036×10^{-9} mole oxidized per rad.

Radiochemistry. The list of radiation-induced chemical reactions grows at a tremendous rate. The mechanisms are all based on the formation of an intermediate very active species under the interaction of photons and secondary electrons, such as ions and especially free radicals. The Dow Chemical Company now manufactures ethyl bromide and ethylene dibromide by irradiation of gaseous mixtures of ethylene and bromine. The cross-linking of polymers such as polyethylene by radiation is carried out on thousands of tons to modify tensile strength, electrical resistance, solubility, etc. Most sensational is the discovery in water, aqueous solutions, and in the human body of the *hydrated electron*, announced by Dr. E. J. Hart of the Argonne National Laboratory in April, 1963. This electron formed by radiation bombardment lasts in a free state for 10^{-4} to 10^{-5} sec until it combines with molecules to form new compounds. Reference may be made to the *Encyclopedia of X-rays and Gamma Rays*, previously mentioned, for an exposition of this discovery and many others. The effects of radiation in rockets upon semiconductors—diodes, transistors, thermistors, infrared sensors, and solar (selenium) cells—which encounter the Van Allen radiation belts have all been investigated recently. The radiation has the ability under proper conditions to knock ions or atoms out of their normal lattice positions into interstitial locations, thus greatly affecting properties such as resistivity, mechanical strength, and the Hall effect which measures the charge carriers in these solid-state representatives. Suffice it to say that radiation such as x-rays and γ-rays is among the most powerful tools of the solid-state scientist. Recently a small group of young adventurers bought by the pound for $100 semiconductor diodes which failed to meet specifications, irradiated these, and sold the resulting effective diodes for $25,000. This is an instance of very useful radiation "damage."

Biological Effects of Radiation. The dangers of x-rays to the human system as well as to all living systems are well known but often overlooked by the radiation research worker using x-ray spectrometers, diffractometers, and other instruments. Burns, anemia, leukemia, and other types of cancer are all on record. A companion handbook[13] presents in detail causes, effects, prevention and protection, and Chap. 6 of this handbook presents the principles of health and safety, so that little more need be said here except to recommend reference to these sources.

REFERENCES CITED

1. J. W. M. DuMond and E. R. Cohen, *Fundamental Formulas of Physics*, p. 145, Prentice-Hall, Inc., Englewood Cliffs, N.J., 1955.
2. A. E. Sandstrom, *Handbuch der Physik*, p. 78, Band XXX, Springer-Verlag OHG, Berlin, 1957.
3. H. A. Liebhafsky, H. G. Pfeiffer, E. H. Winslow, and P. D. Zemany, *X-ray Absorption and Emission in Analytical Chemistry*, John Wiley & Sons, Inc., New York, 1960.
4. P. W. Zingaro, *Norelco Reptr.*, **1**: 67 (1954).
5. S. Fine and C. F. Hendee, Tech. Rept. #86, Philips Laboratories, Irvington on the Hudson, N.Y., 1954.
6. H. R. Moore and F. C. Chalkin, *Proc. Phys. Soc. (London)*, A, **68**:717 (1955).
7. G. L. Rogosa and W. F. Peed, *Phys. Rev.*, **100**:1763 (1955).
8. G. L. Rogosa and W. F. Peed, *Phys. Rev.*, **101**:591 (1956).
9. W. F. Peed, et al., *Phys. Rev.*, **105**:588 (1957).
10. D. S. Flikkema and R. V. Schablaske, Argonne National Laboratory Rept., #ANL-5804, (1957).
11. P. Fisher, R. S. Crisp, and S. E. Williams, *Opt. Acta*, **5**:31 (1958).
12. D. E. Bedo and D. H. Tomboulian, *Phys. Rev.*, **109**:35 (1958).
13. H. Blatz (ed.), *Radiation Hygiene Handbook*, McGraw-Hill Book Company, New York, 1959.

Chapter 2

GENERATION OF X-RAYS

T. H. Rogers

The Machlett Laboratories, Incorporated

1. INTRODUCTION

As discussed in Chap. 1, x-radiation may be excited in a number of ways. This chapter will deal with electrically energized x-ray generators designed for the production of primary x-rays, as required in the practice of research and analysis techniques described in this handbook. In such generators, x-rays are produced by electrons accelerated to a high velocity in an evacuated chamber by an electric field, which are slowed down or stopped by collision with atoms of matter lying in their paths. The accelerating voltages employed in practical x-ray generators in use today will generally fall in the range from 10^4 to 10^8 volts, depending on the spectral characteristics desired.

Vacuum tubes designed specifically to provide for the acceleration of electrons within the vacuum space and their interception by a target for the production of x-rays are known as *x-ray tubes*. The combination of such a tube and an electrical apparatus designed to generate, modify, or control electrical energy for application to x-ray tubes is called an x-ray generator.

2. X-RAY TUBES

Designed for many different applications, x-ray tubes differ widely as to structural detail, with, however, many elements of design in common. Modern x-ray tubes utilize high vacuum as the voltage-insulating medium within which the anode and cathode structures are mounted and the electron beam is accelerated. The residual gas pressure in such tubes is usually less than 10^{-6} mm Hg. (Early x-ray tubes depended on the ionization of the residual gas to produce the electron beam by ion bombardment of the cathode and required gas pressures about 1,000 times higher.) The evacuated chamber is usually permanently "sealed off" from the vacuum pumping system after the accomplishment of a thorough degassing of the elements and evacuation of the envelope, and the necessary high vacuum is self-maintained throughout the useful life of the tube. In some instances, x-ray tubes remain permanently connected to the vacuum pumping system, such tubes having temporary seals and joints to permit replacement or interchange of one or more elements for special or experimental purposes. Such tubes are spoken of as "demountable" tubes.

All x-ray tubes must incorporate a structure which supports and maintains the cathode and target in proper spatial relationship and which insulates these elements from each other at the operating voltage. Usually the envelope of the tube is used as the insulating structure as well as the container of the evacuated space (Fig. 1). The envelope may be immersed in an insulating medium of greater dielectric strength than air, such as oil or compressed gas, which in turn is contained in a grounded metal enclosure which provides protection against electric shock and may shield off unwanted portions of the radiation. Such units are frequently called "shockproof" tubes (Fig. 2). The anode incorporates a target of suitable metal upon which the electron beam impinges and wherein the x-rays are generated. Tungsten is the most commonly used target material, both because of its high atomic number which makes for efficiency in x-ray production and because of its favorable thermal properties of high melting point, high conductivity, and low vapor pressure. Other metals are used when the specific applications require certain characteristic spectra. The area on the target bombarded by electrons, which thus becomes the source of x-rays, is called the focal spot. The size and shape of the focal spot are designed for specific applications and are controlled primarily by the beam-forming structure of the cathode. The cathode includes the source of electrons, usually an incandescible tungsten filament, and an associated beam-forming structure which focuses the electron stream on the target. Some method of cooling is provided to transfer heat from the target to the exterior of the tube.

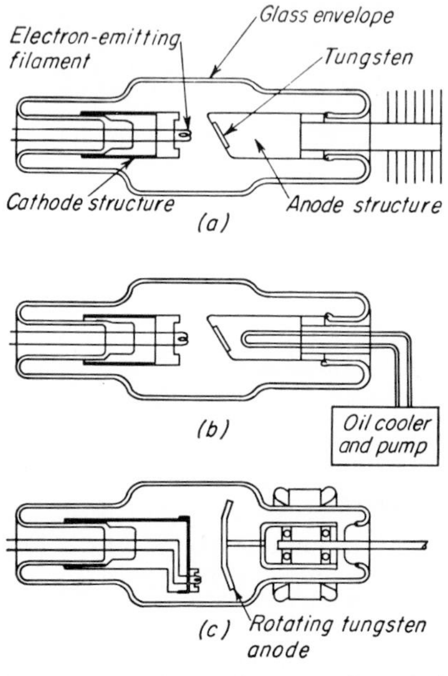

Fig. 1. Schematic diagrams of typical x-ray tubes. (*a*) Air-cooled. (*b*) Oil-cooled. (*c*) Rotating anode.

The bombarded area must be large enough to absorb safely the thermal energy delivered by the electron beam, but not so large as to produce excessive penumbra when the x-rays are required from an approximate "point source." In the design of tubes for such cases, particular attention is paid to the provision of the minimum focal-spot size consistent with the electrical loading factors required for the intended

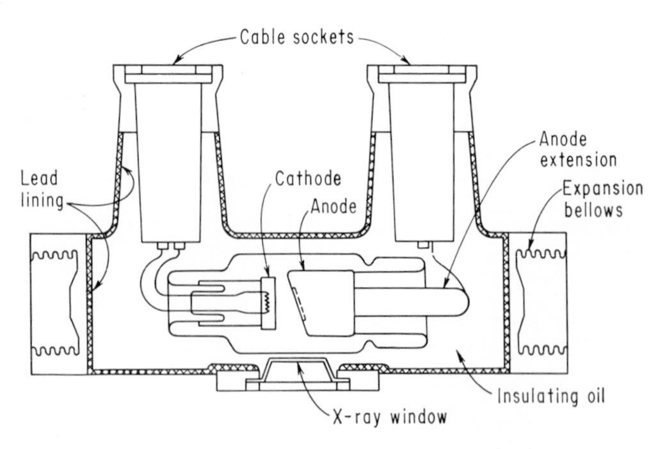

Fig. 2. Schematic diagram of shockproof tube.

service, and to means for rapid removal of heat so that limitations on repetitive operations are minimized. The simplest types employ a tungsten target embedded in a copper member, called the anode, having a portion extending to the exterior of the tube envelope. The heat generated at the focal spot is transmitted into the copper and conducted thereby to the exterior and transferred to the surrounding medium. If the surrounding medium is air, the tube is called an air-cooled x-ray tube. More often, in modern practice, the tube is immersed in a housing filled with insulating oil; such a tube is called an oil-immersed tube. Heat is transferred to and carried away by circulation of the oil. Sometimes other insulating material (e.g., compressed gas such as freon or sulfur hexafluoride) is used. Allowable minimum focal-spot size in such tubes is limited by rate of heat transmission through the tungsten target to the copper backing.

Most tubes in which minimum focal size is required employ the "line-focus" principle (Fig. 3) to reduce the optical size of the focus, by a factor of 3 or more, as compared with the physical size which governs the loading capacity. This "line-focus" principle consists of arranging the plane of the target surface at an angle of 15 to 20° with respect to the center line of the x-ray beam to be projected from the tube. At a 20° projection angle, the gain in actual length of the bombarded area as compared with the "optical" focal spot is 3 (csc 20°). Even smaller angles may be used in those cases where the spread of the x-ray beam that may be utilized is not too small for the required purposes. Sometimes a double-angled anode is used to provide the opportunity for optimizing the compromise to fit special requirements.

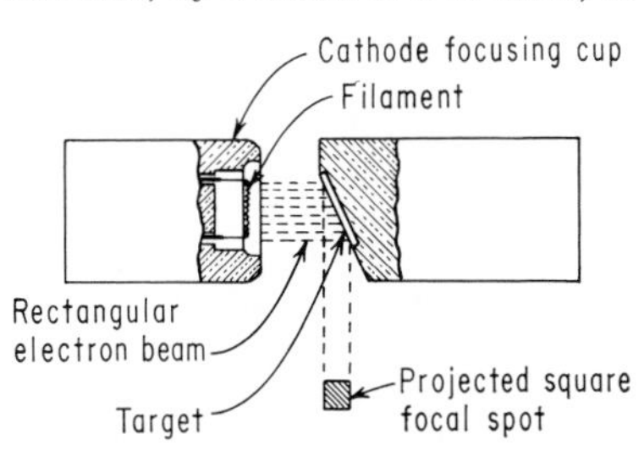

FIG. 3. Diagram of "line-focus" principle.

Tubes designed to provide the smallest possible focal spot for a given loading capacity employ a rotating anode, wherein the target is a relatively large-diameter disk, made to rotate about its central axis at 3,000 or more rpm. The focal spot is near the edge of the rotating disk, remaining stationary with respect to the exterior of the tube. The heat generated is swept rapidly out of the bombarded area by the motion of the target, and thus a much smaller focal spot may be utilized without becoming overheated. Generally, in such tubes, the target is not backed with copper; the heat is spread through the tungsten disk and radiated therefrom with satisfactory efficiency because of the area available for radiation and the high temperature permissible with the all-tungsten target assembly. The rotating anode assembly is mounted on a special ball-bearing system specially designed for operation in vacuum, with a nonvolatile metallic lubricant. It is driven by induction-motor action, an external stator providing the magnetic field.

Diffraction Tubes. Tubes designed to be employed in techniques involving diffraction of x-rays (see Parts 2 and 3) incorporate certain special features necessary to make them most suitable for such use. They must generally provide for the following requirements:

1. Monochromatic radiation of specified wavelength
2. Maximal intensity
3. Minimal focal-spot size
4. Low-absorption x-ray windows
5. Multiplicity of x-ray windows
6. Close proximity of windows to focal spot

Conventional Tubes. Commercially available sealed-off tubes normally sold for diffraction applications are designed to meet these requirements. Most such tubes follow a similar pattern of construction as described in the following paragraphs (see Fig. 4).

In order to provide a "monochromatic" beam, diffraction tubes employ targets of a material whose characteristic spectrum (see Chap. 1, Section 2) provides a "line" of suitable intensity and of the required wavelength, the other wavelengths being essentially eliminated by a filter or other form of monochromator. The choice of target materials is limited not only by suitability of spectrum but by melting point, which

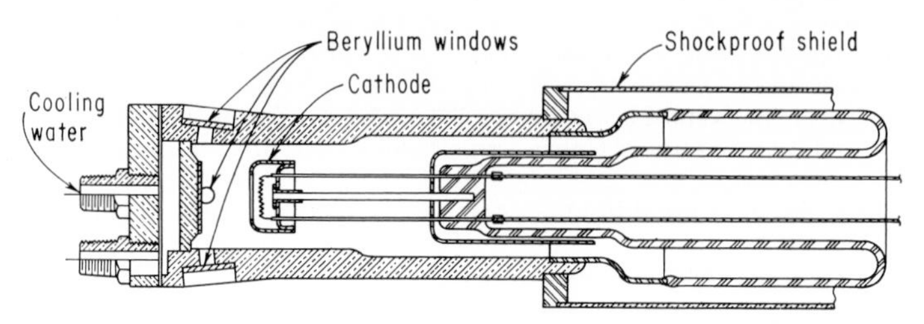

FIG. 4. Schematic diagram of conventional diffraction tube.

must be high enough, and vapor pressure, which must be low enough, for inclusion in a sealed-off high-vacuum tube. These requirements are met by only a certain few metallic elements in pure form; those finding use in commercially available tubes include those shown in Table 1, which also shows their principal characteristic wavelengths and minimum exciting voltages.

Table 1. Standard Diffraction-tube Targets

Material	Emission wavelength, Å		Energy, kv	
	$K\alpha$	$L\alpha$	K	L
Tungsten	0.21	1.47	58.0	8.4
Silver	0.56	4.15	22.1	2.98
Molybdenum	0.71	5.39	17.4	2.29
Copper	1.54		8.03	
Nickel	1.65		7.46	
Cobalt	1.79		6.93	
Iron	1.93		6.40	
Chromium	2.29		5.41	

Once the most suitable operating voltage for optimal line-to-background intensity ratio is resolved, maximal intensity is achieved by operating with the tube current at the maximum permitted by the thermal characteristics of the target material and anode structure. Tubes designed for maximal loading usually have a copper anode to which the target material is affixed in one of several ways to ensure intimate contact for heat transmission. The copper anode is efficiently cooled by circulation of water through ducts therein. Such tubes are usually operated with the anode at ground (zero) potential, to facilitate the provision of water cooling. The cathode will then, of course, be at a high negative potential.

Precision in diffraction-pattern formation requires that the source of x-rays, or focal spot, be reduced to the practical minimum for most applications. To achieve maximal intensity while minimizing effective focal size, the "line-focus" principle is employed to an extreme degree in diffraction tubes. The focal area takes the form of a narrow (1 mm or less) band 10 to 15 mm long. Since the field to be covered by the beam is so small (less than 1° angular divergence), the "viewing angle" from the focal-area plane can be approximately 6° or less, and the "projected" focal spot, viewed from either end, will appear as 1 mm (or less) square.

To minimize loss of intensity, the windows in the vacuum envelope through which the beams emerge must be of a material having a low absorption coefficient for x-rays of the relatively long wavelengths involved, and as thin as possible. The most advantageous material is beryllium. Modern techniques now permit inclusion of beryllium windows only 0.1 to 1 mm thick with permanent high-temperature vacuum-tight seals in conventional sealed-off tubes. Such windows are extremely rugged mechanically, thermally, and electrically, as compared with mica, aluminum foil, or low-absorption glasses formerly employed for x-ray windows to provide similar absorption-loss characteristics.

Diffraction tubes usually are provided with more than one window. A window at each end of the line focus permits two beams to be utilized simultaneously. Either one or two "side" windows, wide enough to "view" substantially the entire length of the focal spot, may be provided as well. The resulting elongated, very narrow, effective focal spot is utilized advantageously in bent-crystal "focusing" cameras (see Chap. 8).

It is advantageous for the windows to be as close as possible to the focal spot, so that the collimators, specimens, radiation-detecting devices, etc., may in turn be located as near as possible to the x-ray source. Hence diffraction tubes are designed with special attention to optimum geometry with respect to these considerations. The portion of the envelope containing the windows and surrounding the target is made to the minimal diameter permissible by the requirements of cooling, electrical clearances, structural ruggedness, etc. It is also of metal, grounded, and self-shielding against electrical and radiation hazards. The high-voltage terminals are located as far from the window area as possible and are arranged so as to facilitate fully shielded connection to the energizing voltage source.

Demountable Tubes. Although most diffraction tubes are of the "sealed-off" type, demountable tubes are sometimes provided for this application. The use of such tubes has certain important disadvantages (e.g., the necessity to provide and maintain a vacuum pumping system, more expensive construction, time required for disassembly, reassembly, and pump-down, etc.). When they are provided, it is usually to meet special requirements of a special application where standard commercially available tubes are not suitable. For example, special target materials and window materials not usable in sealed-off tubes may be employed in demountable tubes.

Rotating Target Tubes. The use of a rotating target permits an increase in the instantaneous loading, and therefore the intensity, of a given focal spot by a factor in the order of ten times. However, it is seldom used in diffraction tubes because of the difficulty of providing for the rapid removal of a great quantity of heat from such a structure in vacuum, as is necessary for the long runs at high intensity generally required for diffraction techniques. In special cases, where the maximum possible intensity must be achieved at all costs, rotating targets have been installed, in demountable tubes, and provided with water cooling through a "vacuum-tight" packing gland. With a sufficiently high-speed vacuum pump, such systems have operated satisfactorily. The bulkiness, complexity, and expense preclude general application.

Tubes for Spectroscopy. Chemical analysis by x-ray fluorescence spectroscopy (see Part 4) is a technique which is rapidly growing in importance. Material to be analyzed is irradiated with x-rays of appropriate intensity and wavelength spectrum, whereupon "fluorescent" x-radiation of specific wavelengths characteristic of the chemical elements in the material is excited therein. This radiation is intercepted, detected, and analyzed spectrographically, providing a means to identify, quantitatively and qualitatively, unknown ingredients of the material under analysis. X-ray tubes for this purpose require operation at relatively high power levels continuously with voltages adjustable in a range of 25 to 100 kv; choice of an assortment of target materials including, most commonly, tungsten, platinum, molybdenum, silver, and chromium; and an x-ray window having the minimum possible absorption for the longer wavelengths of the x-ray spectrum. Hence special tubes have been designed for this purpose which have grounded, water-cooled anodes, thin beryllium windows, large focal spots located in close proximity to the window, and are furnished with a choice of target materials including those mentioned above. These tubes can be operated continuously with power input of 2 kw or more.

The design of tubes for spectroscopy imposes many of the requirements of tubes for diffraction but differs therefrom in several important respects: (1) A maximum of total flux, rather than maximal intensity from a minimal focal spot, is desirable; so a

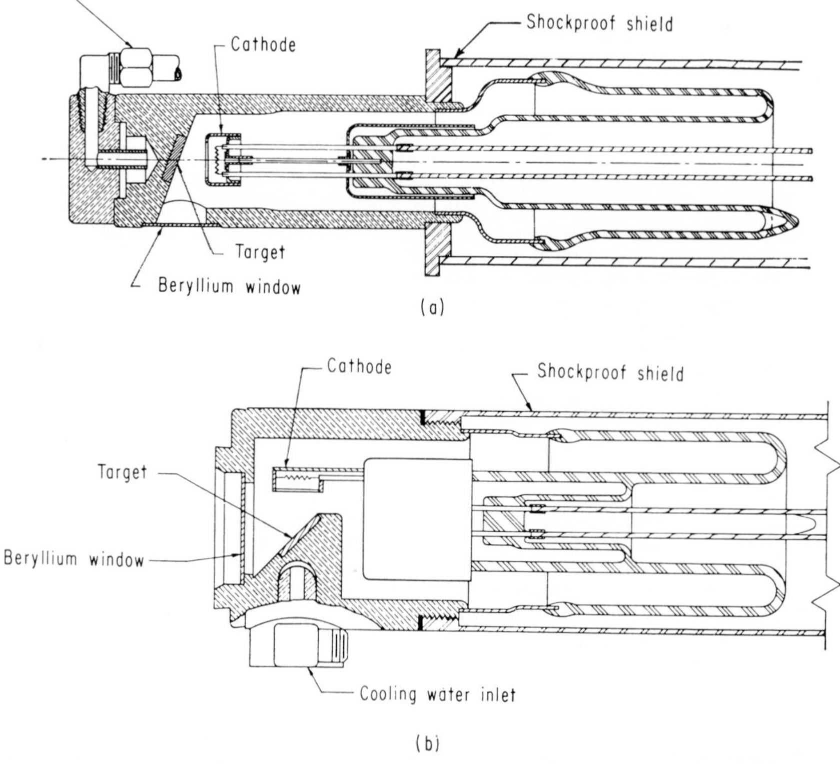

Fig. 5. Schematic diagram of typical tubes for spectroscopy. (*a*) "Side window." (*b*) "End window."

larger focal spot is provided, to maximize loading capacity. (2) A relatively large irradiated area is desired; so the x-ray window is made as large as feasible. (3) Monochromatic radiation is not generally necessary, but characteristic spectral lines of any material other than the specified target material can be very troublesome in the interpretation of the fluorescent spectrum being analyzed; hence an extreme degree of target purity is required.

Typical internal geometries employed in tubes designed for spectroscopy are shown schematically in Fig. 5. Some tubes have a "side-window" configuration, and others are of "end-window" design. It will be noted that in these structures the window is placed as close as possible to the focal spot, and that the window is at the same potential as the anode, normally ground potential. It is important that the window be at ground potential, rather than high potential, because specimens and other apparatus are placed in very close proximity to the window. One important difficulty frequently arises from this internal arrangement; secondary electrons from the focal spot impinge copiously on the window because of its proximity in position and potential. With the high power levels involved, the intensity of bombardment of the window generates sufficient heat so that the temperature of the window rises sufficiently to create problems. Figure 6 represents a modified end-window design, recently introduced, which obviates this difficulty. It will be noted that the window is at cathode potential, which fact prevents bombardment of the window by secondary electrons from the anode. The cathode and window are intended to be held at ground potential, while the anode is designed for operation at high positive potential.

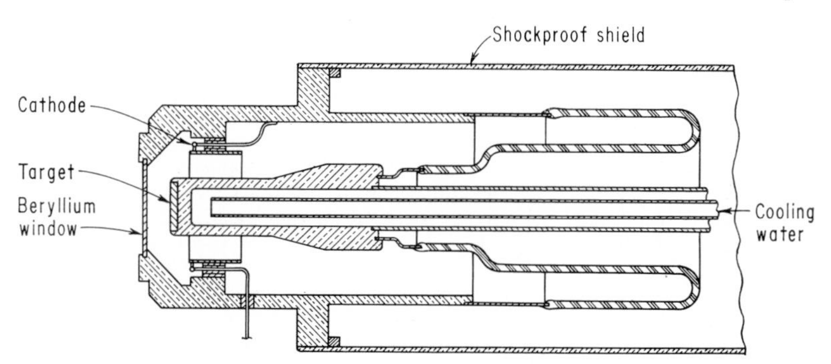

FIG. 6. Spectroscopy tube of advanced design, with window at cathode potential.

Tubes for Other Industrial Applications. Industrial applications of x-rays occur in a number of categories, the most common of which is inspection by radiography. In radiography, x-ray shadow pictures of objects to be inspected for internal defects or structural details are produced on photographic film. Sharp images require small focal spots. For industrial subjects, usually motion is not a factor, so that long exposures requiring relatively low power levels may be used, permitting focal spots as small as may be desired. Voltage employed is governed by the nature and thickness of material to be penetrated, and may range from a very few kilovolts to several million volts.

Tubes for industrial radiography occur in a variety of forms, the most common of which is the oil-cooled type used in units operating at voltages between 100 and 400 kv. This service may require prolonged periods of loading at relatively high power (approximately 4 kw), so that dissipation of this large amount of heat from the anode becomes the primary factor in design. The tungsten target is embedded in a copper anode, as described previously, but instead of being dependent on conduction of heat to the exterior for cooling, the copper anode is made hollow and insulating oil is pumped through it as a coolant to carry the heat away as rapidly as it is generated. Such tubes are usually mounted in a shockproof, rayproof enclosure and insulated therein by the same oil used as the coolant. In operation the anode may be at a potential of 100 to 200 kv from ground; hence good insulating properties are required.

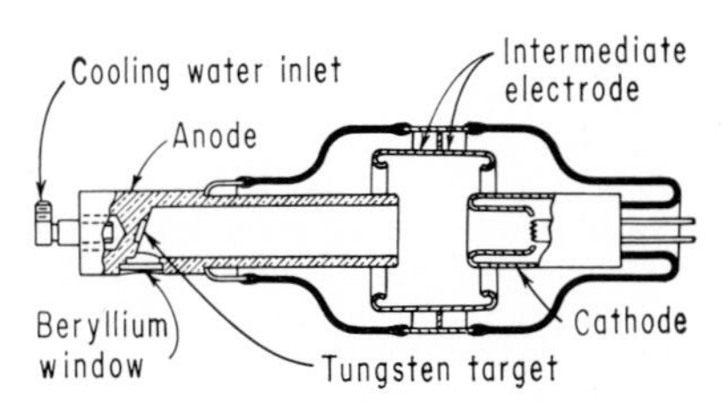

FIG. 7. Water-cooled tube with grounded anode, beryllium window, and multisection construction.

Some radiographic tubes, cooled by water circulating through the anode structure, are designed for operation with the anode at ground potential (Fig. 7). These tubes have the advantage of utilizing the superior cooling properties of water, and also usually have the target located at the extreme end of the envelope, providing certain geometric advantages in application.

Certain radiographic applications, involving thick sections of heavy materials, require the use of extremely high voltages (1,000 kv and above). Tubes for use in this range are frequently called "supervoltage" x-ray tubes (see Fig. 8). Their construction is usually of the grounded-anode type, and also is usually of the multistage type, whereby the envelope is made up of a number of interconnected sections in which the electron beam is subjected to successive accelerating fields as it passes through them in turn. Thus each section is required to insulate only a fraction of the total voltage involved. A "tapped" voltage source is required to energize such tubes. Multistage construction is regularly employed for voltages of 1,000 kv and above, and in some cases for lower voltages down to 250 kv.

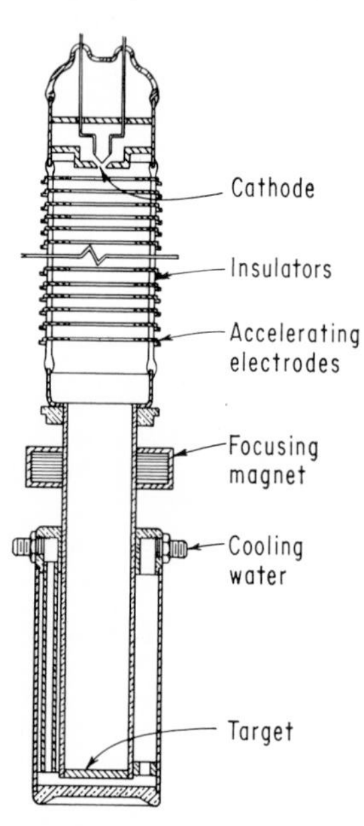

Fig. 8. Schematic diagram of multistage supervoltage tube for use in Van de Graaff generator.

In the range of 5 to 100 Mev, x-rays are generated by the betatron, a device which accelerates electrons to high energies in a circular path through multiple revolutions by means of magnetic induction. The x-ray tube in this case is in the form of a hollow toroid, often called a "donut." The donut contains an electron "injector," similar to the cathode in a conventional x-ray tube, which injects electrons at an initial energy of about 50 kv. A magnetic field causes them to follow the circular path, and linkage of the circular path with an increasing magnetic field provides the accelerating induction. At a time of maximum velocity, the electrons strike a target within the donut and produce x-rays by the usual collision mechanism. The usual target-cooling problems are essentially absent because the efficiency of x-ray generation at such high energy levels is such that little heat generation takes place at the required x-ray output.

A special technique called microsecond radiography is employed to study rapidly moving objects (projectiles, mechanisms, etc.). In tubes for this technique, the cathode contains a small gap between electrodes across which an arc is caused to fire by a suitable trigger-voltage pulse. This arc becomes a copious source of electrons to convey an instantaneous discharge current to the anode, producing a very short highly intense burst of x-rays. In a very recently developed version, a "field-emission" cathode is employed, wherein electrons are drawn directly from an array of sharp points by the intense electric field, permitting better control of focusing and pulse duration than with the "arc" cathode. The discharge current is supplied by a charged condenser bank, or a pulse-forming network, at voltages up to 600 kv. Capacitance and other circuit constants determine the duration of the discharge, which usually is in the order of a microsecond, or less. The target is a block of tungsten, cooled primarily by radiation and by the formation of tungsten vapor. Life of such tubes may be quite short, a few hundred discharges evaporating sufficient tungsten to render the tube inoperable.

Fluoroscopy is also used for industrial inspection. Tubes for this purpose entail essentially the same physical, electrical, and thermal characteristics as for radiography, up to about the 250-kv voltage level. Fluoroscopic screens become increasingly inefficient at the higher voltages, and hence attempts to use fluoroscopy above this level are uncommon. Special rotating-anode tubes capable of continuous operation at relatively high power with extremely small focal spots have been developed, which permit fluoroscopy to be utilized advantageously for many crucial inspections requiring detection of extremely minute defects. These tubes may employ very-large-diameter tungsten-disk targets in the manner described previously in this section, permitting dissipation of heat by radiation at a continuous rate of several kilowatts.

X-ray thickness gauging is employed to monitor or control thickness of continuously moving sheet and strip materials, such as steel, copper, aluminum, and plastics, during their manufacture (see Chaps. 40 and 44). The operating voltage, dependent on the material and thickness involved, may range from 10 to 150 kv. Tube currents are usually quite low (0.2 to 5 ma). The thickness measurement or comparison is based on the reduction in intensity of the x-ray beam in passing through the material whose absorption characteristics are known. Beam intensity is measured by Geiger- or scintillation-counter circuitry and translated into thickness indication or servo-type control signal. Tubes for gauging applications are sometimes required to provide a dual beam, in which case they may be similar or identical to tubes used in diffraction apparatus. Otherwise, tubes as used for conventional industrial radiography in the same voltage range are employed in x-ray thickness gauges. Unusual mechanical ruggedness, requiring special structural design, may be demanded in some cases.

X-rays are sometimes employed for the irradiation of materials to produce chemical or biological changes, such as partial or complete destruction of microorganisms (sterilization), deinfestation, etc. (see Chap. 1, Sec. 6). Special tubes for such purposes have been constructed with large-area beryllium windows and extremely large focal spots, for operation at relatively low voltages and high current (60 kv, 200 ma), for the production of very high dosages of long-wavelength x-rays. Dose rates of the order of 10^7 r/min are produced with such tubes. The low penetration of such rays limits their usefulness to surface and thin-film applications. Other irradiation schemes employ electron beams which are produced and accelerated as in an x-ray tube but allowed to pass through a suitable window to the exterior of the tube and impinge on the material to be irradiated. Such beams must be accelerated by at least ½ million volts (usually more) in order to provide practical results.

Medical and Dental X-ray Tubes. Although it is the plan of this handbook to cover *nonmedical* areas of x-ray science, this discussion of x-ray tubes may well include a brief description of the categories intended primarily for medical and dental applications, since many industrial applications may utilize essentially similar tubes and involve similar principles.

Medical and dental diagnostic x-rays are usually generated at voltages between 40 and 150 kv. Dental and lightweight (portable) medical units are usually limited to 90 kv or less. The usual maximum range for diagnostic equipment is 150 kv. Diagnostic technique may take the form of radiography, wherein x-ray shadow pictures are produced on photographic film, or of fluoroscopy, wherein a visible image is produced by x-rays on a fluorescent screen. Both techniques require small focal spots for sharply defined images. Radiography requires relatively high instantaneous energy applied to the tube so as to produce the radiograph in a period sufficiently short to prevent blurring due to motion. Fluoroscopy requires application of energy to the tube for a period sufficiently long to permit adequate examination. Level of energy is a compromise between those required for adequate image brightness and minimized patient dosage. In recent years, "image intensifiers" have alleviated this compromise.

To provide the smallest possible focal spot for a given loading capacity, particularly for short-exposure radiography, tubes incorporating the rotating-anode principle, described previously in this section, are generally employed. Latest developments provide for "high-speed" rotation up to 10,000 rpm, by supplying 180-cps excitation to the stator. This is done in order to take maximum advantage of the rotating-anode principle, whereby the allowable energy density in the focal spot, for short exposures, is approximately proportional to the square root of the speed of rotation.

A most recent development in diagnostic tubes is the "grid-controlled" x-ray tube. In this design, the cathode incorporates, in addition to the electron source and the beam-forming focusing device, an element whereby the flow of electrons can be controlled by means of control-circuit voltages applied thereto. This "grid-control" action permits timing of exposures independently of the high voltage applied across the tube, and thus facilitates the generation of very short, rapidly repeated exposures required in the recently evolved technique of cineradiography. Tubes of this type now on the market include a model for operation at kilovoltages up to 150 kv in which a grid voltage of -2 kv produces complete "cutoff" of anode current. Full anode current is allowed to pass when the grid-circuit pulses raising the grid to zero (cathode) potential are applied. By this technique, exposure times down to 0.001 sec or less are readily obtainable, at repetition rates of any number per second desired for cine recording.

The energy-loading capability of a tube for radiographic exposures is usually specified by means of "rating charts," which indicate the maximum allowable combination of *kilovolts* and *milliamperes* which may be applied to the tube for any exposure duration (time) within the range covered by the chart (usually from 0.01 sec or less to 20 sec or more). An example of such a chart is shown in Fig. 9. The voltages and currents allowable depend not only on the structural design and focal-spot size of the tube, but also on the type and characteristics of the electric circuit employed to energize it, and, in case of a rotating-anode tube, on the speed of rotation at which it is

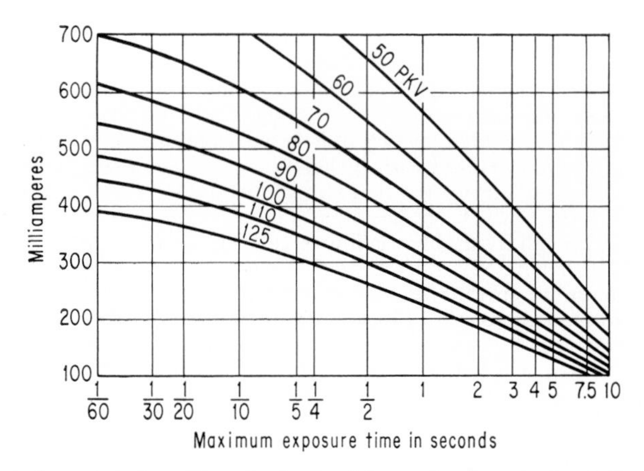

FIG. 9. Typical x-ray tube-rating chart—for 2.0-mm focal spot of rotating-anode tube operated in full-wave rectified circuit.

operated. Hence a different rating chart must be supplied for each combination of these operational variables. Most frequently, diagnostic tubes are provided with two independently operable cathodes, each respectively producing a different focal-spot size so as to increase the versatility of application. Separate sets of rating charts must be supplied for each focus of such "double-focus" tubes.

Focal-spot sizes in stationary-anode diagnostic tubes generally range from 1.0 to 5.0 mm; in rotating-anode tubes from 0.3 to 2.0 mm. Generally, two fixed focal spots of different sizes are provided in all rotating-anode tubes and in some stationary-anode tubes.

Tubes for Medical Therapy. A very wide range of voltage and current is employed in the generation of x-rays for medical therapy, depending on the nature of the therapeutic problem involved. Such therapy is broadly divided into two classes; superficial therapy, pertaining to skin and subcutaneous disorders; and deep therapy, pertaining to more deeply located treatment areas. For superficial therapy, voltages from 6 to 150 kv are employed; for deep therapy, voltages range from 180 kv to 50 Mev.

Superficial-therapy x-ray tubes for the voltage range of 30 to 150 kv are generally similar to those employed for diagnostic techniques. Dosage requirements are usually greater and exposure times are not required to be limited to short duration. Hence overall cooling rather than focal-spot considerations is the primary factor governing design, and rotating-anode tubes are seldom used for this application. For some superficially located conditions, extremely long wavelength radiation of low penetration characteristics is required. Tubes for this class of therapy are operated at voltages between 6 and 50 kv, and are frequently provided with an x-ray exit window of metallic beryllium in the tube envelope. Such beryllium window tubes permit the emission of the longer-wavelength portion of the spectrum which is normally absorbed by other types of x-ray window. The dosage level at the outer surface of the window in such tubes may be over 1,000,000 r/min, and hence special safety precautions are necessary in their use. However, the high absorption coefficient makes the shielding of such radiation relatively easy.

X-rays generated at voltages from 6 to 15 kv are often called grenz rays. Modern grenz-ray tubes are usually equipped with beryllium windows.

For the treatment of lesions located within body cavities, special x-ray tubes are designed for insertion into such cavities so that the x-ray window of the tube can be brought into very close proximity or actual contact with the lesion. Such tubes, usually called contact-therapy x-ray tubes, generally operate at voltages between 40 and 60 kv.

Deep-therapy x-ray tubes occur in a variety of forms, in general similar to those used for industrial radiography in voltage ranges from 200 kv upward. In the "supervoltage" ranges, sectionalized tubes, betatrons, and linear accelerators are used, the structures being generally similar or identical to those described above for industrial usage.

X-ray units used for medical therapy usually operate at dose rates, suitable for treatment routines, ranging from approximately 30 to 100 r/min at the treatment area (usually from 20 to 100 cm from the target). "Quality" (wavelength and homogeneity) of the radiation is controlled by inserting in the beam "filters" of aluminum, copper, tin, lead, etc., which greatly reduce the primary-beam intensity. Precautions to avoid inadvertent treatment without prescribed filters are essential.

3. POWER EQUIPMENT

Conventional Power Supplies. The most commonly employed device for generating high voltage for application to x-ray tubes is a high-ratio step-up transformer, supplied with alternating voltage from power lines at conventional distribution voltage and frequency (in the United States, most commonly 230 volts, 60 cps). Auxiliary apparatus, called the x-ray control, provides means for varying the input and correspondingly the output voltage of the transformer at will over the required range. Some form of multitapped autotransformer is usually used for this purpose. The control also makes provisions for supplying and regulating the heating current to the x-ray tube filament so as to control its electron emission to the desired values. Other control functions are to initiate and terminate exposures and govern their duration, regulate heating current supplied to rectifier-tube filaments, and give indications by meters or otherwise of the various current and voltage values established by the various control settings.

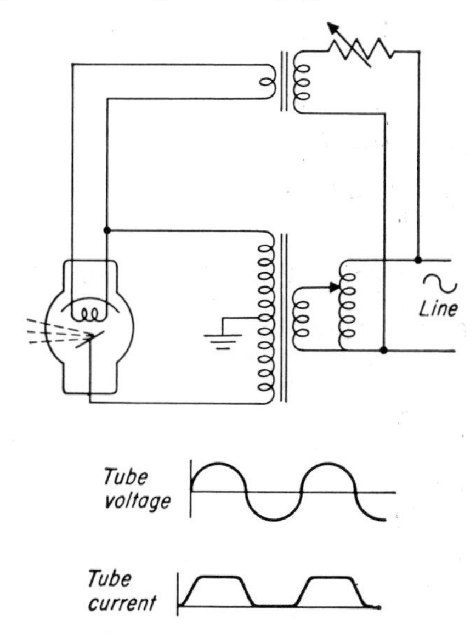

FIG. 10. Diagram of self-rectified circuit.

A self-rectified x-ray generator is one in which the x-ray tube is connected directly across the high-voltage transformer output terminals, so that alternating voltage is supplied to the tube (Fig. 10). Current through the tube is unidirectional by virtue of the ability of the tube to function as a rectifier. This mode of operation requires that loading of the anode be limited to a value below the point at which its temperature will allow electron emission on the reverse polarity of the impressed voltage. By insertion of a high-voltage rectifying tube in series with the x-ray tube, reversal of current is prevented and this limitation on anode loading is removed. Such a unit, with one or two rectifiers, or valve tubes, in series with the x-ray tube, is called a half-wave rectified x-ray generator, since each alternate half of the voltage wave is suppressed (Fig. 11). In a full-wave rectified x-ray generator (Fig. 12), four valve tubes are employed in a bridge circuit so as to supply both half cycles of voltage to the x-ray tube with unidirectional polarity. When very large currents in the x-ray tube are required, a three-phase voltage supply with full-wave rectification, employing six valve tubes, is sometimes used.

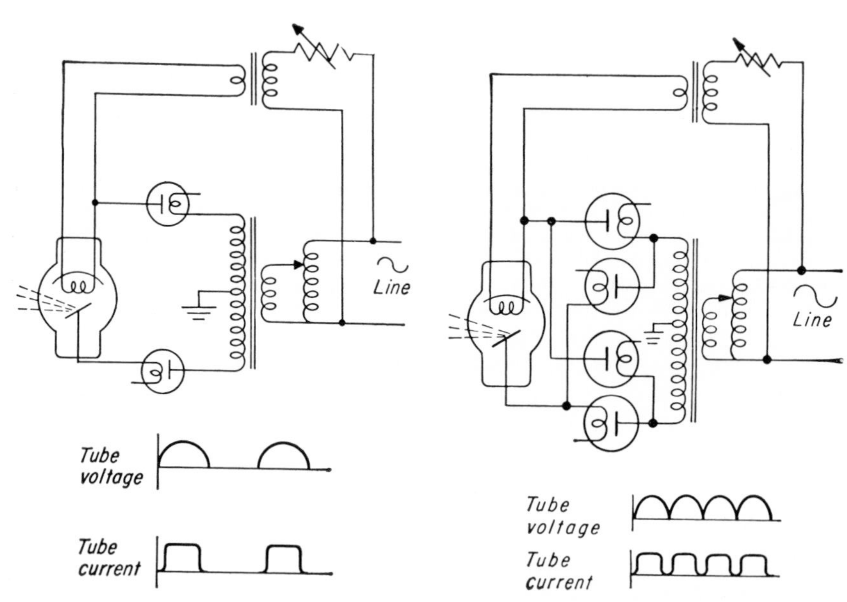

Fig. 11. Diagram of half-wave rectified circuit.

Fig. 12. Diagram of full-wave rectified circuit.

The various types of rectified circuits described above are all in common use. Small, light-duty, and portable units are usually self-rectified. High-current radiographic units are usually full-wave, either single-phase or three-phase. A system for extremely high current, extremely short duration exposures (0.001 to 0.003 sec) employs energy-storage capacitors across the rectified high-voltage source to supply the high-current pulses under control of a high-voltage electrostatic switching tube of the grid-controlled type.

For energizing the end-grounded water-cooled tubes operated at high power levels for x-ray spectroscopy and diffraction, the two-valve full-wave circuit of Fig. 13 is frequently used. A capacitor may be added to this circuit to provide a constant, essentially ripple-free voltage for maximal intensity of radiation output. A so-called constant-potential circuit is often used in units for operation at 200 to 400 kv. In one such circuit (Fig. 14), the transformer, through rectifier tubes, charges separate capacitors on respective half cycles, these capacitors being arranged to discharge in series continuously through the x-ray tube. In this way the output voltage of the transformer is doubled and the voltage to the x-ray tube is approximately constant, resulting in increased x-ray output.

Special-purpose Power Supplies. For voltages ranging from about 200 kv to 2 Mev, the so-called resonant transformer system of generating high voltage has been employed in a number of instances (see Fig. 15). In this system, the inductance represented by the transformer secondary is "tuned" to the operating frequency by means of the capacitance of the secondary and its high-voltage terminal. This tuned circuit is designed with a high Q, so that a high circulating current and a correspondingly high terminal voltage is obtained. By using an elevated frequency, such as 1,000 to 2,000 cps, extremely compact and lightweight units can be designed for relatively high voltages. These units are in the self-rectified category, since the x-ray tube is subjected to alternating voltage.

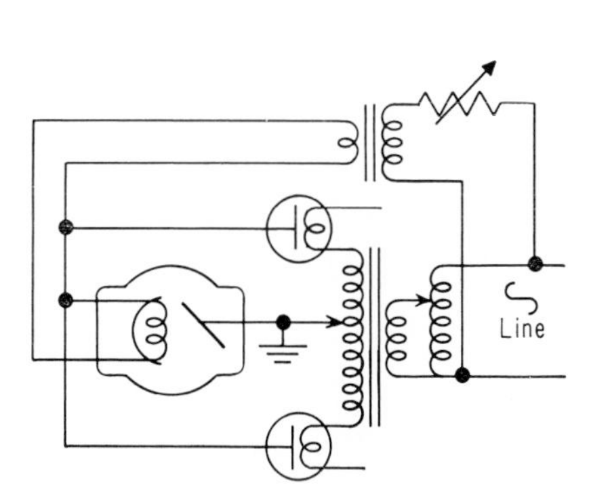

FIG. 13. Two-valve full-wave circuit for operation of end-grounded tubes.

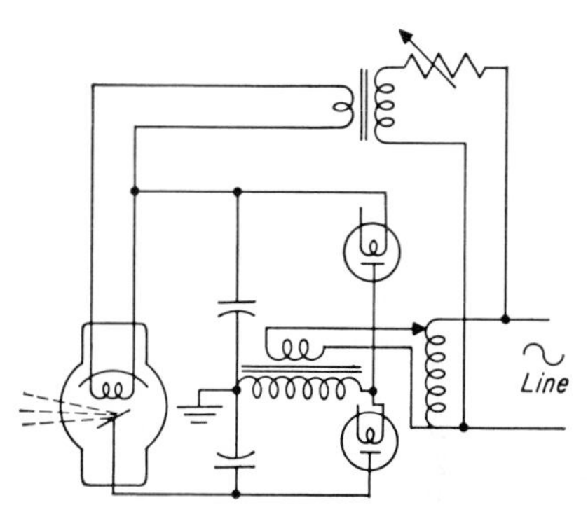

FIG. 14. Diagram of voltage-doubling constant-potential circuit.

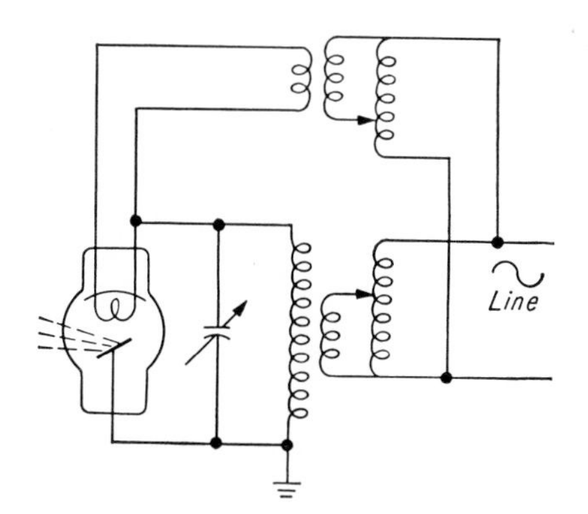

FIG. 15. Diagram of resonant transformer circuit.

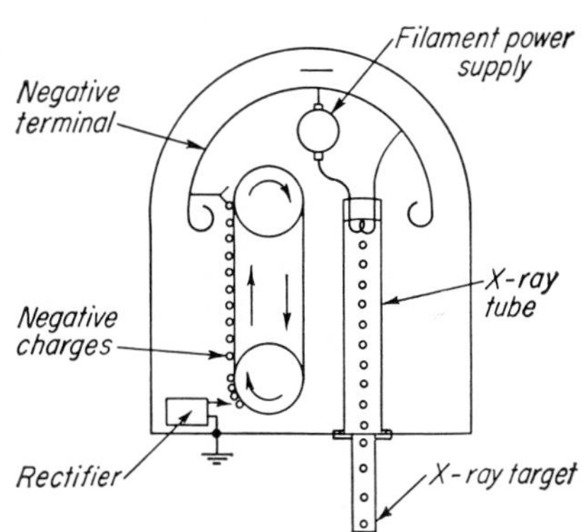

FIG. 16. Diagram of Van de Graaff electrostatic generator.

For voltages in the range of 1 to 6 Mev, the Van de Graaff electrostatic generator has been employed with great success (Fig. 16). In this type of unit, negative electric charges are sprayed on a moving insulating belt at a relatively low voltage (approximately 50 kv). These charges are mechanically transported to the insulated high-voltage terminal of the machine where they are removed and accumulated. The voltage is maintained at any desired constant value by balancing at that voltage the electrons flowing from the terminal via the x-ray tube with the electrons continuously replenished by the charge-carrying belt. Currents ranging from 0.25 to 4.0 ma can be delivered to an electron or positive-ion accelerator tube at voltages up to 10 Mev by this type of device. Over 10 kw output of electron power has been produced by Van de Graaff electrostatic accelerators for radiation processing. Another type of electrostatic generator employing a rotating glass cylinder to transport charges has been developed in France which operates in a range of 100 to 600 kv and is being employed as an x-ray generator.

The betatron (Fig. 17) employs magnetic induction rather than high voltage to accelerate electrons to high energies; this principle is best suited to energy ranges from 5 to 100 Mev. The electrons make hundreds of thousands of revolutions in the circular path provided in the "donut" tube described previously (Sec. 2). The betatron machine is essentially a large magnetic core, energized by alternating current similarly to a transformer, in which the "donut" acts as a secondary winding and the electron revolutions are analogous to the secondary transformer turns. The apparatus

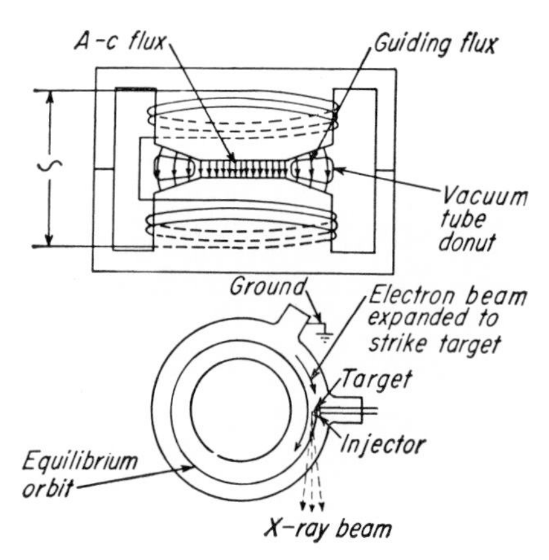

FIG. 17. Diagram of betatron principle.

also includes a large capacitor bank which helps supply the reactive kva required to energize the betatron magnet. Control of betatron injection and the orbit-expanding pulse must also be provided by appropriate circuitry.

Still another device employed for acceleration of electrons and other charged particles is the linear accelerator. This device utilizes extremely high frequency (microwave) energy, in a series of resonant cavities or a waveguide, to set up instantaneous high electric fields which move along in synchronism with the electrons of a beam injected into the system. For x-ray purposes, such accelerators are in use at energy levels from 6 to 50 Mev. The high-frequency energy is supplied by radar-type oscillators, employing klystrons, magnetrons, or other similar devices, in very short but intense bursts or pulses. Average beam-current values are usually well under 100 μa, but because of the high electron energy the x-ray yield may be quite high. For radiation processing, microwave linear accelerators with over 5 kw of output electron power are feasible.

All the "special-purpose" types of generators described above are used for industrial radiography, the required penetrating power determining the selection of the voltage range. All types are also being used in certain instances for deep therapy. All the generator circuits described for voltage ranges above 1 Mev are also used for the production of electron beams for direct application externally of the tube.

Chapter 3

DETECTION AND MEASUREMENT OF X-RAYS

Victor E. Buhrke

Picker Nuclear Western

1. DEFINITIONS

Avalanche. A process by which an ion produces another ion by collision and the new and original ions produce still others by further collisions (cf. Fig. 1).

Background. An unwanted signal from one or more of the following sources: cosmic radiation, electronic noise, thermal noise, spectral impurities from the target and/or window of the x-ray tube, secondary radiation from the collimators, scatter from the analyzing crystal or crystal holder, Compton or modified scatter, scatter from the sample (cf. Chap. 33), and natural radioactivity in building materials.

Characteristic Curve. The plot of counting rate vs. voltage applied to the detector, all pulses counted being greater than the threshold sensitivity of the detecting circuit (cf. Figs. 2 and 3).

Dead Time. The time interval, after recording a count, during which the detector is completely insensitive and does not detect other ionizing events occurring inside it. It is the time interval during which pulses cannot be detected, or the interval between the beginning of a pulse of normal amplitude and the point following it after which the next pulse can be detected (cf. Fig. 4).

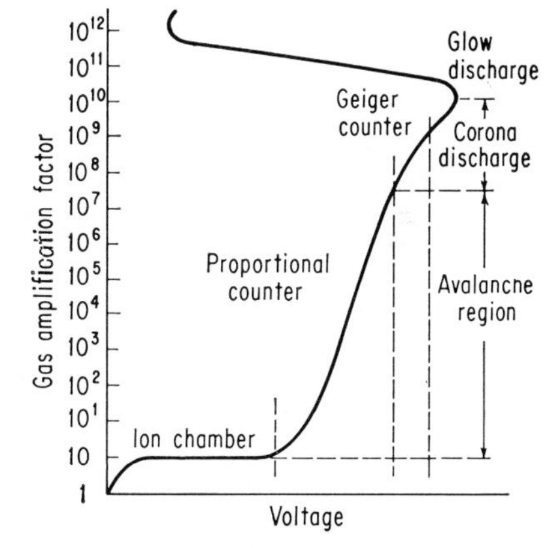

FIG. 1. Effect of voltage on the gas amplification factor. [*Reprinted with permission from H. Friedman, Proc. IRE*, **37**: *791*(*1949*).]

Efficiency. The ratio of the number of x-ray quanta producing counts to the number of quanta incident upon the detector. Quantum counting efficiency (Q.C.E.) is a measure of the probability that a quantum entering the detector will produce a count (cf. Fig. 5).

Escape Peak. A photon loses some energy when it produces secondary fluorescence of the detecting elements of a detector. This photon may, however, retain sufficient energy to produce additional ion pairs along its path through the detector The output of a detector may therefore include pulses from those photons which have the energy of the original pulse minus that required to fluoresce the elements of the

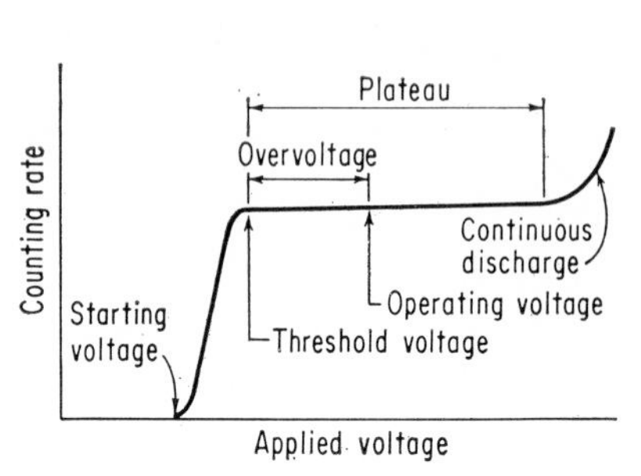

FIG. 2. Effect of voltage on counting rate for constant x-ray intensity.

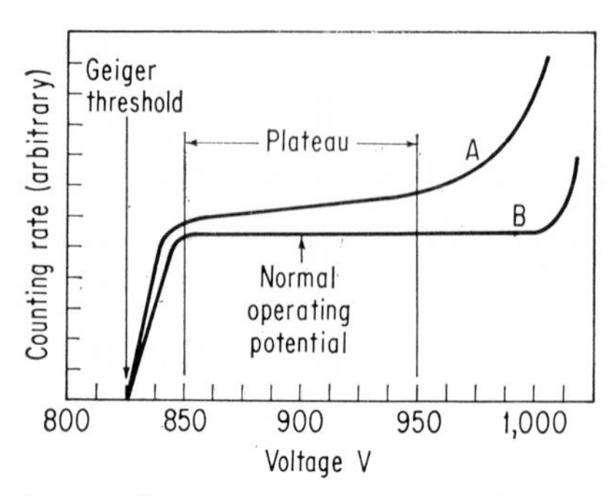

FIG. 3. Geiger counter characteristic. (*a*) Without quenching circuit, slope 0.08 per cent per volt. (*b*) With multivibrator quenching circuit, slope 0.03 per cent per volt.

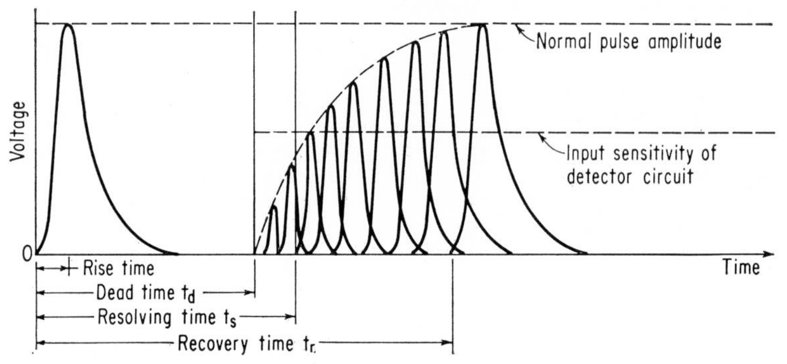

FIG. 4. Characteristic times of radiation detector circuits.

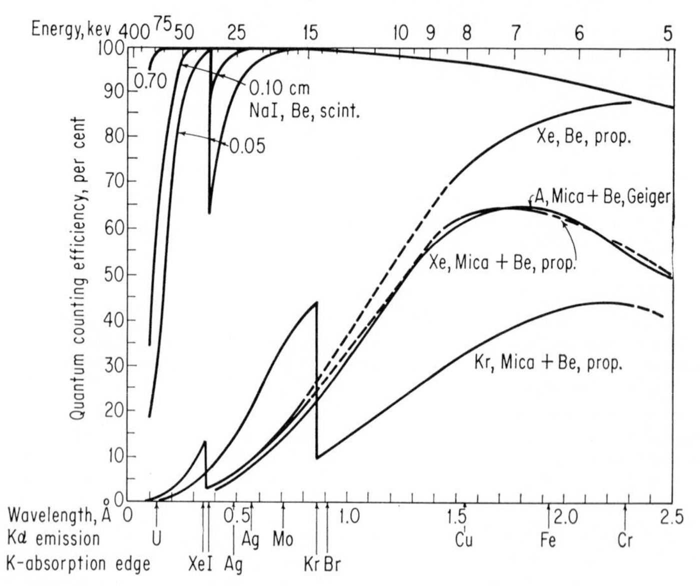

FIG. 5. Quantum-counting efficiency as a function of wavelength. [*Reprinted with permission from J. Taylor and W. Parrish Rev. Sci Instr.*, **26**: *367* (*1955*).]

detector. The escape peak is produced by those photons which have lost some energy in causing the secondary fluorescence. The escape peak can be either useful or troublesome in some analyses (cf. Fig. 6).

Gas-amplification Factor. The ratio of total ion pairs produced in a proportional detector to initial ion pairs resulting from the passage of radiation through the detector (cf. Figs. 7 and 8).

Initial Ion Pairs. Those ionized gas molecules created when a quantum of radiation collides with the gas molecules in a detector in the absence of a potential gradient between anode and cathode (cf. Total Ion Pairs, later in this section).

Ionization. The act or result of any process by which a neutral atom or molecule acquires a charge of either sign, or by which electrons are liberated.

Ionization Potential. The energy required to separate an electron from an atom to produce an ion and an electron (an ion pair). The energy required to produce an ion pair is approximately twice the energy of ionization because the process is inefficient. The change in potential (volts) at an anode is

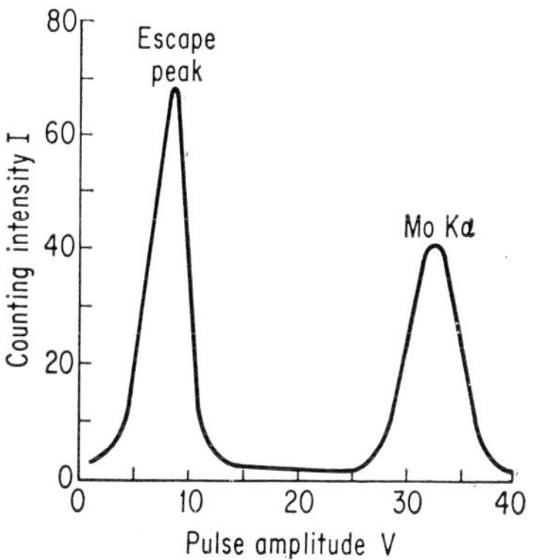

FIG. 6. Observed differential curves showing main and escape peaks for krypton proportional counter with Mo $K\alpha$. (*Reprinted with permission from International Tables for X-ray Crystallography, vol. III, p. 153 Kynoch Press, Birmingham, England,* 1961.)

$$dv = 10^{12}Ane/C = 1.6 \times 10^{-7}An/C \qquad (1)$$

where $e = 1.6 \times 10^{-19}$ coulomb (electronic charge)
A = gas-amplification factor
n = number of original ion pairs formed
C = capacity of counting chamber and circuit, μf

(cf. Tables 1 and 2).

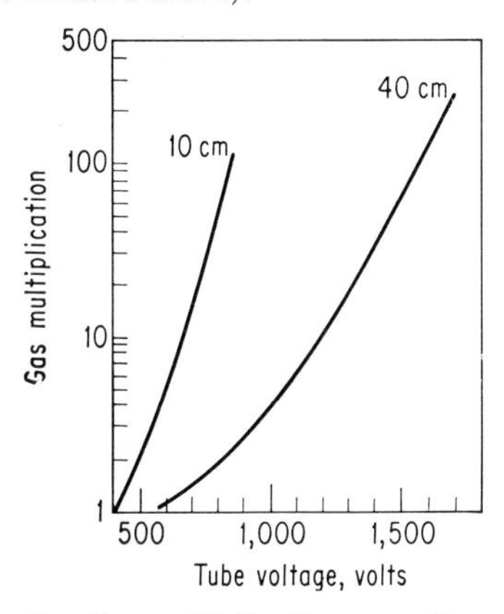

FIG. 7. Gas multiplication vs. voltage for pressure of 10 and 40 cm Hg; argon 99.6 per cent pure; collector diameter, 0.01 in.; cathode diameter, 0.87 in. (*Reprinted with permission from B. B. Rossi and H. H. Staub, Ionization Chambers and Counters, Chap. 4, National Nuclear Energy Series, div. V, vol. 2, McGraw-Hill Book Company, New York, 1949.*)

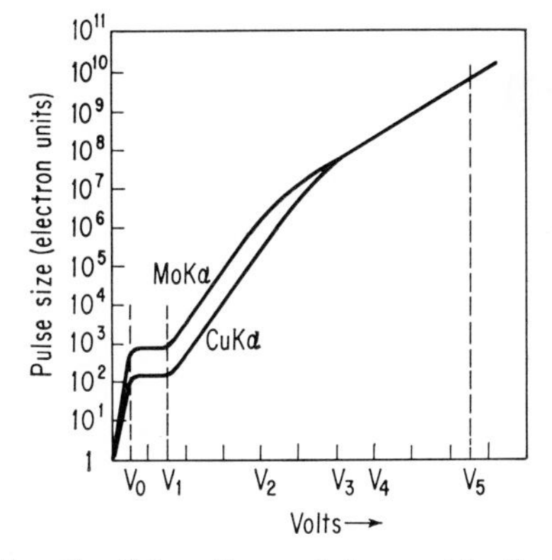

FIG. 8. Below V_0, partial recombination; V_0 to V_1, ionization chamber region A independent of initial ionization; V_2 to V_3, region of limited proportionality; V_4, Geiger threshold voltage; above V_5, continuous discharge. (*Reprinted with permission from H. S. Peiser, H. P. Rooksby, and A. J. C. Wilson, X-ray Diffraction by Polycrystalline Materials, The Institute of Physics and the Physical Society, London, Physics in Industry Series, 1954.*)

Table 1. The Chemical Elements—Ionization Potentials*

Z	Element	Symbol	IP	Ground state	Z	Element	Symbol	IP	Ground state
1	Hydrogen	H	13.595	$1s\ ^2S_{1/2}$	55	Cesium	Cs	3.893	$6s\ ^2S_{1/2}$
2	Helium	He	24.580	$(1s^2)\ ^1S_0$	56	Barium	Ba	5.210	$6s^2\ ^1S_0$
3	Lithium	Li	5.390	$2s\ ^2S_{1/2}$	57	Lanthanum	La	5.61	$5d\ 6s^2\ ^2D_{1\frac{1}{2}}$
4	Beryllium	Be	9.320	$2s^2\ ^1S_0$	58	Cerium	Ce	(6.91)	
5	Boron	B	8.296	$2s^2\ 2p\ ^2P_{1/2}^\circ$	59	Praseodymium	Pr	(5.76)	
6	Carbon	C	11.264	$2s^2\ 2p^2\ ^3P_0$	60	Neodymium	Nd	(6.31)	$4f^4\ 6s^2\ ^5I_4$
7	Nitrogen	N	14.54	$2s^2\ 2p^3\ ^4S_{1\frac{1}{2}}^\circ$	61	Promethium	Pm		
8	Oxygen	O	13.614	$2s^2\ 2p^4\ ^3P_2$	62	Samarium	Sm	5.6	$4f^6\ 6s^2\ ^7F_0$
9	Fluorine	F	17.42	$2s^2\ 2p^5\ ^2P_{1\frac{1}{2}}^\circ$	63	Europium	Eu	5.67	$4f^7\ 6s^2\ ^8S_{3\frac{1}{2}}^\circ$
10	Neon	Ne	21.559	$(2s^2\ 2p^6)\ ^1S_0$	64	Gadolinium	Gd	6.16	$4f^7\ 5d\ 6s^2\ _9D_2^\circ$
11	Sodium	Na	5.138	$3s\ ^2S_{1/2}$	65	Terbium	Tb	(6.74)	
12	Magnesium	Mg	7.664	$3s^2\ ^1S^\circ$	66	Dysprosium	Dy	(6.82)	
13	Aluminum	Al	5.984	$3s^2\ 3p\ ^2P_{1/2}^\circ$	67	Holmium	Ho		
14	Silicon	Si	8.149	$3s^2\ 3p^2\ ^3P_0$	68	Erbium	Er		
15	Phosphorus	P	11.0	$3s^2\ 3p^3\ ^4S_{1\frac{1}{2}}^\circ$	69	Thulium	Tm		$4f^{13}\ 6s^2\ ^2F_{3\frac{1}{2}}^\circ$
16	Sulfur	S	10.357	$3s^2\ 3p^4\ ^3P_2$	70	Ytterbium	Yb	6.2	$(4f^{14})\ 6s^2\ ^1S_0$
17	Chlorine	Cl	13.01	$3s^2\ 3p^5\ ^2P_{1\frac{1}{2}}^\circ$	71	Lutetium	Lu	5.0	$5d\ 6s^2\ ^2D_{2\frac{1}{2}}$
18	Argon	A	15.755	$(3s^2\ 3p^6)\ ^1S_0$	72	Hafnium	Hf	5.5 ±	$5d^2\ 6s^2\ ^3F_2$
19	Potassium	K	4.339	$4s\ ^2S_{1/2}$	73	Tantalum	Ta	6 ±	$5d^3\ 6s^2\ ^4F_{1\frac{1}{2}}$
20	Calcium	Ca	6.111	$4s^2\ ^1S_0$	74	Tungsten	W	7.98	$5d^4\ 6s^2\ ^5D_0$
21	Scandium	Sc	6.56	$3d\ 4s^2\ ^2D_{1\frac{1}{2}}$	75	Rhenium	Re	7.87	$5d^5\ 6s^2\ ^6S_{2\frac{1}{2}}$
22	Titanium	Ti	6.83	$3d^2\ 4s^2\ ^3F_2$	76	Osmium	Os	8.7	$5d^6\ 6s^2\ ^5D_4$
23	Vanadium	V	6.74	$3d^3\ 4s^2\ ^4F_{1\frac{1}{2}}$	77	Iridium	Ir	9.2	$5d^7\ 6s^2\ ^4F_{1\frac{1}{2}}$
24	Chromium	Cr	6.76	$3d^5\ 4s\ ^7S_3$	78	Platinum	Pt	8.96	$5d_9\ 6s\ ^3D_3$
25	Manganese	Mn	7.432	$3d^5\ 4s^2\ ^6S_{2\frac{1}{2}}$	79	Gold	Au	9.223	$(5d^{10})\ 6s\ ^2S_{1/2}$
26	Iron	Fe	7.896	$3d^6\ 4s^2\ ^5D_4$	80	Mercury	Hg	10.434	$6s^2\ ^1S_0$
27	Cobalt	Co	7.86	$3d^7\ 4s^2\ ^4F_{4\frac{1}{2}}$	81	Thallium	Tl	6.106	$6s^2\ 6p\ ^2P_{1/2}^\circ$
28	Nickel	Ni	7.633	$3d^8\ 4s^2\ ^3F_4$	82	Lead	Pb	7.415	$6s^2\ 6p^2\ ^3P_0$
29	Copper	Cu	7.723	$(3d^{10})\ 4s\ ^2S_{1/2}$	83	Bismuth	Bi	8 ±	$6s^2\ 6p^3\ ^4S_{1\frac{1}{2}}^\circ$
30	Zinc	Zn	9.391	$4s^2\ ^1S_0$	84	Polonium	Po		
31	Gallium	Ga	6.00	$4s^2\ 4p\ ^2P_{1/2}^\circ$	85	Astatine	At		
32	Germanium	Ge	8.13	$4s^2\ 4p^2\ ^3P_0$	86	Radon	Rn	10.745	$(6s^2\ 6p^6)\ ^1S_0$
33	Arsenic	As	10 ±	$4s^2\ 4p^3\ ^4S_{1\frac{1}{2}}^\circ$	87	Francium	Fa		
34	Selenium	Se	9.750	$4s^2\ 4p^4\ ^3P_2$	88	Radium	Ra	5.277	$7s^2\ ^1S_0$
35	Bromine	Br	11.84	$4s^2\ 4p^5\ ^2P_{1\frac{1}{2}}^\circ$	89	Actinium	Ac		
36	Krypton	Kr	13.996	$(4s^2\ 4p^6)\ ^1S_0$	90	Thorium	Th	....	$6d^2\ 7s^2\ ^3F_2$
37	Rubidium	Rb	4.176	$5s\ ^2S_{1/2}$	91	Protactinium	Pa		
38	Strontium	Sr	5.692	$5s^2\ ^1S_0$	92	Uranium	U	4 ±	$5f^3\ 6d\ 7s^2\ ^5L_6^\circ$
39	Yttrium	Y	6.6	$4d\ 5s^2\ ^2D_{1\frac{1}{2}}$	93	Neptunium	Np		
40	Zirconium	Zr	6.95	$4d^2\ 5s^2\ ^3F_2$	94	Plutonium	Pu		
41	Columbium	Cb	6.77	$4d^4\ 5s\ ^6D_{1/2}$	95	Americium	Am		
42	Molybdenum	Mo	7.18	$4d^5\ 5s\ ^7S_3$	96	Curium	Cm		
43	Technetium	Tc	....	$4d^5\ 5s^2\ ^6S_{2\frac{1}{2}}$	97				
44	Ruthenium	Ru	7.5	$4d^7\ 5s\ ^5F_5$	98				
45	Rhodium	Rh	7.7	$4d^8\ 5s\ ^4F_{4\frac{1}{2}}$	99				
46	Palladium	Pd	8.33	$4d^{10}\ ^1S_0$	100				
47	Silver	Ag	7.574	$5s\ ^2S_{1/2}$	101				
48	Cadmium	Cd	8.991	$5s^2\ ^1S_0$	102				
49	Indium	In	5.785	$5s^2\ 5p\ ^2P_{1/2}^\circ$	103				
50	Tin	Sn	7.332	$5s^2\ 5p^2\ ^3P_0$					
51	Antimony	Sb	8.64	$5s^2\ 5p^3\ ^4S_{1\frac{1}{2}}^\circ$					
52	Tellurium	Te	9.01	$5s^2\ 5p^4\ ^3P_2$					
53	Iodine	I	10.44	$5s^2\ 5p^5\ ^2P_{1\frac{1}{2}}^\circ$					
54	Xenon	Xe	12.127	$(5s^2\ 5p^6)\ ^1S_0$					

Parentheses denote values that have been determined experimentally but not yet confirmed by series.

* Reprinted with permission from C. E. Moore, *Natl. Bur. Std.* (*U.S.*) *Circ.* 467, 1949.

Ion Pair. One electron and one positive ion. A copper photon (8 kev) produces approximately 300 ion pairs in an argon Geiger-Müller tube. The same photon can produce approximately 350 ion pairs in a xenon proportional detector. About 270 photons (only about 26 effective) are produced by a copper photon when it strikes NaI·Tl in a scintillation detector.

Operating Voltage. The voltage across the detector between cathode and anode. The voltage at which the detector is used to make measurements (cf. Fig. 2).

Photoelectron. An electron produced when an incident photon with sufficient energy collides with an atom and knocks out an orbital electron, thereby causing the

Table 2. Ionization Potentials*
The Elements

El.	At. No.	Ionization potential, volts					
		I	II	III	IV	V	VI
A	18	15.68	27.76	40.75	(61)	(78)	
Ac	89						
Ag	47	7.542	21.4	35.9			
Al	13	5.96	18.74	28.31	119.37	153.4	
As	33	10.5	20.1	28.0	49.9	62.5	
Au	79	9.18	19.95				
B	5	8.257	25.00	37.75	258.1	338.5	
Ba	56	5.19	9.95				
Be	4	9.28	18.12	153.1	216.6		
Bi	83	8.0	16.6	25.42	45.1	55.7	
Br	35	11.80	19.1	25.7	(50)		
C	6	11.217	24.27	47.65	64.22	390.1	
Ca	20	6.09	11.82	50.96	69.7		
Cb	41	......	....	24.2	....	49.3	
Cd	48	8.96	16.84	38.0			
Ce	58	6.54	14.8	....	(36.5)		
Cl	17	12.952	23.67	39.69	53.16	67.4	
Co	27	7.81	17.3				
Cr	24	6.74	16.6	....	....	(73)	
Cs	55	3.87	23.4	(35)	(51)	(58)	
Cu	29	7.68	20.34	29.5			
Dy	66	6.8					
Er	68						
Eu	63	5.64	11.4				
F	9	17.34	34.81	62.35	86.72	113.67	156.37†
Fe	26	7.83	16.16				
Ga	31	5.97	20.43	30.6	63.8		
Gd	64	6.7					
Ge	32	8.09	15.86	34.07	45.5	93.0	
H	1	13.527					
He	2	24.46	54.14				
Hf	72	......	(14.8)				
Hg	80	10.39	18.65	34.3	(72)	(82)	
Ho	67						
I	53	10.6	19.4				
Il	61						
In	49	5.76	18.79	27.9	57.8		
Ir	77						
K	19	4.318	31.66	46.5			
Kr	36	13.93	26.4	36.8	(68)		
La	57	5.6	11.4	(20.4)			
Li	3	5.363	75.26	121.8			
Lu	71						
Ma	43						
Mg	12	7.61	14.96	79.72	108.9		
Mn	25	7.41	15.70	....	....	(76)	
Mo	42	7.35	....	....	....	60.8	
N	7	14.48	29.47	47.40	77.0	97.4	
Na	11	5.12	47.06	70.72			
Nd	60	6.3					
Ne	10	21.47	40.9	63.2			
Ni	28	7.61	18.2				
O	8	13.550	34.93	54.87	76.99	113	137.5
Os	76	(8.7)					
P	15	10.9	19.56	30.012	51.106	64.698	
Pa	91						

Table 2. Ionization Potentials* *(Continued)*

El.	At. No.	Ionization potential, volts					
		I	II	III	IV	V	VI
Pb	82	7.38	14.96	(31.9)	42.11	69.4	
Pd	46	8.3	19.8				
Po	84						
Pr	59	5.8					
Pt	78	8.88					
Ra	88	5.252	10.099				
Rb	37	4.159	27.36	(47)	(80)		
Re	75						
Rh	45	7.7					
Rn	86	10.698					
Ru	44	7.7					
S	16	10.30	23.3	34.9	47.08	63	87.65
Sb	51	8.5	(18)	24.7	44.0	55.5	
Sc	21	6.7	12.8	24.61	(73.9)	(97.0)	
Se	34	9.70	21.3	33.9	42.72	72.8	
Si	14	8.12	16.27	33.35	44.93	165.6	
Sm	62	6.6	11.4				
Sn	50	7.30	14.5	30.5	39.4	80.7	
Sr	38	5.667	10.98				
Ta	73						
Tb	65	6.7					
Te	52	8.96	....	30.5	37.7	60.0	(72)
Th	90	......	....	29.4			
Ti	22	6.81	13.6	27.6	42.98	(99.6)	
Tl	81	6.07	20.32	29.7	50.5		
Tm	69						
U	92						
V	23	6.71	14.1	(26.4)	(48)	(65)	
W	74	8.1					
Xe	54	12.08	(21.1)	32.0	(46)	(76)	
Y	39	6.5	12.3	20.4			
Yb	70	7.1					
Zn	30	9.36	17.89	40.0			
Zr	40	6.92	13.97	24.00	33.8		

Compounds

Compound	Ionization potential I volts	Compound	Ionization potential I volts
Br_2	12.8	CH_3Cl, methyl chloride	10.7
BrCl	12.9 (calc.)	CH_3I, methyl iodide	9.1
C_2	12	CH_4, methane	14.5
CH_2O, formaldehyde	11.3	CN	14
CH_3Br, methyl bromide	10.0	CO	14.1

The degree of ionization is indicated by the numerals I, II, etc. Doubtful values are indicated by parentheses.

* Reprinted with permission from *Handbook of Chemistry and Physics*, 44th ed., Chemical Rubber, 1962.

† Seventh ionization potential of fluorine, 184.26 volts.

emission of characteristic radiation (x-ray fluorescent radiation). The ejected orbital electron is the photoelectron and has a kinetic energy equal to the energy of the photon which ejected it from its orbit minus the binding energy of the orbital electron.

Plateau. That portion of the curve of count rate vs. applied voltage for a proportional detector which shows a minimum increase of count rate for an increase in applied voltage (cf. Figs. 2 and 3).

Pulse-height Analyzer.[32,46–49] An electronic device which permits the passage of only those pulses with voltage amplitudes between selected maximum and minimum values, and blocks all others. The voltage range between the maximum and minimum value is referred to as the channel or window (cf. Sec. 7).

Pulse-height Discriminator. A circuit which passes voltage pulses of a selected minimum amplitude and blocks the smaller pulses (cf. Sec. 7).

Quenching.[36–41] The process of terminating the discharge in a detector. During the migration of positive ions to the cathode, argon (or other noble gas) ions with an ionization potential of about 16 volts collide with the quench-gas molecules which have ionization potentials less than 16 volts (about 11 volts). Because of this difference in ionization potential, the charge is transferred from the positive ions to the quench-gas molecules. The quench-gas molecules then migrate to the cathode to be neutralized. The quench-gas molecules are thereby dissociated, using up energy and thus preventing any further ionization and multiple discharges (avalanches). When a small amount of a polyatomic gas such as an alcohol, ethylene, methane, or chlorine is introduced into the detector, the tube becomes "self-quenching." These polyatomic gas molecules, because of their diffuse rotational-vibrational absorption bands, can absorb the photons emitted by the ionized positive ions when they recombine with an electron. The polyatomic gases suitable as quench agents "prefer" to decompose into neutral particles rather than produce electrons and positive ions. The polyatomic gases may also give an electron to the positive ions by direct collision and then decompose. It should be mentioned that the halogen quench agents do not decompose during or after quenching. They actually do dissociate, but a recombination mechanism (free radical) replenishes the quench-gas supply. This mechanism is a change from molecular to atomic to molecular state, and not a permanent decomposition.

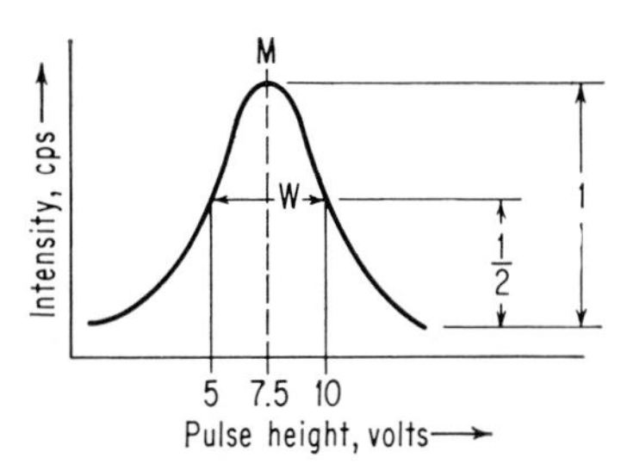

FIG. 9. Typical PHA curve (differential).

The quenching agent prevents the positive ions from ejecting electrons from the cathode and thereby prevents a continuous discharge from being set up in the detector. In halogen-quenched detectors the ionized gas atoms capture electrons from the diatomic halogen molecule, forming neutral gas atoms and ionized halogen. The ionized halogen is neutralized at the cathode and does not cause ejection of electrons.

Electronic circuits have been used to produce the same result as that brought about by quenching agents. These circuits lower the applied voltage at the proper time to bring it below the Geiger threshold and prevent ejection of electrons from the cathode by collisions from the positive ions.

Recovery Time. The time required for the positive-ion sheath (cloud) to travel to the cathode. It is advisable to quench over this time interval in order to avoid spurious counting (cf. Fig. 4).

Resolution of a Detector. When a beam of monochromatic radiation strikes the window of a detector which has the proper voltage applied to it, a series of output pulses of different pulse amplitudes (volts) is produced by the detector. The resolution of a detector for a particular energy (wavelength) of radiation may be expressed as the ratio of the width (in volts) at half maximum of the pulse-amplitude distribution divided by the mean pulse energy (volts) [cf. Fig. 9, Eq. (20)].

Resolving Time. The shortest time interval between counts that can be detected. It is the interval between the start of a pulse of normal amplitude and the time at which the detector and circuitry are first able to produce another pulse of sufficient amplitude to exceed the threshold value of the associated circuitry following the detector (cf. Fig. 1).

Rise Time, Dead Time, Resolving Time, Recovery Time (Notations refer to Fig. 4). A = rise time. The time interval from the beginning of a pulse to the time it takes for the pulse to reach 90 per cent of full amplitude.

B = dead time. The time interval after the beginning of a pulse during which the counter is incapable of producing another pulse.

C = resolving time. The time interval after the beginning of a pulse until the tube is capable of producing a second pulse of sufficient amplitude to trigger the associated circuit.

D = recovery time. The time interval after the beginning of a pulse until the tube is capable of producing a second pulse of full amplitude. The time for the positive-ion sheath to travel to the cathode of a gas-filled detector.

E = threshold amplitude for circuits.

F = 90 per cent of full amplitude.

Recovery time t_r

$$t_r = \frac{(r_c^2 - r_w^2)(P/P_0) \log (r_c/r_w)}{2K_A V} \tag{2}$$

where r_c = radius of cathode
r_w = radius of anode wire
K_A = ion mobility at atmospheric pressure P_0
P = filling pressure of detector
V = voltage applied across cathode and anode

Self-quenching. An internal atomic mechanism within the detector which causes the discharge in the detector to terminate. See Quenching above.

Starting Potential. The voltage which must be applied to a detector to cause it to begin to count.

Total Ion Pairs. Those ionized gas molecules produced when a strong enough potential gradient exists between anode and cathode to accelerate the initial ion pairs (see Initial Ion Pairs above) to a velocity such that they can produce ion pairs upon collision with other molecules in the detector.

2. DESCRIPTION OF DETECTORS

Geiger-Müller (G-M). *Description.* The Geiger-Müller tube usually consists of a cylindrical envelope containing the proper filling gases (cf. Fig. 10), two electrodes, and a thin window which is transparent to x-rays (cf. Table 8). The envelope can be glass with a thin conductive coating to form a cathode, or it can be a metal tube made of stainless steel or some other high-work-function material. The collector (anode) is the other electrode and is usually a coaxially mounted, thin tungsten wire. The filling gases can be noble gases with or without a quenching agent (cf. Sec. 1). The pressure of the filling gas varies from 1 atm down to several centimeters of Hg (cf. Table 7).

Operation. When an ionizing particle is transmitted into the volume of the tube it produces free electrons and positive ions around the anode wire. The electrons have a relatively high mobility (cf. Table 3) and are accelerated to the anode wire. The positive ions being of a much slower mobility form a sheath around the anode. This sheath causes a decrease in the field strength around the anode. The free electrons, however, are under a strong acceleration voltage and each electron can acquire sufficient energy to produce additional ionization of the filling gas. Each photon entering the tube can therefore produce an avalanche (cf. Fig. 1) of electrons because of the high voltage. When the electrons reach the anode they produce a current and this pulse is in turn registered and/or counted. Every discharge in a G-M tube builds up to a constant size, and therefore the size of a pulse in a G-M tube is not a function of the original number of ions produced (or the energy of the incident photon).

Proportional. *Description.* Generally, the proportional tube is similar in construction to the G-M tube. The description of the G-M tube will provide the reader with a word picture of the proportional tube. Differences between G-M and proportional tubes are given in Table 6.

Operation. The proportional detector is a gas-filled chamber which operates in a voltage region between those of the ionization chamber and G-M tube (cf. Fig. 1). This is a region in which there is gas multiplication, and proportionality to particle energy is still present (cf. Fig. 8).

The discharge terminates in a proportional tube when the electrons in the gas volume have all been gathered by the anode. In contrast, the discharge terminates in a G-M tube when the positive-ion sheath covers the anode.

The amount of ionization produced per discharge in a proportional detector is a function of tube characteristics, operating conditions, and the extent of the primary ionization. The extent of ionization is related to the energy of the particle which produced the primary ionization. This is in sharp contrast to the G-M tube, where gas multiplication proceeds to a fixed number of ion pairs, regardless of the primary ionization (energy of the particle).

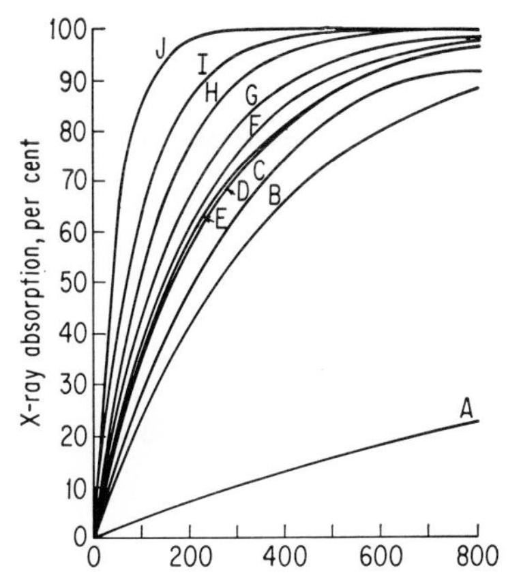

Fig. 10. X-ray absorption as a function of gas pressure and length of column. (*A*) Molybdenum $K\alpha$ in argon. (*B*) Copper $K\alpha$ in argon. (*C*) Molybdenum $K\alpha$ in xenon. (*D*) Cobalt $K\alpha$ in argon. (*E*) Molybdenum $K\alpha$ in krypton. (*F*) Copper $K\alpha$ in kyrpton. (*G*) Iron $K\alpha$ in argon. (*H*) Cobalt $K\alpha$ in krypton. (*I*) Iron $K\alpha$ in krypton. (*J*) Copper $K\alpha$ in xenon. (*Reprinted with permission from H. S. Peiser, H. P. Rooksby, and A. J. C. Wilson, X-ray Diffraction by Polycrystalline Materials, 1st ed., p. 199, The Institute of Physics and the Physical Society, London, Physics in Industry Series, 1954.*)

Scintillation. *Description.* A scintillation detector consists of a crystal, light pipe, and multiplier phototube. An electronic preamplifier is also sometimes considered to be part of the detector. The crystal may consist of many different materials, some of which are activated sodium and lithium iodides. The crystal is frequently coated with a thin layer of beryllium under which is a thin layer of aluminum. These coatings are placed on the surface between the crystal and the opening through which x-rays should pass. The beryllium is not transparent to visible light but is transparent to most x-rays. The aluminum acts as a reflector for light which is created by scintillation in the crystal but directed away from the multiplier phototube. The aluminum is a mirror to reflect this light back to the photoemissive cathode. Between the crystal and multiplier phototube is a material (light pipe) with high transmission for the light scintillated in the crystal. Following the light pipe is the multiplier phototube. This tube is a phototube in which a very large multiplication of the current of photoelectrons from the photocathode of the tube can take place. These photoelectrons are produced by the light from the scintillation crystal.

Operation. When a particle or photon strikes the scintillation crystal the photon or particle can lose some or all of its energy by absorption and produce a scintillation of light within the crystal. The amount of light produced is a function of the energy of the particle or photon. The light is transmitted to the photocathode of the multiplier phototube. The light causes the ejection of electrons from the cathode. These electrons are then permitted to strike the first dynode of the tube. There is a multiplication at each dynode, and the resulting multiplication can reach well in excess of 10^6. These electrons are finally collected at the anode. The current pulse is ampli-

Table 3. Mobilities of Positive and Negative Ions*
(cm/sec)(volt/cm)$^{-1}$(mm Hg)

Gas	Air	Argon	Hydrogen	Nitrogen	CO_2
Positive ion	1,070	1,040	4,300	980	600
Negative ion	1,290	1,290	6,500	1,380	720

* Reprinted with permission from *International Critical Tables*, McGraw-Hill Book Company, New York, 1929.

Table 4. Scintillators*

Material	Wavelength of max emission, Å	Decay time, sec
Anthracene	~4,400	2.7×10^{-8}
Trans-stilbene	~4,100	$3–7 \times 10^{-9}$
NaI(Tl)	~4,100	2.5×10^{-7}
LiI(Sn)	~5,300	
LiI(Eu)	~4,400	
ZnS(Ag)	~4,500	1×10^{-5}

* Reprinted with permission from W. J. Price, *Nuclear Radiation Detection*, 2d ed., McGraw-Hill Book Company, New York, 1964.

Table 5. Characteristics of Representative Scintillation Phosphors*

Material	Wavelength of max emission, Å	Decay constant, μsec	Density, g/cm^3	Relative pulse height†
Inorganic crystals:				
NaI(Tl)	4,100	0.25	3.67	210
CsI(Tl)	4,200–5,700‡	1.1	4.51	55
KI(Tl)	4,100	1.0	3.13	50 (approx)
LiI(Eu)	4,400	1.4	4.06	74
Organic crystals:				
Anthracene	4,400	0.032	1.25	100
Trans-stilbene	4,100	0.006	1.16	60
Plastic phosphors	3,500–4,500	0.003–0.005	1.06	28–48
Liquid phosphors	3,550–4,500	0.002–0.008	0.86	27–49

* Courtesy of Harshaw Chemical Company, Cleveland, Ohio.
† With 10 μsec anode time constant (Robert Swank, *Ann. Rev. Nuclear Sci.*, **4** (1954).
‡ Unpublished data of Bonomomi and Rossel quoted by B. Hahn and J. Rossel in *Helv. Phys. Acta*, **26** (1953).

fied and fed through an analyzer or discriminator (cf. Sec. 1 for definitions) to a scaler and/or rate meter (cf. Sec. 8).

The operation of the scintillation detector can be divided into several consecutive steps:

1. The absorption of the radiation in the scintillator and the consequent excitation and ionization in the scintillator

Table 6. Characteristics of Representative Photomultipliers*

Type	Manufacturer	Photocathode size (min diam, in.)	Spectral class	Avg sensitivity, μa/lumen	Gain	Diam, in.	Overall dimensions (length, in.)
6342-A	RCA	1.5	S-11	50	2.3×10^6†	$2\frac{1}{4}$	$5\frac{13}{16}$
6655-A	RCA	1.7	S-11	50	2.3×10^6†	$2\frac{1}{4}$	$5\frac{13}{16}$
6810-A	RCA	1.7	S-11	60	6.3×10^8‡	$2\frac{3}{8}$	$7\frac{1}{2}$
6199	RCA	1.24	S-11	45	2.8×10^6†	$1\frac{9}{16}$	$4\frac{9}{16}$
6292	Dumont	1.5	S-11	60	2×10^6§	$2\frac{1}{16}$	$5\frac{5}{8}$
6363	Dumont	2.5	S-11	60	2×10^6§	3	$6\frac{1}{8}$
6364	Dumont	4.2	S-11	60	2×10^6§	$5\frac{1}{4}$	$7\frac{1}{8}$
6291	Dumont	1.25	S-11	60	2×10^6§	$1\frac{1}{2}$	$4\frac{1}{4}$
CL 1012	CBS	1.348	S-11	60	2.25×10^5†	$1\frac{1}{2}$	$4\frac{3}{4}$
CL 1002	CBS	1.745	S-11	60	2.25×10^5†	2	$5\frac{5}{8}$
CL 1003	CBS	2.703	S-11	60	2.25×10^5†	3	$6\frac{1}{8}$
CL 1015	CBS	4.250	S-11	70	1.90×10^5†	$5\frac{1}{4}$	$7\frac{3}{4}$
9536B	EMI	1.75	S-11	50	6×10^5	$2\frac{1}{16}$	$5\frac{3}{4}$
9578B	EMI	2.5	S-11	50	....	$3\frac{3}{32}$	$6\frac{1}{8}$
9579B	EMI	4.37	S-11	50	....	5	$7\frac{1}{2}$
8054	RCA	2.59	S-11	75	8×10^4	3	$6\frac{5}{16}$

* Courtesy of Harshaw Chemical Company, Cleveland, Ohio.
† 1,250-volt supply voltage.
‡ 2,300-volt supply voltage.
§ At 145 volts/stage.

2. Conversion of the energy absorbed by the scintillator into light (energy) by means of luminescence
3. Transfer of the light photons to the photocathode of the multiplier phototube
4. Absorption of the light photons by the photocathode and emission of photoelectrons
5. Electron multiplication within the multiplier phototube
6. Analysis of the voltage pulse formed by the multiplier phototube through the application of additional, succeeding electronic circuits

There are losses in each process taking place in the scintillation detector. Approximately 26 electrons arrive at the first dynode of the multiplier phototube when an 8-kev copper photon strikes an NaI·Tl crystal of "optimum" thickness.

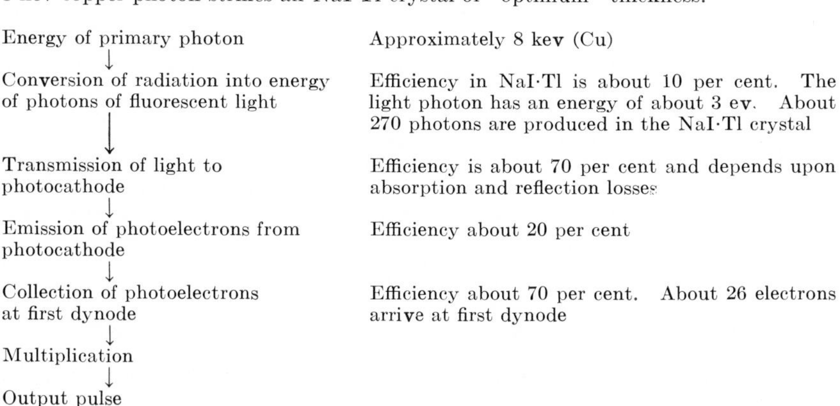

Energy of primary photon
Approximately 8 kev (Cu)
Conversion of radiation into energy of photons of fluorescent light
Efficiency in NaI·Tl is about 10 per cent. The light photon has an energy of about 3 ev. About 270 photons are produced in the NaI·Tl crystal
Transmission of light to photocathode
Efficiency is about 70 per cent and depends upon absorption and reflection losses
Emission of photoelectrons from photocathode
Efficiency about 20 per cent
Collection of photoelectrons at first dynode
Efficiency about 70 per cent. About 26 electrons arrive at first dynode
Multiplication
Output pulse

Resolution of the Scintillation Detector. The resolution R may be defined as

$$R = \frac{(\bar{Q})^2}{Q^2 - (\bar{Q})^2} = \frac{(\bar{Q})^2}{\Delta^2} \tag{3}$$

where R = resolution, a measure of uniformity of pulse size
$\bar{Q}$ = mean pulse amplitude
$(\bar{Q})^2$ = square of the mean
Δ = mean-square deviation of Q

For a series of identical scintillations,[4]

$$\frac{1}{R} \cong \frac{\Delta^2}{n_e^2 M^2} = \frac{\delta_e^2}{n_e^2} + \frac{\delta_1^2}{n_e m_1^2} + \frac{\delta_2}{n_e m_1 m(m-1)} \tag{4}$$

where n_e = average number of electrons reaching first dynode when light input remains constant
δ_e^2 = mean-square deviation of n_e
m_1 = average multiplication factor at first dynode
δ_1^2 = mean-square deviation in m_1
m = average multiplication factor at each of $n - 1$ succeeding dynodes
δ_2 = mean-square deviation in m
M = $m_1 m^{n-1}$, the overall multiplication in n stages

The term δ_e^2/n_e^2 expresses the statistical nature of the photoelectric-emission process and follows the Poisson distribution.

The term $\delta_1^2/n_e m_1^2$ applies to the first dynode.

The term $\delta_2/n_e m_1 m(m - 1)$ applies to successive dynodes.

The equation above can be used to show that increasing the number of electrons n_e which reach the first dynode is a good method to increase resolution. Another method is to increase the voltage on the first dynode. There is an optimum value which can be found experimentally (cf. Sec. 7).

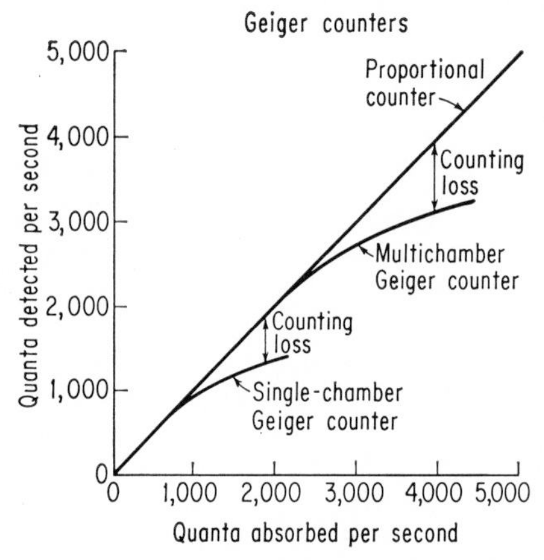

FIG. 11. The effect of counting rate on counting losses.

3. GENERAL REQUIREMENTS OF A DETECTOR

Linearity. The detector should maintain a linear response over a broad range of intensities (cf. Fig. 11).

Stability. It should not be sensitive to variations in ambient temperature and should maintain a stable response to incident radiation over long periods of time.

Signal-to-Noise Ratio. It should be as insensitive as possible to noise or background radiation and be as sensitive as possible to the radiation of interest. That is, it should operate with a high signal-to-background ratio.

Energy Resolution. It should be selective in its response to different wavelengths of radiation. In the case of diffraction from polycrystalline materials or x-ray spectrochemical analysis, this implies sensitivity to characteristic rays and little or no response to white or background radiation. When using a polychromatic beam (Laue work) a high degree of energy resolution is not desirable.

Quantum Efficiency. It should detect a high percentage of the incident quanta of the radiation of interest (cf. Fig. 5).

Sensitivity. A single quantum incident to the sensing portion of the detector should produce a large response.

Lifetime. It should be useful for a long time.
Availability. It should be inexpensive and readily available for purchase.

4. COMPARISON OF DETECTORS

This comparison stresses only the three most commonly used detectors: Geiger, proportional, and scintillation. Some less common detectors are mentioned, but no detailed discussion is given.

Ionization Chamber. This detector is primarily of historical interest. It is difficult to use, lacks the capability of energy resolution, and is insensitive.[1–5]

Direct Photomultipliers. Dynodes are Be-Cu alloys, and the scintillator crystal is absent. The quantum-counting efficiency (QCE) of this detector is low for the wavelengths normally encountered in x-ray diffraction and spectroscopy (10 Å and shorter).[6–9]

Crystal Detectors. These special-application devices use crystals of CdS, AgCl, AgI, and diamond.[10–17]

Magnetic-strip Electron Multiplier. This device converts x-ray photons to secondary electrons. Amplification of the original signal provides a usable output pulse. Its main advantage is that it is windowless. A vacuum is essential at all times to protect the photocathode surfaces.[18,19]

Semiconductor Detectors. These devices rely on charge carriers which are produced when ionizing photons travel along semiconductors. Theoretical resolution is excellent but has not yet been achieved.[20]

Geiger-Müller. This detector is useful for routine diffractometry where pulse-height analysis is unnecessary and counting rates are less than about 600 counts/sec (cps).[21–25]

Sealed Proportional. A very low noise device, this has excellent energy resolution for certain wavelengths, short dead time, high quantum efficiency, and can be used for pulse-height analysis. The proportional tube does not suffer so large an increase in resolving time as the G-M tube when filling pressure is increased. The ratio of anode wire diameter to diameter of the detector is less in the proportional than in the G-M tube.

The accelerating field extends out to only a few wire diameters and in this way helps to hold constant the number of positive-ion–electron pairs which are formed as a result of a single ionizing event. The multiplication factor can be altered by changing the applied voltage. The output pulse amplitude is directly related to the energy of the incident photon because the multiplication factor is independent of the energy of the incident photon. As a result the proportional detector may be used with pulse-height analysis.[26–32]

Flow Proportional. When it is necessary to measure radiation with a wavelength greater than about 3 Å, it is advisable to use a flow counter. This detector uses a window so thin (about 0.1 micron) that gases can diffuse through it. The thin window makes it possible to measure soft radiation while the flow of gas through the detector makes it possible to keep a constant pressure in the chamber.

The G-M and proportional tubes are similar in that they resemble one another in appearance and construction. They usually consist of gas-filled cylindrical tubes with a coaxially mounted collector wire. They are fairly rugged and relatively free of noise.

Scintillation Detector. A very versatile device, these instruments are sensitive to shock and temperature changes. Shock will break the multiplier phototube and temperature changes can introduce variations in output. Energy resolution is not so good as that of the sealed proportional for the same wavelength. It has a very broad range of high quantum-counting efficiencies.[12,33,34,35]

5. GUIDE TO SELECTING A DETECTOR

Selection of the Detector. The proper selection of a detector will be easier if the investigator will ask himself the questions below and then base his selection on the matching of the radiation with the quantum efficiency and linearity of the detector, as well as on a decision as to whether pulse-height analysis (PHA) is necessary or useful for the particular application. Figure 12 shows the useful ranges of the commonly used detectors, and Table 7 gives a detailed comparison.

How is the detector going to be used? X-ray spectrochemical analysis? What elements (energies) are to be measured? Over what counting range will one work? Will there be scatter from the crystal or sample? Will PHA be necessary? What primary radiation will be used?

X-ray diffractometry? What anode (target) material will be used? Counting range? Scatter from sample or collimators? Will PHA be necessary?

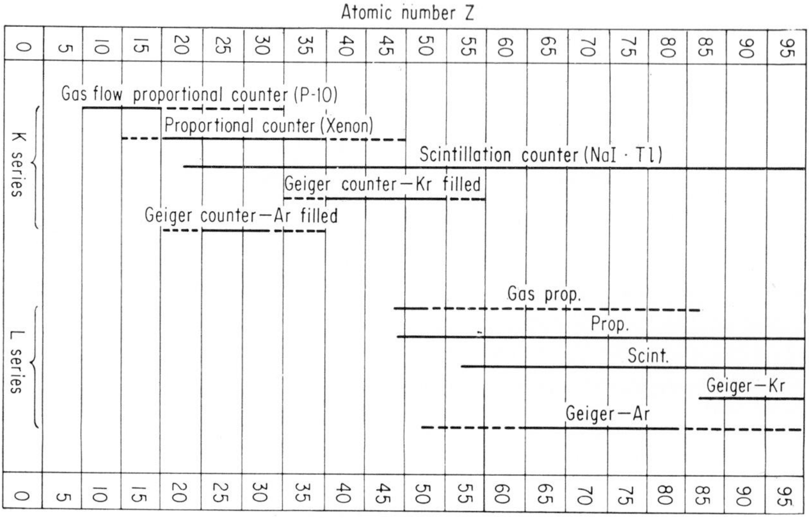

FIG. 12. Suggested guide for selecting a detector.

6. PROCEDURES FOR USE OF DETECTORS

Selection of Applied Voltage and Amplifier Gain. Proper selection of gain and d-c voltage will improve signal-to-noise ratios for all detectors.

Geiger. Try to use maximum d-c voltage and minimum amplifier gain. The noise from the linear amplifier is usually greater than the noise from the Geiger-Müller tube.

Proportional. The proportional and Geiger-Müller tubes contain gases as detecting media. The noise of these two tubes is similar. The smaller signal put out by the proportional detector means that more amplifier gain is required.

Proportional and Scintillation. If several wavelengths (energies) are to be studied, it is advisable to select a voltage that will satisfy the longest wavelength (lowest energy). This will usually assure adequate voltage for the other wavelengths to be measured.

Scintillation. The scintillation detector has a comparatively high noise. The linear amplifier is frequently "quieter" than the scintillation detector; therefore, use of a high gain is often desirable. In practice it is advisable to set the gain to the maximum which the particular circuits and laboratory surroundings will permit and set the d-c voltage to a minimum. Care must be taken to assure that adequate voltage exists on the first dynode; otherwise the performance of the scintillation detector will be below standard.

The pulses from the Geiger tube are often large enough to activate following circuits without need of preamplification. The pulses from proportional and scintillation detectors generally require preamplification to trigger the following scaling

Table 7. Comparison of Detectors

	Geiger-Müller	Proportional	Scintillation
Application	Diffractometry of polycrystalline materials. Spectrochemical analysis (fluorescence). Survey metering	Sealed—diffractometry and spectrochemical analysis (fluorescence). Flow—spectrochemical analysis of elements with Z less than 22	Diffractometry of polycrystalline or single-crystal materials. Spectrochemical analysis of elements with Z greater than 22
Advantages	Simple, stable, rugged, inexpensive, good efficiency, long life (if halogen-quenched), good peak-to-background ratio, small in size	Sealed—linear up to 10^4–10^5 cps. Excellent signal-to-noise ratio. Permits use of pulse-height analysis. Small size. Excellent energy resolution. High efficiency. Stable. *Versatile.* Flow—linear up to 10^4–10^5 cps. Excellent signal-to-noise ratio. Permits use of PHA. Small size. Excellent energy resolution. High efficiency. Very long life. Useful to measure soft (10-Å) radiation with good peak-to-background ratio. Stable	Linear up to 10^4–10^5 cps. Permits PHA. Excellent QCE over wide λ range. Long life. *Versatile.* Even response across crystal face
Disadvantages	Cannot use PHA. Nonlinear at 1,000 cps (single chamber). Limited sensitivity and versatility. Short life if organically quenched	Sealed—some temperature sensitivity. Requires a preamplifier. Escape peaks cause trouble. Each filling gas has a limited QCE for various λ. Has field-strength variation perpendicular to axis of anode wire. Flow—temperature-sensitive. Fragile windows. Escape peaks are troublesome. Requires preamplifier and gas cylinders. Sensitive to changes in flow rate of filling gas. Easily contaminated by "dirty" filling gas	Expensive. Temperature-sensitive! Poor peak-to-background for soft (3-Å) radiation. Poor energy resolution for 3-Å radiation. Fragile. Easily destroyed by overvoltage
Approximate cost	$50–$100	Counter plus preamplifier often exceeds $350	$500 or more (includes preamplifier)

Table 7. Comparison of Detectors (*Continued*)

	Geiger-Müller	Proportional	Scintillation
Operating voltages (depend on gas filling, pressure of filling, gain in amplifier, etc.)	~500–1,500 volts	~Several hundred to 2,000 volts	Usually less than 1,200 volts because of limit set by multiplier phototube
Operating temp, °C	(−50 to 200°C for special tubes) Depends on gas filling and construction. Halogen-quenched tubes can usually be used over bigger temperature range than organic-quenched tubes	Pulse amplitudes are a function of temperature in both sealed and flow types	Very sensitive to changes in temperature. Background counts can double for 10°C increase of temperature of crystal and multiplier phototube
Max. safe voltage	Continuous discharge region must be avoided in the case of organic-quenched tubes. Halogen-quenched counters are not so sensitive to accidental overvoltage	Voltages beyond plateau can cause permanent damage to gas filling and/or cathode and anode in sealed or flow types	Depends on multiplier phototube. Generally advisable not to exceed voltage where abrupt (3–10X) increase in noise pulses is produced by small (10–20 volts) increase in voltage
Life span	Halogen-quenched tubes have theoretically infinite lifetimes. Organic quenching agents render lifetimes of about 10^{10} counts. In practice it is not unusual to get several years of useful service from halogen-quenched G-M tubes	Sealed tubes can last for over 1 year. Flow tubes if kept clean and undamaged have infinite lifetimes. In practice one can expect years of useful service from flow counters and several months to years from sealed counters	Scintillation-counter lifetimes will vary from months to years, the determining factors being the quality of the hermetic seal and the multiplier phototube
Plateau length	100–300 volts	Varies with filling gas and energy of radiation being measured. Not unusual to get 200 volts or more, however	Varies with energy of radiation being measured, type of crystal, type of multiplier phototube
Plateau slope, % per 100 volts	3–15 depending upon filling gas, quenching agent, count rate, and other physical characteristics	About 2–5 depending upon count rate, filling gas, and other variables	When operated near optimum conditions, better than 8 can be obtained
Detection medium	Usually argon or krypton gas with an organic or halogen quenching agent	The xenon sealed detector is the most common. Flow counters usually employ argon-methane mixtures (P-10)	Sodium iodide activated with thallium. Other scintillators available

Table 7. Comparison of Detectors *(Continued)*

	Geiger-Müller	Proportional	Scintillation
Background (unshielded)	This depends on many other conditions being controlled; however, for a tube with an effective volume of about 800 cm³ the count will range about 1–2 counts/min (cpm)	Same as G-M tubes	Voltage on detector, gain in amplifier, shielding, type of multiplier phototube, age of equipment, etc., all affect background counts. Backgrounds of 1–2 counts/sec are usually accepted while doing diffraction or fluorescence work
Dead time	About 50–3,000 μsec	Less than 1 μsec	~1 μsec for NaI(Tl)
Pulse-height analysis	No	Yes	Yes
Type of output	Equal-sized pulses	Pulses proportional to energy of incident photon	Same as proportional counter
Process of detection	Electron and ion migration with Townsend avalanche and production of ultraviolet radiation	Localized reaction to incident absorbed radiation. Only a portion of the volume of the detector is involved in the absorption, ionization, and migration of a particular photon	Conversion of x-rays to light, light to photoelectrons, and secondary electron multiplication
Output pulse size	Volts	~1 mv	Several millivolts
Multiplication factor	10^6–10^8. All pulses have about the same size. See Sec. 2	~10^4	10^5–10^7

circuits. The preamplifier is usually placed near the detector instead of with the amplifier in the counting rack. The reason for this location is that it reduces noise pickup by the cable which connects the detector to the amplifier. If the preamplifier were placed with the amplifier, any noise pulses picked up in the cable would be preamplified and then amplified, resulting in a higher observed noise level.

Figure 8 shows the variation of pulse size with applied voltage:

1. Between voltages 0 and V_0 two processes compete, namely, the recombination of ion pairs and the removal of charge by collection of charges at the electrodes.

2. Between V_0 and V_1 is the saturation region. There is only negligible recombination in this region. This is the ionization-chamber region.

3. V_1 to V_2 is an area in which the charge collected is increased by gas multiplication. The electrons released in primary ionization have sufficient energy to produce additional ionization. Multiplication takes place, and the pulse size is a function of the initial ionization (energy of photon). This is the proportional region.

4. V_2 to V_3 is an area of limited proportionality in which the pulse size is not linearly dependent upon the charge collected during the initial ionization.

5. V_4 to V_5 is the Geiger region in which gas multiplication increases the charge to the limits of the chamber and associate circuits. Pulse size is no longer a function of the energy of the detected radiation.

Counting Loss, Sample Calculation. *Problem.* Estimate the counting rate at which the dead-time loss is 1 per cent for both a typical proportional counter and a G-M tube.

$\dot{m}$ = observed counting rate
$\dot{m}\tau$ = fraction of time during which the counter system is insensitive
τ = resolving time
$\dot{n}\dot{m}\tau$ = number of counts lost per unit time
$\dot{n}$ = counting rate observed if resolving time was negligibly small

$$\dot{n} - \dot{m} = \dot{n}\dot{m}\tau \qquad \text{(dead-time correction)} \tag{5}$$
$$\dot{n} = \dot{m}/(1 - \dot{m}\tau) \tag{6}$$
$$\text{Per cent dead-time loss} = 100\dot{m}\tau$$

Solution: Assuming dead-time values of 0.5 and 250 μsec for proportional and G-M tubes, respectively, leads to counting rates of

$$\dot{m} = \frac{1}{100\tau} = \frac{1}{(10^2)(0.5 \times 10^{-6})} = 2 \times 10^4 \text{ cps} \tag{7}$$

for proportional detectors and

$$\dot{m} = \frac{1}{100\tau} = \frac{1}{(10^2)(250 \times 10^{-6})} = 40 \text{ cps} \tag{8}$$

for G-M tubes.

Table 8. Transmission of Aluminum $K\alpha$ Radiation*

Material	Thickness, in.	% transmission
Aluminum foil	0.00045	22
Aluminum foil	0.0003	51
Beryllium foil	0.0045	1.2
Beryllium foil	0.001	55
Mica	0.0002	18
Mylar	0.00025	30
Formvar	Gives interference pattern	84

* Reprinted with permission from C. F. Hendee, S. Fine, and W. B. Brown, *Rev. Sci. Instr.*, **27**:532 (1956).

Table 9

Symbol	Fe	Co	Cu	Mo
At. No. Z	26	27	29	42
Wavelength, A°	1.94	1.79	1.54	0.71
Excitation voltage, kv	~6.4	~7.0	~8.1	~17.4
Curve for argon*	*G*	*D*	*B*	*A*
Curve for krypton*	*I*	*H*	*F*	*E*
Curve for xenon*	......	......	*J*	*C*

* See Fig. 10.

Suggestions on Use of the Detector. *Geiger*

1. See Fig. 5 for aid in selection of detector which will provide best quantum efficiency for radiation of interest.
2. Use.
   a. Set to pulse-height discrimination (not PHA) (cf. Sec. 7).
   b. Position detector to proper 2θ position.

Table 10. X-ray Attenuation in Spectrographs*

	0.1 Å	1.0 Å	10 Å
Fraction *Transmitted* by 10-cm Beam Path (1 atm; 25.0°C)			
Air	0.9983	0.9665	3×10^{-11}
He	0.9998	0.9996	0.920
Fraction *Transmitted* by Various Windows			
Be, 8 mils	0.9953	0.980	2.5×10^{-6}
Mica, 0.2 mil	0.9998	0.982	0.083
Mylar, 0.25 mil	0.9999	0.9983	0.263
Be, 1 mil†	0.9994	0.9975	0.199
Al, 0.2 mil	0.9998	0.9810	0.491
Fraction *Absorbed* by Counter Gas (3-cm path; 1 atm; 25°C)			
Argon‡	0.0008	0.154	>0.9999
Krypton	0.0045	0.264	>0.9999
Xenon	0.0186	0.806	>0.9999
Fraction *Absorbed* by Scintillation Counter Crystal			
Sodium iodide, 2 mm	0.511	>0.9999	>0.9999

* Reprinted with permission from H. A. Liebhafsky, H. G. Pfeiffer, E. H. Winslow, and P. D. Zemany, *X-ray Absorption and Emission in Analytical Chemistry*, John Wiley & Sons, Inc., New York, 1960.

† 1-mil Be is liable to be porous.

‡ P10 gas, used in flow counters, is 90% argon, 10% CH_4, and absorbs x-rays about like argon.

c. Use maximum voltage and minimum gain.
d. Turn x-rays off and plot counting rate vs. applied voltage for a fixed gain.
e. Turn x-rays on and permit their entry into tube. Plot voltage vs. count rate for fixed gain. Curve should be similar to that shown in Fig. 2.
f. Select voltage which is 50 to 75 volts to high side of knee.

Proportional

1. Select detector (cf. Fig. 5) with filling gas of highest quantum efficiency for desired radiation.
2. Use.
   a. Set analyzer to PHD, not PHA (cf. Sec. 7).
   b. Set detector to appropriate angle.
   c. Select intermediate gain because of low noise of detector relative to amplifier. Care must be taken not to use a gain which is so high that noise pickup by the detector cable starts to interfere.
   d. With x-rays off, run noise curve of detector by plotting counting rate vs. applied voltage for a fixed gain.
   e. With x-rays entering detector, increase applied voltage in about 25-volt steps and plot voltage vs. count rate.

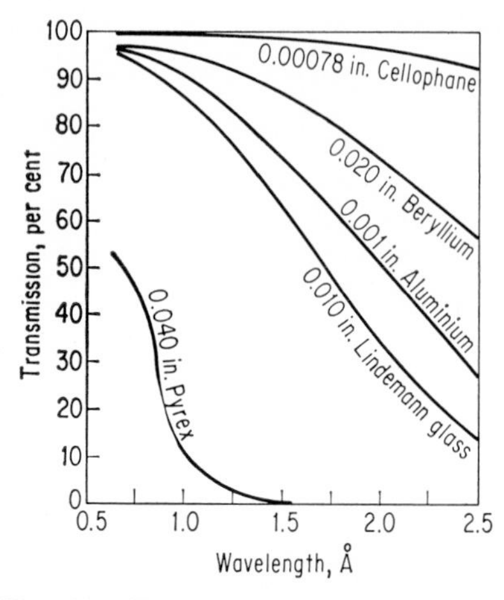

FIG. 13. Transmission characteristics of various materials used as windows in diffraction x-ray tubes. [*Reprinted with permission from H. Brackney and Z. J. Atlee, Rev. Sci. Instr.,* **14:** *59 (1943).*]

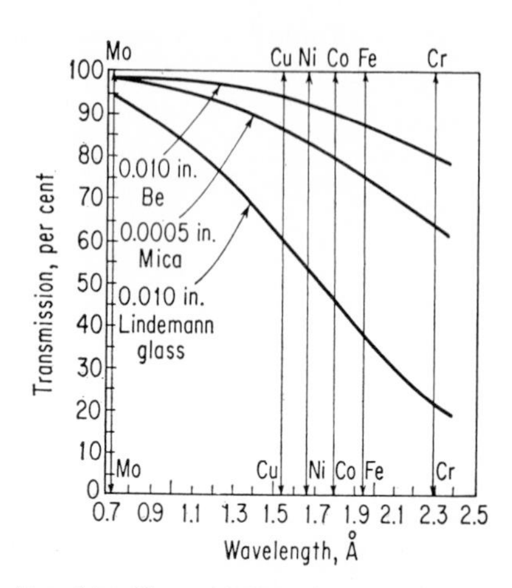

FIG. 14. Transmission of x-ray tube window materials for $K\alpha$ radiation. (*Reprinted with permission from H. Klug and L. E. Alexander, X-ray Diffraction Procedures, p. 64, John Wiley & Sons, Inc., New York, 1954.*)

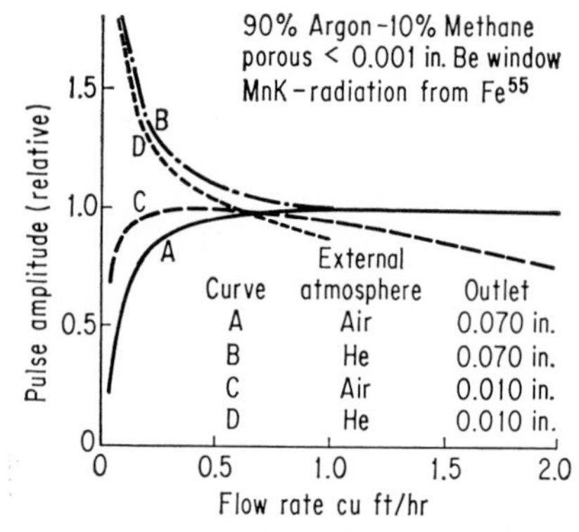

FIG. 15. Pulse amplitude as a function of counter gas flow rate. [*Reprinted with permission from C. F. Hendee et al., Rev. Sci. Instr.,* **27:** *531 (1956).*]

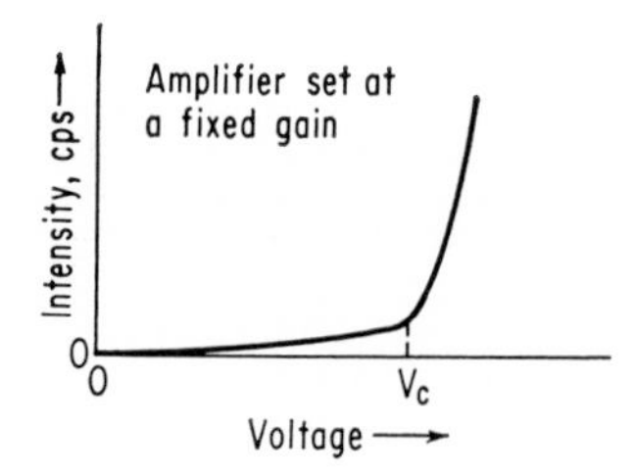

FIG. 16. Noise curve (x-rays off, fixed gain).

f. Select an operating voltage from portion of curve which shows smallest (a minimum) increase in counting rate for an increase in voltage applied to the detector.

Figure 15 can be used to select gas flow rate when using a flow-proportional detector.

Scintillation

1. Consult Fig. 5 to find if scintillation detector has satisfactory QCE for wavelength of interest.
2. Use.
   a. Set analyzer to PHD mode.
   b. Position detector at appropriate two-theta angle.
   c. With x-rays off, run noise curve (see Fig. 16). The relatively high noise of the scintillation detector requires that the operator use an applied voltage well below

the point at which noise pulses can become a serious interference. The noise curve will show an abrupt increase in count rate at a certain voltage for a fixed gain. Any attempt to use the detector with a voltage above this point is useless. The detector should be used to measure only wavelengths (energies) which require voltages below the point at which noise generation becomes excessive (i.e., beyond 2 to 3 cps). Cosmic radiation is approximately 2 particles/cm²-sec at sea level. V_c is maximum voltage which should be used for this detector at the fixed gain. Between 0 and V_c volts, the intensity (counts) produced is perhaps due to the cosmic radiation of high energy. The cosmic ray has such high energy that the total gain of the system required to register counts is very low as compared with those normally encountered in x-ray work.

d. Select a maximum amplifier gain to permit use of a minimum d-c voltage. The multiplier phototube is usually noisy compared with the amplifier. The applied voltage should not exceed $\sim$1,200 volts because many multiplier phototubes are permanently damaged if they are exposed to voltages above this level. The manufacturer usually supplies certificates or instructions which state the maximum voltage the tube can withstand.

e. With x-rays of interest entering the crystal, start at maximum gain and minimum voltage. The curve should look like Fig. 2.

f. Select an operating voltage on the "plateau." The term plateau is inappropriate when discussing scintillation detectors; however, for convenience the term is frequently used in the x-ray laboratory. The purist may find this objectionable. Generally speaking, the noise curves are an excellent (and almost the only) record by which to judge the performance of the tube as time passes. The slope of the plateau, the length of the plateau, and the noise level under certain conditions are all criteria by which to assign merit ratings to tubes. These criteria are applicable to G-M, proportional, and scintillation tubes.

7. PULSE-HEIGHT ANALYSIS (PHA) AND PULSE-HEIGHT DISCRIMINATION (PHD)

Introduction. The function of the *discriminator* is to accept pulses with amplitudes that fall above a threshold value. The function of the *analyzer* is to reject pulses which have amplitudes that fall below the base line and above the upper-level channel or window. It is not always advisable to use PHA instead of PHD. The choice frequently is made when it has been determined which method will yield the highest peak-to-background ratio and provide the most favorable counting statistics.

The size of pulses from proportional or scintillation detectors is inversely related to the wavelength of the x-rays producing them. It is possible to select or reject pulses on the basis of size (amplitude) by inserting special electronic circuits between the detector and the measuring circuit. The PHD and PHA are such special devices.

Application. The pulse-height analyzer is used to reject unwanted low- and high-energy pulses. A common application is the elimination of interfering high-order spectral lines. Many successful applications of PHA have been reported:

1. Determination of low concentrations of silicon in presence of high iron by x-ray spectrochemical analysis.
2. Removal of high background from radiation which has been scattered by slits, analyzing crystals, samples, sample holders, etc.
3. Measurement of low aluminum concentrations in presence of high nickel by x-ray spectrochemical analysis.
4. Removal of radiation whose origin is the continuous (white) spectrum.

Will the Pulse-height Analyzer Improve Counting Statistics? It is not always a simple matter to determine if the PHA will improve statistics. Nor is it always a simple operation to arrive at the ideal settings of the analyzer from the standpoint of counting statistics. The following approach might be useful in some instances. The procedure calls for measuring background and sample counting rates for several different settings of the PHA.

Procedure

1. Measure the background counting rate of your detector with the window of the analyzer out; in other words use PHD. The lower level (base line) should be high enough to reject thermal noise from the scintillation detector and major circuit noises when using gas detectors.

2. Determine the net sample counting rate with the instrument set to integral (PHD) as in step 1 above. The net rate is calculated by subtracting the background rate from the gross counting rate observed when the sample is in position.

3. Set the instrument to PHA with the window centered on the principal energy of x-ray to be measured and select a width of the window which is equal to 2.5 times the width of the resolution of the detector for the particular energy to be measured. (For example, the energy of copper $K\alpha$ photons is about 8 kev, and suppose we have a detector with an energy resolution of 50 per cent for 8-kev photons. Fifty per cent of 8 kev is 4 kev. Therefore, use a window that is $2.5 \times 4 = 10$ kev. The lower level will be at 3 kev and the upper level at 13 kev if the analyzer is centered on 8 kev with a 10-kev window.)

4. Measure the background counting rate of your detector with the window of the analyzer set in accord with instructions in step 3 above.

5. Determine the net sample counting rate of your sample with the window settings used in step 4.

6. Divide the result of step 2 by the result of step 1 and refer to this ratio as A.

7. Divide the result of step 1 by the result of step 4 and refer to this ratio as L.

8. Divide the result of step 2 by the result of step 5 and refer to the resulting ratio as M.

9. Refer to Table 11.

10. If K is larger than A (step 6), then the use of a pulse-height analyzer set as specified in step 3 will improve counting statistics in this case. If K is smaller than A,

Table 11. Table of Values of "Critical" Ratio K of Net CPM to Background CPM*

	$L = 2$	$L = 3$	$L = 4$	$L = 5$	$L = 6$	$L = 7$	$L = 8$	$L = 9$	$L = 10$
$M = 1.1$	7.9	11.9	14.0	15.2	16.0	16.5	17.0	17.3	17.6
$M = 1.2$	2.8	5.2	6.4	7.1	7.6	7.9	8.2	8.4	8.6
$M = 1.3$	1.0	2.9	3.9	4.4	4.8	5.0	5.2	5.4	5.6
$M = 1.4$	0.1	1.8	2.6	3.1	3.4	3.6	3.8	3.9	4.0
$M = 1.5$	...	1.0	1.8	2.2	2.5	2.7	2.9	3.0	3.1
$M = 1.6$	...	0.4	1.2	1.6	1.9	2.1	2.3	2.4	2.5
$M = 1.7$	...	0.1	0.8	1.2	1.5	1.7	1.8	1.9	2.0
$M = 1.8$	...	....	0.5	0.9	1.2	1.3	1.5	1.6	1.7
$M = 1.9$	...	....	0.2	0.6	0.9	1.1	1.2	1.3	1.4
$M = 2.0$	...	....	....	0.4	0.7	0.9	1.0	1.1	1.2
$M = 2.1$	...	....	....	0.2	0.5	0.7	0.8	0.9	1.0
$M = 2.2$	...	....	....	0.1	0.3	0.5	0.7	0.8	0.9
$M = 2.3$	...	....	....	....	0.2	0.4	0.5	0.6	0.7
$M = 2.4$	...	..	....	....	0.1	0.3	0.4	0.5	0.6
$M = 2.5$	...	....	....	....	....	0.15	0.3	0.4	0.5
$M = 2.6$	...	....	....	....	....	0.05	0.2	0.3	0.4
$M = 2.7$	...	....	....	....	....	.....	0.1	0.2	0.3
$M = 2.8$	...	....	....	....	....	.....	0.05	0.15	0.25
$M = 2.9$	...	....	....	....	....	.....	.....	0.05	0.15
$M = 3.0$	...	....	....	....	....	.....	.....	.....	0.10
$M = 3.1$	...	....	....	....	....	.....	.....	.....	0.05

* Reprinted with permission from F. H. Low, *Radioisotope Measurement in Nuclear Medicine*, Picker X-ray Corp., White Plains, N.Y., 1960.

or if there is no value for K given in Table 11, then an analyzer set as prescribed in step 3 will not improve counting statistics; it will make them worse.

11. Increase the size of the window so that it becomes three times as wide as the expected resolution. The window must remain centered; therefore, any adjustment in upper level should be accompanied by an equivalent adjustment in the base line.

12. Repeat steps 4 through 10 with the new settings.

13. Reduce the width of the window so that it is only two times the expected resolution.

14. Repeat steps 4 through 10 with the settings prescribed in 13.

15. If step 12 or step 14 gives a larger value of K than obtained in 10, then the conditions used to obtain the larger K should be used for measurement for they have provided a more favorable set of conditions. The process can be repeated to ensure that the largest K value has been obtained.

It should be remembered that PHA under correct conditions can provide more favorable counting statistics; however, improper settings or even use of PHA when unnecessary can result in poorer statistics.

Derivation of Formula Used to Compute Table of Values of K. The following formula was derived for the statistical error in the net result of a sample measurement:

$$\text{Per cent probable error (P.E.) of net} = \frac{\sqrt{[\text{cps}_{\text{gross}} \times (\text{per cent P.E.}_{\text{gross}}/100)]^2 + [\text{cps}_{\text{bkgd}} \times (\text{per cent P.E.}_{\text{bkgd}}/100)]^2}}{\text{cps}_{\text{gross}} - \text{cps}_{\text{bkgd}}} \times 100 \quad (9)$$

If we use the following symbols:

$$\begin{aligned} N_T &= \text{cps}_{\text{gross}} \\ N_B &= \text{cps}_{\text{bkgd}} \\ N_S &= \text{cps}_{\text{net}} = \text{cps}_{\text{gross}} - \text{cps}_{\text{bkgd}} \\ T_T &= \text{gross counting time} \\ T_B &= \text{background counting time} \\ Q &= \text{a given per cent P.E.} \end{aligned}$$

then the formula can be simplified to read

$$\text{Per cent P.E. of net} = \frac{\sqrt{N_T/T_T + N_B/T_B}}{N_S} = Q \quad (10)$$

$$Q^2 = \frac{N_T + N_B}{T_T} \quad (11)$$

$$T_T = \frac{N_T + N_B}{Q^2 N_S{}^2} \quad (12)$$

If we now assume that you are going to spend the same amount of time counting the sample and counting background separately (which is logical in the case where the two counting rates are similar, i.e., the net sample rate is small compared with the background rate), then we can say

$$T_T = T_B \quad (13)$$

and therefore

$$T_T = \frac{N_T + N_B}{A^2 N_S{}^2} = \frac{N_S + 2N_B}{A^2 N_S{}^2} \quad (14)$$

In this form, the formula can be used to compare the time required to obtain a given error with two different detectors, or with the same detector with and without a pulse-height analyzer. The basis of these procedures is whether A is greater than, equal to, or less than K.

$$\frac{T_{T_1}}{T_{T_2}} = \frac{N_{S_1} + 2N_{B_1}}{N_{S_2} + 2N_{B_2}} \left(\frac{N_{S_1}}{N_{S_1}}\right)^2 \quad (15)$$

Incidentally, this ratio is known as the "figure of merit." If we now choose ratios which are of interest to use,

$$H = N_{S_1}/N_{B_1} = \text{ratio of net cps to background cps without analyzer} \quad (16)$$
$$L = N_{B_1}/N_{B_2} = \text{ratio of background cps without and with analyzer} \quad (17)$$
$$M = N_{S_1}/N_{S_2} = \text{ratio of net cps without and with analyzer} \quad (18)$$

then the ratio of net cps to background cps (i.e., K) at which the pulse-height analyzer begins to help the statistics can be calculated by letting $T_{T_1} = T_{T_2}$ and substituting K, L, and M in the equation. Solving for K, this becomes

$$K = 2\frac{1 - M^2/L}{M - 1} \quad (19)$$

The above procedure was taken from *Picker Scintillator*, vol. 6, Jan. 1, 1962.

A Method of Obtaining a PHA Curve and Setting the PHA Window

1. Insert the proper specimen into the instrument so that the detector will receive the primary or secondary radiation which is to be measured at a later time.
2. Position the detector to the appropriate 2θ position.
3. Adjust the controls so that the circuits will perform as a PHA.
4. Set a window in the order of 0.5 kev.
5. Scan the base line from lower to higher energy settings. The PHA will pass only those pulses which correspond to the energy level between the base line and upper level of the PHA. The scan should resemble that shown in Fig. 17.

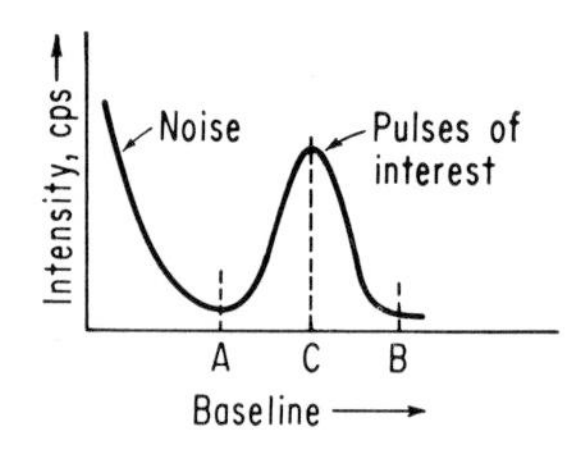

FIG. 17. PHA curve (differential).

6. Select base-line and upper-level settings which are symmetrical about the mean pulse amplitude. In the example of step 5 above, C is the mean pulse amplitude and A represents the lower level while B represents the upper level. A and B have the same energy difference from C. It can be seen that with the PHA set in this fashion the analyzer should pass most of the pulse about energy C, and in addition any fluctuations in A or B as a result of electrical instability are not accompanied by large charges in intensity. One should avoid setting the base line or window on the steep portions of the curve (between A and C, and between C and B).

Figure 18 shows the effect of pulse-height analysis on the spectrum of a copper-target x-ray tube. Peak-to-background ratios with and without discrimination are tabulated in Table 12.

Obtaining a PHD Curve

1. Same as for step 1 above.
2. Same as for step 2 above.
3. Adjust circuits to perform as PHD.
4. Scan base line from low to high values. In this mode all pulses with amplitude above the threshold value will be accepted. The threshold value is that value set by the level of the PHD. The curve should be similar to that shown in Fig. 19.
5. Select setting of lower level at A for PHD. If necessary to use PHA then select A as lower level and B as upper level (window or channel).

Summary. Both techniques (PHD and PHA) can provide useful data. The choice of one over another is often subjective. The operator should run the spectrum first to find if there is any unwanted radiation present. If the spectrum from PHA shows only a monoenergetic distribution then there will probably be little or no advantage in using PHA over PHD. Resorting to the K test described above will sometimes help to make the choice. It has been found that if the intensity with PHA is more than 5 to 10 per cent less than that with PHD, the settings are not optimum for the PHA and should be improved before a measurement is made.

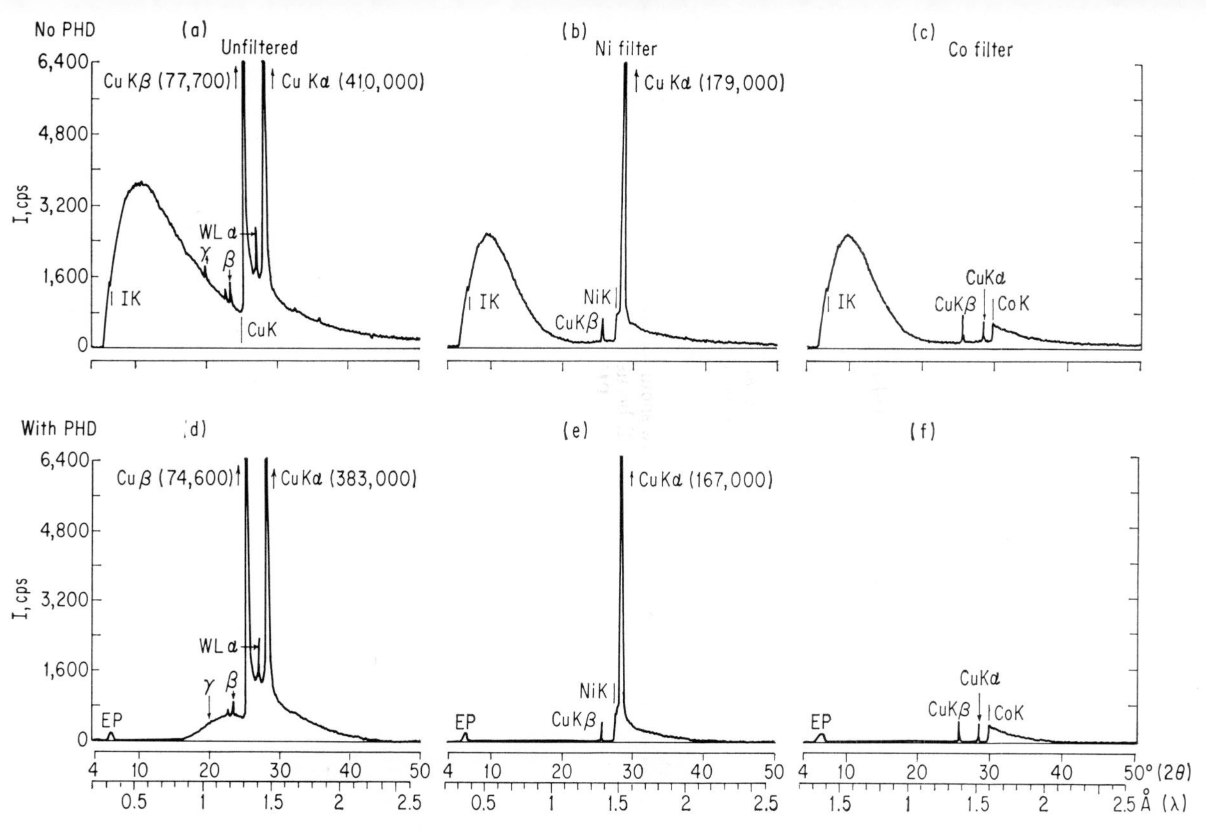

FIG. 18. Spectrum of Cu-target x-ray tube (40 kvp, full-wave rectification). (*a*) Rate-meter recording with silicon crystal plate cut parallel to (111) and scintillation counter. (*b*) Same with Ni filter. (*c*) Same as (*a*), with balanced Co filter. (*d–f*) Same as (*a–c*), with pulse-height analyzer set to pass about 90 per cent Cu $K\alpha$. The WL lines are target impurities; the symbol 1 refers to the *K*-absorption edge; EP, escape peak. (*Reprinted with permission from International Tables for X-ray Crystallography, vol. III, p. 151, Kynoch Press, Birmingham, England, 1961.*)

Table 12. Peak-to-background Ratios for Various Counters with and without Discrimination (Silicon Powder, 111 Line)*

λ	Scintillation counter		Proportional counter (xenon)		Proportional counter (krypton)		Geiger counter (argon), corrected for nonlinearity
	With	Without	With	Without	With	Without	
Mo *Kα*	44	10	44	16	51	29	27
Cu *Kα*	134	12	146	57	64	26	46
Cr *Kα*	93	5	92	16	...	...	18

* Reprinted with permission from *International Tables for X-ray Crystallography*, vol. III, p. 150, International Union of Crystallography, Kynoch Press, Birmingham, England, 1961.

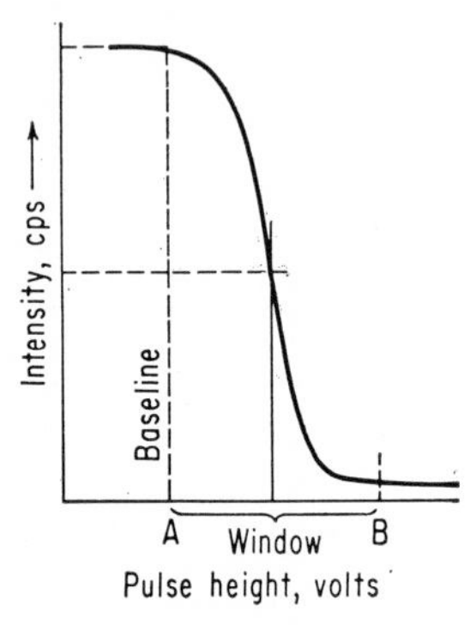

FIG. 19. PHD curve (integral).

Selection of Amplifier Gain. If the level region of the integral curve is not visible, then the gain of the amplifier should be increased. In all probability the gain is too low to bring the pulses above noise level.

If the mean pulse distribution of the PHA curve falls at a level too high to permit setting a proper (symmetrical) window, the total gain of the system should be reduced. This can be done by reducing the applied voltage or the gain of the amplifier. The choice depends upon other conditions such as type of detector and noise of detector.

The noise curve should be run with those instrument settings which will be used for the analysis.

Interferences in PHA. Frequently, the operator encounters polychromatic radiation rather than monochromatic. There are many sources of radiation to interfere with an analysis: cosmic, thermal, higher-order reflections, scatter, electrical pickup, etc. The appearance of the differential and integral curves is altered when two different energies appear and the detector has adequate energy resolution to show their respective pulse distributions. Figures 20 and 21 show the appearance for two energies.

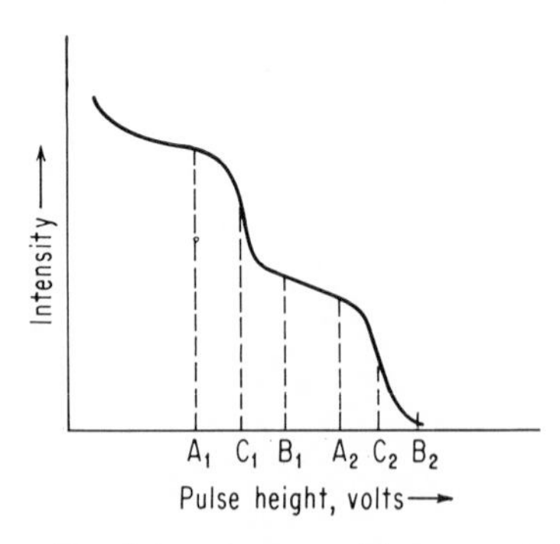

FIG. 20. Integral curve with two energies present. ($A_{1,2}$) Proper base-line positions. ($B_{1,2}$) Proper upper-level positions. ($C_{1,2}$) Mean pulse amplitudes.

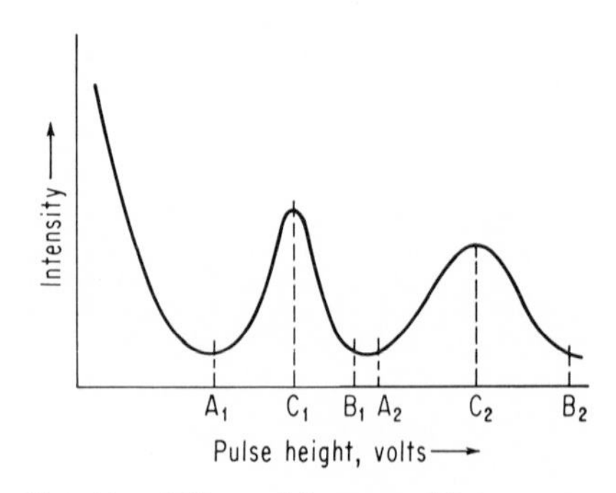

FIG. 21. Differential curve with two energies present. ($A_{1,2}$) Proper base-line positions. ($B_{1,2}$) Proper upper-level positions. ($C_{1,2}$) Mean pulse amplitudes.

A *shift of mean pulse amplitude* can occur with change in incident photon flux when using a proportional detector. The shift is usually less than 10 per cent, relative (see Fig. 22). Resolution changes can be seen as incident photon flux varies. Reports of 10 to 20 per cent relative have been made.

Poor Resolution. The integral curve for two energies and from a detector with "poor" resolution will appear similar to that shown in Figs. 23 and 24. Possible solutions to such a problem would be to:

1. Select a different detector.
2. Consider use of a crystal monochromator.
3. Adjust the kilovolts of the x-ray tube in an attempt to fall below the excitation potential of high-energy pulses.

Escape Peak. This is caused by secondary fluorescence of elements in the detecting media (gas or scintillating crystal). See the definition in Sec. 1 for an explanation of the escape peak.

When molybdenum radiation (17.4 kev) is used with a krypton-filled detector (proportional), a very large escape peak occurs (see Fig. 6).

In the case of the scintillation detector working with copper radiation, one can encounter escape-peak interference from radiation with an energy 28.5 kev greater than that of copper $K\alpha$. For example, the NaI·Tl contains iodine which can be ionized by 28.5 kev. If the copper $K\alpha$ photon has an energy of 8 kev, then a photon with an energy of 36.5 kev will interfere. It will interfere because 28.5 kev of the 36.5 kev will be used by the iodine, leaving 8 kev which in turn will be passed by the PHA along with the 8 kev from copper $K\alpha$ photons.

The escape peak can also be used to measure certain wavelengths and should not always be considered as an interference.

The escape peak is sometimes far enough removed from other peaks of a differential curve so as to permit an analysis to be run using the escape peak as the principal peak.

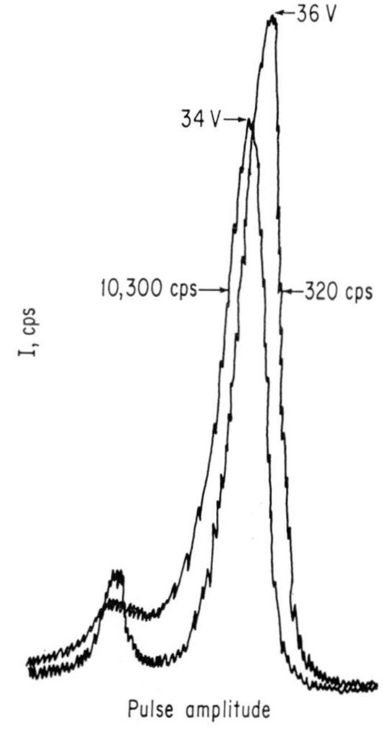

FIG. 22. Shift in pulse amplitude as a function of counting rate. (*Reprinted with permission from W. R. Kiley and J. A. Dunne, Symposium on X-ray and Electron Probe Analysis, Special Technical Publication No. 349, ASTM, 1963.*)

Resolution. *Introduction.* When monoenergetic radiation is absorbed in a detector such as a proportional or scintillation type, and proper operating conditions

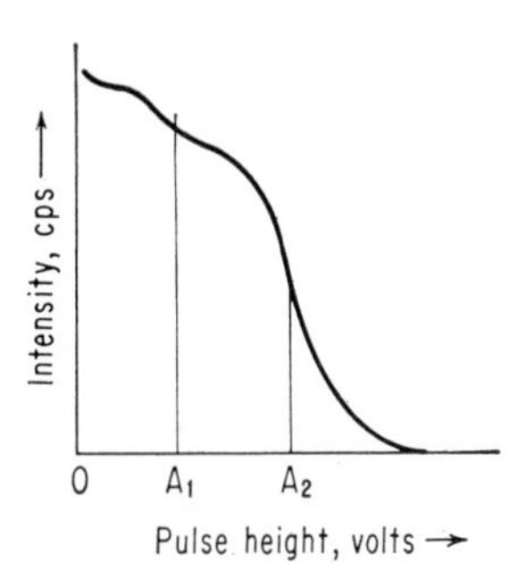

FIG. 23. Incomplete resolution (integral curve).

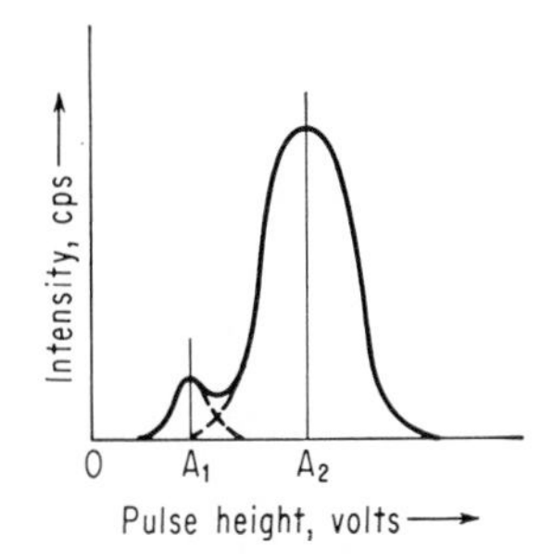

FIG. 24. Incomplete resolution (differential curve).

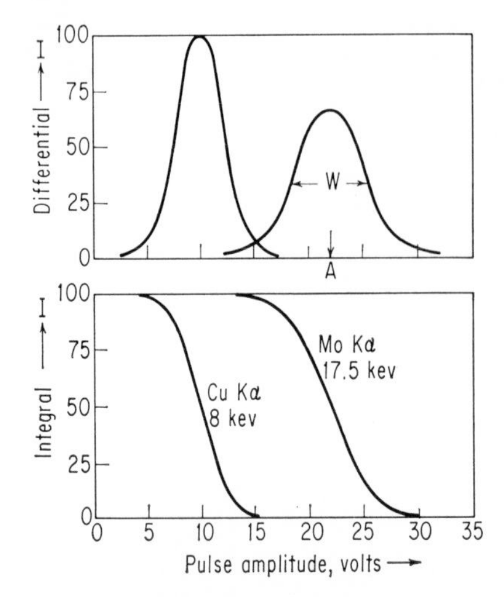

FIG. 25. Differential and integral PHA curves obtained with a scintillation detector. [*Reprinted with permission from W. Parrish and T. R. Kohler, Rev. Sci. Instr.*, **27**: *799* (*1956*).]

have been selected, those pulses from the detector which have passed through the PHA give rise to a curve such as is shown in Fig. 9.

$$W/M = (10 - 5)/7.5 = 5/7.5 \times 100 = \text{resolution, per cent} \quad (20)$$

where W = width of envelope at half maximum, volts

M = mean pulse amplitude, volts

NOTE: Curves such as Fig. 9 are obtained by scanning the spectrum with a small window and varying the base line. The pulses being passed by the analyzer have a mean amplitude equal to the base line plus one-half the value of the window. In plotting the data, it is important to take this fact into consideration. For example, if a curve is run with a 2-volt window, then the intensity should be plotted as a function of the reading of the base-line dial plus half the window (or half of 2 volts).

A further example is shown in Fig. 25.

$$(W_1/A_1)_{Cu} \cong (12.5 - 7.5)/10 = 5/10 = 0.5 \quad (21)$$

$$W/A = \text{term for resolution} \quad (22)$$

$$(W_2/A_2)_{Mo} \cong 7/22 \cong 0.3 \quad (23)$$

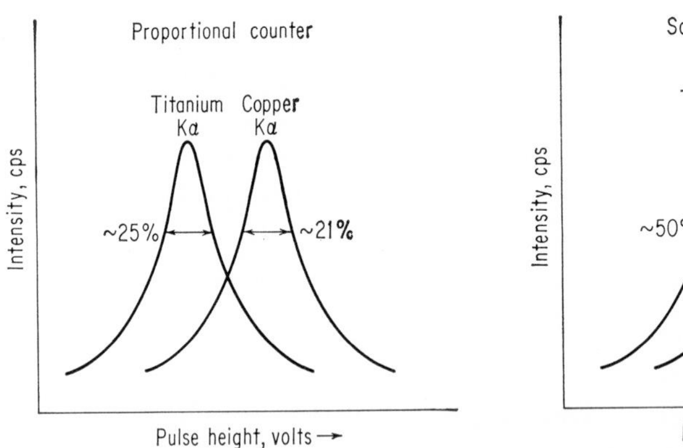

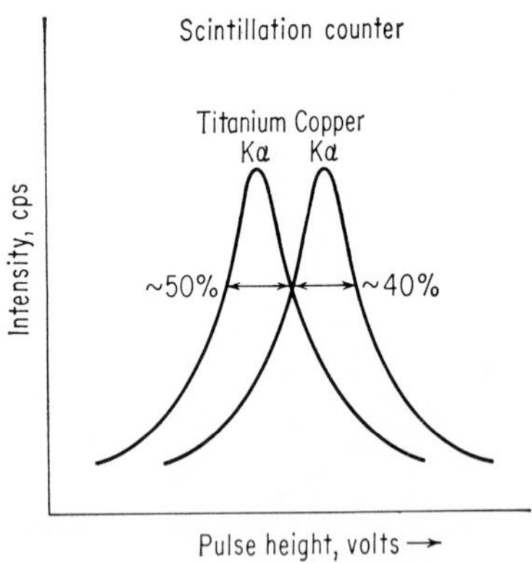

FIG. 26. PHA curves showing the effect of counter resolution in the separation of pulses of similar energy.

NOTE: The proportional detector can be used to resolve pulses from elements which have a difference in atomic number of 2 to 3. The scintillation detector is not capable of this kind of resolution. Approximate energy resolutions for several detectors are shown in Table 13.

Figure 26 shows qualitatively the effect that resolution could play in separation of pulses of similar energies.

Figure 27 shows the effect on pulse-height analyzer transmission as the window is narrowed.

Table 13. Approximate Energy Resolutions*

Detector	Energy, kev	Wavelength, Å	Resolution, %	Count rate, cps
Scintillation (NaI·Tl)..	25	0.49 (Sn $K\alpha$)	~25	3,000
	8.0	1.5 (Cu $K\alpha$)	~48	3,000
	5.4	2.2 (Cr $K\alpha$)	~52	3,000
Proportional (xenon)...	8.0	1.5 (Cu $K\alpha$)	~18	3,000
Flow counter (P-10)...	1.5	8.3 (Al $K\alpha$)	~42	3,000
	2.3	5.3 (S $K\alpha$)	~37	3,000
	8.0	1.5 (Cu $K\alpha$)	~20	3,000

The proportional detector can generally be used to resolve pulses from elements which have a difference in atomic number of 2 to 3. The scintillation detector is not capable of this kind of resolution.

* Reprinted with permission from *International Tables for X-ray Crystallography*, vol. III, p. 150, International Union of Crystallography, Kynoch Press, Birmingham, England, 1961.

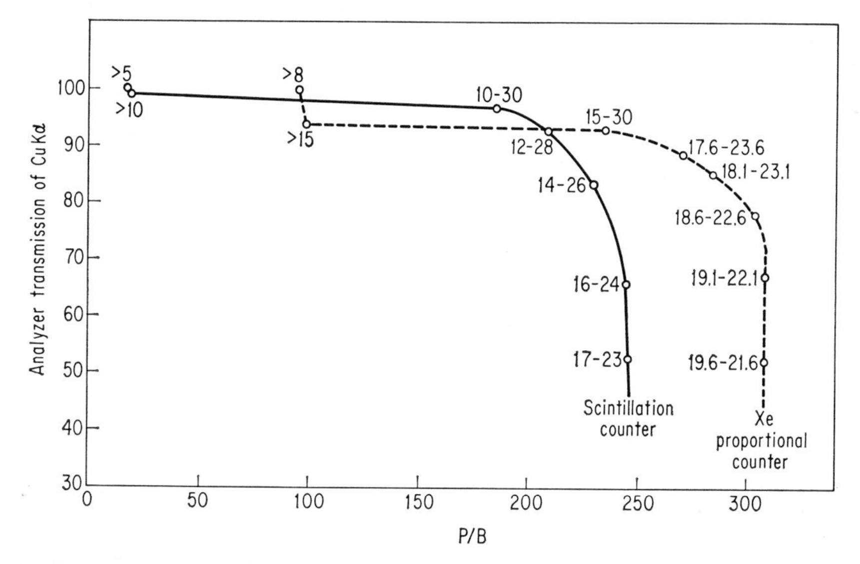

FIG. 27. Analyzer transmission of Cu $K\alpha$ as a function of peak-to-background ratio for narrowing channel settings of the pulse-height analyzer around the pulse-amplitude maximum. Numbers refer to the range of energies accepted. [*Reprinted with permission from C. F. Hendee, S. Fine, and W. B. Brown, Rev. Sci. Instr.*, **27**: *804* (*1952*).]

A Method for "Calibration" of a Pulse-height Analyzer. *Introduction.* The PHA can be used to measure the mean pulse amplitude in volts and thereby make it possible to identify the source of the radiation. The dials of the pulse-height analyzer can be calibrated in volts to make identification of pulse amplitudes more convenient. This calibration makes it easier for an operator to identify various energies when using *nondispersive analysis*.

Procedure

1. Obtain an iron-55 source (Mn $K\alpha$ radiation).
2. Mount the source directly to the face of the detector.
3. Set instrument to PHA mode.
4. Set base line to 4.9 and window to 2 volts, or upper level at 6.9 volts. The Mn $K\alpha$ is 5.9 kev.
5. Select proper gain and apply voltage to detector in increasing steps of about 20 volts.
6. Observe the rate meter and when the intensity passes through a maximum reduce the voltage until the rate meter reads maximum intensity. This procedure is more accurate if one takes a series of scaler readings.
7. At this point, the analyzer is passing all possible pulses of 5.9 kev, provided there are no other sources of radiation near the detector.

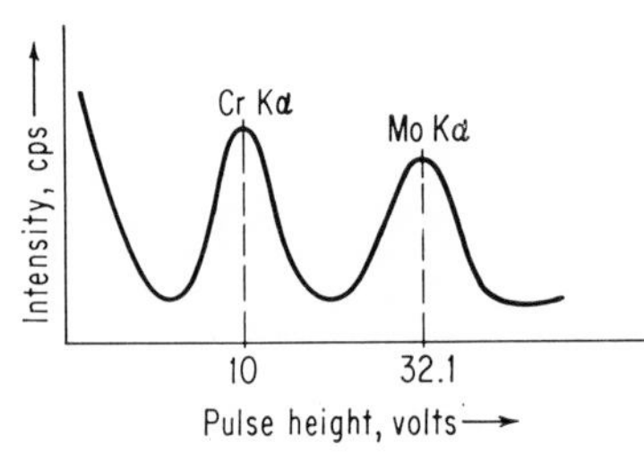

Fig. 28. Pulse-height-distribution curves for Cr $K\alpha$ and Mo $K\alpha$ radiation (differential).

8. The dials of the analyzer can now be read directly in volts to identify the energy of pulses being passed.

Note: Some investigators have used a similar method to arrive at settings for the pulse-height analyzer. In place of the Mn $K\alpha$ radiation, the operator simply uses the primary or secondary radiation from the x-ray tube or sample.

An Alternative Method to Arrive at Energy from PHA Dial. If the dials of the PHA are linear, the ratio of two mean pulse amplitudes as read from the PHA dials is equivalent to the ratio of the energy or wavelengths of the two sources of radiation. Figure 28 shows pulse-height-distribution curves for Cr $K\alpha$ and Mo $K\alpha$. Let us assume that only the identity of the Cr $K\alpha$ radiation is known and that it is desired to identify the other radiation.

$$32.1/10 = 3.21 \qquad \text{(from curve)} \tag{24}$$

$$\lambda_{\mathrm{Cr}\ K\alpha}/\lambda_x = 2.29/\lambda_x = 3.21 \tag{25}$$

$$\lambda_x = 2.29/3.21 = 0.71 = \lambda_{\mathrm{Mo}\ K\alpha} \tag{26}$$

8. SCALERS AND RATE METERS

Scaler. A scaler is an electronic device which counts pulses produced by the detectors. The two main types of scaler are *binary* and *decade.* The binary and decade instruments use scaling factors of 2 and 10, respectively.

Scalers can be used for fixed count or fixed time. The integrated intensity of a line may be measured in several ways:

1. The line may be scanned from one side to another at a constant angular velocity.
2. The detector may be moved stepwise across a line, the scaler being operated continuously except when changing angular position.
3. A large receiving slit may be used (one wider than the line to be measured). The slit is centered on the line and a count taken for a fixed time.

A monitor scaler and counter can be used to compensate for electronic drifts which cause changes in x-ray output and detector response. Variations can then be corrected in the final calculations.

Rate Meter. The rate meter is a smoothing device which gives a measurement of average counting rate without separate measurement of counts and time.

A rate meter is essentially a resistance and capacitance in series. Figures 29 and 30 illustrate typical circuits.

A rate meter consists of a pulse amplifier and pulse shaper. The shaper converts pulses of different amplitudes and shapes into rectangular pulses of fixed voltage and time dimensions. These formed pulses are then fed to a measuring circuit.

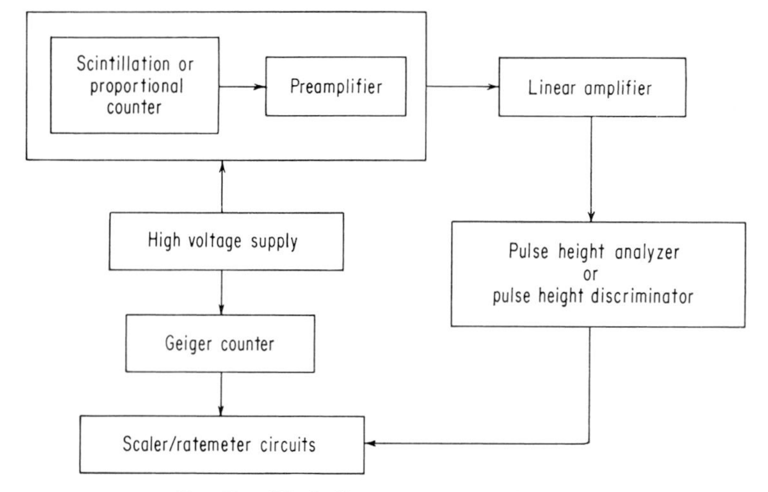

FIG. 29. Block diagram of a typical circuit.

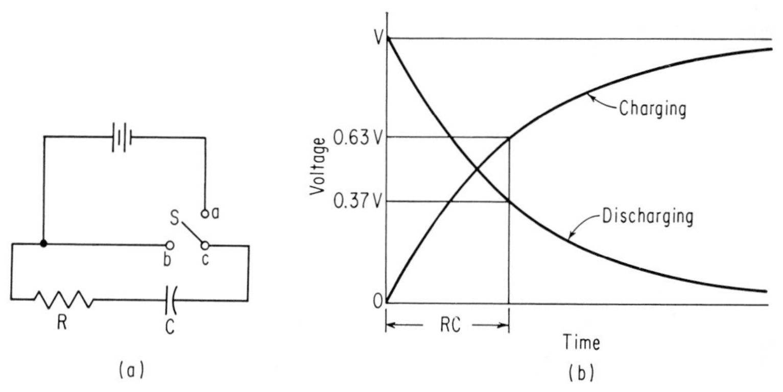

FIG. 30. Capacitor-resistor circuit and curve.

9. TROUBLE SHOOTING

Rules to Follow to Secure Maximum Operational Efficiency

1. A detector should never be operated above its rated voltage.
2. A detector should never be permitted to go into continuous discharge.
3. A detector should be disconnected from the high voltage when it is not in use.
4. The voltage in associated circuits should be free from major fluctuations and should be stabilized.

Some Possible Causes of Short-term Instability

Fatigue. In gas-filled detectors fatigue can be brought about by absorption of the quench gas by other components of the detector.

Temperature. Variations in ambient temperature can be the cause of erratic changes in the characteristic curve of the detector.[60]

Overdose. Excessive ultraviolet light has been known to cause erratic behavior in gas-filled detectors.

Pitting of the anode can cause deterioration of gas detectors.

Breakdown of quench gas and subsequent deposition of products on the cathode and other components can cause decrease in performance.

Changes Which Can Occur in Gas-filled Tubes

Operating potential decreases.

Pressure increases.

Plateau increases in slope.

Efficiency decreases as gas pressure (filling) decreases.

Some Potential Sources of Noise

Applied voltage too high

Amplifier gain too high

Stray radiation from another nearby x-ray unit with poor shielding or radioactive material near the detector

Inadequate grounding of circuits

Line disturbances and poor filtering

Improper use of PHA

Secondary radiation from slits, samples, crystals, etc.

Noise Curve. A noise curve can serve as a quantitative check on the performance of a detector. The permanent record provided by such a curve is a valuable tool in any laboratory.

Iron-55. A source of Mn $K\alpha$ radiation with an energy of 5.9 kev can be purchased for less than $100. The half-life of this source is several years. It is not a radiation hazard when encapsulated. It can be used to calibrate the PHA and also serve as a useful tool to aid in a check of the stability of the counting and recording circuits since it in effect replaces the x-ray generator.

Quantum Efficiency. Selection of a detector should be based largely but not solely upon the quantum-counting efficiency it possesses for the radiation in question. The energy of noise pulses should also be considered and choice of a detector should be made so that the detector has a maximum QCE for the radiation in question and a minimum quantum-counting efficiency for sources of noise For example, the scintillation detector has a much higher efficiency for 1.54-Å radiation than does the xenon proportional detector. However, it also has a higher efficiency for white radiation than does the xenon tube.

Escape Peak. Molybdenum $K\alpha$ radiation produces a very large escape peak when used with a krypton-filled proportional detector.

Poor Grounding. Stability of electronics will be inadequate for quantitative work if grounding is poor. The equipment itself must be grounded, and in addition the grounding in the laboratory should be adequate. It is not impossible for a laboratory to have a poor ground.

Microswitches. Weissenberg and precession cameras can produce noise pulses in recording equipment which is nearby, unshielded, poorly grounded, or used with amplifier gains in excess of those recommended by good practice.

Electron Affinity. Gases with very high electron affinities, such as oxygen, can poison gas detectors by preventing electrons from reaching the anode, thereby reducing the charge collected per energy quantum.

Plateau Length. A good plateau usually has a length in excess of 150 volts and a slope less than 5 per cent per 100 volts. Halogen-quenched tubes are an exception. (See Special Problems with Geiger-Müller Detector later in this section.)

Insulators and Ionizing Radiation. Insulators usually lose their resistivity when they have undergone excessive bombardment by ionizing radiation.

Glowing of Anode Wire. Heating up an anode wire to glow temperature has been used to remove impurities from the wire.

Flush Flow Counter. Washing the inside of a flow counter with organic solvents and then distilled water has been used as a cleaning procedure if contamination is suspected.

Resolving Time of Entire Circuit. Counting losses can be due to coincidence losses in the circuit as well as from the detector itself. The detector is not always the source of losses. The resolving time of the circuit for the upper level of the PHA is often the slowest component in the circuit.

Improper Settings of PHA. If the base line or upper limit is set on the steep portion of the pulse-distribution curve, the change in counting rate per unit change in applied voltage or the instability of the levels themselves will be much greater than if the settings are made properly.

Choking. When too many pulses enter the detector, the detector fails to recover and the observed intensity drops off sharply. This occurs when a detector is passed through the primary beam. *Caution: Avoid this procedure! Do not submit a detector to the primary beam!* The intensity ratio of alpha-1 to alpha-2 radiation should be 2:1. A possible cause of a low ratio is the detector's receiving an excess of pulses at the alpha-1 position but not at the alpha-2 position (see Fig. 31).

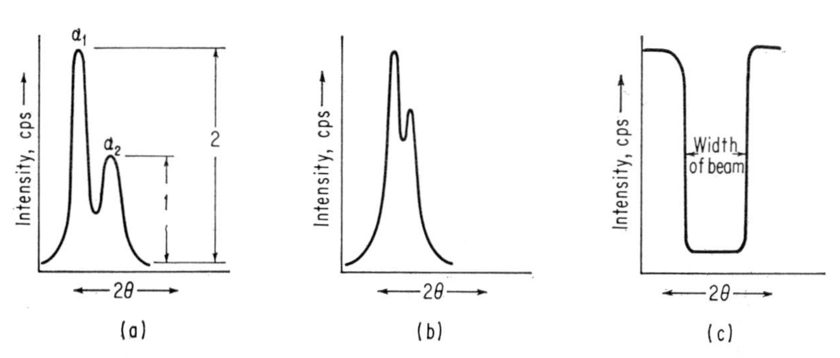

FIG. 31. (*a*) Ratio α_1/α_2 correct. (*b*) Ratio incorrect because of choking at α_1 position. (*c*) Complete choking.

Suggestions

1. Put in attenuation filters.
2. Lower the kilovolts or milliamperes.
3. Change the sample.
4. Select another detector.
5. Compensate with a correction factor.

Correction for Counting Loss

$$N = N_o/(1 - N_o\tau)^{50,59} \tag{27}$$

where N = true counting rate

N_o = observed counting rate

τ = dead time of entire counting system (cf. Fig. 11)

Equation (27) is the most useful when the corrections apply to peak intensity (not integrated intensity) and is for those cases where deviations from linearity are less than about 20 per cent. Equation (27) does not correct for, or take into account, the error caused by the waveform of the x-ray generator.

The kind of generator used to produce x-rays is usually half-wave, full-wave, or constant-potential (filtered and regulated, d-c). The form factor for each generator makes it necessary to apply a different correction factor.

Waveform Correction. Counting-loss corrections should take into account the waveform. The factor K is used to correct for the waveform contribution to nonlinearity:

$$N = N_o/(1 - N_oK\tau) \tag{28}$$

where K = correction factor (form factor)

$$= \frac{\text{root-mean-square intensity of source}}{\text{mean intensity of source}} \tag{29}$$

τ = dead time of entire counting system (not only that of detector tube)

Pepinsky[61] reported a method for determining K. The method consists in varying the dead time of the entire circuit from τ_1 to τ_2 and using a beam of constant intensity to calculate K from Eq. (30).

$$K = \frac{1/(N_o)_1 - 1/(N_o)_2}{\tau_1 - \tau_2} \cong 3.4 \text{ (half-wave)} \quad (30)$$

$$\cong 1.7 \text{ (full-wave)} \quad (31)$$

Values given in Eqs. (30) and (31) illustrate a principle but are not intended for use as a generally accepted value. A correction factor is also required for d-c generators. In some cases, however, the factor K is set to 1 when using d-c generators, and other waveforms are referenced to the direct current since it most nearly approximates a natural source of radiation such as a radioisotope.

Linear and Dead-time Corrections. These corrections should be made with monochromatic radiation. Use a crystal monochromator and PHA to avoid $\lambda/2$ if possible. Also use lower kilovolts to avoid $\lambda/2$.

Differences from 170 to 270 μsec dead time have been reported for Geiger tubes when using constant-potential and full-wave generators (cf. Ref. 11, pp. 146, 147).

Nonlinearity Corrections

1. When coincidence losses exceed 20 per cent, the multiple-foil method has been recommended for making corrections when single-chamber Geiger tubes are used. Counting ranges of 400 to 500 cps and 800 to 900 cps for half-wave and full-wave rectification, respectively, are in this range (20 per cent). Accuracy of the corrected rate is probably no better than ± 5 per cent up to counting ranges of 3,000 cps.
2. When losses are less than 20 per cent, accuracies of 1 to 4 per cent have been reported if the resolving time τ of the Geiger tube and form factor K of the generator have been measured with an accuracy of ± 10 per cent. The expression used to calculate the true count rate was $N = N_o/(1 - N_oK\tau)$.[50,59]

Special Problems with Geiger-Müller Detector. *Ultraviolet* light can cause erratic results with G-M tubes.

Dry weather has caused spurious counting due to a charge buildup on the window of the detector.

Plateau length is not always a positive indication of quality in halogen-quenched tubes because the halogen is not used up in quenching. Shortening of the plateau in organic-quenched tubes is some indication of depletion of the quenching agent. Resolving times of other circuits can also show up in the plateau length.

Alignment of Tube. For maximum efficiency the x-ray beam should be directed as nearly as possible along a path which is parallel to the anode and very close to it while at the same time not striking it.

Dead Space. The efficiency of the G-M tube is a function of the distance between anode and window as well as gas pressure, type of gas, and transmission of radiation by the window material.

Temperature. Wide variations should be avoided.

Background. Should not exceed 1 to 2 cps in most cases.

Special Problems with Proportional Detector. *Dirt.* Should be kept away from the flow-counter inlet. Dirt particles cause spurious counting if they enter the volume of the detector. The field strength around the anode can be altered by dirt particles.

Flush. Flow counters should be flushed with about 1 ft^3/hr of P-10 (if P-10 is used) for 5 to 10 min in the morning.

Ultraviolet can cause spurious counts.

Temperature. Proportional counters are sensitive to temperature changes.

Sagging Anode Wire. If the position of the anode wire is changed with respect to the incoming beam or cathode shell, then the distribution of field strength around the anode will change.

Sagging Windows. Flow-counter windows can sag and change their distance from the anode in the process. When this occurs the field strength can vary. The metal film on the inside of the window can build up a charge, and when it changes its position it can alter the field strength.

Variation in Field Strength. Crystallographers may prefer the scintillation detector over the proportional because of the more uniform response one gets across the scintillation-crystal face, when compared with the nonuniformity which one observes due to the field-strength variation along an axis perpendicular to the anode wire of a proportional detector.

Voltage and Gain. Use care in selection. See previous sections for discussions.

Special Problems with Scintillation Detector. *Decrease in Resolution.* Several factors can cause changes in resolution:

1. Optical imperfections in scintillator
2. Nonuniformity in photocathode
3. Unstable multiplier phototube
4. Fluctuations in applied voltage
5. Excessive thermal noise in multiplier phototube
6. Poor optical coupling

Magnetic Field. Stray magnetic fields can cause deflection of the electron beams in unshielded multiplier phototubes.

Mechanical Shock. Can defocus the tube as well as destroy the envelope. Vibration can defocus the electron beam in the tube.

Uneven Response. An uneven response across the crystal can cause serious problems.

Light Leak. A pinhole of visible light can cause background counts of more than 25 cps. Black paper wrapped around the detector will help disclose light leaks.

Preamplifier Heat. Can cause high thermal noise.

Dark Current Noise. Equivalent to 0.5 to 2.0 kev.

Organic Scintillators. Low absorption compared with NaI·Tl.

10. COUNTING STATISTICS (See also Chap. 36, Sec. 21)

Introduction. Statistics have a very extensive application because any measurement or event when repeated often enough results in a variety of answers. These variations are not all within the control of the experimenter. The generation of x-rays is a random process governed by the laws of statistics; therefore, the measurement of x-rays should be treated as a statistical process.

"While in x-ray fluorescence analysis the random error due to the count distribution is frequently negligible as compared with the systematic errors involved in the method, this is not true when the counting rate is low. Therefore, in trace analysis, microfocus work, and other operations where low net counting rates are obtained, especially when the background counting rates are relatively high, consideration of the effects of count distribution in photon counting is useful."[51]

Definitions

Accuracy. The proximity of an observed value to the absolute value.

Precision. The repeatability of a series of observations.

Addition of Independent Errors. Errors can cancel out one another. Therefore, the errors of individual quantities should not be simply added or subtracted. The following equation presents a statistical method for treating such a problem:

$$s = \sqrt{s_1^2 + s_2^2} \tag{32}$$

s can be the standard deviation or any of the other errors if s_1 and s_2 are the corresponding individual errors.

Chi-square Test

$$\chi^2 = \sum_i \frac{[(\text{observed value})_i - (\text{expected value})_i]^2}{(\text{expected value})_i} \tag{33}$$

where observed value = value obtained in each of a series of identical measurements
expected value = average value of all the values in a series of measurements. In the counting of pulses, the expected value is the average count

The chi-square test is a method of analyzing the results of a series of identical measurements. It can be used to determine how closely a set of data fits the Poisson distribution.

The chi-square test is used to calculate the probability P that a repetition of observations will result in greater deviations from an assumed distribution than those observed in the first trial. Evans[57] gives an example of the use of Pearson's chi-square test (cf. Table 14).

In order to evaluate the data, the value of chi square obtained from a series of measurements can be compared with a table of chi square values. Data are considered valid if chi square falls within the high confidence range 80 per cent of the time, within the average confidence range 90 per cent of the time, and in the basic confidence range 98 per cent of the time (cf. Table 14).

Cooke-Yarborough Method.[53] This is a method of measuring random pulses by adding periodic pulses at a constant, controlled, low rate to the random pulses to be measured.

Table 14. Chi-square Values*

No. of measurements in series being analyzed	Ranges of chi-square values		
	High confidence (80% probability)	Standard confidence (90% probability)	Basic confidence (98% probability)
3	0.211– 4.605	0.103– 5.991	0.020– 9.210
4	0.584– 6.251	0.352– 7.815	0.115–11.345
5	1.064– 7.779	0.711– 9.488	0.297–13.277
6	1.610– 9.236	1.145–11.070	0.554–15.086
7	2.204–10.645	1.635–12.592	0.872–16.812
8	2.833–12.017	2.167–14.067	1.239–18.475
9	3.490–13.362	2.733–15.507	1.646–20.090
10	4.168–14.684	3.325–16.919	2.088–21.666
11	4.865–15.987	3.940–18.307	2.558–23.209
12	5.578–17.275	4.575–19.675	3.053–24.725
13	6.304–18.549	5.226–21.026	3.571–26.217
14	7.042–19.812	5.892–22.362	4.107–27.688
15	7.790–21.064	6.571–23.685	4.660–29.141
16	8.547–22.307	7.261–24.996	5.229–30.578
17	9.312–23.542	7.962–26.296	5.812–32.000
18	10.085–24.769	8.672–27.587	6.408–33.409
19	10.865–25.989	9.390–28.869	7.015–34.805
20	11.651–27.204	10.117–30.144	7.633–36.191
21	12.443–28.412	10.851–31.410	8.260–37.566
22	13.240–29.615	11.591–32.671	8.897–38.932
23	14.041–30.813	12.338–33.924	9.542–40.289
24	14.848–32.007	13.091–35.172	10.196–41.638
25	15.659–33.196	13.848–36.415	10.856–42.980
26	16.473–34.382	14.611–37.382	11.524–44.314
27	17.292–35.563	15.379–38.885	12.198–45.642
28	18.114–36.741	16.151–40.113	12.879–46.963
29	18.939–37.916	16.928–41.337	13.565–48.278
30	19.768–39.087	17.708–42.557	14.256–49.588

* Reprinted with permission from F. H. Low, *Radioisotope Measurement in Nuclear Medicine*, Picker X-ray, White Plains, N.Y., 1960.

Equilibrium Time of Rate Meter (see Fig. 32)

$$\text{Equilibrium time} = t(0.5 \ln 2nt + 0.394) \tag{34}$$

where t = time constant, sec, of rate meter
n = counting rate, cps, shown by rate meter

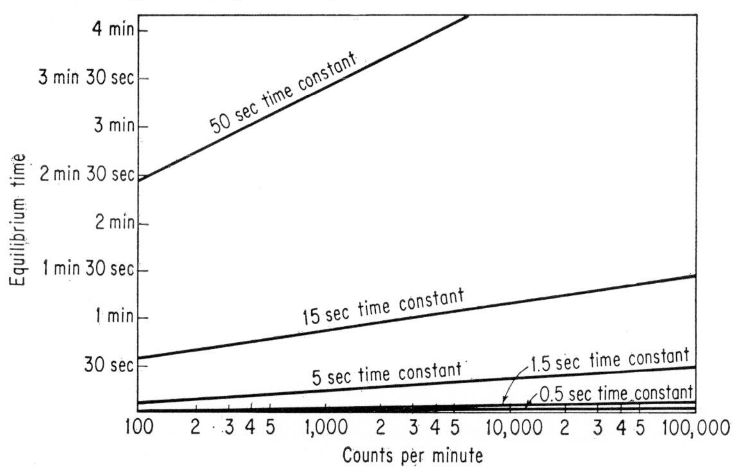

FIG. 32. Equilibrium time of a rate meter. (*Reprinted with permission from F. H. Low, Radioisotope Measurement in Nuclear Medicine, Picker X-ray Corporation, White Plains, N.Y., 1960.*)

The Mean. A mean $\bar{x}$ is calculated by dividing the sum of the individual terms by the number of terms.

$$\bar{x} = \sum_{i=1}^{n} (x_i)/n \tag{35}$$

The mean is an arithmetic average.

Harmonic Mean. The reciprocal of the arithmetic mean of the reciprocals. Most frequently used when reciprocals, such as rates, are involved.

$$\bar{H} = n/\left(\sum_{i=1}^{n} 1/x_i\right) \tag{36}$$

Normal Distribution. Many measurements of a physical nature fall into the normal distribution. The measurement of quantities which vary continuously in magnitude seems to fit a normal distribution. Mathematically, it can be stated that the probability dP that the quantity x will lie between $x + dx$ is

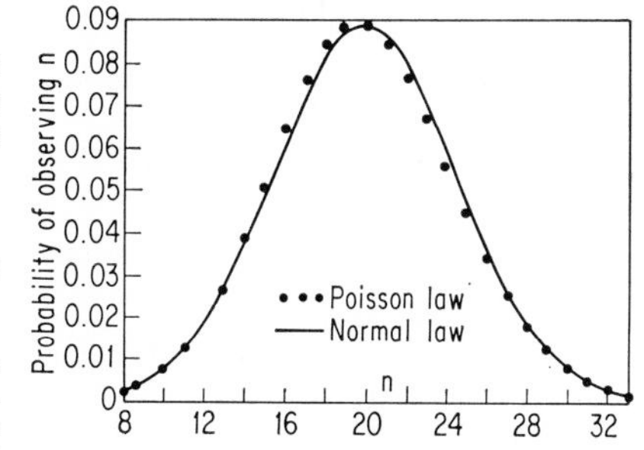

FIG. 33. The normal distribution as an approximation of the Poisson distribution at an average value of 20.

$$dP = (1/s\sqrt{2\pi})\, e^{-(x-m)^2/2s^2}\, dx \tag{37}$$

where m = mean value of the distribution
s = standard deviation (an indication of the width of the distribution curve)

A plot of $y = dP/dx$ versus x gives the familiar "bell-shaped curve" shown in Fig. 33. Table 15 gives fractions of the total data to be found in various ranges about the mean.

A series of measurements will not always fit a normal distribution or any other distribution, and it is precisely such a question of fit which is often answered through the application of statistical methods; namely, does a set of measurements fit a particular distribution?

Poisson Distribution

$$P_x = (m^x/x!)e^{-m} \tag{38}$$

where P_x = probability of observing x events when the average of a large number of attempts is m events

In this distribution, m and x are integers. The variable is continuous in the normal distribution, a difference between the Poisson and the normal distribution.

Table 15. Fractions of Total Normal Distribution for Various Ranges about a Mean*

% of total data	*In the range $\bar{x} \pm$*
50	0.6745 σ†
68.2	1.00 σ
75	1.15 σ
90	1.65 σ
95	1.96 σ
95.45	2.00 σ
99	2.57 σ
99.73	3.00 σ

* From Ref. 55.
† Observed standard deviation.

Poisson Standard Deviation. The Poisson standard deviation for a single reading of a rate meter can be calculated from the following formula:[52]

$$s = \sqrt{a/2RC} \tag{39}$$

where s = standard deviation of a single reading of rate meter
a = counting rate
RC = time constant of rate meter, sec
R = resistance of integrating circuit, ohms
C = capacitance of the integrating circuit, farads

Per Cent Probable Error (Scaler)

$$\text{Per cent probable error} = 67.45/\sqrt{N} \tag{40}$$

where N = number of observed counts (assuming background is negligibly small compared with peak)

Per Cent Probable Error of a Single Rate-meter Reading

$$\text{Per cent probable error} = 67.45/\sqrt{2nt} \tag{41}$$

where n = counting rate, cps
t = time constant of rate meter, sec

Per Cent Reliable Error (Scaler)

$$\text{Per cent reliable (nine-tenths) error} = 164.49/\sqrt{N} \tag{42}$$

where N = number of observed counts (assuming background is negligibly small compared with peak)

Per Cent Ninety-five-hundredth Error (Scaler)

$$\text{Per cent ninety-five-hundredth error} = 196.00/\sqrt{N} \tag{43}$$

where N = number of observed counts (assuming background is negligibly small compared with peak)

Probable Error. This is the error which is just as likely to be exceeded as not. For a normal distribution the probable error is 0.6745σ. Statisticians make frequent use of standard deviation in their work since many tables in the literature use σ to express the data collected.

Standard Deviation Expected. The square root of the total number of events (or counts).

$$\sigma_{\text{expected}} = \sqrt{N} \tag{44}$$

where N = total number of events

Standard Deviation Observed

$$\sigma_{\text{observed}} = \frac{\Sigma d^2}{n - 1} = \frac{\sum_{i=1}^{n} (x_i - \bar{x})^2}{n - 1} \tag{45}$$

where d = difference of the determination from the mean
n = number of determinations

Variance. The square of the standard deviation.

Applications of Statistics. Figure 34 shows the per cent probable error vs. counting rate for a rate meter.[56]

Dead-time Counting Losses. Most electromechanical types of counting equipment and certain non-self-quenching G-M tubes are paralyzable. They are capable of

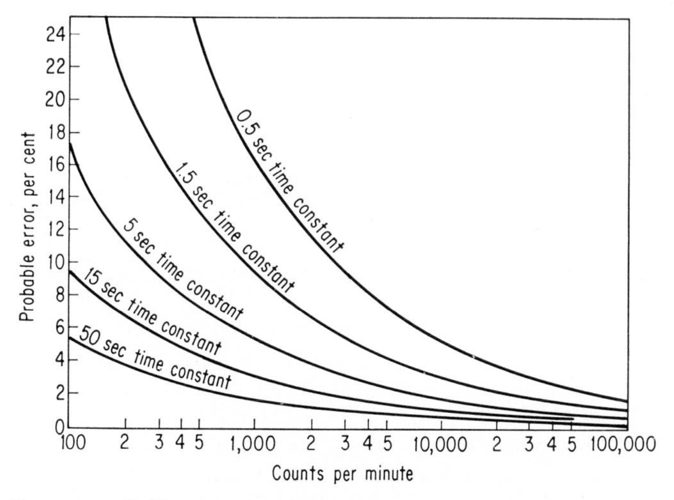

FIG. 34. Per cent probable error vs. counting rate for a rate meter. (*Reprinted with permission from F. H. Low, Radioisotope Measurement in Nuclear Medicine, Picker X-ray Corporation, White Plains, N.Y., 1960.*)

counting only those intervals which are longer than their dead time. If N is the true average pulse rate, the observed is

$$n = Ne^{-NT} \tag{46}$$

when pulses arrive in a nonperiodic (random) fashion.[58]

When a pulse arrives during a dead interval and cannot cause another dead interval, the system is nonparalyzable.

Self-quenching G-M tubes and proportional and scintillation detectors fit into this class. The true pulse rate N can be expressed in terms of the observed rate n and dead time T:

$$N = n/(1 - nT)^{50,59} \tag{47}$$

Scaler vs. Rate Meter. The accuracy of a single measurement of intensity is affected by the number of pulses which are produced by background. The probable error for a single scaler measurement of peak and background can be calculated:

$$\epsilon_{50} = \frac{0.67N + N_B}{N - N_B} \tag{48}$$

where N = total pulses counted
N_B = background pulses

The counting-rate meter produces a different error. It can be calculated:

$$\epsilon_{50} = 0.67/2nRC \tag{49}$$

where n = counting rate
RC = time constant of rate meter

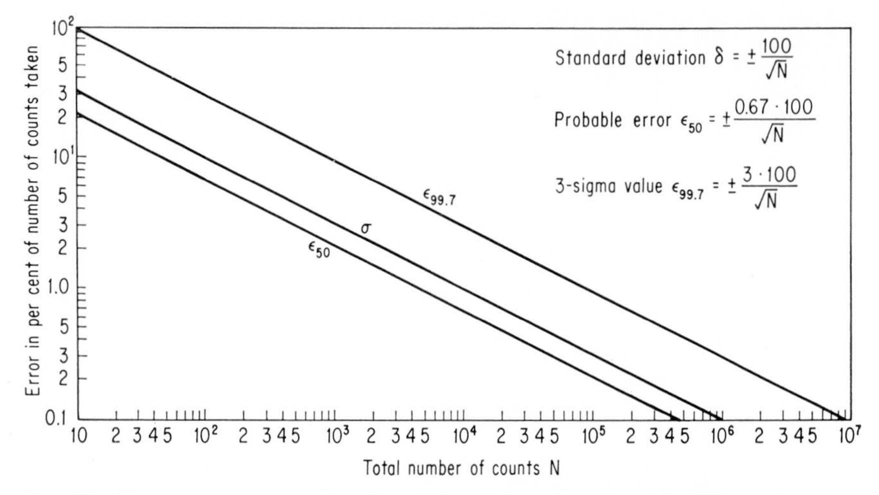

FIG. 35. Percentage error as a function of the total number of counts N for various confidence levels.

Per Cent Error vs. Total Counts. Figure 35 is useful in determining the per cent error for various confidence levels and total accumulated counts.[62] Figure 36 shows the number of counts required to give a desired degree of accuracy for various ratios R of total to background counting rate.

How to Calculate and Use Standard Deviation σ. We usually try to arrive at a value of the mean m of a distribution. This can be done by averaging the observations x to calculate the observed mean $\bar{x}$. When enough measurements have been taken we can estimate sigma (σ). In this way we can find whether the measurements we have taken fit the assumed distribution.

The quantity sigma is estimated by

$$\sigma^2 = \frac{\sum_{i=1}^{n} (x_i - \bar{x})^2}{n - 1} \tag{50}$$

where n = number of observations
$\bar{x}$ = observed mean
x_i = ith observation
σ = standard deviation observed

We never really know the true mean m. We must therefore express it in some "adjusted" form. The following example clarifies the procedure we can use to calculate σ and m:

X_i	$X_i - \bar{X}$	$(X_i - \bar{X})^2$
90	-10	100
112	$+12$	144
98	-2	4

$$\bar{x} = 100 \Sigma(x_i - \bar{x})^2 = 248$$
$$\sigma = \sqrt{248/(3-1)} = \sqrt{124} = 11.1 \tag{51}$$

With only three observations we do not have a reliable estimate of σ. We therefore cannot tell if the set fits a normal distribution.

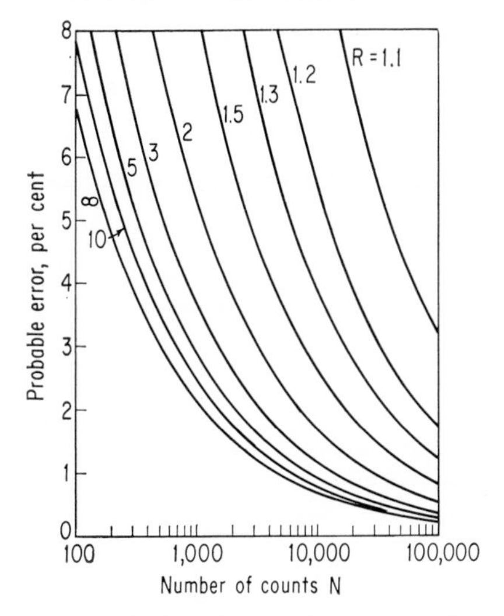

FIG. 36. Number of counts required to give a desired degree of accuracy for various ratios (R) of total to background counting rate. (*Reprinted with permission from H. P. Klug and L. E. Alexander, X-ray Diffraction Procedures for Polycrystalline and Amorphous Materials, p. 273, John Wiley & Sons, Inc., New York, 1954.*)

We are still interested in finding out how close the observed mean comes in value to the true mean. We can calculate the *standard deviation of the mean* σ_m by

$$\sigma_m = \sigma/\sqrt{n} \tag{52}$$
$$\sigma_m = 11.1/\sqrt{3} = 6.4 \tag{53}$$

We could therefore express $m = 100 \pm 6$. This makes use of a standard deviation of 6 as our error.

When Can One Consider a Measurement to Be Invalid? How does one make averages more "true to life" by rejecting individual members in a series because they are so "abnormal" as to distort the average?

The criterion used most frequently for deciding whether a particular reading should be eliminated from a series of measurements because it is not typical of the normal (Poisson) distribution of data is that proposed by Chauvenet, and hence known as "Chauvenet's criterion."[61] It says that a reading can be discarded if the probability

Table 16. Chauvenet's Criterion

No. of measurements in the series n	Individual data discarded if probability of occurrence is no greater than	Min ratio of individual data deviation to standard deviation of avg value which justifies rejection
3	1:6	1.37
4	1:8	1.53
5	1:10	1.64
6	1:12	1.73
7	1:14	1.80
8	1:16	1.87
9	1:18	1.91
10	1:20	1.97
15	1:30	2.13
20	1:40	2.24
25	1:50	2.33
30	1:60	2.39
40	1:80	2.50
50	1:100	2.57
100	1:200	2.80

of its occurrence is not greater than $1/2n$ where n is the number of measurements made in a particular series.

For a reading to fulfill this requirement, the ratio of its deviation from the average to the standard deviation of the series must exceed a certain minimum value (shown in Table 16), which depends upon the number of measurements in the series.

If the measurements are numbers of counts, the ratio is equal to

$$(N_n - N_{\text{av}})/\sqrt{N_{\text{av}}} \tag{54}$$

where N_n is the suspected measurement and N_{av} is the average value of the series, including the suspected measurement.

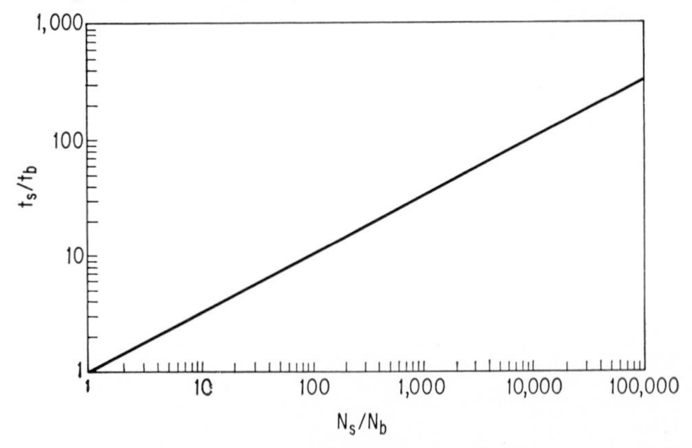

FIG. 37. Graph showing the most efficient distribution of counting time between sample and background. N_s = counting rate of sample plus background. N_b = counting rate of background. t_s = length of time of sample-plus-background count. t_b = length of time of background count. (*Reprinted with permission from Radiological Health Handbook, U.S. Department of Public Health, Education, and Welfare, Public Health Service, Bureau of State Services, Division of Radiological Health, Washington 25, D.C., September, 1960, PB 121784R.*)

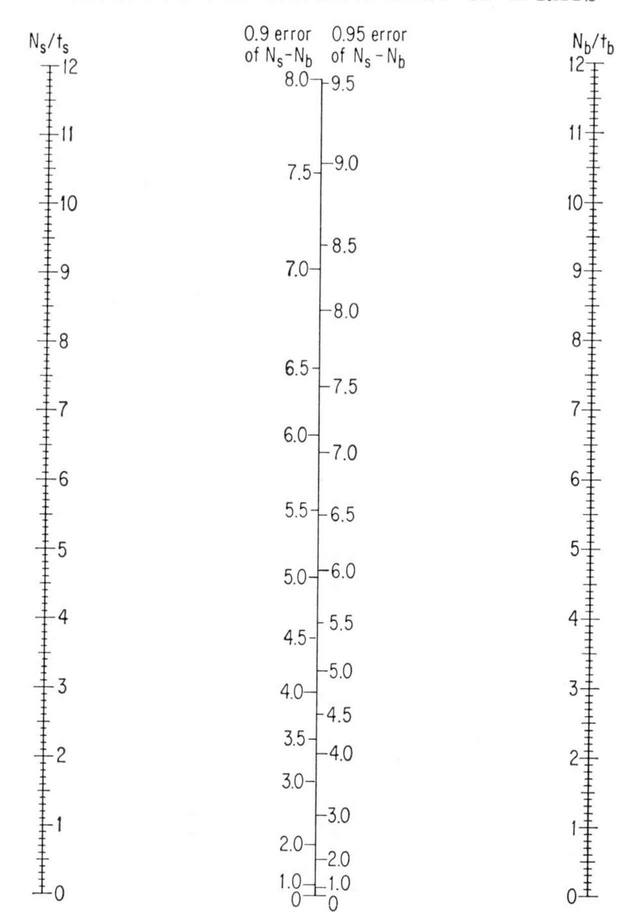

FIG. 38. Nomograph for estimating counting error for very low counting rates. N_s and N_b = counting rates of sample plus background and background, respectively (counts per minute). t_s and t_b = number of minutes sample and background were counted, respectively. [*Reprinted with permission from A. A. Jarrett, Statistical Methods Used in the Measurement of Radioactivity, AECU 262 (MonP-126), Technical Information Division, ORE, Oak Ridge, Tenn., 1950.*]

As an example, a series of 10 counts is shown in Table 17. Can count 2 be rejected?

$$(N_2 - N_{av})/\sqrt{N_{av}} = 139/\sqrt{3{,}121} = 2.49 \quad (55)$$

Since this exceeds 1.97, the minimum ratio for 10 measurements, the count can be rejected.

Nomograms for Count Distribution and Error. Jarrett[60] has devised useful graphs to assist in estimation of the optimum counting time for sample and background, and for estimation of the Poisson counting error (see Figs. 37 and 38).

Figure 37 is used to determine the optimum ratio of sample to background counting *times* from the ratio of the corresponding counting *rates*. Thus, if the counting-rate ratio sample-plus-background to background is 10, sample-plus-background should be counted about three times as long as background.

Table 17

n	N	$N_n - N_{av}$
1	3,210	+89
2	2,982	−139
3	3,105	−16
4	3,217	+96
5	3,088	−35
6	3,142	+21
7	3,074	−47
8	3,101	−20
9	3,204	+83
10	3,089	−32
	31,212	
N_{av}	3,121	

Figure 38 is an example of a nomograph from which a quick estimate of counting error (taking background into consideration) can be obtained for very low counting rates. As an example, consider the case in which sample-plus-background counting rate is 120 cpm, background counting rate is 75 cpm, and counting time for both is 10 min. The 0.95 error of the net count is found to be 8.6 cpm from the nomograph.

REFERENCES CITED

1. W. H. Bragg and W. L. Bragg, *Proc. Roy. Soc.*, **A88**:428 (1913).
2. A. H. Compton and S. K. Allison, *X-rays in Theory and Experiment*, 2d ed., D. Van Nostrand Company, Inc., Princeton, N.J., 1935.
3. S. A. Korff, *Electron and Nuclear Counters*, D. Van Nostrand Company, Inc., Princeton, N.J., 1946.
4. W. J. Price, *Nuclear Radiation Detection*, 2d ed., McGraw-Hill Book Company, New York, 1964.
5. J. A. Carrerall, L. F. Wilson, and J. Trotter, *J. Sci. Instr.*, **35**:393 (1958).
6. J. S. Allen, *Rev. Sci. Instr.*, **12**:484 (1941).
7. J. S. Allen, *Rev. Sci. Instr.*, **18**:739 (1947).
8. J. L. Blankenship and C. J. Borokowski, *Rev. Sci. Instr.*, **33**:778 (1962).
9. E. R. Piore, G. G. Harvey, E. M. Gyorgy, and R. H. Kingston, *Rev. Sci. Instr.*, **23**:8 (1952).
10. R. J. Frerichs, *Appl. Phys.*, **21**:312 (1950).
11. P. J. Van Heerden, Thesis, Utrecht, Netherlands, 1945.
12. J. Taylor and W. Parrish, *Rev. Sci. Instr.*, **26**:367 (1955); **27**:108 (1956).
13. Z. Mihailovic, *Compt. Rend.*, **238**:492 (1954).
14. R. K. Willardson and G. C. Danielson, *U.S. At. Energy Comm. Rept.*, **ISC-163** (1950).
15. G. P. Freeman, Thesis, Utrecht, Netherlands, 1952.
16. R. Frerichs and J. E. Jacobs, *Gen. Elec. Rev.*, **54** (8): 42 (1951).
17. C. H. Bachman, O. J. Gelormini, and H. W. Davis, *Am. J. Roentgenol.*, **73**:98 (1955).
18. G. W. Goodrich and W. C. Wiley, *Rev. Sci. Instr.*, **32**:846 (1961).
19. L. Heroux and H. E. Hinteregger, *Rev. Sci. Instr.*, **31**:280 (1960).
20. G. L. Miller, W. M. Gibson, and P. F. Donovan, *Ann. Rev. Nucl. Sci.*, **12**:189 (1962).
21. L. F. Curtiss, *Natl. Bur. Std. (U.S.) Circ.*, **490** (1950).
22. H. Friedman, *Electronics*, **18**(4):132 (1945).
23. H. Friedman, *Ind. Rad. Non-destructive Testing*, **6**(1) (1947).
24. S. H. Liebson, *Phys. Rev.*, **72**:602 (1947).
25. H. J. Mader, *Z. Physik*, **137**:216 (1954).
26. H. R. Laird and M. J. Zunick, *Commun. and Electron.*, (22):734 (1956).
27. A. R. Lang, *Nature*, **168**:907 (1951).
28. A. R. Lang, *Rev. Sci. Instr.*, **25**:1032 (1954).
29. R. Lindemann and A. Trost, *Z. Physik*, **115**:456 (1940).
30. A. Trost, *Z. Physik*, **117**:257 (1941); *Z. Angew. Phys.*, **2**:286 (1950).
31. D. West, *Progress in Nuclear Physics*, O. R. Frisch, ed., vol. 3, p. 18, Pergamon Press, New York, 1953.

32. S. C. Curran, *Luminescence and the Scintillation Counter*, Academic Press Inc., New York, 1953.
33. H. Berger, *Proc. Natl. Electron. Conf.*, **9**:880 (1953).
34. R. Hofstadter, *Phys. Rev.*, **75**:796, 1611 (1949).
35. J. T. Nelson and R. T. Ellickson, *J. Opt. Soc. Am.*, **45**:984 (1955).
36. S. H. Liebson and H. Friedman, *Rev. Sci. Instr.*, **19**:303 (1948).
37. H. V. Neher and W. W. Harper, *Phys. Rev.*, **49**:940 (1936).
38. W. C. Porter, *Nucleonics*, **11**(3):32 (1953).
39. H. G. Stever, *Phys. Rev.*, **61**:38 (1942).
40. D. Van Zoonen and G. Prast, *Appl. Sci. Res.*, **B**(3):1 (1954).
41. A. L. Ward and A. D. Krumbein, *Rev. Sci. Instr.*, **26**:341 (1955).
42. L. Alexander, E. Kummer, and H. P. Klug, *J. Appl. Phys.*, **20**:735 (1949).
43. H. L. Andrews, *Rev. Sci. Instr.*, **21**:191 (1950).
44. K. Lonsdale, *Acta Cryst.*, **1**:12 (1948).
45. J. L. Putman and E. H. Cooke-Yarborough, *J. Sci. Instr.*, **25**:409 (1948).
46. P. H. Dowling, C. F. Hendee, T. R. Kohler, and W. Parrish, *Philips Tech. Rev.*, **18**:262 (1956/7).
47. C. F. Hendee and S. Fine, *Phys. Rev.*, **95**:281 (1954).
48. T. Mulvey and A. J. Campbell, *Brit. J. Appl. Phys.*, **9**:406 (1958).
49. D. Van Zoonen, *Appl. Sci. Res.*, **B**(4):196 (1955).
50. H. P. Klug and L. E. Alexander, *X-ray Diffraction of Polycrystalline and Amorphous Materials*, p. 290, John Wiley & Sons, Inc., New York, 1954.
51. K. F. J. Heinrich, "Count Distribution and Precision in X-ray Fluorescence Analysis," paper presented at Pittsburgh Analytical Conference, 1960.
52. R. D. Evans, *The Atomic Nucleus*, McGraw-Hill Book Company, New York, 1955.
53. E. H. Cooke-Yarborough, *J. Brit. Inst. Radio Eng.*, **11**:367–380 (1951).
54. L. J. Rainwater and C. S. Wu, *Nucleonics*, **1**(2): pp. 60–69 (October, 1947); **2**(1):42–49 (January, 1948).
55. W. Volk, *Chem. Eng.*, March, 1956.
56. F. H. Low, *Radioisotope Measurement in Nuclear Medicine*, Picker X-Ray, White Plains, N.Y., 1960.
57. R. D. Evans, *The Atomic Nucleus*, McGraw-Hill Book Company, New York, 1955.
58. R. D. Evans, *The Atomic Nucleus*, McGraw-Hill Book Company, New York, 1955.
59. W. J. Price, *Nuclear Radiation Detection*, 2d ed., McGraw-Hill Book Company, New York, 1964.
60. A. A. Jarrett, *Statistical Methods Used in the Measurement of Radioactivity*, AECU 262 (Mon P-126), Technical Information Division, ORE, Oak Ridge, Tenn., 1950.
61. *Picker Scintillator*, **5**(2) (Feb. 24, 1951).
62. W. Parrish, Sec. 3.1, *International Tables for X-ray Crystallography*, vol. III, Physical and Chemical Tables, p. 153, International Union of Crystallography, Kynoch Press, Birmingham, England, 1962.

GENERAL REFERENCES

Baird, A. K., D. B. McIntyre, and E. E. Welday: *Advances in X-ray Analysis*, W. M. Mueller, ed., vol. 6, p. 377, Plenum Press, New York, 1963.
Bessen, I. I.: *Advances in X-ray Analysis*, W. M. Mueller, ed., vol. 1, p. 455, Plenum Press, New York, 1960.
Birks, J. B.: *Scintillation Counters*, McGraw-Hill Book Company, New York, 1953.
Boltz, D. F.: *Selected Topics in Modern Instrumental Analysis*, Prentice-Hall, Inc., Englewood Cliffs, N.J., 1952.
Brentano, J. C. M., and I. Ladany: *Rev. Sci. Instr.*, **25**:1028 (1954).
Burbank, R. D.: *Rev. Sci. Instr.*, **31**:368 (1960).
Chaplin, G. B. B.: *Instruments and Measurements*, Von Koch et al., eds., vol. 2, p. 514, Academic Press Inc., New York, 1961.
Clayton, C. E., and J. B. Whittaker: *Nucleonics*, **21**:60 (1963).
Cullity, B. D.: *Elements of X-ray Diffraction*, Addison-Wesley Publishing Company, Inc., Reading, Mass., 1956.
Curran, S. C.: *J. Sci. Instr.*, **24**:233 (1947).
Curran, S. C., and J. D. Craggs: *Counting Tubes, Theory and Applications*, Academic Press Inc., New York, 1949.
de Wolff, P. M., J. Taylor, and W. Parrish: *J. Appl. Phys.*, **30**:63 (1959).
Dolby, R. M.: *J. Sci. Instr.*, **40**:345 (1963).
du Pre, F. K.: *Philips Res. Rept.*, **8**:411 (1953).
Estabrook, J. N., and S. W. Hughes: *J. Sci. Instr.*, **30**:317 (1953).

Friedman, H.: *Proc. Inst. Radio Engrs. Australia*, **37**:791 (1949).
Geiger, H.: *Verhandel. Deut. Phys. Ges.*, **15**:534 (1913).
Hamacher, E. A., and K. Lowitzsch: *Philips Tech. Rev.*, **17**:249 (1955/6).
Hendee, C. F., S. Fine, and W. B. Brown: *Norelco Reptr.*, **3**:40 (1956).
Hendee, C. F., S. Fine, and W. B. Brown: *Rev. Sci. Instr.*, **27**:531 (1956).
Henke, B. L.: *Advances in X-ray Analysis*, W. M. Mueller, ed., vol. 5, p. 285, Plenum Press, New York, 1962.
Jones, J. L., and K. W. Paschen: *Applied Rad. Labs. Spectrographer's News Letter*, **15**:1 (1963).
Kiley, W. R.: *Norelco Reptr.*, **6**:23 (1959).
Kiley, W. R.: *Advances in X-ray Analysis*, W. M. Mueller, ed., vol. 2, p. 293, Plenum Press, New York, 1960.
Kiley, W. R.: *Norelco Reptr.*, **7**:143 (1960).
Kiley, W. R., and J. A. Dunne: Technical paper presented at Atlantic City Conference, Eastern Analytical Symposium, 1963.
Kohler, T. R., and W. Parrish: *Rev. Sci. Instr.*, **26**:347 (1955).
Kohler, T. R.: *Semiconductor Nuclear Particle Detectors*, Nuclear Sci. Series Report 32, J. W. T. Dabbs and F. J. Walter, eds., Publ. 871, NAS-NRC, Washington, D.C., p. 193, 1961.
Lang, A. R.: *Rev. Sci. Instr.*, **25**:1032 (1954).
LeGalley, D. P.: *Rev. Sci. Instr.*, **6**:279 (1935).
Liebhafsky, H. A., H. G. Pfeiffer, E. H. Winslow, and P. D. Zemany: *X-ray Absorption and Emission in Analytical Chemistry*, John Wiley & Sons, Inc., New York, 1960.
Linden, B. R.: *Nucleonics*, **11**(9):30 (1953).
Mack, M., and N. Spielberg: *Spectrochim. Acta*, **12**:169 (1958).
Mader, H. J.: *Z. Physik*, **137**:216 (1954).
Marshall, F., J. W. Coltman, and L. P. Hunter: *Rev. Sci. Instr.*, **18**:504 (1947).
Mathieson, E., and P. W. Sanford: *J. Sci. Instr.*, **40**:446 (1963).
Miller, D. C.: *Norelco Reptr.*, **4**:37 (1957).
Mueher, R., and H. Weyerer: *Roentgen Bl.*, **10**:340 (1957).
Muehlhause, C. O., and H. Friedman: *Rev. Sci. Instr.*, **17**:506 (1946).
Owen, R. B.: *Instruments and Measurements*, Van Koch et al., eds., vol. 2, p.295, Academic Press Inc., New York, 1961.
Parratt, L. G., C. F. Hempstead, and E. L. Jossen: *Rev. Sci. Instr.*, **23**:1 (1952).
Parrish, W.: *Philips Tech. Rev.*, **17**:206 (1955/6).
Parrish, W., and E. A. Hammacher: *Trans. Instr. Meas. Conf. (Stockholm)*, 1952, p. 95.
Parrish, W., E. A. Hammacher, and K. Lowitzsch: *Philips Tech. Rev.*, **16**:123 (1954).
Parrish, W., and T. R. Kohler: *J. Appl. Phys.*, **27**:1215 (1956).
Peiser, H. S., H. P. Rooksby, and A. J. C. Wilson: X-ray *Diffraction by Polycrystalline Materials*, Chapman & Hall, Ltd., London, 1955.
Pepinsky, R.: *Anal. Chem.*, **22**:1580 (1950).
Rogers, J. L., and F. C. Chalkin: *Proc. Phys. Soc. (London)*, **B67**:348 (1954).
Rossi, B. B., and H. H. Staub: *Ionization Chambers and Counters*, McGraw-Hill Book Company, New York, 1949.
Short, M. A.: *Rev. Sci. Instr.*, **31**:618 (1960).
Tanaka, K.: *Rev. Sci. Instr.*, **31**:467 (1960).
Taylor, A.: *X-ray Metallography*, John Wiley & Sons, Inc., New York, 1961.
Taylor, J., and W. Parrish: *Acta Cryst.*, **9**:971 (1956).
Teves, M. C., and T. Tol: *Philips Tech. Rev.*, **17**:65 (1955/6).
Tournarie, M.: *J. Phys. Radium*, Suppl. 1, **15**:16A (1954).
Trost, A.: *Z. Angew. Phys.*, **10**:404 (1958).
Trott, B. B.: *J. Sci. Instr.*, **37**:336 (1960).
Van Heerden, P. J.: *Physica*, **16**:505 (1950).
Van Rennes, A. B.: *Nucleonics*, **10** (7):20; (8):22; (9):32; (10):50 (1952).
Van Zoonen, D.: *Appl. Sci. Res.*, **B**(5):368 (1956).
Weiss, W. L., and G. M. Whatley: *Nucleonics*, **21**:66 (1963).
Wilkinson, D. H.: *Ionization Chambers and Counters*, Cambridge University Press, New York, 1950.
Winogradoff, N.: *J. Sci. Instr.*, **25**:432 (1958).
The International Dictionary of Physics and Electronics, D. Van Nostrand Company, Inc., Princeton, N.J., 1956.
International Tables for X-ray Crystallography, vol. III, International Union of Crystallography, Kynoch Press, Birmingham, England, 1961.
Radiological Health Handbook, U.S. Department of Public Health, Education, and Welfare, Public Health Service, Bureau of State Services, Division of Radiological Health, Washington 25, D.C., September, 1960, PB121784R.

Chapter 4

THE GEOMETRY OF CRYSTALS

Dan McLachlan, Jr.

The Ohio State University

1. THE CRYSTALLINE STATE

The most common impressions of crystals are gained by casual observations of sugar, salt, quartz, gem stones, etc. Historically, minerals were the first large group of crystals to furnish the variety and consistency necessary for permitting crystallography to become a science. The general characteristics of crystals as determined

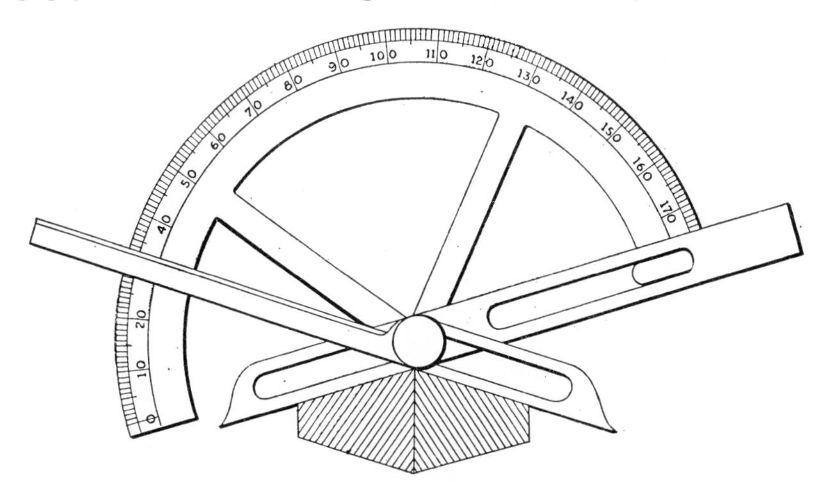

FIG. 1. A contact goniometer for measuring crystal angles.

without modern instrumentation are that they are solid materials having regularly arranged flat faces; in fact the earliest definitions of the crystalline state involved these properties.

Crystal Faces. As in most quantitative sciences something must be measured. In the early stage of crystallography when the flat faces were the most studied characteristic, measurements were made of the angles between adjacent faces. In 1669, this led Nicolaus Sterno to the law of constancy of angle. The first measurements were made by the contact goniometer shown in Fig. 1. The modern method is by

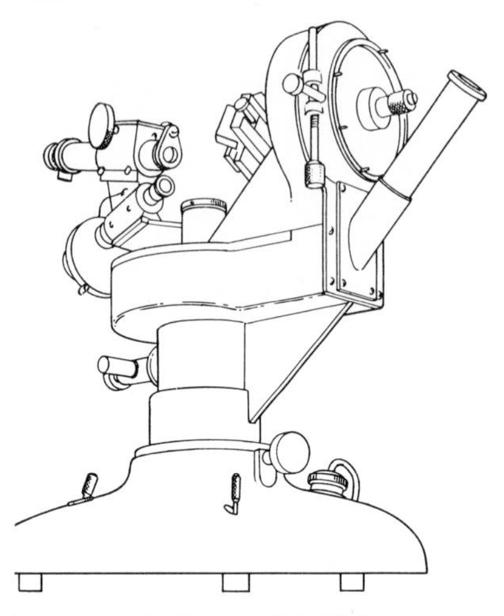

FIG. 2. A late-model Unicam two-circle optical goniometer.

the optical goniometer, either the simple one-circle (horizontal) or the two-circle goniometer.

An example of a relatively recent model of a two-circle goniometer is shown in Fig. 2 as advertised by Unicam of Cambridge. Its working principles are shown in Fig. 3. There is a light and collimator tube A, a telescope B, a rotatable shaft C, and a vertical shaft reaching up from base D. The axes of the telescope B, collimator A, and the two shafts intersect at a common point E as shown and at which the face of a crystal is to be positioned while the crystal is supported on a small glass rod (or such material) attached to a goniometer head F. The crystal after it has been satisfactorily mounted can be rotated about the vertical axis and its position read off scale G, and also can be rotated about the axis of C and the position read off scale H. The accuracy of reading of the scales G and H is enhanced by the microscope I.

Stereographic Projections. As may be seen from Fig. 3, when a strong reflection of light from the collimator A is seen in the telescope B, then one knows that a crystal

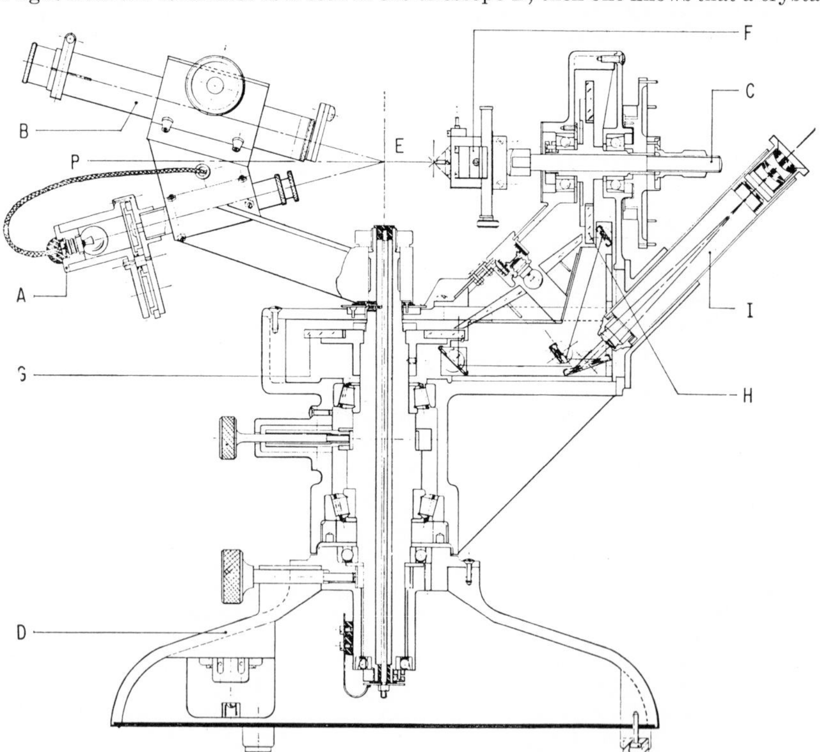

FIG. 3. Schematic drawing of the internal parts of the Unicam goniometer.

face at the position E is so oriented that a perpendicular line through the face at E is directed along the bisector EP. Such a perpendicular is the *pole* of the face (or plane) in question. Figure 4*a* shows a crystal surrounded by a sphere and the perpendiculars extended to the surface of the sphere.

For a crystal with numerous faces the perspective drawings are difficult to draw and unsatisfactory at best, so that one is faced with the old map maker's problem of

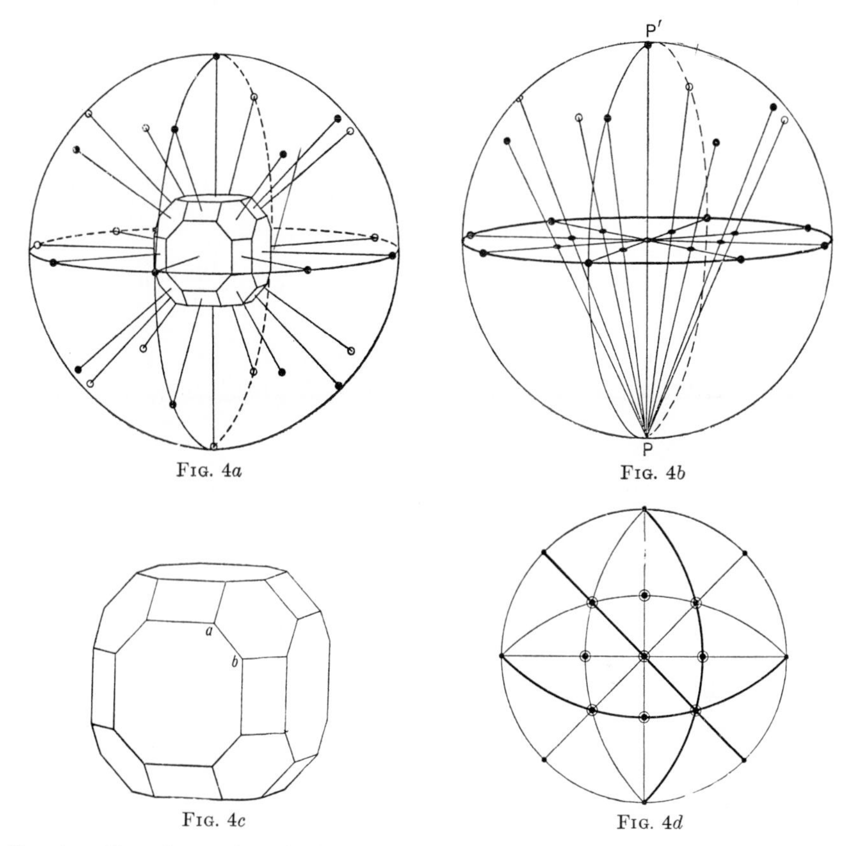

FIG. 4*a* FIG. 4*b* FIG. 4*c* FIG. 4*d*

FIG. 4*a*. Lines drawn through the center of a sphere passing perpendicular to the faces of a crystal and intersecting the surface of a sphere.
FIG. 4*b*. Lines drawn from the "south pole" of a sphere to the points on the surface of the "northern hemisphere" shown in Fig. 4*a*. The array of points where these lines pass through the equatorial plane constitutes a stereographic projection of the poles of the crystal faces.
FIG. 4*c*. The original crystal.
FIG. 4*d*. The stereographic projection of the poles of Fig. 4*c*.

representing the characteristics or detail of the surface of a sphere on a flat page of paper. Of the many ways of accomplishing this, the stereographic projection is most popular with crystallographers. To accomplish a stereographic projection of the points on the surface of the upper hemisphere shown in Fig. 4*b*, lines are drawn from each point to the south pole p of the sphere. Where these lines intersect the equatorial plane dots are made. A similar procedure for the lower (or southern) hemisphere requires drawing lines from the lower points through the equatorial plane toward the north pole p' and open circles drawn on the equatorial plane. The equatorial plane

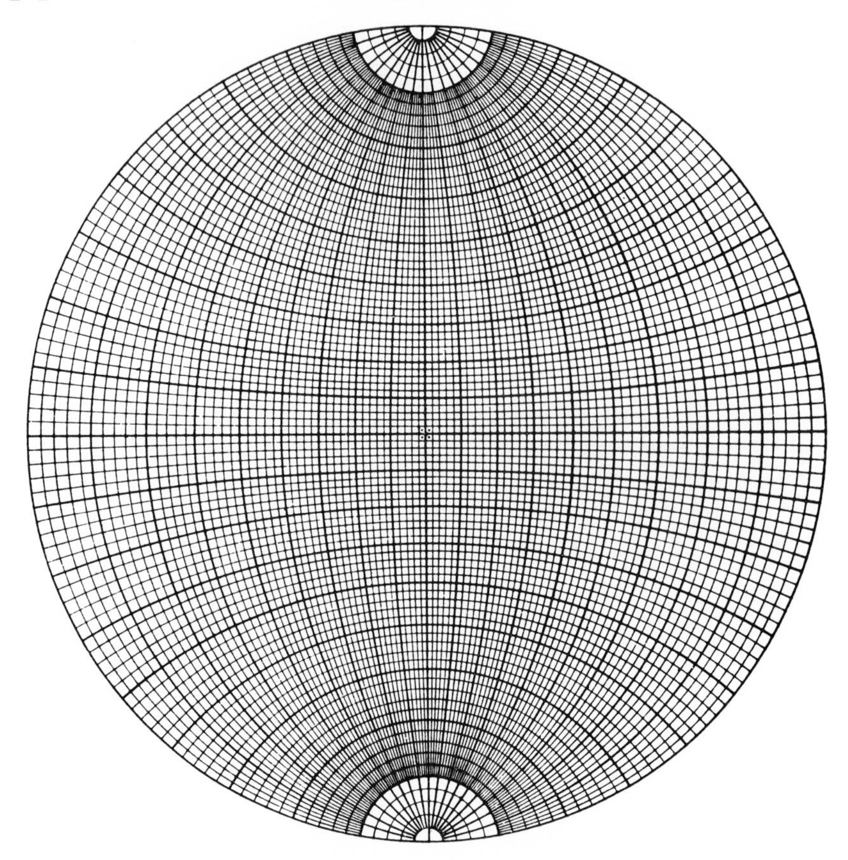

Fig. 5. Wulff net drawn to 2° intervals.

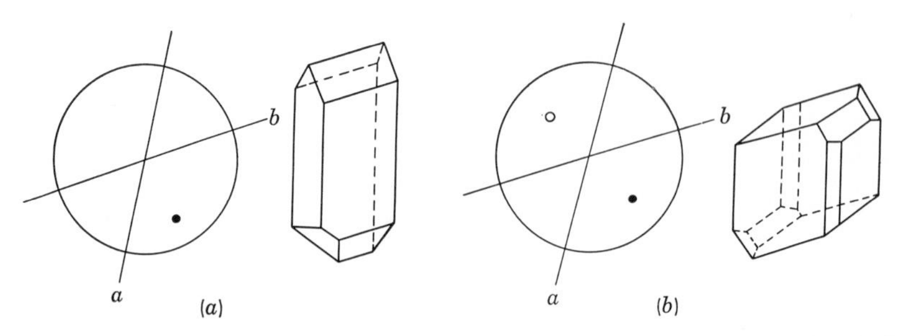

Fig. 6. (*a*) Point group $\bar{1}$ illustrated by the triclinic crystal acid strontium tartrate tetrahydrate. (*b*) Point group $\bar{1}$ as illustrated by the triclinic crystal of the complex mineral axanite.

with its dots and open circles is all that is saved; and one such for the crystal shown in Fig. 4*c* is presented in Fig. 4*d*. The curves in Fig. 4*d* connecting the poles are great circles (on the original sphere) or *zones*.

For convenience in plotting the data from the optical goniometer, the Wulff net (see Fig. 5) is popular. The one illustrated here is marked off in 2° intervals in the

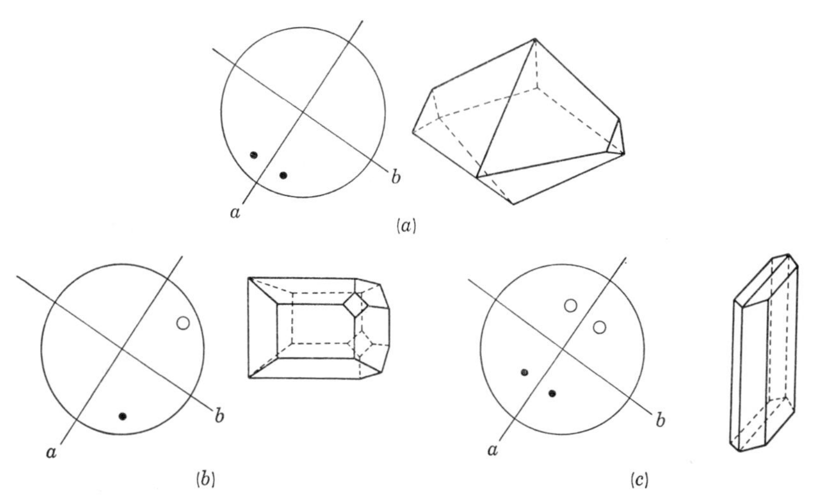

FIG. 7. (*a*) Point group *m* as illustrated by the monoclinic crystal clinohedrite. (*b*) Point group 2, cane sugar, monoclinic. (*c*) Point group $2/m$, gypsum.

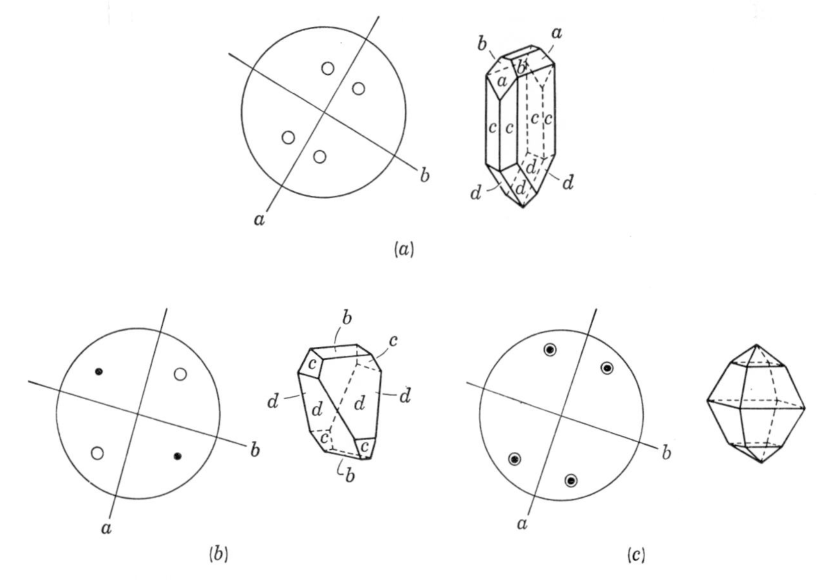

FIG. 8. (*a*) Point group *m*, calomine, orthorhombic. (*b*) Point group 222, illustrated by the growth of the orthorhombic crystal epsonite. (*c*) Point group *mmm*, orthorhombic sulfur.

two Euler angles sometimes designated θ and ϕ for longitude and latitude and sometimes by the symbols γ (gamma) and δ (delta).

It might be observed that the crystal shown in Fig. 4*c*, as well as its projection Fig. 4*d*, exhibits obvious symmetry. However, the symmetry is overdemonstrated (redundant) when represented by all the faces of some well-developed crystals, and it is customary to show only sufficient points on the projection to represent the symmetry. Later we shall enumerate all the 32 kinds of symmetry (point groups). But at present

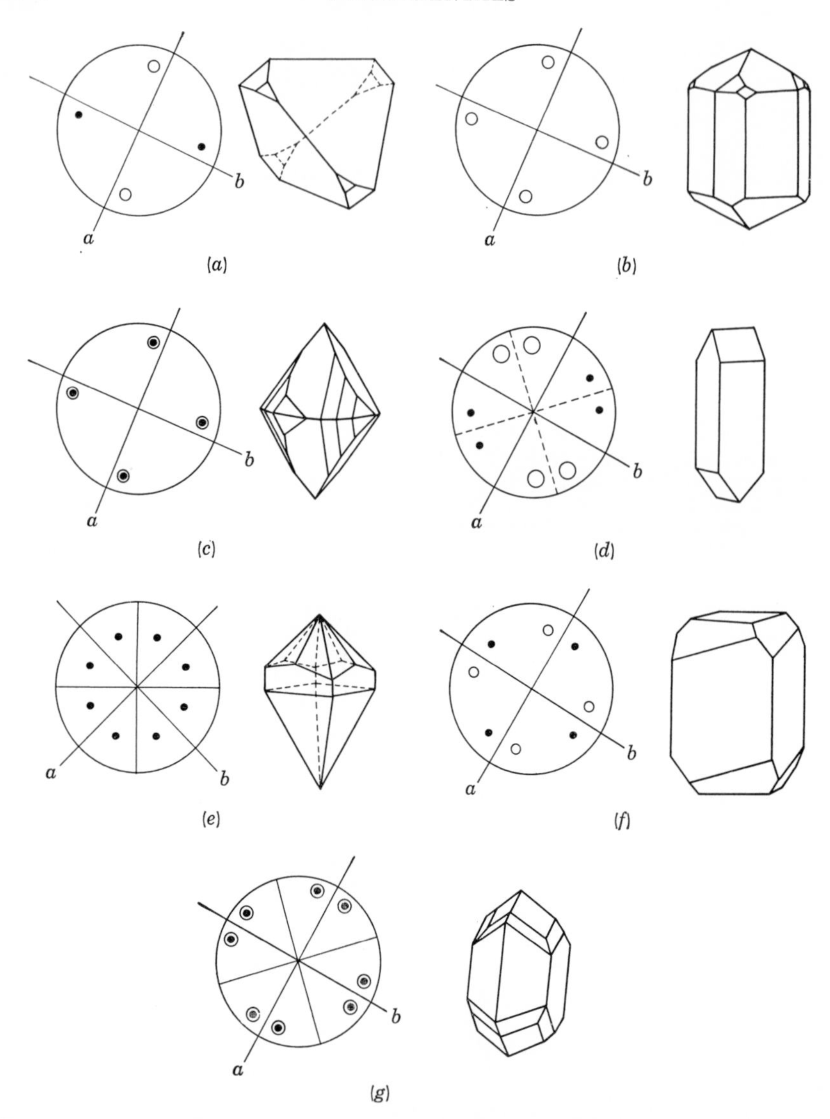

FIG. 9. (*a*) Point group $\bar{4}$, of the tetragonal system, artificially grown $CaO\text{-}Al_2O_3\cdot SiO_2$. (*b*) Point group 4, barium antimonial tartrate. (*c*) Point group $4/m$, scheetite. (*d*) Point group $\bar{4}2m$, urea. (*e*) Point group $4mm$, the hydrate of silver fluoride. (*f*) Point group 42, methylammonium iodide. (*g*) Point group $4/mmm$, zircon.

we shall only show by means of Figs. 6 to 12 the 32 symmetrical shapes for the 32 classes and the stereographic projection that corresponds to each.

We wish to emphasize that the orientation of the faces of crystals is only one of the many ways that crystals exhibit symmetry. The next significant gross property of a crystal is its possible anisotropy, that is, the dependence of physical properties upon direction.

Manifestations of Symmetry. Enumerated below are one atomic property and 15 examples of gross physical properties of crystals in which anisotropy might be exhibited by a crystal dependent upon which of the 32 crystal classes it belongs to.

1. Index of refraction (depicted frequently by a diagram called an *indicatrix*)
2. Optical activity (the power to rotate the plane of polarized light)
3. Pleochroism (the dependence of color upon the direction)
4. Etched figures on the faces
5. Rates of growth in different directions
6. Rates of dissolving in different directions
7. Thermal conductivity
8. Coefficient of thermal expansion
9. Pyroelectricity
10. Elasticity
11. Hardness
12. Magnetic anisotropy
13. Dielectric constant
14. Piezoelectricity
15. Ferroelectricity
16. Atomic arrangement (the big problem in crystal structure)

Insofar as the applied and resultant measurables are linearly related, the gross anisotropic properties can be treated by means of first-rank, second-rank, third-rank, etc., tensors. The dielectric constant, for example, requires a second-rank tensor, piezoelectricity a third-rank tensor, and elastic constants (generalized Hooke's law)

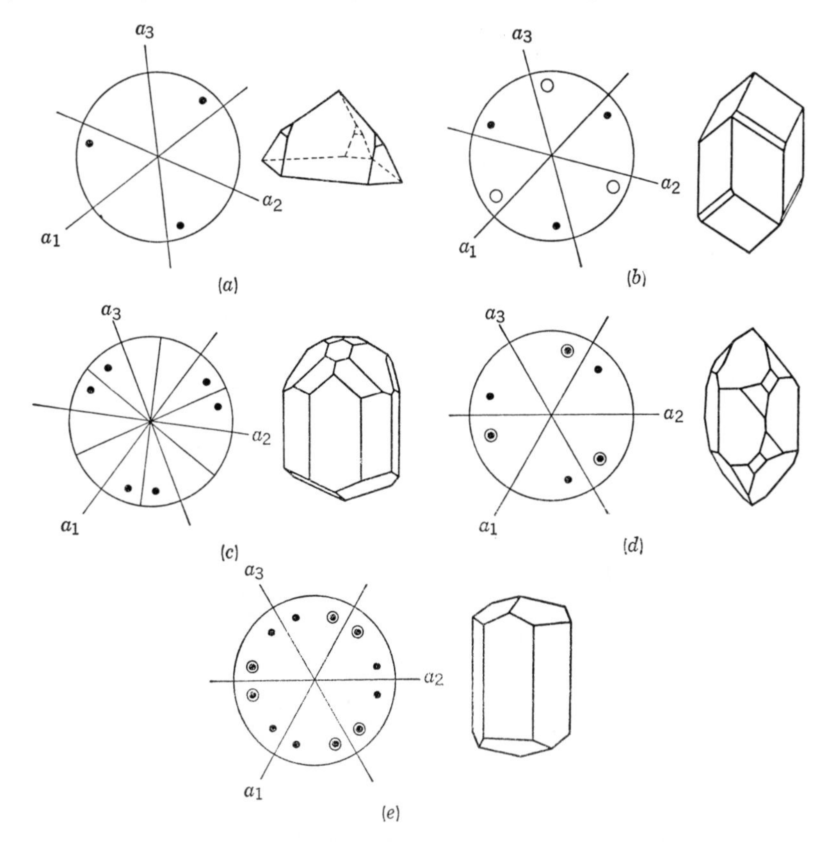

Fig. 10. (*a*) Point group 3, sodium periodate trihydrate, rhombohedral. (*b*) Point group $\bar{3}$, dioptase. (*c*) Point group 3*m*, tourmaline. (*d*) Point group 32, quartz. (*e*) Point group $\bar{3}m$, calcite.

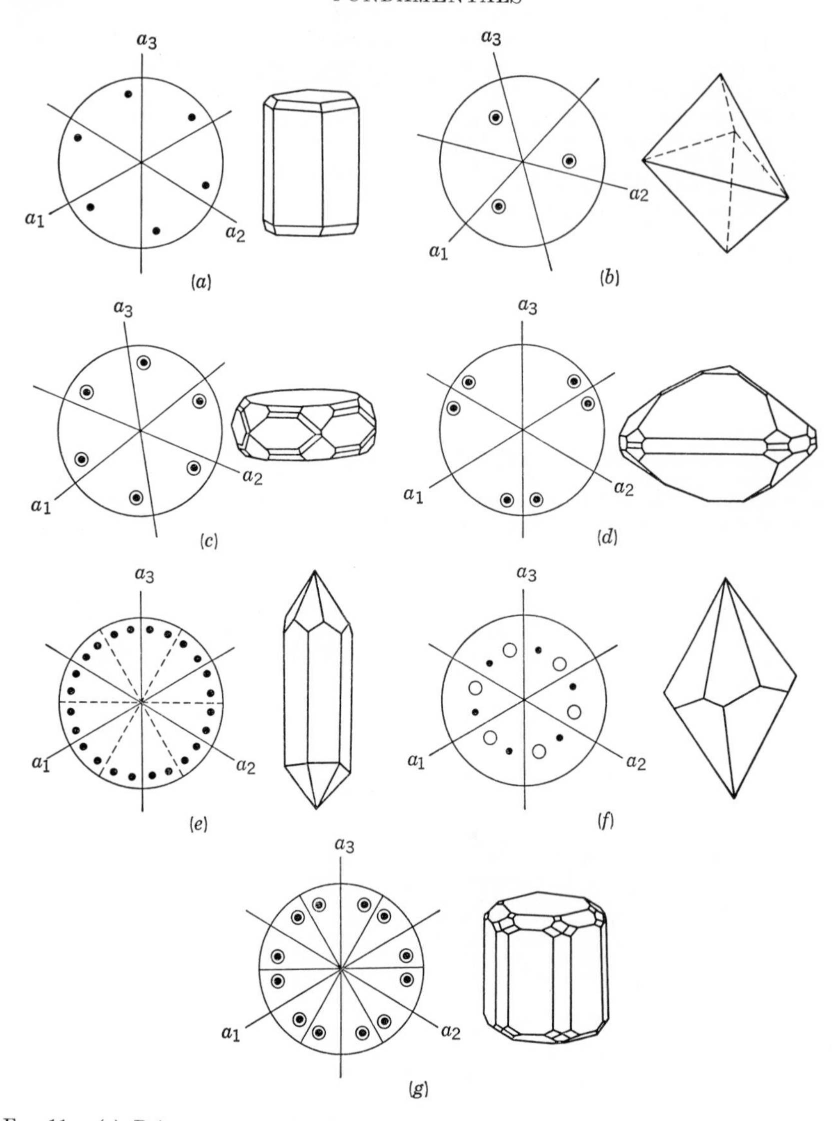

Fig. 11. (*a*) Point group 6, belonging to the hexagonal division of the hexagonal system, potassium sulfate. (*b*) Point group $\bar{6}$ has not been illustrated by any growing crystal. (*c*) Point group $6/m$, apatite. (*d*) Point group $\bar{6}m2$, bentonite. (*e*) Point group $6mm$, triethylammonium chloride. (*f*) Point group 62, high quartz. (*g*) Point group $6/mmm$, beryl.

fourth-rank tensors. This general study of symmetry in the study of anisotropy was once called crystal physics but is too extensive for this handbook. The reader is referred to Warren P. Mason, *Piezoelectric Crystals and Their Application to Ultrasonics*, D. Van Nostrand Company, Inc., Princeton, N.J., 1950; J. F. Nye, *Physical Properties of Crystals*, Oxford University Press, Fair Lawn, N.J., 1957; and similar books.

The sixteenth item in the above tabulation of properties, atomic arrangement, is of most interest to x-ray researchers. Since symmetry in so inherent in the way atoms are arranged, the crystal classes will now be discussed.

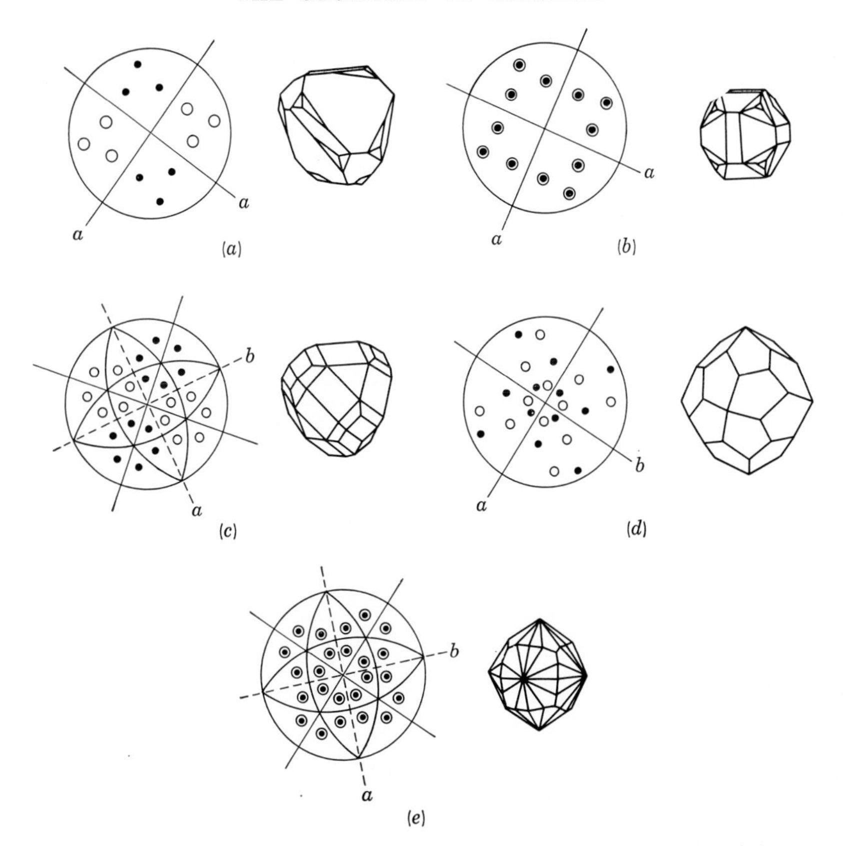

FIG. 12. (*a*) Point group 23, of the cubic system, sodium chloride (never found this complete in development). (*b*) Point group *m*3, pyrite. (*c*) Point group $\bar{4}3m$, copper antimony sulfide. (*d*) Point group 43 has no illustration in nature. (*e*) Point group *m*3*m*, silver.

2. THE CRYSTAL CLASSES

There are 10 elements of symmetry in crystals, as tabulated in Table 1 with their symbols. These 10 elementary operators, as they are called, can be combined in 32 ways to produce the 32 point groups as tabulated in Table 2. To save a long discussion of these operators, Fig. 13*a* and *b* illustrates how the operators 4 and $\bar{4}$ relate the atomic positions, and Fig. 13*c* shows how three perpendicular mirrors operate to produce eight equivalent points.

Table 1

No symmetry	1
Mirror plane of symmetry	*m*
Twofold rotor	2
Threefold rotor	3
Threefold rotatory inverter	$\bar{3}$
Fourfold rotor	4
Fourfold rotatory inverter	$\bar{4}$
Sixfold rotor	6
Sixfold rotatory inverter	$\bar{6}$
Inverter	$\bar{1}$

Table 2. Crystal Classes

Class No. according to Von Groth	Names of classes according to Von Groth	Symmetry symbols	
		Schönflies	Hermann-Mauguin
	Triclinic System		
1	Triclinic asymmetric	C_1	1
2	Triclinic pinacoidal	$S_2 = C_i$	$\bar{1}$
	Monoclinic System		
3	Monoclinic sphenoidal	C_2	2
4	Monoclinic domatic	$C_{1h} = C_s$	$m = \bar{2}$
5	Monoclinic prismatic	C_{2h}	$\frac{2}{m}$
	Orthorhombic System		
6	Orthorhombic disphenoidal	$V = D_2$	222
7	Orthorhombic pyramidal	C_{2v}	$2mm$
8	Orthorhombic dipyramidal	$V_h = D_{2h}$	$\frac{2}{m}\frac{2}{m}\frac{2}{m} = mmm$
	Tetragonal System		
9	Tetragonal disphenoidal	S_4	$\bar{4}$
10	Tetragonal pyramidal	C_4	4
11	Tetragonal scalenohedral	$V_d = D_{2d}$	$\bar{4}2m$
12	Tetragonal trapezohedral	D_4	422
13	Tetragonal dipyramidal	C_{4h}	$\frac{4}{m}$
14	Ditetragonal-pyramidal	C_{4v}	$4mm$
15	Ditetragonal-dipyramidal	D_{4h}	$\frac{4}{m}mm = \frac{4}{m}\frac{2}{m}\frac{2}{m}$
	Trigonal System		
16	Trigonal pyramidal	C_3	3
17	Trigonal rhombohedral	C_{3i}	$\bar{3}$
18	Trigonal trapezohedral	D_3	32
20	Ditrigonal-pyramidal	C_{3v}	$3m$
21	Ditrigonal-scalenohedral	D_{3d}	$\bar{3}\frac{2}{m}$
	Hexagonal System		
19	Trigonal dipyramidal	C_{3h}	$\bar{6}$
22	Ditrigonal-dipyramidal	D_{3h}	$\bar{6}m2$
23	Hexagonal pyramidal	C_6	6
24	Hexagonal trapezohedral	D_6	622
25	Hexagonal dipyramidal	C_{6h}	$\frac{6}{m}$
26	Dihexagonal-pyramidal	C_{6v}	$6mm$
27	Dihexagonal-dipyramidal	D_{6h}	$\frac{6}{m}mm = \frac{6}{m}\frac{2}{m}\frac{2}{m}$
	Cubic System		
28	Cubic tetrahedral-pentagonal-dodecahedral	T	23
29	Cubic pentagonal icositetrahedral	O	432
30	Cubic dyakis-dodecahedral	T_h	$\frac{2}{m}\bar{3} = m3$
31	Cubic hexakis-tetrahedral	T_d	$\bar{4}3m$
32	Cubic hexakis-octahedral	O_h	$\frac{4}{m}\bar{3}\frac{2}{m} = m3m$

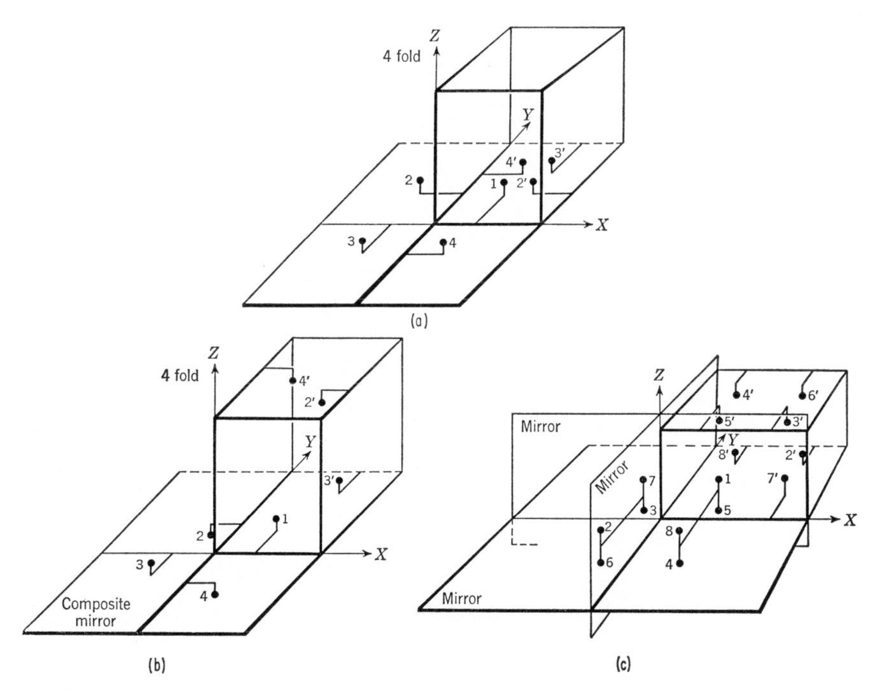

FIG. 13. (*a*) Point group *C*4 or 4. Coordinates of equivalent points: xyz; $\bar{y}xz$; $\bar{x}\bar{y}z$; $y\bar{x}z$. (*b*) Point group *S*4 or $\bar{4}$ of the tetragonal system. Coordinates of equivalent points: xyz; $\bar{y}x\bar{z}$; $\bar{x}\bar{y}z$; $y\bar{x}\bar{z}$. (*c*) Point group D_{2h} or *mmm*. Coordinates of equivalent points: xyz; $x\bar{y}\bar{z}$; $\bar{x}y\bar{z}$; $\bar{x}\bar{y}z$; $xy\bar{z}$; $x\bar{y}z$; $\bar{x}yz$; $\bar{x}\bar{y}\bar{z}$.

3. CRYSTAL SYSTEMS AND SPACE LATTICES

The more modern concept of crystals since the application of x-ray diffraction is that a crystal is a periodic array of ordered atoms in three dimensions. The repeating unit is imagined to be a unit cell whose volume and shape are designated by three distances a, b, and c representing the length of the cell edges and three angles α, β, and γ representing the angles between the cell edges. Figure 14 shows a three-dimensional array of unit cells with a, b, c, α, β, and γ marked on them. There are six shapes which will fit in three dimensions in this manner. These are called the six crystal systems. They are depicted in Fig. 15, and the restrictions are given in Table 3.

Table 3

1. Triclinic	$a \neq b \neq c$	$\alpha \neq \beta \neq \gamma \neq 90°$
2. Monoclinic	$a \neq b \neq c$	$\alpha = \gamma = 90°$, $\beta \neq 90°$
3. Orthorhombic	$a \neq b \neq c$	$\alpha = \beta = \gamma = 90°$
4. Tetragonal	$a = b \neq c$	$\alpha = \beta = \gamma = 90°$
5. Cubic	$a = b = c$	$\alpha = \beta = \gamma = 90°$
6. Hexagonal	$a = b \neq c$	$\alpha = \beta = 90°$, $\gamma = 120°$

To show how the unit cells might be oriented with respect to the outside faces of crystals we present in Fig. 16 the four forms of sulfanilamide.

Referring to Fig. 13, we should say that each of these represents a single unit cell.

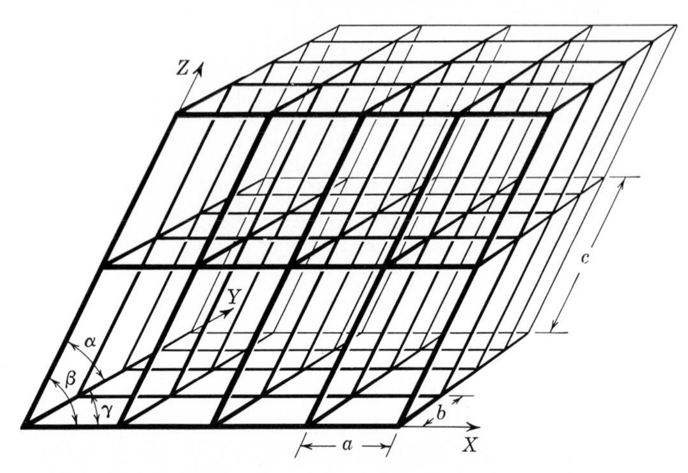

FIG. 14. The general (triclinic) space lattice showing the unit cell dimensions a, b, c and the angles α, β, and γ. It is becoming standard practice among crystallographers, however, to make α, β, and γ represent the obtuse angles.

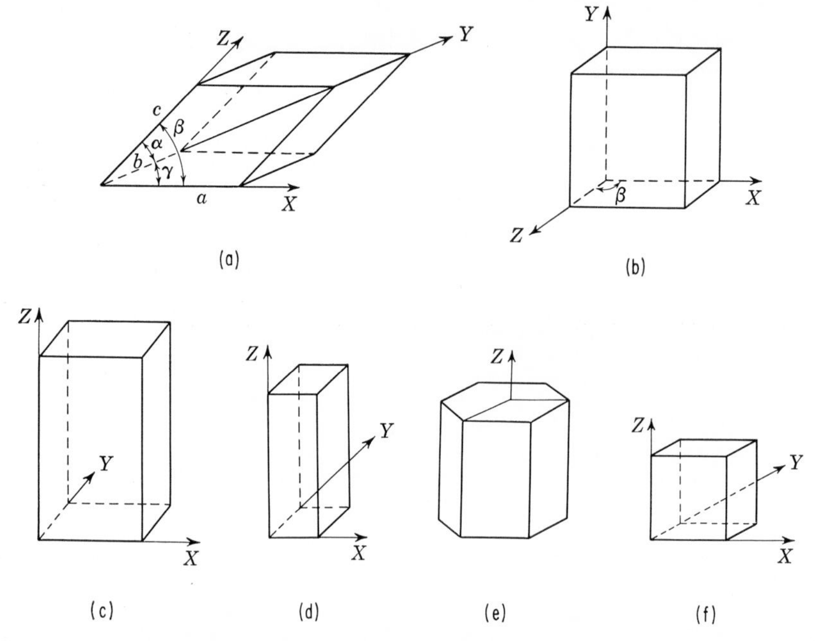

FIG. 15. (*a*) The triclinic cell. (*b*) The monoclinic cell. (*c*) The orthorhombic cell. (*d*) The tetragonal cell. (*e*) The hexagonal cell. (*f*) The cubic cell.

It is to be noted that coordinates of the atoms are given with the corner of the unit cell as the origin. The corner does not have to be the only origin. Other origins are shown in Fig. 17. The six combinations of origins (or centers) are as follows:

P, primitive at corner
A, face-centered on face bound by the edges *b* and *c*

B, face-centered on a *b* face
C, face-centered on a *c* face
F, centered on all faces
I, body-centered

These types of centers cannot be placed in every possible combination on all the six crystal systems but only in 14 ways to produce the 14 Bravais lattices. These are shown in Fig. 19.

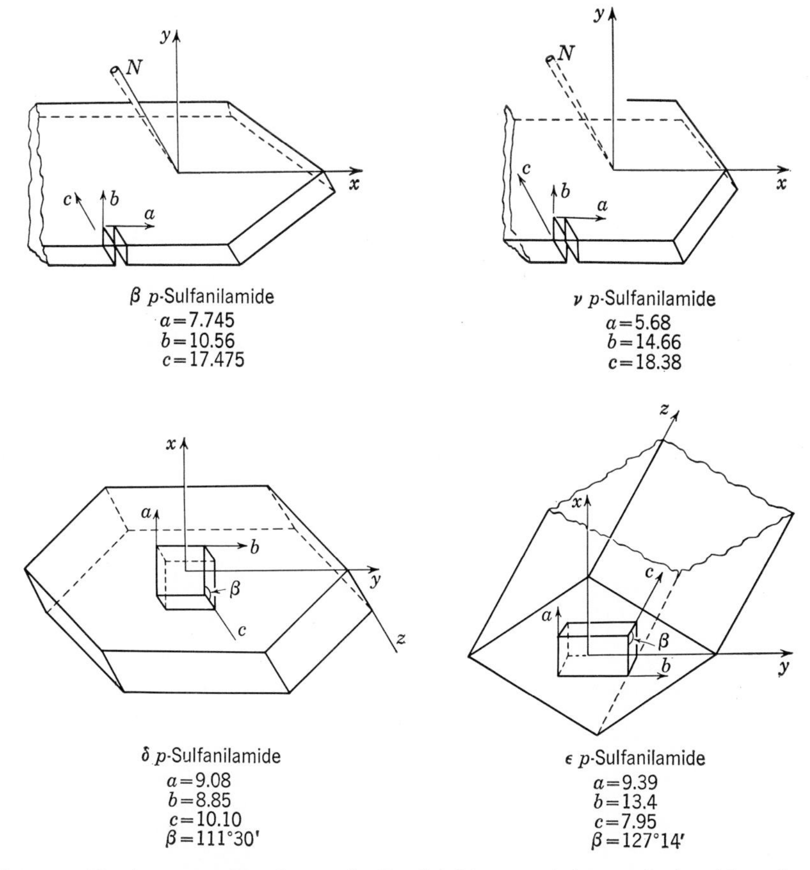

FIG. 16. The four crystalline forms of sulfanilamide, two of them orthorhombic and two monoclinic.

4. MILLER INDICES AND INTERPLANAR SPACINGS

It is possible to pass a plane through a unit cell so that it cuts the a axis at a distance a/h, the b axis at b/k, and the c axis at c/l, where h, k, and l are integers. Figure 20 shows a plane cutting the axes at $a/3$, $b/1$, and $c/2$ so that the integers h, k, and l are 3, 1, and 2. The integers are called Miller indices designated (hkl), in this case (312); the plane (100) is also shown.

When a set of parallel planes is passed through a unit cell so that they are equally spaced, the set is called a *family* of planes. Of great importance to x-ray crystallography is the interplanar spacing d_{hkl}, which can be computed, knowing $h, k, l, a, b, c,$

α, β, and γ, by means of equations appropriate to each of the six crystal systems. These equations are furnished in Table 4.

Also of importance are the cell volumes V given in Table 5.

Table 4

The calculation of interplanar spacings is carried out by means of equations appropriate to each crystal system.

Cubic system:

$$d_{hkl} = \frac{a}{\sqrt{h^2 + k^2 + l^2}}$$

Tetragonal system:

$$d_{hkl} = \frac{1}{\sqrt{(h^2 + k^2)/a^2 + l^2/c^2}}$$

Orthorhombic system:

$$d_{hkl} = \frac{1}{\sqrt{h^2/a^2 + k^2/b^2 + l^2/c^2}}$$

Hexagonal system (indexed on hexagonal lattice):

$$h_{hkl} = \frac{1}{\sqrt{\dfrac{4(h^2 + k^2 + hk)}{3a^2} + \dfrac{l^2}{c^2}}}$$

Monoclinic system:

$$d_{hkl} = \frac{1}{\sqrt{\dfrac{(h^2/a^2 + l^2/c^2 + 2hl \cos \beta/ac)}{\sin^2 \beta} + \dfrac{k^2}{h^2}}}$$

Triclinic system:

$$d_{hkl} = \frac{1}{\sqrt{\dfrac{\dfrac{h}{a}\begin{vmatrix} \frac{h}{a} & \cos\gamma & \cos\beta \\ \frac{k}{b} & 1 & \cos\alpha \\ \frac{l}{c} & \cos\alpha & 1 \end{vmatrix} + \dfrac{k}{b}\begin{vmatrix} 1 & \frac{h}{c} & \cos\beta \\ \cos\gamma & \frac{k}{b} & \cos\alpha \\ \cos\beta & \frac{l}{c} & 1 \end{vmatrix} + \dfrac{1}{c}\begin{vmatrix} 1 & \cos\gamma & \frac{h}{a} \\ \cos\gamma & 1 & \frac{k}{b} \\ \cos\beta & \cos\alpha & \frac{l}{c} \end{vmatrix}}{\Delta}}}$$

where Δ is the determinant

$$\begin{vmatrix} 1 & \cos\gamma & \cos\beta \\ \cos\gamma & 1 & \cos\alpha \\ \cos\beta & \cos\alpha & 1 \end{vmatrix}$$

Table 5

Cubic:	$V = a^3$
Tetragonal:	$V = a^2c$
Hexagonal:	$V = \dfrac{\sqrt{3}\, a^2c}{2} = 0.866a^2c$
Rhombohedral:	$V = a^3 \sqrt{1 - 3\cos^2\alpha + 2\cos^3\alpha}$
Orthorhombic:	$V = abc$
Monoclinic:	$V = abc \sin\beta$
Triclinic:	$V = abc\sqrt{1 - \cos^2\alpha - \cos^2\beta - \cos^2\gamma + 2\cos\alpha\cos\beta\cos\gamma}$

One is also occasionally interested in computing the angle between planes. The angle ϕ between the plane $(h_1k_1l_1)$ of spacing d_1 and the plane $(h_2k_2l_2)$ of spacing d_2 may be computed using the equations compiled in Table 6, where V is the volume of the cell.

Table 6

Cubic:

$$\cos \phi = \frac{h_1h_2 + k_1k_2 + l_1l_2}{\sqrt{(h_1^2 + k_1^2 + l_1^2)(h_2^2 + k_2^2 + l_2^2)}}$$

Tetragonal:

$$\cos \phi = \frac{\frac{h_1h_2 + k_1k_2}{a^2} + \frac{l_1l_2}{c^2}}{\sqrt{\left(\frac{h_1^2 + k_1^2}{a^2} + \frac{l_1^2}{c^2}\right)\left(\frac{h_2^2 + k_2^2}{a^2} + \frac{l_2^2}{c^2}\right)}}$$

Hexagonal:

$$\cos \phi = \frac{h_1h_2 + k_1k_2 + \frac{1}{2}(h_1k_2 + h_2k_1) + \frac{3a^2}{4c^2}l_1l_2}{\sqrt{\left(h_1^2 + k_1^2 + h_1k_1 + \frac{3a^2}{4c^2}l_1^2\right)\left(h_2^2 + k_2^2 + h_2k_2 + \frac{3a^2}{4c^2}l_2^2\right)}}$$

Rhombohedral:

$$\cos \phi = \frac{a^4d_1d_2}{V^2}[\sin^2 \alpha(h_1h_2 + k_1k_2 + l_1l_2) + (\cos^2 \alpha - \cos \alpha)(k_1l_2 + k_2l_1 + l_1h_2 + l_2h_1 + h_1k_2 + h_2k_1)]$$

Orthorhombic:

$$\cos \phi = \frac{\frac{h_1h_2}{a^2} + \frac{k_1k_2}{b^2} + \frac{l_1l_2}{c^2}}{\sqrt{\left(\frac{h_1^2}{a^2} + \frac{k_1^2}{b^2} + \frac{l_1^2}{c^2}\right)\left(\frac{h_2^2}{a^2} + \frac{k_2^2}{b^2} + \frac{l_2^2}{c^2}\right)}}$$

Monoclinic:

$$\cos \phi - \frac{d_1d_2}{\sin^2 \beta}\left[\frac{h_1h_2}{a^2} + \frac{k_1k_2 \sin^2 \beta}{b^2} + \frac{l_1l_2}{c^2} - \frac{(l_1h_2 + l_2h_1) \cos \beta}{ac}\right]$$

Triclinic:

$$\cos \phi = \frac{d_1d_2}{V^2}[S_{11}h_1h_2 + S_{22}k_1k_2 + S_{33}l_1l_2 + S_{23}(k_1l_2 + k_2l_1) + S_{13}(l_1h_2 + l_2h_1) + S_{12}(h_1k_2 + h_2k_1)]$$

5. SPACE GROUPS

In Part 3 of this handbook much discussion will be given to the computation of intensities of diffraction of x-rays from the various (hkl) planes of crystals and to the counterpart, namely, the computation of electron densities (xyz) throughout the space within the unit cells. The diffraction pattern from a crystal is in the form of an array of diffraction maxima arranged regularly throughout "reciprocal space," and the points of maximum intensity are arranged on a *reciprocal* lattice (see Sec. 6 and Chap. 26). This reciprocal lattice has symmetry in itself which helps to determine the point group to which the crystal belongs (see Table 7).

But even more important, the reciprocal space might exhibit a systematic arrangement of lattice points at which the intensity of diffraction is zero. These zero intensities are called systematic extinctions and are used to determine to which of the 230 space groups the crystal belongs. These extinctions are caused by certain kinds of configurations of the atoms which result in the interplanar spacings being reduced by one-half, one-third, one-fourth, or one-sixth. Referring to Fig. 17, we can say, for example, that for a body-centered or I lattice we get extinctions when $h + k + l$ is odd. The entries at the top of Table 8 give the conditions of nonextinction for each lattice in Fig. 17, A, B, C, F, and I, remembering that P gives no extinctions.

In addition to extinctions due to the Bravais lattices, extinctions may occur as a consequence of the presence of *glide* mirrors and screw axes. Figure 18a shows a mirror m, which has symmetry but produces no extinctions, while Fig. 18b shows a

Table 7. Diffraction Symmetry*

Crystal symmetry			Symmetry of x-ray diffraction effects	
Triclinic	C_1	1	C_i	$\bar{1}$
	C_i	$\bar{1}$		
Monoclinic	C_2	2	C_{2h}	$2/m$
	C_v	m		
	C_{2h}	$2/m$		
Orthorhombic	D_2 V	222	D_{2h}	mmm
	C_{2v}	$2mm$		
	D_{2h} V_h	mmm		
Tetragonal	S_4	$\bar{4}$	C_{4h}	$4/m$
	C_4	4		
	C_{4h}	$4/m$		
	D_{2d}	$\bar{4}2m$	D_{4h}	$4/mmm$
	C_{4v}	$4mm$		
	D_4	422		
	D_{4h}	$4/mmm$		
Hexagonal Rhombohedral	C_3	3	C_{3i}	$\bar{3}$
	C_{3i}	$\bar{3}$		
	C_{3v}	$3m$	D_{3d}	$\bar{3}m$
	D_3	32		
	D_{3d}	$\bar{3}m$		
Hexagonal	C_6	6	C_{6h}	$6/m$
	C_{3h}	$\bar{6}$		
	C_{6h}	$6/m$		
	D_{3h}	$\bar{6}m2$	D_{6h}	$6/mmm$
	C_{6v}	$6mm$		
	D_6	622		
	D_{6h}	$6/mmm$		
Isometric	T	23	T_h	$m3$
	T_h	$m3$		
	T_d	$\bar{4}3m$	O_h	$m3m$
	O	432		
	O_h	$m3m$		

* After Buerger, *X-ray Crystallography*, John Wiley & Sons, Inc., New York, 1942.

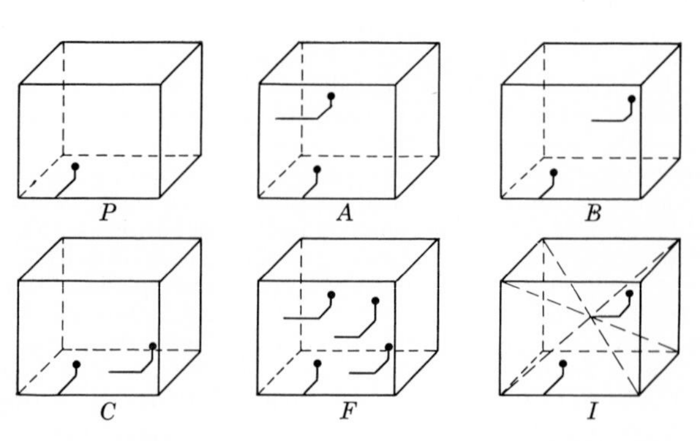

Fig. 17. Showing the primitive lattice *P*, the cell centered on the *A* face, on the *B* face, the *C* face, all faces *F*, and body-centered cell *I*, with one equivalent point at each center.

Table 8. Symmetry Interpretations of Extinctions*

Class of reflection	Condition for nonextinction (n = an integer)	Interpretation of extinction	Symbol of symmetry element
hkl	$h + k + l = 2n$	Body-centered lattice	I
	$h + k = 2n$	C-centered lattice	C
	$h + l = 2n$	B-centered lattice	B
	$k + l = 2n$	A-centered lattice	A
	$\left\{ \begin{array}{l} h + k = 2n \\ h + l = 2n \\ k + l = 2n \end{array} \right\}$ ⇔ h, k, l, all even or all odd	Face-centered lattice	F
	$-h + k + l = 3n$	Rhombohedral lattice indexed on hexagonal reference system	R
	$h + k + l = 3n$	Hexagonal lattice indexed on rhombohedral reference system	H
$0kl$	$k = 2n$	(100) glide plane, component $b/2$	b (P, B, C)
	$l = 2n$	(100) glide plane, component $c/2$	c (P, C, I)
	$k + l = 2n$	(100) glide plane, component $b/2 + c/2$	n (P)
	$k + l = 4n$	(100) glide plane, component $b/4 + c/4$	d (F)
$h0l$	$h = 2n$	(010) glide plane, component $a/2$	a (P, A, I)
	$l = 2n$	(010) glide plane, component $c/2$	c (P, A, C)
	$h + l = 2n$	(010) glide plane, component $a/2 + c/2$	n (P)
	$h + l = 4n$	(010) glide plane, component $a/4 + c/4$	d (F), (B)
$hk0$	$h = 2n$	(001) glide plane, component $a/2$	a (P, B, I)
	$k = 2n$	(001) glide plane, component $b/2$	b (P, A, B)
	$h + k = 2n$	(001) glide plane, component $a/2 + b/2$	n (P)
	$h + k = 4n$	(001) glide plane, component $a/4 + b/4$	d (F)
hhl	$l = 2n$	$(1\bar{1}0)$ glide plane, component $c/2$	c (P, C, F)
	$h = 2n$	$(1\bar{1}0)$ glide plane, component $a/2 + b/2$	b (C)
	$h + l = 2n$	$(1\bar{1}0)$ glide plane, component $a/4 + b/4 + c/4$	n (C)
	$2h + l = 2n$	$(1\bar{1}0)$ glide plane, component $a/2 + b/4 + c/4$	d (I)
$h00$	$h = 2n$	[100] screw axis, component $a/2$	2_1, 4_2
	$h = 4n$	[100] screw axis, component $b/2$	4_1, 4_3
$0k0$	$k = 2n$	[010] screw axis, component $b/2$	2_1, 4_2
	$k = 4n$	[010] screw axis, component $b/4$	4_1, 4_3
$00l$	$l = 2n$	[001] screw axis, component $c/2$	2_1, 4_2, 6_3
	$l = 3n$	[001] screw axis, component $c/3$	3_1, 3_2, 6_2, 6_4
	$l = 4n$	[001] screw axis, component $c/4$	4_1, 4_2
	$l = 6n$	[001] screw axis, component $c/6$	6_1, 6_2
$hh0$	$h = 2n$	[110] screw axis, component $a/2 + b/2$	2_1

* After Buerger, *X-ray Crystallography*, John Wiley & Sons, Inc., New York, 1942.

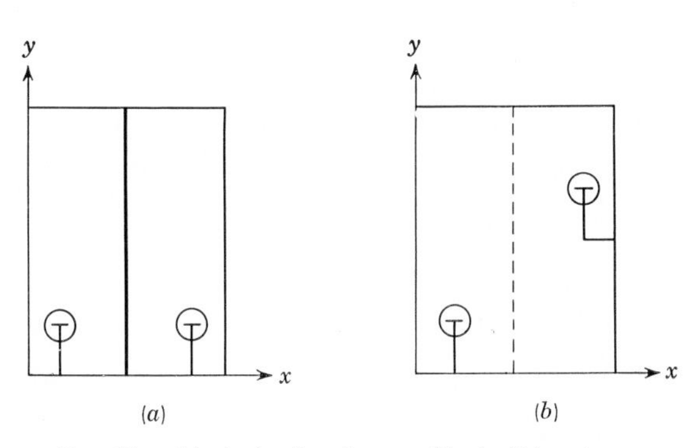

FIG. 18. (*a*) A simple mirror. (*b*) A glide mirror.

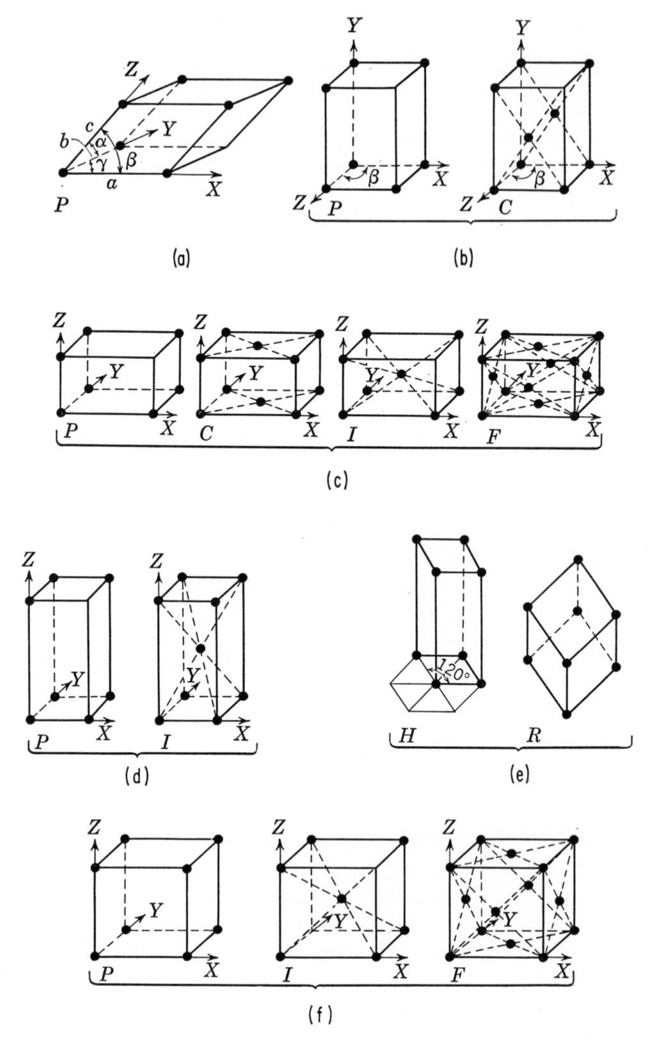

FIG. 19. The 14 Bravais lattices. (*a*) The triclinic lattice is always primitive, *P*. (*b*) The monoclinic lattice may be primitive, *P*, or centered, *C*, i.e., centered on the *ab* face. (Note that in this lattice only the *y* axis is vertical. This long-established practice may some day be abandoned.) (*c*) The orthorhombic lattices are the primitive, *P*, the centered, *C*, the body-centered, *I*, and the face-centered, *F* (centered small faces). (*d*) The tetragonal lattice may be primitive, *P*, or body-centered, *I*. (*e*) The hexagonal system is divided into the hexagonal division *H* and the rhombohedral division *R*. (*f*) The cubic system may be primitive, *P*, body-centered, *I*, or face-centered, *F*.

mirror gliding in the y direction and designated by the symbol b. This glide mirror b causes extinctions on the $hk0$ and $0kl$ planes of reciprocal space when k is odd.

A mirror gliding in the x direction is designated by a and in the z direction by c. A mirror gliding in the direction of a face diagonal is designated by d and in the direction of a body diagonal by n. The conditions for nonextinction for glide mirrors are next shown in Table 8. The last to be shown in Table 8 are the conditions of nonextinction for screw axes. Screw axes can be understood by inspecting the

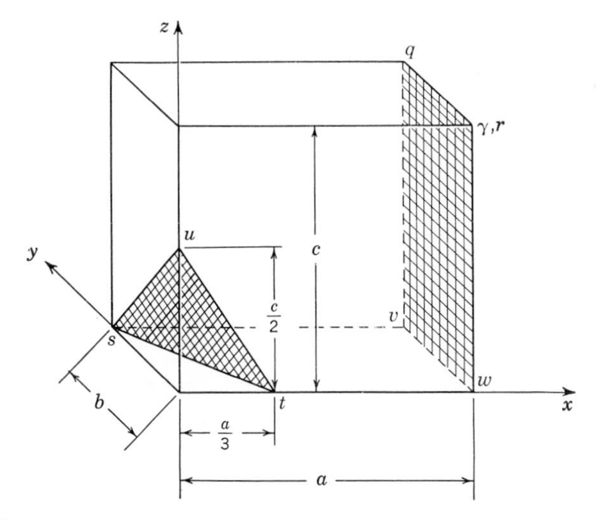

FIG. 20. Showing the position of the (312) plane and the (100) plane in the unit cell.

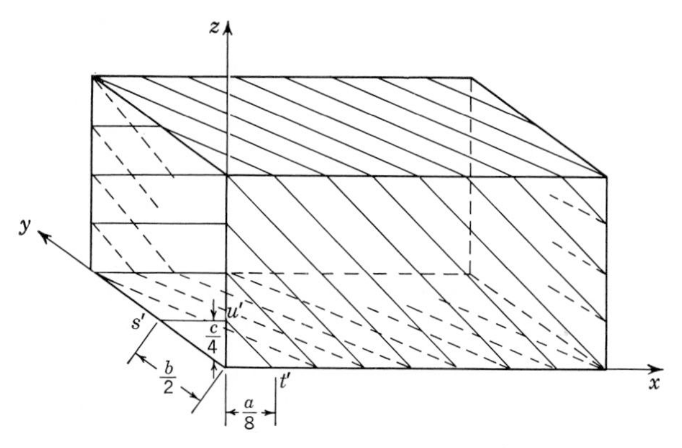

FIG. 21. Showing all the planes belonging to the (824) family of planes. They are all parallel, equally spaced, and commensurate with the unit cell dimensions.

diagrams labeled with numerical subscripts shown in Fig. 22; 3, 4, and 6 being ordinary rotation axes, $\bar{3}$, $\bar{4}$, and $\bar{6}$ rotatory inversions, and 3_1, 3_2, 4_1, 4_2, 4_3, 6_1, 6_2, 6_3, 6_4, and 6_5 screw axes. Combining the contents of Table 1 with the statements that have just been made, we get all the symbols shown in Table 9.

Table 9. Operators

Not causing extinction	*Causing extinction*
P	A, B, C, F, 1
1, $\bar{1}$	
m	a, b, c, d, n
2	2_1
3, $\bar{3}$	3_1, 3_2
4, $\bar{4}$	4_1, 4_2, 4_3
6, $\bar{6}$	6_1, 6_2, 6_3, 6_4, 6_5

The combination of the operators listed in Table 9 according to regulations imposed by group theory produces all the 230 space groups. The Schoenflies symbols and the International symbols for the 230 space groups are listed in Table 10.

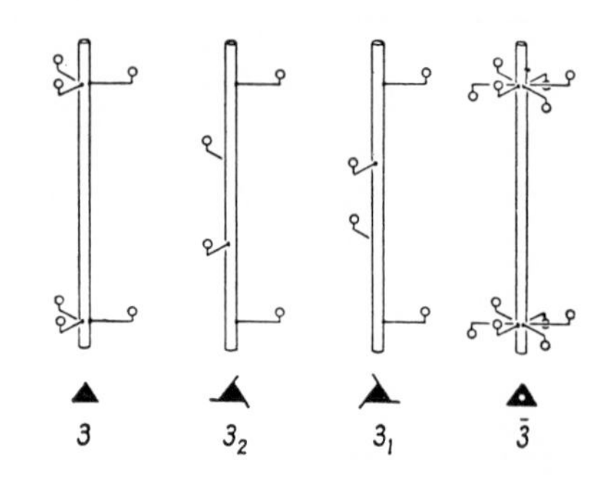

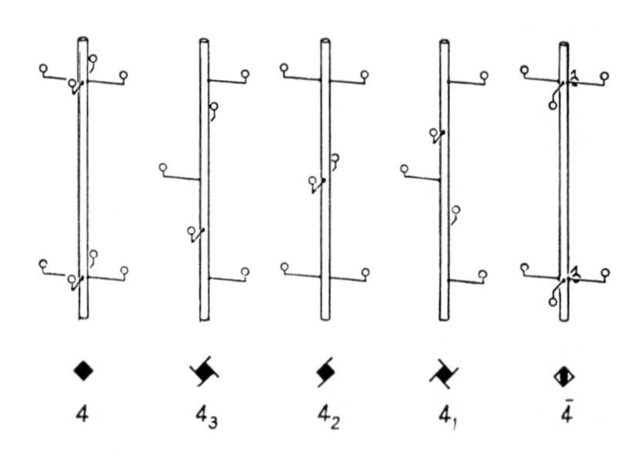

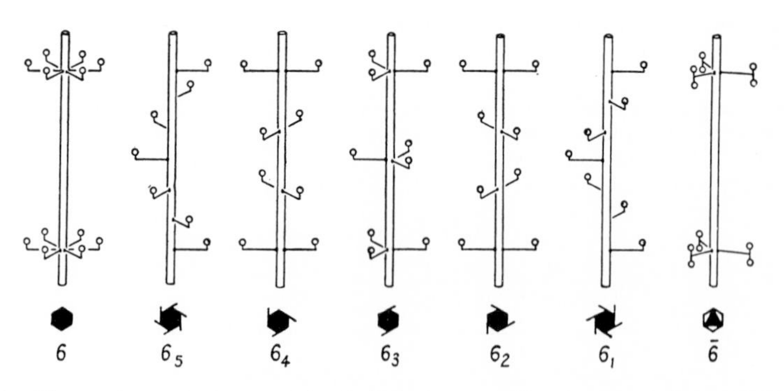

FIG. 22. The various rotation axes (excluding the twofold axis, 2, and the twofold screw axis, 2_1).

Table 10

Number	Schoenflies	1952 International Tables
Triclinic		
1	C_1^1	$P1$
2	C_i^1	$P\bar{1}$
Monoclinic		
3	C_2^1	$P2$
4	C_2^2	$P2_1$
5	C_2^3	$B2$
6	C_s^1	Pm
7	C_s^2	Pb
8	C_s^3	Bm
9	C_s^4	Bb
10	C_{2h}^1	$P2/m$
11	C_{2h}^2	$P2_1/m$
12	C_{2h}^3	$B2/m$
13	C_{2h}^4	$P2/b$
14	C_{2h}^5	$P2_1/b$
15	C_{2h}^6	$B2/b$
Orthorhombic		
16	D_2^1	$P222$
17	D_2^2	$P222_1$
18	D_2^3	$P2_12_12$
19	D_2^4	$P2_12_12_1$
20	D_2^5	$C222_1$
21	D_2^6	$C222$
22	D_2^7	$F222$
23	D_2^8	$I222$
24	D_2^9	$I2_12_12_1$
25	C_{2v}^1	$Pmm2$
26	C_{2v}^2	$Pmc2_1$
27	C_{2v}^3	$Pcc2$
28	C_{2v}^4	$Pma2$
29	C_{2v}^5	$Pca2_1$
30	C_{2v}^6	$Pnc2$
31	C_{2v}^7	$Pmn2_1$
32	C_{2v}^8	$Pba2$
33	C_{2v}^9	$Pna2_1$
34	C_{2v}^{10}	$Pnn2$
35	C_{2v}^{11}	$Cmm2$
36	C_{2v}^{12}	$Cmc2_1$
37	C_{2v}^{13}	$Ccc2$
38	C_{2v}^{14}	$Amm2$
39	C_{2v}^{15}	$Abm2$
40	C_{2v}^{16}	$Ama2$
41	C_{2v}^{17}	$Aba2$
42	C_{2v}^{18}	$Fmm2$
43	C_{2v}^{19}	$Fdd2$
44	C_{2v}^{20}	$Imm2$
45	C_{2v}^{21}	$Iba2$
46	C_{2v}^{22}	$Ima2$
47	D_{2h}^1	$Pmmm$
48	D_{2h}^2	$Pnnn$
49	D_{2h}^3	$Pccm$
50	D_{2h}^4	$Pban$
51	D_{2h}^5	$Pmma$
52	D_{2h}^6	$Pnna$
53	D_{2h}^7	$Pmna$

Table 10 (*Continued*)

Number	Schoenflies	1952 International Tables
54	D_{2h}^{8}	*Pcca*
55	D_{2h}^{9}	*Pbam*
56	D_{2h}^{10}	*Pccn*
57	D_{2h}^{11}	*Pbcm*
58	D_{2h}^{12}	*Pnnm*
59	D_{2h}^{13}	*Pmmn*
60	D_{2h}^{14}	*Pbcn*
61	D_{2h}^{15}	*Pbca*
62	D_{2h}^{16}	*Pnma*
63	D_{2h}^{17}	*Cmcm*
64	D_{2h}^{18}	*Cmca*
65	D_{2h}^{19}	*Cmmm*
66	D_{2h}^{20}	*Cccm*
67	D_{2h}^{21}	*Cmma*
68	D_{2h}^{22}	*Ccca*
69	D_{2h}^{23}	*Fmmm*
70	D_{2h}^{24}	*Fddd*
71	D_{2h}^{25}	*Immm*
72	D_{2h}^{26}	*Ibam*
73	D_{2h}^{27}	*Ibca*
74	D_{2h}^{28}	*Imma*
Tetragonal		
75	C_4^1	$P4$
76	C_4^2	$P4_1$
77	C_4^3	$P4_2$
78	C_4^4	$P4_3$
79	C_4^5	$I4$
80	C_4^6	$I4_1$
81	S_4^1	$P\bar{4}$
82	S_4^2	$I\bar{4}$
83	C_{4h}^1	$P4/m$
84	C_{4h}^2	$P4_2/m$
85	C_{4h}^3	$P4/n$
86	C_{4h}^4	$P4_2/n$
87	C_{4h}^5	$I4/m$
88	C_{4h}^6	$I4_1/a$
89	D_4^1	$P422$
90	D_4^2	$P42_12$
91	D_4^3	$P4_122$
92	D_4^4	$P4_12_12$
93	D_4^5	$P4_222$
94	D_4^6	$P4_22_12$
95	D_4^7	$P4_322$
96	D_4^8	$P4_32_12$
97	D_4^9	$I422$
98	D_4^{10}	$I4_122$
99	C_{4v}^1	$P4mm$
100	C_{4v}^2	$P4bm$
101	C_{4v}^3	$P4_2cm$
102	C_{4v}^4	$P4_2nm$
103	C_{4v}^5	$P4cc$
104	C_{4v}^6	$P4nc$
105	C_{4v}^7	$P4_2mc$
106	C_{4v}^8	$P4_2bc$
107	C_{4v}^9	$I4mm$
108	C_{4v}^{10}	$I4cm$
109	C_{4v}^{11}	$I4_1md$

Table 10 (*Continued*)

Number	Schoenflies	1952 International Tables
110	C_{4v}^{12}	$I4_1cd$
111	D_{2d}^{1}	$P\bar{4}2m$
112	D_{2d}^{2}	$P\bar{4}2c$
113	D_{2d}^{3}	$P\bar{4}2_1m$
114	D_{2d}^{4}	$P\bar{4}2_1c$
115	D_{2d}^{5}	$P\bar{4}m2$
116	D_{2d}^{6}	$P\bar{4}c2$
117	D_{2d}^{7}	$P\bar{4}b2$
118	D_{2d}^{8}	$P\bar{4}n2$
119	D_{2d}^{9}	$I\bar{4}m2$
120	D_{2d}^{10}	$I\bar{4}c2$
121	D_{2d}^{11}	$I\bar{4}2m$
122	D_{2d}^{12}	$I\bar{4}2d$
123	D_{4h}^{1}	$P4/mmm$
124	D_{4h}^{2}	$P4/mcc$
125	D_{4h}^{3}	$P4/nbm$
126	D_{4h}^{4}	$P4/ncc$
127	D_{4h}^{5}	$P4/mbm$
128	D_{4h}^{6}	$P4/mnc$
129	D_{4h}^{7}	$P4/mmm$
130	D_{4h}^{8}	$P4/ncc$
131	D_{4h}^{9}	$P4_2/mmc$
132	D_{4h}^{10}	$P4_2/mcm$
133	D_{4h}^{11}	$P4_2/nbc$
134	D_{4h}^{12}	$P4_2/nnm$
135	D_{4h}^{13}	$P4_2/mbc$
136	D_{4h}^{14}	$P4_2/mnm$
137	D_{4h}^{15}	$P4_2/nmc$
138	D_{4h}^{16}	$P4_2/ncm$
139	D_{4h}^{17}	$I4/mmm$
140	D_{4h}^{18}	$I4/mcm$
141	D_{4h}^{19}	$I4_1/amd$
142	D_{4h}^{20}	$I4_1/acd$
Rhombohedral (trigonal)		
143	C_3^{1}	$P3$
144	C_3^{2}	$P3_1$
145	C_3^{3}	$P3_2$
146	C_3^{4}	$R3$
147	C_{3i}^{1}	$P\bar{3}$
148	C_{3i}^{2}	$R\bar{3}$
149	D_3^{1}	$P312$
150	D_3^{2}	$P321$
151	D_3^{3}	$P3_112$
152	D_3^{4}	$P3_121$
153	D_3^{5}	$P3_212$
154	D_3^{6}	$P3_221$
155	D_3^{7}	$R32$
156	C_{3v}^{1}	$P3m1$
157	C_{3v}^{2}	$P31m$
158	C_{3v}^{3}	$P3c1$
159	C_{3v}^{4}	$P31c$
160	C_{3v}^{5}	$R3m$
161	C_{3v}^{6}	$R3c$
162	D_{3d}^{1}	$P\bar{3}1m$
163	D_{3d}^{2}	$P\bar{3}1c$
164	D_{3d}^{3}	$P\bar{3}m1$
165	D_{3d}^{4}	$P\bar{3}c1$

Table 10 (*Continued*)

Number	Schoenflies	1952 International Tables
166	D_{3d}^5	$R\bar{3}m$
167	D_{3d}^6	$R\bar{3}c$
Hexagonal		
168	C_6^1	$P6$
169	C_6^2	$P6_1$
170	C_6^3	$P6_5$
171	C_6^4	$P6_2$
172	C_6^5	$P6_4$
173	C_6^6	$P6_3$
174	C_{3h}^1	$P\bar{6}$
175	C_{6h}^1	$P6/m$
176	C_{6h}^2	$P6_3/m$
177	D_6^1	$P622$
178	D_6^2	$P6_122$
179	D_6^3	$P6_522$
180	D_6^4	$P6_222$
181	D_6^5	$P6_422$
182	D_6^6	$P6_322$
183	C_{6v}^1	$P6mm$
184	C_{6v}^2	$P6cc$
185	C_{6v}^3	$P6_3cm$
186	C_{6v}^4	$P6_3mc$
187	D_{3h}^1	$P\bar{6}m2$
188	D_{3h}^2	$P\bar{6}c2$
189	D_{3h}^3	$P\bar{6}2m$
190	D_{3h}^4	$P\bar{6}2c$
191	D_{6h}^1	$P6/mmm$
192	D_{6h}^2	$P6/mcc$
193	D_{6h}^3	$P6_3mcm$
194	D_{6h}^4	$P6_3/mmc$
Cubic		
195	T^1	$P23$
196	T^2	$F23$
197	T^3	$I23$
198	T^4	$P2_13$
199	T^5	$I2_13$
200	T_h^1	$Pm3$
201	T_h^2	$Pn3$
202	T_h^3	$Fm3$
203	T_h^4	$Fd3$
204	T_h^5	$Im3$
205	T_h^6	$Pa3$
206	T_h^7	$Ia3$
207	O^1	$P432$
208	O^2	$P4_232$
209	O^3	$F432$
210	O^4	$F4_132$
211	O^5	$I432$
212	O^6	$P4_332$
213	O^7	$P4_132$
214	O^8	$I4_132$
215	T_d^1	$P\bar{4}3m$
216	T_d^2	$F\bar{4}3m$
217	T_d^3	$I\bar{4}3m$
218	T_d^4	$P\bar{4}3n$
219	T_d^5	$F\bar{4}3c$

Table 10 (*Continued*)

Number	Schoenflies	1952 International Tables
220	T_d^6	$I\bar{4}3d$
221	O_h^1	$Pm3m$
222	O_h^2	$Pn3n$
223	O_h^3	$Pm3n$
224	O_h^4	$Pn3m$
225	O_h^5	$Fm3m$
226	O_h^6	$Fm3c$
227	O_h^7	$Fd3m$
228	O_h^8	$Fd3c$
229	O_h^9	$Im3m$
230	O_h^{10}	$Ia3d$

Table 11. Reciprocal Cell Dimensions from Direct Cell Dimensions

$$a^* = bc \sin \alpha/V$$
$$b^* = ca \sin \beta/V$$
$$c^* = ab \sin \gamma/V$$

where V is given in Table 5.

$$\cos \alpha^* = \frac{\cos \beta \cos \gamma - \cos \alpha}{\sin \beta \sin \gamma}$$

$$\cos \beta^* = \frac{\cos \gamma \cos \alpha - \cos \beta}{\sin \gamma \sin \alpha}$$

$$\cos \gamma^* = \frac{\cos \alpha \cos \beta - \cos \gamma}{\sin \alpha \sin \beta}$$

Table 12. Direct Cell Dimensions from Reciprocal Cell Dimensions

$$a = b^*c^* \sin \alpha^*/V^*$$
$$b = c^*a^* \sin \beta^*/V^*$$
$$c = a^*b^* \sin \gamma^*/V^*$$

where $V = a^*b^*c^*(1 - \cos^2 \alpha^* - \cos^2 \beta^* - \cos^2 \beta^* + 2 \cos \alpha^* \cos \beta^* \cos \gamma^*)^{1/2}$

$$\cos \alpha = \frac{\cos \beta^* \cos \gamma^* - \cos \alpha^*}{\sin \beta^* \sin \gamma^*}$$

$$\cos \beta = \frac{\cos \gamma^* \cos \alpha^* - \cos \beta^*}{\sin \gamma^* \sin \alpha^*}$$

$$\cos \gamma = \frac{\cos \alpha^* \cos \beta^* - \cos \gamma^*}{\sin \alpha^* \sin \beta^*}$$

6. THE RECIPROCAL LATTICE (Also see Chap. 26)

The array of diffraction maxima in reciprocal space can be thought of as points located at the corners of "reciprocal cells." These cells are considered to have edge lengths a^*, b^*, and c^* and interedge angles α^*, β^*, and γ^* with volume V^*. The relationships between cell constants in reciprocal and direct space are

$$a^* = 1/d_{100} \qquad d_{100} = 1/a^* = \lambda/(2 \sin \theta_{100})$$
$$b^* = 1/d_{010} \qquad d_{010} = 1/b^* = \lambda/(2 \sin \theta_{010})$$
$$c^* = 1/d_{001} \qquad d_{001} = 1/c^* = \lambda/(2 \sin \theta_{001})$$

The distance from the origin (000) of the reciprocal lattice to any point (hkl) in the lattice is

$$hkl = (h^2a^{*2} + k^2b^{*2} + l^2c^{*2} + 2hka^*b^* \cos \gamma^* + 2klb^*c^* \cos \alpha^* + 2hlc^*a^* \cos \beta^*)^{1/2}$$

This can be recognized as the equation for the length of the body diagonal of a parallelepiped.

Additional relationships are given in Tables 11 and 12.

7. A REMARK REGARDING TABLES

The *International Tables for X-ray Crystallography* (vol. I, *Symmetry Groups;* vol. II, *Mathematical Tables;* and vol. III, *Physical and Chemical Tables,* published for the International Union of Crystallography by the Kynoch Press of Birmingham, England, under the editorship of Norman F. M. Henry and Kathleen Lonsdale and an editorial committee) are indispensable for anyone doing serious x-ray crystallography research. As an example of information that can be only illustrated here in Fig. 13*a*, *b*, and *c*, the International Tables give the coordinates of the equivalent positions (general and special) for the entire 230 space groups, with drawings.

Chapter 5

DESIGN OF TYPICAL X-RAY LABORATORY

W. R. Whitford and John Moskal

Philips Electronic Instruments

1. GENERAL CONSIDERATIONS

There are a number of factors to be considered when planning the x-ray analytical laboratory: (1) the analytical work to be done, (2) the analytical approach to be used, (3) the quality and quantity of available personnel needed, and (4) the finances available for the installation. It is axiomatic that the analyst keep cost in mind as one of the main factors that he must consider. He must try to get the required analyses done as effectively as possible within the scope of his activity. In his selection of equipment, he must weigh sensitivity, versatility, precision, accuracy, and price. He must also consider ultimate operating expense of the x-ray laboratory in terms of staffing and training laboratory personnel, overhead and equipment service costs, and future upgrading of the equipment when it becomes advantageous to broaden the analytical capabilities of the laboratory. Reluctance on the part of the laboratory administration to budget adequately for these operating contingencies after the initial laboratory has been set up may severely hamper the performance of the x-ray laboratory.

2. OPERATIONS

The analyst does more than just operate the equipment and interpret his instrumental results. Much of his time must be spent in the laboratory preparing specimens suitable for analysis. These and other important operations which the analyst must do in the course of his work are:

1. Specimen procurement and general preparation, including cutting, grinding, polishing, etc.
2. Specific preparation procedures required for special analytical work, such as pelletizing, solubilizing, concentrating and dilution techniques, and the development of new techniques
3. Routine upkeep of the equipment, including alignment, calibration, and general testing to obtain optimum performance
4. Film loading, unloading, and photographic development
5. Maintenance and repair of a mechanical or electrical nature
6. Filing and classification of analytical data

These operations and functions apply basically to any x-ray laboratory installation, regardless of size, scope, or extent of its analytical program.

Instrument accessibility is of prime importance in maintenance. In case there is any need to remove large components from the consoles (i.e., transformers, line stabilizers, etc.) there must be ample space around the instrument to allow free access for this purpose. For this reason it is advisable to locate the equipment near the center of the room or at a suitable distance from the wall.

The final product of any x-ray laboratory is the analytical data produced, whether they be x-ray film, diffractometer or spectrographic recordings, or printed tapes. This represents the information which the analyst must interpret and, from time to time, review and have readily available. These data are frequently valuable, and provision should be made for keeping reference files for this information in an orderly manner to avoid loss or damage.

3. SPECIMEN PREPARATION

Specimen preparation is the key to success in any analytical work, but the accommodations for this important phase are often inadequate and, in some instances, hazardous.

Provision for good housekeeping in the sample area is needed. A room separate from the main x-ray laboratory is desirable from the standpoint of reducing airborne dust and noxious fumes. Adequate ventilation to remove heat, dust, and fumes can be provided with suitable blowers and ducts. General cleanliness should be stressed to prevent cross contamination of samples. Noisome operations can be controlled by personnel to reduce any discomfort to coworkers. Table 1 indicates the general type of specimen-preparation equipment employed in the x-ray analytical laboratories of various industries.

4. THE X-RAY LABORATORY PLAN

A suggested layout for a two-man x-ray laboratory is shown in Fig. 1. A modular concept has been used for convenience to the laboratory planner, based upon an average module size of 7 ft 0 in. by 24 ft 0 in. It can be seen that, for the two-man laboratory, three of these average modules have been allocated. With the exception of the outside wall, all inner walls are movable and the service utilities are considered to be supplied from vertical utility stacks in the outside walls. The spaces and facilities as planned are regarded as minimum for a modern x-ray laboratory for research or control. The actual floor space occupied by most pieces of x-ray equipment is 20 to 25 sq ft. The arrangement provides convenient circulation between the sample-preparation area, the x-ray equipment, and the darkroom, if necessary. Similarly, the film-measuring facilities, calculator, and the files are handy to the analyst. The room for film viewing, instrument alignment, and microscopic work may be darkened at will by means of a dark shade.

Adequate storage can be provided in this plan, by means of suitable shelves and cupboards, for all phases of the work. Bulky equipment not in daily use, such as oscilloscopes used for servicing, vacuum pumps, and special specimen-preparation apparatus, may be caster-mounted. Usually suitable storage, in less costly space on the same floor of the building, can be provided for such equipment. Modification of the floor plan to suit modules of other dimensions will be evident with a little study.

Most domestic commercial x-ray analytical units have a maximum power demand of 3 to 5 kva and can usually be obtained to operate on 200/250-volt single-phase 50- to 60-cycle current. In some rare instances up to 10 kva may be required. Although most x-ray equipment may be purchased with built-in voltage regulation (usually optionally offered by the manufacturer) a wise precaution is to provide separate line regulation or isolation transformer for the x-ray laboratory power supply. This is particularly true at those industrial plants where it is difficult to obtain a "clean" line for the laboratory. The local representative of your power company can usually be prevailed upon to survey the proposed laboratory and make specific recommendations as to the type of independent regulator needed. The number and make of the x-ray units will determine the exact power requirements of the room in which the equipment will be used. A suitable 120/240 a-c circuit should be provided for auxiliary equipment such as hot plates, grinders, metallurgical polishers, and ovens. A source of water (preferably filtered) with drain facilities is needed for cooling the x-ray tubes

Table 1. Specimen-preparation Equipment Requirements for Selected Industries

Equipment	Agri-cultural	Cement	Clinical	Con-sumer	Distilla-tion	Elec-tronics	Food	Glass	Metals	Mining	Organics	Paint	Petro-leum	Pharma-ceutical	Polymer	Steel
Analytical balance	1	1	1	...	1	1	1	1	1	1	1	1	1	1	1	1
Blender	1	1	...	...	...	2	2	1	...	...	1	1	...	1	1	
Chromatography	...	...	...	2	...	...	...	...	...	...	2	...	2	2		
Cutting wheel	...	...	...	...	...	...	...	2	2	...	...	...	...	...	2	1
Drying oven	...	2	2	2	2	...	2	...	...	...	1	2	1	2	2	
Electrolytic	...	...	2	2	...	2	...	...	2	2	...	...	...	2	2	2
Evaporating	1	...	1	2	...	...	...	...	...	...	1	1	2	1	2	
Filters	1	...	...	...	1	...	1	...	...	...	1	2	1	2	2	
Impact grinder	1	1	...	2	...	...	...	1	2	1	...	2	...	2	2	
Lathe	...	...	...	2	...	...	...	2	2	...	...	...	...	...	...	1
Metallograph	...	...	...	...	...	...	...	2	1	2	...	...	...	...	...	1
Microscope	1	...	...	2	...	1	...	2	1	...	2	1	2	1	2	2
Muffle furnace	1	1	...	2	...	2	1	1	1	1	1	1	2	2	1	1
Pellet press	1	1	...	...	...	...	1	1	...	1	...	...	...	2	1	2
Sieves	1	1	...	1	...	...	...	...	...	2	2	2	...	2	1	
Surface grinder	...	...	...	1	...	...	...	1	...	2	...	...	...	...	2	1
Volumetric devices	1	2	1	...	...	...	2	...	...	...	...	2	1	1	2	

1 = essential; 2 = optional.

and transformers. Many laboratories have provided temperature-mixing controls in addition to the filters on the cooling-water supply. By this means they are able to control the temperature of the water during seasonal variations and avoid condensation within the x-ray generator that could cause damage to the equipment due to high-voltage arcing.

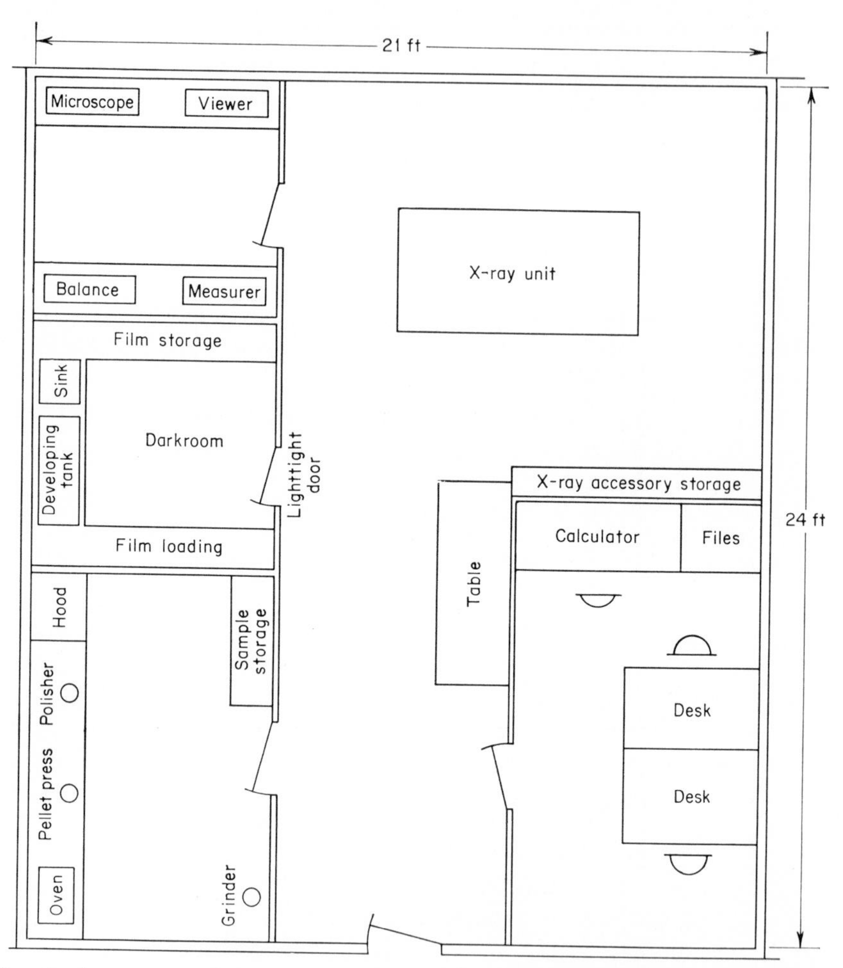

FIG. 1. Layout of typical x-ray analysis laboratory. Note separate areas allocated for darkroom, desks, and specimen preparation. Samples can be delivered and prepared without entry into actual analysis area.

The hood and specimen-preparation area should have the usual utilities of a chemical laboratory: 120 volts a-c, gas, compressed air, water, drain, and vacuum. Modern commercial x-ray equipment is designed to be suitably rayproof and shockproof for operating-personnel protection.* All special setups for x-ray studies must be similarly designed to protect the operator. The planner of the x-ray laboratory, as well as all present and future members of their staff, should be familiar with the local state codes concerning radiation protection, the *Safety Code for the Industrial Use of X-rays,*

* See Chap. 6 for a discussion of radiation and electrical safety.

published by the American Standards Association, and the current publications of the U.S. Bureau of Standards concerning the daily tolerance dose recommended. The manufacturer's operating instructions for the equipment should be thoroughly read and understood by all concerned with the use of the equipment.

Convenient, small film-badge dosimeters are available from several suppliers for monitoring personnel subject to accidental exposure. A recent addition to the personnel-monitoring line is a pen-light-sized battery-operated ionization detector which gives not only a visual indication of the radiation striking it but an audible "chirp" as well. The main disadvantage, however, is that it does not register the total accumulated dosage received and may be subject to "jamming" at high radiation levels. It does serve the purpose of alerting the operator that a radiation leak is present and may prove useful in locating such leaks.

In a well-run x-ray laboratory an operator can work an 8-hr day around the equipment and not receive as much as one-tenth the daily permissible dose of radiation, but through inattention and carelessness, he can obtain an injurious exposure. Radiation protection then is an extremely subjective thing, and it must be continually watched that familiarity does *not* breed contempt. The manufacturer of the x-ray equipment has given serious consideration to the incorporation of safety devices in his equipment, and it is only the irresponsible operator who will circumvent these devices to facilitate his work. To protect the inexperienced or untrained it is strongly recommended that the x-ray laboratory be made a restricted, limited-access area for only those people authorized to enter.

In some laboratories the desks of the staff have been placed in the same room with, and sometimes very near to, the x-ray units. This practice is to be avoided and discouraged since there is always some slight scattering of radiation, so that unnecessary exposure, as when doing desk work, is not wise. Good planning will place the x-ray equipment away from the specimen-preparation and office areas. Distance will then decrease the small amounts of scattered radiation to insignificant levels, and the intervening walls, plus the added distance, will afford considerable protection in the case of an accidental direct-beam leak. For those occasional instances during alignment or adjustment of the x-ray equipment when it is necessary to work with an unshielded x-ray beam, the use of a frame-mounted piece of leaded glass, ½ in. thick and on a movable stand, is advantageous. Flashing red warning lights may be wired through a relay to the start circuit of the x-ray equipment, if desired.

Air Conditioning and Lighting. Air conditioning is desirable in all laboratory rooms and may be essential in some of the areas, especially where critical sample preparation is required and in the darkroom where adequate natural ventilation becomes a serious problem. In planning for air-conditioning the x-ray laboratory it must be borne in mind that the electronic equipment is the major source of heat generated in the area and should be considered when sizing the cooling capacity of the system. The heat produced by the equipment can be determined from the rated wattage as supplied by the manufacturer. The temperature should be regulated for comfort between 70 and 75°F at a relative humidity of 50 per cent. The air should be filtered, and in critical installations, electrostatic filtration should be employed.

If air conditioning is an economic impossibility there should at least be provision for a mechanical air exhaust.

Whether the rooms are air-conditioned or have a simple supply and exhaust, it is important to have the blowers sized so that the incoming supply exceeds the exhaust. This will keep the laboratory under a slight air pressure and will allow an outward leakage of air rather than inward. This will cut down infiltration which will bring in airborne dust and other sources of contamination.

In general the laboratory lighting levels for general work should be designed for about 30 to 35 ft-candles/sq ft. For close alignment work levels up to 100 ft-candles/sq ft may be required and can usually be satisfactorily met by using individual extension lamps operated from outlets distributed throughout the laboratory. The installation of dimmer controls for the x-ray laboratory general lighting may be an advantage to the operator in obtaining his dark-adaptive vision when working with fluorescent screens or other low-illumination-level work such as film measuring and recording.

Photographic Darkroom. An x-ray laboratory doing diffraction-camera work will require darkroom facilities. Frequently this requirement can be met with a one-man darkroom unless the volume of work demands that it be larger. A larger darkroom, used by several groups, is usually inconvenient and unsatisfactory because of the different light requirements for various films, the need for different processing chemicals, and the divided responsibility for keeping the equipment clean and in order.

Suitably ventilated or air-conditioned inner rooms are preferred for darkrooms. Outside-wall rooms are difficult to maintain at a constant temperature and may be difficult to make absolutely lighttight to daylight. The darkroom should be equipped with incandescent fixtures rather than fluorescent fixtures because the latter's very appreciable and rather persistent afterglow may be sufficient to fog uncovered film quickly. Spot illumination, in addition to the proper safelights, directly over the work areas has proved to be the most satisfactory.

Vibration. Vibration has not been a serious problem in the x-ray laboratory, but where single-crystal diffraction work is being done it may prove bothersome and may limit the measurement of precise lattice parameters. However, each vibration problem is almost a unique one, and what will satisfactorily solve the problem in one location may be useless in another. The solution usually revolves around the design of a vibrationless support for mounting the affected equipment. Actually, a vibrationless support is merely an oscillating system loosely coupled mechanically to the building. The natural period of the support must be long compared with that of the building vibrations. The support itself must be damped to suppress its own natural vibrations. The vibrationless support may take the form of a heavy mass, such as a stone slab or concrete block, resting on a pile of newspapers, layers of rubber, felt, cork, or other materials. Shearing fraction of the newspapers and internal fraction of the other materials damps out vibrations. If the source of the vibration can be isolated, such as a nearby compressor or motor, it may be more expedient to vibration-damp the source itself. Frequently vibration problems can be overcome in the x-ray laboratory simply by redistributing the x-ray equipment within the laboratory.

GENERAL REFERENCES

Klug, Harold P., and Leroy E. Alexander: *X-ray Diffraction Procedures*, John Wiley & Sons, Inc., New York, 1954.

Lewis, H. F. (ed.): *Laboratory Planning for Chemistry and Chemical Engineering* (a project of the Committee on Design, Construction, and Equipment of Laboratories; Division of Chemistry and Chemical Technology, National Academy of Sciences, National Research Council), New York, 1962.

Sproull, Wayne T.: *X-rays in Practice*, McGraw-Hill Book Company, New York, 1946.

Chapter 6

HEALTH AND SAFETY

Mark R. Rosumny

Picker X-ray Corporation

1. THE MAXIMUM PERMISSIBLE DOSE

About thirty days after Roentgen's announcement of his discovery of x-rays, in December, 1895, Emil Grubbe of Chicago reported radiation damage to himself in the form of dermatitis on his hands.[1] Thus the first attempts to establish maximum permissible limits were based on the dose required to produce skin erythema. Subsequently, the haemopoietic system was included in this tolerance-dose concept. In the last ten years, emphasis has shifted to the genetic effects, which are not thought to be subject to the repair process, and hence there can be no tolerance dose. Consequently, the accumulative population dose from all sources of radiation including background is the prime consideration rather than the individual dose, and a small number of radiation workers may be subjected to somewhat higher levels of radiation as long as the hazard of genetic effects to the total population is not considered to be increased.

In 1958, the International Committee on Radiation Protection[2] recommended a maximum-accumulation whole-body dose for occupational personnel of $5(N - 18)$ rems, where N is the age of the individual. This amounts to an average dose of 5 rems/year over age eighteen. It was further specified that no more than 3 rems should be accumulated in any 13-week period. Medical exposures are excluded. It was recommended that nonoccupational people or persons outside a controlled area should receive no more than 0.5 rem/year from external radiations. The Federal regulations (Title 10, Sec. 20) are more restrictive but apply only to the use of by-product radioactive material. However, the U.S. Atomic Energy Commission is now permitting the various states to set up their own regulatory agencies provided that certain minimum requirements are met. Several states have already qualified, and the AEC will not duplicate its requirements within the approved state area. The state regulations cover all types of ionizing radiations, and probably within the next few years most of the fifty states will have such regulations. The situation is confused by the fact that some local communities place restrictions on all types of radiation-producing equipment, and require licenses and inspections.

As far as can be determined, the state and local authorities follow the recommendations of the ICRP as to the maximum permissible dose to radiation personnel but additionally have adopted some of the practices of the AEC, particularly in regard to nonradiation personnel, which will have considerable bearing on the radiation shielding required in uncontrolled or unrestricted areas. Generally, an unrestricted area is defined as an area which is not controlled by the licensee or any area used for residential quarters. The radiation in such an area shall be such that no individual, if continuously present, could receive in excess of 2 mrems in any 1 hr, 100 mrems in 7 consecutive days, or 0.5 rem in 1 year. Thus, in ordinary practice in which the area immediately surrounding a radiation room or radiation cabinet is not controlled, the shielding must be sufficient so that the leakage is no more than 2 mr in any 1 hr for the very minimum requirement. If it is shown that the x-ray equipment is incapable of continuous operation but has only a 10 per cent duty cycle, for example, the *rate* of leakage could be 20 mr/hr but the accumulative or total dose would be only 2 mr in any 1 hr. Work loads, use factors, and occupancy factors can be applied as design considerations toward the 1-week and 1-year limits. However, the appropriate state and local regulatory agencies should be consulted to be certain that the design conforms to their minimum requirements, since a license is frequently required. While the state requirements when approved by the AEC are remarkably uniform, interpretations may be made in ways unforeseen.

On the subject of maximum permissible dose, the motto of the St. John X-ray Laboratory, Califon, N.J., is worthy of consideration: "Think of minimum possible exposure instead of maximum permissible dose."

2. RADIATION HAZARDS ASSOCIATED WITH X-RAY DIFFRACTION TECHNIQUES*

The primary beam at the window of an x-ray tube may have a radiation level of the order of 10^5 r/min, and serious permanent skin burns can occur with only a few seconds of exposure at this proximity.

In various countries a number of regulations already exist which usually apply to the use of equipment in factories, educational establishments, etc., and to which individuals are required, or advised, to adhere. The International Commission on Radiological Protection has, in its broad survey,[3] made recommendations relevant to x-ray analysis. There is also an article on Protection against Radiation Injury in vol. 3 of *International Tables for X-ray Crystallography;*[4] this deals with x-ray, neutron, and electron diffraction. While the Commission on Crystallographic Apparatus of the International Union of Crystallography believes that it is therefore inappropriate for it to formulate further regulations, there are certain matters, not necessarily relevant for inclusion in regulations, which should be drawn to the attention of crystallographers and others for their guidance in the use, or the consideration of design details, of x-ray diffraction equipment.

The following notes deal only with x-ray diffraction. Neutron and electron diffraction, x-ray fluorescence spectroscopy, microprobes, microradiography, radiography, and the use of radioisotopes, etc., are not included.

Sources of Unwanted Radiation. X-ray crystallographic techniques involve the use of an x-ray generator to which is coupled some form of apparatus such as a photographic camera or counter diffractometer. In operation, dangerous leakage and scattering of radiation can occur in the following ways:

1. Escape of primary x-rays when a tube-housing window is open and apparatus is not in position at that window
2. By scattering of the primary x-ray beam at interfaces between an open window of a tube housing and the diffraction apparatus being used at that window
3. Escape of the residual primary x-ray beam from the diffraction apparatus
4. Leakage, from openings in the diffraction apparatus or through the walls of the apparatus, of radiation (including unwanted fluorescent radiation) scattered by the air or by mechanical parts of the apparatus
5. Leakage of radiation generated by valve rectifiers in the high-voltage power units of x-ray generators
6. Penetration of radiation through the walls and (closed) window shutters of an x-ray tube housing

* This section consists of the major portion of the report of the Commission on Crystallographic Apparatus of the International Union of Crystallography and is reproduced with permission from *Acta Cryst.*, **16**: 324–328 (1963).

No one should be permitted to use x-ray apparatus until he has received proper instruction in safe practices. When new apparatus is being mounted, or existing apparatus modified or realigned, it is necessary to survey the apparatus (see Sec. 4). Regular departmental meetings on safety practices, reviewing the safety of existing apparatus, etc., are useful and often necessary to emphasize the importance of the problem.

Factors Responsible for the Hazards. Each of the various possible sources of radiation hazard listed above results from one or more of the following:

1. Negligence by the user
2. Failure by the user to recognize and deal with incompatibility of design when coupling diffraction apparatus to x-ray generators of different manufacturing origin
3. Faulty equipment
4. Unsatisfactory design of equipment

Comments Concerning the Hazards. *Hazard* 1. If, while an x-ray tube is energized, a tube window is open when apparatus is not in the operating position at that window, there can be an extremely dangerous escape of the primary beam. It is essential that this must not occur and that some safety interlock device between tube housing and diffraction apparatus be used. Safety measures adopted should (*a*) have a fail-safe characteristic and (*b*) not restrict the responsible operator from making those adjustments recognized as an essential part of the procedure associated with the particular apparatus involved.

Various designs have been described[7,8,9,10] to eliminate this hazard.

Hazard 2. Leakage and scattering of x-rays, from the region of coupling between an x-ray tube window and the apparatus in use at that window, is one of the most serious hazards and is likely to give rise to narrow but intense beams of stray radiation. Separate consideration is necessary according to whether or not the tube housing and apparatus (camera, diffractometer, etc.) are made by the same manufacturer.

a. Equipment from same manufacturer. Much equipment exists in which radiation is strongly scattered from the region where the camera or diffractometer, etc., locates against the window of a tube housing. The user should therefore check his apparatus and, if necessary, make modifications (see below).

b. Components from different manufacturers. Here, it is the user's responsibility to recognize and deal with the problems which arise. Designs have been published for labyrinths,[11,12,13] and some of the devices referred to under Hazard 1 also incorporate this feature.

From a design point of view this hazard should be considered in conjunction with Hazard 1. As far as possible, the primary beam leaving the tube window should be limited, at the window, to the cross section to be used. The process of adjusting diffraction apparatus at a tube window presents a potential danger to the operator: suitable flexibility of alignment with maintenance, at the same time, of full protection is therefore essential in any design, and the use of x-rays only in the final stages of alignment, when this condition obtains, is advocated. When fluorescent screens are used for viewing a beam, they should be mounted on long supports to avoid accidental insertion of the fingers into the beam. To minimize unnecessary repetition of alignment procedures, the design of film cameras should, when practicable, allow the separate removal of the film cassette; if, however, it is necessary to remove the whole camera for each exposure, then the design should be such as to ensure high accuracy in repositioning the camera at the tube window and thus make realignment unnecessary.

Hazards 3 *and* 4. These are largely determined by the basic design of the apparatus, and thus it is hoped that manufacturers will ensure that all future designs will eliminate these hazards. Apparatus should be carefully monitored by the user.

Hazard 5. Thermionic rectifiers used in x-ray generators can act as powerful sources of penetrating x-rays. Causes include underrunning of rectifier filaments and, in a faulty valve, the passage of some inverse current at high voltage. Walls of high-voltage circuit tanks have not always been adequate to prevent this radiation from escaping. Monitoring of equipment should include this region of the generator.

Hazard 6. With most modern x-ray generators using sealed tubes in safety shields, leakage of radiation through the tube housing and window shutters does not appear to present any hazard. There may be exceptions, and it is hoped that all commercial designs will give complete safety rather than be based on an arbitrary "permissible" leakage.

General Recommendations. In experimental work, operators need to be able to make adjustments, etc., when apparatus is in operation. Stray radiation must therefore be minimized at origin even where safety regulations depend on having the entire generator and apparatus placed in an enclosure fitted with door safety interlocks. No method is completely foolproof, and appropriate scientific training and awareness of responsibility are the eventual requirements of personnel.

The use of x-ray "warning" signs at the entrance to an x-ray laboratory, small signs attached to the x-ray units, lights indicating when apparatus is in operation, etc., is useful in minimizing the risk of accidental exposure. Wherever possible it is preferable to place x-ray units in a room separate from the place where personnel do other work.

Various publications deal with safety, and reference has been made to the existence in some countries of regulations which are enforced (e.g., in factories). No attempt is made here to criticize or override such publications.

The latest (1959) revision of the *Recommendations of the International Commission on Radiological Protection*[3] (ICRP) suggests that, with installations for x-ray analysis, "the leakage radiation at any accessible point at a distance of 5 cm from the surface of the tube-housing shall not exceed 25 mr in 1 hour at every specified rating." The Commission on Crystallographic Apparatus suggests that a similar criterion should be applied to the combined assembly of tube housing and apparatus, in operation. For two reasons the figure of 25 mr in 1 hr needs reduction when applied to the whole assembly. First the existing ICRP figure for tube housing alone is based on only 3 hr exposure time per week at the indicated proximity: in counter diffractometry, for example, the operator may be located near a working assembly for a considerably longer period than this each week. Secondly, the combined assembly represents a much larger "source" and attenuation due to the inverse-square law is less marked. For these reasons it is suggested that the leakage radiation, at any accessible point at a distance of 25 cm from the effective bounding surface of the combined working assembly of tube housing and diffraction apparatus, should be less than 2 mr in 1 hr at every specified tube rating. While this may be taken as an upper limit, it should not be regarded as a satisfactory working level. Every effort should be made to reduce the amount of stray radiation to a level not sensibly detectable with a monitor appropriate for the energy range involved. This applies particularly in locating those sharply defined beams of scattered radiation which are likely to escape from inadequately shielded apparatus.

If each apparatus (camera or other device as previously defined), and the tube housing at which it is operating, is regarded as a single "combined assembly" and made safe according to the above recommendations, then hazards will not arise (1) through multiplication of apparatus operating in a similar way at other windows of the same generator, (2) through increasing the number of generators in the same room.

High-voltage generator units containing thermionic rectifiers should be subjected to the same criteria, for reasons given under Hazard 5.

It is hoped that manufacturers will use the above criteria of safety and give the user some quantitative reassurance as to the safety levels achieved in each type of equipment marketed.

3. DOSIMETERS AND FILM BADGES

When x- or gamma rays interact with matter, a large share of the energy absorbed eventually is dissipated in the form of ionization. This is true especially in gases with energy levels of radiation below 5 Mev. Because of the practicability of the method, air ionization was accepted as a means of measuring the x-ray or gamma-ray dose, particularly since air may be considered as an approximate tissue-equivalent material.

Pocket dosimeters are about the size and shape of fountain pens. They have a small collecting volume of air or similar gas, a quartz-fiber electrometer, and a calibrated lens-reticule system for viewing the quartz fiber. Exposure to radiation changes the relative position of the fiber to the calibrated reticule, and the accumulative dosage can be read directly. The range most commonly used for personnel dosimetry is 0 to 200 mr. The dosimeter is charged in a separate "charger" by inserting it in a socket provided for the purpose and adjusting a dial on the charger to bring the reading to 0.

Since any leakage of charge will produce a reading, the resistance of the insulation must be extremely high. The collecting electrode and insulation are protected from atmospheric conditions by a sealed diaphragm containing an external electrode. The diaphragm is collapsed on charging so that the electrodes make contact. This may be a source of erratic readings in a new dosimeter since the outer electrode retains some of the charge which influences the inner system as the external charge bleeds away very slowly. In used units, because of the accumulation of small amounts of dust and dirt on the diaphragm, the external charge bleeds away rapidly and the instrument becomes stable. With new dosimeters, the effect can be simulated by grounding the outer electrode by touching it with the end of something like a paper clip held in the fingers. The initial reading may be disturbed to the extent of 2 or 3 mr in the 200-mr-range unit, but increased stability will result. Sometimes it may be necessary to "age" the dosimeter by exposing it to radiation in order to achieve maximum stability.

The pocket chamber is a device exactly like the dosimeter except that the reading unit is mounted in the charger. Here, all advantage of instantaneous reading is lost since the instrument must be brought to the charger to be read. Furthermore, the charge is lost upon reading so that the chamber must be recharged again before reuse. However, because the reading unit is not integrated with the chamber, the unit can be manufactured more economically. The "blind" feature is an advantage in instances where workers unfamiliar with radiation effects may decide erroneously that they have received injury from observing that the dosimeter has increased a few milliroentgens.

Both the dosimeter and the pocket chamber are designed to have a nearly linear response to radiation from several Mev down to 50 kev or so where the absorption of the radiation by the walls of the unit becomes appreciable. The accuracy within this range is usually guaranteed to ± 10 per cent. The dosimeter seems to be a little more reliable than the pocket chamber as usually manufactured, although the chamber can be made as a precision instrument.

A common source of error is caused by the effect of temperature. A dosimeter or chamber charged at several degrees below room temperature and then worn next to the body may suddenly show an increase of 6 to 8 mr because of the warming up of the instrument. It is good practice to warm up the units by wearing them a half hour or so before charging if this effect is noticed.

Both instruments may be discharged or damaged by a shock such as a drop to the floor. In case of damage, the cost of repair is usually higher than the price of a new instrument. However, these instruments are usually quite rugged, and a life of several years can be expected with normal handling.

Both a film badge and either a pocket dosimeter or a pocket chamber are required to be worn by radiation workers using isotopes and by all radiation workers in agreement states. The greatest advantage of the film badge is the permanent and authoritative record it provides since the result usually is obtained by an independent and expert agency. The greatest disadvantage is the length of time necessary to obtain the result since the badge must be mailed to the laboratory, processed, read, and the result mailed back. It may take as long as 2 weeks before the radiation dosage is known. Therefore, it is good practice, as well as a necessary requirement in many instances, to provide radiation workers with dosimeters or pocket chambers for the determination of the immediate radiation dose, and film badges for the permanent and legal record.

All films are very energy-dependent, with an order of sensitivity of about 25 times greater for about 40-kev radiation than for 1-Mev radiation. Corrections are made by the use of filters in two general methods. In the first method a combination of filters is used to obtain as flat a response as possible over a wide energy range. The second method determines the energy of the incident radiations by the various filter combinations and, therefore, the proper corrections to apply. Since both methods have serious limitations, the test film must be compared eventually with calibrated films exposed to known energies and doses of radiations. The problem is still more complex when the film badge is exposed to a wide variety of different energies of radiations. Extremely careful control of the development process is required to prevent errors of great magnitude. At least one control badge usually is furnished with monitoring badges. This film is not designed to be intentionally exposed but to show the effect of any adverse storage condition or accidental exposure to the film badges during transit or storage so that proper corrections may be made if possible.

In spite of all the corrections and possible sources of error, the film badge has proved to be a reliable device for personnel monitoring. Many laboratories claim ± 10 per cent accuracy. However, when the energies of the radiations are unknown to the laboratory or when a wide variety of different energies are used, the accuracy is not likely to be this high. Variation of response with temperature, angle of incidence of the radiation to the filter-film combination, and position of the badge on the wearer's body relative to the incident radiation are factors which may cause considerable variation in results. Most film badges will cover the range from a few milliroentgens to 1,000 r or more. Special badges may be obtained for other ranges.

Many people are concerned because the film-badge readings do not check closely with the readings from the pocket dosimeter or chamber. It is not unusual for the dosimeter or chamber to drift as much as 5 to 6 mr a week. If the total accumulative dose for the week is in the same order of magnitude, an apparent error of 100 per cent can be easily obtained. Also with very small doses, particularly with 1-Mev radiations, the blackening of the film in the badge will be so slight that it becomes difficult to determine above the fog level of the film itself. Here again, the error may be as much as 100 per cent. However, the accuracy of both units increases rapidly as the accumulative dose is increased until in the area of most concern the film badge usually checks within ± 25 per cent of the dosimeter or chamber. If the two systems do not check this closely in the 100 mr per week range, checks should be made to determine if the units are worn properly. One discrepancy may be caused by the fact that the dosimeters or chambers are rate-dependent. If a high-intensity dose is applied for a short time, these units almost invariably will read lower than the film badges under the same circumstances. The dosimeter may be easily checked for excessive drift and improper calibration. Finally, an additional badge service from another laboratory may be obtained temporarily for additional comparisons.

4. MONITORING DEVICES

Because of scatter, emphasis is placed on the fact that the radiation hazard cannot be estimated entirely from a knowledge of the radiation output but must be determined from actual measurement. The most useful monitoring and measuring device is the ionization-type rate meter. These have considerably larger ionization chambers than the pocket dosimeters and have a compact amplifier system with self-contained batteries to produce a portable lightweight survey meter. Units of this type have a nearly flat response from low-energy to high-energy radiation and are guaranteed usually to ± 10 per cent accuracy. Two general types are in use. The most popular standard type is characterized by its ruggedness and fast response to radiation. However, the lowest limit it can measure accurately is of the order of 1 or 2 mr/hr. Moreover, the walls of the ionization chamber have appreciable absorption at low energies so that the range of the instrument is from about 50 kev to several Mev. Consequently, this instrument may underestimate scatter by a large percentage in the low-energy ranges, as seen in Table 1.

The other type of ionization meter, characterized by most "Cutie Pie" instruments, has a very thin window in the ionization chamber. The response of some of these instruments is very good down to 10 kev with about ± 10 per cent accuracy. Recently Victoreen Model 440 was introduced, responding down to 6.5 kev with ± 15 per cent accuracy. Lower-energy radiation can still be detected, but air absorption at such low energies becomes an appreciable factor. Such instruments usually can measure small radiation levels as little as 0.1 mr/hr or so, as well as much higher levels, but the time constant is rather inconveniently long. Moreover, they require care in handling since they are delicate by comparison with the standard survey meter. However, for diffraction and other low-energy work, the thin-window ionization meter is a necessity.

Geiger-counter-type instruments, in spite of their great sensitivity, are not usually recommended for the precise measurement of radiation because of their severe energy dependence. However, units of this type are used in automatic monitoring and warning systems. Below a preset level, usually about 2 mr/hr, one type of instrument will

Table 1. Scatter Measurements with Standard and Thin-window Ionization Meters

Radiation	Standard meter, mr/hr	Thin-window meter, mr/hr
Scatter from iridium-192.......	11	12.5
Scatter from 160-kv x-ray.....	31	47
Scatter from 100-kv x-ray.....	19	40
Scatter from 50-kv x-ray......	4	24

Table 2. Relative-exposure-time Factors

Eastman AA = 1.00

Type	Film	Cobalt-60	Iridium-192	270 kv	150 kv	100 kv	50 kv
3	Eastman KK	0.18	0.21	0.21	0.17	0.15	0.13
	Ansco C	0.26	0.32	0.28	0.23	0.20	0.19
	Ilford G	0.36	0.38	0.32	0.26	0.23	0.21
2	Eastman AA	1.00	1.00	1.00	1.00	1.00	1.00
	Ansco A	0.78	0.80	0.74	0.76	0.78	0.70
	Du Pont 506	0.96	0.96	1.0	1.0	1.05	1.0
	Ilford CX	1.64	1.47	1.20	1.10	0.94	0.92
	Ilford B	0.78	0.75	0.69	0.60	0.53	0.53
1	Eastman M	5.3	4.9	3.8	3.5	3.3	2.8
	Ansco B	2.14	2.07	1.85	2.0	2.2	2.2
	Du Pont 510	4.2	3.8	3.3	3.0	3.1	2.9
	Ilford F	4.8	4.1	2.9	2.4	2.0	2.0

The above is valid only at a density of 2.0.

NOTE: In addition to the above, a new, finer-grain, slower type of film has been introduced. This is exemplified by Eastman Single Coated M and Ansco HD (high definition). Both these films are about the same speed and require about two times the exposure of Eastman M.

indicate "safety" by a green light. Above this level, a red flashing light will be actuated. Alarms and door interlocks can be actuated with the warning light. These units are, without doubt, the greatest system for preventing accidents now in use since they operate independently of the source of radiation and are not "fooled" by faulty operation of other safety devices. Reliable dosimeters, film badges, meters, and automatic warning systems may be obtained from any reputable dealer in x-ray equipment. All the above instruments will read accurately only if the whole chamber is covered by the field of radiation. Pinpoint leaks in radiation shielding will be determined inadequately or missed entirely by most instruments for this reason. Location and severity of such leaks can be determined by the use of x-ray films covering the joints in the radiation shielding or location of suspected leaks. The relative speeds of various industrial x-ray film at various energy levels are given in Table 2.

5. INTERLOCKS

Radiation Interlocks. A very economical and desirable safety feature is a door or cabinet interlock system which will interrupt the x-ray current when the door or cabinet is opened inadvertently and will prevent the x-ray current from being turned on when the door is open. However, the interlock must be considered only as an additional safety feature and not as a foolproof system. With constant-potential units, the x-ray tube may emit radiation for a short period of time after the unit is

Fig. 1. Shutter *A* has been closed to permit retraction of slider *E*, which in turn permits removal or replacement of shield *B*. [*Norelco Reptr.*, **10**:92 (1963).]

Fig. 2. Extension rod *G* has been removed to reveal the slider which is guided by the bearings for accessory part *D* and the bracket *F* which is offset to provide clearance for the collimating-slit assembly *C*. [*Norelco Reptr.*, **10**:92 (1963).]

turned off if the capacitors are not discharged by a properly working resistor-bleeding system. One case is known with a self-rectified unit where the kv and ma meters were improperly connected. The door interlock interrupted the meter circuit but not the x-ray circuit. Severe burns to the operator resulted.

A number of safety devices, designed by users of x-ray equipment, have been reported. A mechanical interlock has been added to a Norelco x-ray diffractometer in use at the laboratories of the Portland Cement Association, Skokie, Ill., which ensures that the x-ray beam shutter is closed before the goniometer shield is removed or replaced.[14]

In Fig. 1, parts *E*, *F*, and *G* comprise the interlock: parts *A*, *B*, *C*, and *D* are original equipment parts. In Fig. 2, shield *B* has been replaced and slider *E* extended to

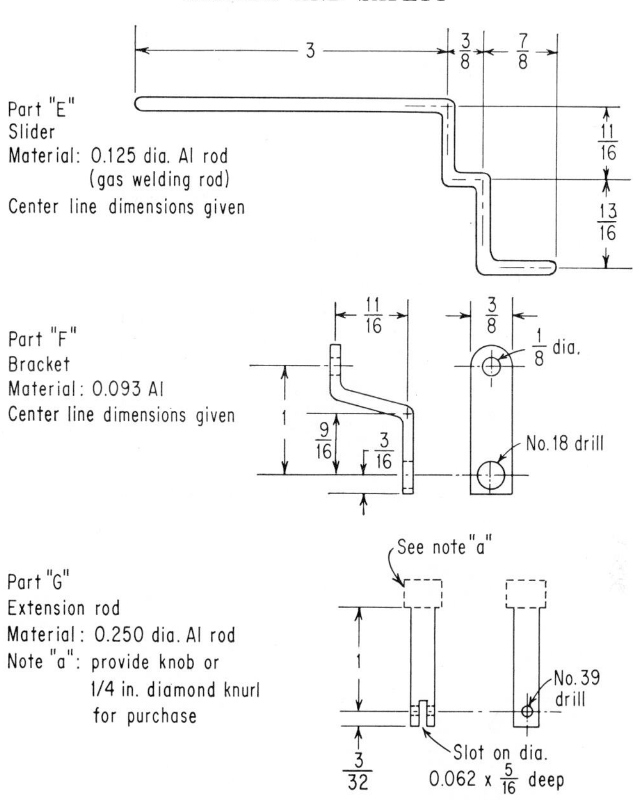

FIG. 3. Parts for x-ray safety interlock. Aluminum, as indicated, has proved satisfactory. [*Norelco Reptr.*, **10**:92 (1963).]

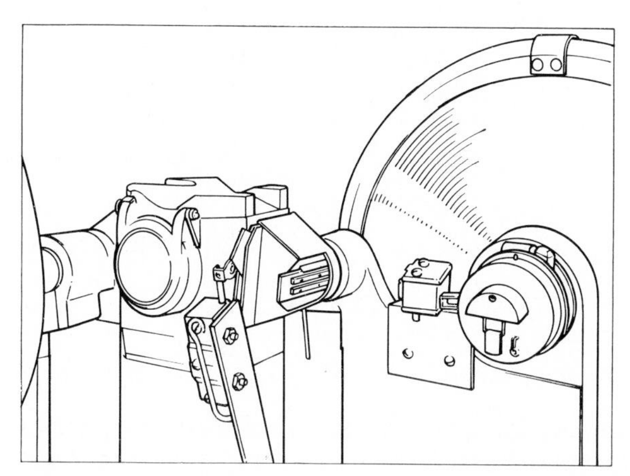

FIG. 4. Microswitches for x-ray warning system. [*Norelco Reptr.*, **5**:110 (1958).]

permit the opening of shutter A. In Fig. 3, dimensions are given for parts E, F, and G. They are made at negligible cost, are easily installed, and do not complicate the use of the equipment. With occasional cleaning and light lubrication, the entire mechanism works smoothly.

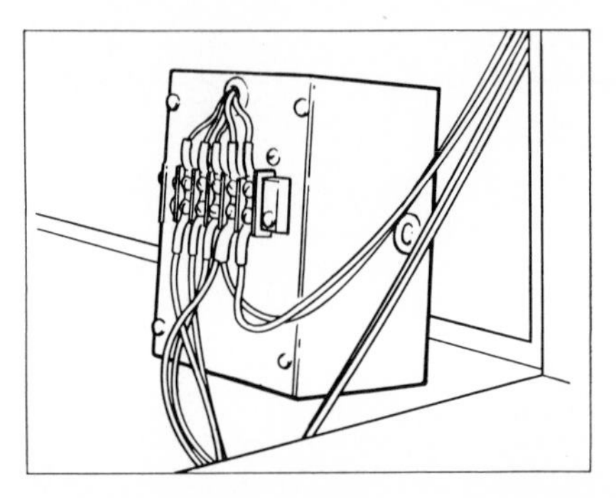

Fig. 5. Buzzer and transformer supply. [*Norelco Reptr.*, **5**:110 (1958).]

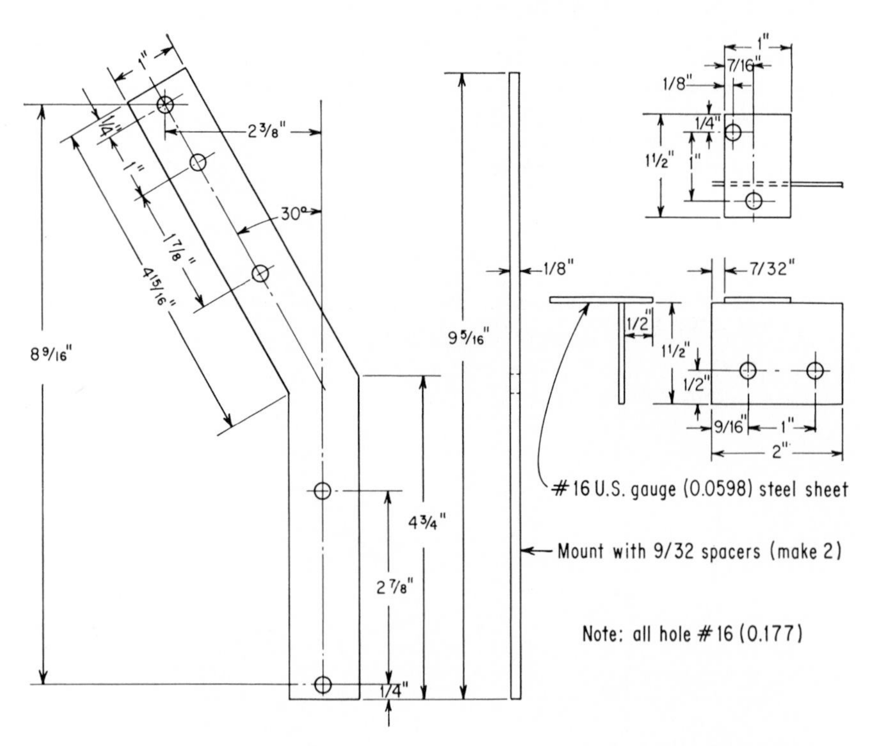

Fig. 6. Mounting brackets for microswitches. [*Norelco Reptr.*, **5**:110 (1958).]

A simple safety warning system has been added to the Norelco diffractometers at the Pure Oil Company Research Center, Crystal Lake, Ill., to protect the laboratory technicians who run the equipment.[15]

The warning system actuates a loud buzzer if the x-ray shield is removed with the beam shutter open or if the shutter is opened with the shield removed. It consists of two microswitches (Fig. 4) mounted on the goniometer. One microswitch is normally open but is closed by the shutter when it is pulled out. The other switch is normally closed but is opened by the flange of the x-ray shield. The buzzer and transformer supply are mounted inside the basic unit (Fig. 5). Figure 6 shows the mounting brackets for the microswitches. The circuit arrangement will be left to the individual user who can employ components suited to his specific requirements and especially atmospheric conditions prevailing in his laboratory.

An arrangement in use at Monsanto Company[16] is similar to the above except that the switches are used to interrupt the x-ray power rather than to actuate a buzzer.

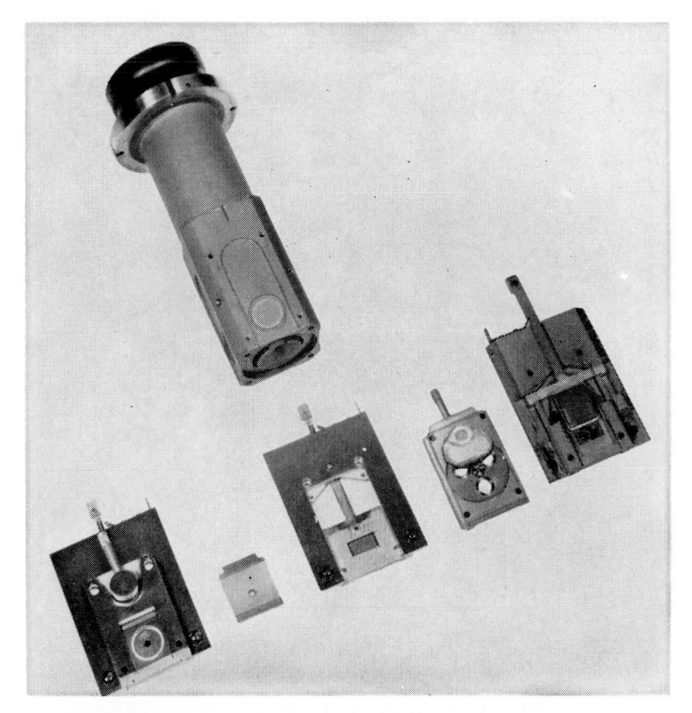

Fig. 7. Partial assembly, front and back views of the Picker safety shutter and radiation leakproof accessory adapter for use with Dunlee diffraction tube.

The switches can be mounted as shown in Fig. 4, and are connected in series with the door interlocks on the Norelco x-ray generator unit.

The Picker X-ray Corporation supplies a novel shutter and collimator adapter arrangement (Patent 3113214 to T. C. Furnas, Jr.) which allows a camera or other accessory to be removed or connected with safety from either direct or scattered radiation, and without interrupting the tube current or operations at the other windows of the same tube. Details are shown in Figs. 7 and 8.

It may be noted that the Eindhoven Philips equipment, which generally is not available in the United States, incorporates a shutter adjacent to the x-ray tube port such that the camera or other accessory can be installed or removed safely with the tube current on.

Electrical Interlocks. Modern x-ray machines are shielded very carefully against electrical hazards. No wiring or contacts are exposed, and if the manufacturer's directions are followed, all metallic exterior surfaces are grounded. Because of the complexity of the electric circuits, inexperienced personnel cannot make extensive repairs. Consequently the use of interlocking switches to prevent electrical hazards has declined. However, in experimental units where access to the circuitry must be maintained, such interlocks are a necessity for the safety of the operator and should be designed carefully to afford the proper protection.

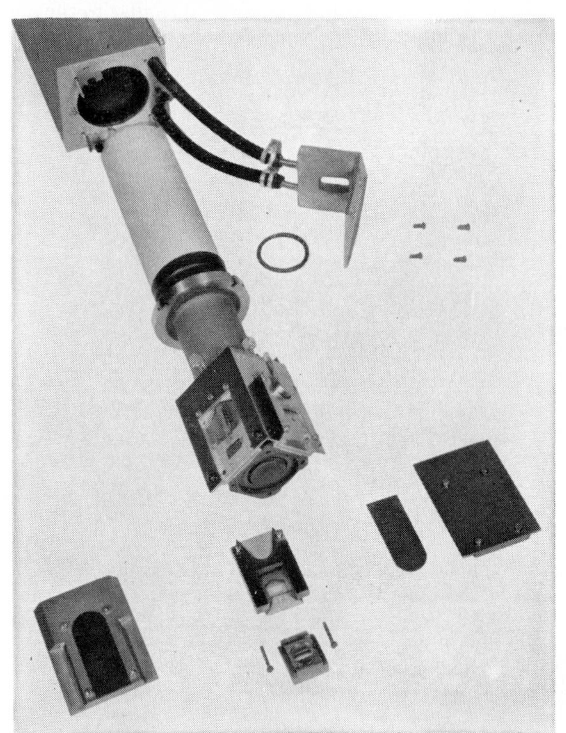

FIG. 8. Partial assembly of Picker safety shutter on Dunlee diffraction tube with exploded view of radiation leakproof accessory adapter and tube shield.

6. SAFETY RULES AND PROCEDURES

Experience has indicated that a formalized safety procedure generally should be adopted and enforced by the management rather than allow the operators to exercise their own judgment under conditions of stress or fatigue. Depending upon the scope of the operation and the type and intended use of the equipment many, if not all, of the following categories, which were condensed from the AEC requirements,[14] should be considered:

A. Organizational structure
  1. Chain of command
    a. Duties and responsibilities of each individual and especially those responsible for the enforcing of the safety procedures
  2. System of periodic reports on safety record as a means of maintaining active management control

B. Operating procedure
  1. Handling and use of the source equipment

2. Use of dosimeters, film badges, survey and monitoring equipment
3. Instructions and occasions for making radiation surveys
4. Methods for controlling access to radiation areas
5. Methods and occasions for locking and securing the radiation equipment
6. Instructions covering transportation of equipment

C. Emergency procedure

1. Specific instructions to minimize exposure in event of accident including possible malfunction of equipment
2. Procedure for notifying the proper persons in event of accident. Names and telephone numbers of the persons to contact should be provided. Possible alternative telephone numbers should be listed

D. Maintenance of individual exposure records and records of surveys

In the event of a serious overexposure of radiation to an individual, there is as yet nothing which can be done in the way of first aid. Indeed, the first symptoms may not show up for several hours, or even days in the case of a lesser dose. The individual should be placed in the care of a competent physician as soon as possible, and every effort should be made, immediately, to estimate his probable radiation dose from a time study of the radiation field and from the individual's own detailed description of the incident. Immediate reading of his film badge should be facilitated.

In the event of a serious electrical shock, the electric power should be immediately turned off, or if this is impossible, the patient should be separated from the source of electricity by means of insulated poles. If the patient is unconscious, most first-aid manuals will recommend immediate application of artificial resuscitation to be continued for several hours or until the patient revives. However, some physicians hold this to be of little use, particularly if the patient's heart is in a state of fibrillation. In any case, it is necessary to place the patient in the care of a competent physician as quickly as possible.

It is necessary to consider all possible malfunctions of equipment and disasters in advance so that minimum time will be lost in the application of emergency procedures which may save life and minimize further hazard. However, industry has proved able to take care of radiation and associated hazards in the same competent manner in which it handles poisons, explosives, combustibles, and other potentially dangerous materials. The probability of receiving an overexposure of radiation in industry is much lower than the chance of having an accident in the home. There is no place for hysteria but only a need for a calm survey of the possible hazard. The reader is encouraged to consult the references listed below for more detailed information on the important subject of x-ray safety.

REFERENCES CITED

1. E. Dale Trout, The History of Radiation Protection in the United States, *Proceedings of the First National Symposium on Nondestructive Testing of Aircraft and Missile Components*, pp. 14-2 to 14-7, Southwest Research Institute and the Society for Nondestructive Testing, Inc., 1960.
2. *Permissible Dose from External Sources of Ionizing Radiation*, NBS Handbook 59, pp. 2, 3, addendum, dated Apr. 15, 1958, Government Printing Office, Washington, D.C.
3. *Recommendations of the International Commission on Radiological Protection*, Pergamon Press, New York, 1959.
4. *International Tables for X-ray Crystallography*, vol. 3, pp. 333–338, The Kynoch Press, Birmingham, England, 1962.
5. T. R. Kohler and W. Parrish, *Rev. Sci. Instr.*, **27**:705 (1956).
6. U.S. National Commission on Radiation Protection, *Radiology*, **63**:428 (1954).
7. American Crystallographic Association Project, *Safety Considerations in the Design of X-ray Tube and Collimator Couplings on X-ray Diffraction Equipment.* [Details from K. E. Beu, Chairman of the A. C. A. Apparatus and Standards Committee (Goodyear Atomic Corporation, P. O. Box 628, Piketon, Ohio).]
8. D. C. Barnes and A. Franks, *J. Sci. Instr.*, **39**:648 (1962).
9. F. Chambers, M. Okrasinski, and H. Cole, *IBM J.*, **5**:69 (1961).

10. W. Hughes, *J. Sci. Instr.*, **39**:93 (1962).
11. S. C. Abrahams and W. R. Blackmore, *Rev. Sci. Instr.*, **24**:885 (1953).
12. O. Kennard, A. J. P. Martin, and L. Woodget, *J. Sci. Instr.*, **36**:48 (1959).
13. W. Hughes and C. A. Taylor, *J. Sci. Instr.*, **38**:493 (1961).
14. J. B. Ricks and W. G. Hime, *Norelco Reptr.*, **10**:92 (1963).
15. G. Brunton and L. Ellison, *Norelco Reptr.*, **5**:110 (1958).
16. E. F. Kaelble, E. D. Fortenberry, and C. E. Hemler, unpublished, Monsanto Company, Inorganic Research Department, St. Louis, Mo.
17. *A Guide on Radiation Safety Considerations in the Preparation of License Applications*, pp. 5–11, Division of Licensing and Regulation, U.S. Atomic Energy Commission, Washington, D.C.

GENERAL REFERENCES

Blatz, H. (ed.): *Radiation Hygiene Handbook*, McGraw-Hill Book Company, New York, 1959.

Braestrup, C. B., and H. O. Wyckoff: *Radiation Protection*, Charles C Thomas, Publisher, Springfield, Ill., 1958.

Part 2

DIFFRACTION OF X-RAYS BY POLYCRYSTALLINE AND AMORPHOUS MATERIALS

Chapter 7

INTRODUCTION TO POWDER DIFFRACTION

James W. Starbuck

Mallinckrodt Chemical Works

The diffraction of x-rays by crystalline materials provides many avenues of study ranging from qualitative analysis to the study of internal defects in the arrangement of atoms. The techniques which will be described in this section come under the general heading often referred to as the "powder" method. These techniques apply to the study of polycrystalline materials whether they be in powder form, as supplied by nature or process, or in a compacted form, as pellets or metallic mass.

The x-ray diffraction studies involve the interpretation of the powder pattern with respect to the values of the Bragg angle θ that it represents and the intensities of the diffraction lines.

X-ray diffraction studies have had increased importance in scientific studies in recent years; consequently, several fine texts have appeared upon which most investigators have had to rely for their education about the principles and practices of x-ray diffraction. The reader is referred to these in the General References.

1. THE POWDER PATTERN

A single crystal, when exposed to monochromatic x-rays, gives rise to diffraction maxima according to the Bragg relationship $n\lambda = 2d \sin \theta$. In this reaction the incident beam, the normal to the diffracting plane, and the diffracted beam lie in a plane. If the crystal is rotated about the axis of the x-ray beam, a cone of diffracted rays is generated, the apex of the cone being at the crystal and its solid angle being equal to 4θ. This cone of diffracted rays is also produced by dividing the crystal into smaller segments and arranging them so that various increments of rotation about the x-ray beam axis are represented. By continued subdivision of the crystal (within limits) one may arrive at a "powdered" state which statistically furnishes all increments of rotation. In addition, the random positioning in space of each "crystallite" will satisfy the Bragg condition for other sets of lattice planes with their respective cone of diffracted x-rays. The random positioning is further augmented by a rotation of the powdered specimen, usually about an axis which is normal to the beam. These cones of diffracted x-rays may be recorded by camera techniques using x-ray sensitive film (see Chap. 8) or by diffractometer techniques using a suitable detector and its associated electronic equipment (see Chap. 9).

A flat photographic film placed perpendicular to the x-ray beam will record the intersection of the diffraction cones and the film, producing a pattern of concentric rings, i.e., a powder photograph. A strip of film placed about the sample will record arcs of these concentric rings. The counter diffractometer is essentially an electronic means of observing arcs of the diffraction rings.

Subsequent chapters deal with the application of specific techniques; however, there are certain general considerations which are applicable to each.

Characteristics of the Powder Pattern. *Effect of Crystallite Size.* The character of the diffraction ring or "halo" is affected by the size of the crystallites. If they are too large, the ring will consist of discrete spots. As the crystallite size decreases, so does the spot size; however, the number of spots increases until an optimum size is reached where the spots have merged into a continuous, sharp photographic image. If the crystallites are further reduced in size, another phenomenon, called line broadening, occurs which gives a wider, less contrasting, ring.

The term crystallite should not be confused with particle; crystallite infers a small, single crystal. The term grain in metals is considered synonymous with crystallite. A particle, on the other hand, may be an agglomerate or cluster of crystallites.

The spottiness of a ring is the result of failure to represent statistically all increments of rotation about the direct x-ray beam. The relationship between spottiness and crystallite size is therefore dependent upon the amount of material exposed to the beam, the degree of motion imparted to the specimen, and the crystal symmetry of the sample.

Generally, a crystallite size of less than 50 microns (passing a 325-mesh screen) will produce smooth rings when employing rotation of the specimen. For stationary samples, crystallites less than 5 microns in diameter are required to produce continuous rings.

Broadening of the rings begins to occur when the crystallites are 2,000 to 3,000 Å in diameter and increases as the crystallites get smaller. Line broadening is discussed in detail in Chap. 17.

Effect of Nonrandom Orientation. Failure to have the crystallites represent all orientations in space will be manifested in the characteristics of the powder pattern in two ways.

Nonrandom distribution of orientations, i.e., preferred orientation, results in a nonuniform density along arcs of a diffraction ring. This condition is readily recognized in flat-plate photographic techniques but is not always apparent in other techniques.

The second result of preferred orientation is the alteration of the density (intensity) of one ring with respect to another. This condition is easily recognized in all techniques if there has been any prior experience with relative intensities from the material in question. Determination of preferred orientation is discussed in Chap. 18.

Crystallite size and orientation effects must be reduced if not eliminated when using diffraction techniques for qualitative and quantitative analyses.

Effect of Lattice Variations. Any condition which introduces deviations from the mean interplanar spacings for a given reflection will produce broadened diffraction lines. Broadening of this kind may originate in the crystal itself because of thermal motion of the atoms or imperfection in the periodicity of the lattice. The most frequent source of the latter over which the crystallographer has any control is cold work, i.e., bent, sheared, or otherwise stressed crystals. Nonhomogeneous solid solutions as from hydration or oxidation reactions with the sample surface also can introduce lattice variations.

2. SELECTION OF RADIATION (cf. Chap. 8, Sec. 6)

Kα Radiation. The production of a useful powder-diffraction pattern depends upon the selection of the characteristic $K\alpha$ radiation best suited for the application. In Chap. 2, Sec. 2, commonly available x-ray tubes from which selection may be made are discussed.

Improper choice of radiation can produce fluorescent radiation from the sample of sufficient intensity to mask the diffracted pattern. Fluorescence occurs when the wavelength of the impinging beam is just shorter than the absorption edge of an element in the sample. It can therefore be predicted by comparing the wavelength being considered for use with the absorption edges, both K and L, of the metallic elements of the sample. This information is found in Chap. 1, Sec. 3. Those elements which fluoresce with the commonly available target elements are shown in Table 1.

Two general rules to follow for avoiding fluorescence are to select a target of the same element as the sample or one which has a wavelength as far removed as possible from the K or L edges of the metallic component of the sample.

The choice of radiation must also take into account the range of interplanar d spacings of primary interest to the investigator. Since $\sin\theta$ in the Bragg equation cannot exceed 1.00, only d spacings greater than $\lambda/2$ are recorded. The range of θ is further restricted at high and low angles by design criteria of the camera or diffractometer.

The requirements for d-spacing range depend upon the type of x-ray analysis being conducted. Identifications and structure determinations require the widest range while line-broadening studies for crystallite size and/or strain measurement require a somewhat shorter range. In precision lattice techniques, it is desirable to have strongly reflecting d spacings registered at Bragg angles greater than 50 to 60°. Normally, only a very narrow range of d spacings is required for quantitative analyses where only one or two diffraction lines from each phase are measured.

Table 1. X-ray Tube Data

Target	Wavelength, Å		Beta filter		Fluorescing elements
	$K\alpha$	$K\beta$	Material	Thickness, mils	
Chromium	2.290	2.085	Vanadium	0.5	Titanium
			V_2O_5	1.6	
Iron	1.936	1.756	Manganese	0.5	Chromium
			MnO_2	1.1	
Cobalt	1.789	1.621	Iron	0.4	Manganese
Copper	1.541	1.392	Nickel	0.6	Iron, cobalt
Molybdenum	0.709	0.632	Zirconium	3.2	Yttrium

For identification work, short wavelengths from Ag or Mo are preferred for inorganic or metallic materials which usually have high-symmetry structures with small unit-cell sizes. Medium wavelengths, such as Cu or Co, are preferred for lower-symmetry structures, which have more complex patterns, for mixtures, and for larger unit cells. Finally, the longer wavelengths of Fe or Cr are necessary for materials such as organic or clay minerals which have very large, low-symmetry unit cells.

Closely related factors in the selection of target are the resolution and accuracy requirements of the investigation. Examination of the Bragg equation reveals that maximum resolution or separation of the diffraction lines is achieved by increasing λ. As θ approaches 90°, a small change in d produces a relatively large change in θ; therefore, for purposes of accuracy, λ should be chosen so as to register the stronger, low-order (hkl) reflections at high angles.

Accompanying the list of factors for selecting the radiation is the economy of operation with respect to exposure times. For a given exposure time, the softer wavelengths of Fe or Cr yield lower-density patterns because of factors such as higher absorption of the beam by the air path, the sample holder, or the sample itself, and lower operating wattages of the tube.

$K\beta$ Radiation. In the above considerations only the $K\alpha$-doublet component of the characteristic radiation has been inferred. The $K\beta$ component should be kept in mind as either a wanted or unwanted component of the radiation. While most techniques call for its elimination by filtering, its presence in some instances is inconsequential and in other instances can be useful. An example of its use is to supply additional lines for measuring lattice constants of metals or alloys. This author has employed Cu $K\beta$ radiation exclusively for crystallite size and strain measurements in UO_2 powders, thereby avoiding the problem of accounting for $K\alpha$-doublet separation.

3. BACKGROUND RADIATION

In addition to the diffracted pattern generated by the $K\alpha$ doublet and $K\beta$ wavelengths of the target, other components of radiation make their way to the film or detector. These constitute the background upon which the pattern is superimposed.

Fluorescence. This phenomenon, which was considered earlier, can be the most intense source of background occurring at all angles. While this effect may be reduced by proper choice of radiation, filter techniques can lessen the effect when the investigator is confronted with no other choice but that of using a wavelength which excites the sample.

Continuum or White Radiation. Accompanying the characteristic spectrum from a target is the continuous or white spectrum which was described in Chap. 1, Sec. 2. This radiation can produce background effects by secondary fluorescence of the sample or by diffraction from the crystal planes in the sample. Reduction of continuum effects is achieved by filter techniques and/or pulse-height discrimination.

Target Impurity Radiations. As the name implies, contaminating elements in the target can produce unwanted components of radiation, the most common being tungsten which evaporates from the tube filament and iron in the target material. These impurities can lead to a general increase in background or to additional diffraction lines. An extremely sensitive check of target purity can be made by making an x-ray spectrographic analysis of the target using a diffractometer. This is done by inserting a suitable analyzing crystal, such as rock salt, with a known d spacing, in the sample position. Any peaks which appear from a 2θ scan may be identified by solving the Bragg equation for λ and referring to the tables of wavelengths for identification of the peaks. Of course, under these conditions the characteristic wavelengths of the primary target material will produce exceedingly intense peaks which will have to be attenuated.

4. ELIMINATION OF BACKGROUND RADIATION

The reduction or elimination of the unwanted portions of the x-ray spectrum can be accomplished in several ways. The applicable technique is dependent upon the degree of monochromatization required by the investigation and the problem.

The goal of the diffractionist is to achieve a high peak-to-background ratio P/B with as little loss in P as possible. In this way maximum contrast on films or statistical precision with counter measurements is realized.

All the methods which follow result in a reduction of the peak intensity to some degree, and the crystallographer is confronted with increased losses with increasing degrees of monochromatization required.

Single-filter Techniques. A single filter composed of an element which has an absorption-edge wavelength just short of the $K\alpha$ wavelength of the target may be used to reduce the $K\beta$ intensity. The ratio of the intensity of the $K\beta$ to that of the $K\alpha$ is usually 0.15 to 0.30. Reduction of this ratio to about 0.01 is accomplished by employing the filters indicated in Table 1. These filters will cause an approximately 50 per cent reduction in the $K\alpha$ intensity. The calculation of the fraction of incident intensity transmitted by a filter can be made using the equation

$$I/I_o = e^{-(\mu/\rho)\rho t}$$

where μ/ρ is the mass absorption coefficient of the filter for the incident wavelength, ρ is the density, and t is the thickness.

Example. The fraction of the Cu $K\alpha$ doublet transmitted by a 0.0006-in. Ni foil is

$$\begin{aligned} \ln (I/I_o) &= -(46)(8.9 \text{ g/cc})(0.0006 \text{ in.})(2.54 \text{ cm/in.}) \\ \ln (I/I_o) &= -0.624 \\ I/I_o &= 0.535 \text{ or } 53.5 \text{ per cent} \end{aligned}$$

The single filter also reduces the continuum or "white" radiation. The effectiveness of this reduction depends upon the position of the $K\alpha$ with respect to the continuum. For example, the reduction of the Mo continuum is greater than for Cu since the Mo K lines are closer to the peak of the continuum.

A single filter may be used also to reduce lines caused by target impurities, the most common being an Ni filter for absorbing tungsten L lines. While the level of contaminant lines may be too low to be observed from a standard sample, such as silicon powder, they may appear in other samples when the crystals are too large or the sample is highly oriented. The proper selection of a filter for contaminant lines cannot be made until the contaminant wavelength is known.

There is always present, to some degree, sample fluorescence caused by either the continuum or line spectrum. The longer wavelengths, however, are usually absorbed by the air path or counter-tube window. The role of the beta filter in reducing fluorescence depends on its position with respect to the x-ray tube, the sample, and the film or detector. Placing the filter between tube and sample attenuates that part of the target spectrum which is just below the absorption edges of the sample. Placing the filter between sample and film may absorb the fluorescence from the sample.

Table 2. Ross Balanced-filter Components*

Target material	Filter pair		Thickness, 10^{-3} in.	
	A	*B*	*A*	*B*
Ag	Pd	Mo	1.08	1.53
Mo	Zr	Sr	1.54	4.09
Cu	Ni	Co	0.38	0.42
Co	Fe	Mn	0.38	0.44
Fe	Mn	Cr	0.37	0.42
Cr	V	Ti	0.38	0.58

* The data in this table were taken from *International Tables for X-ray Crystallography*, vol. III, p. 79, Kynoch Press, Birmingham, England, 1962, and are used with permission.

The fluorescent rays from the sample caused by the characteristic rays of the target are softer, i.e., longer-wavelength. A second filter, such as aluminum foil, placed between the sample and film or detector will preferentially absorb the secondary radiation.

Balanced-filter Technique. A narrow-wavelength band may be isolated by using a combination of two filters with absorption edges close to each other. More commonly these edges are chosen to lie just above and just below the $K\alpha$-doublet wavelengths of the target. The filter pair then consists of the usual $K\beta$ filter plus an additional filter. This technique is known as the Ross balanced-filter technique. The balancing of the filters is achieved by adjusting the thickness of the second filter so that its attenuation of the $K\beta$ wavelength is the same as that of the $K\beta$ filter. The balanced pair attenuate all the wavelengths to the same degree except those between the absorption edges. Ross filter data are given in Table 2. The thickness data were calculated assuming metal foils chosen to attenuate the $K\alpha$ doublet to 67 per cent of the incident intensity.

The Ross technique consists in recording two patterns, first with the A filter in place (preferably between the specimen and film or detector), then with the A filter removed and the B filter in its stead. The difference between the two patterns corresponds to the monochromatized pattern. Obviously, the technique is most applicable to counter diffractometer traces, but it can be applied to microdensitometered film patterns.

The subject of Ross balanced filters is discussed in Refs. 1 to 4.

Crystal-monochromator Techniques. Various studies such as radial-distribution analyses, low-angle scatter, precise line-profile analyses, or lattice-parameter studies, and general studies of radioactive materials require more strict monochromatization than is afforded by single or balanced filters. Here the investigator is faced with a wider choice of materials and methods from which the optimum condition may be found.

The details of the many choices are too voluminous for handbook presentation, and therefore only brief consideration will be given. Roberts and Parrish[5] have presented an excellent review along with an extensive bibliography.

The crystal monochromator is a means of separating the $K\alpha$ radiation from the other components by using a crystal-diffracted beam as the primary beam incident upon the sample. One such monochromator, termed a "flat monochromator," is a single crystal which has one face cut parallel to the set of the crystal planes. The width of the beam can be shortened with an increase in intensity by using "tilted-surface monochromators." In this instance the crystal is cut at some angle α, preferably so that the diffracted beam is parallel to the crystal surface. Another type is the "singly bent" monochromator where the crystal is bent to a cylindrical surface with no further shaping of the crystal surface. In this manner a widely diverging bundle of rays may be brought to geometric focus. In this instance, there are reflection-type and transmission-type crystals. An extension of the singly bent crystal is the logarithmic-spiral form. Aberrations inherent to singly bent crystals are overcome in "bent and ground" crystals. In this instance, the reflecting planes are bent to a radius of $2R$ while the scattering surface of the crystal is shaped to lie on the focusing circle of radius R. Another class of monochromator is the "point-focus" type which employs special single or double curvatures of the crystal surface.

The application of focusing monochromators to camera techniques requires special camera designs. Two notable designs are available commercially. P. M. DeWolff designed a version of the Guinier camera which is manufactured by N. V. Nederlandsche Instrumentfabriek "Nonius," Delft, Netherlands.* (See Fig. 11 of Chap. 8.) Another is the Guinier-Jagodzinski double-cylinder camera, manufactured by Rich. Seifert Co. of Hamburg, Germany.

The application of focusing monochromators to counter diffractometers is covered in considerable detail by Lang.[6]

Pulse-amplitude Discrimination. Scintillation or proportional counters with associated pulse-amplitude discriminators offer effective means for reducing unwanted radiation. The alteration of a rate-meter–recorded trace of the x-ray spectrum is dependent upon several factors. Some of these factors such as quantum-counting efficiency for various wavelengths and detector-tube operating conditions (i.e., the applied voltage and amplifier gain) were discussed in Chap. 3. These factors should be recognized as contributing to monochromatization.

The more important consideration is the use of the pulse-height analyzer for discriminating within narrower limits with a minimum loss in intensity of the $K\alpha$. Since the pulse amplitudes from scintillation or proportional detectors are proportional to the energy of the absorbed x-ray quanta, the unwanted portions of the spectrum may be electronically rejected with a single-channel analyzer having an adjustable base line and adjustable channel width (window). The base line serves to pass only those pulses which exceed a selected amplitude while the window serves to reject pulses which exceed a selected amplitude.

Lack of resolution in the analyzer makes it impossible to discriminate $K\alpha_1$ from $K\alpha_2$, and only a very small reduction in $K\beta$ can be realized without extensive reduction in intensity of the $K\alpha$. See Chap. 3 for a complete discussion of pulse-amplitude discrimination.

REFERENCES CITED

1. P. A. Ross, *Phys. Rev.*, **28**: 425 (1926).
2. P. A. Ross, *J. Opt. Soc. Am.*, **16**: 327 (1928).

* Nonius cameras are distributed in the United States by the General Electric Company.

3. P. Kirkpatrick, *Rev. Sci. Instr.*, **4**: 14 (1933).
4. P. Kirkpatrick and C. K. Chang, *Phys. Rev.*, **66**: 159 (1944).
5. B. W. Roberts and W. Parrish, Filter and Crystal Monochromator Techniques, *International Tables for X-ray Crystallography*, vol. III, p. 73, Kynoch Press, Birmingham, England, 1962.
6. A. R. Lang, *Rev. Sci. Instr.*, **27**: 17 (1956).

GENERAL REFERENCES

Azaroff, L. V., and M. J. Buerger: *The Powder Method in X-ray Crystallography*, McGraw-Hill Book Company, New York, 1958.
Barrett, C. S.: *Structure of Metals*, 2d ed., McGraw-Hill Book Company, New York, 1952.
Bragg, W. H., and W. L. Bragg: *The Crystalline State*, vols. I–III, G. Bell & Sons, Ltd., London, 1949.
Buerger, M. J.: *X-ray Crystallography*, John Wiley & Sons, Inc., New York, 1942.
Bunn, C. W.: *Chemical Crystallography*, Oxford University Press, Fairlawn, N.J., 1945.
Clark, G. L.: *Applied X-rays*, 4th ed., McGraw-Hill Book Company, New York, 1955.
Compton, A. H., and S. K. Allison: *X-rays in Theory and Experiment*, D. Van Nostrand Company, Inc., Princeton, N.J., 1960.
Cullity, B. D.: *Elements of X-ray Diffraction*, Addison-Wesley Publishing Company, Inc., Reading, Mass., 1956.
Henry, N. F. M., H. Lipson, and W. A. Wooster: *The Interpretation of X-ray Diffraction Photographs*, St. Martin's Press, Inc., New York, 1951.
International Tables for X-ray Crystallography, Kynoch Press, Birmingham, England, vol. I, 1952; vol. II, 1959; vol. III, 1962.
Klug, H. P., and L. E. Alexander: *X-ray Diffraction Procedures*, John Wiley & Sons, Inc., New York, 1954.
Peiser, H. S., H. P. Rooksby, and A. J. C. Wilson: *X-ray Diffraction by Polycrystalline Materials*, Institute of Physics, London; Chapman & Hall, Ltd., London; and Reinhold Publishing Corporation, New York, 1955.
Sproull, W. T.: *X-rays in Practice*, McGraw-Hill Book Company, New York, 1946.
Taylor, A.: *X-ray Metallography*, John Wiley & Sons, Inc., New York, 1961.
Wilson, A. J. C.: *X-ray Optics*, Methuen & Co., Ltd., London, 1949.

Chapter 8

CAMERA TECHNIQUES

Tibor Zoltai

University of Minnesota

1. INTRODUCTION

X-ray powder diffraction is among the most widely used instrumental techniques in the various branches of material science. It is a fast and nondestructive technique for the identification of compounds and for the detection of structural changes produced in a compound by physical and chemical processes. Although it is not the most sensitive and quantitative analytical technique available today, it is relatively inexpensive and is consequently available to the majority of the students of solid state. It requires little effort to master the principles of x-ray powder diffraction and to enable one to apply it in the course of his scientific or engineering projects with appreciable immediate success.

The development of the x-ray powder-diffraction technique began with the systematic studies and camera designs of Debye and Scherrer[1] in 1916 in Germany, and Hull[2] in 1917 in the United States. The original cameras were quickly accepted and improved by many leading scientists in the field. Numerous new designs of powder cameras were introduced, some of which were designed for better precision and some for specific types of investigations; among the latest improvements is the use of electronic detectors in place of the photographic film. Electronic detectors have many advantages; however, the film techniques are still preferable in some instances. For example, (1) they are less expensive and require very little maintenance, (2) they permit the use of smaller quantities of samples, and (3) faint diffraction lines are more readily detected with film than by electronic detection techniques. Film cameras do not require well-stabilized current and voltage and do not need the expensive electronic accessories of the diffractometers. A simple Debye-Scherrer camera can yield good powder patterns from a few micrograms of sample, and some other cameras can accept even smaller amounts. The electronic instruments give considerable variation in the background, often obscuring important weak diffraction peaks, which can be recovered only with special techniques. On the other hand, the photographic-film technique offers smooth background and permits immediate resolution of faint diffraction lines.

The Principle of X-ray Powder Photography. X-ray powder photography is, of course, based on the principle of diffraction, which is so conveniently expressed by the Bragg equation

$$\lambda = 2d_{hkl} \sin \theta \tag{1}$$

and means that diffraction will take place only from those lattice layers which are inclined to the incident x-ray beam at the proper angle θ. The ideal powder sample contains many thousands of small, randomly oriented crystals, and consequently many grains are expected to be in the proper position at all times to permit diffraction from all the permissible lattice planes.

Figure 1*a* illustrates a single grain in a powder sample which has a lattice layer oriented perpendicular to the page of the book and is inclined to the incident x-ray beam at the appropriate diffraction angle θ. The diffracted beam, still in the plane of the paper, is inclined to the lattice layer by the same angle θ and to the direct beam by angle 2θ. Since there are many thousands of grains in the powder sample, several of them will be in a position such that they have the same lattice layer inclined to the

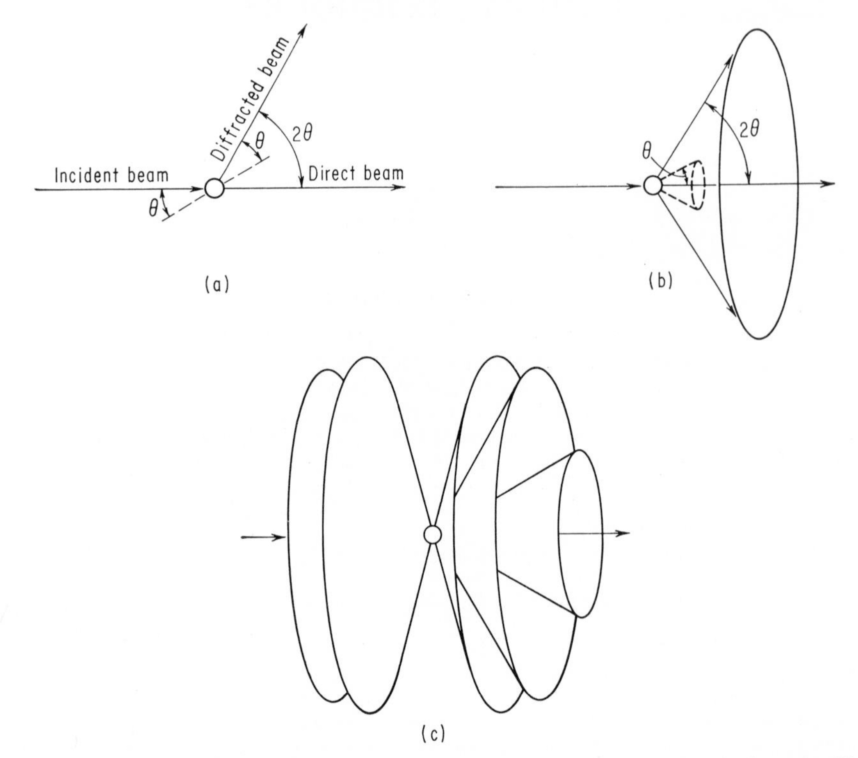

Fig. 1. Illustration of the diffraction of x-rays (*a*) by a lattice layer of a single grain, (*b*) by identical lattice layers from many grains, and (*c*) by different lattice layers of many grains.

incident beam by the same angle θ of Fig. 1*a*, and since the Bragg equation defines the inclination of the lattice plane in one dimension only, there will be identical lattice layers in the proper diffraction position oriented tangentially along the surface of a cone whose inclination with the direct beam will be θ. Similarly there will be a cone of diffracted beams inclined to the direct beam by an angle of 2θ (see Fig. 1*b*). Simultaneously, other lattice layers with different interplanar spacing and, consequently, with different θ inclination will be in diffracting position, thus giving rise to various diffraction cones. Several diffraction cones are illustrated in Fig. 1*c*.

All the powder cameras are designed to record these diffraction cones; however, many of them differ in the geometry and construction of the design. There are three major types of powder cameras: (1) the Debye-Scherrer camera, (2) the focusing cameras, and (3) the flat-film cameras. These three cameras select different ranges of the diffraction spectrum, record the diffraction cones in different ways, and emphasize different aspects of the powder pattern; but they all give essentially the same powder pattern. In addition, there are some specific modifications of these cameras which change the physical environment of the sample or alter the powder pattern for specific investigation. Such special cameras are, for example, the high- and low-temperature, the controlled-atmosphere, and the integrating cameras. The most important cameras will be discussed and evaluated briefly in the following sections.

2. THE DEBYE-SCHERRER CAMERA

Camera Characteristics. This camera is the most widely used, probably because it gives more information than do most of the other cameras, and it has a versatile design which is easily adaptable for specific investigations. It is extremely simple. The sample is placed in the center of a cylinder and a narrow strip of film is wrapped around the inside wall of the cylinder to record the diffraction cones.

FIG. 2. Photograph of a Debye-Scherrer camera. (*Courtesy of Philips Electronic Instruments.*)

The incident beam is usually filtered to enhance monochromation and is then passed through a collimator designed to produce a narrow and almost nondivergent beam.

In most Debye-Scherrer cameras the specimen is rotated during the period of exposure to radiation in order to bring more particles into position for diffraction and, through that, to increase the intensity of the diffraction lines. A photograph of a typical Debye-Scherrer camera is given in Fig. 2.

The geometry of the Debye-Scherrer camera is essentially that of the illustration of the powder-diffraction principle in Fig. 1*c*. Consequently, the distance on the film between the two sides of a diffraction cone corresponds to the angle 4θ, and from the measurement of this distance the interplanar spacing of the diffraction lattice planes can be calculated.

$$d_{hkl} = \lambda/(2 \sin \theta) \tag{2}$$

The diameter of the camera may be selected arbitrarily; cameras with 9 in. diameter, for example, are frequently used. However, it is more advantageous to fix the camera diameter so that a certain measurement unit on the film corresponds to 1 or 2° of θ. Since the arc length of a cone is equal to $R4\theta$ (where R is the radius of the camera) and maximum 4θ is equal to 360°, the camera diameter should be such that its circumference is 360 or 180 units of measure. That is,

$$\pi D = 360 \qquad \text{and} \qquad D = 360/\pi = 114.6 \tag{3}$$

The most convenient Debye-Scherrer cameras in practice have a diameter of 114.6 or 57.3 mm.[3] In the former camera 1 mm on the film corresponds to 1°; in the latter to 2° of θ. That is, if the angle of incidence θ is $x°$, it corresponds to x mm on the film in the 114.6-mm-diameter camera. The corresponding diffraction line, however, is inclined to the direct beam by 2θ; therefore, the line will be at $2x$ mm from the center of the direct beam position on the film. In powder photographs taken with such cameras the distance between the center of the direct beam and the diffraction lines can be measured with a millimeter scale, and the interplanar spacings can be calculated by using Eq. (2), or the measurement can be converted directly into interplanar spacing with the aid of tables[4,5,6] or of templates which are constructed for various wavelengths and camera diameters.

The number of diffraction lines recorded in a powder pattern, obviously, depends upon the lattice of the compound and the wavelength of the radiation used. That is, since d is inversely proportional to λ, fewer diffraction cones can be obtained with longer and more with shorter wavelengths of x-ray. The smallest possible interplanar spacing obtainable is equal to

$$d_{hkl} \min = \lambda/2 \tag{4}$$

since maximum θ is 90° and sin 90° is equal to 1.

Consequently, the selection of an appropriate wavelength offers advantages in obtaining good pictures from compounds having very small or very large unit cells. For example, Cr $K\alpha$ (λ = 2.229 Å) radiation is recommended for compounds having large unit cells, and Mo $K\alpha$ (λ = 0.7107 Å), for compounds of small unit cells.

Sample Preparation and Mounting. In order to facilitate observation and measurement, the lines on the film should be narrow, continuous, and strong. Even though these features of the diffraction lines can be improved with finer collimation of the direct beam, more sensitive film, and longer exposure to radiation, and by other technical means, the proper preparation and mounting of the sample still offers the simplest means to assure satisfactory results. The size and relative orientation of the particles in the sample, the quantity of the sample, and the shape of the powder mount are therefore of utmost importance.

Large particles in the powder mount either give spotty, discontinuous diffraction lines or require an unreasonably large quantity of sample. Particles which are too small, on the other hand, cause broadening of the diffraction lines. The most advantageous particle size is between 200- and 350-mesh diameter depending on the perfection and symmetry of the crystal structure of the sample. Crystals with well-developed mosaic and lineage structure and with high degree of stacking disorder produce broader lines and consequently should be ground finer. Crystals possessing high symmetry yield fewer diffraction lines than do crystals of low symmetry, since symmetry requires several lattice planes to have identical interplanar spacings. Consequently, crystals of high symmetry will give fewer difficulties in the resolution of the diffraction lines, and their fine grinding is not so essential.

A mount which is excessively large should also be avoided, especially if the elemental composition of the sample has high absorption for the selected radiation. An element will have very high absorbing power for radiation whose wavelength is slightly shorter than the wavelength of one of the absorption edges of the element. Figure 3 illustrates the mass absorption coefficient of the elements for Cu $K\alpha$ radiation. The wavelength of Cu $K\alpha$ is 1.542 Å, the wavelength of the K absorption edge of cobalt is 1.608 Å, of iron is 1.743 Å, and of nickel is 1.488 Å; therefore, cobalt and iron in the sample will be highly absorbent in copper radiation, whereas nickel will have low absorption. Similarly, the L absorption edge of dysprosium is 1.579 Å, and of holmium is 1.535 Å; consequently, the former element will have high and the latter low absorption for Cu $K\alpha$ radiation. In many cases, as when taking powder patterns of iron compounds using Cu $K\alpha$ radiation, it may be necessary to use radiation with a different characteristic wavelength in order to obtain usable photographs. In most cases, however, decreasing the quantity of the sample may prove sufficient. As a general rule, the quantity of the sample should be as small as permitted by the minimum number of particles and the desired mounting technique. If the permissible quantity of the sample is too small to handle, it should be diluted with a low-absorbent and amorphous binder.

If we assume that the diameter of the powder mount is smaller than that of the x-ray beam, the width of the diffraction line is larger or at least equal to the diameter of the sample. The width of the diffraction lines, therefore, can be decreased by decreasing the size of the powder mount.

Figure 4 illustrates the combined effect of absorption and powder-mount size on the width and the intensity profile of a diffraction line. Figure 4*a* illustrates the intensity profile of the ((111)) diffraction line produced by a 0.5-mm-diameter rod-type powder mount of 50 per cent galena and 50 per cent collodion, and Fig. 4*b* the same line produced by a 2-mm-diameter similar powder mount. The splitting of the diffraction

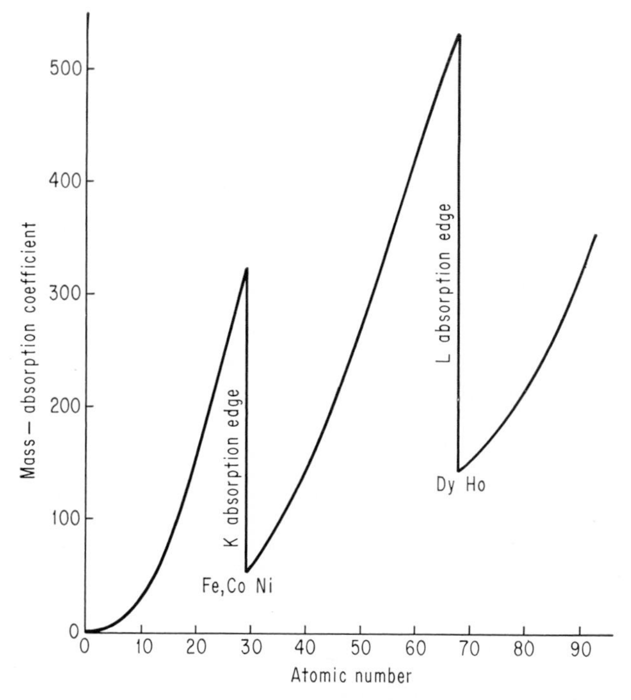

FIG. 3. Illustration of the absorption coefficient of the elements for Cu $K\alpha$ radiation.

line in the latter case will, obviously, seriously interfere with the interpretation of this diffraction line.

It is quite obvious that some crystals cleave along certain planes when ground. There will be a tendency for particles to align parallel to the cleavage faces when the powder is compressed or settled during the powder-mount preparation. This preferred orientation of the particles will obviously increase the number of particles in the diffraction position for certain lattice layers and decrease the number for others. In most cases this exaggeration and depression of some diffraction lines is highly undesirable and should be avoided. In some investigations, however, the improvement of the intensity of one particular diffraction line caused by preferred orientation may be desirable.

We can summarize that, in general, the powder sample should be ground to 200- to 350-mesh size and as small quantity of the sample should be worked into the powder mount as is feasible. Several types of powder mounts are used in powder photography; the following are the most popular.

Rod Mount. A small quantity of powdered sample, a few milligrams, is mixed with an amorphous binder such as collodion or gum tragacanth and is rolled into a rod of 0.1 to 0.5 mm diameter. Alternatively, a fine glass fiber may be dipped into an amorphous glue, and rolled over the powdered sample. Both these techniques give similar cylindrically shaped mounts. The former requires shorter radiation time and

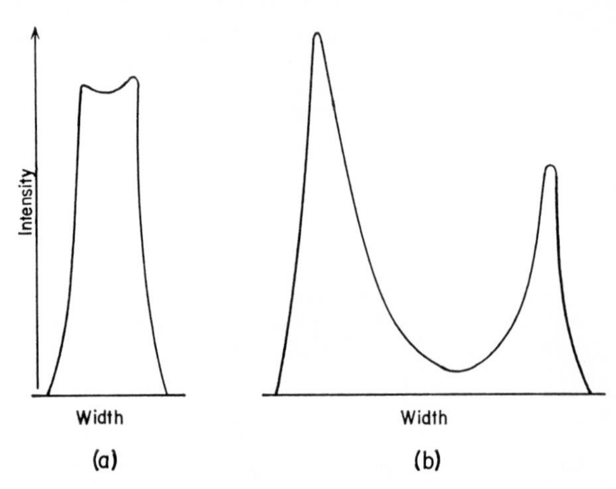

FIG. 4. Intensity profile of the ((111)) diffraction line of PbS. Cu $K\alpha$ radiation, sample mixed with 50 per cent collodion. (*a*) 0.5-mm- and (*b*) 2-mm-diameter rod mount.

yields sharper diffraction lines; however, the second is more advantageous for high-absorbent elements.

The rod sample is mounted with its axis parallel to the surface of the film and is rotated around its longitudinal axis. If the collimator has an oval-shaped slit system, this type of mount yields diffraction lines of unusual shape described as "umbrella effect." The cause of the umbrella effect is illustrated in Fig. 5. When the slit system is changed to a circular pinhole system, the umbrella shape of the diffraction lines becomes less apparent but is still present, assuming that the cross section of the incident beam is greater than the diameter of the rod.

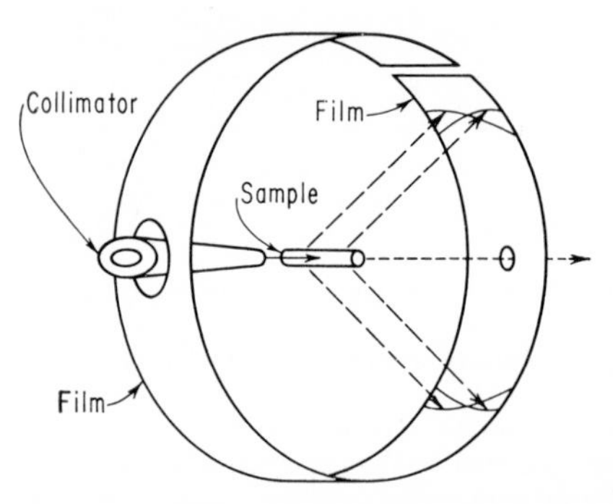

FIG. 5. Illustration of the "umbrella effect."

Ball Mount. A very small quantity of the powder is mixed with an amorphous binder, such as collodion or clear fingernail polish, shaped into a small sphere, and glued to the end of a glass fiber with the same binder. A ball about 0.1 mm in diameter can be prepared on the stage of a binocular microscope, and a few micrograms of powder can be sufficient. Such a ball would require longer exposure to radiation than would rod mounts but in most cases would give satisfactory patterns.

The ball mount offers several advantages as opposed to the rod mount: (1) smaller quantity of sample may be handled, (2) the umbrella effect is practically absent, (3) preferred orientation is negligible, (4) the specimen diameter may be made smaller, and (5) absorption is also minimized.

Capillary Mount. Samples which may dissolve in the binder call for a special, dry sample preparation. They can be mounted in capillary tubes, and if necessary, the tubes can be sealed with wax to prevent hydration. Funnel-shaped capillary tubes can be prepared or purchased. Pyrex glass capillaries should be satisfactory in most cases; however, thin silica or Lindeman glass capillaries offer less absorption and are more advantageous.

In addition to the above commonly used types of powder mounts, there are many others offering special advantages in certain cases. For example, a rod can be cut directly from a soft polycrystalline material or a rod mount can be ground from a piece of metal without powdering it first. These techniques offer added information concerning the orientation of the grains.

Film Mounting. In the first types of powder cameras, the film was mounted by joining the two free ends of the film at the collimator. This is called the Bradley-Jay mounting and is illustrated in Fig. 6*a*. The hole provided for the direct-beam catcher is in the center of the film strip and all the diffraction lines can be measured with

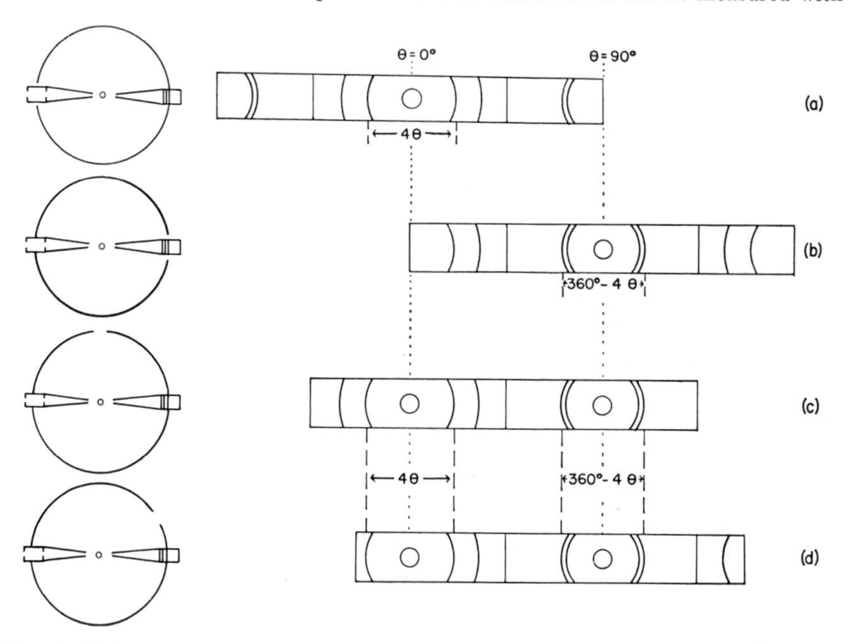

FIG. 6. Film mounting in the Debye-Scherrer camera. [*After* (*a*) *Bradley-Jay*, (*b*) *van Arkel*, (*c*) *Straumanis*, and (*d*) *Wilson*.]

respect to the center of the hole. The van Arkel mounting joins the free ends of the film at the direct-beam catcher and the film permits the measurement of the diffraction lines with respect to the hole provided for the collimator (see Fig. 6*b*). The exact center of the hole, which represents $\theta = 0°$ in the former case and $\theta = 90°$ in the latter, is established by dividing the distance between several pairs of diffraction lines.

The most popular film mounting is the Straumanis mounting, illustrated in Fig. 6*c*. This mounting contains holes for both the collimator and the beam catcher at $\theta = 0°$ and $\theta = 90°$ within the film strip and permits the establishment of both reference positions from a few pairs of diffraction lines. Unfortunately, many compounds have no diffraction lines in the back-reflection region and prohibit the determination of the position at which $\theta = 90°$. The Wilson mount (Fig. 6*d*) remedies this problem by joining the two ends of the film closer to the beam-catcher hole. Consequently, some of the front-reflection lines will be paired on the film around the collimator hole and permit the determination of both the $\theta = 0°$ and $\theta = 90°$ positions from front-reflection lines.

Analysis of Errors. There are several sources of error in the Debye-Scherrer powder technique which should be kept in mind, checked for, and corrected when necessary. These errors can be divided into two groups according to the two diffraction-line characteristics which are measured: (1) position and (2) intensity of the diffraction lines.

The position of the diffraction lines and the determination of the interplanar spacings can be in error because of the following major causes: (1) difference between assumed and actual camera diameter, (2) film shrinkage and expansion, (3) eccentricity of the powder mount, (4) divergence and refraction of the x-ray beam, and (5) absorption of x-rays by the specimen.

The first two errors can easily be corrected in the Straumanis and Wilson film-mounting techniques by determining the centers of the direct-beam and collimator holes (which represent, respectively, $\theta = 0°$ and $90°$) from a few pairs of diffraction lines. The distance between these two centers should be 90 or 180 mm if the camera diameter is 57.3 or 114.6 mm, respectively. If it is found to differ from one of these two values, the difference is attributed to an error in the assumption of camera radius or to film shrinkage, and spacing values for all diffraction lines can be corrected. In the Bradley-Jay and the van Arkel types of film mounting, the same errors can be determined from the change in the position of the reference marks on the film or from the observed positions of the known diffraction lines of an internal standard.

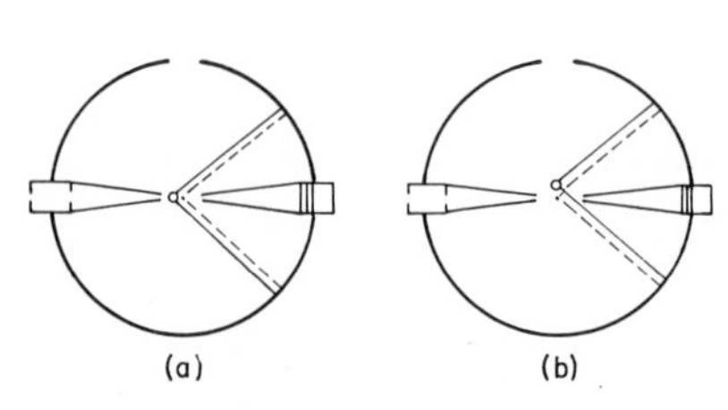

FIG. 7. Effect of the eccentricity of the powder mount on the separation between diffraction-line pairs. Mount displaced (*a*) parallel, (*b*) perpendicular to the direction of the direct beam.

The eccentricity of the powder mount may cause serious errors; if the camera is in good adjustment, however, and the powder mount has been centered with the centering screw, such errors should not be significant. It should be pointed out that eccentricity errors can be of two types or the combination of both. The first type of eccentricity error occurs when the powder mount is displaced along the direction of the x-ray beam, in which case the diffraction cone is intersected by the film at shorter or longer distance from the sample, and consequently the position of the diffraction lines will indicate longer or shorter (Fig. 7*a*) interplanar spacing. In the second type of eccentricity error, the powder mount is displaced perpendicular to the direction of the incident x-ray beam. The diffraction cone then will be asymmetrically intersected by the film (see Fig. 7*b*); however, the arc length will be correct and no error in d arises when both lines of a diffraction cone are measured.

Perfectly parallel x-ray beams cannot be obtained in practice; they are usually divergent. This divergence of the beam causes some errors in the location of the diffraction lines. The arc becomes longer in the front and shorter in the back-reflection region; however, this error is usually negligible. The error due to refraction of x-rays by the sample is also negligible. The index of refraction of most substances for x-rays used in diffraction is between 0.99996 and 1.00004, and therefore, this effect is obviously insignificant.

The effect of absorption, on the other hand, is very severe and may cause serious misinterpretation. Figure 4*b* illustrates one effect of absorption; here the diffraction line is practically split into two separate lines. This illustration, of course, shows the extreme effect of absorption, which is, however, quite common. The distortion of the intensity profiles of the diffraction lines caused by absorption varies as a function of θ. In the front-reflection region the profile tends to be split as in Fig. 4*b*. As θ increases, the peak on the lower θ side becomes smaller relative to the one on the higher θ side. Around $\theta = 45°$ the peak on the lower θ side almost completely disappears, resulting in an asymmetric profile falsely indicating a peak center at higher than the correct θ angle. As θ approaches $90°$ the intensity profile becomes more symmetrical. Figure 8 illustrates this change in the intensity profile with increasing θ.

Most of these errors, their correction, and special techniques for the precision determination of interplanar spacings from Debye-Scherrer powder patterns are further discussed in Chap. 10.

The intensity of the diffraction lines of the Debye-Scherrer powder pattern is greatly affected by absorption. Because of the design of the camera, the x-ray beam in part penetrates through the sample and in part is diffracted only from the surface. Consequently, the shape of the sample is critical in the absorption correction. Table 1 gives the absorption correction for rod and capillary mounts* and Table 2 for ball mounts. R in these tables refers to the radius of the specimen and μ to the mean linear absorption coefficient of the sample. R is relatively simple to measure with a calibrated microscope eyepiece, but the determination of the proper value of μ

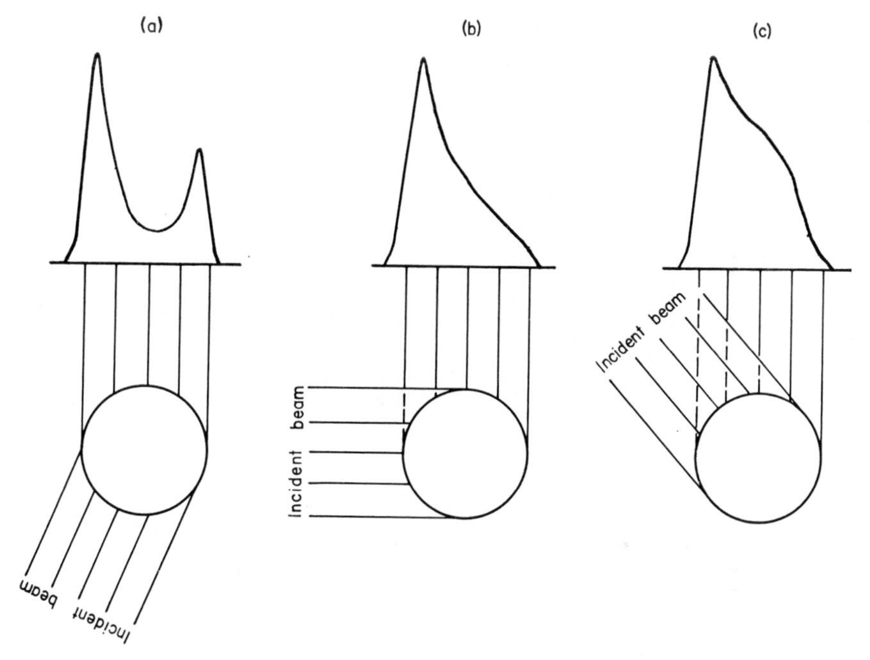

FIG. 8. Intensity profile of diffraction lines of highly absorbent samples for (a) low θ, (b intermediate θ, and (c) high θ diffraction angles.

involves, in most cases, some approximation. The mean value of μ can be obtained from the mass absorption coefficient of each element (μ_m) in the sample:

$$\text{Mean } \mu = (w_1\mu_{m1} + w_2\mu_{m2} + \cdots + w_n\mu_{mn} + w_b\mu_{mb})(v_s\rho_s + v_b\rho_b) \tag{5}$$

where the subscripts 1 to n refer to the elements of the sample, b to the binder, w is the atomic-weight fraction, v is the volume fraction, and ρ is the density of the sample (s) and of the binder (b).

If no binder is used or if the binder does not fill up all the space between the grains of the sample, a packing coefficient has to be determined. The absorbing power of air is very low, and consequently there is no need to account for the absorption of x-rays by air in the voids.

* For the type of mount where the powder is glued around a glass fiber and for the capillary mount a better correction can be obtained if, instead of using the mean linear absorption coefficient, the absorption of the glass is accounted for separately in the calculation of the correction.

Table 1. Absorption Correction for Rod Mount*
(No binder added, 0 per cent porosity)

μR†	θ				
	0°	22½°	45°	67½°	90°
0.0	1.0000	1.00000	1.0000	1.0000	1.0000
0.1	0.8470	0.8480	0.849	0.850	0.851
0.2	0.7120	0.7160	0.719	0.724	0.729
0.3	0.6000	0.6060	0.614	0.627	0.635
0.4	0.5100	0.5170	0.527	0.545	0.556
0.5	0.4350	0.4420	0.458	0.478	0.490
0.6	0.3690	0.3780	0.398	0.423	0.436
0.7	0.3140	0.3240	0.348	0.378	0.393
0.8	0.2680	0.2785	0.305	0.337	0.356
0.9	0.2300	0.2410	0.271	0.305	0.324
1.0	0.1977	0.2095	0.242	0.2785	0.295
1.1	0.1698	0.1828	0.2170	0.2550	0.2715
1.2	0.1459	0.1600	0.1954	0.2350	0.2510
1.3	0.1256	0.1403	0.1770	0.2170	0.2335
1.4	0.1084	0.1233	0.1611	0.2010	0.2180
1.5	0.0938	0.1091	0.1469	0.1866	0.2050
1.6	0.0811	0.0973	0.1352	0.1746	0.1932
1.7	0.0710	0.0871	0.1247	0.1641	0.1824
1.8	0.0615	0.0780	0.1154	0.1542	0.1730
1.9	0.0537	0.0702	0.1074	0.1459	0.1644
2.0	0.0471	0.0635	0.1005	0.1384	0.1567
2.1	0.0416	0.0579	0.0944	0.1315	0.1493
2.2	0.0367	0.0531	0.0889	0.1250	0.1426
2.3	0.0324	0.0486	0.0838	0.1189	0.1365
2.4	0.02865	0.0447	0.0791	0.1135	0.1309
2.5	0.0255	0.0412	0.0750	0.1086	0.1256
2.6	0.0227	0.0382	0.0711	0.1040	0.1211
2.7	0.0202	0.0355	0.0675	0.0998	0.1167
2.8	0.01803	0.0330	0.0641	0.0962	0.1127
2.9	0.01607	0.0308	0.0610	0.0925	0.1089
3.0	0.01436	0.0288	0.0582	0.0889	0.1054
3.1	0.01288	0.02705	0.0558	0.0857	0.1021
3.2	0.01159	0.0255	0.0535	0.0830	0.0990
3.3	0.01049	0.02415	0.0514	0.0804	0.0961
3.4	0.00955	0.0229	0.0495	0.0778	0.0933
3.5	0.00871	0.0217	0.0477	0.0755	0.0906
3.6	0.00796	0.0206	0.0460	0.0733	0.0881
3.7	0.00729	0.01968	0.0444	0.0711	0.0858
3.8	0.00670	0.01875	0.0429	0.0692	0.0836
3.9	0.00617	0.01787	0.0415	0.0673	0.0815
4.0	0.00568	0.01706	0.0402	0.0653	0.0794
4.1	0.00525	0.01629	0.0389	0.0635	0.0774
4.2	0.00488	0.01563	0.0377	0.0618	0.0755
4.3	0.00453	0.01500	0.0366	0.0602	0.0738
4.4	0.00420	0.01445	0.0356	0.0587	0.0721
4.5	0.00391	0.01390	0.0347	0.0573	0.0705
4.6	0.00364	0.01343	0.0338	0.0561	0.0689
4.7	0.00340	0.01300	0.0329	0.0547	0.0675
4.8	0.00316	0.01259	0.0321	0.0535	0.0661
4.9	0.002945	0.01222	0.0313	0.0525	0.0647
5.0	0.002755	0.01189	0.0305	0.0514	0.0635

* After Bradley.[25]
† Linear absorption coefficient times radius of rod.

Table 2. Absorption Correction for Ball Mount*
(No binder added, 0 per cent porosity)

μR	θ				
	0°	22½°	45°	67½°	90°
0.0	1.000	1.000	1.000	1.000	1.000
0.1	0.862	0.862	0.863	0.869	0.872
0.2	0.742	0.742	0.743	0.748	0.753
0.3	0.646	0.646	0.647	0.655	0.661
0.4	0.560	0.560	0.567	0.580	0.589
0.5	0.489	0.490	0.502	0.520	0.531
0.6	0.422	0.424	0.441	0.462	0.476
0.7	0.368	0.372	0.391	0.415	0.432
0.8	0.321	0.326	0.348	0.374	0.393
0.9	0.281	0.287	0.313	0.340	0.359
1.0	0.245	0.252	0.281	0.310	0.330
1.1	0.215	0.224	0.256	0.285	0.306
1.2	0.189	0.200	0.233	0.263	0.286
1.3	0.167	0.179	0.214	0.245	0.267
1.4	0.147	0.159	0.196	0.228	0.250
1.5	0.131	0.143	0.180	0.215	0.236
1.6	0.115	0.128	0.166	0.201	0.222
1.7	0.102	0.116	0.154	0.190	0.210
1.8	0.0910	0.105	0.143	0.179	0.199
1.9	0.0814	0.0953	0.134	0.169	0.189
2.0	0.0731	0.0874	0.125	0.161	0.181
2.1	0.0653	0.0797	0.117	0.152	0.173
2.2	0.0585	0.0729	0.109	0.145	0.165
2.3	0.0528	0.0673	0.103	0.138	0.159
2.4	0.0476	0.0621	0.0977	0.132	0.152
2.5	0.0430	0.0575	0.0925	0.126	0.147
2.6	0.0388	0.0532	0.0877	0.121	0.141
2.7	0.0352	0.0496	0.0835	0.116	0.136
2.8	0.0321	0.0463	0.0796	0.112	0.131
2.9	0.0290	0.0433	0.0760	0.108	0.126
3.0	0.0267	0.0405	0.0726	0.104	0.122
3.1	0.0244	0.0381	0.0695	0.100	0.118
3.2	0.0224	0.0359	0.0666	0.0971	0.114
3.3	0.0205	0.0338	0.0638	0.0939	0.111
3.4	0.0189	0.0319	0.0614	0.0911	0.108
3.5	0.0174	0.0302	0.0590	0.0883	0.105
3.6	0.0161	0.0287	0.0569	0.0857	0.102
3.7	0.0149	0.0273	0.0549	0.0833	0.0991
3.8	0.0138	0.0260	0.0530	0.0809	0.0967
3.9	0.0128	0.0247	0.0512	0.0786	0.0941
4.0	0.0119	0.0235	0.0494	0.0765	0.0918
4.1	0.0111	0.0224	0.0481	0.0744	0.0895
4.2	0.0103	0.0214	0.0466	0.0725	0.0873
4.3	0.00960	0.0205	0.0457	0.0705	0.0852
4.4	0.00899	0.0197	0.0439	0.0688	0.0833
4.5	0.00841	0.0189	0.0427	0.0672	0.0815
4.6	0.00787	0.0182	0.0415	0.0656	0.0797
4.7	0.00738	0.0175	0.0403	0.0641	0.0780
4.8	0.00693	0.0169	0.0393	0.0627	0.0765
4.9	0.00650	0.0163	0.0383	0.0612	0.0749
5.0	0.00613	0.0157	0.0373	0.0600	0.0734

* After Evans and Ekstein.[26]

3. FOCUSING CAMERAS

The principle of the focusing cameras is illustrated in Fig. 9*a*. The x-ray beam enters the cylindrical camera at S; either this is placed at the focal point of the primary x-ray beam, or the camera has a narrow slit at S to create a focus. The divergent beam then is diffracted by the crystals of the sample, and the diffracted rays are focused on the inside wall of the cylinder. The particles in the sample are randomly oriented, and many of them will be in the proper diffraction position for various lattice layers. Particles A and B, for example, have the same lattice layer identically oriented with respect to S, so that the rays reaching A and B make the proper θ with this lattice layer. Consequently, both angles SAF and SBF must be equal to $180° - 2\theta$, and since S is a common point of the primary rays, the geometry of a circle requires that F be a common point of the diffracted rays.

The first focusing cameras were independently developed by Seemann[7] in 1919 and by Bohlin[8] in 1920, and focusing cameras are therefore frequently referred to as

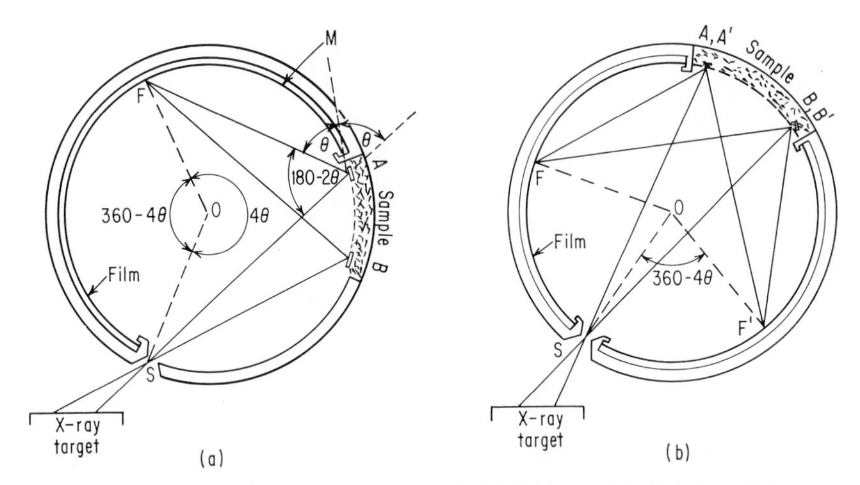

FIG. 9. Principle of (*a*) the asymmetric and (*b*) the symmetric focusing cameras.

Seeman-Bohlin focusing cameras. The focusing cameras offer the advantage of sharper diffraction lines and, consequently, better measurements. However, they record only the lines of the front- or the back-reflection region and lose the self-correcting features of the Straumanis film mounting of the Debye-Scherrer camera. On the other hand, the relative intensity of the diffraction lines in the focusing cameras is practically unaffected by the usual errors of the Debye-Scherrer cameras, and for most investigations they require only corrections for the Lorentz-polarization factors.

The two major types of focusing cameras are the asymmetric and the symmetric varieties. The former is illustrated in Fig. 9*a* and the latter in Fig. 9*b*. The asymmetric camera restricts recording of diffraction lines to a narrow range and to one side of the familiar diffraction cone. Several modifications of this camera were designed by Phragmen and first employed by Westgren[9] to record the low, medium, and high θ ranges of the diffraction lines. The symmetrical cameras, on the other hand, usually restrict data collection to the region of high θ, that is, the back-reflection lines, but they permit recording of both sides of the diffraction cones. Since the back-reflection lines permit more accurate interplanar-spacing determination than do the front-reflection lines, and the symmetrical back-reflection focusing camera gives better resolution than the Debye-Scherrer camera, this type of focusing camera is very popular in precision interplanar-spacing determination. Another less popular type of symmetrical focusing camera is the symmetrical front-reflection camera illustrated in Fig. 10*a*. Here the incident beam is transmitted through the specimen and the focal point of the beam is adjusted so that it is on the circle opposite the specimen. It is possible to place a slit at the focal point of the direct beam and add a symmetrical back-reflection camera in line with the front-reflection camera, as illustrated in Fig. 10*b*.

Since the focusing cameras have no provision for the rotation of the powder mount, fine grinding of the sample is even more important than when using the Debye-Scherrer techniques. For the same reason they also require more powder in order to yield continuous diffraction lines.

The film, similarly to the Debye-Scherrer practice, is placed firmly against the inside wall of the cylinder as illustrated in Fig. 9*a* and *b*. Since these cameras do not offer the possibilty of using Straumanis or similar camera-diameter correcting mounting of the film, the camera diameter must be precisely determined or internal standards should be used. The use of internal standards also helps detect film shrinkage. In the symmetrical camera the position of $\theta = 90°$ can be obtained from a pair of

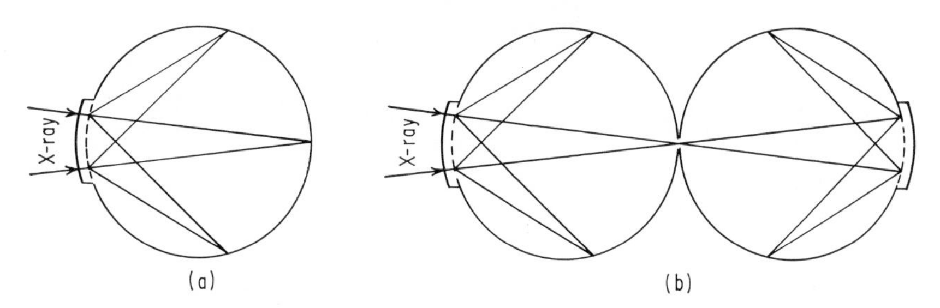

FIG. 10. Illustration of the (*a*) symmetrical front-reflection and (*b*) combined front- and back-reflection focusing cameras.

lines, while in the asymmetric cameras a reference mark (M in Fig. 9*a*) must be established. In the asymmetric cameras the diffraction lines are measured with respect to the reference mark, and in the symmetrical cameras with respect to the $\theta = 90°$ point.

Since the angles SAF and SBF are equal to $180° - 2\theta$, the angle SOF around the same arc of the asymmetric camera is equal to $2(180° - 2\theta)$, and around the arc containing the sample it is equal to 4θ. The distance along the inside wall of the camera between S and F on the sample side is equal to $4\theta R$ where R is the radius of the camera. Therefore, the distance D measured from the reference point M to the diffraction line on the film can be used to determine θ,

$$\theta = \frac{D + SM}{4R} \tag{6}$$

where SM refers to the predetermined distance between the slit and the reference point M and is constant for a given camera.

In the symmetrical focusing cameras the distance between the corresponding pairs of diffraction lines D is measured, and θ can be obtained as

$$(4\pi - 8\theta)R = D$$
$$\theta = (\tfrac{1}{2}\pi - \tfrac{1}{8}R)D \tag{7}$$

where $(\frac{1}{2}\pi - \frac{1}{8}R)$ is a camera constant.

It is obvious that the addition of a curved monochromator to a focusing camera with the focal point of the monochromator located at the slit of the camera would improve not only the monochromation of the incident beam but also the intensity and the resolution of the diffraction lines. Since the addition of the curved monochromator was most strongly advocated by Guinier,[10] the back-reflection symmetrical camera combined with a curved-crystal monochromator is frequently called the Guinier camera. The photograph of a commercially available Guinier camera is shown in Fig. 11.

FIG. 11. Photograph of a Guinier camera. (*Courtesy of N. V. Nederlandsche Röntgen Apperatenfabriek Evershed-Enraf.*)

4. FLAT-FILM CAMERAS

These cameras, also called pinhole cameras, differ from the Debye-Scherrer cameras by the exchange of the cylindrically mounted film strip with a flat film, placed in either the front- or the back-reflection side of the powder, or in both sides simultaneously. The diffraction cones, consequently, will be registered on the film as complete circles rather than arcs. The presence of the full circle is advantageous in the study of the preferred orientation of the crystals in polycrystalline material and in the structural investigation of amorphous material. Since the film-to-powder distance can be varied, these cameras offer definite advantages in the study of compounds having unusually large or small unit cells.

The back-reflection flat-film camera can also serve as a semifocusing camera when the incident beam is made to pass through a pinhole at the film. This creates a divergent beam with its focus at the pinhole, and the beam diffracted from the flat-powder mount will be near to the focal point again at the film. This focusing effect can be improved by the addition of a curved-crystal monochromator. Back-reflection flat-film cameras are advantageous in the study of stress effects (cf. Chap. 19) and grain orientation (cf. Chap. 18). In the latter case the specimen is not powdered as usual, but an undisturbed slice is cut directly from the solid sample.

The determination of the interplanar spacings is somewhat more difficult with the flat-film camera than with the Debye-Scherrer camera; first, since the film-to-powder distance is not so well defined as in the cylindrical cameras; and second, the calculations are somewhat more involved, and tables for the conversion of measurements to interplanar spacing due to the variable film-to-powder distance are less readily available. For the partial solution of these difficulties, the sample is usually mixed with an internal standard of known interplanar spacing.

Another disadvantage of the flat-film cameras is that only a small portion of the front- and/or the back-reflection cones can be recovered, and approximately half of the diffraction spectrum is completely lost. Flat-film cameras are, consequently, used only as complementary cameras to the Debye-Scherrer cameras for special investigations.

From Fig. 12 one can easily derive the relationship between the diameter of the

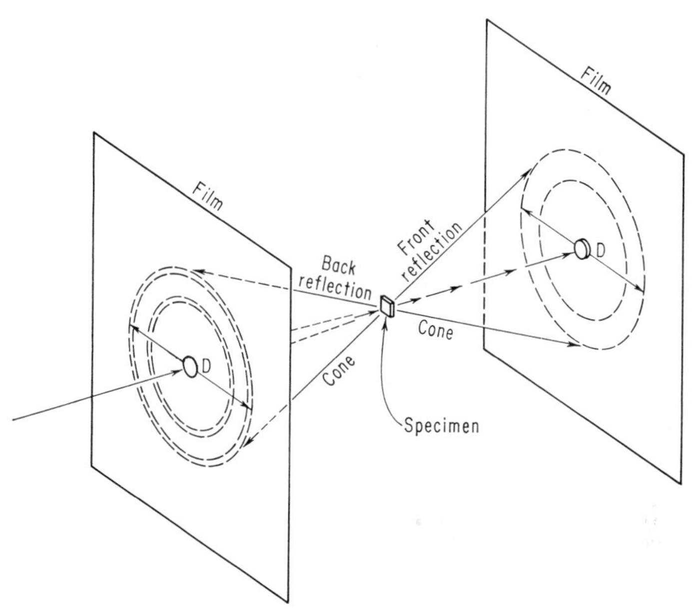

FIG. 12. Illustration of the geometry of the front- and back-reflection flat-film cameras.

FIG. 13. Photograph of a back-reflection flat-film (Lane) camera. (*Courtesy of the General Electric Company.*)

diffraction rings D and the diffraction angle θ. For the front-reflection type this is

$$\tan 2\theta = D/2F$$
$$\theta = \tfrac{1}{2} \tan^{-1} (D/2F) \tag{8}$$

where F is the film-to-powder distance.

In the back-reflection camera the angle between the center of the diffraction cone (i.e., where the angle $\theta = 90°$) and the surface of the diffraction cone is not 2θ but $(180° - 2\theta)$. Consequently, Eq. (8) gives the value of $(90° - \theta)$ instead of θ.

Several variations of flat-film cameras are available. Some have provisions for the rotation of the film, the specimen, or both to reduce the spottiness of the diffraction rings caused by too large or too few grains in the sample. Figure 13 is the photograph of a back-reflection flat-film camera.

5. SPECIAL CAMERAS

There are many variations of the above-described three basic powder cameras which are designed for specific types of investigation. Some are manufactured and marketed; most of them, however, are homemade and obviously vary a great deal in construction. An attempt to describe these cameras in any detail would be impractical; rather than attempt that, the function of the more important ones will be discussed briefly.

Glancing-angle Cameras. The so-called glancing-angle or flat-specimen cameras are designed to handle flat rather than cylindrical or spherical-shaped powder samples; to obtain sharper lines, especially in the front-reflection range; and to minimize the absorption effect. The basic geometry of these cameras can be visualized by replacing the usual powder mount of the Debye-Scherrer camera with a flat specimen set stationary in an inclined position with respect to the incident beam. This camera will obviously permit the recovery of a certain range of the diffraction spectrum only, but it is semifocusing and eliminates most of the distortion or doubling of the front-reflection lines, caused frequently by highly absorbent samples in the Debye-Scherrer cameras. Brindley and Spiers,[11] for example, have designed and successfully used a glancing-angle camera.

Scanning Cameras. The scanning, moving-film, or integrating cameras are designed either for studying the orientation of the grains in polycrystalline samples or for eliminating the spottiness of the diffraction lines. One of the earlier moving-film powder cameras was conceived by Kratky.[12] His camera is very similar to the modern Weissenberg single-crystal camera. A few years later, Fink and Smith[13] came out with a scanning camera to be used for obtaining continuous diffraction lines from coarse-grained polycrystalline samples.

Microbeam Cameras. These cameras are designed to satisfy one or more of the following special requirements: to give diffraction patterns of very small (down to 5 to 6 microns) samples or of small areas of a larger sample; to reduce the exposure time; and to record low-angle diffraction lines. One of the most important points in the design of a microbeam camera is the collimation of the x-ray beam. Collimators using pinholes cut in thin lead sheet or high-absorbent glass capillaries can achieve beam diameters of 10 microns. The first microbeam camera designed by Kratky[14] is a modification of the front-reflection flat-film camera. He employed a short-focal-distance convergent beam (angle of convergence approximately 30°) with the sample placed at the focus of the beam and the film a few millimeters behind it. A more recent design of Chesley[15] uses a fine capillary collimator, short film-to-specimen distance, and has provisions for obtaining vacuum in the camera.

Low-angle Cameras (cf. Chap. 16). Diffraction lines corresponding to higher than 50 Å interplanar spacing are shadowed by the direct-beam catcher in most powder cameras. Front-reflection flat-film cameras can be adopted for low-angle diffraction studies by increasing the film-to-crystal distance, by using longer wavelengths, by the adaptation of very fine and long collimation, and by minimizing the air scattering, which is significantly strong in this region. This latter can be achieved by creating a reasonable vacuum in the camera. There are many low-angle cameras designed especially for the study of organic materials. One of the first was designed and used successfully by Bear.[16]

The use of crystal monochromators is advantageous in obtaining better resolution and, consequently, is desirable in low-angle diffraction. Guinier and Fournet[17] found the use of two curved crystals in series especially advantageous.

More recently, Hawes[18] proposed a cylindrical camera for the better measurement of low-angle diffraction lines. The axis of the cylinder in his camera coincides with the incident beam and the axis of the diffraction cones. The position of the diffraction lines on the film with this geometry becomes proportional to d rather than to θ, which permits more reliable measurements in the low-angle diffraction region than usual.

High-pressure Cameras. The first high-pressure camera was designed by Jacobs,[19] who obtained up to 5,000 atm of pressure. In his helium-gas camera, however, the film was also in the pressure chamber, which was found disadvantageous by Lawson and Riley,[20] who have placed the sample in a small (½ by ¼ in.) bomb and placed the film in the normal-pressure portion of the camera. The bomb has a wall a few millimeters thick made of low-absorbent beryllium metal permitting efficient transmission of the x-ray beam. With this camera they were able to obtain good photographs at various pressures up to 15,000 atm.

One of the most important groups of special powder cameras includes the high- and low-temperature cameras. These cameras, however, are more important in today's research than some of the ones discussed above and, consequently, they are discussed separately in Chaps. 14 and 15, respectively.

6. CHOICE OF FILM AND RADIATION

Film (cf. Chap. 3). The characteristics of the satisfactory x-ray films can be summarized in a few points: (1) high sensitivity for the wavelength of the characteristic radiation of common x-ray tube targets, (2) fine-grained texture and homogeneous emulsion layer or layers, (3) low fogging, (4) low expansion due to changes in temperature and humidity, and (5) wide range of linear relationship between the darkening of the film and the logarithm of the exposure time.

Many suitable x-ray films are available on the market. The most frequently used types are the Kodak Industrial Type K, Ansco Medical Non-screen, and the Ilford Industrial G films. The Commission of Crystallographic Apparatus of the International Union of Crystallography studied the characteristics of various x-ray films. The results of this study can be of significant help in the selection of films.[21] Most x-ray films have double emulsion; that is, they are sensitive on both sides. This yields the advantage of speed in obtaining sufficiently strong diffraction lines; however, because of the thickness of the film, the apparent camera diameter is shorter on the inner side than on the outer side of the film. In routine work this creates no complication; however, in precision work and in focusing cameras single-emulsion films are preferable.

It is advisable that, once the film has been chosen, the recommendation of the manufacturer be followed carefully in the processing of the film. The quality of the film can be maintained only by clean and constant darkroom procedure. When the film is used for quantitative analysis or for crystal-structure investigation, it is essential to use fresh chemicals and controlled temperature in the various baths.

In some cases it may be impossible to obtain strong diffraction lines and to decrease the darkness of the background. If the film is sensitive on both sides, the darkness of the background can be decreased by scraping the emulsion surface off the inside of the film. The film itself absorbs x-rays, and a significant portion of the fluorescence radiation, the air scattering, and the white radiation is absorbed by the film, while most of the stronger characteristic radiation penetrates through the film.

Radiation (cf. Chap. 7). The choice of the proper characteristic radiation, that is, the x-ray tube target, depends on many factors which can be summarized: (1) it should have the lowest possible absorption for the elements of the investigated material; (2) short $K\alpha$ wavelength is desirable for the investigation of compounds having small unit cells, or for the collection of the diffraction lines corresponding to short interplanar spacing; (3) long $K\alpha$ wavelength is desirable for compounds having relatively large unit cells or in precision work; (4) it is also desirable to select a target which can be operated at high power in order to allow short exposure time.

If one cannot afford to own more than one x-ray tube, this, in general, should be a tube with a copper target. The wavelength of Cu $K\alpha$ is such that it gives the best results for the majority of compounds, it can be operated at relatively high power, and it has a relatively long lifetime. If one can afford several x-ray tubes, the following targets are recommended: Mo (short $K\alpha$ wavelength); Cr (long $K\alpha$ wavelength); Fe (low absorption for compounds containing Fe, Mn, and Co).

The necessary exposure time of a sample is a function of (1) the elemental composition of the compound; (2) the crystal structure of the compound; (3) its degree of crystallinity; (4) its absorption coefficient for the given radiation; (5) the packing, the quantity, and the shape of the sample and the mount; and (6) the characteristic wavelength of the x-ray tube target besides the obvious differences between the various types of cameras and techniques. Consequently, the intensities of the diffraction lines of one compound cannot be simply compared with those of another for quantitative interpretation. For example, using Cu $K\alpha$ radiation and a Debye-Scherrer camera, the strongest line of fluorite is more than twice as intense as the strongest line of an equal quantity of rutile.

A feel can be developed in practice, however, for the estimation of the proper exposure time. A few practical points, like the following, may be helpful: the denser phase of a compound usually requires shorter exposure time than a less dense phase; compounds containing elements with high scattering factor require relatively short exposure; compounds with imperfect crystal structure usually require longer exposure time; and high x-ray absorbent materials require longer exposure time than usual. In general, the exposure time for a ball mount of 0.1 mm diameter in the 114.6-mm-diameter Debye-Scherrer camera with Cu $K\alpha$ radiation varies between 4 and 14 hr.

7. MEASUREMENT OF X-RAY POWDER PHOTOGRAPHS

According to the nature of information needed, two types of measurements can be taken from the x-ray powder photographs: (1) the position and (2) the intensity of the diffraction lines. The former measurement yields data for the calculation of the lattice parameters of the sample and the latter for the calculation of its structure or for the quantitative determination of its composition. In most investigations, such as identification, both measurements are necessary. In some cases, however, one of the two measurements may be sufficient. For example, in most stress-strain or substitution problems, information concerning the lattice is sufficient, whereas in the study of order-disorder, only intensity measurements are generally needed.

Measurement of the Position of Lines. The position of the diffraction lines is usually measured with reference to the $\theta = 0$ or $90°$ position or to a reference mark on the film. The diffraction lines always have a measurable width and, under normal conditions, are measured at the center, tangential to the curvature. A simple ruler with the appropriate scale can be used for these measurements; however, more accurate measuring devices equipped with vernier plates are recommended; several models are commercially available. The measuring device of Fig. 14 is a commercial model designed for the 114.6-mm-diameter Debye-Scherrer camera; however, it can be used with or without alteration for measuring films taken with other types of cameras. More elaborate measuring instruments are used occasionally in x-ray laboratories in order to assure more precise measurements. For example, a measuring device such as that of Fig. 14 can be attached to a densitometer, and the center of the diffraction lines can be located more reliably. With or without the densitometer, the powder photograph can be blown up with an appropriate projector to aid further in the determination of the center of the lines. These more elaborate measuring instruments can also help to detect asymmetry in the intensity profile of a diffraction line, the cause of which can then be interpreted and the true center of the diffraction line located.

Since the position of the diffraction lines is determined by the Bragg equation (1), the diffraction angle θ and the interplanar spacing d can be calculated from the position of the diffraction lines. It should be kept in mind that, since d is related to $\sin\theta$, the interplanar spacing can be determined more accurately from the back- than from the front-reflection lines. Figure 15 illustrates that a line measured with the same reliability in the front- and another in the back-reflection region give different degrees of reliability in the value of the corresponding interplanar spacings. Consequently, it is easier to obtain good lattice parameters from back-reflection lines than to obtain the same reliability in the lattice parameters derived from front-reflection lines by using better measuring devices. If an x-ray tube with longer-wavelength characteristic radiation is used, the determination of the interplanar spacings can be improved since all the diffraction lines will be shifted to higher θ positions. This also facilitates the visual separation of lines having similar interplanar spacings.

Another way to improve the measurements of the position of the diffraction lines is the use of internal standards. A small quantity of powder of a substance which has well-known lattice parameters is mixed with the sample. The diffraction lines of the sample can then be measured with respect to the position of the lines of the standard. This technique is especially advantageous where the lines are measured with respect to a mark on the film rather than to well-definable $\theta = 0$ or $90°$ positions, or where no adequate film-shrinkage control is available.

FIG. 14. Photograph of an x-ray powder-film measuring device. (*Courtesy of Philips Electronic Instruments.*)

The exposure time of taking a powder photograph can be significantly decreased with the use of intensifying screens placed behind the film. These screens fluoresce in the x-ray beam and augment the darkening of the film. This method has obvious advantages in routine work; however, it should be avoided in precision work and when intensities are measured, since (1) the effective diameter of the camera is decreased by the thickness of the intensifying screen, and (2) the darkening of the film is seriously affected by the homogeneity and other characteristics of the intensifying screen.

Measurement of the Intensity of Lines. While the position of the diffraction lines is a simple function of the interplanar spacings, the intensity is a complex function of the crystal structure and of many other factors. The intensity of a diffraction line can be expressed as

$$I_{hkl} = I_0 C F^2_{hkl} V m L p T A \qquad (9)$$

where I_0 is the intensity of the incident beam; C is a physical constant; F_{hkl} is the structure factor which depends on the scattering power and the spatial arrangement of the atoms in the compound; V is the volume of the sample in the powder mount; m is the multiplicity factor representing the number of symmetrically identical planes which all contribute to the intensity of one diffraction line (Table 3 gives this m for the 11 centric crystal classes); Lp is the Lorentz-polarization factor which depends solely on θ* and can be corrected for easily (Table 4 gives the values of Lp for a set of

* For powder diffraction $Lp = \dfrac{1 + \cos^2 2\theta}{\sin^2 \theta \cos \theta}$.

diffraction angles); T* is the temperature factor, which is a function of temperature, θ, and λ; A is the effect of absorption (absorption corrections for rod and ball mounts are given in Tables 1 and 2).

The relationship between the intensity of the x-ray beam striking the film and the resulting darkening of the film is illustrated in Fig. 16. In the range of the curve, where the darkening of the film increases linearly with increasing log intensity, measurements and estimations of intensities can be made satisfactorily. If not all the diffraction lines of a photograph have intensities within this "linear range," it is advantageous to take two or three pictures with different exposure times rather than to obtain intensities in the nonlinear portion of the curve. If the exposure times of three photographs are properly selected, the intensities of the weak lines in the first film, of the medium lines in the second film, and of the strong lines in the third will fall in the "linear range." A correlation factor between the intensity scales of these

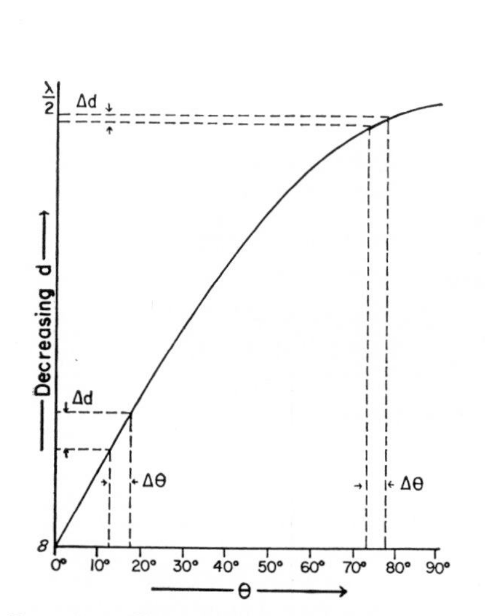

Fig. 15. Illustration of the higher reliability of interplanar-spacing determinations from diffraction lines of higher θ angles.

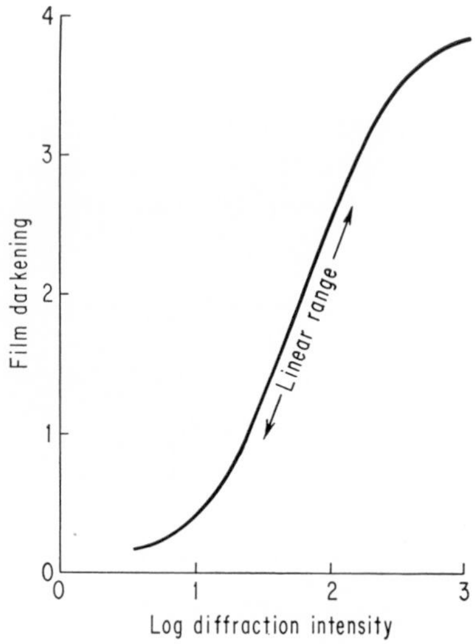

Fig. 16. Illustration of the typical relationship between diffraction intensity and film darkening.

films can then be established from the intensities of lines which are in the "linear range" of two films. A more convenient technique, the so-called multiple-film technique, achieves the same result by placing, for instance, three films in the camera. The first two films will act as absorbers of x-rays, and if the exposure time is chosen properly, the weak lines will be in the "linear range" in the first film, the medium lines in the second, and the strong lines in the third.

In routine x-ray powder photography the intensity of the diffraction lines is usually estimated by eye and is recorded without corrections. There are two types of notations used frequently in intensity estimations: (1) five degrees of intensities are distinguished and called very strong (*vs*), strong (*s*), medium (*m*), weak (*w*), and very weak (*vw*); (2) the darkest line is assigned an intensity of 100 and the others between 1 and 100 according to their intensities with respect to the darkest line. The estimation of intensities can be facilitated by preparing and using a reference film showing the darkening of the film with increasing exposure time.

The intensity of the diffracted beam is proportional to the total darkening of the

* $T = e^{-\frac{B \sin^2 \theta}{\lambda^2}}$ where B is the temperature coefficient, and its usual value at room temperature varies between 1 and 4 for most of the atoms in inorganic compounds.

Table 3. Multiplicity Factors and Coincidences for Powder-diffraction Lines*

Crystal system	Crystal class	Diffraction symmetry	Lattice symmetry	Reflection type	Multiplicity factor	Additional coincidences in d due to symmetry
Triclinic	1, $\bar{1}$	$\bar{1}$	$\bar{1}$	hkl	2	
Monoclinic	2	$\frac{2}{m}$	$\frac{2}{m}$	hkl	4	
	m			$hk0$ (first setting)	2	
	$\frac{2}{m}$			$h0l$ (second setting)	2	
				$h00$, $0k0$, $00l$	2	
Orthorhombic	222	$\frac{2}{m}\frac{2}{m}\frac{2}{m}$	$\frac{2}{m}\frac{2}{m}\frac{2}{m}$	hkl	8	
	$mm2$			$hk0$, $h0l$, $0kl$	4	
	$\frac{2}{m}\frac{2}{m}\frac{2}{m}$			$h00$, $0k0$, $00l$	2	
Tetragonal	4	$\frac{4}{m}$	$\frac{4}{m}\frac{2}{m}\frac{2}{m}$	hkl	8	hkl, khl
	$\bar{4}$			hhl	8	
	$\frac{4}{m}$			$h0l$	8	
				$hk0$	4	$hk0$, $kh0$
				$hh0$	4	
				$h00$	4	
				$00l$	2	
	422	$\frac{4}{m}\frac{2}{m}\frac{2}{m}$		hkl	16	
	$4mm$			hhl	8	
	$\bar{4}2m$			$h0l$	8	
	$\frac{4}{m}\frac{2}{m}\frac{2}{m}$			$hk0$	8	
				$hh0$	4	
				$h00$	4	
				$00l$	2	
Hexagonal	3	$\bar{3}$	$\frac{6}{m}\frac{2}{m}\frac{2}{m}$	hkl†	66	khl, $\overline{hkl}$, $\overline{khl}$
	$\bar{3}$			hhl	6	hhl
				$h0l$	6	$0hl$
				$hk0$	6	$kh0$
				$hh0$	6	
				$h00$	6	
				$00l$	2	
	32	$\bar{3}\frac{2}{m}$		hkl	12	khl
	$3m$			hhl	12	
	$\bar{3}\frac{2}{m}$			$h0l$	6	$0hl$
				$hk0$	12	
				$hh0$	6	
				$h00$	6	
				$00l$	2	
	6			hkl	12	khl

Table 3. Multiplicity Factors and Coincidences for Powder-diffraction Lines* (*Continued*)

Crystal system	Crystal class	Diffraction symmetry	Lattice symmetry	Reflection type	Multiplicity factor	Additional coincidences in d due to symmetry
Hexagonal (*continued*)	$\bar{6}$	$\frac{6}{m}$		hhl	12	
	$\frac{6}{m}$			$h0l$	12	
				$hk0$	6	$kh0$
				$hh0$	6	
				$h00$	6	
				$00l$	2	
	622	$\frac{6}{m}\frac{2}{m}\frac{2}{m}$		hkl	24	
	$6mm$			hhl	12	
	$\bar{6}m2$			$h0l$	12	
	$\frac{6}{m}\frac{2}{m}\frac{2}{m}$			$hk0$	12	
				$hh0$	6	
				$h00$	6	
				$00l$	2	
Isometric	23	$\frac{2}{m}\bar{3}$	$\frac{4}{m}\bar{3}\frac{2}{m}$	hkl	24	khl
	23			hhl	24	
	$\frac{2}{m}\bar{3}$			$hk0$	12	$kh0$
				$hh0$	12	
				hhh	8	
				$h00$	6	
	432	$\frac{4}{m}\bar{3}\frac{2}{m}$		hkl	48	
	$\bar{4}3m$			hhl	24	
	$\frac{4}{m}\bar{3}\frac{2}{m}$			$hk0$	24	
				$hh0$	12	
				hhh	8	
				$h00$	6	

* After Buerger.[27]
† Indexed on hexagonal coordinates.

film across the width of the diffraction line and not necessarily to the maximum darkness of the line. This means that a broader diffraction line with lower darkness at its center may represent more intensive diffraction than a narrow line with higher darkness. The intensities obtained by measuring the maximum darkness of the lines are called "peak intensities" while intensities representing the total darkening of the film for the full width of a diffraction line are referred to as "integrated intensities." Most of the intensity estimations as well as simple photometer measurements give only peak intensities. Most frequently the peak intensity is proportional to the integrated intensity. In some cases, however, the peak intensities are incorrect; for example, when because of the design of the camera, low θ lines are more focused than are high θ lines; or when the crystal has structural imperfections, such as mozaic or lineage structure, stacking disorder, or partial amorphous structure. Consequently, the measurements of integrated intensities are more reliable, and in structural and quantitative work they are highly preferable.

Many intensity-measurement methods have been proposed for the collection of integrated intensities. Some of the popular ones are:

The Photometer-trace Method. This method requires that the darkness (or transmittance) be measured at regular intervals, or that continuous measurements be taken with a scanning photometer along the center line of the powder photograph.

The darkness profile of the film can be plotted in the former case and recorded automatically on a chart in the latter case. One ordinate of the chart will be proportional to the darkness and the other to the distance on the film. From the film-calibration curve the intensity values corresponding to darkness values can be obtained, and using the intensity values for one ordinate (instead of darkness) the area under the peaks, and consequently the integrated intensity, can be calculated or measured with a planimeter.[22]

The Density-wedge Method. This method is similar to the above, in general, except that the intensity ordinate of the profile is not obtained from photometer measurements, but from the comparison of darkness with that of a density wedge. The density wedge is prepared on the same kind of film as the one used for the powder photography with a set of exposures of regularly increased exposure time. Thus the density wedge gives darkness directly in terms of intensity. This method calls for a special photometer which has two identical light paths, one for the powder photograph and one for the density wedge, and two identical photocells to identify equivalent darkness on the two films.[23]

Table 4. *Lp* Corrections for Powder Intensities[28]

sin θ	Lp
0	∞
0.025	3,197
0.050	797.0
0.075	352.6
0.100	197.0
0.125	125.0
0.150	85.95
0.20	47.11
0.25	29.17
0.30	19.48
0.35	13.68
0.40	9.973
0.45	7.487
0.50	5.774
0.55	4.576
0.60	3.744
0.65	3.189
0.70	2.869
0.75	2.730
0.80	2.808
0.85	3.148
0.90	3.921
0.95	5.848
1.00	∞

The Dawton Method. If a contact print of the powder photograph is made on the same kind of film with properly controlled procedures, the total light transmission of the print will be proportional to the integrated intensity. This is so because the darkening of the film is a function of the log of exposure time (i.e., the intensity) when the powder photograph is made and again when the print is made; and because of the log of log relationship, the darkening of the print will be a function of the true intensity. The photometer, in this method, is equipped with a large enough aperture to cover the full width of the widest diffraction line of a given powder photograph. The light transmission of the diffraction lines is measured with this photometer, and the readings will give integrated intensity directly.[24]

The Plateau Method. In this method the Debye-Scherrer camera is oscillated around the axis of the cylinder of the camera during the exposure. The oscillation angle is selected so that a reasonably wide section of the center of the diffraction lines in the photograph will have a plateau of equal darkness. The darkness of the plateau will be a function of the sum of intensities at all points across a single diffraction line; thus, the darkness of the plateau is proportional to integrated and not to peak intensity.

The darkness of the plateau of the diffraction lines can be measured with a photometer, and with the use of the film-calibration curve this can be converted into relative integrated intensities directly. The need for the film-calibration curve can be avoided by using the density-wedge technique and an appropriate densitometer.

REFERENCES CITED

1. P. Debye and P. Scherrer, *Nachr. Kgl. Ges. Wiss. Göttingen, Math-Physik. Kl.*, 1 (1916).
2. A. W. Hull, *Phys. Rev.*, (2)**9**:84 (1917).
3. M. J. Buerger, *Am. Mineralogist*, **21**:11 (1936).
4. G. Switzer, J. M. Axelrud, M. L. Lindberg, and E. S. Larsen, *U.S. Geol. Surv. Circ. 29* (1948).
5. *Natl. Bur. Std., Appl. Math. Ser. 10* (1950).
6. H. J. Garrett and R. E. Brocklehurst, *USAF, WADC Tech. Rept. 57-381* (1958).
7. H. Seemann, *Ann. Physik*, **59**:455 (1919).
8. H. Bohlin, *Ann. Physik*, **61**:421 (1920).
9. A. F. Westgren, *Trans. AIME*, **93**:13 (1931).
10. A. Guinier, *Compt. Rend. (Paris)*, **204**:1115 (1937).
11. G. W. Brindley and F. W. Spiers, *Proc. Phys. Soc. (London)*, **50**:757 (1934).
12. O. Kratky, *Z. Krist.*, **72**:529 (1930).
13. W. L. Fink and D. W. Smith, Symposium on Radiography and X-ray Diffraction Methods, *ASTM*, Philadelphia, Pa., p. 200, 1937.
14. O. Kratky, *Z. Krist.*, **76**:261 (1931).
15. F. G. Chesley, *Rev. Sci. Instr.*, **18**:422 (1947).
16. R. S. Bear, *J. Am. Chem. Soc.*, **66**:1297 (1944).
17. A. Guinier and G. Fournet, *Compt. Rend. (Paris)*, **226**:656 (1948).
18. L. L. Hawes, *Acta Cryst.*, **12**:443 (1959).
19. R. B. Jacobs, *Phys. Rev.*, **54**:325 (1938).
20. A. W. Lawson and N. A. Riley, *Rev. Sci. Instr.*, **20**:763 (1949).
21. *Acta Cryst.*, **9**:520 (1956).
22. J. C. M. Brentano, *Opt. Soc. Am.*, **35**:382 (1945).
23. B. Wheeler Robinson, *J. Sci. Instr.*, **10**:233 (1933).
24. Ralph H. V. M. Dawton, *Proc. Phys. Soc. (London)*, **50**:919 (1938).
25. A. J. Bradley, *Proc. Phys. Soc. (London)*, **47**:879 (1935).
26. H. T. Evans, Jr., and Miriam G. Ekstein, Tables of Absorption Factors for Spherical Crystals, *Acta Cryst.*, **5**:540 (1952).
27. *Crystal-structure Analysis*, modified after M. J. Buerger, p. 188, John Wiley & Sons, Inc., New York, 1960.
28. *Internationale Tabellen zur Bestimmung von Kristallstrukturen*, vol. II, p. 568, Gebrüder Borntraeger, Berlin-Nicolasse, 1935.

GENERAL REFERENCES

Azaroff, L. V., and M. J. Buerger: *The Powder Method*, McGraw-Hill Book Company, New York, 1958.
Barrett, C. S.: *Structure of Metals*, 2d ed., McGraw-Hill Book Company, New York, 1952.
Buerger, M. J.: *X-ray Crystallography*, John Wiley & Sons, Inc., New York, 1942.
Bunn, C. W.: *Chemical Crystallography*, Clarendon Press, Oxford, 1945.
Cullity, B. D.: *Elements of X-ray Diffraction*, Addison-Wesley Publishing Company, Inc., Reading, Mass., 1956.
Guinier, A.: *X-ray Crystallographic Technology* (English translation by T. L. Tippell), Hilger and Watts, London, 1952.
Henry, N. F. M., H. Lipson, and W. A. Wooster: *The Interpretation of X-ray Diffraction Photographs*, Macmillan & Co., Ltd., London, 1951.
International Tables for X-ray Crystallography, Kynoch Press, Birmingham, England, vol. I, 1952; vol. II, 1959; vol. III, 1962.
Klug, H. P., and L. E. Alexander: *X-ray Diffraction Procedures*, John Wiley & Sons, Inc., New York, 1954.
Peiser, H. S., H. P. Rooksby, and A. J. C. Wilson: *X-ray Diffraction by Polycrystalline Materials*, Institute of Physics, London; Chapman & Hall, Ltd., London; and Reinhold Publishing Corporation, New York, 1955.
Sproull, W. T.: *X-rays in Practice*, McGraw-Hill Book Company, New York, 1946.
Taylor, A.: *X-ray Metallography*, John Wiley & Sons, Inc., New York, 1961.
Wilson, A. J. C.: *X-ray Optics*, Methuen & Co., Ltd., London, 1949.

Chapter 9

DIFFRACTOMETER TECHNIQUES

L. F. Vassamillet

Mellon Institute

and

H. W. King

Imperial College of Science and Technology

1. DIFFRACTOMETER DESIGN

The x-ray diffractometer* is a mechanical device for obtaining x-ray intensities as a function of the angle between the incident and the diffracted beams. Originally used by the Braggs[1] for the measurement of reflections from single crystals, it is most frequently used now to measure reflections from powder samples (diffractometry) or x-ray fluorescence (spectroscopy). The latter is covered in Part 4 of this handbook. Furthermore the relative positions of the x-ray source, sample, and receiver usually satisfy a modified Seeman-Bohlin parafocusing arrangement[2] so as to obtain maximum intensities. The major components are the principal protractor (or main gear), the 2θ-angle bisecting mechanism, the slit system (optics), the sample holder, and the detector (counter tube). Associated with the detector, which may be a Geiger-Müller, proportional, or scintillation counter, are the power supplies, preamplifiers, amplifier and pulse shaper, scaling circuit, counting-rate meter, recorder, and/or printer. There are several commercial diffractometers on the market which possess a variety of special accessories such as monochromators, limit switches, reversing switches, step-scanning drives, and sample spinners. The primary differences among the several commercial instruments relate to the manner in which the angular position of the sample (θ) is obtained from the angular position of the detector (2θ). Under Sec. 2 are listed the pertinent differences among the various makes.

In Fig. 1 are shown the essential features of the parafocusing arrangement as they apply to the diffractometer. The flat sample is tangent to the focusing circle at S. The source-to-sample distance FS and sample-to-detector distance SD are the same and equal R, the radius of the goniometer arc. The radius of the focusing circle depends on θ according to the relation

$$r = R/(2 \sin \theta) \tag{1}$$

* The original description for such an instrument was "x-ray spectrometer." In August, 1952, the Committee on Equipment of the International Union for Crystallography decided that this unnatural designation should be replaced by the distinctive term "x-ray diffractometer."

The scanning range of the diffractometer is shown as ψ, and may be negative as well as positive. For most diffractometers the upper limit of ψ is 165°. For accurate lattice-parameter work the use of negative values of ψ permits a direct measurement of 4θ and the accurate determination of 0° 2θ.[3]

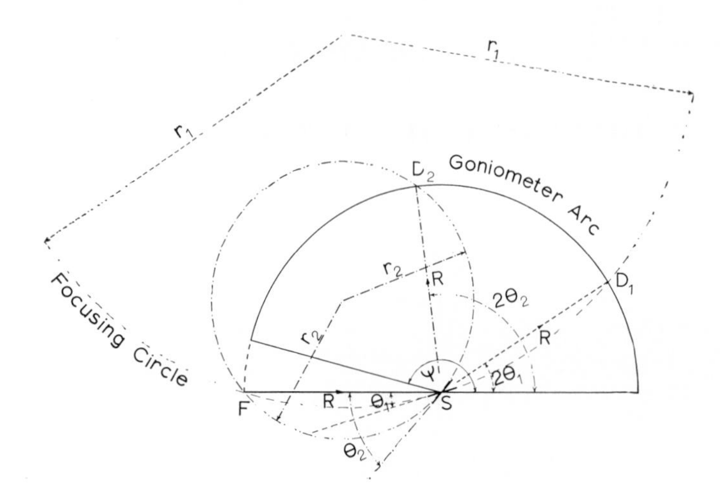

FIG. 1. Parafocusing arrangement of the x-ray diffractometer.

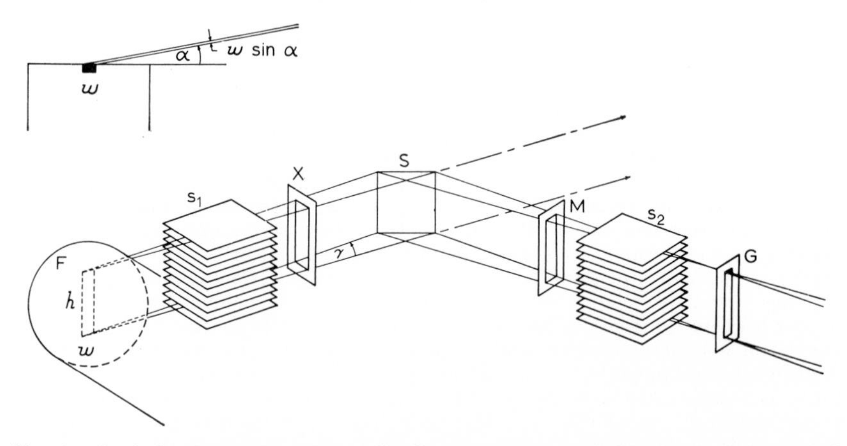

FIG. 2. Optical arrangement using a "line" x-ray source and Soller slits to limit vertical divergence. (*Reprinted with permission from H. Klug and L. Alexander, X-ray Diffraction Procedures, John Wiley & Sons, Inc., New York,* 1954.)

The x-ray optics (Fig. 2) consist of the focal line F, divergence slit X, sample S, receiving slit G, antiscatter slit M, and Soller slits S_1 and S_2. The effective width of the focal line is determined by its true width ω and the takeoff angle α according to the relation $\omega_{\text{eff}} = \omega \sin \alpha$. The angular width of the source as seen by the detector in degrees 2θ is

$$\Delta 2\theta = 180\omega_{\text{eff}}/\pi r = 180\omega_{\sin\,\alpha}/\pi r \tag{2}$$

Table 1. Characteristics of Counter Tubes

Characteristic \ Counter	Geiger-Müller	Proportional	Scintillation
Linearity with counting rate; resolving time τ	Poor; $\tau \sim 200$ μsec. Corrections needed for counting rates above 100 counts/sec	Good: $\tau \sim 0.2$ μsec. Counting rate limited by scaler: 1% error at 10,000 counts/sec	Good; $\tau \sim \frac{1}{2}$ μsec. Counting rate limited by scaler: 1% error at 10,000 counts/sec
Quantum-counting efficiency	Dependent on filler gas, pressure of gas, path length, window; strongly wavelength-dependent		Very good over wide-wavelength region
Proportionality	No relationship between pulse amplitude and wavelength	Linear dependence over wavelengths used in diffraction. However, pulses of single wavelength produce distribution of pulse amplitudes. Energy resolution; width of distribution/energy at peak amplitude. Typical valves (Cu $K\alpha$ radiation): Xe-proportional counter, 20%; scintillation counter, 50%	
Plateau	Determined by voltage necessary to trigger discharge	Determined by voltage necessary to produce pulse height greater than discrimination level of counting circuits	
Non-x-ray background	Counter-tube noise negligible. Cosmic background $\sim$ 1 count/sec		Counter-tube noise high. Interferes with measurement of long-wavelength radiation
Escape peak	Not present	Presence depends on absorption edges of atoms in gas or crystal. Size of escape peak depends on geometry, gas pressure of detector	
Stability Reproducibility Lifetime	Good Good Unlimited	As good as GM. Some designs show temperature dependence. Presence of organic quench limits lifetime to $\sim 10^9$ counts	Good if crystal not damaged, crystal is hydroscopic. Unlimited

beam according to the relation

$$A = \gamma R/2 \sin \theta$$

The considerable advances in electronics have resulted in a wide range of possible detectors and read-out systems (Fig. 4). We shall limit ourselves to the most common arrangements. The primary radiation detectors are of two types: the counter tube,[4,5] which is a gas-filled tube with a central electrode or electrodes, and the scintillation counter.[6] See Chap. 3 for a complete discussion of x-ray counters. Sensitivity vs. wavelength for several typical detectors is shown in Fig. 5. The important characteristics of the tube are linearity with counting rate, quantum-counting efficiency, proportionality, plateau, non-x-ray background, escape peak, stability, reproducibility, and lifetime. These are summarized in Table 1. The most important characteristic of the associated circuitry is the overall stability and linearity of amplification; i.e., the amplified pulses from a given monochromatic signal must have identical sizes and shapes, and the output pulse height must be strictly proportional to the input pulse height. The amplifier must be nonoverloading for very large pulses. Other common specifications are the reproducibility of the high-voltage setting (~0.03 per cent), its stability (~0.005 per cent for 1 percent variation of input voltage), and temperature independence (~0.005 per cent variation/10° F). Another measure of stability is the voltage change on warm-up, and this value can be held to a few hundredths of a per cent over the first ½ hr. Subsequent drift will then depend on line-voltage drift. The upper limit of the counting rate will be determined as much by the counting circuitry as by the dead time of the detector tube. Usually nonlinearity in the amplifier, scaler, or rate meter due to coincidence losses will be negligible for counting rates below 10,000 cps. However, the scaler or rate meter saturates at counting rates in the range of 1 to 5×10^5 cps. This is no limitation; in diffraction work peak intensities rarely exceed a few thousand counts per second.

2. REPRESENTATIVE COMMERCIAL INSTRUMENTS

Examples of some commercial diffractometers are shown in Figs. 6 through 11, and the basic specifications of these instruments are listed in Table 2. All diffractometers have one feature in common, namely, they all make use of a worm-gear mechanism to drive the 2θ scan, though not all of them use full-throated gears to reduce the wear on the gear teeth. In most instruments, the angular position of the detector is read off an odometer located on the main drive shaft. Any backlash in the worm gear will thus result in an error in the measured value of 2θ. In practice the backlash is removed by spring loading the gear drive. Most manufacturers claim an accuracy of better than 0.01° for an individual measurement of 2θ, and to accomplish this the gears have to be hobbed to a precision of 0.002 to 0.003°. The accuracy of measurement of the finished diffractometer is checked by optical means.[7] Many manufacturers are willing at an additional cost to supply a calibration certificate for the 2θ scale, should this be required for very high precision work.

Most of the instruments in Table 2 have their detectors set to scan in a horizontal plane, which means that the weight of the detector arm, counter tubes, or any attachments built around the sample holder will not give rise to an error in the measurement of 2θ. This arrangement also provides adequate space around the sample for building high- or low-temperature attachments, etc. Such a horizontal diffractometer will require a horizontal x-ray tube (with a vertical line focus) so that only limited use can be made of the other windows. In practice, it is often found that a horizontal x-ray tube is used solely for the purpose of supplying a single horizontal diffractometer. The vertical Philips/Norelco diffractometer, on the other hand, is designed specifically to scan in a vertical plane and to be used with a four-window x-ray tube so that the remaining three windows may be used simultaneously if required. In the Picker and Siemens diffractometers, the x-ray tube is supported by the diffractometer, and scanning can be performed in either a vertical or horizontal plane, ad lib. Diffractometers which scan in a vertical plane do have the disadvantage, however, that the moment of force exerted by the weight of the detector (plus that of any accessories

Fig. 6. General Electric spectrogoniometer. (*Courtesy of General Electric Co., U.S.A.*)

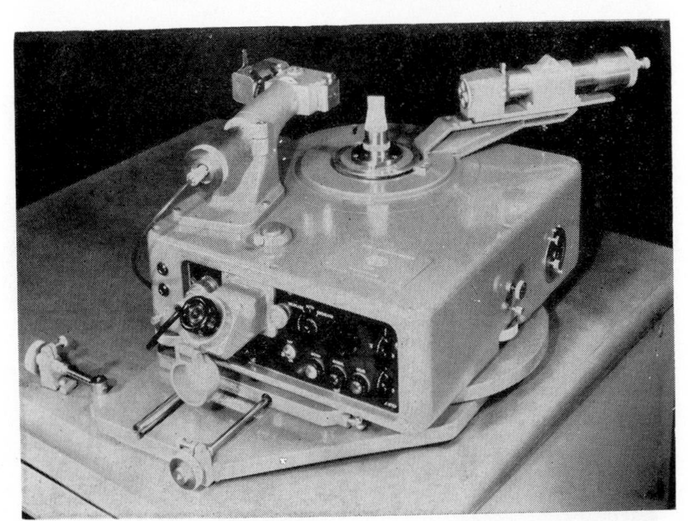

Fig. 7. Hilger and Watts diffractometer. (*Courtesy of Hilger and Watts, Ltd., England.*)

mounted on the detector arm) will tend to either oppose or reinforce the spring loading of the worm gear. Thus a significant error may result in the value of 2θ read off an odometer if the moment of force of the detector is of the same order of magnitude as that of the strength of the spring loading. Vertical diffractometers do have the advantage that they can be modified to have a $\theta - \theta$ scan, in which the x-ray tube and the detector move in opposition while the specimen stays constant and horizontal. This technique enables diffraction patterns to be obtained from liquid specimens.

The maximum angle ψ through which the detector can scan is determined primarily by the position and design of the x-ray source. All instruments can scan to at least

a

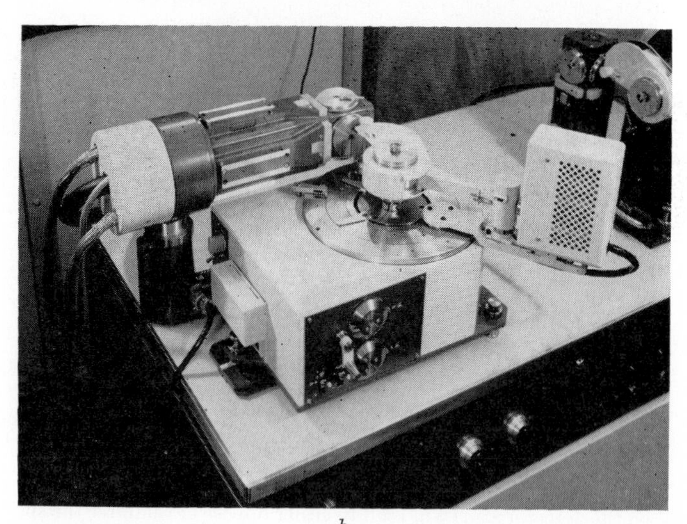

b

FIG. 8. Philips/Norelco (*a*) vertical and (*b*) horizontal diffractometers. (*Courtesy of N. V. Philips, Netherlands.*)

$+160°$ 2θ, but the range on the negative side of the direct beam when using the manufacturers specified x-ray tube varies from -10 to $-100°$. Larger negative angles can be achieved if the size of the x-ray tube is diminished; e.g., negative angles of the order of $-155°$ can be obtained by using the Siemens diffractometer in conjunction with the Hilger Micro-focus x-ray tube.[8]

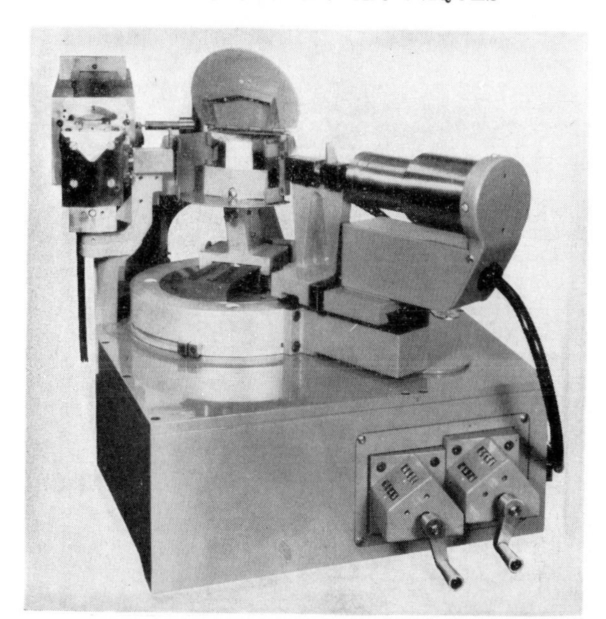

FIG. 9. Picker biplane diffractometer. (*Courtesy of Picker X-ray Corporation.*)

FIG. 10. Siemens Type F diffractometer. (*Courtesy of Siemens and Halske A. E., West Germany.*)

Perhaps the greatest difference between commercial diffractometers lies in the variety of methods used to rotate the sample at half the angular speed of the detector, i.e., the so-called $2\theta{:}\theta$ drive. The Hilger, horizontal Philips, Picker, and Wooster instruments use two equal-size gear wheels mounted concentrically one above the other and linked by a differential or spur mechanism. This drive has the advantage that the $2\theta{:}\theta$ coupling can be easily uncoupled and the sample rotated independently of the detector—the so-called ω drive which has its use in single-crystal investigations. This

Table 2. Basic Specifications of Some Commercial Diffractometers*

Specification	AEI Raymax	Berthold	General Electric	Hilger & Watts	Philips/Norelco	Picker	Siemens	Wooster
Diffractometer plane	Horizontal	Horizontal	Horizontal	Horizontal	Vertical or horizontal	Horizontal or vertical	Horizontal or vertical	Horizontal
Diffractometer radius	15.2 cm	25 cm	14.6 cm	18 to 20 cm	17 cm	5.73 cm	17.25 cm or 18.25 cm	8 to 15 cm
Scanning range, °2θ	−1 to +138° with radiation screens −100 to +140° without radiation screens	−100 to +165°	−10 to +165°	−135 to +165°; special attachment to +172°	Vertical: −38 to +165° Horizontal: −100 to +165°	−55 to +165°; with change in tube stand position −90° angle attainable	−100° to +162°, left or right side of tube. −30° to +150° with vertical tube	−90° to +170°
Main drive mechanism and gear contact	Worm gear	Worm gear	Worm gear; partially throated	Worm gear; partially throated	Worm gear; rectangular teeth	Worm gear; partially throated	Worm gear, line contact	Worm gear; partially throated
Backlash protection	Spring loading		Spring loading	Spring loading	Spring loading	Spring loading	Spring loading	Spring loading
$2\theta:\theta$ mechanism	Spur gearing	Ring and planetary gears	Lever arm and slide	Gear train and worm gear	Vertical: Gear train Horizontal: Spur gear	Differential bisector	Ring gear and planetary gears	Electronic stepping motors
Independence of 2θ and ω drives	Yes	No	No	Yes	Vertical: No Horizontal: Yes	Yes	No	Yes
Determination of counter position on 2θ scale	Odometer and vernier drum	Vernier scale	Odometer and vernier drum	Odometer and vernier drum	Odometer and vernier drum	Odometer and vernier drum	Odometer and vernier drum	Odometer and vernier drum
Factory calibration of 2θ scale	Quality control on gears	Not quoted	Quality control on gears	Calibrated and checked by optical polygons	Optically by means of polygons. Calibration service now available. Standard silicon specimen supplied	Quality control on gears. Use of optical polygons on occasional units	Quality control check on $2\theta:\theta$ settings by optical means	Checked by optical means
Accuracy of individual measurement of 2θ	0.01°	0.016°	0.01°	0.01°	0.0025°	±005°	±0.01°	0.01°
and precision of gears	...	...	0.001° − 0.002°	0.002°	Not quoted	Better than 0.001°	Not quoted	
Location of Soller slits between:								
Source-sample	Yes	...	Yes	Yes	Yes	Yes	No	Yes
Sample-detector	Yes	...	Yes	Yes	Yes	Yes	Yes	Yes
Location of filters	...	...	Sample-detector	Sample-detector	Sample-detector or source-sample	Source-sample or sample-detector	Sample-detector	Source-sample or sample-detector
Alignment	Special tools	...	Special tools; alignment manual	Removable telescope pentagonal prism, and special fitment	Special tools—optional Instructions being revised	Special tools and technique, alignment manual	Special tools, technique, alignment manual	Left to operator's judgment
Specimen surface position	Factory adjustment	Adjusting plate	Factory adjustment	Factory adjustment	Factory adjustment	Adjustable by operator	Factory adjustment	Factory adjustment

* Based on information supplied by the manufacturers.

coupling also means that any error in $2\theta:\theta$ following is not accumulative with increasing 2θ but is repeated over every cycle of $2°$ 2θ. The General Electric diffractometer makes use of a gearless lever arm bisecting mechanism with very precise $2\theta:\theta$ following. Any error arising from a minor mismatching of the arms will be progressively increased with increasing 2θ. Any errors arising from backlash or lack of precision in the gear ring and planet gears of the Berthold and Siemens, or in the matched gear train used in the vertical Philips/Norelco, will be spread out over an intermediate range of 2θ.

The precise location of the sample surface with respect to the axis of the diffractometer is an important source of error in the measured value of 2θ. With the exception of the Berthold and Picker instruments, the alignment of the sample surface is set by the manufacturer of the diffractometer and the operator can make no adjustments apart from the possible use of shims, which in any case can move the surface in only one direction (toward a position outside the focusing circle in Fig. 1).

The use of synchronous motors is standard practice for all drives for worm gears and strip-chart recorders. To ensure that the graduations on the chart coincide with selected fractional values of 2θ, most manufacturers specify sequential starting methods for the 2θ scan and the recorder. An additional pen is also provided in the

FIG. 11. Wooster diffractometer. (*Courtesy of Crystal Structures, Ltd., England.*)

strip-chart recorder so that a mark can be printed every integral value of 2θ, to check shrinkage or expansion of the chart subsequent to the printing of the graduations.

Commercial diffractometers also possess a variety of special accessories to assist in the measurement of the position or intensity of a diffraction profile. As may be seen from the list in Table 3, some of these features are supplied as standard equipment and others as optional extras, depending on the instrument. Most diffractometers can handle block specimens in addition to powders and have additional attachments for spinning a powder sample in its own plane to increase the intensity of the diffracted beam by bringing more particles into positions to diffract rays in the focusing plane.

Limit switches to prevent the detector from colliding with the divergent slit housing or the x-ray tube are standard equipment. However, in many instruments these limit switches are adjustable so that the 2θ scan can be arrested at any preselected value of 2θ. A further development is that the direction of scan can be reversed on tripping a limit switch so that the detector can be set to scan in an oscillatory manner over a selected range of 2θ.

When investigating very weak profiles, or when the shape of the profile is required, it is convenient to be able to scan in a stepwise manner across the profile and to note the impulse count after a predetermined interval of time spent at each angular position. The facility to step-scan automatically is either built into the instrument or is available as an optional attachment.

Table 3. Special Facilities of Some Commercial Diffractometers

Facility	AEI Raymax	Berthold	General Electric	Hilger & Watts	Philips/ Norelco	Picker	Siemens	Wooster
Block samples........	Up to 0.5″	Yes	Yes	Optional—extra	Optional—extra	Yes	Not thicker than 1 in.	Yes
Sample spinner.......	Yes	....	Yes. Also for wire samples	Optional—extra	Optional—extra	No	Optional extra. Also sample oscillator ($\pm 1°$)	Yes
Step scanning.........	No	....	Optional—extra	Standard	Standard	Optional—extra	Mechanical and counter controlled automatic. Both extra attachments	Yes
Oscillatory scanning...	No	....	Optional—extra	Optional	Standard	Standard	No	Yes
Print-out facilities:								
Preset time.........	No	Yes	Yes	Yes	Yes	Yes	Yes	Yes
Preset counts.......	No	Yes	Yes	Yes	Yes	Yes	Yes	Yes
Running index......	No	....	Yes	No	Yes	No	Yes	No
Accumulated time..	No	....	Yes	No	Yes (extra)	No	Yes. Accumulated counts and time simultaneously	Yes (extra)
Monochromators:.....	No	....		No	Standard extra less crystals	Standard extra	Standard extra	Standard extra
Between source and specimen.....	....	....	Yes	....	No	Yes	Yes	Yes
Between specimen and counter......	....	....	Yes	....	Yes	Yes	Yes	No

Whenever data are collected in a time-consuming manner such as in step scanning, which also involves the rapid reading of several impulse-counting dials, the operation becomes tedious and susceptible to operator error. Both these drawbacks can be eliminated by using an automatic printer which prints out the values on the impulse-counting scales after a preset time, or conversely the value on the time clock after a preset number of counts. Such printers are available as standard extras for most diffractometers (see Table 3), and in the case of the General Electric XRD 6 and the Siemens they will also print out a sequence number and the accumulated time or counts.

Facilities to increase the peak-to-background ratio by pulse-height discrimination, in conjunction with a scintillation or proportional counter, are now regarded almost as standard items for commercial diffractometers. Curved-crystal monochromators to

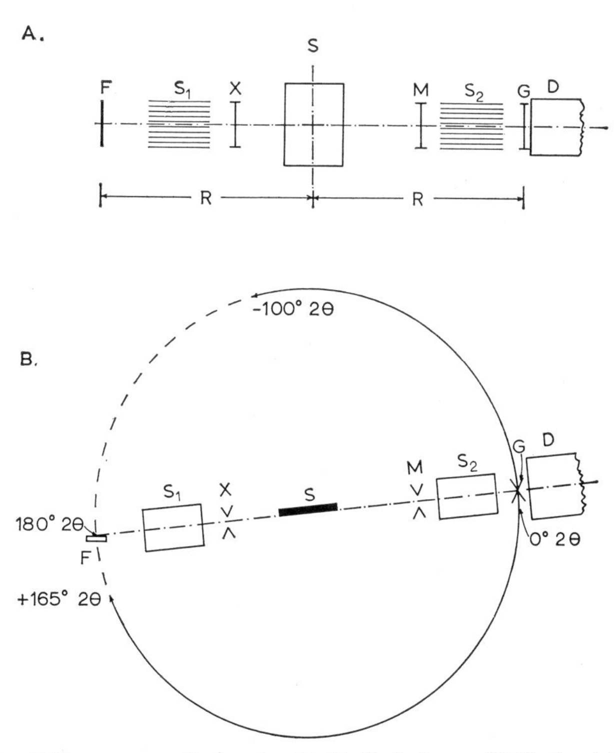

FIG. 12. Diffractometer alignment. (*a*) Vertical plane. (*b*) Horizontal plane.

eliminate the $K\alpha_2$ and $K\beta$ components of the characteristic radiation, in addition to lowering the intensity of the background, are available with most instruments. The locations of these monochromators with respect to source, sample, and detector are given in Table 3.

3. PRINCIPLES OF ALIGNMENT

To obtain a diffracted beam at the correct angular reading, and with the maximum possible intensity and resolution, the alignment of the diffractometer must fulfill the following conditions. (1) The central ray of the x-ray beam must pass through the half-height positions of all collimating and Soller slits (Fig. 12*a*) and lie in the same plane as that defined by the locus of points of the mid-point of the receiving slit G as it scans through $\pm 180°\ 2\theta$. (2) The central ray of the beam must originate from the 180° 2θ point of the diffractometer circle and, with the detector set at 0° 2θ, just graze the sample surface and pass through the center of all slits and through the 0° 2θ

point of the diffractometer circle (Fig. 12*b*). (3) The sample surface must coincide with its axis of rotation, which in turn must coincide with the axis of the diffractometer. Fortunately, not all these adjustments have to be made by the operator. In most commercial instruments the slits are aligned in both vertical and horizontal directions with respect to the diffractometer axis and, except for the Berthold and Picker, the sample reference surface is also aligned to conform with condition 3 above. Thus in general the process of aligning the diffractometer is reduced to a number of adjustments of the instrument with respect to the x-ray tube. Most manufacturers specify an alignment procedure to be used in conjunction with special jigs or templates. The following is a general procedure which is applicable to all instruments, but for convenience the various movements are described in terms of a horizontal instrument. It is important to note that since several of the adjustments require an uncollimated beam with the detector arm set at 0° 2θ the detector should be protected from damage by an excess of radiation with a thin sheet of lead, copper, etc.

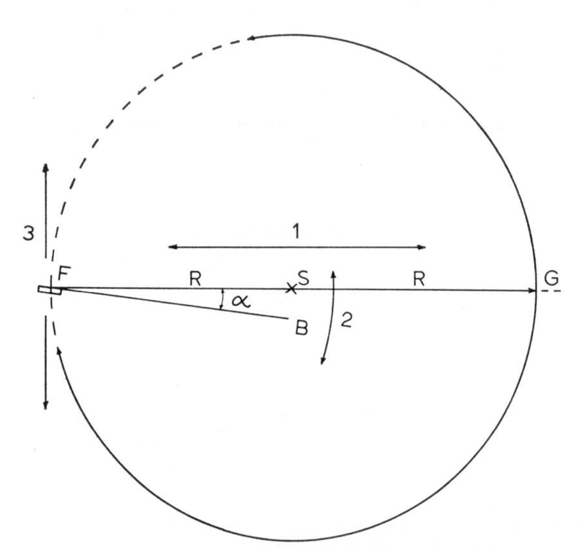

FIG. 13. Diffractometer alignment, adjustment directions.

1. The x-ray tube is adjusted in its mounting to ensure that the central ray emerging from the relevant window is exactly horizontal (i.e., in the plane of the focusing circle).

2. The diffractometer height is adjusted so that the collimating system is the same height as the window of the tube.

3. The instrument is accurately leveled in directions both perpendicular and parallel to the x-ray beam so that the central ray conforms to condition 1. This adjustment may be checked by removing the Soller slit S_1 and comparing the height of the midpoint of the divergent slit X with the height of the mid-point of its image cast on a fluorescent screen placed in front of the receiving slit G.

4. Where an adjustment is provided (see Table 2) the value of the radius R of the diffractometer is adjusted by moving the receiving slit along the detector arm so that, when the divergent slit assembly is snug against the x-ray tube, the distance from source to sample is equal to that from sample to receiving slit. If the position of the receiving slit, i.e., the radius R, is fixed (see Table 2), the entire diffractometer must be moved along the direction 1 in Fig. 13 until the distance FS is equal to SG. This setting is difficult to accomplish in practice without the use of special templates.

5. The diffractometer is rotated, preferably about the point F, to obtain the required takeoff angle α, which may be measured in terms of a displacement SB of the axis of

the diffractometer, i.e., from Fig. 13,

$$SB = \alpha R \tag{4}$$

For the usual takeoff angle of 6° and using a diffractometer of radius 17 cm, SB is equal to 0.89 cm. In practice a fluorescent card with two vertical lines ruled a distance SB apart may be placed at the center of the instrument with one line coincident with the optical axis. With the divergent slit X and the Soller slit S_1 removed, the diffractometer may then be rotated along the direction 2 in Fig. 13 until the diffuse edge of the beam caused by the shadow of the target moves from S to B as measured on the card.

6. The entire diffractometer, or if not the point F, is translated along the direction 3 in Fig. 13, i.e., along the tangent to the diffractometer circle at F, until maximum intensity is obtained using the finest divergent slit. If in this adjustment only the point F moves, the beam will tend to shift off the optical axis of the diffractometer requiring a rotation about its own axis (S) until maximum intensity is obtained through the finest receiving slit set at 0° 2θ, i.e., to satisfy the condition of Fig. 12*b*.

7. The static $2\theta{:}\theta$ setting is aligned by disengaging the θ drive and rotating the sample holder until it exactly bisects the uncollimated beam when the detector is set at 0° 2θ. Most manufacturers provide a special collimating slit which replaces the specimen holder and facilitates precise alignment of the $2\theta{:}\theta$ setting. If the sample surface position is adjustable, it too must be aligned to bisect the uncollimated x-ray beam when the detector is set at 0° 2θ.

The above procedure will have to be repeated several times to obtain optimum intensity and resolution. The factors which have the greatest effect on the intensity of the diffracted beam are the takeoff angle α, the horizontal alignment of the Soller slits, and the vertical alignment of the collimating slits. If the intensity is found to be below expectation, steps 1, 2, 3, 5, and 6 should be repeated carefully. The resolving power of the instrument is a direct function of the fineness of the focusing achieved in steps 4 and 7. A common test for the degree of resolution is to determine the lowest 2θ angle at which the $K\alpha_1$ and $K\alpha_2$ peaks can be separated. Using a horizontal divergence angle of 1°, a 6° takeoff angle, and a receiving slit of about 0.02°, the α_1 and α_2 peaks for copper radiation will be resolved between 30 and 35° 2θ for a well-aligned instrument. This check should preferably be performed by step scanning. If continuous scanning must be used, a scanning speed of $\frac{1}{8}$°/min with an electronic time constant (RC) of 4 to 5 sec is recommended.

The correct angular readings for 2θ are not easily established. The factors which strongly influence the angular position of the diffracted beam are discussed in Sec. 4. As summarized in Eq. (9) the critical alignment errors are an error ΔF in the position of the focal spot (movement 3 in Fig. 13) and an error ΔS in the position of the sample surface with respect to the diffractometer axis. As mentioned earlier, the latter adjustment is usually fixed by the manufacturer, and so the most important alignment procedure is step 6. For example, if it is required to measure 2θ to 0.01° using a diffractometer of radius R = 17 cm, ΔF must be less than 0.03 mm.[34] It is thus a great advantage to have some form of mechanical traverse to accomplish step 6 with precision. A direct check on the alignment of F is possible only for the Picker and Siemens diffractometers. All other manufacturers recommend that the 2θ readings be checked against the theoretical values for the Bragg reflections of a standard crystalline powder, usually quartz. However, as discussed in Sec. 4 to follow, most of the errors affecting the angular position of a diffraction profile vary systematically with 2θ and in general they tend to become smaller as 2θ tends to 180°. Hence, if the instrument is aligned by matching low-angle reflections with the theoretical values, the high-angle reflections may be in error and vice versa. The accuracy of an individual measurement of 2θ using this method of calibration is thus of the order of 0.05°, though the reproducibility of the measurement may be better than 0.005°.

In the Picker and Siemens instruments, the x-ray tube is clamped directly to the diffractometer in such a manner that it is free to rotate about an axis which passes along the focal line. This means that the takeoff angle α can be varied without disturbing the alignment of the focal line. The adjustment of F (step 6) can thus be accomplished with precision by moving the tube along the direction 3 in Fig. 13 until the measured angular position of a sharp reflection is independent of the takeoff angle. The Siemens instrument has the facility to scan on both sides of the direct beam. The sample surface is rotated through 180° when scanning on the negative side, and so any errors due to a misalignment of ΔS will be in the same direction on both sides of the beam. Alignment of the focal line is accomplished to within the error of the reproducibility of 2θ (0.005°[3]) by moving the diffractometer along the direction 3 in Fig. 13 until peaks measured on either side of the beam are superimposed on a chart recording.

4. FACTORS INFLUENCING THE POSITIONS AND PROFILES OF DIFFRACTION MAXIMA

The various factors which affect the shape, intensity, or angular position of diffraction maxima when using the diffractometer method may be conveniently grouped as follows:

1. Physical effects
   a. Wavelength
   b. Dispersion, Lorentz, and polarization
   c. Filters and monochromators
   d. Refraction
2. Geometrical effects
   a. Flat specimen and horizontal divergence
   b. Axial (or vertical) divergence
   c. Absorption
   d. Source profile and width
   e. Detector slit width
3. Instrumental effects
   a. Calibration of principal protractor
   b. Accuracy in $2\theta:\theta$ for all values of θ
   c. Backlash
4. Alignment effects
   a. Focal-spot displacement
   b. Specimen surface not coincident with diffractometer axis
   c. X-ray beam not in diffractometer plane
   d. $\theta \neq 0$ when $2\theta = 0$
   e. °0 2θ not on beam path
5. Measurement effects
   a. Time constant of electronic circuits
   b. Peak position vs. center of gravity
   c. Counting statistics
   d. Backlash

Physical Effects. Errors in the conversion of wavelengths from kX to angstrom units have been discussed by Lonsdale,[9] who has listed the "characteristic" wavelengths for various target materials. These so-called characteristic radiations are in fact distributed asymmetrically over a small band of wavelengths so that the peak value of the spectral distribution may differ significantly from its center of gravity (centroid) or any other weighted mean of the distribution,[10] causing a problem as to which value of the wavelength should be used in the Bragg equation. The problem may be overcome by using wavelengths determined from peak values when Bragg reflections are measured using peak position and centroid values of wavelength for Bragg angles measured from the centroid of diffraction profiles, etc., for the various methods of measuring diffraction profiles. This principle is not so easy to apply in practice, however, since in most cases the methods used to measure the generally accepted values of the characteristic radiations are not described in sufficient detail. The error in angular position of a diffraction profile, because of an error $\Delta\lambda$ in wavelength, has tan θ dependence. However, unless the value of 2θ is required specifically, it is usually more convenient to make a correction for $\Delta\lambda$ by adding (or subtracting) an amount to the calculated d spacings or lattice parameters. The uncertainty in the absolute value of λ is important when accuracies greater than 1 part in 20,000 are required.[10]

Since the relationship between λ and θ in the Bragg equation is not linear, the spread in θ resulting from an asymmetrical spread in λ will vary according to the Bragg angle θ, becoming most pronounced in the back-reflection region.[11] This effect, known as dispersion, causes the centroid of the diffraction profile to be shifted to higher values of θ. The centroid is also shifted toward higher values because of a variation of the Lorentz-polarization factor across the diffraction profile; i.e., the three effects are additive. Neglecting higher terms, the resultant shift in the centroid can be expressed as[12–14]

$$\Delta 2\theta = (3V/\tilde{\lambda}) \tan^3 \tilde{\theta} \tag{5}$$

where V is the mean square of the breadth of the profile and $\tilde{\lambda}$ and $\tilde{\theta}$ the wavelength and Bragg angle, respectively, as indicated by centroid measurements. This equation also includes the error in 2θ because of a variation in the absorption of the sample with wavelength.[14,15] The effects of Lorentz and dispersion on the peak position are also found to vary as $\tan^3 \theta$, but in contrast to the centroid, these errors are now of opposite sign and so tend to cancel out, leaving only a residual $\tan \theta$ dependence for the error $\Delta 2\theta$ in peak position.[4]

The spread in wavelength of the x-ray source can often be reduced, but not completely eliminated, by the judicious use of filters, curved-crystal monochromators, and if the detector is a proportional or scintillation counter, by applying pulse-height discrimination. These devices, however, modify the wavelength distribution of the characteristic radiation, thereby introducing a further source of error in the Bragg angle θ.[16,17] The latter effect may be reduced by placing all filters, monochromators, etc., in the *diffracted beam*, so that any modification in wavelength will occur after Bragg reflection has taken place within the sample. The wavelength distribution also depends on the waveform of the voltage applied to the x-ray tube. Hence, for precision measurements of wavelength peaks or profiles it is desirable to specify a highly stabilized d-c voltage. The constant d-c source is a feature now being included with many commercial x-ray power supplies.

The influence of refraction has been discussed by Wilson.[18,19] For the case of small, roughly spherical crystals such as those used in powder specimens the change in the direction of the x-rays on entering and leaving the crystals may cause either an increase or a decrease in the Bragg angle, the net effect being that the diffraction profile is broadened symmetrically about 2θ but not shifted in angle. An error does occur with respect to λ, however, because the wavelength of the radiation inside the crystal differs slightly from that in air. Calculated values of d spacings or in the case of a cubic crystal the lattice parameter a are usually corrected for refraction by adding an amount given by[18]

$$+\Delta d = 2.70 \times 10^{-6} \lambda^2 \rho d \, \Sigma Z / ZA \tag{6}$$

$$+\Delta a = 4.48 \times 10^{-6} (\lambda a)^2 \Sigma Z \tag{7}$$

where λ is measured in angstroms, ρ is the density in g/cm^3, ΣZ is the sum of the atomic numbers, and ΣA the sum of the atomic weights of the atoms in the unit cell.

Geometrical Effects. The influence of geometrical factors on the shape and angular position of diffraction profiles has received considerable attention.[20–32]

Figure 14, for example, shows the contributions to the broadening of a profile by the six geometrical factors (source width, flat sample, vertical divergence, absorption, receiving-slit width, and misalignment) for two types of diffractometers. The essential differences between the two sets of curves are source width and vertical divergence, which correspond to the great improvement in resolution brought about by using a fine-line focus with Soller slits. Notice that the flat sample, vertical divergence, and absorption effects introduce asymmetry into the profile whereas the effect of the finite width of the source and the receiving slits is to broaden the diffraction profile but not to change its position, except in the low-angle region where the $K\alpha_1$-$K\alpha_2$ doublet is not resolved. Here a wider slit causes the *peak* to be shifted toward the centroid of the two reflections.

In most instances the influence of geometrical effects on the angular position of a diffracted beam has been analyzed in terms of a shift in the centroid of the profile.

Shifts in the peak position are much more difficult to analyze, the only detailed treatment being for the effects of flat specimen and absorption[24] which were found to cause peak shifts similar in direction and magnitude to those of the centroid. Recently[32] it has been shown that shifts in peak position for all the geometrical errors follow quite closely the form analyzed in detail for the centroid and hence only the latter need be considered.

The following equation summarizes the various analyses of the shift of the centroid because of the geometry of the method:

$$\Delta\theta = \frac{-\sin 2\theta}{4}\left[\frac{1}{\mu R} + \frac{\gamma^2 + \delta_1{}^2}{3(1 - \cos 2\theta)}\right] + \frac{\delta_2{}^2}{6 \sin 2\theta} \tag{8}$$

where θ is the Bragg angle, γ the horizontal divergence angle, $\delta_{1,2}$ the effective axial divergence angles, μ the linear absorption coefficient of the sample, and R the radius of the diffractometer circle. The first term inside the brackets is the contribution of the absorption of the specimen. It should be noted that, in contrast to the Debye-Scherrer film method, a highly absorbing specimen causes less error than one with a

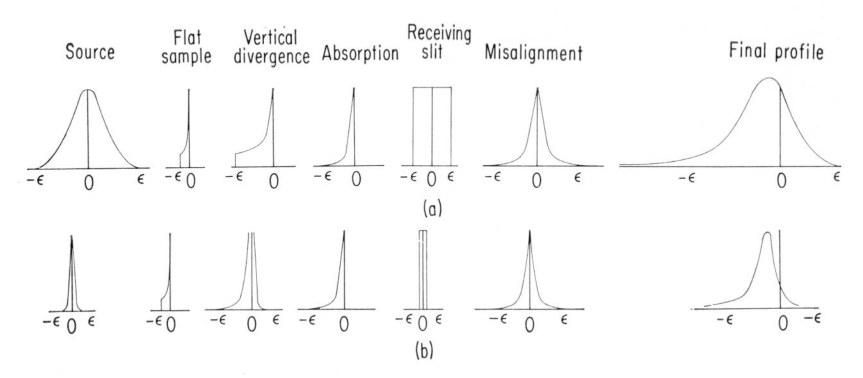

FIG. 14. The six instrumental weight functions for diffractometers of (*a*) old and (*b*) new designs computed for typical experimental conditions. (*L. Alexander, J. Appl. Phys.*, **25**: 155, 1954.)

low absorption coefficient. The other term inside the brackets refers to the contribution from the horizontal divergence angle γ and that part of axial divergence error which has $\sin 2\theta$ dependence. The results of Pike's[33] analysis of axial divergence are used here and the effective vertical divergence angles δ_1 and δ_2 are given by

$$\delta_1 = (h/R)\sqrt{2Q_1} \qquad \delta_2 = (h/R)\sqrt{Q_1 - Q_2} \tag{9}$$

where Q_1 and Q_2 are constants for a given Soller-slit system, and $2h$ is the height of the irradiated portion of the sample. Q_1 and Q_2 are rather complicated functions of the aperture q of the Soller slits. Typical examples of q, Q_1, Q_2, δ_1, and δ_2 are given in Table 4. Rows A and B are applicable to the Norelco and Siemens instruments where $q \sim 1.20$; C and D apply to the G.E. diffractometer where $q = 0.85$ for the medium-resolution slits.

All the terms inside the brackets in Eq. (8) have $\cos^2 \theta$ dependence when the errors are analyzed in terms of the fractional error in d spacings $\Delta d/d$ and can therefore be eliminated by extrapolation procedures to $2\theta = 180°$. The δ_2 part of the axial divergence has $1/\sin^2 \theta$ dependence when analyzed in terms of $\Delta d/d$ and is thus a maximum at $180°\ 2\theta$. This error must therefore be added on to the extrapolated value of d. The magnitude of the shift in centroid position due to specimen absorption (transparency) and flat-specimen aberration is shown in Figs. 15 and 16, respectively.

Instrumental Effects. There are two sources of error inherent in the mechanism of the diffractometer: (1) the angular scale of 2θ and (2) the accuracy with which

Table 4. Effective Axial Divergence Angles for Some Conventional Diffractometers

No. Soller slits	Q_1	Q_2	δ_1, °	δ_2, °	$\delta_2/12 \times 10^{-5}$
	$q = 1.20$		$h = \frac{1}{2}$ cm	$R = 17$ cm	
A. One set*	1.24	0.29	2.65	1.65	6.92
B. Two sets*	0.59	0.09	1.8	1.2	3.67
	$q = 0.85$		$h = \frac{1}{2}$ cm	$R = 14.6$ cm	
C. One set†	1.07	0.15	2.9	1.9	9.15
D. Two sets†	0.37	0.026	1.55	1.05	2.8

* Siemens-Halske and Norelco: $\delta_1 = (h/R)\sqrt{2Q_1}$ $\quad \delta_2 = (h/R)\sqrt{Q_1 - Q_2}$
† General Electric (medium resolution): $q = (R/h)\Delta$, where Δ = foil spacing/length

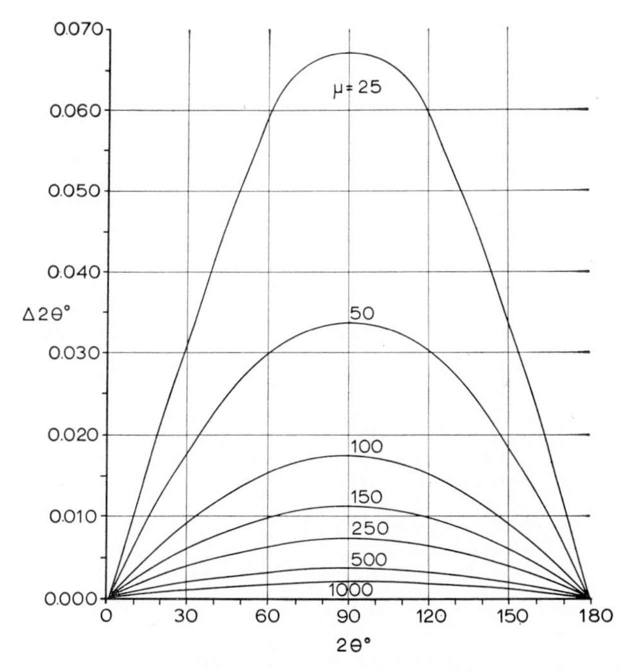

Fig. 15. Shift of center of gravity due to specimen transparency aberrations ($\Delta 2\theta = \sin 2\theta/2\mu R$, $R = 17$ cm) for various values of μ. [*W. Parrish and A. J. C. Wilson, International Tables for Crystallography (gen. ed. K. Lonsdale), vol. II, p.* 216, 1959.]

$\theta = \frac{1}{2}(2\theta)$. In addition to any lack of precision in the manufacture of the gear, random errors in 2θ can arise from uneven wear on the main gear teeth and the variation of an oil film on the gear. Systematic errors in 2θ may also occur if the gear circle has some slight ellipticity or the center of the gear circle does not exactly coincide with the axis of rotation of the diffractometer. The displacement of 2θ (peak or centroid) because of the latter errors will vary sinusoidally with increasing 2θ.[34,35] Thus, for precision work it is recommended that the goniometer scale be at least checked, if not completely calibrated, by optical means.[2]

An error in $2\theta:\theta$ following upsets the focusing of the method, causing the diffraction profile to become broadened with a consequent loss in maximum intensity, but the angular position is not significantly affected unless the peak is very asymmetrical.

Alignment Effects. Improper alignment of the diffractometer will result in a broadened and displaced peak. The broadening effect for a well-aligned system is generally small, with a half breadth that is of the order of the source width. Klug and Alexander[36] found that a misalignment function of a Cauchy form was necessary

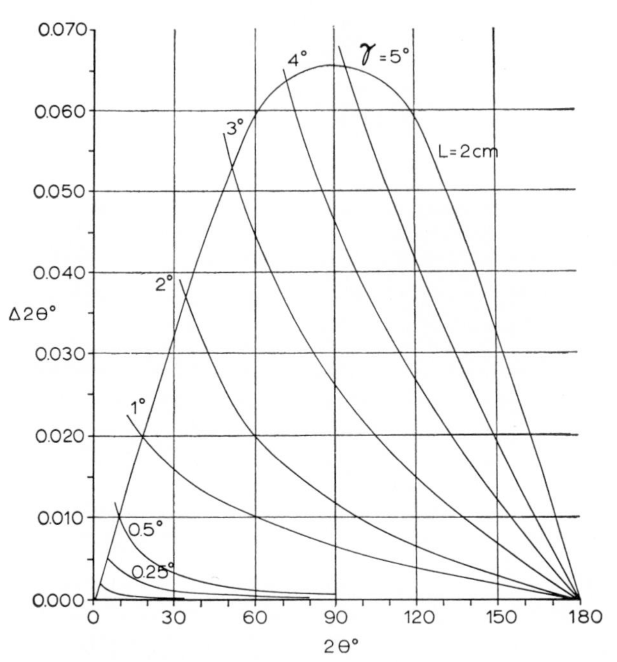

FIG. 16. Shift of center of gravity due to flat-specimen aberration ($\Delta 2\theta = \gamma^2 \cot \theta$, $R = 17$ cm) for various values of γ. (In the original paper the horizontal divergence angle was designated as 2α.) [*W. Parrish and A. J. C. Wilson, International Tables for Crystallography (gen. ed. K. Lonsdale), vol. II, p.* 216, 1959.]

in some cases in order to obtain good agreement between theoretical and observed line profiles.

The important effects of a misalignment on the angular position of the diffracted beam have been analyzed by Wilson[24] and by Vassamillet and King.[34] The shift in 2θ is given by

$$\Delta 2\theta = -\Delta F/R - (2\Delta S \cos \theta)/R \tag{10}$$

where ΔF is the displacement of the focal spot from the 180° 2θ position along the tangent to the diffractometer circle and ΔS is the displacement of the sample surface from the rotation axis. This analysis applied to both the peak and the centroid of the diffraction profile and the resultant shift in 2θ is quite significant, particularly in the low-angle regions.

A misalignment of the angle η between the central ray and the plane of the diffractometer circle is not nearly so critical.[37] The resultant error in $\Delta\theta$ is given by $(1 - \cos \eta) \tan \theta$, meaning that for accuracy of 1 part in 20,000 the magnitude of η must not exceed $\pm 0.57°$ (or $+33$ min). This limit can usually be achieved in practice. An additional error, similar in behavior and magnitude, arises if there is a tilt of the specimen surface with respect to the axis of rotation. This, too, is easily kept below the prescribed limit.

The effect of an error in the static $2\theta:\theta$ setting, i.e., the specimen surface not being parallel to the central ray of the x-ray beam when the detector is set at 2θ = zero, has been studied experimentally.[34] It was found that if the diffractometer was otherwise well aligned a change in $2\theta:\theta$ setting affected the breadth and maximum intensity of the diffraction profile but not its peak position or centroid to within the experimental reproducibility of 0.001° 2θ. If, however, there was also a misalignment ΔF, a change in $2\theta:\theta$ setting resulted in a shift in both the peak and the centroid of the profile. However, the maximum intensity of the profile is sufficiently sensitive to the $2\theta:\theta$ setting that the misalignment is detectable by superimposing peaks from both sides of the primary beam.

Measurement Effects. Distortion and displacement of the diffraction profile occur when the profile is obtained from a strip-chart recorder fed by the output of a counting rate meter. When maximum accuracy is desired, the more time-consuming, point-counting (or step-scanning) method is required. However, nearly as good results can be obtained by scanning in both the clockwise and counterclockwise directions and taking the average of the two results.[3]

The effects of the time constant of the rate-meter circuit, the scanning rate, the angular aperture of the detector slit, and strip-chart speed have been considered in some detail by Klug and Alexander[36] and by Parrish.[38] The proper choice of the above factors depends on whether resolution, intensity, or minimum time of operation is the primary goal of a particular measurement.

As discussed by Parrish and Wilson[39] and others, [40,41] the justification for using the centroid as the measure of the position of a diffraction profile is that this property of the profile can be determined to an accuracy of 0.001° 2θ and is more amenable to analysis (of errors) than the peak position. Peaks, on the other hand, are in general much easier (i.e., quicker) to measure, and in the important high-angle region they are less sensitive to errors arising from physical effects. There still remains some doubt concerning the displacement of the peaks because of geometrical effects, and so the accuracy must be limited to 0.005° 2θ. A choice between the two methods of measuring 2θ is thus a compromise between a slightly greater accuracy on one hand and a much greater amount of labor in measurement on the other.

The intensity of diffraction maxima is such that there is in any measurement of the position of the line profile an uncertainty in that position (be it peak, centroid, or any other feature of the profile) because of the counting statistics. There are several discussions of the problem of statistics in x-ray measurements.[42,38,36] See also Chap. 3 and Chap. 37, Sec. 21, of this handbook. The relation between accuracy of the centroid position and counting statistics for well-resolved profiles has been studied in detail by Pike and Wilson.[40] The position of the centroid can be written as

$$2\theta_{\text{c.g.}} = 2\theta_z - \frac{\Delta 2\theta}{1 - r} \frac{\sum_{m=1}^{n} m f_m}{\sum_{m=1}^{n} f_m} - \frac{r b_0}{\Delta 2\theta} - 1 \tag{11}$$

where $b_0 = \dfrac{n-1}{3}\dfrac{2a+z}{a+z}$ = centroid of trapezoidal background

$2\theta_z$ = final limit, step n

r = ratio of integrated background to integrated total intensity

$= \dfrac{n\frac{1}{2}(a+z)}{\sum_{m=1}^{n} f_m}$

f_m = intensity at step m

$a = f_1$, intensity at starting position

$z = f_n$, intensity at final position

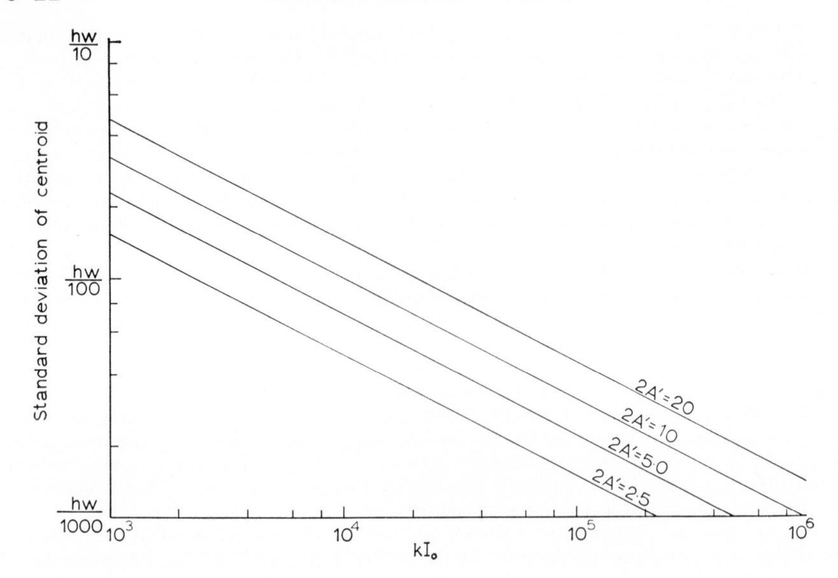

FIG. 17. The standard deviation of a centroid of a Cauchy profile due to counting statistics when step scanning by fixed-time method is used. Variation with range of integration I_0 = number of counts at the peak, k = number of steps in profile half width, $2A'$ = number of half widths in range of integration. (*E. R. Pike and A. J. C. Wilson, Brit. J. Appl. Phys.*, **10**: 57, 1959.)

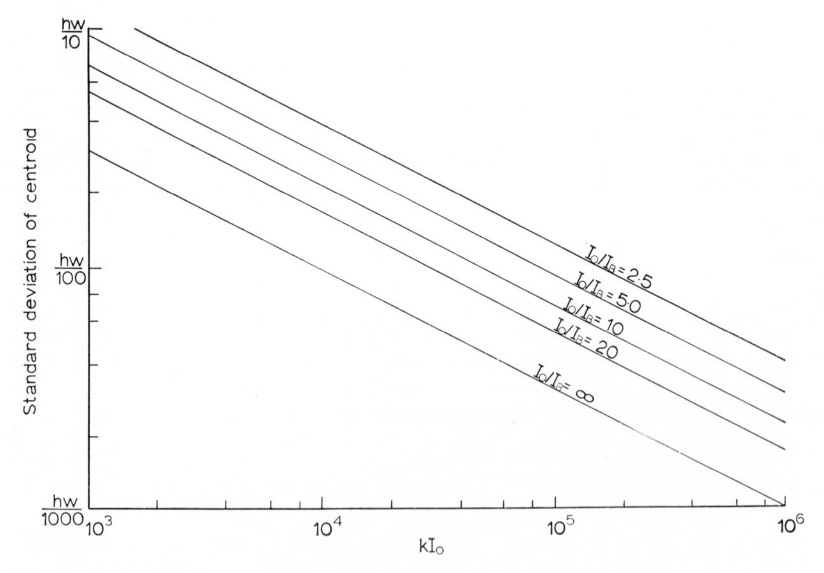

FIG. 18. As for Fig. 17. Variation with peak-to-background ratio I_0/I_B for $2A' = 10$.

The standard deviation for the centroid is shown in Figs. 17, 18, and 19. In all cases it is assumed that the x-ray tube is fully stabilized, or if a monitor signal M is used to determine counting times, $M \gg f_m$.

Use of the centroid method does not completely eliminate subjective considerations. The determination of the limits of integration $2\theta_a$ and $2\theta_z$ is somewhat arbitrary. Pike and Wilson[40] observed that the shift in centroid position on shifting the integration limits was approximately one-twentieth the distance between the mid-point of the range and the centroid. In addition a minimum range corresponding to a wavelength range of 0.0125 Å was required. The centroid shifted markedly for ranges less than this amount. The authors have observed that a satisfactory rule of thumb is to take a range of approximately five half widths. Shorter ranges will be acceptable whenever the profile breadth is very large because of physical causes.

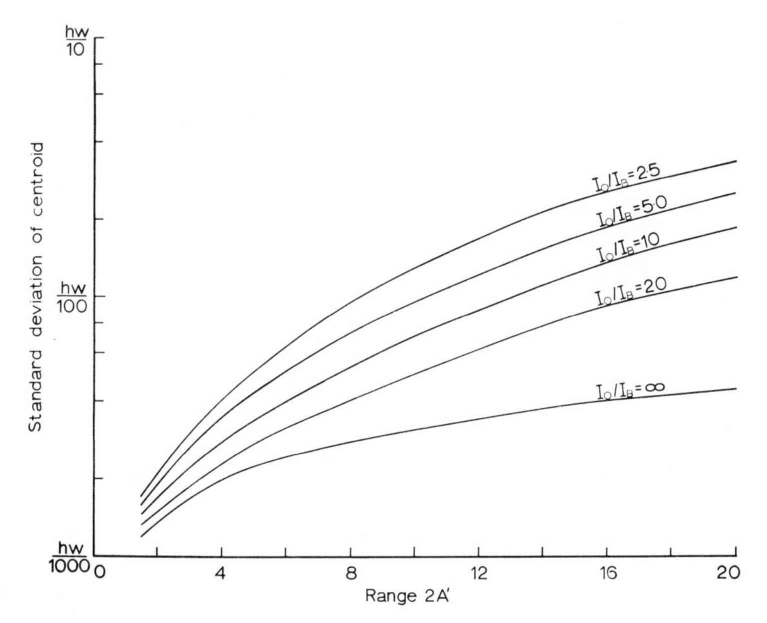

Fig. 19. As for Fig. 17. Variation with range for various values of peak-to-background ratio for $kI_0 = 10^5$.

The effect of backlash in the gear train serves only to displace the profile. The appropriate method of handling it depends on the manner in which °0 2θ has been established. In a sense the backlash error either can be divided between the two scanning directions or can be assigned entirely to one direction.[3] The major sources of error in counter diffractometry are summarized in Table 5.

5. CHOICE OF INSTRUMENTAL CONDITIONS

The successful operation of a diffractometer is dependent upon a proper choice of experimental conditions. It is frequently necessary to make compromises between such factors as peak intensity, resolution, and scanning time. Except for some few isolated cases, the x-ray tube is run at its maximum rated loading, although the particular value of excitation voltage used will depend on the variation of the peak-to-background ratio with voltage and on possible interference of the characteristic radiation with higher orders ($\lambda/2$, $\lambda/3$, etc.).

Table 5. Sources of Major Errors in Counter Diffractometry[39]

Source of error	Max effect on reflection angle at	Direction of shift (2θ)*		Variation with θ of		Remarks
		0–90°	90–180°	2θ	d	
Instrument misalignment	....	....	....	....	....	Minimize by careful alignment and center c.g. of primary beam on axis of rotation
2:1 missetting	....	....	....	....	~ 0	Causes asymmetric broadening, little effect on c.g., small shift of peak to higher 2θ. Eliminated by careful alignment
Zero-angle calibration	....	+ or −	+ or −	Constant	$\cot\theta$	Requires accurate mechanical calibration with pinhole or knife-edge. d error not linear
Flat specimen	Small 2θ (α constant)	−	−	$\cot\theta$	$\cot^2\theta$	Causes asymmetrical broadening toward small 2θ. Extrapolates to zero
	90° 2θ (L constant)	....	....	$\sin 2\theta$	$\cos^2\theta$	
Transparency	90° 2θ	−	−	$\sin 2\theta$	$\cos^2\theta$	Same as for flat specimen. Reduce by use of thin specimens of materials with small absorption
Axial divergence	Small and large 2θ	Complex: − at small angles, + at large angles		....	....	Extrapolates to a constant. Minimize by use of small 2δ†
Specimen displacement	Small 2θ	+ or −	+ or −	$\cos\theta$	$\cos\theta\cot\theta$	Usually source of largest error but extrapolates to zero. Minimize by careful specimen preparation
Rate-meter recording	....	+ or −	+ or −	Constant	$\cot\theta$	Time constant and scan speed cause asymmetric broadening and shift of c.g. and peak toward scanning direction. Eliminated by fixed-count intensity measurements and reduced by use of small time constant and scan speed
Dispersion and Lorentz factor	Large 2θ	Negligible	+	$\tan^3\theta$	$\tan^2\theta$	Largest error in c.g. at very high 2θ. Does not extrapolate to zero (little effect on peak)

* + = toward higher 2θ; − = toward lower 2θ.
† $\delta = \tan s/l$, where s = spacing, l = length of Soller slits.

The following general principles will serve as a guide toward reasonable operating conditions:

1. Increasing resolution (by decreasing slit widths) results in a lowering of the peak and integrated intensities (Fig. 20).

2. Increasing the smoothness of the line (increasing the time constant RC) results in decreasing the resolution, shifting peaks in the scanning direction, increasing line asymmetry, and lowering peak intensities (Fig. 21).

3. The amount of peak shift due to the time constant of the detector circuit will depend on the scanning speed and receiving-slit width. To avoid excessive effects it is generally desirable to choose an RC constant equal to or less than one-half the time width of the slit. The time width is defined as the ratio of the receiving-slit width in degrees ν to the scanning velocity ω in degrees per minute times 60, i.e.,

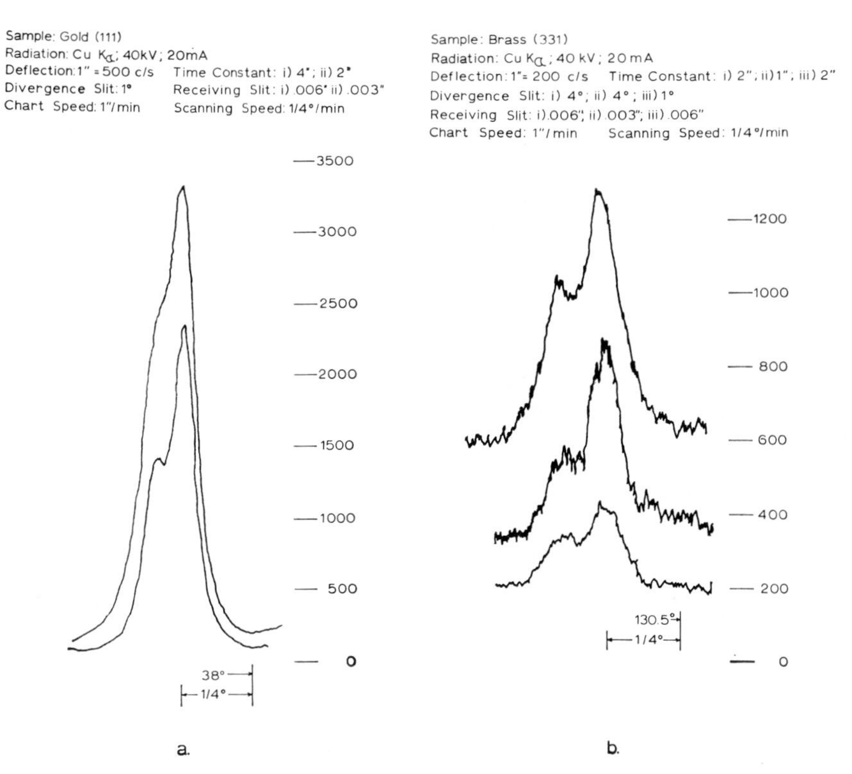

FIG. 20. Effect of resolution on peak intensities.

$$\text{Time width} = 60(\nu/\omega) \qquad \text{sec} \tag{12}$$

Table 6 gives some suggested choices of time constant RC for several values of scanning speeds and receiving-slit widths.

The relationship between resolution and intensity is most clearly shown in Table 7, which gives a comparison of conditions promoting resolution with those promoting intensity of the diffracted maxima.

With operating conditions set for maximum resolution, as in Table 8 (item 4), the $\alpha_1\alpha_2$ doublet of Cu $K\alpha$ radiation will be partially resolved at $2\theta = 35°$ if the sample

Table 6. Scanning Speeds, Receiving-slit Width, and Suggested Time Constants for Several Commercial Diffractometers

Instrument	Scanning speeds ω, °/min	Receiving-slit width		Time width* W_t, sec	RC range, sec	Max time const RC, sec	Remarks
		ν, °	As marked				
Norelco	2, 1, ½, ¼, ⅛	0.05	0.006 in.	3	½–16	1.5	
		0.025	0.003 in.	1.5	(multiples of 2)	0.75	
Siemens-Halske	4, 2, 1, ½, ¼, ⅛, 1/16	0.35	1.0 mm	21	<0.01–1,200	10.5	The time constant depends on the setting of the statistical error and the full-scale counting rate
		0.14	0.4 mm	8.4	....	4.2	
		0.07	0.2 mm	4.2	....	2.1	
		0.035	0.1 mm	2.1	....	1.0	
		0.018	0.05 mm	1.0	....	0.5	
General Electric	2.0, 0.2	0.2	....	12	½–8	6	Higher RC values may be obtained by adding capacitance
		0.1	....	6	(multiples of 2)	3	
		0.05	....	3	....	1.5	
		0.02	....	1.5	....	0.75	
Picker	2, 1, ½, ¼, ⅛	0.2	0.02 in.	12	⅓–9	6	Higher RC values may be obtained by adding capacitance
		0.1	0.01 in.	6	(multiples of 3)	3	
		0.05	0.005 in.	3	....	1.5	
		0.02	0.002 in.	1.2	....	0.6	
		0.01	0.001 in.	0.6	....	0.3	
Hilger	2, 1, ½, ¼, ⅛, 1/16	0.07	0.2 mm	4.2	1–8	2.1	Higher RC values may be obtained by adding capacitance
		0.035	0.1 mm	2.1	(multiples of 2)	1.0	

* Time width for a scanning speed of 1°/min. To find time width or time constant for any other speed, divide the time (W_t or RC) corresponding to the appropriate receiving-slit width by ω.

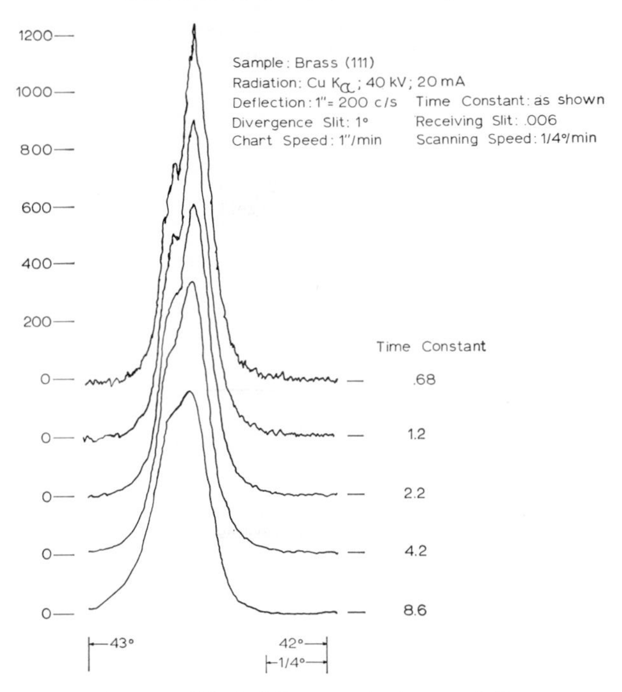

FIG. 21. Effect of time constant on resolution.

Table 7. Comparison of Conditions Promoting Resolution with Those Promoting Intensity of Diffracted Maxima

Factor	Proper adjustment of factor to	
	Increase resolution	Increase intensity
Source:		
Direction of view	Lateral (with Soller slits)*	Longitudinal*
Angle of view	3° or less	Not less than 6°
Receiving-slit width	Small*	Large*
Absorption of x-ray beam by sample	Thin layer of powder	Thick layer of powder
Horizontal divergence γ	Moderately small	Large*
Vertical divergence δ	Small (Soller slits)	Large

* The more influential items are starred.

introduces no particle size, strain, or deformation broadening. In the back-reflection region ($2\theta > 90°$) the breadths of the line profiles are determined more by the dispersion of the x-rays than by the sources of instrumental widths (horizontal and vertical divergence angles, receiving-slit width, etc.) (Fig. 20*b*). Consequently, it is possible to use larger source and receiving slits in this region without suffering any loss in resolution.

Table 8. Typical Objectives and Experimental Conditions for Preparing Recorder Traces

Objective	Divergence slit, °	Receiving slit, °	Scanning speed, °/min	Time const, sec	Recording scale
1. To obtain a pattern over a large angular range for qualitative identification of major constituents	2 (medium)	0.05–0.01 (medium to large)	2	~1	Linear or logarithmic
2. To obtain accurate measurements of integrated intensities of sharp peaks	4 (large)	0.1 (large)	1/8–1/4	12	Linear
3. Same as 2 but for broad peaks	4 (large)	0.2 (very large)	1/4–1/2	12	Linear
4. To obtain high resolution of diffraction detail	1 (small)	0.02–0.05 (small)	1/8	5	Linear
5. Accurate lattice-parameter measurements	1 (small)	≤0.035	1/8	8	Linear
6. To obtain pattern over large angular range for qualitative identification of minor constituents	4 (large)	0.1 (large)	2	~1	Logarithmic

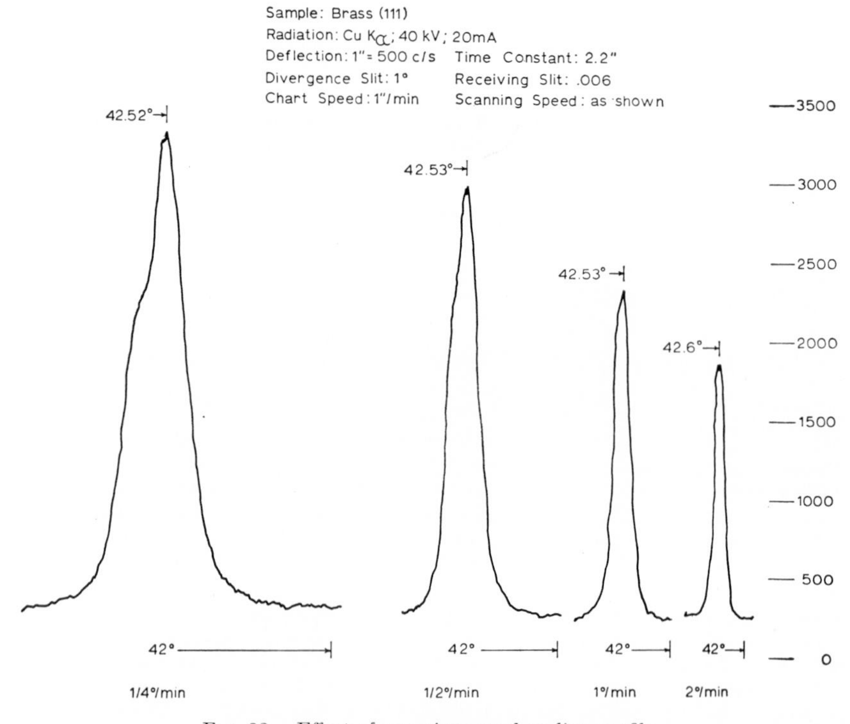

Fig. 22. Effect of scanning speed on line profile.

The effects of the various operating conditions are demonstrated in the following figures:

Figure 22. Effect of scanning speed on the line profile. With an increase in scanning speed, intensity and resolution both decrease and the peak position shifts in scanning direction.

Figure 23. Effect of scanning direction on profile shape and peak position. Note the change in the intensity of the α_2 component on change in scanning direction as well as the change in the peak position.

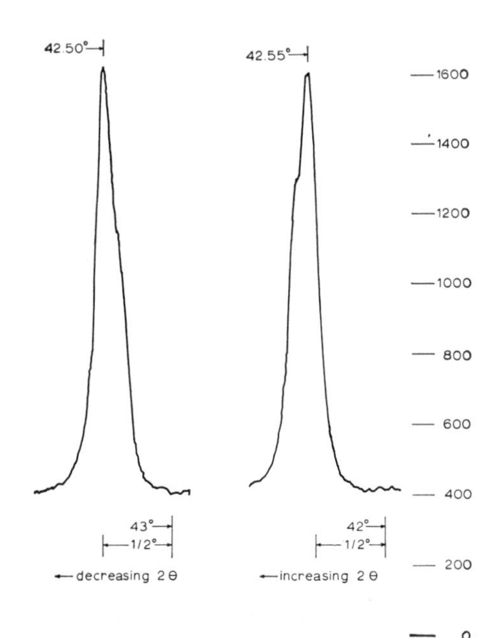

FIG. 23. Effect of scanning direction on profile shape and peak position.

Figure 20. The effect of receiving-slit width on resolution and peak intensities: (*a*) Trace of the (111) peak of gold. Upper trace (i) is with a 0.006-in. receiving slit and a 4-sec time constant. Lower trace (ii) was with a 0.003-in. receiving slit and a 2-sec time constant. The scanning rate was ¼°/min. (*b*) In the back-reflection region, the (331) peak of brass at ¼°/min with (i) 4° divergence slit, 0.006-in. receiving slit, 2-sec time constant; (ii) 4° divergence slit, 0.003-in. receiving slit, 1-sec time constant; (iii) 1° divergence slit, 0.006-in. receiving slit, 2-sec time constant.

Note that there is essentially no loss in resolution by using wider receiving or divergence slits, but considerable gain in intensities. The signal-to-noise level stays nearly constant.

Typical objectives and suggested experimental conditions for preparation of recorder traces are listed in Table 8.

Proper operating conditions for the counter tube depend on the nature of the tube: its type and design, the filler gas, etc. For the proportional counter the operating voltage will depend on the preamplifier, amplifier, and discriminating circuits (if used) as well. The response curve[36,4] should be determined for each tube since it is from this curve that the proper operating voltage is chosen. Instructions for obtaining this curve are usually supplied by the manufacturer. Examples from some response

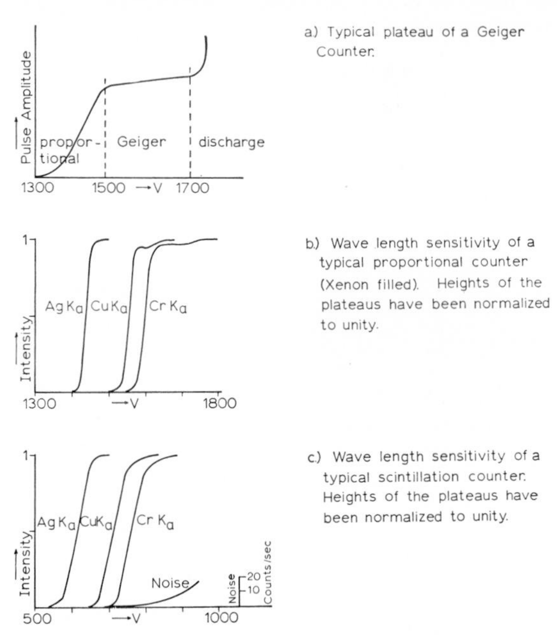

FIG. 24. Sensitivity of various types of detectors with voltage and wavelength.

curves of the various types of detectors with their typical operating-voltage ranges are shown in Fig. 24. The latter are:

	Volts
Geiger-Müller counter	1,500–2,000
Proportional counter	1,400–1,700
Scintillation counter	500– 900

Because the scintillation counter operates at considerably lower voltages than the other detectors and because even momentary operation of a Geiger counter in the discharge region will seriously damage or considerably reduce its life as a Geiger tube, great care should be exercised in placing these tubes in operation.

The Geiger counter differs from a proportional counter by the presence of a quenching component in the filler gas. However, the Geiger counter may be used as a proportional counter (by operating 200 to 300 volts below the Geiger region) even when the quenching gas has been used up and the counter no longer operates in the Geiger region.

6. SPECIMEN HANDLING

The form of the average specimen is such that only rarely can it be placed directly into the diffractometer for analysis. The problems arising in specimen preparation are (cf. Sec. 4) (1) particle size, (2) sample thickness, (3) preferred orientation, (4) strain and cold working, and (5) surface flatness.

Particle Size. The particle size of a powder specimen for diffractometer studies must be closely controlled. For example, Alexander, Klug, and Kummer[43] have shown that unless the mean particle size of a quartz powder is less than 5 microns the reproducibility of successive intensity measurements exceeds 2 per cent. The cause of this difficulty lies in the relatively small number of grains correctly oriented for diffraction even though the total number of grains in the sample might be quite large. Care must also be taken when sieving heterogeneous samples since fractions of different size may contain different amounts of the various constituents present in the sample. The effect of crystallite-size statistics on x-ray intensities has been discussed in considerable detail by DeWolff, Taylor, and Parrish.[44] They demonstrate the improvement in reproducibility obtained using a sample spinner, a device which permits rotation of the sample in its own plane during the measurement time. Warren[45] has shown how the counting statistics can be used to determine grain size of grains >1 micron (see Sec. 4).

Thus far no convenient universal method or laboratory appliance exists for producing powders with a uniform particle size less than 25 microns in diameter. Extended grinding in a mill* can sometimes reduce particle sizes below this value, but usually a few large crystallites will escape to produce fluctuations in intensity. If maximum accuracy is required (<5 per cent reproducibility), special techniques for sample preparation and the use of the sample spinner which can reduce mean deviations in intensity by a factor of 2 to 4 are recommended.

If the sample is a mixture of various materials with differing hardnesses and crystal habits, additional complications during grinding occur. The softer or more easily cleaved fraction will reduce more rapidly and by a coating action protect the larger, harder particles. It may be necessary in such cases to sieve and grind intermittently so as to remove the finer fraction. This essentially is the principle behind the selective uniform-particle-size grinder mentioned above. Before packing in the sample holder the entire sample must be well mixed. Mechanical shakers do this step most conveniently.†

Sample Thickness. For maximum intensity from a flat sample the thickness t must satisfy the following relation:[36]

$$t \geqq (3.2/\mu)\ (\rho/\rho')\sin\theta \tag{13}$$

where μ is the linear absorption coefficient, ρ and ρ' the true and effective densities of the powder, respectively. For example, the minimum thickness for the high-angle lines of a silicon powder, 325 mesh, with a packing efficiency of 50 per cent ($\rho/\rho' = 2$) is about 0.4 mm. Only in the case of very light materials with small mass absorption coefficients are especially thick samples required. The aluminum sample plates are usually about 1 mm thick.

From the above equation we see that the effective diffracting volume, which is approximately the illuminated area times the thickness t, depends critically on the absorption coefficient. This in turn determines the particle statistics. In Fig. 25 is shown the dependence of deviation in diffraction intensities upon crystallite size for various values of the linear absorption coefficient μ. This shows that, for materials with very high absorption coefficients, extremely small (<5 microns) particle sizes are required.

Preferred Orientation. Even more serious from the standpoint of reproducibility of intensities is the problem of packing the sample into the holder without introducing

* There is a variety of special devices for grinding purposes in addition to the hand- or motor-driven mortar grinder commonly found in the laboratory. Motor-operated, they utilize a vial of metal, glass, or plastic and an insert, rod or ball, of metal or glass. The vial capacities range from 1 to 25 ml of material. Typical of the products available are (in order of decreasing costs):

Selective uniform-particle-size grinder, Pitchford Scientific Instruments Co., 10 and 50 ml capacity, minimum mean size 27 microns.

Pica blender-mill, Pitchford Scientific Instruments Co., 3 samples 10 to 15 ml capacity.

Wig-L-Bug grinder, Spex Industries, Inc., 1, 2.5, 6, 10, and 25 ml capacity.

Dental Mix, Master Appliance Mfg. Co., 1 ml capacity.

† See preceding footnote.

preferred orientation. For those materials which cleave easily or are obtained as plates or rods, the effects of packing on the intensities can be very great, changing intensities sometimes by orders of magnitude. There is no universal remedy for this problem. The sample spinner does not reduce preferred orientation effects. Extensive grinding (minimum particle size) helps as does front loading of the specimen holder with as little packing as possible. Sifting onto a tacky surface sometimes reduces preferred orientation but at the same time gives a very rough sample plane. Mixing a small amount of an isotropic material (like MgO) usually reduces the orientation effect, and if an internal standard is desired, the proper choice of the standard can serve two purposes. See Chap. 18 for a complete discussion of preferred orientation.

Specimen Preparation. Specimen holders supplied with most instruments are simply small rectangular metal plates (usually aluminum) with a hole or depression of the right size cut into them. The dimensions of the hole required depend on the amount of material available, and whether measurements are to be made in the

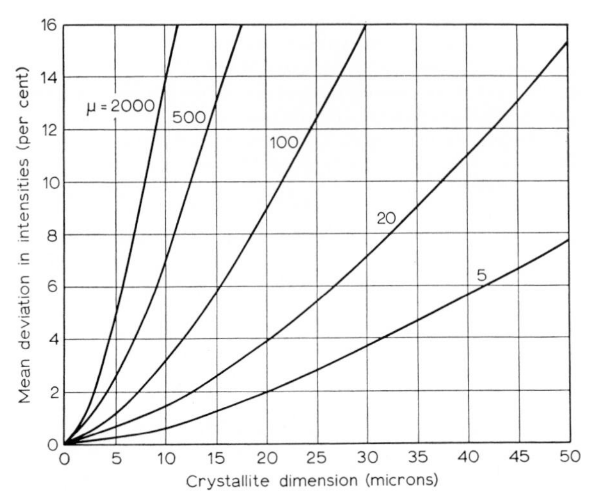

FIG. 25. Dependence of deviation in diffraction intensities upon crystallite size for various values of the linear absorption coefficient μ. (*Reprinted with permission from H. Klug and L. Alexander, X-ray Diffraction Procedures, John Wiley & Sons, Inc., New York,* 1954.)

region of small Bragg angle or in the back-reflection region. The size of area needed for a given horizontal divergence angle and Bragg angle can easily be determined by placing a fluorescent screen in the sample position. McCreery[46] has given extensive instructions for sample preparation by the back-loading technique. This procedure is also described in detail in Klug and Alexander.[36] Careful observance of the procedure will minimize preferred orientation if the powder is not too anisotropic and will also produce a plane surface. Briefly the steps are:

1. A glass microscope slide is attached to one side of the metal plate with cellophane adhesive tape.
2. Using a small sieve, an excess of powder is sifted into the cavity.
3. The powder is tamped gently but firmly and *uniformly* with the edge of a spatula.
4. Excess powder is sliced off with a razor blade.
5. Additional loose powder is sifted onto the cavity, then pressed into it with the flat side of the spatula or another glass slide. Excess powder again is sliced away. For greater uniformity in packing this step may be repeated more than once, but at the risk of increasing preferred orientation.
6. Another piece of glass, larger in area than the cavity, is taped into place over the cavity.
7. With considerable caution the glass slide covering the front of the plate can now

be removed. There should be no cellophane tape on the front of the plate to interfere with the positioning of the sample in the diffractometer.

For small amounts of sample three procedures are useful. The easiest to accomplish is to fill the ¾-in. depression of a glass slide (biological). Very fine powders will stay in place without binders. For coarser powders a drop of dilute collodion will act as a suitable binding fluid. Another method is to mix the powder into a very liquid slurry which is then poured onto a glass slide. By tilting the slide a nearly uniform layer can be obtained. When dry the sample is ready for use. This method, however, does not provide a flat, smooth, well-defined surface. A third method uses the standard sample holder with a piece of very thin Mylar film stretched over the hole. Wetting the surface of the plate with very dilute collodion before laying down the Mylar will make it adhere but not bond to the metal. With care the Mylar can be stretched tight and uniform. The powder is then sifted onto the back. This can be done over a light box so as to obtain uniform deposition. A couple of drops of very dilute adhesive serves to hold the powder in place. For metal films passed through 325 mesh, the same dilute collodion is ideal. When dry the Mylar can be stripped off, leaving a self-supporting film of material with a flat front surface and a minimum amount of preferred orientation. This latter result is a consequence of sifting since the smallest particles pass through first, establishing a rough plane for the larger particles to rest upon.

Strain and Cold Working. In the case of most nonmetallic crystals, fracture and cleavage do not introduce measurable amounts of deformation. Thus there is no visible broadening of the diffraction profiles until the crystallite size has been reduced to less than 1,000 Å. For some materials that cleave very readily, such as graphite, line broadening due to the particle-size effect is observed after moderate grinding times. For metallic materials filing is a common way of obtaining a powder. However, filing is an extremely brutal process and introduces extensive deformation. Unless the deformation itself is being studied, the filings must be annealed. The time and temperature of annealing will depend on the metal system. It is usually preferable to pick an annealing temperature at which only recovery takes place. At higher temperatures, recrystallization and subsequent grain growth may result in each particle's being a single crystal, whereas in the recovery stage each particle may consist of many nearly perfect subgrains with slightly differing orientations. This last condition is desirable, since it will reduce primary extinctions as well as improve the sample statistics.

If there is any danger of oxidation during the annealing, the powder should be sealed in glass, vycor, or quartz capsules, evacuated and partially filled with an inert gas such as He, A, or N_2.

There is no rule of thumb for the recovery temperature of a metal system as it is related not only to the melting point but also to the amount of cold work and the composition.

Metal specimens with very small grain size can often be prepared without filing, but by deforming (rolling, etc.) and annealing the bulk material. For most materials, however, a preferred-orientation texture will result. Since flat plates can be obtained directly by rolling, this method can sometimes be very useful if the resulting preferred orientation can be tolerated.

Surface Flatness. Deviations from true flatness of the sample surface result in (1) broadening of the diffraction profile, (2) displacement of the peak, and (3) incorrect intensity measurement. The first two effects become progressively more and more serious as the optimum thickness t becomes smaller. The effect on correct intensity measurements becomes serious when absolute intensities are being measured.[47] If a choice has to be made between preferred orientation and sample surface flatness, it is probably better to choose a sample-preparation procedure that favors the former rather than the latter.

7. TYPICAL PATTERNS

Some typical patterns obtained using a strip-chart recorder are illustrated in Figs. 26 through 29. The experimental conditions used are given in Table 9.

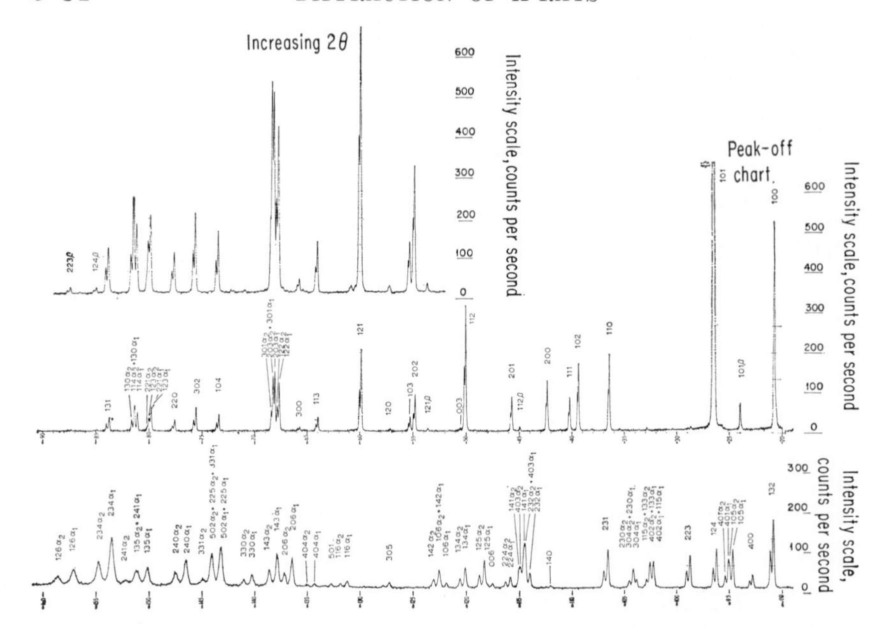

FIG. 26. Recorder trace of permaquartz. ("Permaquartz" is the General Electric X-ray Company name for a permanent specimen of novaculite, an exceedingly fine-grained quartzose rock. This reasonably inexpensive material is not represented as an absolute "standard," as differences in detail from sample to sample are observed. However, the data obtained will correspond reasonably well to standard data for pure quartz with respect to angular position, resolution, and relative intensity of the diffraction lines.) The structure is trigonal. For operating conditions see Table 9.

Table 9. Experimental Conditions for Diffractometer Traces of Some Standard Substances

Radiation: Cu $K\alpha$, 35 kv, 20 ma. Takeoff angle, $\alpha = 6°$.
Filter, Ni except as noted. Temperature, 24° C. Soller slit, $\delta = 2°$.
Detector, scintillation counter, 750 volts, pulse height 9.5 volts, channel width 10 volts.

Sample and range, ° 2θ		Divergence slit, °	Receiving slit, °	Scale, counts/sec	Chart speed, cm/min	Scan speed, °/min	Time const, sec
Permaquartz	<90°	1	0.035	666	¼	¼	3.5
	>90°	4	0.07	666	¼	¼	7.5
Gold	<90°	½	0.07	666	½	½	1.9
	>90°	1	0.14	1,666	½	½	3
Silicon	<90°	1	0.035	1,666	½	½	1.3
	>90°	4	0.07	1,666	½	½	3
Zinc oxide	<90°	1	0.07	1,666	1	1	1.3
	>90°	4	0.14	1,666	1	1	3

Figure 26 shows the pattern of "permaquartz," a naturally occurring mineral composed of crystallites of quartz. This material is recommended as a reference standard by the General Electric X-ray Company. It has the advantage that it can be lapped to give a plane bulk sample with a flat surface and, in comparison with a powder specimen, is virtually indestructible. Permaquartz produces a large number of reflections so that at least one will be found in any range of 2θ which may be of particular interest. The extent of the separation of the five peaks which occur near $2\theta < 68°$ is a useful guide to the resolving power of the instrument.

The Siemens-Halske Company supplies a standard specimen of a fine layer of gold deposited on a glass slide. This specimen is relatively indestructible. Its face-centered cubic diffraction pattern is shown in Fig. 27.

The diamond cubic diffraction pattern of powdered silicon as used in the I.U.Cr. lattice-parameter project[48] is shown in Fig. 28. This trace was made without a Ni filter, except in the low-angle region and the very high angle region ($2\theta \sim 160°$) where traces with and without the Ni filter are superimposed. Silicon is recommended as a standard substance by Philips, who supply a compacted silicon powder standard. Since the lattice parameter of silicon is known with great precision the angular values

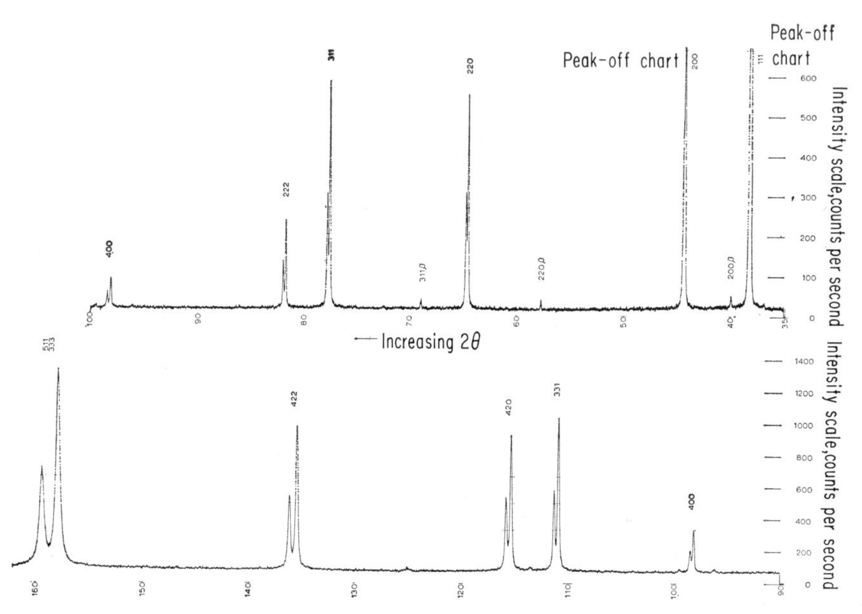

FIG. 27. Recorder trace of gold (face-centered cubic). For operating conditions, see Table 9.

of its reflections can be accurately calculated. With respect to quartz the small number of reflections obtainable under Cu $K\alpha$ radiation is a slight disadvantage.

Another material recommended as a standard substance is zinc oxide (Hilger and Watts). The diffraction pattern of this hexagonal substance, taken under typical conditions for rapid scanning (1°/min), is shown in Fig. 29.

The experimental conditions (Table 9) were changed at $2\theta = 90°$, by increasing the size of the collimating slits and adjusting the time constant in accord with Eq. (11). This is done to increase the intensity of the profiles and results in only a small loss of resolution, as shown in Fig. 26, where the region from 52 to 90° has been scanned using both sets of conditions. Line broadening due to dispersion increasingly dominates the instrumental broadening above $2\theta = 90°$. Compare the width of the $132\alpha_1$ reflection (91°) with that of the $126\alpha_1$ reflection (157°).

Diffraction patterns obtained with strip-chart recorders frequently show a considerable fall in intensity with increasing 2θ that may be offset by increasing the widths of the slits as described above. Peak intensities throughout the 2θ range depend primarily on the scattering factor and multiplicity of each reflection; the

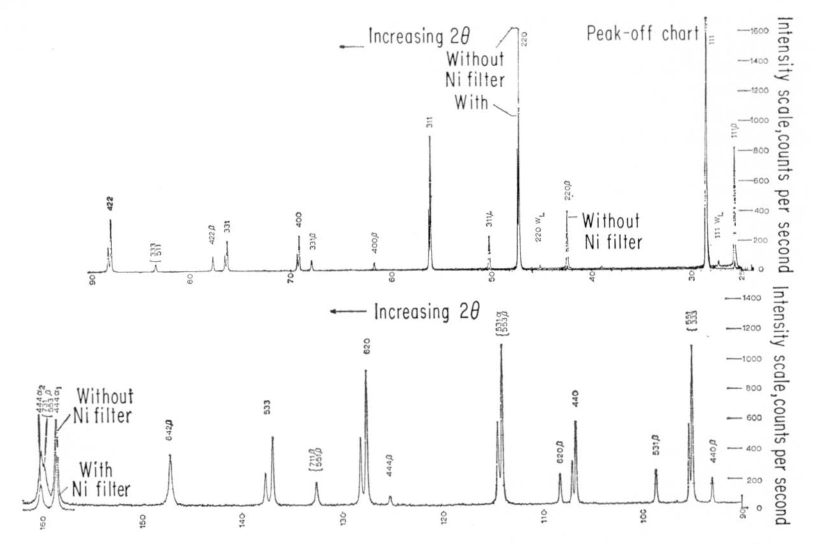

Fig. 28. Recorder trace of silicon (diamond cubic). The presence of the W_L line is a common occurrence for any tube that has had a long life. For operating conditions, see Table 9.

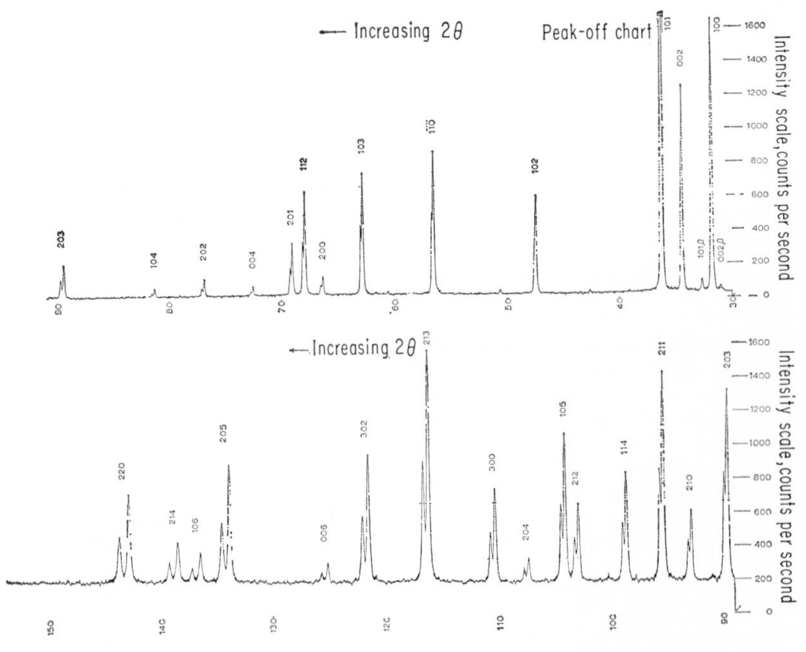

Fig. 29. Recorder trace of zinc oxide (hexagonal). For operating conditions, see Table 9.

Lorentz-polarization factor which has a minimum near $2\theta = 90°$ but is somewhat lower in the back-reflection region than in the forward region; and the dispersion effect which spreads the reflection out over a much wider region of 2θ at the high angles. In a comparison of peak intensities with those obtained by the Debye-Scherrer film method, an additional factor must be considered: absorption. In the diffractometer method, absorption is constant with angle whereas with solid cylindrical specimens (normal Debye-Scherrer techniques) the absorption decreases markedly with increasing angle, particularly in the forward direction.

The several diffraction patterns (Figs. 26 through 29) illustrate the resolving power of the technique under the different experimental conditions used. The pattern which best shows the resolving power of the diffractometer is Fig. 26, where the scanning speed of ¼°/min was used. Here the $K\alpha_1$-$K\alpha_2$ doublet was resolved in the region of $2\theta = 40°$.

For rapid conversion of 2θ values as measured on a chart to d spacings, transparent plastic d scales for diffractometer charts are available,* graduated in d values in angstrom units for Cu radiation. Those presently available cover the 2θ range from 4.4 to 100° for chart speeds of 2 and 5° 2θ/in.

8. COMPARISON OF DIFFRACTOMETER AND CAMERA TECHNIQUES

Registration. The essential feature of the diffractometer is that it uses a localized detector which scans each profile in turn, whereas with the film camera all diffraction lines are recorded simultaneously. Though both methods produce a measurement of the angular position of each peak, the profile of the diffracted beam is obtained directly with the diffractometer and indirectly (with the aid of a microphotometer) in the camera method. It is possible with both methods to partially differentiate between various wavelengths in the incident or diffracted beam by means of filters, but in the case of diffractometry the use of pulse-height discrimination (PHD) is a great added advantage, particularly in improving the signal-to-noise ratio and in eliminating interference due to fluorescence or higher-order (λ/n, $n = 1, 2$, etc.) radiation. Although most of the other advantages of the diffractometer can be matched by camera techniques,[49] special focusing, or measuring devices,[50] elaborate precautions are necessary.[51] In terms of cost, a good Debye-Scherrer camera will cost only one-tenth that of a commercial diffractometer, unless the special requirements just mentioned are included, making costs of cameras and diffractometers more nearly comparable.

Sample Volume. The minimum volume of powder required to obtain a good diffractometer trace is of the order of 0.1 cc. If the precise intensity of the profile is unimportant, smaller quantities (0.02 cc) along with special preparation procedures may suffice. Note, however, that focusing cameras which utilize a line-focus x-ray tube require much the same volume of sample as a diffractometer. If, however, only very small volumes of powder are available the Debye-Scherrer method is much to be preferred. A perfect diffraction pattern can be obtained with as little as 0.0015 cc. The Debye-Scherrer method has an advantage in identifying the various phases of differing hardness or particle size in a heterogeneous sample. On the other hand, the diffractometer has an advantage in that fine-grain, flat, bulk specimens can be examined directly, i.e., without reducing them to powder.

Sample Preparation. This has been discussed in great detail in Sec. 6. Usually sample preparation is much simpler with the Debye-Scherrer film method than for the diffractometer. The capillary method of preparing a Debye-Scherrer sample also affords protection, if necessary, from effects of the atmosphere.

Speed vs. Accuracy. Choice of the method to be used depends on the type of information required. Since diffraction profiles are recorded directly on the diffractometer trace, the angular position of a single profile, if required, can thus be obtained rapidly. On the other hand, the film camera records all diffraction lines simultaneously and is particularly useful when seeking the presence or positions of several weak

* N. P. Nies, 969 Skyline Drive, Laguna Beach, Calif.

lines. Accuracy is also a function of operating speed. For example, the lattice parameter of silver can be obtained to an accuracy of 1/15,000 from a Debye-Scherrer film with a 3-hr exposure, but as much as 8 hr are needed to double-scan all high-angle peaks at the rate of ¼°/min using the diffractometer. At this accuracy level the peak positions can be obtained quickly from the diffractometer trace, but for greater accuracy the more time-consuming point-counting method would be required. Similarly, with film techniques, it is recommended that the film be read several times.[51]

There is another aspect of speed that frequently is important. When it is necessary to follow phase transformations with changes in single specimens in either time[52] or temperature,[53] the diffractometer has an obvious advantage. One can then concentrate on the particular range of 2θ where the changes in pattern are expected to occur. The sample can be removed from the instrument, treated in accordance with the experiment, and quickly reinserted for study. A trace of a single line can usually be obtained in a fraction of a minute.

Resolving Power. The resolving power of the diffractometer is superior to that of the Debye-Scherrer camera. Under good alignment conditions the Cu $K\alpha_1$-$K\alpha_2$ peaks can be resolved on a diffractometer trace at values of 2θ in the region of 30 to 35°, but it is very rare for these peaks to be resolved below $2\theta = 90°$ on a Debye-Scherrer film. Similarly, the angular breadth of a peak on a diffractometer trace is only about one-third of that of a Debye-Scherrer line in the region of $2\theta = 90°$.

Accuracy. The accuracy of an individual measurement of 2θ is not easy to establish. Peak positions on a diffractometer trace can be measured to 0.005° by double scanning, and accuracies of 0.001° 2θ are claimed for the measurement of the position of the centroid of a profile.[40,41] By contrast, the vernier scales commonly used to measure line positions on a Debye-Scherrer film can be read to 0.02 mm, i.e., to 0.02° 2θ for a 11.46-cm camera. Reading the vernier to higher precision is of little advantage since the reader's uncertainty in estimating the center of the line becomes a limiting factor. The technique of taking the average of several readings of low accuracy (often by different operators) has been criticized by Parrish.[48] Focusing cameras exceed the Debye-Scherrer camera in accuracy measurement of angular position. An accuracy of 2 sec of arc is claimed[50] for a specially constructed back-reflection camera with a built-in comparator scale. The absorption by the specimen affects the accuracy whenever extrapolation procedures are used. Accuracy increases in the diffractometer method with increasing absorptivity and in the Debye-Scherrer method with increasing transparency of the specimen.

Sensitivity. The counter-tube detectors used on the diffractometer are inherently more sensitive to x-ray quanta than is photographic film. In addition, the sensitivity range for linear counting rates is very large, going frcm the typical background level of 1 count/sec to values of the order of 10^4 counts/sec. Hence by properly setting the conditions of detection and scan, relative intensities of both weak and intense peaks can be measured to better than 1 per cent. With photographic film, 10^4 to 10^5 x-ray quanta are required before a line can be distinguished. Since the maximum range of intensities on a single film is about 20:1 the use of film methods to study intensities is severely limited, as intensity ranges of 100:1 for a single pattern are quite common. In practice this limitation is overcome by using several layers of film, often interspersed with thin metal foils, but this makes film calibration more complicated and less accurate. The diffractometer method is subject to errors arising from possible variations in the intensity of the x-ray source or in the efficiency of the counter tube during the experiment. These errors can be minimized by using stabilized circuitry for the x-ray tube and detector and/or using a split beam and monitoring counter. Although all diffraction lines are recorded simultaneously on a film the intensity of each line has to be measured separately with a microphotometer, so that similar precautions must be taken to avoid drift in the intensity of the light source or in the efficiency of the photocell.

Choice of Techniques. It is evident from the above that the choice between a diffractometer and a camera technique is usually based on either the form of the sample or the nature of the information required. The recommended technique to be applied under some typical conditions imposed by these factors is given in Table 10.

Table 10. Suggested Techniques for Some Typical Experimental Conditions

Experimental condition	*Technique*
Sample identification	Debye-Scherrer
	Diffractometer (fast trace)
Very limited supply of material	Debye-Scherrer
Very weak lines	Debye-Scherrer (many lines)
	Diffractometer (one line)
Line shape, breadth, or asymmetry	Diffractometer
Relative intensities	Diffractometer (point counting)
Lattice parameter to 1/15,000	Debye-Scherrer
	Diffractometer (peak positions from slow trace)
Lattice parameter above 1/15,000	Focusing camera (back reflection)
	Diffractometer (point counting)
Long-range order	Focusing camera (transmission)
	Diffractometer
Peak shifts in the low-angle region (α_1 and α_2 peaks not fully resolved)	Focusing camera (transmission)
	Diffractometer (centroid)
Materials tending to have preferred orientation	Debye-Scherrer
Materials needing protection from atmosphere	Debye-Scherrer
Materials with large crystallite size	Debye-Scherrer
Interference: Fluorescence (e.g., study of Fe-containing materials with Cu $K\alpha$ radiation). Higher orders present in white radiation (λ/n, $n = 1$, 2, etc.). Radioactivity (presence of β and γ radiations in sample)	Diffractometer (with PHD and scintillation or proportional counter)
Rapid following-phase transformations	Diffractometer

Acknowledgment. The authors wish to thank Dr. Harold Klug and Dr. Sidney Pollack for helpful discussions. We acknowledge the extent to which we have relied on the book *X-ray Diffraction Procedures* (H. Klug and L. Alexander, John Wiley & Sons, Inc., New York, 1954). We also wish to recognize the very considerable amount of assistance given by the manufacturers of the several diffractometers, and their accredited representatives, who readily made available the technical information.

REFERENCES CITED

1. W. H. Bragg and W. L. Bragg, *Proc. Roy. Soc. (London)*, **88A**:428 (1913).
2. A. Friedman, *Electronics*, 132 (April, 1945).
3. H. W. King and L. F. Vassamillet, *Advances in X-ray Analysis*, vol. 5, p. 78, W. M. Mueller (ed.), Plenum Press, New York, 1962.
4. W. Parrish and T. R. Kohler, *Rev. Sci. Instr.*, **27**:795 (1956).
5. W. Parrish, *Philips Tech. Rev.*, **17**:206 (1956).
6. H. I. West, Jr., W. E. Meyerhof, and R. Hofstadter, *Phys. Rev.*, **81**:141 (1951).
7. J. C. Evans, and C. O. Taylerson, N.P.L. Notes Appl. Sci., no. 26, H.M. Stationery Office, London, 1961.
8. H. W. King and C. M. Russell, *Advances in X-ray Analysis*, vol. 8, p. 1, W. M. Mueller, G. R. Mallett, and M. Fay (eds.), Plenum Press, New York, 1965.
9. K. Lonsdale, *International Tables for X-ray Crystallography*, Kynoch Press, Birmingham, England, **3**:41 (1962); *Acta Cryst.*, **3**:400 (1950).
10. A. J. C. Wilson, *Z. Krist.*, **3**:471 (1959).
11. A. R. Lang, *J. Appl. Phys.*, **27**:485 (1956).
12. E. R. Pike, *Acta Cryst.*, **12**:87 (1959).
13. J. Ladell, M. Mack, W. Parrish, and J. Taylor, *Acta Cryst.*, **12**:567 (1959).
14. E. R. Pike and J. Ladell, *Acta Cryst.*, **14**:53 (1961).
15. A. J. C. Wilson, *Mathematical Theory of X-ray Powder Diffractometry*, Philips Technical Library, Eindhoven, 1962.
16. A. J. C. Wilson, *Proc. Phys. Soc. (London)*, **72**:924 (1958).
17. J. Cermak, *Acta Cryst.*, **12**:832 (1960).
18. A. J. C. Wilson, *Proc. Comp. Phil. Soc.*, **36**:485 (1940).
19. A. J. C. Wilson, *Proc. Phys. Soc. (London)*, **80**:303 (1962).

20. L. Alexander, *J. Appl. Phys.*, **19**:1068 (1948).
21. L. Alexander, *J. Appl. Phys.*, **21**:126 (1950).
22. L. Alexander, *J. Appl. Phys.*, **25**: 155 (1954).
23. L. S. Birks, Report H-2517, Problem H-75, Physical Optics Div., NRL, Washington, D.C., April, 1945.
24. A. J. C. Wilson, *J. Sci. Instr.*, **27**:321 (1950).
25. J. N. Eastbrook, *Brit. J. Appl. Phys.*, **3**:349 (1952).
26. E. R. Pike, *J. Sci. Instr.*, **34**: 355 (1957); **36**: 52 (1959).
27. J. I. Langford, *J. Sci. Instr.*, **39**: 515 (1962).
28. B. W. Delf, *Brit. J. Appl. Phys.*, **12**:421 (1961).
29. M. E. Milberg, *J. Appl. Phys.*, **29**:64 (1958).
30. C. G. Vouk, *Norelco Reptr.*, **8**:92 (1961).
31. J. I. Langford and A. J. C. Wilson, *J. Sci. Instr.*, **39**:581 (1962).
32. A. J. C. Wilson, *Proc. Phys. Soc. (London)*, **78**:249 (1961).
33. E. R. Pike, *J. Sci. Instr.*, **36**:52 (1959).
34. L. F. Vassamillet and H. W. King, *Advances in X-ray Analysis*, vol. 6, p. 142, W. M. Mueller (ed.), Plenum Press, New York, 1963.
35. J. C. Evans and C. O. Taylerson, N.P.L. Notes Appl. Sci., no. 26, H. M. Stationery Office, London.
36. H. Klug and L. Alexander, *X-ray Diffraction Procedures*, John Wiley & Sons, Inc., New York, 1954.
37. W. L. Bond, *Acta Cryst.*, **13**:814 (1960).
38. W. Parrish, *Philips Tech. Rev.*, **17**:206 (1956).
39. W. Parrish and A. J. C. Wilson, *International Tables for Crystallography* (gen. ed. K. Lonsdale), vol. II, p. 216, Kynoch Press, Birmingham, England, 1959.
40. E. R. Pike and A. J. C. Wilson, *Brit. J. Appl. Phys.*, **10**:57 (1959).
41. J. Ladell, W. Parrish, and J. Taylor, *Acta Cryst.*, **12**(253): 561 (1959).
42. P. William Zingaro, *Norelco Reptr.*, **V**:99 (1958).
43. L. Alexander, H. P. Klug, and E. Kummer, *J. Appl. Phys.*, **19**:742 (1948).
44. P. M. DeWolff, J. Taylor, and W. Parrish, *J. Appl. Phys.*, **30**:63 (1959).
45. B. E. Warren, *J. Appl. Phys.*, **31**:2237 (1960).
46. G. L. McCreery, *J. Am. Ceram. Soc.*, **34**:141 (1949).
47. B. W. Batterman, D. R. Chipman, and J. J. DeMarco, *Phys. Rev.*, **122**:68 (1961). The authors describe a method of checking on the effect of surface roughness by comparing the amount of fluorescence from the powder sample at an angle well removed from a Bragg peak with that from a highly polished solid sample of the same material. Surface roughness will attenuate the fluorescent signal.
48. W. Parrish, *Acta Cryst.*, **13**:838 (1960).
49. A. Guinier, *Advances in X-ray Analysis*, vol. 5, p. 1, W. M. Mueller (ed.), Plenum Press, New York, 1962.
50. A. Franks, Ref. 49, vol. 3, p. 69, 1960.
51. M. Straumanis and I. Ievins (K. E. Beu, translator), *The Precision Determination of Lattice Constants by the Asymmetric Method*, Goodyear Atomic Corp., April 15, 1959 (GAT-T-643).
52. H. W. King and T. B. Massalski, *Trans. AIME*, **221**:1063 (1961).
53. Several papers in *Advances in X-ray Analysis*, vol. 5, W. M. Mueller (ed.), Plenum Press, New York, 1962.

GENERAL REFERENCES

Birks, L. S.: *X-ray Spectrochemical Analysis*, Interscience Publishers, Inc., New York, 1959.
Brown, G. (ed.): *The X-ray Identification and Crystal Structures of Clay Minerals*, Mineralogical Society, London, 1961.
Klug, H., and L. Alexander: *X-ray Diffraction Procedures*, John Wiley & Sons, Inc., New York, 1954.
Liebhafsky, H. A., H. G. Pfeiffer, E. H. Winslow, and P. D. Zemany: *X-ray Absorption and Emission in Analytical Chemistry*, John Wiley & Sons, Inc., New York, 1960.
Mueller, William M. (ed.): *Advances in X-ray Analysis*, vols. 1–6, Plenum Press, New York, 1960–1963.
Parrish, W. (ed.): *Advances in X-ray Diffractometry and X-ray Spectrography*, Centrex Publishing Co., Eindhoven, 1962.
Peiser, H. S., H. P. Rooksby, and A. J. C. Wilson (eds.): *X-ray Diffraction by Polycrystalline Materials*, Institute of Physics, London, 1955.
Taylor, A.: *X-ray Metallography*, John Wiley & Sons, Inc., New York, 1960.
Wilson, A. J. C.: *Mathematical Theory of X-ray Powder Diffractometry*, Philips Technical Library, Eindhoven, 1962.

Chapter 10

THE PRECISE AND ACCURATE DETERMINATION OF LATTICE PARAMETERS

Karl E. Beu

Goodyear Atomic Corporation

1. INTRODUCTION

Lattice parameters are a measure of unit cell dimensions of crystalline materials, and, in the case of simple crystal structures, they provide a direct measure of internuclear distances. The precise and accurate determination of the lattice parameters (constants) of crystalline materials has assumed increasing importance in recent years. For example, such data are essential in helping to solve many problems in solid-state physics.

Lattice-parameter data have been used (1) in developing more satisfactory concepts of bonding energies in crystalline solids, (2) in studying the physical characteristics of interstitial and substitutional solid solution, (3) in determining some of the more subtle effects of radiation damage in solids, (4) in developing phase-equilibrium diagrams, (5) in determining residual stresses in such materials as hardened steels, (6) in the quantitative determination of dislocation densities and atomic weights, and (7) in determining true densities and thermal-expansion coefficients of materials for which these properties are difficult or impossible to determine by conventional methods because of the physical state of the material; i.e., if it is a powder, porous material, etc. Finally, the precise and accurate determination of lattice parameters is of importance wherever data of this type, including x-ray identification methods, are used in interlaboratory comparisons. Whenever the differences in diffraction patterns among crystalline compounds become rather subtle, an accurate and precise knowledge of lattice parameters or d values will help to resolve the identification problem. Although others could be cited, these examples should indicate the scope and magnitude of lattice-parameter applications.

Except for the section on noncubic materials, discussion shall be confined to cubic materials having only one lattice parameter—the unit cell edge, designated a_0—to simplify discussion. a_0 may be determined by x-ray diffraction techniques using the Bragg equation $n\lambda = 2d_{hkl} \sin \theta$ and the relationship $a_0 = d_{hkl} \sqrt{h^2 + k^2 + 1^2}$, where d_{hkl} is the interplanar spacing, in angstroms, of the Bragg planes having Miller indices (hkl), θ is the Bragg angle of reflection from these planes, n is the order of reflection, and λ is the wavelength, in angstroms, of x-rays used. Equations of the latter type for crystal systems of lower symmetry are discussed in Sec. 4.

Basically, the problem of determining a_0 precisely and accurately depends (1) on the precision and accuracy with which θ and λ can be determined and (2) on the relationship of precision between a_0 and θ illustrated in Fig. 1. From this figure it can be seen, for a given precision in θ, the precision in a_0 improves with increasing θ. It is no great problem to obtain high precision alone as long as diffraction lines are measured at sufficiently large Bragg angles. For example, a precision of about 1 part in 10,000 (0.01 per cent) in a_0 can be obtained merely by measuring a diffraction-line position with a precision of $0.05°\theta$ at about $83°\theta$ ($166°\ 2\theta$) provided, of course, that a sharp diffraction line occurs at this angle. This precision in θ can easily be achieved with most modern powder cameras or diffractometers. The best precisions claimed in the

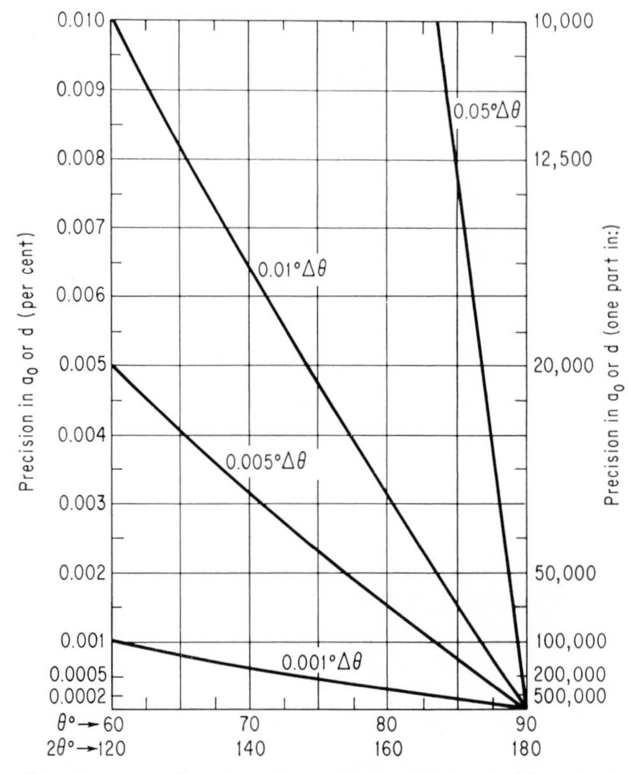

FIG. 1. Precision in a_0 as a function of θ or 2θ for various precisions in θ according to $|\Delta a_0|/a_0 = \cot\theta|\Delta\theta|$.

literature are on the order of $0.001°\theta$. At about $87°\theta$ (the highest measurable angle obtainable in a practical film powder camera), this corresponds to a precision in a_0 of about 1 part in 1,000,000 (0.0001 per cent).

Such potentially high precision serves as a great inducement to use x-ray diffraction techniques for the problems mentioned above. Precision alone can be useful when analyzing a series of similar samples using the same x-ray equipment in an identical manner from sample to sample; however, precision without corresponding accuracy is of dubious value in many other practical cases. Where both accuracy and precision are required, some difficulties arise.

Accuracy requires the removal of all significant systematic errors from the data within the precision of the θ and λ measurements. The major effort in developing lattice-parameter techniques has been concerned with the understanding and removal of systematic errors from the data. Table 1 lists the major sources of systematic

Table 1. Principal Sources of Systematic Errors in Lattice-parameter Determinations

Major factor involved	Film cameras			Diffractometer
	Cylindrical	Flat plate, back reflection	Symmetrical focusing, back reflection	
Sample.......	Absorption (diameter)	Transparency (thickness)	Transparency (thickness)	Transparency, absorption
	Eccentricity	—*	Displacement from focusing cylinder	Displacement from rotation axis
	Wobble	Tilt with respect to x-ray beam axis	Tilt with respect to focusing cylinder	Tilt with respect to rotation axis
	—	—*	Curvature variation from focusing cylinder	Surface flatness
Instrument...	Camera radius†	Sample-film distance†	Camera radius†	Diffractometer radius†
	Radial divergence	Radial divergence	—‡	Radial (horizontal) divergence
	—	—	—	2:1 missetting or tracking
	(Nonuniform film shrinkage)	(Nonuniform film shrinkage)	(Nonuniform film shrinkage)	Angular scale
	—	—	—	Misalignment
Detector.....	—	—	—	Rate-meter recording§
	Uniform film shrinkage	Uniform film shrinkage	Uniform film shrinkage	—
	—	—	Film displacement from focusing cylinder	—
	Irregular film-cylinder contact	Film buckling	Irregular film-cylinder contact	—
	Double coating of film¶	Double coating of film¶	Double coating of film¶	—

Factors common to all methods:
- Sample temperature control and measurement
- Instrumental zero setting and/or calibration†
- Instrumental axial (vertical) divergence
- Observer bias in measuring line positions
- X-ray source profile asymmetry
- Lorentz and polarization factors
- Dispersion of x-rays
- Refraction of x-rays
- X-ray wavelength distribution
- Absolute value of x-ray wavelength

* Equivalent to sample-film distance error.

† Including gauge, knife-edge, or notch calibration procedures used, if any.

‡ Method depends on radial divergence of primary x-ray beam.

§ Can be eliminated by step scanning or point-by-point counting.

¶ This can be eliminated if single-coated film is used.

errors for film cameras and diffractometers. An effort has been made in Table 1 to sort out the error sources according to the major factors which give rise to the various errors. Corresponding error sources are listed on the same line to show these relationships among the various instrument types. A dash (—) indicates that there is no corresponding source or that it is usually considered to be negligible for that particular type of equipment. These error sources will be discussed below in more detail as they apply to the various methods for determining lattice parameters.

All error sources except wavelength (and wavelength change in the diffracting crystal) affect the accuracy of the lattice parameter through their effect on θ, the Bragg angle. Wavelength error, on the other hand, affects lattice-parameter accuracy through λ in the Bragg equation, and since wavelength errors are somewhat different in nature from the other errors, their effects will be discussed separately.

The major limitation on lattice-parameter accuracy due to wavelength is the limited accuracy with which some x-ray wavelengths are known. Many wavelengths are known accurately only to 1 part in 50,000; however, the peak values for some are estimated to be known accurately to about 1 part in 1,000,000, e.g., the Cu $K\alpha_1$ and Fe $K\alpha_1$ wavelengths which are widely used in lattice-parameter measurements.[1] Another wavelength-type factor which affects lattice-parameter accuracy is the conversion from angstroms (the unit commonly used to express lattice-parameter values) to kX units (the unit commonly used by spectroscopists in reporting x-ray wavelengths) or vice versa. A widely used factor for converting kX units to angstroms is 1.00202, and this factor is known accurately only to about 1 part in 30,000.[2]*

A lattice-parameter value can never be determined more accurately than the wavelength or conversion factor used to calculate it. For those cases in which a precision and accuracy of 1 part in 30,000 or less are satisfactory, this is no problem. It is unfortunate in those cases where it is important to know the absolute magnitude of the lattice parameter to an accuracy better than that corresponding to the wavelength accuracy. However, in the equally important case where it is desired to make interlaboratory or interequipment comparisons, it is entirely practical to restrict the definition of accuracy in the following sense: by stating a numerical value of the characteristic (peak, centroid, etc.) used to define a wavelength value, a lattice-parameter value may be calculated based on the precision and accuracy of the θ measurements alone. That lattice-parameter value may then be compared on the basis of its precision and accuracy in θ with other values as long as these other values are calculated using the same wavelength. Thus, with this restriction, lattice-parameter and wavelength accuracies can be handled separately and advantage may be taken of the apparently higher precision and accuracy in lattice parameters attainable based on θ measurements. It is understood, of course, that any improvements in x-ray wavelength accuracy[41h] can be immediately reflected in an improvement in true lattice-parameter accuracy via the Bragg equation. Further discussion will be based on the premise that the effects of wavelength and of θ on lattice-parameter accuracies can be handled separately.

The magnitude of the systematic error problem in determining θ has already been indicated; i.e., when precisions of about $0.05°\theta$ are satisfactory, the systematic errors can be kept down to this level using modern x-ray equipment, a moderately careful experimental technique, and any of the several calculation procedures to be described. At this level the systematic errors can, to a large extent, "take care of themselves." At the $0.01°\theta$ level, it becomes much more important to evaluate the magnitudes of the systematic errors as they apply to the particular experimental conditions used. At the $0.001°\theta$ level, the detailed nature of *all* systematic errors needs to be closely evaluated before *any* can be said to be insignificant. Significant errors ($>0.001°\theta$) need to be corrected in a valid manner in order to obtain a precise and accurate value of a_0 at this level.

The difficulties in correcting for systematic errors in θ in a valid manner were vividly demonstrated in a recent interlaboratory comparison sponsored by the International Union of Crystallography (IUCr).[3] The lattice parameters of powder samples of silicon, tungsten, and diamond were determined by 16 laboratories around the world. In spite of using subsamples of the same homogeneous sample, and the same wave-

* In a recent tabulation of x-ray wavelengths[41h] (including those commonly used in lattice parameter determination), the absolute accuracy in angstroms for Cu $K\alpha_1$ is estimated to have been determined to better than one part in 200,000.

In spite of using subsamples of the same homogeneous sample, and the same wavelength and conversion-factor values, the agreement (a measure of accuracy) was only about 1 part in 10,000 (0.01 per cent), although precisions as high as 1 part in 550,000 (0.00018 per cent) were reported.

One of the significant factors leading to this relatively poor accuracy was the lack of a valid statistical test to determine when the systematic errors in θ had been removed from the data within the precision of measurement. Such a test has recently been devised and is incorporated in a method for the precise and accurate determination of lattice parameters. It is called the likelihood-ratio method (LRM).[4,4a] [Using the LRM, the lattice-parameter data for zone-refined silicon,[5] IUCr silicon,[57b, 57e] and for tungsten powder,[6,42a] have recently been shown to be precise and accurate at the 1 part in 150,000 level or better (corresponding approximately to the 0.001°θ level).] Any lattice-parameter data of a precision higher than about 1 part in 20,000 should be tested for accuracy using the LRM or a comparable statistical method if such data are to be used in future interlaboratory tests.

Several methods have been developed which are capable of precision and accuracy at the 0.01°θ and 0.001°θ levels. These will be discussed in the next section. The methods at the 0.01°θ level are of primary interest for most practical lattice-parameter work and will be discussed on this basis, while the methods at the 0.001°θ level are primarily useful for the development of reference standards and in looking for extremely subtle lattice-parameter effects. The 0.001°θ-level methods require greater experimental finesse and (usually) more expensive equipment than the 0.01°θ methods; however, once these objectives have been attained, the 0.001°θ methods can, in general, be used as routinely as the 0.01°θ methods.

2. STRAUMANIS FILM METHOD (0.01 TO 0.002° ϕ LEVEL)

Shortly after the discovery of the principles of powder x-ray diffraction by Debye, Scherrer, and Hull in 1915, lattice parameters of many substances were determined with a precision of about 2 per cent. Technique improvements were made using cylindrical and back-reflection cameras, with or without standard calibrating substances. By the early 1930s the precision of measurement had increased to about 1 part in 20,000 (0.005 per cent). At this time, further improvements took place in two directions, beginning with the experimental reduction of systematic errors by Straumanis[7] and the extrapolation methods of Kettmann[8] and Bradley and Jay.[9]

Combining the best of available experimental techniques with some of his own, Straumanis et al.[11] obtained a precision of about 1 part in 200,000 (0.0005 per cent) on aluminum in 1936. This is based on measuring diffraction-line positions with a precision of about 0.002°ϕ. (ϕ is defined using the Bragg equation in the form $n\lambda = 2d \cos \phi$. Since the angle measured in the Straumanis method is 4ϕ, the precision in ϕ is better by a factor of 2 than that in θ based on measuring the 2θ angle.) In developing his method, Straumanis claims to have reduced systematic errors experimentally within the precision of measurement; hence, his accuracy would also correspond to about $\pm 0.002°\phi$. Although Straumanis has offered no rigorous proof to demonstrate accuracy of this magnitude, a quantitative evaluation[57a,57d] of some of the systematic errors inherent in the Straumanis method for certain experimental conditions indicates that his claims are substantially correct. With minor modifications[10] the Straumanis technique still represents one of the most precise and accurate methods available for lattice-parameter determination.

The Straumanis method can also be used at lower levels of precision. In fact, various facets of it can be, and are, used in connection with much routine powder-identification work; however, for work at the 0.001°θ level, this method needs to be followed in painstaking detail and will be described briefly on this basis. Each individual can then judge for himself what factors are required to attain the level of precision and accuracy in which he is interested.

Basic Requirements. The basic requirements for obtaining precise and accurate lattice-parameter values of powders (or single crystals) using the Straumanis method include the following:

1. A sample powder or crystal that gives sharp diffraction lines (0.5 to 1.5° 2θ half

width in the 160 to 175° 2θ range) which can be measured with a precision of about 0.005 mm on the film

2. A low-absorbing cylindrical sample of 0.2 mm diameter or less

3. The sample centered to better than 0.01 mm with respect to the film cylinder in a camera of 50 to 120 mm diameter and a means for rotating the sample spindle with respect to the film cylinder

4. Asymmetric film loading with uniform contact between the film and film cylinder

5. A collimator system which minimizes axial divergence, i.e., double pinholes of 0.6 mm diameter or less when using a spot-focus x-ray source

6. Sample-temperature control to $\pm 0.1°$ C or better during the exposure

7. Measurement of the film in a linear measuring instrument accurate to about 0.001 mm over a length of about 250 mm; the film to be contained in an atmosphere of constant humidity and temperature during measurement

8. Measurement of the diffraction line at the smallest available 4ϕ angle (corresponding to the largest 2θ angle) in calculating the lattice parameter

9. Application of a refraction correction to the lattice-parameter calculation

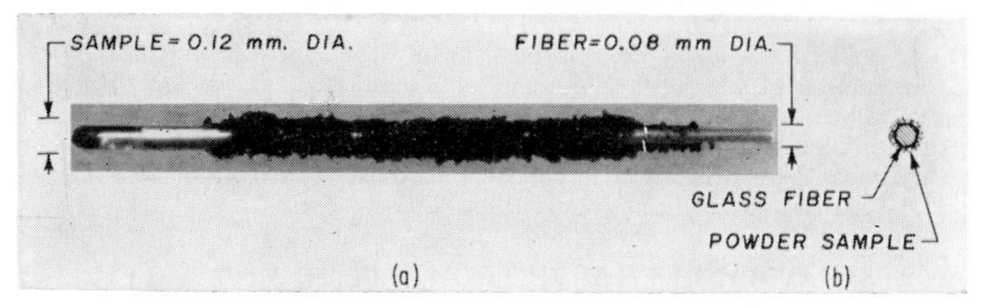

FIG. 2. Straumanis-type powder sample. WO_2 powder on Lindemann glass fiber. (*a*) Photomicrograph. (*b*) Schematic cross section. (*Courtesy of M. E. Straumanis.*)

These nine points constitute a recipe for obtaining precise and accurate lattice-parameter values at the $0.002°\phi$ level. Using this recipe, a majority of the systematic error sources for cylindrical film cameras listed in Table 1 may be reduced experimentally to the measurement precision level. The effects of the remaining error sources will be discussed after a brief review of each of these nine points.

Sharp Diffraction Lines. Unless a powder sample has relatively strain-free crystallites of the proper size to give very sharp, smooth diffraction lines with sample rotation, it is impossible to measure the lines to a maximum precision of about $0.002°\theta$ or ϕ. If it is impossible to have crystallites of optimum size, it is better that they be slightly larger rather than smaller. The spottiness of lines due to slightly larger crystallites can be eliminated by translation as well as rotation of the sample. Translation-rotation mechanisms have been described.[10,13]

Low-absorbing Small-diameter Samples. If a Lindemann (low-absorbing) glass fiber is coated with a thin layer of the sample powder* to a total diameter of no more than 0.2 mm (see Fig. 2), the absorption characteristics for such a sample can result in a nearly symmetrical absorption profile, the peak of which is not displaced by more than about $0.001°\theta$ from the true 2θ position at angles of 160° 2θ and larger.[57c] Such a sample would cause no measurable shift in the peak of the diffraction profile at or above 160° 2θ due to absorption. Great care is required to achieve this condition. For example, any or all of the following factors could cause a significant peak shift due to absorption: a highly absorbing powder sample, too thick a powder layer on the fiber, or measurements made at angles much less than 160° 2θ. With single crystals 0.2 mm in diameter, the shift due to absorption is usually appreciable.

Sample Eccentricity. If the sample axis of rotation deviates from the center of the film cylinder by more than about 0.01 mm in a camera 50 to 120 mm in diameter, it

* A nondrying adhesive such as silicone grease should be used to cause the powder to adhere to the fiber. If the adhesive is of the drying type, it may induce strains in the crystallites which could affect the measured ϕ value and lattice-parameter determination.

is necessary to adjust the sample spindle until the eccentricity is less than this amount. [Sample wobble is eliminated (<0.002 mm) in a separate step by aligning the cylindrical sample on its own axis of rotation under a microscope at about 20× magnification. This can be done externally to the camera body if desired.] A correction for residual eccentricity (below 0.01 mm) can be made by rotating the sample-spindle and cover-plate assembly until the eccentricity vector is parallel to the x-ray beam in the camera. This orientation eliminates the need for assumptions ordinarily used in eccentricity-correction procedures.[9] Correction for residual eccentricity is then made by obtaining two exposures, one with the eccentricity vector in the direction of the x-ray beam and the other with the vector in the opposite direction. The average lattice-parameter value obtained from these two exposures is free of eccentricity error. The Straumanis method does not permit making eccentricity corrections to individual line measurements as required when using the LRM;[4] however, an exact eccentricity-correction procedure which permits doing this has been developed.[14] In developing this exact procedure, it was shown that, if the sample-spindle and cover-plate assembly is rotated until the vector is perpendicular to the x-ray beam, the eccentricity correction in measuring 4ϕ is less than $0.0001°\phi$ for a vector of magnitude about 0.01 mm in a 57.3-mm-diameter camera and for ϕ angles in the range of 5 to 45°. Hence the effects of eccentricity can be reduced to negligible values more simply by directing the vector perpendicular to instead of parallel to, the x-ray beam.

Cameras larger than about 120 mm in diameter make it easier to reduce the percentage eccentricity error mechanically; however, such cameras usually require inordinately long exposure times and are subject to greater film-measuring problems and temperature fluctuations than smaller cameras. Straumanis has shown that there is no real advantage to be gained in measurement precision in terms of degrees θ when using cameras larger than 50 to 75 mm in diameter. This is based on the premise that the angular width of a given diffraction line is essentially constant, the larger the camera, the greater the separation of lines, but the wider a given line (in millimeters) on the film. The lower limit on camera size for high precision and accuracy is dictated by the accuracy of the film-measuring instrument, the graininess of the film, and the ability to minimize eccentricity mechanically. Straumanis prefers a 64-mm-diameter camera as a useful compromise.

Asymmetric Film Loading. This, is perhaps, the most widely known and used feature of the Straumanis method. The film is placed asymmetrically in the camera so that forward- and back-reflection lines are registered symmetrically about zero and 180° 2θ, respectively. The lines around 0° 2θ are registered at one end of the film, the lines around 180° 2θ at the other end. [If there are no lines in the back-reflection region, the Wilson[15] modification of the asymmetric film-loading procedure may be used. This modification involves obtaining some forward-reflection lines on the (normal) back-reflection end of the film.] By measuring lines about these two points, the zero and 180° 2θ positions can be accurately determined within the precision of measurement even though these positions are physically unavailable because they are located in the holes drilled (rather than punched) in the film to admit the collimator and beam stop tubes. After these two positions are determined, the effective camera radius and corrections for uniform film shrinkage may be calculated. It has been found that the zero-degree position can be determined even more accurately by using a beam stop internal to the camera and by registering a shadow of the sample capillary on the film. The center of the shadow is in the zero-degree 2θ position.[16,57a,57d] In processing the film, it is desirable to eliminate the second image on double-coated film. This can easily be done by applying a waterproof tape to the second emulsion prior to development and then removing the tape prior to fixing the film.[17]

Collimator Dimensions. A double-pinhole collimator system is recommended by Straumanis, with the pinhole diameter no larger than 1 mm. A 1-mm-diameter pinhole system is useful in order to minimize exposure time; however, the shift in diffraction peak position due to axial divergence for a collimator of this size may become significant at large diffraction angles. As a point of reference, the peak shift due only to axial divergence at $87.5°\theta$ for a 0.6-mm double-pinhole collimator in a 64-mm-diameter camera is on the borderline of significance ($0.001°\theta$).[18]

Sample Temperature. Lattice parameters vary with temperature such that a change of 0.1° C affects the lattice-parameter value, in angstroms, in the fifth or sixth decimal place, depending on the thermal expansion coefficient of the material. The fifth or sixth decimal place corresponds approximately to the $0.001°\theta$ level of precision and accuracy. Thus, sample temperatures need to be measured and controlled to about ±0.1°C so that the lattice parameter will not fluctuate significantly during an exposure and so that the lattice-parameter determination can be related to an absolute temperature value. This latter is required (1) when interlaboratory comparisons are made and the lattice parameters are determined at different temperatures or (2) when thermal expansion coefficients are to be determined from lattice-parameter measurements. Straumanis has developed several thermostatic devices[10] for controlling camera temperature, including air and water media for control to ±0.02° C. A thermometer is used to measure the air or water temperature inside the thermostat-equipped housing which is adjacent and exterior to the camera body.

Film Measurements. In order to measure line positions to a precision of about $0.002°\phi$ it is necessary to measure them to about 0.005 mm on films using a 57.3-mm-diameter camera (1 mm on film $= 2°\ 2\theta = 2°\ 4\phi$; hence

$$0.005 \text{ mm} = 0.010°\ 4\phi = 0.0025°\ \phi$$

Measurements to a precision of about 0.005 mm at 95 per cent confidence limits are about the best that can be attained with film technique, and this precision can best be achieved using a measuring instrument that is somewhat more precise and accurate than 0.005 mm over the measuring range of about 250 mm. While measuring the film it is important to protect it from changes in temperature and humidity. A simple way to accomplish this is to place the film between two pieces of plate glass and to seal the edges with a waterproof tape. The film in its glass envelope is then placed on the measuring-instrument table and allowed to come to thermal equilibrium. It is important that the light source for the measuring instrument be sufficiently far away from the film so that thermal equilibrium can be established. Measuring instruments in which the light source is close to the film are particularly difficult to use because thermal (and hence, humidity) equilibrium is nearly impossible to establish at the 0.005-mm measuring level.

It is also important to align the equator of the film exactly (within 0.05 mm) along the line of measurement and parallel to the direction of motion of the instrument table. Measurement errors here are due not so much to lack of parallelism as to the rapidly increasing effect of axial divergence as the position of measurement moves away from the equatorial position of a line on the film.[18] Alignment along the equator can easily be attained within 0.03 mm by registering sample shadow marks[16,57a,57d] at two positions on the film prior to processing.

Measurements at the Smallest Usable 4φ Angle. Nearly all systematic errors—except zero, axial divergence, Lorentz, polarization, and dispersion—tend to become smaller, the smaller the 4ϕ angle. This and the increased precision in lattice parameter obtainable with decreasing 4ϕ angle are the primary reasons why Straumanis recommended the calculation of a lattice parameter from the "last line" at the smallest 4ϕ angle. There are two reasons for measuring the 4ϕ angle rather than the 2θ angle: (1) The precision in measuring and calculating ϕ is two times better than that of measuring and calculating θ if the 2θ angle is measured. [The precision in millimeters is about the same regardless of the (sharp) line being measured in the range of 120 to 175° 2θ, and the precision in ϕ is equivalent to mm/4 while the precision in θ is equivalent to mm/2.] (2) The effect of a nonuniform x-ray source in shifting the peak of a profile is essentially eliminated when measuring 4ϕ instead of 2θ.[19,57e]

Refraction Correction. After the d value or lattice parameter is calculated from measurements of the smallest 4ϕ angle, a correction has to be made for refraction of x-rays in the crystal. Straumanis recommends a refraction correction for cubic substances[20] of the form $a_0 = a_{hkl}(1 + \partial/\sin^2 \theta_{hkl})$ where a_0 is the lattice parameter corrected for refraction, a_{hkl} is the lattice parameter calculated from the θ_{hkl} measurement, and $\partial = 1 - \mu$; μ is the index of refraction.

Systematic Errors Not Discussed Explicitly by Straumanis. There are six sources of error which Straumanis does not discuss explicitly. These are axial divergence, dispersion, Lorentz and polarization factors, nonuniform film shrinkage, and observer bias in measuring-line positions. Axial divergence has been handled implicitly (comparison of slit and pinhole collimator data)[10] and may be minimized to the point of insignificance by suitable choice of collimator dimensions. This has been discussed. Dispersion and Lorentz and polarization factors cause no shift in the peak position[5] and hence may be ignored. (Pike and Wilson[21] have pointed out that the peak position is not affected by the combined dispersion plus Lorentz factors. Either alone may have a slight effect.)

Nonuniform film shrinkage on the order of 0.01 mm/mm has been observed occasionally[57a,57d] and can be corrected on individual films as indicated in the section on the

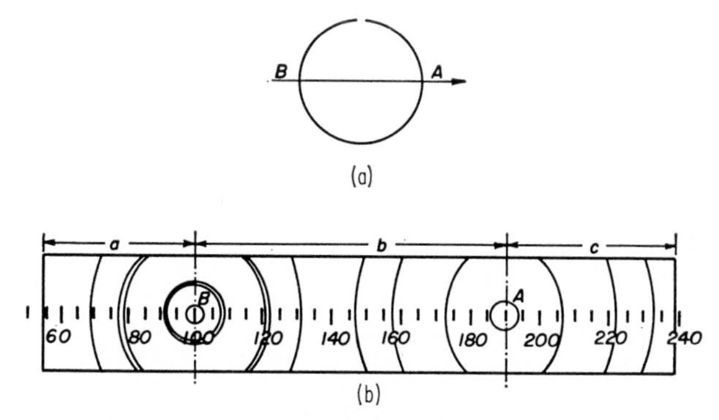

FIG. 3. Schematic drawing of Straumanis-type film. (*a*) Film mounted asymmetrically in camera. (*b*) Film laid out flat on measuring instrument.

Convolution-film Method. It is also possible to consider nonuniform shrinkage as a random error and to average out its effect by making several exposures on the same sample. This procedure tends to reduce precision; hence it should not be used when the highest precision and accuracy are desired.

Observer bias in measuring line positions visually on a film is a rather complex problem. It is tacitly assumed by Straumanis and others that the line position actually measured is the position of maximum line blackening (peak position). This has been demonstrated to be true in connection with some x-ray wavelength measurements;[23] however, there is evidence from diffraction-pattern measurements that this is not universally true.[24,57a,57d] Some of the factors affecting line-position measurements are (1) the inherent asymmetry of the line, (2) the proximity to other lines, and (3) the graininess of the film. Any or all of these factors can conspire to cause a bias in measurement with respect to the experimental peak position. That characteristic of the diffraction profile actually measured visually on any one film can be determined from difference measurements on microphotometer records of diffraction plus calibration lines as pointed out in the section on the Convolution-film Method. In summary, it is felt that the systematic errors neglected by Straumanis can be maintained at or below the 0.002° ϕ level if the above factors are properly evaluated and handled before lattice-parameter values are calculated.

Example of Straumanis Calculation. Figure 3 is a schematic drawing of a diffraction pattern of aluminum obtained in a 57.7-mm-diameter camera using copper radiation. The scale shown in this figure is a part of the film-measuring instrument. A represents the angular position $4\phi = 360°$ $(2\theta = 0°)$ and B represents the position $4\phi = 0°$ $(2\theta = 180°)$. To determine the film-shrinkage correction ϕ, and a_0 for a given film, corresponding diffraction-ring segments are measured in regions a, b, and c about positions A and B, as follows:

a. Determination of effective film circumference and mm/degree:

Aluminum (hkl)	(224) α_1	(111) β
Measured in region a and c, respectively	78.334	207.230
Measured in region b	120.986	172.510
Sum	199.320 mm	379.740 mm

379.740 − 199.320 = 180.420 mm effective film circumference = 360° on the film. mm/degree (corrected for film shrinkage) = 180.420/360 = 0.50117.

b. Determination of 4ϕ, ϕ, and a_0:

(hkl) of "highest-angle" line	$(333)\alpha_1$
Measured in region b	108.440
Measured in region a	90.910
Difference	17.530 mm

$4\phi = 17.530/0.50116 = 34.978°$.
$\phi = 8.745°$.

from which

$a_0 =$ 4.04944 Å
+0.00004 Å refraction correction

$a_0 =$ 4.04948 Å for aluminum at 23.1° C, based on Cu $K\alpha_1$ = 1.54051 Å and corrected for refraction

3. EXTRAPOLATION METHODS FOR CYLINDRICAL AND BACK-REFLECTION FILM CAMERAS (0.01°θ LEVEL)

Principles and Useful Extrapolation Functions. In 1932, Bradley and Jay[9] showed that the magnitudes of certain systematic errors in cylindrical film cameras were proportional to $\cos^2 \theta$ in the range of about 50 to 90°θ and would reduce to zero for $\cos^2 \theta = 0$ ($\theta = 90°$). Thus, by plotting lattice-parameter values calculated from several (hkl) reflections in this range against $\cos^2 \theta$ and extrapolating linearly to $\cos^2 \theta = 0$, this would yield a lattice-parameter value free from these systematic errors. If these were the only systematic errors, the extrapolated lattice parameter would be an accurate value within the precision of measurement.

The $\cos^2 \theta$ extrapolation function was derived based on the assumptions that systematic errors are due to absorption in a highly absorbing capillary sample and to eccentricity of this sample with respect to the film cylinder. The absorption portion of the derivation is based on a divergent x-ray beam while the eccentricity portion is based on a parallel beam. Although absorption and eccentricity are, indeed, two of the major systematic errors in film powder cameras, they are not necessarily the only ones. Furthermore, the assumptions of a highly absorbing sample and parallel radiation are by no means universal in their application. Finally, the graphical method of drawing in the "best-fitting" extrapolation line gives rise to a degree of subjectivity on the part of the observer which does not lend itself particularly to accuracy.

In spite of these limitations, the $\cos^2 \theta$ extrapolation method has been successfully applied and it and similar functions are in widespread use today. A reason for its success is that a precision of about 0.01°θ is satisfactory for much lattice-parameter work. In many cases of practical interest this level of precision is sufficiently low to mask some of the effects of the approximations used as well as systematic errors not included in deriving the $\cos^2 \theta$ function.

The $\cos^2 \theta$ extrapolation function has been the basis of much additional lattice-parameter development. For example, Cohen[25] in 1935 developed an analytical method for $\cos^2 \theta$ extrapolation by means of a "linear least-squares fit" to the data. Cohen's method eliminates the subjectivity of fitting the "best" straight line graphically; however, it imposes an arbitrarily equal weight on each lattice-parameter value regardless of the precision with which the diffraction line can be measured.

It was realized that lattice-parameter values could be determined with higher precision at larger θ angles because of the cot θ effect (see Fig. 1) and hence should be given more weight. Hess[26] and others developed weighting functions to overcome this limitation of the Cohen analytical extrapolation; however, these developments are limited by the $\cos^2 \theta$ function itself and the fact that the weighting is still based on a more or less arbitrary function rather than on the precision with which the diffraction lines themselves can be measured.

Among the extrapolation functions widely used for cylindrical cameras at present is the one developed independently in 1945 by Taylor and Sinclair[27] and Nelson and Riley.[28] This extrapolation function, $\xi = \frac{1}{2}(\cos^2 \theta/\sin \theta + \cos^2 \theta/\theta)$, was derived based on using cylindrical samples of intermediate absorption having no eccentricity with respect to the film cylinder and an exponential x-ray source distribution. The advantages of this function over $\cos^2 \theta$ are that it takes into account the highly practical case of samples of intermediate absorption and that it is linear over a wider range (from 30 to 90°θ). Its major disadvantage is that it ignores other systematic errors.

An extrapolation function widely used for symmetrical back-reflection focusing cameras or for the back-reflection region of cylindrical cameras is $\phi \tan \phi$, where $\phi = \pi/2 - \theta$. A $\phi \tan \phi$ extrapolation is linear for $\phi < 30°$ and the extrapolation is made to $\phi = 0°$, corresponding to $\theta = 90°$. The function $\phi \tan \phi$ is virtually identical with $\sin^2 \phi (= \cos^2 \theta)$ and hence the same advantages and disadvantages of the $\cos^2 \theta$ extrapolation function apply in essence to $\phi \tan \phi$; however, it is recommended that $\phi \tan\phi$ be used for symmetrical back-reflection cameras instead of $\cos^2 \theta$.

Extrapolation functions are not generally useful with flat-plate back-reflection cameras because of the difficulty in obtaining the necessary number of back-reflection lines in the small angular range available for this type of camera. However, Hess[26] has derived an expression $\Phi = -(\Delta p/p) \sin \Phi \cos \Phi$ where Δp is the error in the specimen-to-plate distance p and $\Phi = \pi - 2\theta = 2\phi$, which gives a measure of the systematic error in Φ for flat-plate back-reflection cameras. The corresponding extrapolation function is $\cos^2 \theta \cos 2\theta$. In those cases where extrapolation is inappropriate, it is recommended that a calibrating substance such as aluminum or silver be applied to the sample surface as a thin film about 0.02 mm thick. The angle ϕ, and hence the lattice parameter, for the sample may then be determined using the relationship $\tan 2\phi = (D/D_c) \tan 2\phi_c$ where the subscript c refers to the calibrating substance. D and D_c refer to diffraction-ring diameters.

For diffractometers, if the sample flatness or transparency errors are predominant, the $\cos^2 \theta$ extrapolation function is useful. On the other hand, if sample surface displacement from the diffractometer rotation axis is the principal error, a useful extrapolation function is $\cot \theta \cos \theta$.

The development of extrapolation functions has continued to the present day, including nonlinear least-squares extrapolations;[29] however, all such functions suffer in principle from the major limitation that no one function can be developed the extrapolation of which will universally result in the elimination of all systematic errors within the precision of measurement.

An ingenious way of exploiting this limitation of extrapolation functions has been recently developed by Mueller et al.,[30] who have prepared computer programs for calculating lattice parameters using several extrapolation functions and weighting factors in various combinations. Because of the speed of computation, many combinations can be calculated quickly. The lattice parameter obtained using the "best" combination is then chosen as the correct (accurate) value. "Best" is defined here in terms of a function v_i where

$$v_i = \sin^2 \theta_i(\text{computed}) - \sin^2 \theta_i(\text{observed})$$

v_i's are calculated for several diffraction lines using a given extrapolation combination, and these values are plotted against θ. The "best" combination is that which shows the smallest deviations of the v_i's from zero. A potential difficulty with this method occurs if the deviations of the v_i's cannot be satisfactorily minimized, regardless of which extrapolation and weighting combination is used. The method offers no obvious guide to help improve this situation.

In summary, the precision and accuracy of extrapolation methods are limited by two major factors: (1) the precision and accuracy with which the cameras and diffractometers are built and used, and (2) the magnitude of the approximations inherent in the extrapolation functions as they are used in conjunction with specific experimental arrangements. In general, these approximations limit the accuracy to the equivalent of about 0.01°θ. The precision can be this good or better for diffractometers and for cylindrical cameras using the experimental guide lines already discussed in the section on the Straumanis method. These guide lines, together with the systematic error sources given in Table 1, also provide a means of evaluating precision and accuracy as applied to focusing and flat-plate back-reflection cameras.

Examples of Extrapolation Methods. Several examples of the major extrapolation methods as they apply to cubic crystals will be given to aid in the application of these methods to specific problems. No attempt will be made to describe cameras or

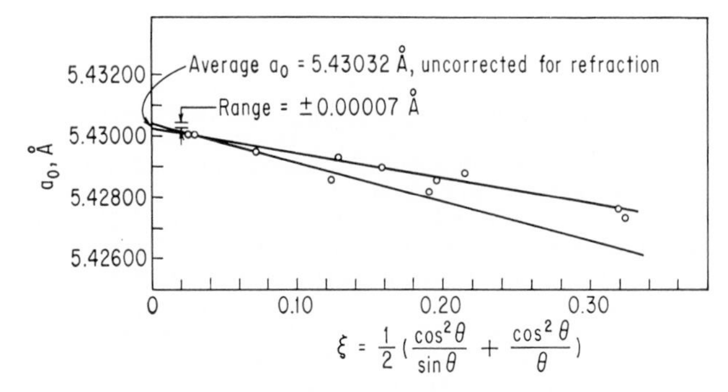

FIG. 4. ξ extrapolation plot for IUCr silicon sample.

diffractometers which may be used in conjunction with these methods, as these have already been described in Chaps. 8 and 9. The calibration of these instruments using knife-edges, notches, pinholes, etc., and the errors inherent in the calibration procedures are also described in those two chapters. Reference should be made to Table 1 for all possible systematic error sources to aid in evaluating the factors which may affect the specific experimental conditions to be used. The extrapolation methods to be discussed can be used in determining lattice parameters for crystal systems having symmetries lower than cubic; however, these applications will be discussed separately in Sec. 4.

Graphical Extrapolation against $\cos^2\theta$, ξ, *or* $\phi \tan \phi$.* Graphical extrapolations are simply carried out by drawing the "best" straight line through the calculated parameter values and extrapolating to $\cos^2\theta$, ξ, or $\phi \tan \phi = 0$. The definition of "best" is somewhat subjective; however, a common practice is to draw the line so as to give greatest weight to the parameter values closest to $\cos^2\theta$, ξ, or $\phi \tan \phi = 0$. A useful modification of this is to draw two extrapolation lines to cover the extreme data-point values, using the most reliable point at the highest angle essentially as a pivot point, as illustrated in Fig. 4 for a ξ function extrapolation. The two parameter values thus defined by the two extrapolation lines at $\xi = 0$ constitute a range which gives a measure of precision while the average of the two is used as the final parameter value, subject to temperature and refraction corrections.

The ξ extrapolation function may be used most effectively for samples which have intermediate (less than infinite) absorption characteristics, as demonstrated by examining the data for Cu_9Al_{14} in Table 2 and the ξ extrapolation plots in Fig. 5. The Cu_9Al_{14} samples were prepared to cover a wide range of absorption characteristics. This was

* Tables of $\cos^2\theta$, ξ, and $\phi \tan \phi$ are given on pp. 228–232 of *International Tables for X-ray Crystallography*, vol. II. (See General References following this chapter.) These tables are of particular value for graphical extrapolation procedures when using these functions.

accomplished by varying sample diameter and by sample dilution with gum tragacanth. Although there are large differences in the slopes of the extrapolation lines (Fig. 5), the maximum variation from the average of the extrapolated lattice-parameter values is only about 1 part in 30,000 (Table 2). In general, ξ extrapolation plots are most useful for small-diameter low-absorption samples which minimize the slope of the plot and permit a fairly precise and accurate determination of the extrapolated

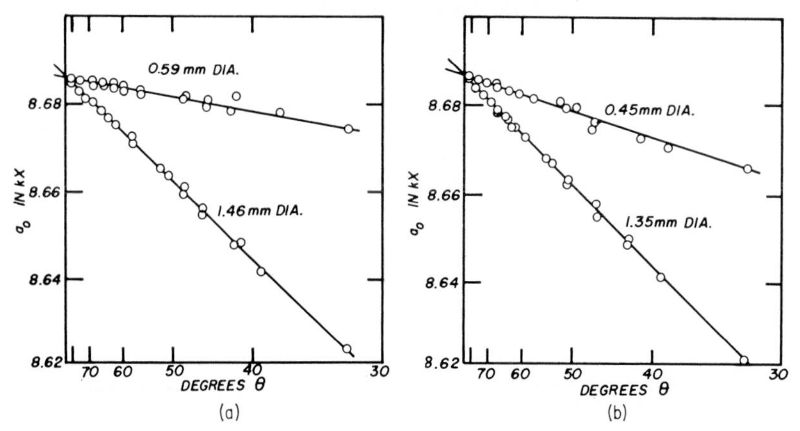

FIG. 5. ξ extrapolation plots for annealed Cu_9Al_{14} filings. (*a*) Samples diluted with gum tragacanth. (*b*) Undiluted samples. [*Courtesy of J. B. Nelson and D. P. Riley, Proc. Phys. Soc. (London)*, **57**:160 (1945).]

lattice-parameter value. For the best results, the plots should extend to ξ values no lower than the equivalent of about 30°θ and should include at least one good point for $\theta > 80°$.

Table 2. Values of a_0 for Cu_9Al_{14} Obtained from Extrapolations against

$$\xi = \frac{1}{2}\left(\frac{\cos^2\theta}{\sin\theta} + \frac{\cos^2\theta}{\theta}\right)^*$$

(Camera diameter = 19 cm)

Diam of specimen, mm	Diluted with gum tragacanth	Temp, ° C	a_0, Å	a_0, kX
0.59	Yes	15.8	8.7038	8.6863
0.45	No	16.2	8.7041	8.6866
1.46	Yes	15.4	8.7036	8.6861
1.35	No	16.4	8.7039	8.6864

Mean value of a_0 = 8.7039 Å (8.6864 kX).
See Fig. 5 for ξ extrapolation plots.
* Data from Nelson and Riley.[28]

Analytical Extrapolation against $\cos^2\theta$, ξ, or $\phi \tan \phi$. The analytical extrapolation method of Cohen[25] was developed based on the assumption that the combined systematic errors are proportional to $\cos^2\theta$; i.e.,

$$\Delta a_0/a_0 = \Delta d/d = K \cos^2\theta$$

An error (or observation) equation may then be derived for cubic crystals and is given as follows: $A_0\alpha_i + D\partial_i = \sin^2\theta_i$, where $A_0 = \lambda^2/4a_0^2$, $\alpha_i = (h^2 + k^2 + l^2)_i$, ∂_i (error term) $= \sin^2 2\theta_i$, and D = a "drift" constant which is a fixed quantity for any one film but differs from one film to another.

The "best" values of A_0 and D (for which the sum of the squares of the random observational errors is a minimum) may be determined by means of normal equations, derived from the error equation using the principle of least squares. The normal equations are

$$A_0\Sigma\alpha_i^2 + D\Sigma\alpha_i\partial_i = \Sigma\alpha_i \sin^2\theta_i$$
$$A_0\Sigma\alpha_i\partial_i + D\Sigma\partial_i^2 = \Sigma\partial_i \sin^2\theta_i$$

An application of the normal equations to parameter data for spectrographic lead (essentially infinite absorption suitable for a $\cos^2\theta$ extrapolation) is given in Table 3. It should be noted that the ∂_i values are multiplied by 10 so that the coefficients of the normal equations will be of the same general magnitude. This, of course, has no effect on the calculated values of A_0 and a_0. Also, the term $D\Sigma\partial_i^2$ is of much smaller magnitude than the term $A_0\Sigma\alpha_i^2$, with the result that values of ∂_i need only be calculated to two significant figures while $\sin^2\theta_i$ need be calculated to five or six significant figures.

Table 3. a_0 Calculations for Spectrographic Lead Using an Analytical Least-squares Extrapolation against $\cos^2\theta$*

Camera diameter = 114.6 mm (1 mm on film = 1.00307° 2θ). Cu $K\alpha$ radiation, sample at 25° C

Line	*hkl*	α	λ	$\theta°$	$\sin^2\theta$	$\sin^2\theta \rightarrow K\alpha_1$	∂‡
1	531	35	$K\alpha_1$	67.080	0.84833	0.84833	5.1
2	531	35	$K\alpha_2$	67.421	0.85258	0.84835†	5.0
3	600	36	$K\alpha_1$	69.061	0.87230	0.87230	4.5
4	600	36	$K\alpha_2$	69.467	0.87698	0.87263†	4.3
5	620	40	$K\alpha_1$	79.794	0.96861	0.96861	1.2
6	620	40	$K\alpha_2$	80.601	0.97332	0.96849†	1.0

$\Sigma\alpha_i^2 = 8{,}242.0 \quad \Sigma\alpha_i\partial_i = 758.3 \quad \Sigma\alpha_i \sin^2\theta_i = 199.6853$

$\Sigma\partial_i^2 = 92.2 \quad \Sigma\partial_i \sin^2\theta_i = 18.3767$

Normal equations:

$$8{,}242.0A_0 + 758.3D = 199.6853$$
$$758.3A_0 + 92.2D = 18.3767$$
$$A_0 = 0.0242082 \qquad D = 0.000213$$
$$a_0 = 4.95052 \text{ Å}$$
$$a_0 = 4.95066 \text{ Å (corrected for refraction)}$$

* Data from Klug and Alexander, p. 470 (see General References).

† Values obtained by multiplying $\sin^2\theta$ values for $K\alpha_1$ by $(\lambda\alpha_1/\lambda\alpha_2)^2$.

‡ Values multiplied by 10 and calculated from observed θ and $\sin^2\theta$ values *before* converting α_2 to α_1 values.

In using the ξ function for a least-squares extrapolation, it is necessary only to redefine the error term ∂_i in the normal equations. In this case, $\partial_i = \sin^2 2\theta_i\,(1/\sin\theta_i + 1/\theta_i)$. In using the $\phi \tan\phi$ function, ∂_i is defined by $\partial_i = \phi_i \sin 2\phi_i$. In either of these extrapolation functions, the other terms in the normal equations remain the same and a calculation is carried out in the same manner as for the $\cos^2\theta$ extrapolation.

Analytical extrapolations of this type have the advantage over graphical "eyeball" extrapolations in that they tend to be more objective in data interpretation; however, they must be used with care, taking into account (1) limitations on weighting of the experimental θ values and (2) limitations of the approximations used in deriving the extrapolation functions themselves. Hess[26] has developed a weighting function ($w = \csc^2 \Phi$) for the Bragg-angle measurements which, while still somewhat arbitrary, corresponds more closely to normal experimental conditions than the unitary weighting ($w = 1$) inherent in the original Cohen method.

Analytical Extrapolation by Computer. The Hess modification of Cohen's method has been further developed by Vogel and Kempter[31] for computation on an IBM 704 computer. The program was written in Fortran code for symmetrical back-reflection focusing cameras ($\phi \tan \phi$ extrapolation function), for cylindrical cameras [$\cos^2 \theta$, $\frac{1}{2}(\cos^2 \theta/\sin \theta + \cos^2 \theta/\theta)$, or $\phi \tan \phi$ extrapolation functions], and for diffractometers ($\cos \theta \cot \theta$ extrapolation function). The computer method is exact in that there are no approximations made in the solution of the normal equations. Furthermore, the iterative process used in this procedure is carried out to convergence rather than stopping after the first cycle as suggested by Hess.[26]

Although the Vogel and Kempter method is available in program form for the IBM 704 computer, the principles of this method will be reviewed briefly to illustrate both the Hess method and Vogel and Kempter's modification. The reader is referred to the literature[26,31,32] for additional details.

For cubic materials the error equation as developed by Hess is

$$F = A_0\alpha + K_0\partial - \gamma$$

where
$$\begin{aligned} A_0 &= 1/a_0^2 \\ \alpha &= \tfrac{1}{2}\lambda^2 n^2(h^2 + k^2 + l^2) \\ K_0 &= \text{“drift” constant} \\ \partial &= \Phi \sin \Phi^* \qquad \Phi = \pi - 2\theta = 2\phi \\ \gamma &= 1 + \cos \Phi = 2 \sin^2 \theta \end{aligned}$$

Hess obtained a weighting function $\csc^2 \Phi$ based on the simplifying assumption of setting $K_0 = 0$. The Vogel and Kempter modification does not make this assumption. Rather it involves minimizing the function

$$Q = \sum_{e=1}^{N} w_e F_e^2$$

where $F_e = \sum_{i=1}^{m} a_i x_{ie} - y_e$ (a generalized form of the normal equation)
w_e = weight associated with each F_e
e ranges from 1 to N (experimental points)
$m = 2$ for cubic materials

By the method of maximum likelihood[33] it can be shown that w_e is inversely proportional to the variance of F_e, $\sigma_{F_e}^2$. Furthermore, the random error in θ_e is essentially constant, as has been observed experimentally, especially in the range of θ larger than 60°; hence it may be ignored in the development of this method since it acts as a proportionality constant. On this basis, weighting functions w_e for four extrapolation functions have been developed and are given in Table 4. (See Ref. 32 for definition of θ as used in Table 4.)

Because w_e is a function of the parameters, an iterative method[34] is used to minimize Q, the iteration proceeding until the corrections to the parameter estimates are considered to be "sufficiently small." A reasonable criterion for "sufficiently small" is based on observing the differences between the observed and least-squares-calculated a_0's over a range of extrapolation function values. If the signs of the differences are randomly distributed the corrections are considered to be "sufficiently small." Once

* ∂ is derived here for the symmetrical back-reflection case (focusing or Debye-Scherrer cameras) using the $\phi \tan \phi$ extrapolation function. If the $\cos^2 \theta$ or ξ functions are used, the values of ∂ are $\sin^2 2\theta$ and $\sin^2 2\theta\,(1/\sin \theta + 1/\theta)$, respectively. For the diffractometer, if specimen surface displacement is the major systematic error, this error is proportional to $\cos \theta \cot \theta$ and $\partial = \sin \theta \cos^2 \theta$ in this case.

Table 4. Weighting Functions w_e for Four Extrapolation Functions

Extrapolation function	Weighting function w_e
$\phi \tan \phi$	$\dfrac{1}{4[K_0(\pi - \theta)\cos^2\theta - (K_0 + 1)\sin 2\theta]^2}$
$\cos^2 \theta$	$\dfrac{1}{4[K_0 \sin 4\theta - \sin 2\theta]^2}$
$\dfrac{1}{2}\left(\dfrac{\cos^2\theta}{\sin\theta} + \dfrac{\cos^2\theta}{\theta}\right)$	$\dfrac{1}{\left[K_0\left(4\cos^3\theta - 8\sin^2\theta\cos\theta + \dfrac{2\sin 4\theta}{\theta} - \dfrac{\sin^2 2\theta}{\theta^2}\right) - 2\sin 2\theta\right]^2}$
$\cos\theta \cot\theta$	$\dfrac{1}{[K_0\cos\theta(\cos^2\theta - 2\sin^2\theta) - 2\sin 2\theta]^2}$

this has been achieved, standard-deviation and confidence-limit estimates may be calculated for the parameters.

Vogel and Kempter have demonstrated that their exact method and Hess's approximate method ($K_0 = 0$) are in excellent agreement, and they cite several lattice-parameter calculations using both methods. In some cases, however, especially where K_0 was significantly different from zero, differences were observed between the two methods, and the exact method is to be preferred.

4. LATTICE PARAMETERS OF NONCUBIC MATERIALS (0.01°θ LEVEL)

The analytical extrapolation methods can all be carried out by hand calculation in reasonable time for cubic materials; however, the calculation time tends to become prohibitive for noncubic materials and the utility of a computer method such as that of Vogel and Kempter becomes obvious. Nevertheless, there are several practical hand-calculation methods which, in certain specialized cases, can be used for noncubic materials, primarily at the 0.01°θ level. These as well as computer methods will be outlined in this section.

Straumanis Method. If two diffraction lines of indices ($h_1k_1l_1$) and ($h_2k_2l_2$) are obtained at angles at or above 80°θ, the Straumanis method can be used directly in determining the lattice constants of tetragonal and hexagonal materials. In favorable cases the precision and accuracy may reach the 0.002°ϕ level as described in the cubic case. In general, large values of $(h^2 + k^2)$ lead to improved precision in a_0 and large values of l^2, to improved precision in c_0. For equal precision and accuracy in a_0 and c_0, it is necessary that $\Sigma(h^2 + k^2)_i$ and Σl_i^2 be approximately equal.

The equations for a_0 and c_0 for tetragonal and hexagonal materials using two lines having indices ($h_1k_1l_1$) and ($h_2k_2l_2$) are given in Table 5. Equations are also included for two different wavelengths λ_1 and λ_2. Two wavelengths may be necessary to obtain two lines having satisfactory (hkl) values at about 80°θ or higher. In each case, c_0 is calculated after a_0 using the values of h, k, l, and θ appropriate for the desired reflection.

Graphical Extrapolation Methods. *Direct Method and Method of Successive Approximations.* If several ($hk0$) and several ($00l$) reflections are available in the range of 30 to 90°θ, two separate graphical extrapolations using the ξ function may be made to determine a_0 and c_0 directly for tetragonal and hexagonal materials. If suitable ($hk0$) and ($00l$) reflections are not available, the method of successive approximations of Lipson and Wilson[35] may be used as follows: An approximate axial ratio a/c* is assumed. Using this a/c ratio, ξ function extrapolations are then made for

* $a/c = a_0/c_0$. This designation is used for simplicity of notation.

Table 5. Equations for a_0 and c_0 for Tetragonal and Hexagonal Materials Using the Straumanis Method

Number of wavelengths used	Crystal system	a_0	c_0*
One	Tetragonal	$a_0 = \frac{\lambda}{2}\sqrt{\frac{l_1^2(h_2^2 + k_2^2) - l_2^2(h_1^2 + k_1^2)}{l_1^2 \sin^2\theta_2 - l_2^2 \sin^2\theta_1}}$	$c_0 = \frac{\lambda a_0 l}{\sqrt{4a_0^2 \sin^2\theta - \lambda^2(h^2 + k^2)}}$
Two	Tetragonal	$a_0 = \frac{\lambda_1\lambda_2}{2}\sqrt{\frac{l_1^2(h_2^2 + k_2^2) - l_2^2(h_1^2 + k_1^2)}{\lambda_1^2 l_1^2 \sin^2\theta_2 - \lambda_2^2 l_2^2 \sin^2\theta_1}}$	c_0 = same as for one wavelength, tetragonal case
One	Hexagonal	$a_0 = \lambda\sqrt{\frac{l_1^2(h_2^2 + h_2k_2 + k_2^2) - l_2^2(h_1^2 + h_1k_1 + k_1^2)}{3(l_1^2 \sin^2\theta_2 - l_2^2 \sin^2\theta_1)}}$	$c_0 = \frac{\lambda a_0 l}{2}\sqrt{\frac{3}{3a_0^2 \sin^2\theta - \lambda^2(h^2 + hk + k^2)}}$
Two	Hexagonal	$a_0 = \lambda_1\lambda_2\sqrt{\frac{l_1^2(h_2^2 + h_2k_2 + k_2^2) - l_2^2(h_1^2 + h_1k_1 + k_1^2)}{3(\lambda_1^2 l_1^2 \sin^2\theta_2 - \lambda_2^2 l_2^2 \sin^2\theta_1)}}$	c_0 = same as for one wavelength, hexagonal case

* c_0 is calculated after a_0, using appropriate values of λ, h, k, l, and θ.

a_0 using reflections having large h and k indices and for c_0 using reflections having large l indices. The a_0 and c_0 values for the ξ extrapolations are determined using the following equations (for hexagonal materials):

$$a_0 = (\lambda/2 \sin \theta) \sqrt{(4/3)(h^2 + hk + k^2) + (a/c)^2 l^2}$$
$$c_0 = (\lambda/2 \sin \theta) \sqrt{(4/3)(c/a)^2(h^2 + hk + k^2) + l^2}$$

The extrapolated values of a_0 and c_0 are then used to compute a refined a/c ratio; a_0 and c_0 values are recomputed using the new a/c ratio; and new a_0 and c_0 extrapola-

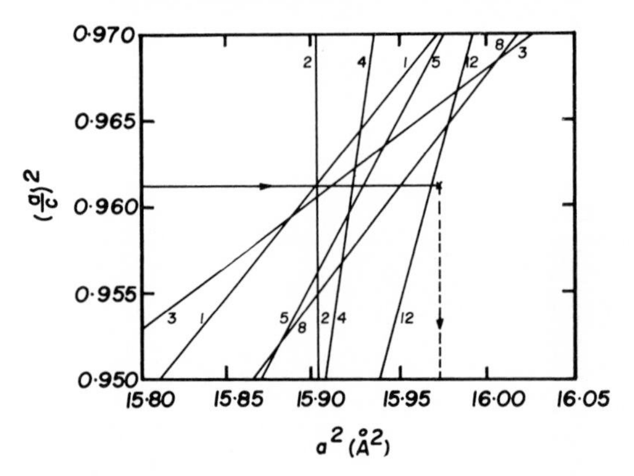

FIG. 6. $(a/c)^2$ vs. a^2 plot for tetragonal Ti-Al alloy. [*Courtesy of E. J. Myers and F. C. Davies, Acta Cryst.*, **14**:194 (1961).]

tions are made. This sequence is repeated until the extrapolated values of a_0 and c_0 remain constant at the desired precision level.

Single-step Method. This graphical method of Myers and Davies[36] can be used to obtain a_0 and c_0 values in a single step instead of requiring successive approximations.

Table 6. Experimental Data, Single-step Graphical Extrapolation for a_0 and c_0 of Tetragonal Ti-Al Alloy*

Diffraction line No.	(hkl)	$\theta°$	Equation of line†
1	202	32.76	$(a/c)^2 = 0.1233a^2 - 1$
2	220	33.12	$a^2 = 15.9020$ (vertical line)
3	113	39.07	$(a/c)^2 = 0.0744a^2 - 0.2222$
4	131	39.73	$(a/c)^2 = 0.6884a^2 - 10$
5	222	41.62	$(a/c)^2 = 0.1859a^2 - 2$
8	313	56.40	$(a/c)^2 = 0.1299a^2 - 1.1111$
12	422	70.26	$(a/c)^2 = 0.3733a^2 - 5$

* Courtesy of E. J. Myers and F. C. Davies, *Acta Cryst.*, **14**:194 (1961).
† $(a/c)^2 = (4 \sin^2 \theta/\lambda^2 l^2)a^2 - (h^2 + k^2)/l^2$ (general)
$a^2 = \lambda^2(h^2 + k^2)/4 \sin^2 \theta$ (for $hk0$ planes)

This method utilizes the ξ function and is based on plotting $(a/c)^2$ vs. a^2. Figure 6 represents such a plot for tetragonal Ti-Al alloy diffraction lines based on the equations

$$(a/c)^2 = (4 \sin^2 \theta/\lambda^2 l^2)a^2 - (h^2 + k^2)/l^2 \qquad \text{(general)}$$
$$a^2 = \lambda^2(h^2 + k^2)/4 \sin^2 \theta \qquad \text{(for } hk0 \text{ planes)}$$

These lines fail to intersect at a common point because of scatter and drift in the experimental data (data for Fig. 6 are given in Table 6). By using an extrapolation fan plotter (Fig. 7) and fitting the plotter to the $(a/c)^2$ vs. a^2 graph until the lines match in sequence and magnitude in a horizontal direction (indicated by the horizontal line with the arrow on Fig. 6), the correct value of $(a/c)^2$ may be read off directly. a^2 corresponds to the abscissa value $\xi = 0$ on the fan plotter (vertical arrow in Fig. 6). (a/c), a_0, and c_0 may then be calculated. For the tetragonal Ti-Al alloy used in the illustration, $a_0 = 3.997$ Å, $c_0 = 4.077$ Å, and $a/c = 0.9804$.

The equations used in this one-step graphical extrapolation for hexagonal crystals are

$$(a/c)^2 = (4 \sin^2 \theta/\lambda^2 l^2)a^2 - 4(h^2 + hk + k^2)/3l^2 \qquad \text{(general)}$$
$$a^2 = \lambda^2(h^2 + hk + k^2)/3 \sin^2 \theta \qquad \text{(for } hk0 \text{ planes)}$$

Taylor and Floyd Method. Another graphical method[37] is useful if there are a number of $(hk0)$ reflections available but only one $(00l)$ reflection in the region of 30 to 90°θ. In this case, the a_0 value is determined by direct extrapolation using the $(hk0)$ reflections and the ξ function. The c_0 value is determined by extrapolation through the one $(00l)$ point using a slope for the c_0 extrapolation line calculated from the slope of the a_0 line. The slope of the c_0 line is c/a times that of the a_0 line. An approximate c/a ratio is determined by a direct calculation for c_0 from the uncorrected Bragg angle of the $(00l)$ reflection; a_0 had already been determined by extrapolation. The error introduced by using this value of c_0 instead of a more accurate value is a second-order effect because this c/a ratio is used only to calculate the slope of the c_0 line. The final (more accurate) c/a ratio may then be obtained after the extrapolated value of c_0 has been determined. The precision and accuracy in the determination of c_0 and c/a ratio depend on the quality (sharpness) of the $(00l)$ reflection and the diffraction angle (the higher, the better) at which it appears.

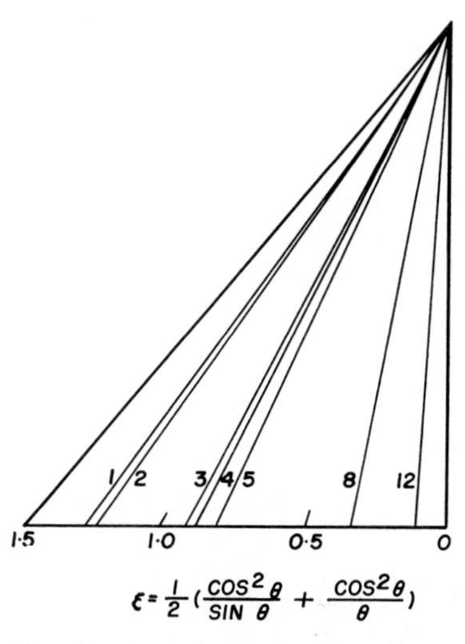

FIG. 7. ξ extrapolation fan plotter for diffraction data from Ti-Al alloy. [*Courtesy of E. J. Myers and F. C. Davies, Acta Cryst.*, **14**:194 (1961).]

Analytical Methods. *$\cos^2 \theta$ Extrapolation.* For tetragonal or hexagonal materials, the error equation for a $\cos^2 \theta$ analytical extrapolation[25] is

$$A_0\alpha_i + C_0\gamma_i + D\partial_i = \sin^2 \theta_i$$

where the terms are defined as follows:

Term	Tetragonal	Hexagonal
$A_0 =$	$\lambda^2/4a_0^2$	$\lambda^2/3a_0^2$
$\alpha_i =$	$(h^2 + k^2)_i$	$(h^2 + hk + k^2)_i$
$C_0 =$	$\lambda^2/4c_0^2$	$\lambda^2/4c_0^2$
$\gamma_i =$	l_i^2	l_i^2
$D =$	Drift constant	Drift constant
$\partial_i =$	$\sin^2 2\theta_i$	$\sin^2 2\theta_i$

The normal equations for tetragonal and hexagonal materials are

$$\begin{aligned} A_0\Sigma\alpha_i^2 + C_0\Sigma\alpha_i\gamma_i + D\Sigma\alpha_i\partial_i &= \Sigma\alpha_i \sin^2\theta_i \\ A_0\Sigma\alpha_i\gamma_i + C_0\Sigma\gamma_i^2 + D\Sigma\gamma_i\partial_i &= \Sigma\gamma_i \sin^2\theta_i \\ A_0\Sigma\alpha_i\partial_i + C_0\Sigma\gamma_i\partial_i + D\Sigma\partial_i^2 &= \Sigma\partial_i \sin^2\theta_i \end{aligned}$$

These equations are then solved for A_0, C_0, and D, and finally for a_0 and c_0 using the appropriate relations tabulated above. Other than the added tediousness of the calculations, the procedure is essentially the same for tetragonal and hexagonal materials as it is for cubic materials.

Computer Method. The Vogel and Kempter analytical extrapolation computer method has been further developed for tetragonal, hexagonal, and orthorhombic materials using $\cos^2\theta$, ξ, $\Phi\tan\Phi$, and $\cos\theta\cot\theta$ extrapolation functions. Since this method has already been outlined for cubic crystals, it will not be described further; however, the error and normal equations will be presented. The error equations are

Tetragonal: $$F = A_0\alpha + B_0\beta + K_0\partial - \gamma$$

where $A_0 = 1/a_0^2 \qquad B_0 = 1/c_0^2$
$\alpha = \frac{1}{2}\lambda^2(h^2 + k^2) \qquad \beta = \frac{1}{2}\lambda^2 l^2$

Hexagonal: $$F = A_0\alpha + B_0\beta + K_0\partial - \gamma$$

where $A_0 = \frac{4}{3}a_0^2 \qquad B_0 = 1/c_0^2$
$\alpha = \frac{1}{2}\lambda^2(h^2 + hk + k^2) \qquad \beta = \frac{1}{2}\lambda^2 l^2$

Orthorhombic: $$F = A_0\alpha + B_0\beta + C_0\epsilon + K_0\partial - \gamma$$

where $A_0 = 1/a_0^2 \qquad B_0 = 1/b_0^2 \qquad C_0 = 1/c_0^2$
$\alpha = \frac{1}{2}\lambda^2 h^2 \qquad \beta = \frac{1}{2}\lambda^2 k^2 \qquad \epsilon = \frac{1}{2}\lambda^2 l^2$

K_0, ∂, and γ are defined as they have been previously for the cubic case. The normal equations based on F_e and Q are the same as those for the cubic case and are solved in the same manner.

5. CENTROID METHOD FOR ASYMMETRIC DIFFRACTOMETERS (0.001°θ LEVEL)

Principles. With the advent of asymmetric diffractometers (asymmetric only in the sense that measurements are made on one side of zero and 180° 2θ or one-half of the complete diffraction circle) employing Geiger, proportional, or scintillation counter detectors, a new avenue of lattice-parameter determination was opened up. This method was given its initial impetus in 1950 by Wilson[38] in his evaluation of systematic errors as they apply to diffraction profiles obtained with diffractometers. In this paper, Wilson developed expressions for the shifts of the centroids and peaks of diffraction profiles due to radial (horizontal) divergence, specimen, and transparency errors. This was followed by a suggestion of Parrish and Wilson[39] that corrections for systematic errors can be made more readily using the centroids instead of the peaks of the diffraction profiles; hence the development of the centroid method for diffractometers.

In addition to being able to use point-by-point scanning techniques or to obtain diffraction profiles directly on charts, diffractometers have the apparent advantage over film methods of providing greater precision and accuracy in angular measurements. However, this is not always observed in practice for commercially available diffractometers—partly because of mechanical problems in obtaining driving-gear systems for the sample and detector tables which are free of systematic error (angular scale in Table 1) within the precision of measurement. The precision of measurement for diffractometers is on the order of 0.001° 2θ according to Pike and Wilson[40] who, with Parrish et al.,[41] have been largely responsible for the development of the centroid method for diffractometers.

The centroid method involves determining the centroid position $2\theta_g$ of a suitably truncated diffraction profile ($\alpha_1 + \alpha_2$ in the case of the $K\alpha$ doublet)—the profile being obtained using point-by-point scanning on the diffractometer. It is necessary to truncate the profile to obtain a finite area for which a centroid can be determined. (Diffraction profiles have a divergent, Cauchy-like distribution, the centroid of which is indeterminate.) Several truncation procedures have been described.[40,41,41d,41f] After determining the centroid of the truncated profile, systematic-error corrections in degrees 2θ are applied algebraically to $2\theta_g$. The corrected $2\theta_g$ value is accurate provided the systematic-error corrections have been made properly. An accurate lattice-parameter value may then be calculated from the corrected $2\theta_g$ using a centroid-based wavelength value.

A major advantage of the centroid method is that corrections for geometric systematic errors can be made in a purely additive manner based on the centroids of the error (aberration) functions. Other methods of making systematic error corrections to diffraction profiles require a much more elaborate mathematical approach involving convolution (unfolding) of the aberration profiles from the observed profile to obtain the pure diffraction profile and a measure of its angular displacement with respect to the observed profile. Furthermore, the centroid of an aberration profile can be determined more readily than the profile itself. Finally, the centroid method does not depend on the resolution of the $K\alpha$ doublets, as do methods based on peak measurements, since the centroid of the doublet (resolved or unresolved) is the measured quantity.

In spite of these obvious advantages of the centroid method, there are certain difficulties that still need resolving. These include: (1) The wavelength problem; i.e., x-ray wavelengths based on spectral profile centroids have not yet been published and, according to some x-ray spectroscopists, are not likely to be published in the near future since the pure spectral profiles are not known theoretically or experimentally with sufficient accuracy.[23] This problem is perhaps a little more serious for centroids than for peak measurements since the centroid is more intimately related to the shape of the diffraction profile than the peak. Nevertheless, by stating the wavelength value used, accurate centroid parameter determinations can be made based on the precision and accuracy of the centroid Bragg-angle measurements corrected for systematic errors. (2) Certain systematic-error factors are inherently difficult to evaluate using the asymmetric diffractometer. For example, the sample-surface displacement error requires great experimental finesse in its evaluation and control. The angular-scale calibration is another systematic error difficult to evaluate completely over the angular range of interest at the $0.001°\theta$ level. (3) The centroid method depends on having diffraction profiles which, except for the $\alpha_1 - \alpha_2$ doublets, do not overlap. Profile overlap creates an almost insuperably problem in applying the centroid method, and this overlap is unavoidable in many cases of interest. In spite of these difficulties, centroid lattice-parameter values precise and accurate at the $0.001°\theta$ level have been obtained. The approach used in obtaining such values is discussed next.

The centroid method continues to be under active development[41a–41e] but still suffers, among other things, from a lack of published centroid wavelengths necessary for lattice parameter determinations. An attempt at calculating centroid wavelengths has been made, with results of uncertain accuracy.[41g]. On the other hand, a table of centerline peak wavelengths has been published recently[41h] with claimed accuracies (in angstroms, including the kX-to-angstrom conversion factor) of a few parts per million.

Experimental Requirements and Systematic-error Corrections. The diffractometer method developed in Prof. Wilson's laboratory has been used to determine the lattice parameter of tungsten with a precision and accuracy at the $0.001°\theta$ level as demonstrated by means of the LRM[4] (see Sec. 8 on the Likelihood-ratio Method in this chapter for an example of the centroid method). Using a weighted mean Cu $K\alpha$ wavelength of 1.541760 Å, the lattice parameter $\hat{a}_0$ of tungsten, based on the LRM hypothesis of "no remaining systematic errors" in the Bragg-angle measurements, was found to be 3.164944 Å* at 18°C, with a 95 per cent confidence interval of

* Not corrected for refraction. The refraction correction is $(1 - n)\hat{a}_0$ to be added to $\hat{a}_0$, where n is the refractive index and $(1 - n)$ is 49.6×10^{-6} for tungsten and Cu $K\alpha$ radiation. $\hat{a}_0$, corrected for refraction, is 3.165101 Å. Since the refraction correction in powders is primarily due to a change in x-ray wavelength in the crystallites,[42] the LRM does not evaluate the significance of this type of correction. This is contrasted with the refraction correction for single crystals in which refraction at the air-crystal interface plays an important role in addition to the wavelength change within the crystal. In this case, the LRM does evaluate the significance of the refraction correction. In fact, the refraction correction turns out to be the only significant calculated systematic-error correction for the lattice-parameter data on single crystals of silicon to be discussed in Sec. 6 on Single-crystal Methods.

±0.000018 Å. This corresponds to a precision and accuracy of about 1 part in 180,000. The experimental details and systematic-error correction procedures used in attaining this precision and accuracy will now be outlined. The details and procedures are based on published information as noted and have recently been summarized[42a] by Dr. B. W. Delf of Prof. Wilson's laboratory. It is assumed that the diffractometer to be used has been aligned as precisely and accurately as possible. For diffractometer-alignment procedures see Chap. 9, Sec. 3.

Measurement and Recording of a Diffraction Profile. A Norelco diffractometer is used in conjunction with an electromechanical system which permits automatic recording of intensity vs. diffraction angle for profiles in steps of 0.02° 2θ.[43] After counting a predetermined number of counts on a "monitor" scaler, the "sample" (Dekatron decade) scaler count is recorded photographically along with the angular-position reading.* The counters and camera are then reset automatically, the diffractometer moves 0.02° 2θ, and the sequence is repeated. The angular limits of the profile (or profiles in the case of the $K\alpha$ doublet) are determined in a preliminary experiment, and the profile is then scanned automatically between these limits.

Calculation of the Centroid Position $2\theta_g$. 1. Nomenclature. After the intensity vs. 2θ data are recorded for a profile, $2\theta_g$ is determined using the following equation:

$$2\theta_g = 2\theta_z - \left[\frac{\Sigma S}{T} + \frac{r}{1-r}\left(\frac{\Sigma S}{T} - \frac{n}{2} + \frac{(n+2)\partial}{12b}\right)\right]\Delta 2\theta$$

where $\Delta 2\theta$ = step width
$2\theta_a$ = initial limit, step zero
$2\theta_z$ = final limit, step n
n = number of steps $(2\theta_z - 2\theta_a)/\Delta 2\theta$
$S_{(n+1)} = T$ = integrated total intensity between $2\theta_a$ and $2\theta_z$; i.e.,
$T = S_1 + S_2 + S_3 + \cdots + S_{(n+1)}$
$\sum_{i=1}^{n} s_i = \Sigma S$ = sum of partial sums of intensity; i.e.,

$$\Sigma S = (S_1) + (S_1 + S_2) + (S_1 + S_2 + S_3) + \cdots + (S_1 + S_2 + S_3 + \cdots + S_n)$$

a = intensity at $2\theta_a$
z = intensity at $2\theta_z$
$b = (a + z)/2$ = average background intensity
$\partial = z - a$ = increase in background intensity
$B = (n + 1)b$ integrated background intensity
$r = B/T$ = ratio of integrated background intensity to integrated total intensity

2. Truncation procedure. Any method of determining the centroid of an x-ray diffraction line involves some truncation procedure in order to eliminate the difficulties caused by the slow decay of intensity in the tails of the line. In this method centroid positions are determined over a series of angular ranges which are symmetrical about the centroid position.

The intensity of the line profile at the extremes of the greatest range used, $2\theta_a$ to $2\theta_z$, is taken as defining the background level. The values of a, z, and ∂ for any other range are calculated assuming the background variation to be linear between $2\theta_a$ and $2\theta_z$. The line profile is therefore truncated as shown in Fig. 8.

In calculations using the maximum range ($2\theta_a$ to $2\theta_z$) the centroid of the line profile above the line AZ is determined. In the case of calculations over a shorter range, $2\theta_a'$ to $2\theta_z'$, for example, the centroid of the shaded area is determined.

3. Calculation of centroid

a. $2\theta_a'$ is chosen.

b. $2\theta_z'$ is chosen. The initial choice is such that $\Sigma S/T$ is approximately equal to $n/2$.

c. a, z, and ∂ are determined as described above.

* The instrument has been modified so that data are now punched directly onto tape for greater convenience in the subsequent computations.

d. An approximate value of centroid position $2\theta_g'$ is calculated using the equation given above.

e. The asymmetry of the line $2\theta_g' - (2\theta_a' + 2\theta_z')/2$ is calculated.

f. If the asymmetry of the line is greater than $\Delta 2\theta/4$, steps *b* to *e* are repeated.

g. The centroid position $2\theta_g$ is the value of $2\theta_g'$ for which the asymmetry is less than $\Delta 2\theta/4$.

The variation with range of the centroid position thus determined is shown in Fig. 9. The centroid position associated with the plateau of this curve is taken as defining the line position.

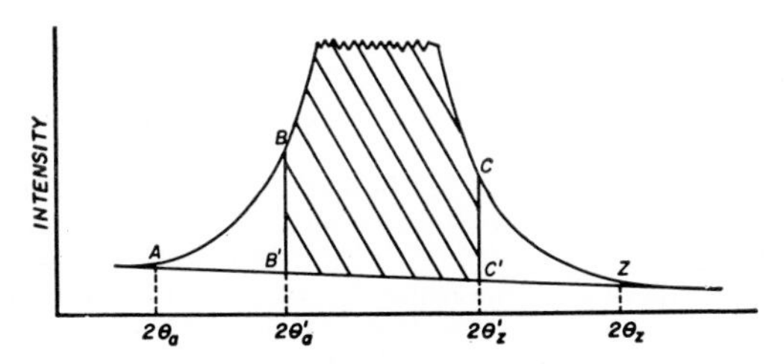

FIG. 8. Schematic of a diffraction profile showing truncation procedure used in calculating centroid Bragg angle $2\theta_g$. (*Courtesy of B. W. Delf.*)

Zero Correction. The method used is essentially a combination of the pinhole and knife-edge techniques described previously.[44] A plate containing a pinhole and a knife-edge, aligned along a diameter of the pinhole, is mounted on a shaft which fits in the hole on the diffractometer normally used for the specimen post. The knife-edge diameter of the pinhole is aligned as closely as possible with the axis of rotation of the diffractometer. A series of intensity vs. angle readings on the diffractometer dial is

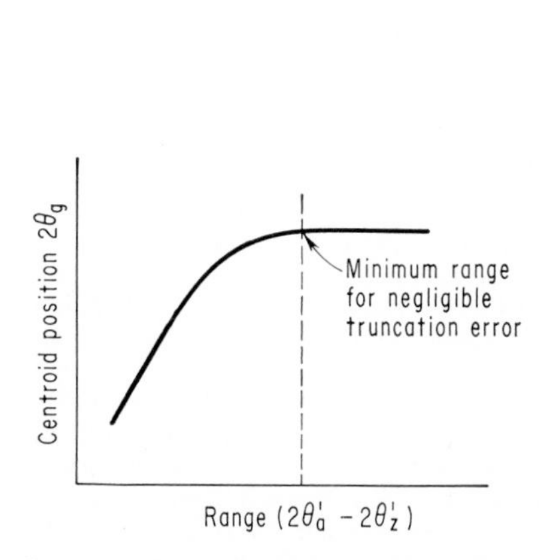

FIG. 9. Determination of minimum range $(2\theta_a' - 2\theta_z')$ essentially free of truncation error. (*Courtesy of B. W. Delf.*)

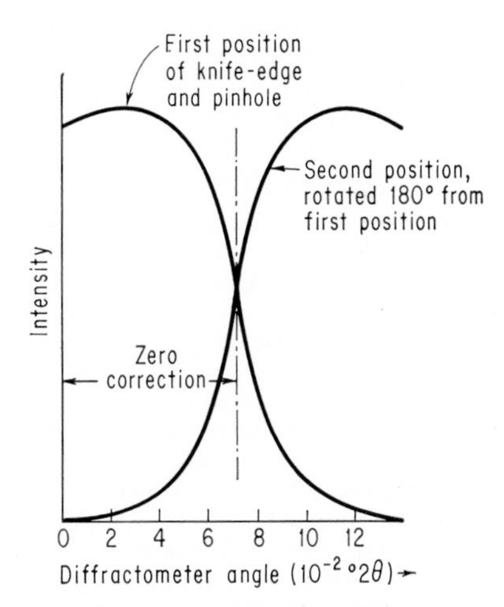

FIG. 10. Zero calibration data for diffractometer using knife-edge and pinhole. (*Courtesy of B. W. Delf.*)

made in the region of zero degrees 2θ, with the plane of the pinhole perpendicular to the primary beam. The shaft (with pinhole and knife-edge) is then turned 180° and a second series of readings made. These data are then plotted as shown in Fig. 10. The diffractometer dial reading corresponding to the intersection of the two curves represents the zero correction to be applied to all subsequent Bragg-angle measurements on that diffractometer.

The intensity data for the curves of Fig. 10 are due primarily to the interaction of the primary beam with the knife-edge; however, a pinhole (about 0.1 mm diameter) is used to reduce the primary-beam intensity to a useful level without requiring filtering of the beam or reduction of tube current or voltage from normal operating conditions. It is important that normal operating conditions be maintained during this procedure to obtain the most accurate zero-correction value. The zero correction can be determined with a precision of about 0.0002° 2θ and an accuracy of better than 0.001° 2θ using this method.

Specimen-surface Displacement Correction. A method for determining the displacement of the specimen surface with respect to the rotation axis of the diffractometer, designated S-S displacement, has been described by Delf.[45] This method can be used to correct for S-S displacement with a precision and accuracy corresponding to 0.004° 2θ or better. The method is described for a diffractometer having a horizontal axis of rotation. It involves fastening a thin (0.01 mm diameter) glass rod with plasticine on the banking surface of the diffractometer specimen post and adjusting the rod until there is no movement of an easily viewed and identified point on the rod when the specimen post is rotated. The centered rod is then viewed from above with a traveling microscope which can be used for measuring distances along its axis with a precision of about 0.001 mm. The microscope is focused on the top edge of the rod, the rod removed and replaced with a glass slide, and the microscope refocused on the top surface of the slide. The distance between the top edge of the rod and the slide is the S-S displacement of the slide.

The mean S-S displacement is determined by making these measurements on the glass slide at various distances from the front edge of the banking surface and the "average" position corresponding to the mean displacement noted. The average S-S displacement of the glass slide is then used as a reference for determining average S-S displacement of a sample surface when measured in the "average" position. The specimen S-S displacement is the algebraic sum of the rod-to-slide and the slide-to-specimen S-S displacements.

The specimen S-S displacement in millimeters, designated s, is then related to the S-S correction in radians* by the equation[40] $\Delta\theta = -(s/R)\cos\theta$ where

$$\Delta\theta \text{ (or } \Delta\theta_g) = \psi - \theta \text{ (or } \psi_g - \theta_g)$$

where ψ or ψ_g is based on the measured Bragg angle, θ or θ_g is based on the true Bragg angle, and R = radius of diffractometer in millimeters.

The S-S displacement correction applies equally to centroid, peak, or other measures of profile position. Delf points out that great care is required in locking the specimen holder in the diffractometer so that the S-S displacement calibration will remain constant. It is also very important that the specimen surface be flat within 0.005 mm and that the sample grains be no larger than 300 mesh (0.004 mm) so that it may be possible to achieve this degree of flatness.

Flat-specimen Correction. The flat specimen surface usually used in diffractometry is an approximation to the curved surface defined by the focusing-circle geometry of the diffractometer, and this approximation requires a correction.[38] In the usual arrangement where the angular divergence of the primary beam is limited to 2α radians by means of a slit so that only a portion of the specimen length is irradiated, the flat-specimen correction to the centroid value θ_g is $\Delta\theta_g = \alpha^2 \cot\theta/3$.

Transparency Correction. The primary x-ray beam usually penetrates the sample surface and diffracts from a volume rather than from a geometric surface. Thus the geometric sample surface only approximates the sample volume actually seen by the

* Note that the corrections $\Delta\theta$ or $\Delta\theta_g$ given here and in subsequent correction procedures are in terms of θ in radians and not 2θ. $\Delta\theta$ or $\Delta\theta_g$ corrections converted from radians to degrees are required for application to the Bragg equation; however, diffraction-angle measurements are made in degrees 2θ. Finally, θ as used in all subsequent centroid-correction equations shall imply θ_g.

x-rays, and this requires a correction of the form[38]

$$\Delta\theta_g = \frac{\sin 2\theta}{4\mu R} - \frac{t \cos \theta}{R[\exp(2\mu t \csc \theta - 1)]}$$

where μ = effective linear absorption coefficient of the sample*
t = sample thickness
R = diffractometer radius

If $\mu t \csc \theta$ is large, this correction has the limiting value of $\sin 2\theta/4\mu R$. If $\mu t \csc \theta$ is small, the limiting value is $t \cos \theta/2R$.

Axial (Vertical) Divergence Correction. The divergence of the x-ray beam out of the equatorial plane and parallel to the diffractometer axis of rotation is called axial or vertical divergence. This divergence may be limited by the use of Soller slits in the primary and/or diffracted beams; however, it cannot be eliminated completely and a correction is required.[46] This correction to θ_g is given by

$$\Delta\theta_g = (h^2/6s^2)[Q_1(q) \cot 2\theta + Q_2(q) \csc 2\theta]$$

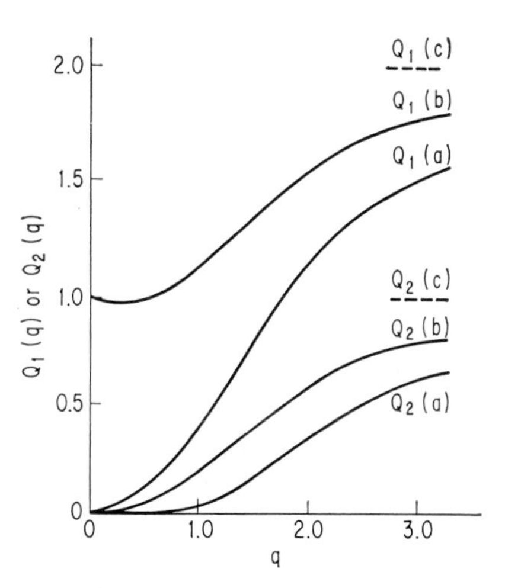

FIG. 11. Values of $Q_1(q)$ and $Q_2(q)$ for Philips diffractometer with (*a*) two sets of Soller slits, (*b*) one set of Soller slits, (*c*) no Soller slits.[46] (*Reproduced by permission.*)

where $h = 2F$ ("height" of x-ray source) $= 2R$ ("height" of receiving slit) $= 2P$ ("height" of flat specimen), s = diffractometer radius, $Q_1(q)$ and $Q_2(q)$ are functions of the collimator geometry, especially as it pertains to Soller-slit dimensions. Values for these functions based on the Philips diffractometer geometry are given in Fig. 11. In this figure, the function $q = s\Delta/h$ where Δ = spacing between adjacent foils in a Soller-slit unit divided by the length of a foil.

Dispersion, Lorentz, Polarization and Absorption† Corrections. Corrections for these factors are given by the following equation (Eq. 4 of Ref. 48):[47,48]

$$\Delta\theta_g = -\frac{V}{2\bar{\lambda}^2} \tan^3 \theta \left(3 - 4 \cot^2 \theta - \frac{16 \cos 2\theta \cos^2 \theta}{1 + \cos^2 2\theta}\right)$$

where V = variance of the spectral distribution of the characteristic wavelength used
$\bar{\lambda}$ = centroid value of the wavelength distribution

Angular-scale Correction. The lattice parameters of a number of standard substances have been determined, and the parameter values calculated at various angles have shown systematic variations from the mean values. If the corresponding angular variations are plotted against angle, the points for all the substances fall on a smooth curve which has the form of a normal angular-calibration curve. The only corrections which are the same for each specimen are axial divergence, Lorentz, polarization, etc., and the curve bears no relationship to these factors. Thus it may be assumed that the resultant curve is a measure of the variations between the true angular scale and the diffractometer dial readings.

The success of this method of angular-scale calibration is attested by the fact that

* Assuming the sample powder to be uniformly packed in the sample holder, the effective coefficient may be calculated for that sample by measuring the reduction in monochromatized intensity of the characteristic x-rays used in the diffractometer with a sample of thickness t in the beam. If the sample is too opaque to be measured in this way, the effective density of the sample powder packed in the specimen holder may be determined by weighing the powder, measuring the volume it occupies, and calculating the effective absorption coefficient from these data and a knowledge of the mass absorption coefficient.

† Absorption here is the effect on the diffraction profile due to differential absorption in the sample over the range of wavelengths encountered in the spectral profile used to calculate the centroid position.

corrections based on this calibration scale for tungsten were necessary and adequate to reduce the systematic errors below the precision of measurement of the Bragg angles (see Sec. 8). Another method for calibrating diffraction angles directly involves using optical tools such as a precision polygon and an autocollimator.

Refraction Correction. The refraction correction for powder samples is normally due to the change in wavelength within the crystallites[42] as contrasted to the single-crystal case where true refraction at the crystal-air interface is an important additional factor. The powder-refraction correction is therefore made after calculating the lattice parameter from Bragg-angle measurements corrected for all other systematic errors. The correction is made by adding $(1 - n)a_0$ to the calculated lattice parameter a_0; n is the index of refraction for the substance and the x-ray wavelength used in obtaining the diffraction data.

6. SINGLE-CRYSTAL METHODS

Peak Method for Symmetrical Diffractometers (0.001°θ Level). This method was developed by Bond[5] in 1960. It is, in some ways, the diffractometer counterpart of the Straumanis film method and has been used to determine the lattice parameter of silicon with a precision and accuracy at the 0.001°θ level as shown by the

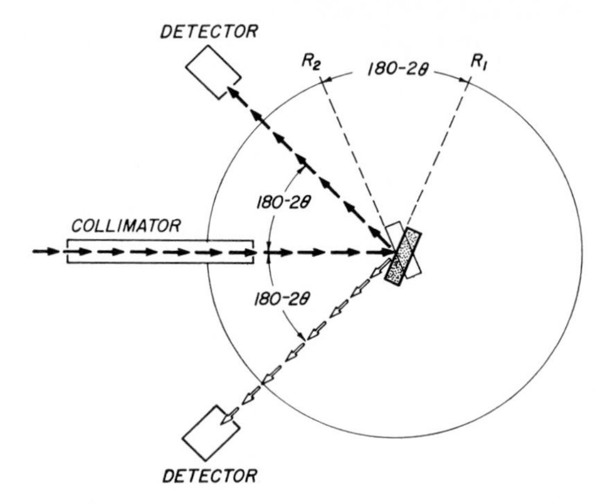

FIG. 12. Schematic illustrating the geometry of Bond's symmetrical diffractometer method. [*Courtesy of W. L. Bond, Acta Cryst.*, **13**:814 (1960).]

LRM.[4] This diffractometer method involves (1) measuring angles symmetrically about zero and 180° 2θ as contrasted to the asymmetric diffractometer in which diffraction angles are measured only on one side of zero and 180° 2θ, (2) measuring the peaks of diffraction profiles rather than the centroids, and (3) eliminating most major systematic errors experimentally rather than by calculation.

This method is somewhat restricted in application in that it can be used only with single crystals; however, advantage is taken of this fact by measuring crystal-angle position instead of diffraction angle for a given (hkl) reflection. By measuring crystal-angle positions symmetrically, it is possible to eliminate certain systematic errors experimentally and to minimize the remaining errors.

The geometry of Bond's method is illustrated in Fig. 12. The flat-slab crystal sample, indicated in two (symmetrical) positions by the stippled and open rectangles, is mounted on a graduated circle (clinometer), the angular position of which can be read to 1 sec of arc (0.0003°). This graduated circle is provided with calibration data indicating irregular errors (corresponding to angular-scale error) having a maximum value of 0.0014° 2θ. This corresponds to a maximum error of 0.0007°θ, part of which can be eliminated by using the calibration data. Two detectors with apertures considerably wider than the diffracted x-ray beam width are placed at a given Bragg-angle position symmetrically with respect to 180° 2θ as indicated.

The crystal is placed first in the stippled position to reflect from a given set of (hkl) planes into the upper detector, and a series of count-rate (intensity) vs. crystal-angle readings is made in the vicinity of R_1. The crystal is then rotated to the position indicated by the open rectangle to reflect into the lower detector for the same (hkl) reflection, and a series of intensity vs. angle readings is made in the vicinity of R_2.

A typical plot for the silicon $(444)\alpha_1$ reflection is shown in Fig. 13. The peak position is determined using the center-line method.* The difference between peak-position readings at R_1 and R_2 is equal to $(180 - 2\theta)$ degrees, from which θ, d, and a_0 can be calculated.

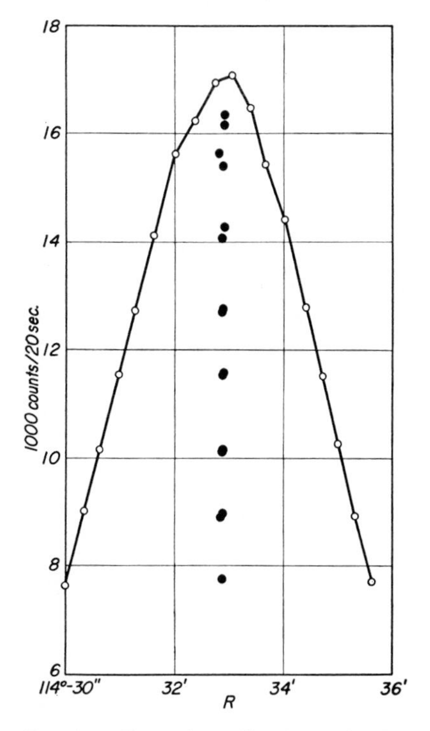

FIG. 13. Typical profile obtained using Bond's method [silicon (444) reflection using Cu $K\alpha_1$ for which $\theta = 79°18'45''$]. [*Courtesy of W. L. Bond, Acta Cryst.*, **13**:814 (1960).]

By measuring crystal angle in this manner instead of diffraction angle and by using wide detector apertures, it can be shown that errors due to eccentricity, surface flatness, misalignment, absorption, zero, source profile, radial divergence, and diffractometer radius can be eliminated experimentally. The principle which justifies this statement is based on the idea that the shape of the diffraction profile or its absolute position in space does not affect the measured difference between corresponding crystal-angle positions as long as a major portion of the profile falls within the detector aperture (hence the need for wide detector apertures).

The experimental validity of this idea can most easily be illustrated in terms of sample-surface displacement (eccentricity) error. A crystal 1 mm thick is mounted so that crystal angles can be measured from the front or back side without remounting the crystal. Thus, if one surface lies on the axis of rotation of the graduated circle, the other will be displaced from this axis by 1 mm, introducing a very large sample-surface displacement error. However, upon measuring crystal angles as described, the difference in diffraction angles [$(180 - 2\theta)$ degrees] thus determined for the front and back surfaces is not detectable within the precision of the graduated circle. Zero, misalignment, and diffractometer-radius errors are also eliminated since θ depends only on the difference in crystal-angle positions observed at R_1 and R_2 and not on these geometrical factors.

The asymmetry of absorption and source profiles modified by radial divergence and surface flatness may affect the position of maximum intensity at the detector apertures, but since the detectors are used only to measure intensities and not angular positions, these error sources, like eccentricity, have essentially no effect on the crystal-angle readings. Rate-meter recording errors do not affect these measurements since the detectors are used only for point-by-point counting. Results obtained with this

* The center-line method involves the upward extrapolation of the mid-points of diffraction profile chords. The intersection of this extrapolated line with the experimentally determined profile is defined as the peak position.

method are not affected by 2:1 tracking error because there is no 2:1 tracking as with most commercial asymmetric diffractometers. Thus the application of this technique to single crystals results in the experimental elimination of nine important systematic errors at the 0.001°θ level.

Another possible error is that due to tilt of the crystal planes being measured with respect to the axis of rotation of those planes. Bond describes a method for aligning the crystal to about 1 min of arc and then shows that an error of about 5 min due to crystal tilt would cause an error in d or a_0 of about 1 ppm. Thus crystal-tilt error can be controlled well within 1 ppm and, for practical purposes, is negligible at the 0.001°θ level.

A factor which can also affect the accuracy of a_0 is the measurement and control of sample temperature. By using thin crystals mounted on an insulated copper block, the temperature of which is regulated to better than ±0.1° C, the temperature of the sample may be determined to better than ±0.1° C. This corresponds to a variation in lattice parameter for silicon of less than 1 ppm, well below the 0.001°θ level.

Bond describes how to eliminate, by calculation, those errors which cannot be removed experimentally. These include dispersion,* axial divergence, Lorentz and polarization factors, and refraction. Thus, except for wavelength, Bond has accounted for all the systematic-error factors listed in Table 1 and has obtained a lattice-parameter value for a silicon single crystal free from systematic error at the 0.001°θ level according to the LRM.

In an example used by Bond,[5] namely, the lattice-parameter determination of zone-refined silicon, it was shown by means of the LRM that corrections required for axial divergence and Lorentz and polarization factors were negligible; i.e., the value of the likelihood-ratio function W_m was not changed significantly, after applying these residual corrections to the raw data. On the other hand, the application of the refraction correction reduced W_m below $w\epsilon$ at the 0.05 significance level. $\hat{\bar{a}}_0$ could then be calculated, and it was found to be 5.430736 ±0.000014 Å at 95 per cent confidence limits based on the x-ray wavelength of 1.540510 Å for Cu $K\alpha_1$ and a sample temperature of 25° C. This represents a precision and accuracy of 1 part in 390,000.

As an additional point of interest, symmetrical diffractometers are being developed for powder samples[49,50] and will probably become more and more important in the precise and accurate determination of lattice parameters. Their symmetry has the potential advantage of reducing systematic errors such as zero-setting and sample-surface displacement which are inherently more difficult to handle when using asymmetric diffractometers.

Kossel-line Method for Films (Equivalent to 0.001°θ Level). This lattice-parameter method was proposed by Kossel et al.[51] in 1935 and was further developed by Lonsdale,[52] who called it divergent-beam x-ray photography. With the development of the electron microbeam-probe analyzer as a point source of x-rays, this method has received renewed attention,[53,54] especially in the study of irradiation effects on the lattice parameters of metal single crystals.

It is a unique claim of this method that, under the right circumstances, it can be used to determine lattice-parameter values with a precision and accuracy of about 1 part in 100,000 using an extremely simple technique and essentially no precision equipment.[52,54] The Kossel-line method is based on obtaining diffraction conics (right circular cones) which are generated from a point source of x-rays in or near the surface of a single crystal slab of the proper thickness. These conics are transmitted through the crystal to register on a film placed roughly parallel to the crystal slab (Fig. 14). The Kossel lines are formed by the intersections of the conics with the film. The major experimental requirements are that the x-ray source be as small as possible (point source), that the x-rays be generated near the crystal surface, and that the crystal be of optimum thickness.† It is unnecessary for the film to be exactly parallel to the crystal or for the crystal-film distance to be known accurately.

* Since this method employs peak measurements, Bond claims the error due to dispersion is negligible (less than 0.001°θ).

† For metallic crystals, a thickness of $x = 1/0.2\mu_L$ is recommended,[54] where μ_L is the linear absorption coefficient for the $K\alpha$ radiation used.

The only experimental measurements required involve determining two lengths L between the intersections of appropriate pairs of conics (one pair is indicated by the lens-shaped figure in Fig. 14) having different Miller indices. If this is done for two slightly different wavelengths such as the $K\alpha_1$ and $K\alpha_2$ characteristic radiations, the specimen-film distance t may be eliminated as a variable. As with other methods, the accuracy of the Kossel-line method depends on the accuracy of the x-ray wavelength values used. In applying this method, the wavelength within the crystal is used, rather than the wavelength in vacuum or air.[52]

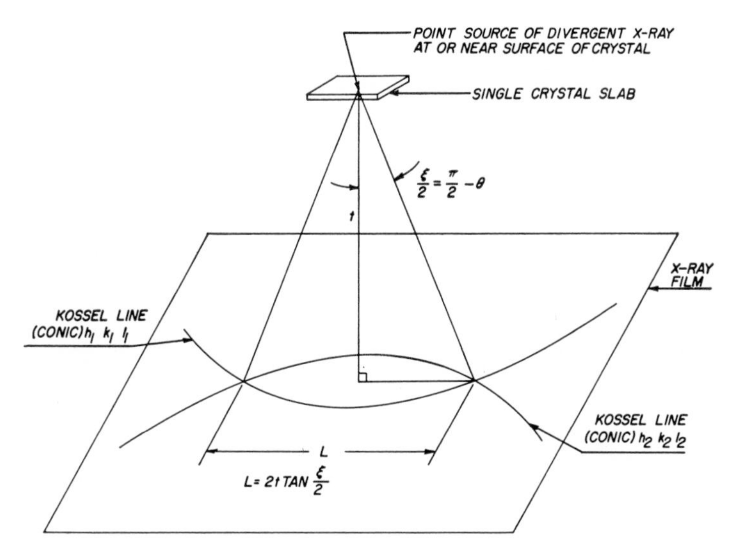

FIG. 14. Schematic of Kossel-line method showing two intersecting conics.

A specific pattern of Kossel lines (lens figure) useful in obtaining a precise and accurate lattice-parameter value is illustrated in Fig. 15. By measuring L_1 and L_2 and by using the appropriate values for the Miller indices and wavelengths, the lattice parameter a_0 is calculated using the equation

$$\left(\frac{L_1}{L_2}\right)^2 = \frac{\lambda_2^2(2a_0^2 - 9\lambda_1^2)}{\lambda_1^2(2a_0^2 - 9\lambda_2^2)}$$

For a lens figure to exist, $2a_0^2$ must be greater than either $9\lambda_1^2$ or $9\lambda_2^2$. Instead of solving this equation directly for a_0, it is advantageous for reasons of sensitivity to plot $(L_1/L_2)^2$ against a function of a_0 as is done in the course of the following example:

A 0.1-mm-thick nickel crystal gives rise to two lens figures of interest when using nickel radiation (fluorescent x-rays generated at the crystal surface by a 29-kv* electron microbeam) and a specimen-film distance of about 6 cm. These lens figures are due to the (004) and (222), $K\alpha_1$ and $K\alpha_2$ Kossel lines. By measuring L_1 and L_2 on a fine-grained film (such as Kodak type M) after an exposure of a few minutes and subsequent processing, $(L_1/L_2)^2$ was found to be 3.21. By plotting $(L_1/L_2)^2$ against $(a_0 - 3.5200)$ Å as shown in Fig. 16, and reading off the abscissa value corresponding to $(L_1/L_2)^2 = 3.21$, a_0 was found to be 3.5286 Å. In other Kossel-line work on nickel single crystals using essentially the same approach,[54] a_0 for unirradiated nickel was found to be 3.52606 ± 0.00002 Å (a precision of better than 1 part in 100,000). Since the crystal temperatures were not given, it is assumed that the differences in these lattice-parameter values for nickel may be due to temperature differences.

* A higher voltage is undesirable because it gives rise to a larger effective point source.

The only systematic errors affecting this method are (1) thermal effects of the electron beam generating the divergent x-ray beam at the crystal surface when using the electron microbeam-probe analyzer, (2) refraction and wavelength effects, and (3) film shrinkage. The other systematic errors are essentially eliminated either because they do not exist for this method or because they are of a second-order nature owing

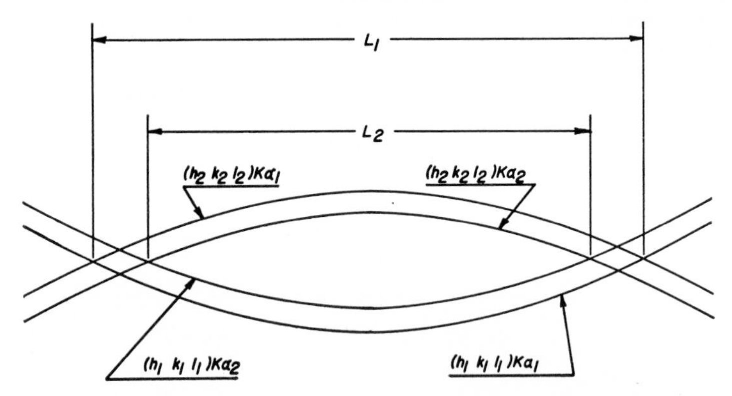

FIG. 15. Kossel-line lens figures for the precise and accurate determination of lattice parameters. [*Courtesy of B. H. Heise, J. Appl. Phys.*, **33**:938 (1962).]

to the slight differential effects between the $K\alpha_1$ and $K\alpha_2$ wavelengths. The thermal effect has been estimated to be small for nickel (about 2° C rise);[54] refraction and wavelength corrections, where needed, can be handled adequately as described for other methods; and film shrinkage, unless excessive or nonuniform, has a negligible

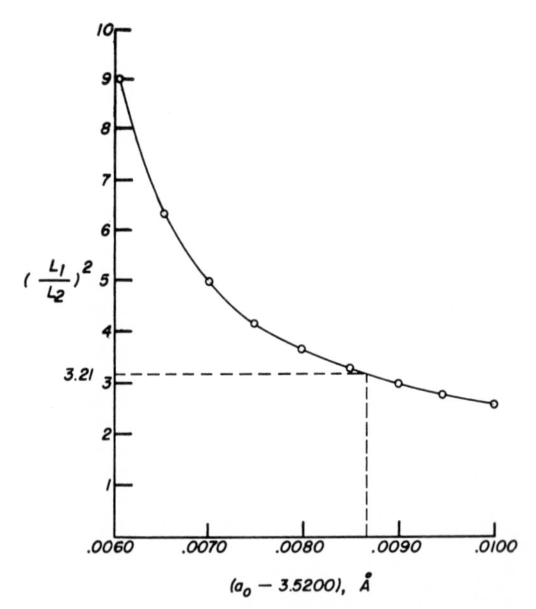

FIG. 16. Graph for determining a_0 from Kossel-line measurements L_1 and L_2 on the (004) and (222) reflections of nickel. [*Courtesy of B. H. Heise, J. Appl. Phys.*, **33**:938 (1962).]

effect because of the small absolute difference between L_1 and L_2 measured in the same regions on the film. Furthermore, uniform shrinkage can be corrected for in terms of the $K\alpha_1$-$K\beta$ separation. In general, measurement, rather than systematic, errors are the limiting factors in lattice-parameter accuracy and precision.

This method has its greatest sensitivity when using high-order Kossel lines having well-resolved α_1-α_2 doublets where the intersections occur at relatively small angles to form "thin" lens figures. These conditions are sometimes difficult to achieve simultaneously. It is also desirable to have the x-ray source as close to a true point source as it is physically possible to achieve. This can best be done using a relatively expensive instrument such as the electron microbeam-probe analyzer for an x-ray source. The sample should be a single crystal which is neither too perfect nor too imperfect. If it is too perfect, it will not give Kossel lines at all, while if it is too imperfect, the α_1-α_2 doublets will not be resolved. These requirements, while simple, are fairly rigorous and perhaps explain why the Kossel-line method has been so rarely used.

Another method involving diffraction-line ratio measurements was developed for powder samples using cylindrical or flat-plate cameras.[55,56] It has been developed for cubic, hexagonal, and tetragonal crystals. It will not be described here since it seems to be applicable primarily to lattice-parameter calculations of relatively low precision and accuracy (about 1 part in 10,000). One advantage of this method is that most of the calculations can be carried out with a slide rule.[56] The reader is referred to the literature for further details.

7. CONVOLUTION-FILM METHOD (0.002°ϕ LEVEL)

Beu et al.[4,14,16,18,57a-e] have developed a film method for the precise and accurate determination of lattice parameters at the 0.002°ϕ level based on a modification of the Straumanis method.[7,10] The basis of this modification is to measure several diffraction-line positions for $\theta > 60°$, to correct these measurements for residual systematic errors, and from these corrected measurements, to calculate the maximum-likelihood estimate of the lattice parameter $\hat{a}_0$ under the hypothesis of "no remaining systematic errors" using the LRM.[4]

Since this method utilizes measurements related to the profile peak, the additive method of correcting for certain systematic errors, which is a feature of the centroid method, cannot be used here. Rather, error profiles have to be determined, and these are convoluted to obtain a measure of the total displacement of the measured (peak) position from the true 2θ position, undistorted by these systematic errors. In particular, profiles due to absorption and radial divergence are calculated using a modified Taylor-Sinclair line-contour matrix method[57c,58] which takes into account the experimentally determined absorption coefficient of the sample powder together with the capillary or fiber on which the powder is mounted, the sample diameter, and the pertinent camera dimensions.* The profiles due to axial divergence are also calculated for the same sample and camera geometry.[18] This type of convolution-profile synthesis was originally described by Klug and Alexander in connection with the determination of diffraction-profile shapes using an asymmetric diffractometer.[59]

The Lorentz and polarization factors do not have profiles associated with them. Rather, they are multiplicative factors to be applied point by point to the profile in the vicinity of the peak. Correction for dispersion is also a multiplicative factor except that it has no significant effect on the peak position[5] and can be ignored at the 0.001°θ level.† Other systematic-error factors such as eccentricity[14] are additive and are applied to the measured θ values after they have been corrected by the necessary convolution and multiplicative procedures. Refraction is also an additive correction

* Another modification of the Taylor-Sinclair method, which also takes into account absorption in the capillary or fiber used for mounting the powder sample is described by Boom and Smits.[58a]

† Pike and Wilson[21] have pointed out that the peak position is not affected by the combined dispersion plus Lorentz factors. Either alone may have a slight effect.

usually applied to the lattice parameter, $\bar{a}_0$. Using the Straumanis method (symmetry of measurement about zero and 180° 2θ, and asymmetric film loading) no corrections are required for camera radius or zero position.

Measurements of diffraction peak positions and calibration lines are made on profiles obtained from a film pattern using a manual densitometer having a linear accuracy of 0.001 mm or better. The peak of a diffraction profile is determined with a precision of 0.002°ϕ or better using the centerline method (see first footnote in Sec. 6) to calculate the peak position. [Visual measurements of peak positions are no longer made because they are unreliable. In particular, it seems that each observer tends to read a (highly repeatable) diffraction line position suited to his own taste and this position may or may not agree with the peak position (maximum blackening) or the positions measured by other observers.] Corrections for nonuniform film shrinkage are made using hairline type calibration lines printed on the film in the vicinity of the diffraction lines of interest.[57a,57d] Uniform shrinkage over the entire film is handled automatically by the Straumanis method. Other experimental details have already been discussed in the section on the Straumanis Film Method.

After the diffraction lines are measured with a precision of about 0.002°ϕ and are corrected for systematic errors as described above with an accuracy of 0.001°θ or better, the lattice parameter $\bar{a}_0$ is calculated using the LRM. The convolution-film method has been successfully developed, as attested by the fact that the LRM indicates complete removal of systematic errors in Bragg angle at the 0.002°ϕ level of precision for a sample of IUCr silicon powder.[57b,57e]. The fully corrected Bragg angle centerline peak measurements obtained with the convolution-film method, along with recent centerline peak wavelengths of Bearden[41h], permit the precise *and* accurate determination of lattice parameters to about one part in 100,000 or better.

8. LIKELIHOOD-RATIO METHOD (LRM) FOR TESTING ACCURACY OF LATTICE-PARAMETER CALCULATIONS

Principles. The LRM is a method for evaluating the accuracy of lattice parameters based on the criterion of internal consistency of the Bragg-angle diffraction data.[4,4a] This involves a statistical comparison of the measurement precision of several corrected diffraction-line positions of a given sample with lattice-parameter values calculated for those lines. If the lattice parameters thus calculated differ by less than the precision of measurement, an accurate value of the lattice parameter, designated $\bar{a}_0$, for cubic materials may then be calculated. As pointed out previously, $\bar{a}_0$ represents the *maximum-likelihood estimate* of the lattice parameter under the hypothesis of "no remaining systematic errors" in the diffraction-angle measurements. The hypothesis formulated as follows:

$$e_1 = e_2 = e_3 = \cdots = e_m = 0 \qquad \text{or} \qquad e_i = 0$$

where e_i is the remaining systematic error in degrees θ at the ith diffraction angle and m is the number of diffraction lines measured; e_i* is defined by the equation $e_i = \psi_i - \theta_i$ where ψ_i is the average of n_i measurements of $\psi_{i\alpha}$, $\psi_{i\alpha}$ is the αth measurement of the ith diffraction angle, and θ_i is the true but unknown value of the Bragg angle θ.

The LRM is applicable to all diffractometer or film methods for which systematic-error corrections can be applied to individual diffraction-line measurements and has been developed by Beu et al. for cubic,[4] tetragonal, and hexagonal[60] materials. The LRM involves obtaining two estimates of a_0; $\hat{a}_0$, which is based on the assumption that $\sum_i e_i = 0$, and $\bar{a}_0$, which has already been defined. In obtaining these estimates, a function $W(a_0)$ is obtained, the minimum of which, W_m, is distributed like the chi-square function.† By comparing W_m with w_ϵ a critical value of the chi-square dis-

* e_i is the variable component of systematic error. The LRM has been generalized to include both variable (e_i) and constant (e) components of systematic error[4a]. LRM analysis based on e_i alone, however, is still the most important aspect of analysis for residual systematic errors in Bragg angle.

† The chi-square function or distribution is a statistical device for testing hypotheses.

tribution, the extent of systematic-error removal can be determined statistically. If $W_m \geq w_\epsilon$, the systematic errors have not been removed from a_0 within the precision of measurement and an accurate value of a_0 cannot be determined. On the other hand, if $W_m < w_\epsilon$, it may be concluded that the systematic errors have been removed within the precision of measurement at the ϵ significance level and $\hat{\hat{a}}_0$ may be calculated. An estimate of the standard deviation of $\hat{\hat{a}}_0$, designated s_{a_0}, may then be calculated. The inequalities between W_m and w_ϵ which are the crux of this method are postulated based on a theorem related to the likelihood ratio,[61] hence the name of the method.

Features of the LRM

1. The most important feature of the LRM is that it provides a valid statistical criterion for determining the accuracy of a lattice-parameter calculation based on the premise of internal self-consistency of the data; i.e., a lattice-parameter value for a given sample is the same within the precision of measurement regardless of which (hkl) reflection is used to calculate this parameter.

2. All systematic-error factors which are related directly to θ will be included in the LRM evaluation of accuracy. Even those factors which require a constant correction in θ for each diffraction angle will be included in this evaluation. The zero-setting error is a factor of this type and is of special importance in diffractometer work. The major factors which do not enter directly into the LRM evaluation are the x-ray wavelength and the change in x-ray wavelength part of the refraction correction. As was pointed out in the Introduction, wavelength accuracy can be handled separately from θ accuracy.

3. A comparison of W_m (calculated after making each systematic-error correction) with the critical value w_ϵ (obtained from the chi-square distribution) will indicate if the correction is valid. If W_m remains about the same or increases, then the correction is either insignificant or improper. The correction is useful only if W_m decreases. Finally, after all corrections are made, if W_m is still greater than w_ϵ, either one or more corrections are of the wrong magnitude or there are additional unknown systematic errors. Only if $W_m < w_\epsilon$ can it be claimed that all systematic errors have been removed within the precision of measurement at the ϵ significance level.

4. If $W_m < w_\epsilon$, this implies further that asymmetry of the characteristic wavelength distribution and its resolution or lack of resolution into the α_1-α_2 doublet, for example, has a negligible effect at the ϵ significance level on the calculated value of the lattice parameter based on the self-consistency criterion. This does not, however, indicate whether the wavelength characteristic (peak, centroid, etc.) used to calculate the lattice parameter is an accurate value.

5. After correcting the diffraction-line measurements for systematic errors, one at a time, the magnitude of the $\hat{e}_i$ values may be observed for $\sum_i e_i = 0$. If the absolute values of the $\hat{e}_i$ do not decrease significantly after a given systematic-error correction has been made, then the magnitude of, and the technique for making, the correction for that particular diffraction line should be reexamined. Thus the LRM is useful in pinpointing the sources of systematic error and in evaluating the techniques used in correcting for systematic errors.

Example Using Delf's Centroid Data on Tungsten.[6,*] *Experimental Data.* Dr. B. W. Delf kindly supplied the author with centroid data on tungsten for LRM evaluation. The experimentally determined centroid-angle values (corrected to 18° C) are given in Table 7 for the four diffraction lines of tungsten that were measured by Delf. The average 2θ and ψ_i (uncorrected θ_i) values are based on n_i measurements per line. s_i and s_i^2, the standard deviation and variance estimates of the average values, respectively, were calculated using the equation

$$s_{i\alpha} = (1/n_i) \sum_\alpha (\psi_{i\alpha} - \psi_i)^2$$

* The LRM evaluation of these data was presented as paper no. 32, "The Precise and Accurate Determination of the Lattice Parameter of Tungsten Using the Likelihood Ratio Method," by K. E. Beu, Pittsburgh Diffraction Conference, Mellon Institute, Pittsburgh, Pa. Nov. 7–9, 1962.

Table 7. Delf's Centroid Data for Tungsten
(Corrected to 18° C)

(hkl) of diffraction lines measured	(110)	(211)	(310)	(321)
Avg $2\theta^\circ$ (measured)	39.50121	72.47161	99.93921	130.60921
Avg $\theta^\circ = \psi_i$ (uncorrected)	19.75061	36.23581	49.96961	65.30461
n_i (measurements per line)	7	7	9	8
$s_i^2(\theta^\circ)^2$	60.9×10^{-8}	29.9×10^{-8}	75.8×10^{-8}	602×10^{-8}
$s_i(\theta^\circ)$	0.00078	0.00055	0.00087	0.00245

Systematic-error Corrections (°2θ)

(hkl)	Error No.*					
	1	2	3	4	5	6
(110)	+0.7675	+0.0053	+0.0080	+0.0160	0	−0.0015
(211)	+0.7675	+0.0045	+0.0039	+0.0050	0	+0.0039
(310)	+0.7675	+0.0036	+0.0391	0	0	−0.0003
(321)	+0.7675	+0.0023	+0.0212	−0.0074	−0.0050	−0.0020

* Coding for systematic-error corrections:
1. Zero
2. Specimen-surface displacement
3. Flat specimen
4. Axial (vertical) divergence
5. Dispersion, Lorentz, and polarization
6. Angular scale

The transparency correction was taken as zero for all lines.

The six corrections to be applied to the ψ_i values are also listed in Table 7 along with the numerical values for the corrections. The transparency error was assumed to be zero because of the extremely high absorption coefficient of tungsten.

The algebraically combined corrections and the corrected ψ_i values are listed in the third and fourth columns from the left of Table 8 for several systematic-error combinations (column 1) to show how the $\hat{e}_i$ and W_m are reduced as additional systematic-error corrections are applied. Sample calculations for $\hat{e}_i$, $\hat{a}_0$, $\bar{\hat{a}}_0$, and W_m are given in the next two sections using the data for the "all correction" case (Table 8) as an example.

Calculation of $\hat{a}_0$ and $\hat{e}_i$ for "All correction" Case. Values for $\hat{e}_i$ for each diffraction line are determined using the equations

$$a_0 \sin \theta_i = K_i$$

where the θ_i are calculated from estimates of a_0 and $K_i = [n\lambda(h^2 + k^2 + l^2)^{1/2}]/2$ for cubic materials, and

$$e_i = \psi_i - \theta_i$$

where the ψ_i are the corrected values given in the fourth column of Table 8 and the θ_i have been calculated using estimates of a_0 and the previous equation.

Only two estimates of a_0 are required, such that the corresponding values of $\sum_i e_i$ are respectively positive and negative and close to zero. Since estimates of a_0 plotted against $\sum_i e_i$ have a linear relationship, a linear interpolation can easily be made graphically or analytically for the point $(a_0, \sum_i e_i = 0)$. This interpolation provides the estimate $\hat{a}_0$ since, by definition, $\hat{a}_0$ is that value of a_0 for which $\sum_i e_i = 0$. After $\hat{a}_0$ is obtained, $\hat{\theta}_i$ and $\hat{e}_i$ for the individual diffraction lines can be calculated using the two equations above.

Table 8. Summary of LRM Calculations from Delf's Data on Tungsten at 18° C

Type of systematic-error correction*	(hkl)	Correction to ψ_i, $\theta°$	Corrected ψ_i, $\theta°$	$\hat{e}_i$, $\theta°$	$\sum_i \hat{e}_i$, $\theta°$	$\hat{a}_0$, Å	$\hat{\hat{a}}_0$, Å	$\hat{a}_0 - \hat{\hat{a}}_0$, Å	W_m
1 + 2 + 3	110	+0.39040	20.14101	−0.00734					
	211	+0.38795	36.62376	−0.00362					
	310	+0.40510	50.37471	+0.00124					
	321	+0.39550	65.70011	+0.00972	0.00000	3.164997	3.164939	+0.000058	80.0
1 + 2 + 3 + 6	110	+0.38965	20.14026	−0.00809					
	211	+0.38990	36.62571	−0.00168					
	310	+0.40495	50.37456	+0.00107					
	321	+0.39450	65.69911	+0.00870	0.00000	3.164997	3.164947	+0.000050	71.3
1 + 2 + 3 + 4 + 6	110	+0.39765	20.14826	−0.00064					
	211	+0.39240	36.62821	−0.00030					
	310	+0.40495	50.37456	−0.00074					
	321	+0.39080	65.69541	+0.00168	0.00000	3.164914	3.164937	−0.000023	8.95
1 + 2 + 3 + 4 + 5 + 6 (all)	110	+0.39765	20.14826	−0.00044					
	211	+0.39240	36.62821	+0.00012					
	310	+0.40495	50.37456	−0.00007					
	321	+0.38830	65.69290	+0.00039	0.00000	3.16494415	3.16494374	+0.00000041	2.50

$\hat{\hat{a}}_0 = 3.164944$ Å (for $W_m < w_\epsilon$)

$w_\epsilon = 7.815$ for 0.05 significance level, 3 degrees of freedom

$s_{a_0} = 0.000009$ Å

95 per cent limit of error of $\hat{\hat{a}}_0 = \pm 0.000018$ Å

$\lambda = 1.541760$ Å for weighted mean Cu $K\alpha$

* See Table 7 for coding of corrections.

Table 9. Calculation of $W(a_0)$ for Delf's Data on Tungsten (All Corrections)

Line No.	(hkl)	ψ_i	s_i^2	Estimate of a_0, Å	$\sin\theta_i$	θ_i	$e_i = \psi_i - \theta_i$	$\frac{e_i^2}{s_i^2}$	$\log_{10}\left[1 + \frac{e_i^2}{s_i^2}\right]$
1	(110)	20.14826	60.89×10^{-8}	3.16494280	0.344457883	20.14871	−0.00045	0.3316	0.124374
				3.16494380	0.344457774	20.14870	−0.00044	0.3223	0.121330
				3.16494490	0.344457665	20.14869	−0.00043	0.3122	0.118000
2	(211)	36.62821	29.89×10^{-8}	3.16494280	0.596618680	36.62811	+0.00010	0.0312	0.013385
				3.16494380	0.596618491	36.62810	+0.00011	0.0405	0.017242
				3.16494490	0.596618303	36.62808	+0.00013	0.0506	0.021437
3	(310)	50.37456	75.75×10^{-8}	3.16494280	0.770231234	50.37466	−0.00010	0.0139	0.005995
				3.16494380	0.770230990	50.37464	−0.00008	0.0084	0.003633
				3.16494490	0.770230747	50.37461	−0.00005	0.0046	0.001993
4	(321)	65.69291	602.03×10^{-8}	3.16494280	0.911349855	65.69256	+0.00035	0.0195	0.008387
				3.16494380	0.911349567	65.69252	+0.00039	0.0245	0.010512
				3.16494490	0.911349279	65.69248	+0.00043	0.0299	0.012795

Estimate of a_0, Å	$W(a_0)$*
3.16494280	2.516
3.16494380	2.503
3.16494490	2.525

$$* \; W(a_0) = \log_e 10 \sum_{i=1}^{i=4} \left[7 \log_{10}\left(1 + \frac{e_1^2}{s_1^2}\right) + 7 \log_{10}\left(1 + \frac{e_2^2}{s_2^2}\right) + 9 \log_{10}\left(1 + \frac{e_3^2}{s_3^2}\right) + 8 \log_{10}\left(1 + \frac{e_4^2}{s_4^2}\right) \right]$$

For Delf's "all corrections" data on tungsten, $\hat{a}_0$ was found by interpolation to be 3.164944 Å, and using this estimate of a_0, the $\hat{e}_i$'s (in degrees θ) were determined to five decimal places as follows:

(hkl)	(110)	(211)	(310)	(321)	$\sum_i \hat{e}_i$
K_i*	1.090190	1.888264	2.437738	2.884370	
ψ_i	20.14826	36.62821	50.37456	65.69290	
θ_i	20.14870	36.62809	50.37463	65.69251	
$\hat{e}_i$, $\theta°$	−0.00044	+0.00012	−0.00007	+0.00039	0.00000

* λ = 1.541760 Å (weighted mean Cu Kα).

These calculations need to be made only if it is desired to explore the magnitudes of the $\hat{e}_i$'s and to pinpoint sources of difficulty in making systematic-error corrections. $\hat{e}_i$ and $\hat{a}_0$ are not needed otherwise.

Calculation of W_m and $\hat{\hat{a}}_0$ for "All Correction" Case. W_m is a statistical function used to determine whether or not systematic errors have been removed from the data within the precision of measurement. This is done by comparing W_m with w_ϵ, a critical value of the chi-square distribution[62] at the ϵ significance level. If $W_m < w_\epsilon$, the systematic errors have been removed within the precision of measurement and a value of $\hat{\hat{a}}_0$ which satisfies the hypothesis of "no remaining systematic errors" may be calculated.

It can be shown[4] that W_m is the minimum of the function

$$W(a_0) = \sum_i n_i \ln (1 + e_i^2/s_i^2)$$

By calculating $W(a_0)$ for several estimates of a_0 in the vicinity of $\hat{a}_0$, a plot of $W(a_0)$ vs. a_0 will reveal the minimum W_m. From this plot, it can be determined if $W_m < w_\epsilon$. If this is so, then $\hat{\hat{a}}_0$ is that estimate of a_0 which corresponds to W_m.

The method for calculating $W(a_0)$ is indicated in Table 9. Values of $W(a_0)$ in the vicinity of W_m are given in this table, and a plot of these values against estimates of a_0 is given in Fig. 17. As can be seen from this figure, $W_m = 2.503$. On the other hand, $w_\epsilon = 7.815$ at the 0.05 significance level and for three degrees of freedom[62] corresponding to the four measured diffraction lines. Thus $W_m < w_\epsilon$ for Delf's data when all corrections are applied, and hence $\hat{\hat{a}}_0 = 3.16494374$ Å,* corresponding to W_m. As a matter of general interest, $W(a_0)$ vs. a_0 curves for various correction combinations are given in Fig. 18. The steady decrease in W_m from 90 for corrections (1 + 3) to 2.5 for all corrections (1 + 2 + 3 + 4 + 5 + 6) can be readily observed.

Calculation of s_{a_0} and 95 per cent Limits of Error. s_{a_0} is an estimate of the standard deviation of $\hat{\hat{a}}_0$ and can be calculated once $\hat{\hat{a}}_0$ has been determined, using the following equation:

$$s_{a_0}{}^2 = \frac{\hat{\hat{a}}_0{}^2}{\sum_i (n_i/\hat{\sigma}_i{}^2) \tan^2 \hat{\hat{\theta}}_i}$$

s_{a_0} for Delf's data was 0.000009 Å (calculations are given in Table 10). The 95 per cent limit of error $= \pm 1.96\, s_{a_0} = \pm 0.000018$ Å.

* Only six decimal places are significant based on s_{a_0} (see next paragraph); however, the reason for including eight decimal places will become clear under Some Implications of the LRM Calculations on Delf's Data.

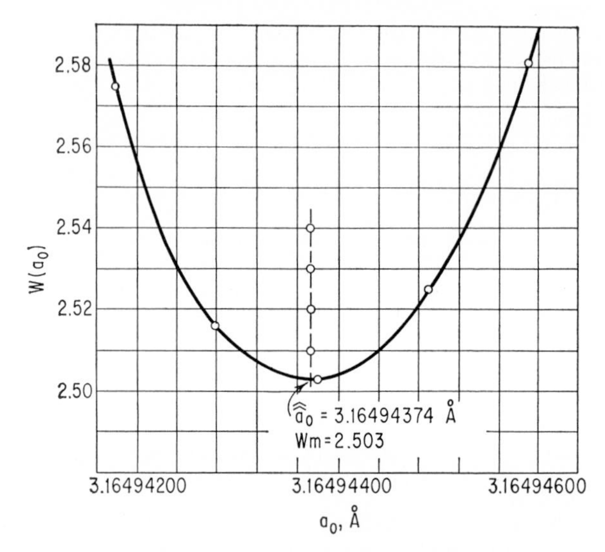

FIG. 17. $W(a_0)$ vs. a_0 for Delf's data on tungsten corrected for all systematic errors (expanded scale).

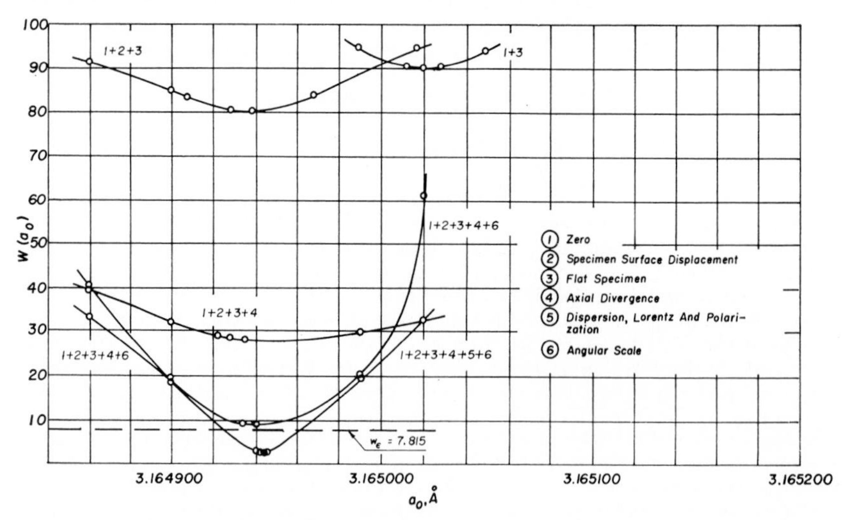

FIG. 18. $W(a_0)$ vs. a_0 for Delf's data on tungsten (various combinations of systematic-error corrections).

Thus the lattice parameter of tungsten under the hypothesis of "no remaining systematic errors" was found to be $\hat{\hat{a}}_0 = 3.164944$ Å and an estimate of its precision and accuracy for 95 per cent limit of error is ± 0.000018 Å, or 1 part in 180,000. This is based on a weighted mean copper $K\alpha$ wavelength of 1.541760 Å and a sample temperature of 18° C.

Some Implications of the LRM Calculations on Delf's Data. Figure 18 shows that, as additional systematic-error corrections were included in the measured ψ_i values, W_m decreased regularly, indicating all corrections to be valid. Furthermore W_m became less than w_ϵ only after all the corrections were made. The sensitivity of the LRM to

Table 10. Calculation of s_{a_0} for Delf's Data on Tungsten (All Corrections)

(hkl)	(110)	(211)	(310)	(321)
$s_i^2 \times 10^{-8} (°\theta)^2$	60.89	29.89	75.75	602.03
$\hat{\hat{\theta}}_i$ (calculated using $\hat{\hat{a}}_0$)*	20.14870	36.62810	50.37464	65.69252
$(\psi_i - \hat{\hat{\theta}}_i)^2 \times 10^{-8}, (°\theta)^2$	18.80	1.73	0.36	18.57
$\hat{\hat{\sigma}}_i^2 \times 10^{-8}, (°\theta)^2$†	79.69	31.62	76.11	620.60
$\hat{\hat{\sigma}}_i^2 \times 10^{-10}$, radians²	2.43	0.96	2.32	18.90
n_i	7	7	9	8
$(n_i/\hat{\hat{\sigma}}_i^2) \times 10^{10}$	2.88	7.27	3.88	0.42
$\tan \hat{\hat{\theta}}_i$	0.367	0.743	1.208	2.214
$\tan^2 \hat{\hat{\theta}}_i$	0.135	0.553	1.459	4.902
$(n_i/\hat{\hat{\sigma}}_i^2) \tan^2 \hat{\hat{\theta}}_i \times 10^{10}$	0.388	4.017	5.663	2.074

$$s_{a_0}^2 = \frac{\hat{\hat{a}}_0^2}{\sum_i (n_i/\hat{\hat{\sigma}}_i^2) \tan^2 \hat{\hat{\theta}}_i} = \frac{(3.165)^2}{12.142 \times 10^{10}} = 83.75 \times 10^{-12}$$

$$s_{a_0} = 9.1 \times 10^{-6} = 0.000009 \text{ Å}$$

* $\hat{\hat{a}}_0 = 3.164944$ Å

† $\hat{\hat{\sigma}}_i^2 = s_i^2 + (\psi_i - \hat{\hat{\theta}}_i)^2$

small corrections is evident by comparing W_m before and after applying correction 5 (see Table 7) as the last correction (correction 5 is very small, zero for three diffraction lines and $-0.005°$ 2θ for the fourth). Before applying correction 5, $W_m = 8.95$ (greater than w_ϵ, which is 7.815); while after applying it, $W_m = 2.503$ (less than w_ϵ). Thus correction 5 reduced W_m below w_ϵ when applied as the last correction, indicating that it was a necessary correction in spite of its small magnitude.

Except in one case, the absolute values of the $\hat{e}_i$'s listed in Table 8 can be observed to be reduced for each diffraction line as each additional systematic-error correction is made. This is to be expected for valid systematic-error corrections. Although all systematic-error corrections were valid, based on reductions in W_m as each was made, $\hat{e}_i$ for correction 6 and the (110) diffraction line increased slightly in absolute value, indicating that the magnitude of this correction was not quite correct for this line. The discrepancy apparently was not great enough to prevent reducing W_m below w_ϵ for all corrections; however, the increase in correction 6 for the (110) reflection indicates the sensitivity of the $\hat{e}_i$'s to corrections which are even slightly improper. Furthermore, it illustrates the ability of the LRM to pinpoint difficulties in systematic-error correction procedures right down to the diffraction line and to the type and magnitude of the correction involved.

A final point involves the quantity $(\hat{a}_0 - \hat{\hat{a}}_0)$, which is a physical measure of the systematic error remaining in the lattice-parameter calculations, as contrasted to W_m, which is a relatively abstract statistical quantity. The physical significance of $(\hat{a}_0 - \hat{\hat{a}}_0)$ can be readily visualized if it is recalled that $\hat{a}_0$ is an estimate of a_0 based on $\sum_i e_i = 0$, while $\hat{\hat{a}}_0$ is an estimate of a_0 based on the hypothesis of "no remaining systematic errors," e.g., $e_i = 0$.*

The quantity $(\hat{a}_0 - \hat{\hat{a}}_0)$ has been given in Table 8 for the various error-correction combinations listed.† $(\hat{a}_0 - \hat{\hat{a}}_0)$ decreases in absolute value with W_m; however, except

* It should be noted that $\sum_i e_i = 0$ and $e_i = 0$ have different implications; e.g., the e_i can have significant values even though their sum may be equal to zero. On the other hand, $e_i = 0$ implies that each e_i is separately equal to zero.

† $\hat{\hat{a}}_0$ may be calculated when $W_m \geq w_\epsilon$; however, it has no physical significance in this case other than to observe the semiquantitative aspects of $(\hat{a}_0 - \hat{\hat{a}}_0)$ illustrated in Table 8.

for the "all-correction" case, $(\hat{a}_0 - \bar{a}_0)$ is greater than s_{a_0}. In the "all-correction" case, $(\hat{a}_0 - \bar{a}_0)$ is +0.00000041 Å or about one-twentieth the value of s_{a_0} (0.000009 Å). This indicates that the systematic errors have indeed been removed from the data within the precision of measurement.

$\hat{a}_0$ and $\bar{a}_0$ have been given to eight decimal places for the "all-correction" case to show the small difference between these two estimates; however, these quantities are significant only to six decimal places based on the precision estimate s_{a_0}, and they should be rounded off to six places in actual practice.

REFERENCES CITED

1. J. A. Bearden and C. H. Shaw, *Phys. Rev.*, **48**:18 (1935).
2. K. Lonsdale, *Acta Cryst.*, **3**:400 (1950).
3. W. Parrish, *Acta Cryst.*, **13**:838 (1960).
4. K. E. Beu, F. J. Musil, and D. R. Whitney, *Acta Cryst.*, **15**:1292 (1962).

4*a*. K. E. Beu and D. R. Whitney, *Further Developments in the Likelihood Ratio Method for the Precise and Accurate Determination of Lattice Parameters*, USAEC Report GAT-T-1289/Rev. 1, 1965, Goodyear Atomic Corporation. Submitted for publication.

5. W. L. Bond, *Acta Cryst.*, **13**:814 (1960).
6. B. W. Delf and A. J. C. Wilson (unpublished data), University College, Cardiff, Wales, 1962.
7. M. E. Straumanis and A. Ievins, *The Precision Determination of Lattice Constants by the Asymmetric Method*, Springer-Verlag, OHG, Berlin, 1940. Reprinted by Edwards Brothers, Inc., Ann Arbor, Mich., 1948.
8. G. Kettmann, *Z. Physik.*, **53**:198 (1929).
9. A. J. Bradley and A. H. Jay, *Proc. Phys. Soc.* (*London*), **44**:563 (1932).
10. M. E. Straumanis and A. Ievins, *The Precision Determination of Lattice Constants by the Asymmetric Method*, Springer-Verlag, OHG, Berlin, 1940. (Translated by K. E. Beu, USAEC Rept. GAT-T-643, 1959. Goodyear Atomic Corp.)
11. A. Ievins and M. E. Straumanis, *Z. Physik. Chem.*, **34**:402 (1936).
12. K. E. Beu, *An Evaluation of Systematic Errors of the Straumanis Method by Means of Error Profiles*, in preparation.
13. R. R. Garlits and C. C. Bolt, *Norelco Reptr.*, **8**:37 (1961).
14. K. E. Beu and D. L. Scott, *Acta Cryst.*, **15**:1301 (1962).
15. A. J. C. Wilson, *Rev. Sci. Instr.*, **20**:831 (1950).
16. K. E. Beu and D. L. Scott, *Modifications of a Commercial Powder Diffraction Camera for Precise and Accurate Lattice Parameter Measurements*, USAEC Rept. GAT-T-973, 1962, Goodyear Atomic Corp.
17. W. Parrish, *Norelco Reptr.*, **2**:67 (1955).
18. K. E. Beu, D. K. Landstrom, D. R. Whitney, and E. R. Pike, *Acta Cryst.*, **17**:(1964).
19. M. E. Straumanis, *Acta Cryst.*, **13**:818 (1960).
20. M. E. Straumanis, *Acta Cryst.*, **8**:654 (1955).
21. E. R. Pike and A. J. C. Wilson, *Proc. Phys. Soc.* (*London*), **72**:908 (1958).
22. K. E. Beu and D. L. Scott, *The Precise and Accurate Determination of Lattice Parameters Using Film Powder Methods: Film Measuring Technique*, USAEC Rept. GAT-392/Part IB, Goodyear Atomic Corp., in preparation.
23. J. O. Porteus and L. G. Parratt, *Precise Wavelength of a Wide Spectral Line and Precise Lattice Parameter of a Crystal*, Cornell University, Ithaca, N.Y., May 1, 1959, Tech. Rept. no. 3, AFOSR-TN-59-305, ASTIA-AD-213-089.
24. H. Ekstein and S. Siegel, *Acta Cryst.*, **2**:99 (1949).
25. M. U. Cohen, *Rev. Sci. Instr.*, **6**:68 (1935).
26. J. B. Hess, *Acta Cryst.*, **4**:209 (1951).
27. A. Taylor and H. Sinclair, *Proc. Phys. Soc.* (*London*), **57**:126 (1945).
28. J. B. Nelson and D. P. Riley, *Proc. Soc.* (*London*), **57**:160 (1945).
29. H. Weyerer, *Z. Krist.*, **109**:338 (1957).
30. M. H. Mueller, L. Heaton, and K. T. Miller, *Acta Cryst.*, **13**:828 (1960).
31. R. E. Vogel, and C. P. Kempter, *Acta Cryst.*, **14**:1130 (1961).
32. R. E. Vogel and C. P. Kempter, *A Mathematical Technique for the Precision Determination of Lattice Constants*, Rept. LA-2317, Los Alamos Scientific Lab, 1959.
33. A. Hald, *Statistical Theory with Engineering Applications*, John Wiley & Sons, Inc., New York, 551, 1952.
34. W. E. Deming, *Statistical Adjustment of Data*, John Wiley & Sons, Inc., New York, 1943.
35. H. Lipson and A. J. C. Wilson, *J. Sci. Instr.*, **18**:144 (1941).

36. E. J. Myers and F. C. Davies, *Acta Cryst.*, **14**:194 (1961).
37. A. Taylor and R. W. Floyd, *Acta Cryst.*, **3**:285 (1950).
38. A. J. C. Wilson, *J. Sci. Instr.*, **27**:321 (1950).
39. W. Parrish and A. J. C. Wilson, *Systematic Errors in Lattice Constant Measurements with the Diffractometer*, Paper no. 59, Am. Cryst. Assoc. Meeting, Harvard University, April 5–9, 1954.
40. E. R. Pike and A. J. C. Wilson, *Brit. J. Appl. Phys.*, **10**:57 (1959).
41. J. Ladell, W. Parrish, and J. Taylor, *Acta Cryst.*, **12**:561 (1959).
41*a*. M. Mack, W. Parrish, and J. Taylor, *Acta Cryst.*, **16**:1179 (1963).
41*b*. W. Parrish, M. Mack, and J. Taylor, *J. Appl. Phys.*, **34**:2544 (1963).
41*c*. W. Parrish, J. Taylor, and M. Mack, *Advances in X-ray Analysis, Vol. 7.*, Plenum Press, New York, 1964.
41*d*. J. Taylor, M. Mack, and W. Parrish, *Acta Cryst.*, **17**:1229 (1964).
41*e*. L. S. Zevin, M. M. Umanskii, and D. H. Kheiker, *Sov. Phys. Cryst.*, **8**:528 (1964).
41*f*. B. W. Delf, *Acta Cryst.* **17**:770 (1964).
41*g*. M. Mack, W. Parrish, and J. Taylor, *J. Appl. Phys.*, **35**:1118 (1964).
41*h*. J. A. Bearden, *X-ray Wavelengths*, USAEC Report NYO-10586, Johns Hopkins University, 1964.
42. A. J. C. Wilson, *Proc. Cambridge Phil. Soc.*, **36**:485 (1940).
42*a*. B. W. Delf, *Brit. J. Appl. Phys.*, **14**:345 (1963).
43. E. R. Pike and J. W. Hughes, *J. Sci. Instr.*, **36**:212 (1959).
44. W. Parrish and K. Lowitsch, *Am. Mineralogist*, **44**:765 (1959).
45. B. W. Delf, *Brit. J. Appl. Phys.*, **12**:421 (1961).
46. E. R. Pike, *J. Sci. Instr.*, **34**:355 (1957).
47. J. Ladell, *Acta Cryst.*, **14**:47 (1961).
48. E. R. Pike and J. Ladell, *Acta Cryst.*, **14**:53 (1961).
49. H. M. Otte, *J. Appl. Phys.*, **34**:1536 (1961).
50. H. W. King and L. F. Vassamillet, *Precision Lattice Parameter Determination by Double Scanning Diffractometry*, presented at 10th Annual Conference on Applications of X-ray Analysis, Denver, Colorado, August 7–9, 1961.
51. W. Kossel, *Gott. Nachr. Math. Physik.*, **1**:229 (1935).
52. K. Lonsdale, *Phil. Trans. Roy. Soc. (London)*, **A-240**:219 (1947).
53. B. H. Heise, *J. Appl. Phys.*, **33**:938 (1962).
54. R. E. Hanneman, R. E. Ogilvie, and A. Modrzejewski, *J. Appl. Phys.*, **33**:1429 (1962).
55. M. Cernohorsky, *Acta Cryst.*, **13**:823 (1961).
56. M. Cernohorsky, *Czech. J. Phys.*, **B10**:225 (1960).
57. K. E. Beu, et al., *The Precise and Accurate Determination of Lattice Parameters Using Film Powder Diffraction Methods*, USAEC Rept. GAT-392, Goodyear Atomic Corp., in preparation.
57*a*. D. L. Scott and K. E. Beu, *Experimental Techniques for the Precise and Accurate Determination of Lattice Parameters by Film Powder Methods*, paper B-4, Pittsburgh Diffraction Conference, Nov. 3–5, 1965.
57*b*. K. E. Beu and D. L. Scott, *The Convolution-film Method for the Precise and Accurate Determination of Lattice Parameters and Its Application to IUCr Silicon*, paper B-5, Pittsburgh Diffraction Conference, Nov. 3-5, 1965.
57*c*. K. E. Beu, D. L. Scott, and L. E. Alexander, *Precise and Accurate Lattice Parameters by Film Powder Methods. V. Absorption Profiles and Corrections for Cylindrical Cameras*, USAEC Report GAT-T-1372, 1966, Goodyear Atomic Corporation. To be published.
57*d*. K. E. Beu and D. L. Scott, *Precise and Accurate Lattice Parameters by Film Powder Methods. VI. Experimental Techniques for Cylindrical Film Cameras*, USAEC Report GAT-T-1373, 1966. Goodyear Atomic Corporation. To be published.
57*e*. K. E. Beu and D. L. Scott, *Precise and Accurate Lattice Parameters by Film Powder Methods. VII. The Convolution-Film Method and Its Application to IUCr Silicon*, USAEC Report GAT-T-1374, 1966, Goodyear Atomic Corporation. To be published.
58. A Taylor and H. Sinclair, *Proc. Phys. Soc. (London)*, **57**:108 (1945).
58*a*. G. Boom and D. W. Smits, *Koninkl. Nederl. Akad. v. Wetenschappen, Amsterdam, Proceedings*, Series B, **68**:46 (1965).
59. H. P. Klug and L. E. Alexander, *X-ray Diffraction Procedures*, p. 246–60, John Wiley & Sons, Inc., New York, 1954.
60. K. E. Beu, F. J. Musil, and D. R. Whitney, *Acta Cryst.*, **16**:1241 (1963).
61. A. M. Mood, *Introduction to the Theory of Statistics*, 259, McGraw-Hill Book Company, New York, 1950.
62. *Handbook of Chemistry and Physics*, 40th ed., 218–219, Chemical Rubber Publishing Company, Cleveland, 1959.

GENERAL REFERENCES

Azaroff, L. V., and M. J. Buerger: *The Powder Method in X-ray Crystallography*, chap. 15, McGraw-Hill Book Company, New York, 1958.

Buerger, M. J.: *X-ray Crystallography*, chap. 20, John Wiley & Sons, Inc., New York, 1942.

Cullity, B. D.: *Elements of X-ray Diffraction*, chap. 11, Addison-Wesley Publishing Company, Inc., Reading, Mass., 1956.

Henry, N. F. M., H. Lipson, and W. A. Wooster: *The Interpretation of X-ray Diffraction Photographs*, chap. 13, Macmillan & Co., Ltd., London, 1953.

Kasper, J. S., and K. Lonsdale: International Tables for X-ray Crystallography, vol. II, chap. 4.7, Kynoch Press, Birmingham, England, 1959, (by W. Parrish and A. J. C. Wilson).

Klug, H. P., and L. E. Alexander: *X-ray Diffraction Procedures*, chap. 8, John Wiley & Sons, Inc., New York, 1954.

Peiser, H. S., H. P. Rooksby, and A. J. C. Wilson: *X-ray Diffraction by Polycrystalline Materials*, chap. 15, Institute of Physics, London, 1955.

Taylor, A.: *X-ray Metallography*, pp. 163–191, John Wiley & Sons, Inc., New York, 1961.

Chapter 11

QUALITATIVE ANALYSIS BY POWDER DIFFRACTION

Emmett F. Kaelble

Monsanto Company

1. INTRODUCTION

Every crystalline powder produces a characteristic diffraction pattern. This is the basis of qualitative analysis by powder diffraction. Identification is usually accomplished by systematic comparison of an unknown pattern with a catalogue of standard data such as the *X-ray Powder Data File** published by the American Society for Testing and Materials. Specialized techniques have been devised for certain situations. Frevel's method of identification by isomorphism, for example, is frequently useful when the patterns sought are not included in the data file. Other techniques are particularly useful for the identification of clay minerals or surface deposits.

The techniques given in Part 3, Determination of Crystal Structure, can also be useful in compound identification. Once the unit cell for an unknown material has been determined, it can be used to identify the material by comparison with similar values listed in one of several compendia,[1-4] which give data for some materials not included in the *X-ray Powder Data File*. Even in the absence of such data, molecular-weight determinations from x-ray data may provide useful evidence if not unequivocal identification. With crystals of low symmetry, such a procedure would be very time-consuming. Moreover, it would be unsuccessful if the unknown were a mixture. Still, it provides a valuable adjunct to the procedures described in this chapter.

Diffraction patterns of mixtures consist of the superimposed patterns of the individual components. Therefore, powder diffraction is useful in analyzing mixtures as well as pure materials. Interpretation becomes more complicated, the degree of complication depending on the number of components, the occurrence of line superposition, and the amount of prior information which is available about the mixture. Again, special techniques, limited only by the ingenuity of the analyst, are helpful in certain situations. Modern data-retrieval systems, such as IBM punched cards and the Termatrex system now being used, facilitate qualitative interpretation of powder diffraction patterns, particularly those of mixtures.

As is true with all analytical procedures, x-ray powder diffraction is most powerful when used in conjunction with other techniques, such as emission spectroscopy, x-ray fluorescence, and chemical analysis. An important advantage of x-ray diffraction over these and other techniques is that the results obtained are in terms of materials

* Since this printing, the name *X-ray Powder Data File* has been changed to *Powder Diffraction File.*

as they occur in the sample, not in terms of elements or ions present. It is often the only satisfactory method of distinguishing among polymorphs or detecting a compound in the presence of others containing the same elements.

Furthermore, the sample is not consumed in x-ray diffraction, so that it may be saved or subsequently analyzed by other techniques. The term "nondestructive," frequently applied to x-ray analysis, is not always appropriate here because crushing or other manipulation is frequently required to prepare the sample for powder diffraction.

2. THE *X-RAY POWDER DATA FILE*

The use of powder diffraction for identification was given a firm foothold in 1938 by Hanawalt, Rinn, and Frevel, who compiled data on 1,000 compounds in a manner

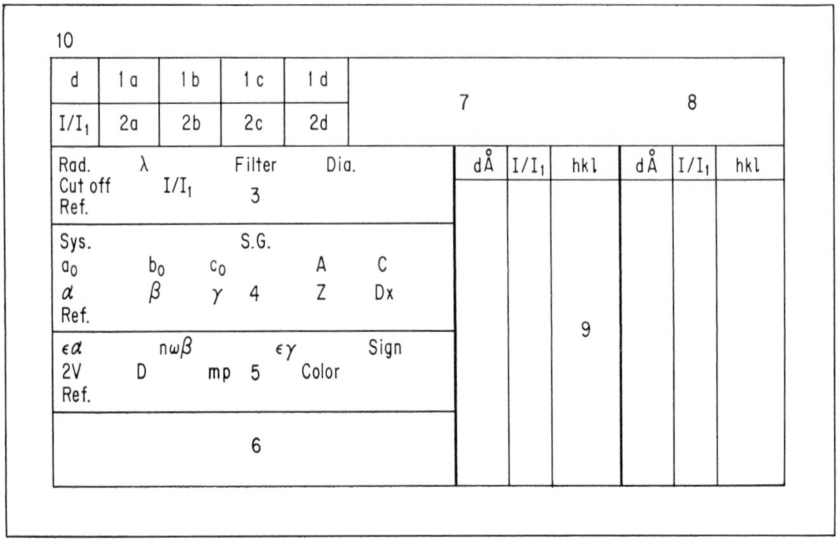

10

d	1a	1b	1c	1d	7	8
I/I_1	2a	2b	2c	2d		

	dÅ	I/I_1	hkl	dÅ	I/I_1	hkl
Rad. λ Filter Dia. Cut off I/I_1 3 Ref.						
Sys. S.G. a_0 b_0 c_0 A C α β γ 4 Z Dx Ref.			9			
εα nωβ εγ Sign 2V D mp 5 Color Ref.						
6						

FIG. 1. Format of plain cards in the *X-ray Powder Data File*. (*Courtesy of the Joint Committee on Chemical Analysis by Powder Diffraction Methods.*)

which formed the basis for a reference catalogue. Their data and procedure led to the development of the *X-ray Powder Data File,* compiled under the auspices of a joint committee representing the American Society for Testing and Materials, the American Crystallographic Association, the British Institute of Physics, and the National Association of Corrosion Engineers. At present the file contains data for 8,000 materials and is growing at the rate of 800 patterns a year. It is by far the most important instrument for qualitative analysis by powder diffraction. The data file is available in a variety of forms for either manual or machine data retrieval. Information regarding purchase of the file is available from the American Society for Testing and Materials, X-ray Department, 1916 Race Street, Philadelphia 3, Pa.

Plain Cards. The *X-ray Powder Data File* is available on 3 by 5 cards commonly referred to as "plain cards," to distinguish them from the other forms in which the *File* is available. The format of these cards is shown in Fig. 1. Various areas of the card are reserved for specific kinds of information. Not all the following information is found on every card.

Spaces 1a, 1b, 1c: Interplanar spacings of the three strongest lines. Only lines for $2\theta < 90°$ are recorded, so that the minimum d value depends on the wavelength of the radiation used.

Space 1d: Largest d value found for the specimen.

Spaces 2a, 2b, 2c, 2d: Relative intensities of the above lines referred to the strongest line as 100.

Space 3: Experimental conditions used in obtaining the pattern.

Space 4: Crystallographic data.

Space 5: Optical data, measured density, melting point, and color.

Space 6: Chemical analysis, source and treatment of specimen, temperature at which data were obtained, etc.

Space 7: Chemical formula and name.

Space 8: "Dot" or structural formula and mineralogical or common name.

Space 9: Interplanar spacings, relative intensities, and Miller indices.

Space 10: Sequence number of the card.

5-0628 minor correction

d	2.82	1.99	1.63	3.258	NaCl ★
I/I_1	100	55	15	13	Sodium chloride (Halite)

Rad. CuKα λ 1.5405 Filter Ni
Dia. Cut off Coll.
I/I_1 G.C. Diffractometer d corr. abs.?
Ref. Swanson and Fuyat, NBS circular 539, vol. II, 41 (1953)

Sys. cubic S.G. O_H^5 = Fm3m
a_0 5.6402 b_0 c_0 A C
α β γ Z 4
Ref. Ibid.

$\varepsilon\alpha$ $n\omega\beta$ 1.542 $\varepsilon\gamma$ Sign
2V D_x 2.164 mp Color colorless
Ref. Ibid.

An ACS reagent grade sample recrystallized twice from hydrochloric acid.
X-ray pattern at 26°C.

Replaces 1-0993, 1-0994, 2-0818

d Å	I/I_1	hkl	d Å	I/I_1	hkl
3.258	13	111			
2.821	100	200			
1.994	55	220			
1.701	2	311			
1.628	15	222			
1.410	6	400			
1.294	1	331			
1.261	11	420			
1.1515	7	422			
1.0855	1	511			
0.9969	2	440			
0.9533	1	531			
0.9401	3	600			
0.8917	4	620			
0.8601	1	533			
0.8503	3	622			
0.8141	2	444			

2003

FIG. 2. Plain card from the *X-ray Powder Data File*. (*Courtesy of the Joint Committee on Chemical Analysis by Powder Diffraction Methods.*)

Figure 2 shows a typical card from the file. The sequence number is in two parts: The number before the hyphen is the set number. (New data are issued periodically in sets.) The number following the hyphen represents sequence within the set. Data for sets 1 to 5 are now also available in the same format but printed in book form, three compounds to a page, rather than on cards. The acceptance of this alternate form will determine whether the other sets will be so offered.

The *Index to the X-ray Powder Data File* is used in conjunction with the plain cards. This volume has a numerical section, alphabetical sections for inorganic and organic compounds and minerals, and an organic formula index. Entries in the *Index* consist of the d values of the three strongest lines, their relative intensities, the name and formula of the substance, and the sequence number of the data card in the *File*. The *Index* is used to select likely identities for a set of powder data. Verification is then made by comparing the selected data cards with the unknown data.

Data in the numerical section of the *Index* are divided into 87 "Hanawalt" groups according to d values, as is shown in Table 1.

Each pattern in the file is entered three times in the numerical section of the *Index*, in the Hanawalt groups corresponding to each of the three most intense lines of the pattern d_1, d_2, and d_3. In the group corresponding to d_1, the d values are shown in the order d_1, d_2, d_3. In the other two entries, the order is d_2, d_1, d_3 and d_3, d_1, d_2, respectively. Within each group, entries are arranged in decreasing order of the d values in the second column. If two or more entries have the same second d values, the third value determines the sequence. The threefold listing makes it possible to find the desired entry in the *Index* despite minor variations in the observed d values and intensities arising from different experimental techniques or conditions. When an experimental d value falls close to the limit of a Hanawalt group, it is advisable to search also the adjacent group to allow for experimental variations. If two or three of the strongest lines of a pattern are greater than 10 Å, additional entries are made for the three strongest lines below 10 Å. This is for the benefit of users of the *File* whose equipment cannot record spacings beyond 10 Å.

The alphabetical sections of the *Index* are useful if supplementary information about a sample indicates that it is or contains a specific compound, or that particular elements are present. Similarly, the organic-formula section is useful if information

Table 1. The Hanawalt Groups

d values, Å	*Grouping interval*
20 and larger	One group
19.9–12.0	Steps of 2 Å
11.9–10.0	Steps of 1 Å
9.99–6.00	Steps of 0.5 Å
5.99–5.00	Steps of 0.25 Å
4.99–3.50	Steps of 0.1 Å
3.49–1.00	Steps of 0.05 Å
0.99–0.80	Steps of 0.1 Å
Smaller than 0.80	One group

about the empirical formula of an organic compound is known. The sequence followed in the organic-formula index is essentially the same as that used in *Chemical Abstracts*.

Procedure for Using the X-ray Powder Data File Plain Cards. A table of the experimental data is prepared listing d values in decreasing order along with relative intensities. The general procedure is then as follows: In the numerical section of the *Index*, locate the proper Hanawalt group for the strongest line of the unknown pattern. Read down the second column to find a match for the second strongest line of the pattern. Find the entry or entries for which the third strongest line also agrees with the pattern within experimental error. Verify the tentative identification by comparing all experimental d values and relative intensities with values on the indicated data card or cards. When the unknown is a single crystalline material which is listed in the *File*, this procedure leads to an unequivocal identification in a matter of minutes.

More often, however, the unknown is a mixture of two or more components, and the procedure is not so straightforward. It is worthwhile to examine the sample under a microscope prior to x-ray analysis. This will often indicate whether the material is a pure compound or a mixture. In some cases, interpretation can be simplified by physical separation of the phases in a mixture and examination of the patterns of the separated components.

If one component of a mixture is present at a level of about 75 per cent or more, interpretation will probably be straightforward, for the three most intense lines on the pattern will probably be those of the major constituent. The preceding general procedure will then lead to the identification of the major constituent, with some minor lines remaining unaccounted for. Repeating the procedure for these lines will then yield the identity of the minor constituent(s).

More trouble is encountered when the components in a mixture are present in similar concentrations. Here the three most intense lines will very likely not all be due to one component. One must always be alert to the possibility of line overlap, which results in two or more lines showing up as a single one with unexpectedly high intensity. No straightforward procedure can be given for this case. One simply tries various combinations of lines in an effort to identify one of the components. When this is accomplished, the procedure is repeated on the remaining lines.

Keysort Punched Cards. A system of mechanical sorting is of great value to the *X-ray Powder Data File* in that it allows ready coordination of numerical diffraction data with known chemical-composition data or other information which may be

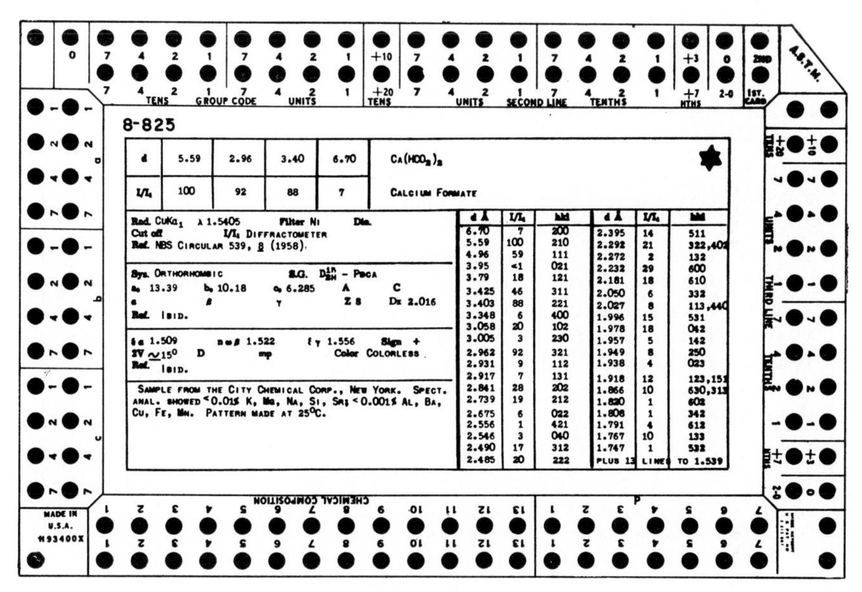

8-825

d	5.59	2.96	3.40	6.70	$Ca(HCO_2)_2$
I/I_1	100	92	88	7	Calcium Formate

Rad. $CuK\alpha_1$ λ 1.5405 Filter Ni Dia.
Cut off I/I_1 Diffractometer
Ref. NBS Circular 539, 8 (1958).

Sys. Orthorhombic S.G. D_{2h}^{15} - Pbca
a_0 13.39 b_0 10.18 c_0 6.285 A C
α β γ Z 8 Dx 2.016
Ref. Ibid.

εα 1.509 nωβ 1.522 εγ 1.556 Sign +
2V ~15° D mp Color Colorless
Ref. Ibid.

Sample from the City Chemical Corp., New York. Spect. anal. showed <0.01% K, Mg, Na, Si, Sr; <0.001% Al, Ba, Cu, Fe, Mn. Pattern made at 25°C.

d Å	I/I_1	hkl	d Å	I/I_1	hkl
6.70	7	200	2.395	14	511
5.59	100	210	2.292	21	322,402
4.96	59	111	2.272	2	132
3.95	<1	021	2.232	29	600
3.79	18	121	2.181	18	610
3.425	46	311	2.050	6	332
3.403	88	221	2.027	8	113,440
3.348	6	400	1.996	15	531
3.058	20	102	1.978	18	042
3.005	3	230	1.957	5	142
2.962	92	321	1.949	8	250
2.931	9	112	1.938	4	023
2.917	7	131	1.918	12	123,151
2.841	28	202	1.866	10	630,313
2.739	19	212	1.820	1	602
2.675	6	022	1.808	1	342
2.556	1	421	1.791	4	612
2.546	3	040	1.767	10	133
2.490	17	312	1.747	1	532
2.485	20	222	plus 13	lines	to 1.539

FIG. 3. Keysort card from the *X-ray Powder Data File*. (*Courtesy of the Joint Committee on Chemical Analysis by Powder Diffraction Methods.*)

available about the material to be identified. The first system of mechanical sorting used with the *File* was based on Keysort punched cards. This system has now been superseded by the IBM and Termatrex systems, and very likely will be discontinued in the future.

A typical card is shown in Fig. 3. The interior portion of the 4- by 6-in. card contains the same data as given on the plain cards. The surrounding double row of holes provides for coding diffraction and chemical data according to codes suggested by the developer of the system, F. W. Matthews.[5]

IBM Cards. In 1951, the *X-ray Powder Data File* was made available on standard IBM punched cards, primarily through the efforts of L. E. Kuentzel. The design of the cards, the sorting system, and the codes used are an outgrowth of similar work in the fields of infrared, ultraviolet, and visible absorption spectroscopy. The rather small use of the IBM x-ray cards to date is a tribute to the excellence of the plain cards. It may also indicate, however, an incomplete appreciation of the usefulness of the IBM cards, particularly in the identification of multicomponent mixtures. The ease and accuracy with which the IBM decks can be reproduced make them inexpensive, so that any laboratory which uses machine sorting for other purposes can add the x-ray cards at only a slight extra cost.

A standard IBM punched card contains 80 columns and 12 rows, providing 960 punch positions. Sorting is done by column, with each card being sent to one of 13 bins, corresponding to the 12 rows plus a reject bin (for no punch), depending on which row in the given column is punched. Cards are sorted at a rate of 250 to 650 per minute, depending on the sorter model, and decks of 2,000 cards can be handled readily at one time.

Using a double punch per column code, the entire alphabet can be punched into a single column. Nearly all the punches in the x-ray cards, however, are independent, single, direct code punches. A general description of the code follows.

Interplanar spacings of all lines having relative intensity 10 or more are punched into the cards. Lines of less intensity are included if there are fewer than 10 lines in the pattern having the required intensity. Intensities are not punched in.

A typical card from the file is shown in Fig. 4. *Columns* 1 to 35 contain *d* values in angstroms. Below 1.00 Å, values are given to the nearest 0.1 Å. In the range

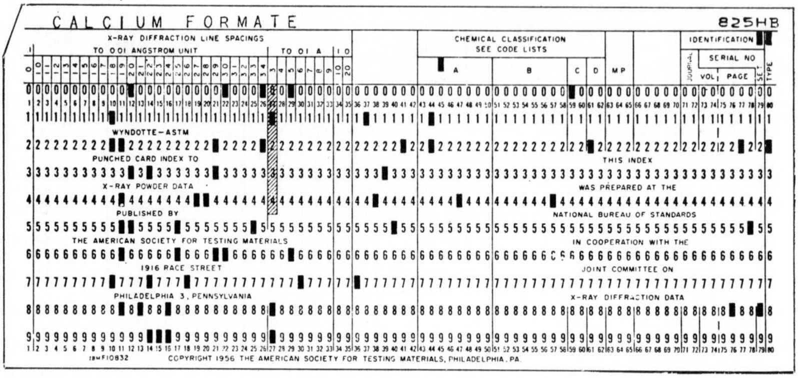

CALCIUM FORMATE 825HB
X-RAY DIFFRACTION LINE SPACINGS TO 0.01 ANGSTROM UNIT — TO 0.1 A — 1.0
CHEMICAL CLASSIFICATION SEE CODE LISTS — A B C D — MP
IDENTIFICATION — JOURNAL — SERIAL NO — VOL. PAGE — SET — TYPE
WYNDOTTE–ASTM
PUNCHED CARD INDEX TO X-RAY POWDER DATA PUBLISHED BY THE AMERICAN SOCIETY FOR TESTING MATERIALS 1916 RACE STREET PHILADELPHIA 3, PENNSYLVANIA
THIS INDEX WAS PREPARED AT THE NATIONAL BUREAU OF STANDARDS IN COOPERATION WITH THE JOINT COMMITTEE ON X-RAY DIFFRACTION DATA
IBM F10832 COPYRIGHT 1956 THE AMERICAN SOCIETY FOR TESTING MATERIALS, PHILADELPHIA, PA.

Fig. 4. IBM card from the *X-ray Powder Data File*. Cf. Fig. 3. (*Courtesy of the Joint Committee on Chemical Analysis by Powder Diffraction Methods.*)

1.00 to 3.49 Å, punching resolution is 0.01 Å. From 3.5 to 9.9 Å, resolution is again 0.1 Å, and from 10 to 29 Å, resolution is 1 Å. All values 29 or greater are punched in as 29.

Columns 36 *and* 37 enable one to sort the cards according to Hanawalt groups using a specific code in which each group is assigned a number between 1 and 87. A punch of 1, 2, or 3 in *column* 27 indicates whether the Hanawalt group punch in the card was based on the first, second, or third strongest line, respectively.

Columns 38 *to* 42 are reserved for future use.

Columns 43 *to* 62 contain chemical classification data according to specific codes: elements, inorganic radicals, organic structure types, and such miscellaneous data as whether or not the compound is hydrated and whether it is inorganic or organic.

Columns 63 *to* 65 are reserved for melting points although these data are not punched in. Melting points can be punched in directly with any value 999 or higher being punched in as 999.

Columns 66 *to* 70 are reserved for individual users to use as they see fit.

Columns 71 *to* 79 serve to identify the source of the x-ray data punched into the card. At present, only the *X-ray Powder Data File* sequence number is entered, although provision is made for entering a literature reference as source. On the IBM cards, the set number is indicated by a letter at the end of the sequence number rather than by a number at the beginning. Thus card 8-417 would be indicated by punching

4, 1, and 7 in columns 76, 77, and 87, respectively, and H in column 79. A double punch per column code is used for the letters. The sequence number is printed at the top of each card. Beginning with set G, the compound name is also printed on each card. With cards from previous sets, it is necessary to consult a numerical index provided with sets A to G to identify a compound from its sequence number.

Column 80 identifies the type of data on the card, i.e., x-ray, infrared, ultraviolet, etc. X-ray cards are punched with a B, which is also printed on the card following the sequence number. Specific codes are available from ASTM.

General Sorting Techniques.[6] Since each position on an IBM card is independent of all others and may be sorted for independently, the final result is not affected by the order in which the individual data are sorted. But an intelligent searching procedure can greatly reduce the time required to reach the desired conclusion. By choosing what appears to be the most characteristic or unique piece of data for the first sort, one can eliminate the maximum number of cards which then need not be handled again. Examples of unique data are a diffraction line (not necessarily one of the strongest) which has a rather uncommon value or the presence of an uncommon element. Each sort separates cards which represent compounds having the sorted-for data in common. The number of cards usually reduces to six or fewer in four or five sorts.

The resolution with which d values are punched into the cards and the possibility of slight deviations between data from different experimental setups must always be kept in mind. Sorting should be done over a broad enough range to ensure inclusion of the line in question. Consulting the corresponding plain cards (which give more complete data, including intensities and Miller indices) is generally desirable as the final step in the identification of an unknown substance.

Procedure for Multicomponent Mixtures. The extensive cross-indexing possible with punched-card techniques may be used to full advantage in the analysis of multicomponent samples, where each of the three strongest diffraction lines may arise from different compounds and extensive line overlap may occur. The difficulties encountered with the plain-card file in such a situation have already been mentioned.

Beukelman[7] has devised a systematic sorting procedure based on the statistical distribution of punches in the IBM card file. The method may also be used with the IBM files of other types of spectral data (infrared, ultraviolet, etc.). It is not a rapid or short-cut method. Rather, it is a method for searching all the available data in a comprehensive manner, and it is recommended only after more rapid techniques have failed.

The general procedure includes the following steps:

1. Reduction of the pattern to a list of d values and relative intensities.
2. Removal from the file of cards which may be rejected on the basis of prior chemical knowledge.
3. Removal from the remaining file of cards carrying the Hanawalt designation of a region in which no diffraction lines occur in the unknown pattern.
4. Searching for the most probable matches.
5. Checking probable compounds chosen by the IBM sorter against the complete data given on the plain cards.

Step 4 is the heart of the method. Compounds having the greatest number of diffraction lines matching the unknown pattern are the most probable. The sorting technique is as follows: First, a sort is made on the strongest line, dividing the deck into two parts, one having the line and the other not having it. Then these two decks are sorted on the second strongest line. This leads to four decks, one with both the strongest lines, one with neither, and two with one each. The last two decks are combined, leaving three decks. These three decks are then sorted on the third strongest line, leading to six decks. This process of sorting and recombination is continued as shown in Fig. 5 until the deck of most probable cards contains few enough cards, perhaps two or three, to permit easy checking with the plain-card file. If no identification is made, the procedure is continued. Usually, after identification of each component, it is necessary to delete the lines of that component and repeat the entire procedure on the remaining lines.

The Matthews (Termatrex) Coordinate Index. As the *X-ray Powder Data File* grows by hundreds of patterns each year, methods of indexing capable of saving time and cost become desirable. One such method is the new Matthews Coordinate Index, named for its developer, F. W. Matthews,[8] who also developed the Keysort system described earlier in this chapter.

A coordinate index is distinguished from other data-retrieval systems by the following important feature: In the usual systems (IBM, for example), each card represents an item and contains characteristics of that item. In a coordinate index, on the other hand, each card represents a characteristic and contains items having that characteristic. Thus, in the Matthews Coordinate Index, one card represents compounds having d values in a certain range; another, those containing a certain element, etc.

Punched cards have been used for coordinate indexes for various purposes since 1915. Each indexed item has a unique position on the characteristic cards which is punched if the item has the corresponding characteristic. Items having any combination of characteristics can be easily identified by superimposing the proper cards and visually observing the coincidence of holes.

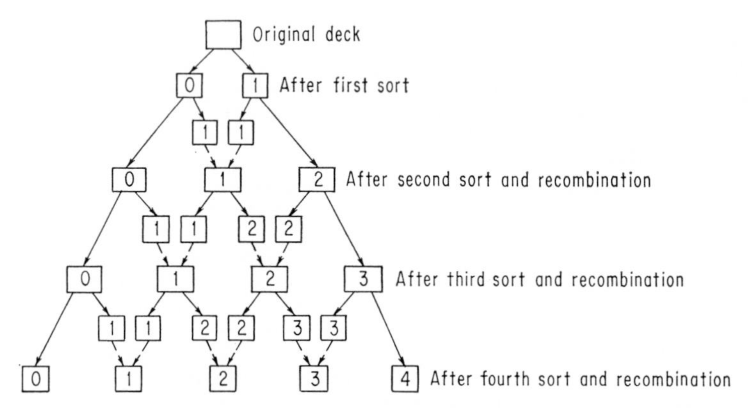

Fig. 5. Schematic diagram of sorting procedure used with IBM cards for the identification of multicomponent mixtures. Numbers in boxes refer to number of individual matches in that particular deck. [*Reprinted from Anal. Chem.*, **29**:1271 (1957). *Copyright,* 1957, *by the American Chemical Society and reprinted by permission of the copyright owner.*]

The Matthews Coordinate Index utilizes the Termatrex cards and associated equipment produced by Jonker Business Machines, Inc. Termatrex cards are made of plastic and measure 9⅝ by 11½ in. The cards contain 10,000 positions arranged in a 100 × 100 matrix (see Fig. 6). The cards are examined in a special viewing device and stored in a convenient holder (see Fig. 7).

The present Index covers data for the inorganic compounds in sets 1 to 13 of the *X-ray Powder Data File*. It contains cards representing the following categories: the Matthews groups of d values, elements or groups of elements (for both positive and negative sorting), alloys, minerals, and hydrates. There are also colored transparent cards for hydrogen and oxygen which allow either positive or negative sorting based on these elements. A set of cards is also available which represent Matthews groups displaced in range by half a group. These cards are very useful when an unknown d value falls close to the group division of the standard set. Thus one of the standard cards covers a range of 8.500 to 9.999 Å, and one of the optional cards covers the range 8.000 to 9.199 Å. For an unknown d value of 8.51, one would choose the latter range. When the standard and optional sets are used together, groups of half the range of the standard set are displayed.

Procedure for Using the Matthews Coordinate Index. Normally, five lines are punched per compound. The procedure for identifying an x-ray pattern is as follows:

1. Select the Termatrex cards which represent characteristics of the unknown material (x-ray or chemical data).

2. Superimpose these cards on the viewer and record the coordinates of the lighted holes (which represent compounds having the desired characteristics). A special grid and scales are provided for reading coordinates.

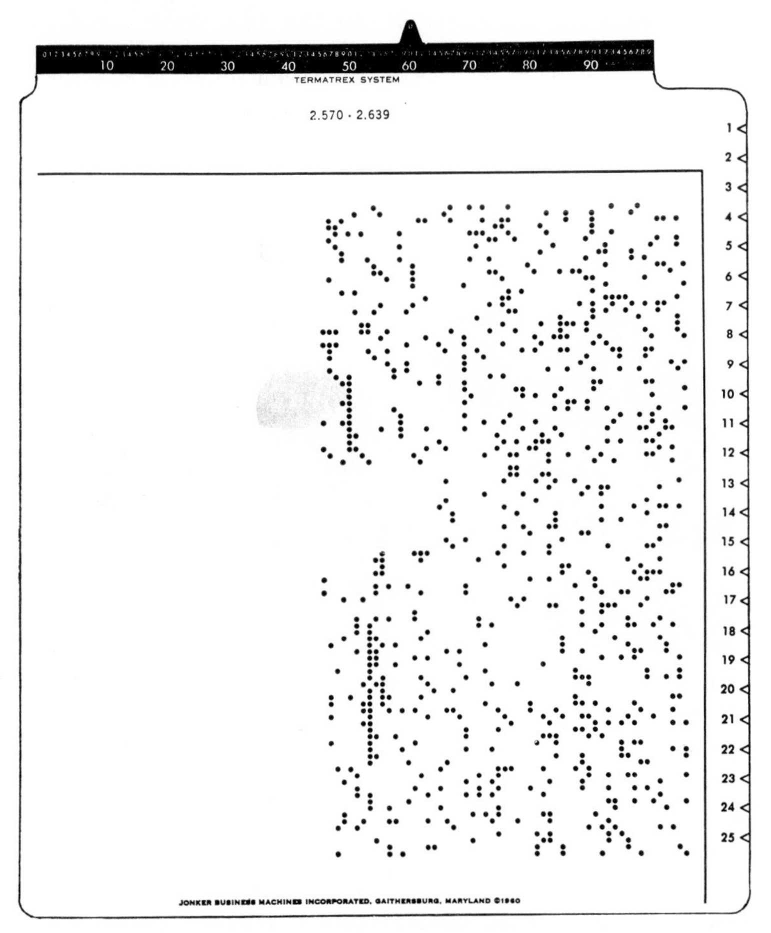

FIG. 6. Termatrex card from Matthews Coordinate Index. Punches represent inorganic substances having major diffraction peaks in the range 2.570 to 2.639 Å. (*Courtesy of the Joint Committee on Chemical Analysis by Powder Diffraction Methods.*)

3. Look up the coordinate numbers in an index booklet which gives chemical and/or mineral name and the plain-card sequence number.

4. Return the cards to the card holder. Because of a unique system of colored tabs, cards bearing line-position data can be stored in random order. Element cards are stored in alphabetical order.

5. Make final positive identification by comparison of the unknown data with the indicated card(s) in the plain-card file.

Features planned for future editions include a deck for organic compounds and cards for melting point and specific gravity. As new data are issued, customers can return cards for partial credit on an updated set. When the number of compounds to be indexed exceeds the capacity of the cards (10,000), a new set will be begun. Edge notches are provided for differentiating between sets. Blank cards and a wide variety of punching equipment are available from Jonker for users who desire to index their own internal x-ray data. No space on the existing cards is reserved for this purpose.

While retaining features of earlier mechanical sorting systems (such as ability to cross-reference x-ray and chemical data), the Coordinate Index possesses several advantages: The number of cards remains small even as the number of items indexed increases. In addition, the cards and associated equipment are small, portable, easy to handle, and relatively inexpensive.

The Fink *d*-Value Index.* A recent addition to the *X-ray Powder Data File* is the Fink *d*-Value Index, developed by the Editorial Board of the Joint Committee on Chemical Analysis by Powder Diffraction Methods and named in honor of Dr. W. L. Fink, who fostered its development. Beginning with set 13, this Index is provided (along with the Hanawalt Index) with each set of data cards purchased. The primary purpose of the Fink Index is to facilitate the identification of powder diffraction

FIG. 7. Jonker equipment used with Matthews Coordinate Index. *Left:* viewer; *right:* card holder.

patterns which do not provide reliable values for the relative intensities of the diffraction lines, such as those frequently obtained in electron diffraction work and in x-ray diffraction studies of mixtures and specimens having preferred orientations of the crystallites. It is expected, however, that this Index will ultimately find wide use for the identification of all types of patterns.

Organization of the Fink Index. The Fink Index uses the *d* values of the eight strongest lines less than 9.99 Å in spacing to characterize each pattern contained in the *Data File*. No relative intensity values are listed in the Index, nor are they used in determining the order of listing of the data or the patterns in the Index. Values greater than 10 Å are used only if their relative intensity is 100. In cases where fewer than eight *d* values are given on the data cards, all the *d* values given are used and the remainder of the eight entries are listed as 0.00 in the Index.

All eight of the *d* values used to characterize each pattern are entered eight different places in the Index. For the first entry of each pattern, the eight *d* values are arranged in decreasing numerical order, from left to right, and cyclic permutation establishes the order in the remaining seven entries, as is shown in Table 2.

To facilitate searching the Index on the basis of two or more *d* values simultaneously, the *d*-value range from above 10 Å to below 1.0 Å is divided into 101 intervals, and the

* This description of the Fink Index was adapted, with permission of the Joint Committee on Chemical Analysis by Powder Diffraction Methods, from instructions prepared by W. C. Bigelow and J. V. Smith for using the Index.

entries separated into 101 corresponding groups by assigning each entry to the group whose interval includes the first d value (counting from the left) of the entry. Entries within each group are arranged in numerical order of their second d values. The d-value interval for the appropriate group is printed on every page of the Index book. In addition to the eight d values, each entry in the Index includes the mineral name and chemical name of the substance (with the latter shortened if necessary to fit into the available space) and the number of the card in the *X-ray Powder Data File* from which the data were taken.

Procedure for Using the Fink Index. The use of the Fink Index in identifying unknown materials from their powder diffraction patterns is relatively simple and straightforward. In general the design and execution of an identification procedure include the following steps:

1. Note all available information concerning the chemical composition of the unknown.
2. Note, in descending numerical order, the d values of the high-intensity lines (i.e., those with I/I_1 greater than 30, or those which would be qualitatively rated as of "medium" intensity or stronger) of the unknown diffraction pattern.
3. Choose an appropriate one of these (d_s) and the next smaller one (d_{s-1}), for use in starting the search.

Table 2. Order within Entries in the Fink Index

Entry	*Order of listing of d values*
1	$d_1, d_2, d_3, d_4, d_5, d_6, d_7, d_8$
2	$d_2, d_3, d_4, d_5, d_6, d_7, d_8, d_1$
3	$d_3, d_4, d_5, d_6, d_7, d_8, d_1, d_2$
.	. . . .
.	. . . .
.	. . . .
7	$d_7, d_8, d_1, d_2, d_3, d_4, d_5, d_6$
8	$d_8, d_1, d_2, d_3, d_4, d_5, d_6, d_7$
with $d_1 > d_2 > d_3 > \cdots > d_8$	

4. Enter the Fink group whose d-value interval includes d_s (making suitable allowance for experimental uncertainties). Examine the second column of the index to find the section of this group which extends from 1 to 3 per cent above and below the value of d_{s-1}. Examine the data for the patterns listed in this section of the group for agreement with the unknown pattern to effect a preliminary identification.
5. If a preliminary identification is achieved, compare the data for the unknown pattern with the data on the corresponding card in the *Data File* to achieve a final identification.
6. If a satisfactory identification is not achieved:
   a. Compare the unknown pattern successively with data in sections of the same group which include the d values d_{s-2}, d_{s-3}, etc., for the successively smaller d values selected in step 2.
   b. Make a new choice of d_s and repeat the process in steps 3, 4, and 5.

The identification of single compounds can generally be accomplished without difficulty. However, the identification of the constituents of even simple mixtures from their diffraction patterns can be a difficult and challenging task. In all cases where there is a possibility of an unknown mixture, primary emphasis should be placed on achieving a fully confirmed identification of one of the components, since this will greatly simplify the identification of the remaining components. Therefore, the corresponding card in the *Data File* should be checked as soon as a reasonable agreement is found for any entry in the Index book. Once one or more components have been identified, the search procedure for the remaining components must be based on the lines of the unknown pattern which have the highest intensities and largest d values that do not belong to patterns of the components already identified; therefore, d_s will generally be chosen from among lines of this group. However, allowance must be made for possible coincidence of lines in the several patterns, and so the d values of patterns already identified should be included in choosing d_{s-1}, d_{s-2}, etc., in steps 3 to 6 of the search procedure outlined above.

Limitations of the *X-Ray Powder Data File*. Despite the rapid growth of the *X-ray Powder Data File*, many crystalline compounds are not included. The situation is particularly bad for organic compounds, of which fewer than 3,000 are catalogued at the present time. Of course, negative results are not entirely worthless. If, after a diligent search of the *File*, one fails to identify an unknown pattern, he can say with confidence that the unknown is not one of over 8,000 substances. The growth of the *File* is the result of constant efforts on the part of the Joint Committee to make it more complete. Users can ensure the success of these efforts by contributing data, as well as corrections and suggestions, to the editor of the *X-ray Powder Data File*.

Difficulties can arise, even when the pattern to be identified is catalogued in the *File*. The presence of errors in the *File* has been recognized for many years. Errors probably result most commonly from improper identification or purity of the "standard" sample, e.g., incorrect degree of hydration; original substance altered by reaction with water, oxygen, carbon dioxide, etc.; the presence of contaminants; or solid-solution effects. Errors in x-ray line positions and intensities are also possible as a result of contamination of the x-ray tube target, failure to record the innermost reflections of a pattern, absorption effects, faulty alignment, inadequate filter, improper exposure, and a host of other experimental parameters. Indeed, such errors can hardly be avoided in a compilation of data from many sources. In 1949, a research fellowship was established at the National Bureau of Standards to review data, remove errors, and produce high-quality standard patterns. Because of this effort, many of the early errors in the *File* have been removed and new ones are less likely to occur. Sets 1 to 5 have been completely revised. Improved equipment should also reduce the probability of errors. The high-quality data obtained by the National Bureau of Standards have been published in circular form (*NBS Circular* 539).

The user of the *X-ray Powder Data File* must, of course, also guard against making the errors enumerated above when preparing the pattern of his unknown sample. Solid-solution effects may so alter the cell dimensions of the unknown that the strong lines fall well outside the appropriate index group. Furthermore, solid-solution, crystal-size, or strain effects may change the order of the relative intensities of the lines. Nonrandom-defect structures and superstructures can cause additional lines to appear. Discrepancies in relative intensities can also arise because of the Lorentz-polarization factor if the unknown and standard patterns were obtained with different wavelength x-rays.

Wrong identification of a complex chemical substance can result from isomorphism. In large molecules, the substitution of one small radical for another or the occlusion of a foreign molecule may not change the powder pattern perceptibly.

Finally, the *X-ray Powder Data File*, and any other file which catalogues d values numerically, suffers from inability to take into account the line profiles which on direct comparison of x-ray patterns sometimes are helpful. Therefore, many laboratories find that catalogues of patterns of frequently encountered materials are a very useful supplement to the *X-ray Powder Data File*, even if many of the patterns are also included in the *File*.

Crystalline materials differ widely in the intensity of the powder diffraction patterns they produce. Depending on the composition of a mixture, one substance may be detectable at levels of less than 1 per cent, while another may be missed even at levels as high as 50 per cent. Thus x-ray powder diffraction does not always yield a complete analysis of a mixture, and the importance of supplementary analytical techniques cannot be overstressed.

3. IDENTIFICATION BY ISOMORPHISM

Frevel has developed procedures for indexing and comparing powder diffraction patterns of isomorphous substances[9] which form the basis of an identification scheme frequently applicable when the pattern to be identified is not included in the *X-ray Powder Data File.* The method involves systematically comparing the diffraction pattern of the unknown substance with representative patterns of the various known crystal structures in an attempt to establish isomorphism between the unknown and one of the standard structures. For purposes of comparison, log d values are plotted vs. relative intensities (arithmetically averaged values for representative members of the isomorphous group). Frevel and coworkers have published such diagrams for 33 cubic,[10] 40 tetragonal,[11] and 53 hexagonal[12] structure types.

The general procedure for identifying a pattern by this method is as follows: (1) Using the scale of the standard diagrams, plot the log d values and corresponding relative intensities of the unidentified pattern on a narrow strip of paper. (2) Verify the pattern as cubic or noncubic by comparison with an index scale on the standard diagrams. (3) Using the appropriate set of diagrams, find an isomorphous prototype of the unknown phase. In this comparison, all lines must be accounted for. (4) Compute the lattice constants and check appropriate classification tables. (5) Confirm the identification by qualitative spectrographic or chemical tests.

4. SPECIAL IDENTIFICATION TECHNIQUES

Identification of Clay Minerals. The identification of clay minerals is worthy of special mention because of the many specialized techniques which have been brought to bear on these seemingly unpromising materials. The procedures, which have been impressively described in a 345-page monograph[13] and elsewhere,[14,15] might well serve as an object lesson on the use of x-ray diffraction for identification even to those not directly interested in clays.

It is remarkable that the clays, which form under a wide variety of natural conditions, nearly all belong to a restricted range of structural types, to which the micas and chlorites also belong. They are layer structures with pronounced basal cleavages and lamellar or platy habits.

Clays present numerous problems to x-ray analysis. The characteristic spacings of the basal layers must be used for identification. Since these spacings are large, the x-ray equipment should be able to record lines up to at least 50 Å. Imperfections arising from random isomorphous substitution, irregular superposition of layers, and stacking of layers of different composition may also complicate the pattern and its interpretation.

The layer structure of clays causes a tendency toward nonrandom orientation of the particles. This is used to advantage in the preparation of oriented aggregates, which enhance the basal reflections to the point that they are sometimes the only ones visible, thus greatly simplifying interpretation. Oriented aggregates are prepared by allowing a suspension of the clay to settle onto a flat glass plate, or by gradually drying out the suspension.

Several other special sample-preparation techniques are also common in the identification of clay minerals. The formation of organic complexes aids in the identification of minerals of variable hydration, such as the montmorillonite group. Simply moistening the clay with a suitable organic liquid such as glycerol or ethylene glycol results in stable complexes which are much more regular in structure than the natural water complexes. Selective destruction of various clay components is also useful. Amorphous hydrous oxides and hydroxides of iron and aluminum mask the diffraction pattern and prevent the formation of oriented aggregates. These materials are frequently leached out by various treatments. Heat-treatment, usually to a temperature of 500° C, results in changes in clay composition which are helpful in characterization. Kaolinite and halloysite are completely destroyed by this treatment, leaving an amorphous residue. Other minerals lose adsorbed water molecules but generally not structural OH groups.

The following standard procedure[14] involves the taking of three diffraction patterns:

1. A diffraction pattern is made of the whole untreated clay. If much organic matter is present, it should be removed by a preliminary treatment with hydrogen peroxide.

2. The clay is treated to dissolve the free sesquioxides, and a pattern is then made of a glycerol- or glycol-saturated oriented aggregate.

3. A pattern is made of an oriented aggregate which has been heated to 500° C for several hours.

Surface Deposits. Reflection methods of x-ray powder diffraction are frequently useful in the identification of surface deposits, e.g., oxide or sulfide films on metal surfaces. This is because of the shallow penetration of the x-ray beam in these methods. The diffractometer is ideal for this purpose, with strong diffraction patterns often resulting from films which are barely visible. The individual crystals which make up surface deposits are rarely randomly oriented. Therefore, one must be alert for marked differences between observed relative intensities and those given for specimens composed of randomly oriented particles, as in the *X-ray Powder Data File.*

Electron diffraction is another commonly used technique for the identification of surface deposits because of the very shallow penetration of a beam of electrons. This technique is discussed in Chap. 23 of this book.

REFERENCES CITED

1. V. Goldschmidt and S. G. Gordon, Crystallographic Tables for the Determination of Minerals, *Acad. Nat. Sci. Phila. Spec. Publ.* 2, 1928.
2. I. A. Knaggs, B. Karlik, and C. F. Elam, *Tables of Cubic Crystal Structure,* Adam Hilger, London, 1932.
3. M. W. Porter and R. C. Spiller, *The Barker Index of Crystals,* W. Heffer & Sons, Ltd., Cambridge, England, 1952.
4. J. D. H. Donnay and W. Nowacki, Crystal Data, *Geol. Soc. Amer. Mem.* 60, New York, 1954.
5. F. W. Matthews, *Anal. Chem.,* **21**:1172 (1949).
6. L. E. Kuentzel, *Codes and Instructions for Wyandotte Punched Cards Indexing X-ray Diffraction Data,* Wyandotte Chemicals Corp., Wyandotte, Mich., 1951.
7. T. E. Beukelman, *Anal. Chem.,* **29**:1269 (1957).
8. F. W. Matthews, *Mater. Res. Std.,* **2**:643 (1962).
9. L. K. Frevel, *J. Appl. Phys.,* **13**:109 (1942).
10. L. K. Frevel, *Ind. Eng. Chem., Anal. Ed.,* **14**:687 (1942).
11. L. K. Frevel, H. W. Rinn, and H. C. Anderson, *Ind. Eng. Chem., Anal. Ed.,* **18**:83 (1946).
12. L. K. Frevel and H. W. Rinn, *Anal. Chem.,* **25**:1697 (1953).
13. G. W. Brindley, *X-ray Identification and Crystal Structures of Clay Minerals,* The Mineralogical Society, London, 1951.
14. D. M. C. MacEwan, *Research,* **2**:459 (1949).
15. G. F. Walker, *Nature,* **164**:577 (1949).

GENERAL REFERENCES

Azároff, L. V., and M. J. Buerger: *The Powder Method in X-ray Crystallography,* McGraw-Hill Book Company, New York, 1958.

Cullity, B. D.: *Elements of X-ray Diffraction,* Addison-Wesley Publishing Company, Inc., Reading, Mass., 1956.

Klug, H. P., and L. E. Alexander: *X-ray Diffraction Procedures,* John Wiley & Sons, Inc., New York, 1954.

Peiser, H. S., H. P. Rooksby, and A. J. C. Wilson: *X-ray Diffraction by Polycrystalline Materials,* Institute of Physics, London, 1955.

Chapter 12

QUANTITATIVE ANALYSIS BY POWDER DIFFRACTION

Robert H. Bragg

Lockheed Missiles and Space Company

1. INTRODUCTION

The x-ray diffraction pattern of a powder mixture consists of the superposition of the diffraction patterns of its constituent compounds. Each compound contributes its own pattern with an intensity proportional to the amount present in the mixture. Quantitative x-ray diffraction analysis consists of determining the amount of a compound from measurements of this intensity. Since the intensity is not generally a linear function of composition, it is usually necessary to make analyses by comparing the pattern of a mixture of unknown composition with patterns or calibration curves prepared from standard mixtures. By far the best method employs an internal standard, a substance added in a fixed proportion to the unknown to serve as a reference.

Usually it is best to use the strong lines of a compound in quantitative analyses, and these may sometimes be superimposed upon the lines of other compounds of the sample. But this complication does not render the analysis unfeasible. It may in some instances even be advantageous to add to a mixture containing the unknown a known amount of the material to be determined. These methods are all based on a basic equation relating x-ray intensities to the absorptive properties of powder mixtures.

2. BASIC PRINCIPLES

In deriving the basic equation, Bragg reflections from the surface of a flat powder specimen such as that used in a diffractometer are considered. The specimen is a uniform mixture of particles small enough to make extinction and microabsorption effects negligible, and it is sufficiently thick that the diffracted x-rays have maximum intensity. The crystallites comprising the specimen are oriented randomly and the porosity is assumed constant in all comparisons. Under these conditions the basic equation relating the intensity of the diffracted x-rays to the absorptive properties of the specimen is[1]

$$I_{ij} = \frac{K_{ij}x_j}{\rho_j[x_j(\mu_j^* - \mu_M^*) + \mu_M^*]} \qquad (1)$$

where I_{ij} = intensity of the ith line (hkl reflection) in the powder pattern of component j whose concentration is sought
x_j = concentration (weight fraction) of component j, g/g of specimen
ρ_j = density of component j
μ_j^* = mass absorption coefficient of component j
μ_M^* = mass absorption coefficient of the matrix (the material which would remain if component j were removed)
K_{ij} = a constant which depends upon the characteristics of the apparatus, the x-ray wavelength, and the structure of component j

Equation (1) refers to the integrated intensity when corrected for the background radiation. It may also be written

$$I_{ij} = \frac{K_{ij}x_j}{\rho_j\mu_T^*} \tag{2}$$

where μ_T^* is the total mass absorption coefficient of the specimen *including* component j.

It sometimes happens that the lines due to two or more components of the mixture are partially or completely superimposed. It is then necessary to generalize Eq. (2). The total intensity in the composite x-ray line due to the superposition of n components is[2]

$$I_i = \Sigma_j I_{ij} \tag{3}$$

in which I_{ij} is now the contribution to the ith line due to component j and is given by an equation similar to Eq. (2). Corresponding to each line a similar equation can be written, and so the complete diffraction pattern consisting of m lines can be written

$$I_i = \Sigma_j c_{ij}x_j \qquad i = 1, 2, \ldots, m \tag{4}$$

where $c_{ij} = K_{ij}/\rho_j\mu_T^*$. Since not all lines are composite some of the c_{ij} are zero. Equation (4) is the complete generalization of the basic equation of x-ray quantitative analysis. All methods reported to date are based on Eqs. (1), (2), or (4). The most widely used are discussed below.

3. TECHNIQUES

Absolute-intensity Method. When only one component is sought Eq. (1) or Eq. (2) applies. These equations show that x_j can be determined directly from absolute-intensity measurements of I_{ij} provided K_{ij}, ρ_j, and μ_T^* are known. All are susceptible to measurement with varying degrees of difficulty. However, it is convenient to refer the measured intensities to a scale corresponding to pure component j, i.e., for $x_j = 1$. When this is done the relative intensity can be written

$$\frac{I_{ij}}{I_{ij}(x_j = 1)} = \frac{\mu_j^*}{\mu_T^*}x_j = \frac{\mu_j x_j}{x_j(\mu_j^* - \mu_M^*) + \mu_M^*} \tag{5}$$

In this case only μ_T^* is unknown. Three cases can be distinguished: $\mu_j^* < \mu_M^*$, $\mu_j^* > \mu_M^*$, and $\mu_j^* = \mu_M^*$. Except for the last case there will not be a linear proportionality between the intensity ratio and the weight ratio x_j. Typical examples are shown in Fig. 1, where it is seen that the experimental data can be decidedly nonlinear. The linearity can be restored by determining μ_T^* in a separate measurement and correcting for it. Although the example of Fig. 1 is for binary mixtures the results are quite general and Eq. (5) applies equally well to mixtures containing any number of components.

The normalization of Eq. (5) cannot be applied in the general case of overlapping lines as in Eq. (4), for then there is no unique relationship between intensities and concentrations x_j. However, the c_{ij} can be determined from intensity measurements on pure components and a separate measurement of μ_T^*. Methods of analysis based on absolute-intensity measurements, using direct determinations of μ_T^*, have been reported for binary[3,4] and multicomponent systems.[5,6] Satisfactory results have often been obtained with the absolute-intensity methods, especially where rapid measurements of moderate accuracy are acceptable. However, the necessary calibrations are usually numerous, complex, and variable. For these reasons the internal-standard methods are more widely used.

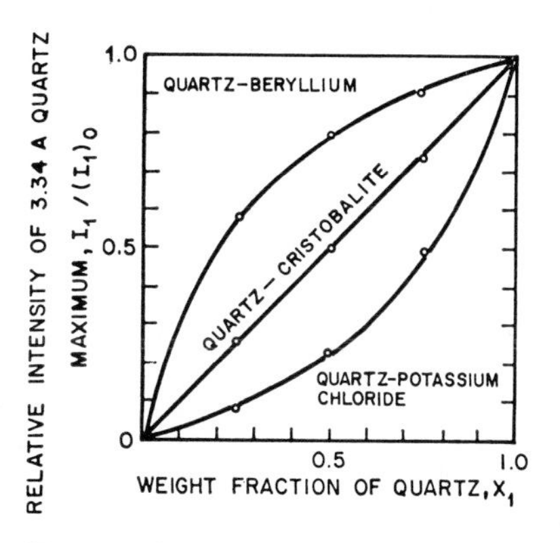

FIG. 1. Comparison of theoretical intensity-concentration curves (solid lines) with experimental measurements (open circles) for several binary mixtures. (*From Ref.* 1.)

Internal-standard Method. *Basic Equation.* For binary and higher-order mixtures the intensity of the kth line in the x-ray pattern of component l is given by an expression similar to Eq. (2),

$$I_{kl} = \frac{K_{kl}}{\rho_l \mu_T^*} x_l \tag{6}$$

where ρ_l is the density of component l and x_l is its weight fraction in the mixture. The ratio of the intensities for components j and l is

$$\frac{I_{ij}}{I_{kl}} = \frac{K_{ij}\rho_l x_j}{K_{kl}\rho_j x_l} \tag{7}$$

in which the common factor μ_T^* has canceled out. Component l in this case serves as an *internal standard* to which component j is referred.

Equation (7) is the basic equation for the internal-standard method derived first by Alexander and Klug,[1] and it is fundamental to all internal-standard methods of x-ray quantitative analyses. It shows that the curve of the intensity ratio I_{ij}/I_{kl} obtained from mixtures of components j and l plotted against the weight ratio x_j/x_l is a straight line passing through the origin. The slope of this curve is a unique constant characteristic of components j and l which is independent of the absorption characteristics of the specimen, or even the other components which may be present.

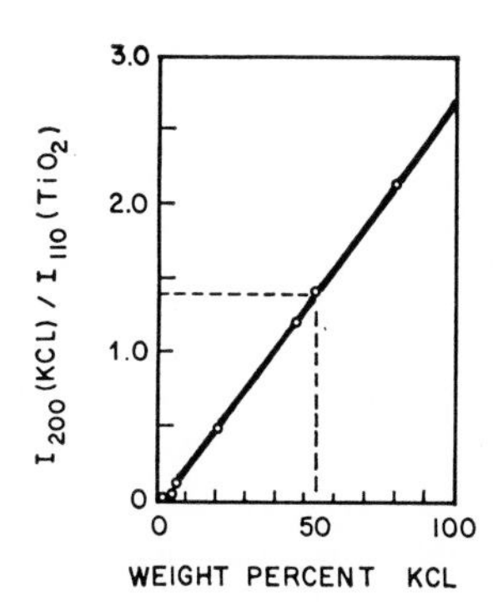

FIG. 2. Internal-standard calibration curve for KCl-TiO_2. Dashed lines show analysis of unknown mixture. (*From L. V. Azaroff and M. J. Buerger, The Powder Method in X-ray Crystallography, p.* 207, *McGraw-Hill Book Company, New York,* 1958.)

A typical internal-standard curve demonstrating this fact is shown in Fig. 2. The data in this case were obtained from microphotometer measurements on x-ray films of Debye-Scherrer powder patterns. The specimens in this case were of conventional rod shape. Although the absorption factors here differ from those of Eqs. (2) or (6) the intensity ratios are also independent of absorption effects as in Eq. (7).

To determine the amount of component j in a specimen, a known amount of component l, the internal standard, is intimately mixed with it. The intensity ratio I_{ij}/I_{kl} is measured, and using the previously determined constant of Eq. (7), the value of x_j is calculated by substituting the known quantities in Eq. (7). In Fig. 2, for example, the 110 reflection of rutile (d_{110} = 3.24 Å) is used as a standard to which the 200 reflection of KCl (d_{200} = 3.14 Å) is referred. From the calibration curve this example shows that the weight ratio of KCl to TiO_2 in an unknown mixture is 54 per cent.

Dilution with Unknown. It is sometimes advantageous to dilute the specimen with known amounts of component j, the compound whose concentration is sought, in order to analyze for it. This case arises when a mixture is at hand which already contains another component l having a strong line suitable for reference in intensity measurements. The amount (and even the identity!) of component l need not be known. When a weight fraction ξ_j per gram of original specimen is added to it the equation appropriate to the new situation is

$$\frac{I_{ij}}{I_{kl}} = \frac{K_{ij}\rho_l}{K_{kl}\rho_j}\frac{x_j + \xi_j}{x_l} = (\text{const})(x_j + \xi_j) \tag{8}$$

In this case a curve of I_{ij}/I_{kl} plotted vs. the additions ξ_j will be a straight line but it will not pass through the origin. The vertical intercept at $\xi_j = 0$ is I_{ij}/I_{kl} determined for the original specimen. Extrapolation of the curve to $I_{ij}/I_{kl} = 0$ gives the value of ξ_j at which $(x_j + \xi_j) = 0$. Consequently, the quantity sought x_j is just the absolute value of the ξ axis intercept. Prior knowledge of the constant of proportionality is unnecessary because it is actually determined by means of measurements on the original specimen and at least one other diluted with component j.

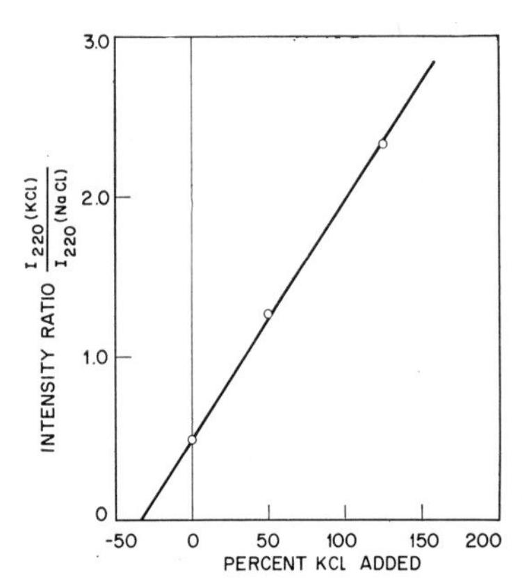

FIG. 3. Determination of KCl in NaCl matrix by dilution with KCl ("unknown" contained 25 per cent KCl). (*From Ref. 2 and unpublished work.*)

In Fig. 3 an analysis of a mixture of NaCl and KCl for KCl is demonstrated. In this case the original unknown actually contained 25 per cent KCl whereas a routine dilution analysis showed 28 per cent.

General Case with Overlapping Lines. In the foregoing instances a unique line is available to characterize the component sought, even though the specimen may contain many other compounds. It is always desirable but not necessary to use well-resolved lines. The internal-standard method also applies to the case of overlapping lines provided a substance can be found having at least one line which is not superimposed on any of the others. Under these conditions the corresponding set of equations is

$$\begin{aligned} I_i &= \Sigma_j(K_{ij}/\rho_j\mu_T^*)x_j \qquad i = 1, 2, \ldots, n \\ I_{kl} &= (K_{kl}/\rho_l\mu_T^*)x_l \end{aligned} \tag{9}$$

where now the first n lines are composite lines but the $(n + 1)$st is due only to the internal standard, component l. The ratio obtained by dividing the first n equations by the last is

$$I_i/I_{kl} = \Sigma a_{ij}(x_j/x_l) \qquad i = 1, 2, \ldots, n \tag{10}$$

where $a_{ij} = K_{ij}\rho_l/K_{kl}\rho_j$. These coefficients are the slopes of calibration curves prepared from binary mixtures of each component j and the internal standard l.

This general internal-standard method, as well as the generalized absolute-intensity method of Eq. (4), requires one further step beyond those required for binary mixtures, i.e., solution of Eq. (10) for the ratios x_j/x_l. (The final step from these ratios to the corresponding x_j is trivial.) Equation (10) is a set of at least n linear equations in n unknowns. This solution is usually not troublesome, for rarely are analyses for more than three compounds attempted, in which event it is merely necessary to solve a system of three equations in three unknowns. In any case the computation presents no unusual problem.

There is one interesting case of Eq. (10) where a strong line of the internal standard overlaps a strong line of the unknown component j, but a second strong line of the standard is clearly resolved. The equations for the two intensities characterizing this situation are

$$I_1 = K_{11}x_1/\rho_1\mu_T^* + K_{12}x_2/\rho_2\mu_T^*$$
$$I_2 = K_{22}x_2/\rho_2\mu_T^*$$

and the intensity ratio is

$$I_1/I_2 = (K_{11}\rho_2/K_{22}\rho_1)\,(x_1/x_2) + K_{12}/K_{22} \tag{11}$$

This equation is linear in x_1/x_2 but does not pass through the origin. A typical example is shown in Fig. 4 for mixture of $Ca(OH)_2$ and $Mg(OH)_2$. The intensities of the partially superimposed $Ca(OH)_2$ 001 reflection ($d_{001} = 4.90$ Å) and the $Mg(OH)_2$ 001 reflection ($d_{001} = 4.76$ Å) are the numerator for the intensity ratio, and that of the $Mg(OH)_2$ 101 reflection ($d_{101} = 2.38$ Å) is the denominator. Evidently an accurate calibration curve of this type can be as useful in an analysis as those conforming to Eq. (7).

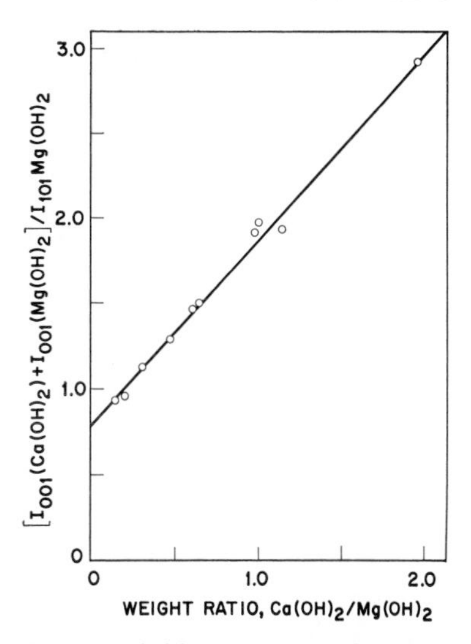

FIG. 4. Calibration curve for overlapping lines using $Mg(OH)_2$ internal standard. (*From Ref.* 2.)

Typical data obtained using this calibration curve are given in Table 1.

Table 1. Analysis of Test Mixtures for $Ca(OH)_2$

Diluent	Amount taken, %	Amount found, %
β Ca_2SiO_4	17.9	19.6
$Ca_3Si_2O_7 \cdot 3H_2O$	39.4	37.4
Portland cement	9.9	9.9
Ca_3SiO_5	29.8	29.4
$CaSiO_3 \cdot H_2O$	39.8	39.9
MgO	64.5	63.0

4. PREPARATION OF SAMPLES

Choice of Standard. If possible an internal standard is chosen to have a strong well-resolved line adjacent to the lines of the unknown(s). This is best done by reference to the *X-ray Powder Data File* (see Chap. 11). Usually several materials will be found which satisfy these criteria. Further restrictions are imposed by the conditions of use or measurement, the hygroscopicity, reactivity with the matrix or unknown, ignition loss during heating, ease of grinding, and sometimes availability. For highest accuracy the purity of the standard must also be constant in all comparisons. Furthermore the reproducibility will be high when reflections of high multiplicity are employed in an analysis. Thus it is desirable to choose for an internal standard a compound which has a strong, high-multiplicity x-ray line close to that of the unknown, is chemically inert, readily available, and of known purity.

Amount to Use. In preparing calibration curves a set of standard mixtures sufficient to cover an intensity ratio of about 0.5:3.0 is used. These intensity ratios are measured with a precision compatible with the specimen reproducibility. For this reason some preliminary measurements of specimen reproducibility are desirable.

Once the slope of the calibration curve is obtained it is possible to choose the amount of internal standard to add to an unknown in order to obtain the highest accuracy. Elementary statistical considerations show that an intensity ratio is determined with the highest precision in the shortest time when the numerator and denominator are equal. Thus for the best results after a preliminary survey of the unknown, an amount of internal standard is added sufficient to obtain an intensity ratio about equal to unity.

Blending the Unknown with the Internal Standard. Even in the absence of errors in the intensity measurements themselves, the precision of the observed intensity ratios will be determined by specimen reproducibility. X-ray quantitative analyses are based on the assumption that the correct proportions of crystallites are oriented so as to give rise to the desired Bragg reflections. As discussed in Chap. 3, repeated measurements will show that this proportion has a statistical distribution. The standard deviation of this crystallite-orientation distribution is determined largely by crystallite size, and the coefficient of variation (standard deviation divided by the average) is proportional to $\Sigma\sqrt{v/p}$. Here v is the effective particle volume and p is the ideal fraction of favorably oriented crystallites for the random case. With materials of intermediate atomic number, particle sizes in the range 2 to 10 microns are required to achieve a sample reproducibility better than 1 per cent. Evidently specimens which merely pass the 325-mesh screen (47 microns) are too coarse to attain high precision.

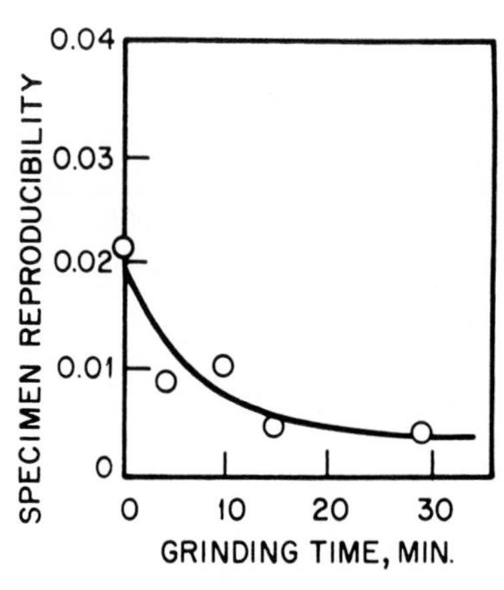

Fig. 5. Effect of grinding in vibratory ball mill on specimen reproducibility. Ordinate is standard deviation divided by average of intensity ratio

$$I_{001}[Ca(OH)_2]/I_{101}[Ca(OH)_2]$$

(*From L. E. Copeland and R. H. Bragg, ASTM Bull.* 228, *p.* 2, 1958.)

The foregoing applies to intensity variations due to specimen reproducibility for a single reflection. For intensity *ratios* under optimum conditions the crystallite size must be reduced by a factor of about 1.5 in order to maintain the same precision. Consequently the fineness requirements for x-ray quantitative analyses are very stringent.

In addition to the fineness requirement it is necessary to produce a uniform blend of standard and specimen, because the total amount of sample used for an analysis may not include all the original specimen and standard. In any event an arbitrary sample taken from the total amount prepared will also be characterized by a statistical variation which is also a function of crystallite size. While it is possible to estimate the overall effects of particle size as it affects crystallite-orientation reproducibility and completeness of blending, this does not ensure the latter. This is best done by an experimental demonstration based upon fine grinding.[7]

In one highly successful method the starting material is first ground to pass the 200-mesh sieve. It is then alternately ground and measured for successive periods until a limiting precision in the intensity measurements is obtained. A typical curve is shown in Fig. 5. In this instance specimens of $Ca(OH)_2$ in a hydrated calcium silicate matrix were ground to a maximum particle size of 2.5 microns in about 15 min.

Results obtained in 10 replicate intensity measurements on properly ground material are given in Table 2.

Since the inherent error due to counting statistics alone is ± 0.65 in this case, the specimen reproducibility was actually ± 0.85 per cent. For comparison, grinding periods of 2 and 24 hr were required to obtain equivalent specimen reproducibility using a conventional laboratory grinder and a ball mill, respectively.

Table 2. Reproducibility of $Ca(OH)_2$ 101 Reflection*

Run	*Integrated intensity per 256 counts*
1	107.2
2	106.9
3	106.9
4	106.1
5	104.3
6	106.0
7	106.4
8	104.3
9	104.8
10	105.8
Avg	105.6 ± 1.1

* After Copeland and Bragg.[7]

5. MEASUREMENT OF INTENSITY

The basic principles enunciated above apply equally well to determinations made by film or diffractometer methods. Both methods have their advantages. The film method, such as employed with a Debye-Scherrer type camera, is satisfactory when the highest precision is not required, and is the only alternative when the original specimen size is only a few milligrams. The major problems with the film methods are lack of speed and the well-known limitations in all quantitative photometry. The diffractometer is capable of higher precision, and the results are obtained in much shorter times. In both cases in addition to the problem of specimen reproducibility, the errors in intensity measurements must be reduced to acceptable magnitudes.

Microphotometer Measurements of Film Patterns (cf. Chap. 8, Sec. 7). When using film techniques for quantitative analyses it is necessary to obtain diffraction intensities from film densities. The attendant problems such as the need for rigid control of exposure and film processing are well known. Fortunately, it is often not necessary to determine absolute intensities, but merely to compare relative intensities within a given pattern. X-ray films have a linear density vs. intensity characteristic and obey the reciprocity law over an appreciable range of exposures. Consequently under some conditions intensities can be compared with high precision. Where rough approximations are acceptable the intensities can even be estimated visually by comparing densities on the specimen film with a reference film prepared in a graded series of exposures.[8] Since visual comparisons cannot be made with an accuracy better than 15 to 20 per cent, it is usually necessary to use a photometric technique.

Powder diffraction lines on typical Debye-Scherrer films, about 35 mm wide and 180 to 360 mm long, can be measured easily with present-day commercial microphotometers. The latter are usually designed for spectrometric work for which the range of film densities is smaller than for the x-ray case. X-ray films are rather grainy by comparison with spectroscopic emulsions, and the microphotometer recorder traces for a well-focused light beam have erratic intensity variations, particularly in the background. Usually defocusing the intrument slightly produces smoother lines.

Photometers have a linear output vs. density characteristic, and since the films have a linear density vs. intensity characteristic, the resulting charts can be used for intensity comparisons directly. It is convenient to zero the recorder ordinate (output) on the background adjacent to the line to be measured. In this way charts are obtained which already have the background subtracted from them. With care, intensity measurements reproducible to within a few per cent can be made. The procedure to use in obtaining integrated intensities is discussed in the next section.

Intensities from Diffractometer Recorder Charts (for related discussions, see Chap. 3 and Chap. 9, Sec. 5). Whether intensities are recorded directly as with the automatic recording diffractometer or indirectly via a recording microphotometer, or are plotted from manual or automatic scaling as with a counting-rate computer, a chart similar to Fig. 6 is eventually obtained. There is a background level indicated by the dashed line, and it is the integrated intensity above the background which is required for analyses.

It should be noted that some lines are sharp and some are broad, and some may overlap. For crude estimates it suffices to use the product of the peak height times the width at half maximum as a substitute for the integrated intensity. Furthermore where the line widths are identical it suffices to compare peak heights. While these short-cut estimates are useful in rough work their use is a dubious economy in most instances. The correct quantity is the integral

$$I = \int P(2\theta)\, d2\theta \tag{12}$$

where $P(2\theta)$ is the line-profile counting rate vs. Bragg angle 2θ.

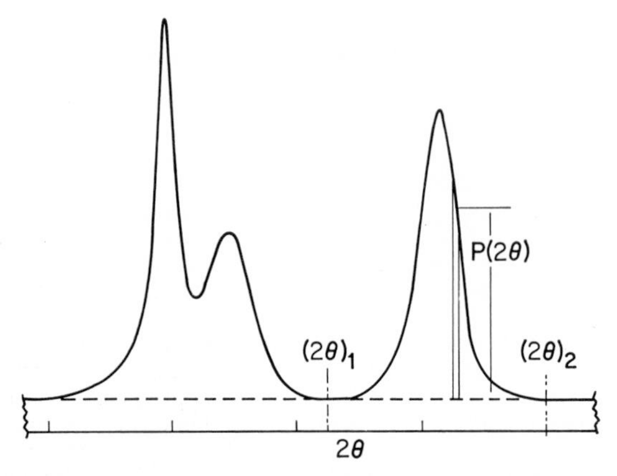

Fig. 6. Typical x-ray charts showing partially superimposed lines and scheme for obtaining integrated intensity.

When the data are recorded on a chart having a sufficiently large scale a typical line can be integrated directly from the chart using a planimeter in about 1 min with a precision of about ±0.5 per cent. If a planimeter is not available the area can be estimated arithmetically by summing ordinates at intervals of 0.05° 2θ using a desk calculator. Less than 5 min is needed to integrate a typical peak in this way with a precision of a few tenths of a per cent. Increments smaller than 0.05° 2θ do not improve the precision appreciably, but since most materials give line half widths of the order of 0.15 to 0.30° 2θ, the approximation of the integral by a finite sum at larger angular increments, say 0.10° 2θ, is a poor one.

The data should always be recorded at a speed slow enough so that errors due to the recorder response itself are small. The recorder displays a fluctuating output whose statistics are a smoothed version of the x-ray intensity itself. Recording with a small time constant comes closest to the ideal situation, i.e., reproducing the instantaneous counting rate as the diffractometer scans a line. The recorder can at best reproduce the actual intensity variations, and therefore nothing is gained by employing large time constants. In fact this practice usually results in highly distorted lines whose background is difficult to estimate accurately.

The major problem with rate-meter (automatic) recording is that with weak intensities it is often impossible to scan sufficiently slowly to obtain enough counts for accurate work, as discussed later. This lack of control can be compensated for by replicate scans of the line of interest and combining the results in one grand total. It is readily shown that a composite of n replications reduces the spread of the composite results by a factor $1/\sqrt{n}$.

Typical results obtained with rate-meter recording (one scan at $\frac{1}{8}°$ 2θ/min) are shown in Fig. 7. In this case the maximum counting rates ranged from about 300 down to about 100 counts/sec.

Counting Techniques (cf. Chap. 3). For the highest accuracy, or optimum accuracy in a given situation, it is necessary to adopt a strategy in measuring intensities based upon a detailed analysis of the factors which influence the overall result. Corresponding to Fig. 6 there is a profile $P(2\theta)$ whose integral I above the background is sought. If the total area from $2\theta_1$ to $2\theta_2$ is I_T and that in the corresponding background is I_B then

$$I = \int P(2\theta)\, d2\theta = I_T - I_B \tag{13}$$

A commonly described procedure is to cause the scaling circuits of the diffractometer to accumulate counts automatically while the goniometer scans at constant angular velocity between, say, points $2\theta_1$ and $2\theta_2$. In this way a total count I_T is obtained. I_B is obtained by determining the average of the counting rates at $2\theta_1$ and $2\theta_2$ and multiplying by the time previously taken to scan from $2\theta_1$ to $2\theta_2$. The precision of the resulting intensity measurement is well known to be

$$\frac{\sqrt{I_T + I_B}}{I_T - I_B}$$

In this case the diffractometer scans through equal angular intervals in equal times, and the result is equivalent to having measured intensities at equally spaced points for a *fixed time*. However, this procedure devotes the same attention to all intensities, with the result that not all points are determined with equal precision.

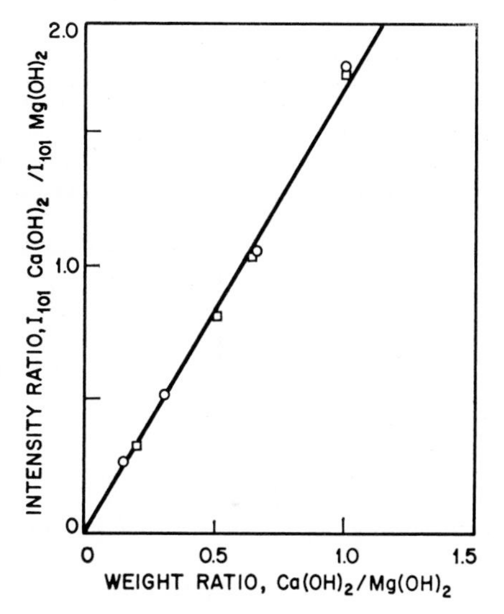

FIG. 7. Calibration curve for $Ca(OH)_2$ determination using $Mg(OH)_2$ internal standard. Open circles are data obtained using automatic recording; squares are for manual scaling. (*From Ref. 2 and unpublished work.*)

It is possible that an equally good overall result could be obtained by spending more time at some points than at others. This can be done in one way by accumulating a *fixed count* at each point, in which case all points are determined with equal precision. However, it is not certain that this procedure produces the better overall result either. Certainly very long times are required to measure weak intensities if a larger number of counts are to be accumulated. What is needed is a method of deciding the best strategy, i.e., an optimum procedure which will produce a desired overall precision in the least time.

Conditions for optimum procedures can be deduced by extending an analysis due to Beers.[9] This has been done in unpublished work by L. E. Copeland and R. H. Bragg, and similar results have been obtained by F. Ordway.

The integrated intensity is represented as the sum

$$I = \int P(2\theta)\, d2\theta \cong \Sigma P(2\theta_i)\, \Delta 2\theta_i = \Sigma\, \Delta I_i$$

Each element ΔI_i has a mean and variance and so has the sum. It is found that the variance of I will be a minimum for a fixed total count I provided each element ΔI_i is measured for the same period of time. However, if the total time is fixed the variance of I will be least, i.e., the precision will be greatest, when the time spent on individual observations is proportional to the square root of the counting rate.

The foregoing discussion shows that while automatic recording (fixed time) corresponds to one optimum situation for integrated intensity measurements, the other commonly used method, fixed count, does not. Unfortunately there is no machine at present which automatically pursues the optimum least-time strategy just discussed. However, in unpublished studies of typical contours L. E. Copeland and R. H. Bragg found that excellent overall precision in I can be obtained using what appear to be very crude individual measurements of ΔI_i. Probably the intuitive explanation for the success of the least-time strategy is that most of the contribution to the sum I comes from the large elements ΔI_i, and hence more is gained by concentrating upon these at the expense of small elements which have a relatively small effect.

6. SENSITIVITY

Sensitivity means the ability to discern small amounts of the material sought in a specimen. Clearly it depends upon the factors which control I_{ij} in Eq. (1) or (2), for it is the minimum excess of this quantity above background which is of interest. For a given substance the only remaining variable is $\mu_T{}^*$. That is, the threshold sensitivity ultimately depends upon the absorptive properties of the matrix. For small x_j Eq. (1) can be expanded (approximately) as

$$I_{ij} \approx (K_{ij}/\rho_j\mu_m{}^*)\, x_j \qquad \mu_m{}^* \gg \mu_j{}^*$$
$$I_{ij} \approx (K_{ij}/\rho_j\mu_j{}^*)\, x_j \qquad \mu_m{}^* = \mu_j{}^*$$
$$I_{ij} \approx K_{ij}/\rho_j\mu_j{}^* \qquad \mu_m{}^* \ll \mu_j{}^*$$

By considering these limiting situations it can be seen that the minimum detectable x_j may be very small if $\mu_j{}^*$ is large, or it may be very large if $\mu_m{}^*$ is large. For medium-atomic-number elements in medium-density inorganic compounds, about 0.2 to 0.5 per cent is detectable using manual-counting techniques or may be seen as a trace in Debye-Scherrer films. Since variations of $\mu_T{}^*$ by a factor of 10 are easily possible the general range of sensitivity depending upon the situation may be put at about 0.05 to 2 per cent, with special cases reaching as high as 20 per cent.

7. PRECISION AND ACCURACY

Precision. As discussed earlier, the precision of an intensity measurement obtained in an analysis is influenced only by random errors and can be made smaller by a suitable adjustment of counting strategy. However, an ultimate upper limit is set by the stability of the x-ray apparatus itself. Modern diffractometers have electronically regulated tube voltage and tube currents and maintain the mean value of each to about ± 0.1 per cent for short periods and ± 0.25 per cent for extended periods. Thus the ultimate precision of an intensity ratio currently attainable is about 0.14 to 0.35 per cent. However, when measurements are restricted to reasonable counting times (about 1 hr per peak) and average counting rates (500 counts/sec), the total accumulated counts will be less than 10^6. Hence the precision of the relative-intensity measurement due to counting statistics alone will be ± 0.14 per cent. Thus a maximum practical precision in the intensity measurements alone is in the range 0.3 to 0.5 per cent.

The precision of the determination also depends upon the specimen reproducibility. Even for extreme fineness, about 1 to 2 microns, the unavoidable spread in intensities will range from 0.1 to 0.5 per cent. This error is independent of the errors discussed above. Consequently we must include the errors due to this quantity, and it then develops that the practical limit of overall precision in x-ray quantitative analysis lies in the range 0.5 to 1.0 per cent.

Accuracy. Whereas the precision obtainable in analysis is capable of a detailed analysis the accuracy is not. This is because the accuracy of a determination depends primarily upon the texture of a specimen, i.e., preferred orientation. The problem of preferred orientation has engaged the attention of investigators since the first x-ray quantitative analysis, and divers schemes more or less successful have been proposed (and according to the authors demonstrated) for eliminating it.[7,10] The only certain method of determining if a specimen has preferred orientation is by measuring it. It does not appear to be generally recognized that, with a complete pole figure at hand, these preferred-orientation data can be used to calculate the intensity for random orientation.[11] Unless this is done the best alternative procedure (which is not guaranteed to eliminate preferred orientation!) seems to be the following: (1) Grind the powder as fine as possible but avoid line-broadening effects. (2) Introduce the specimen into its holder in such a way, e.g., by gentle sifting, that it falls and settles freely and is not compacted. The resulting specimens are highly porous, particularly if the crystallites are platy or rodlike, and will collapse if shaken sharply. However, the intensities obtained from these specimens are highly reproducible and give good results in analyses.[2]

8. QUANTITATIVE ANALYSIS BY LATTICE-PARAMETER MEASUREMENT

The lattice parameters of primary solid solutions vary nearly linearly with the atomic percentage of the solute element; this is known as Vegard's law. Typical data are shown in Fig. 8 for additions of Zn to Ag.[12] This suggests a natural method of determining the composition of alloys by means of a lattice-parameter measurement only. In this case the analysis depends on having an accurate curve of lattice parameters vs. composition and thereafter making accurate parameter measurements, but it is unaffected by the relative intensities of powder lines. Such analyses are capable of high accuracy. However, they are limited to applications in which there are no

Table 3. Applications

Substance	Internal standard	Reference
Quartz	CaF_2	G. L. Clark and D. H. Reynolds, *Ind. Eng. Chem., Anal Ed.*, **8**:36 (1936)
Quartz, cristobalite, and tridymite	α Al_2O_3	C. Legrand and A. Bertrand, *Soc. Franc. Ceram. Bull.*, **50**:69 (1961)
$CaCO_3$, SiO_2	CaF_2	A. Bertrand and M. Loisel, *Soc. Franc. Ceram. Bull.* **50**:53 (1961)
Portland cement clinker alite, C_4AF, C_3A, β C_2S	NaCl	M. Von Euw, *Silicates Ind.*, **23**:643 (1958)
Fe_2O_3, Fe_3O_4	CaF_2	M. Robert, G. Pomey, and M. Angeli, *Chim. Anal. Paris*, **42**:533 (1960)
αFe, Fe_3C, Fe_2C, FeC	FeC, $CaCO_3$, αFe	F. H. Herbstein, J. Smuts, and J. N. Van Niekerk, *Anal. Chem.*, **32**:20 (1960)
Quartz, tridymite, and cristobalite	Pure components	S. R. Holmquist, J. F. Berry, and L. Zwell, *Am. Ceram. Soc. Bull.*, **37**:317 (1958)
Cubic and monoclinic ZrO_2	Pure components	P. Duwez and F. Odell, *Am. Ceram. Soc. J.*, **32**:180 (1949)
$Ca(OH)_2$	$Mg(OH)_2$	L. E. Copeland and R. H. Bragg, *Anal. Chem.*, **30**:196 (1958)
Kaolinite	Pure component	G. W. Brindley and S. S. Kurtossy, *Am. Mineralogist*, **46**:1205 (1961)
Quartz	CaF_2	G. L. Clark, W. F. Loranger, and S. J. Bodnar, *Anal. Chem.*, **26**:1413 (1954)

complications due to other substances, such as binary systems or ternary solid solutions for which due account can be taken.

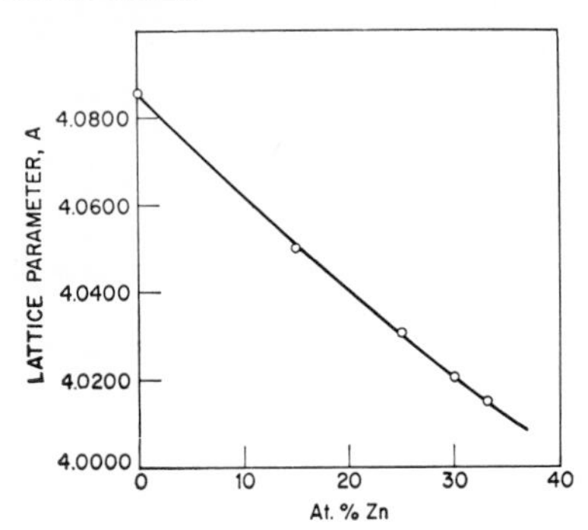

FIG. 8. Variation of lattice parameters with Zn additions. Ag-Zn alloy at 20°C. (*From Ref.* 12.)

REFERENCES CITED

1. L. Alexander and H. P. Klug, *Anal. Chem.*, **20**:886 (1948).
2. L. E. Copeland and R. H. Bragg, *Anal. Chem.*, **30**:196 (1958).
3. J. Leroux, D. H. Lennox, and K. Kay, *Anal. Chem.*, **25**:740 (1953).
4. P. P. Williams, *Anal. Chem.*, **31**:1842 (1959).
5. F. H. Herbstein, J. Smuts, and J. N. Van Niekerk, *Anal. Chem.*, **32**:20 (1960).
6. R. H. Black, *Anal. Chem.*, **25**:743 (1953).
7. L. E. Copeland and R. H. Bragg, *ASTM Bull.* 228, p. 56, 1958.
8. H. P. Klug and L. E. Alexander, *X-ray Diffraction Procedures*, pp. 364–376, John Wiley & Sons, Inc., New York, 1954.
9. Y. Beers, *Rev. Sci. Instr.*, **13**:72 (1942).
10. C. W. Brindley and S. S. Kurtossy, *Am. Mineralogist*, **46**:1205 (1961).
11. B. D. Cullity and A. Freda, *J. Appl. Phys.*, **29**:25 (1958).
12. D. Stockdale, *J. Inst. Metals*, **66**:287 (1940).

GENERAL REFERENCES

Specimen Reproducibility

Alexander, L., H. P. Klug, and E. Kummer: Statistical Factors Affecting the Intensity of X-rays Diffracted by Crystalline Powders, *J. Appl. Phys.*, **19**:742 (1948).

Ballard, J. W., H. L. Oshry, and H. H. Shrenk: Sampling, Mixing, and Grinding Techniques in the Preparation of Samples for Quantitative Analysis by X-ray Diffraction and Spectrographic Methods, *J. Opt. Soc. Am.*, **33**:667 (1943).

Forziatti, F. H., W. K. Stone, J. W. Rowen, and W. D. Appel: Cotton Powder or Infrared Transmission Measurements, *J. Res. Natl. Bur. Std.*, **45**:109 (1950).

Legrand, C., and A. Bertrand: Effect of Crushing in Quantitative Analysis by Diffraction of X-rays, *Soc. Franc. Ceram. Bull.*, **50**:69 (1961).

General Theory

Alexander, L. E., and H. P. Klug: Basic Aspects of X-ray Absorption in Quantitative Diffraction Analysis of Powder Mixtures, *Anal. Chem.*, **20**:886 (1948).

Copeland, L. E., and R. H. Bragg: Quantitative X-ray Diffraction Analysis, *Anal. Chem.*, **30**:196 (1958).

Unusual Methods

Black, R. H.: Analysis of Bauxite Exploration Samples, *Anal. Chem.*, **25**:743 (1953).

Brindley, G. W., and S. S. Kurtossy: Quantitative Determination of Kaolinite by X-ray Diffraction, *Am. Mineralogist*, **46**:1205 (1961).

Leroux, J., D. H. Lennox, and K. Kay: Direct Quantitative X-ray Analysis, *Anal. Chem.*, **25**:740 (1953).

Williams, P. P.: Direct Quantitative Diffractometric Analysis, *Anal. Chem.*, **25**:740 (1953).

Chapter 13

HIGH-TEMPERATURE DIFFRACTOMETER TECHNIQUES

William J. Campbell

U.S. Bureau of Mines

1. INTRODUCTION

High-temperature x-ray diffraction cameras were developed as early as 1921, with interest in this field increasing steadily. The B.S.A. Unicam camera has been in widespread use, both in this country and abroad, for approximately a decade.

Shortly after the commercial development of x-ray diffractometers in the mid-1940s several laboratories adapted furnaces to these units. Design and application of high-temperature x-ray diffractometers were reviewed by Campbell, Stecura, and Grain[1] and later by Lang and Franklin.[2] Ten papers on high-temperature x-ray diffraction were published in vol. 5 of *Advances in X-ray Analysis* (Plenum Press, New York, 1962). All are recommended for supplementary reading.

Successful application of high-temperature diffraction methods requires both the full-time effort of skilled personnel and a well-designed furnace. For example, Dr. H. J. Goldschmidt[3] successfully investigated numerous difficult problems with his x-ray camera; this camera is the prototype of the commercially available B.S.A. Unicam model. In contrast, many laboratories have had only moderate success using the commercial model, their operators having limited experience in high-temperature x-ray technology.

A realistic attitude is also necessary in regard to the accuracy of the temperature measurements. In the temperature range 1500 to 2500° C, errors of 25 to 50° C are the rule. Although some authors claim accuracies of $\pm 2°$ C in the temperature range 500 to 1000° C, others report $\pm 20°$ C or greater, using furnaces of similar design.

Schossberger[4] stated, "Although there was definite progress in the design of high-temperature x-ray cameras during the decade 1940–1950, an investigation in the field leads to the impression that it is probably easier to design than to operate such cameras. The investigation of superlattice limits, thermal expansion, and exact transformation temperatures is still a difficult problem if both the specimen temperature and the thermal gradients in the specimen must be known with a high accuracy and if these temperatures have to be kept constant for a period of five or more hours." His comments are equally applicable to high-temperature furnaces for x-ray diffractometers.

Furnaces for x-ray diffractometers can be conveniently divided into two main classes: highly complex instrumentation designed for specific applications at extreme temperatures or pressures, and furnaces designed for general laboratory use; the latter class is emphasized in this chapter.

Requirements for a versatile high-temperature furnace are: sample temperatures of up to 1300 to 1400° C while maintaining a long heater life, sample temperatures to be accurately measurable, thermal gradients to be small, low heat capacity, to be operative in selected atmospheres or vacuum, adapted for both solid and powder samples with sample position readily accessible, to be designed for use on a commercially available precision wide-angle goniometer (0 to 160° 2θ), and sample to be adjustable to focusing circle while at elevated temperature.

2. METHODS OF HEATING

Four methods of heating x-ray diffraction samples are: passage of electricity through the sample, induction heating, focused high-intensity light source, and electric resistance heaters external to the sample. Only the latter technique is adaptable to a low-cost general versatile furnace.

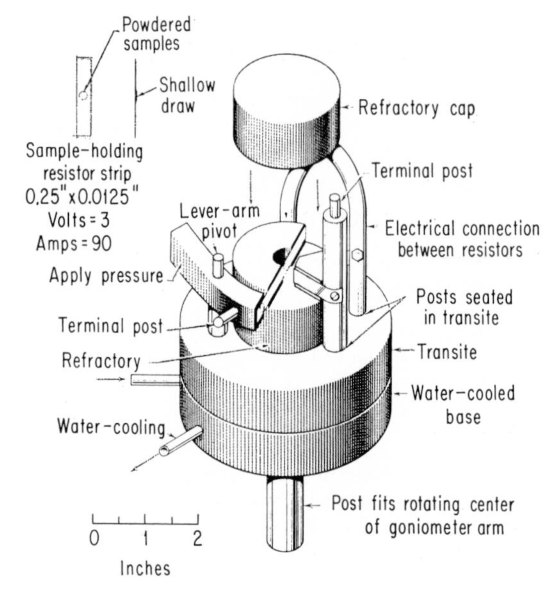

FIG. 1. Platinum strip heater. (*Sowman and Andrews.*[7])

Birks[5] passed electric current through metallic specimens in studies of metals under controlled stress at elevated temperatures. This method is limited by the electrical characteristics of the sample; the maximum temperature depends upon the melting point of the sample. Furnaces of this type can be designed with very low heat capacity. Birks reported that a sample was heated from room temperature to 870° C in less than 1 min and quenched with nitrogen to 150° C in 4 sec.

Kellett and Steward[6] described an internal resistance heater in which the sample is graphitic carbon. Temperatures approximating 2500° C were achieved with their furnace. At temperatures below 1000° C an appreciable fraction of the heat is lost by conduction down their sample support rods, resulting in large thermal gradients. At higher temperatures, heat dissipation is primarily a radiative process giving more uniform sample temperatures.

One modification of the internally heated sample design is to mount the sample directly on the heated metallic strip. Sowman and Andrews[7] (see Fig. 1) developed a platinum–20 per cent rhodium resistance strip heater in which a small flat-bottomed draw holds the powdered sample. A second strip, without the draw, placed opposite the sample serves as a temperature booster. Temperatures as high as 1750° C were reported, the temperature measurements stated to be accurate to ±20° C at 1500° C.

A strip-heater furnace, described by Intrater and Hurwitt,[8] is available commercially from Materials Research Corporation. The flat-specimen area of the platinum–40 per cent rhodium strip is stated to be both mechanically stable and uniform in temperatures up to 1500° C. Temperature stability has been found to be better than ±2° C for 1 hr at 1400° C.

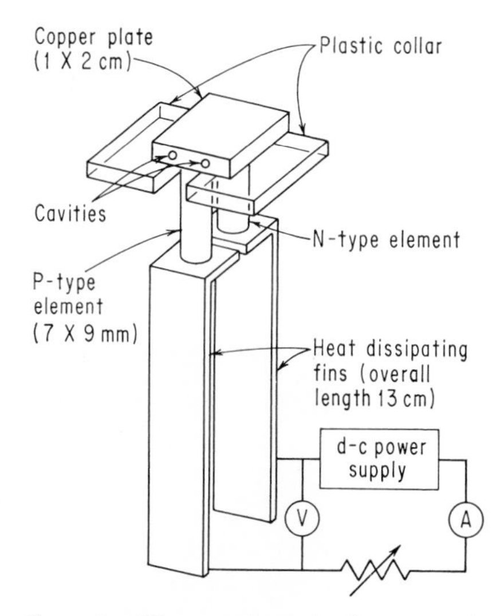

FIG. 2. Thermoelectric thermostat. (*Horne, Croft, and Smith.*[9])

Horne, Croft, and Smith[9] (see Fig. 2) designed a thermostat which utilizes a thermoelectric couple for both heating and cooling the sample. This thermostat consists of a copper plate having two cavities for the measuring and controlling thermocouples, a *p*-type and an *n*-type thermoelectric element, and two copper heat-dissipating fins, all of which are thermally and electrically insulated from the x-ray equipment. The sample, in the form of a fine paste, is painted directly on the upper surface of the copper plate to form a coating 0.001 in. thick.

A versatile induction-heated furnace was designed by Lang and Franklin[2] (see Fig. 3). Sample temperature fluctuations of less than 1 and 2° C are attained over the temperature ranges 130 to 1000° C and 1000 to 1600° C, respectively. Thermal equilibration of the sample requires less than 1 min. Specimen temperatures of approximately 1600° C, either in air, argon, nitrogen, or in vacuo, are easily attained with a 60 per cent platinum–40 per cent

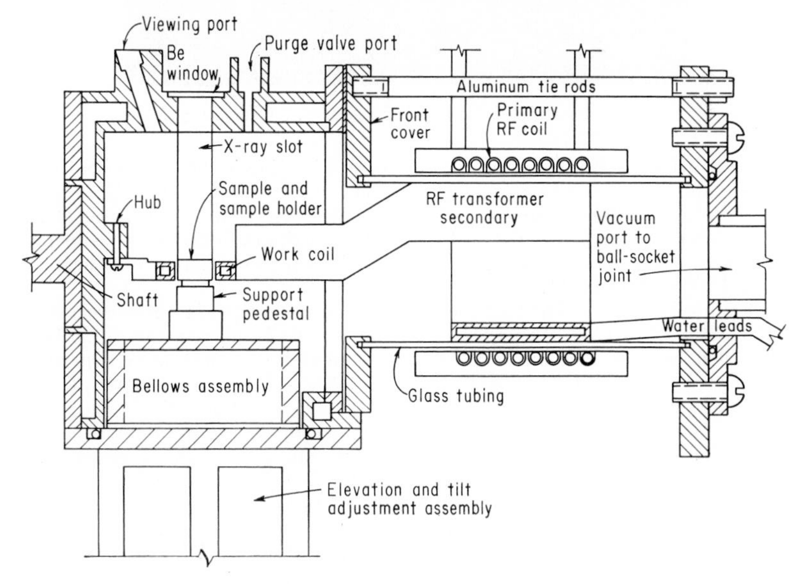

FIG. 3. Induction heater. (*Lang and Franklin.*[2])

rhodium specimen holder using about 40 to 60 per cent of the available power. During one of the trial runs, a tantalum specimen holder was heated in vacuo to approximately 2000° C.

Focused high-intensity light sources can be used for heating samples in controlled atmospheres to temperatures approximating 3000° C.[10] With this type of heating, the sample must remain at the focus of the second mirror; thus rotation of the sample on the x-ray focusing circle is not permitted. An x-ray diffractometer designed by the Bureau of Mines at College Park rotates both the x-ray tube and detector in a horizontal plane about a vertical axis in which the sample is stationary (see Fig. 4). Kruh (University of Arkansas, private communication) constructed a goniometer that rotates both the x-ray tube and detector in a vertical plane around a horizontal stationary sample which is heated by resistance windings. Although high-intensity light sources probably will not be widely employed in x-ray diffraction because of cost and complexity of instrumentation, their potential for studies above 2000° C is of major importance.

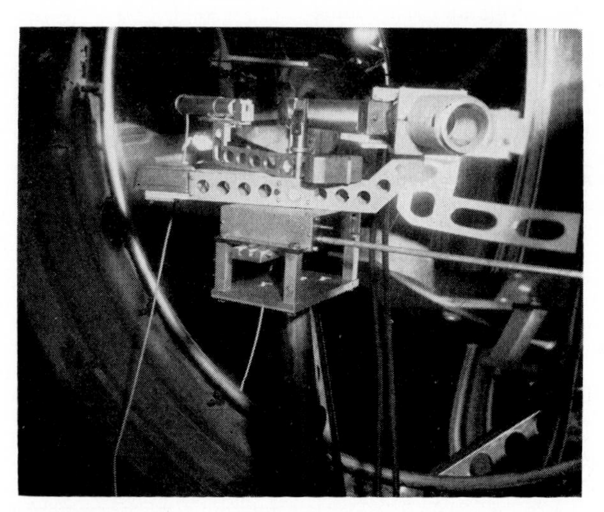

FIG. 4. Focused high-intensity light source. (*Bureau of Mines.*)

External-current Heating. External-current heating is the only method adaptable to a wide variety of furnace designs and is the only method considered in detail in this chapter. External-current heaters can be divided into two main classes—wirewound and metal-foil. Table 1 lists the maximum operating temperatures reported for all types of furnaces. Various designs for external-current heaters are shown in Figs. 5 through 11.

Commercial Furnaces. Diffractometer furnaces are available commercially from Robert L. Stone Co., 3314 Westhill Dr., Austin Tex.;[11] Tem-Pres, Inc., 1526 William St., State College, Pa. (see Fig. 7); Materials Research Corporation, 47 Buena Vista Ave., Yonkers, N.Y.;[8] J. J. Maguire Co., 742 Investment Bldg., Washington, D.C.[1,12,13] (see Figs. 8 and 12); and Rigaku-Denki Co., Ltd., Tokyo, Japan.[14]

Platinum Metals. Most of the furnaces designed for operation in oxidizing atmospheres use platinum (melting point 1770° C), platinum–10 per cent rhodium (melting point 1850° C), or platinum–20 per cent rhodium (melting point 1900° C) windings. Various factors to be considered in the design of platinum wirewound furnaces are discussed by Priddis;[15] attention to all these factors is essential for long furnace life at elevated temperatures. A general discussion of wirewound furnaces is available from Norton Company.[16]

Approximately 1500° C was obtained with a platinum–20 per cent rhodium wire

Table 1. Maximum Temperatures Reported for Various Furnace Designs

Type of heater	Atmosphere	Temp, ° C	Reference
Thermoelectric	Oxidizing	100	9
Gas circulation	Selected	900	38
Hot plate	Nonoxidizing	800, 1200	26, 25
Tube type	Oxidizing	1200, 1300, 1500, 1500+	50, 12 14, 18
Tube type	Nonoxidizing	1500, 1500, 1800	12, 14 50
Parallel plates	Selected	1400	21
Foil	Nonoxidizing	1800, 2000+	32, 30
Strip	Oxidizing	1500	8
Strip	Nonoxidizing	1800	8
Induction	Oxidizing	1600	2
Induction	Nonoxidizing	1900+	2
Internal heating	Nonoxidizing	2500	6
Image furnace	Oxidizing	2000–2500*	10

* Estimated for diffraction samples.

wound on a double core[17] (see Fig. 5). Using a single platinum–20 per cent rhodium wound core, 1400° C was reached in the author's laboratory. Van Niekerk[18] designed a double-core platinum-rhodium wound furnace which he considered to be operational up to 1600° C after a slight modification of the sample holder. By positioning heating elements both in back and in front of the sample, more uniform sample temperatures are achieved. Shimura[14] described a double-core furnace which is available from Rigaku-Denki Company, Ltd. This furnace can be operated either in selected atmospheres or in vacuum. Using both front and back heaters only 210 and 410 watts are required to maintain 1200 and 1500° C, respectively.

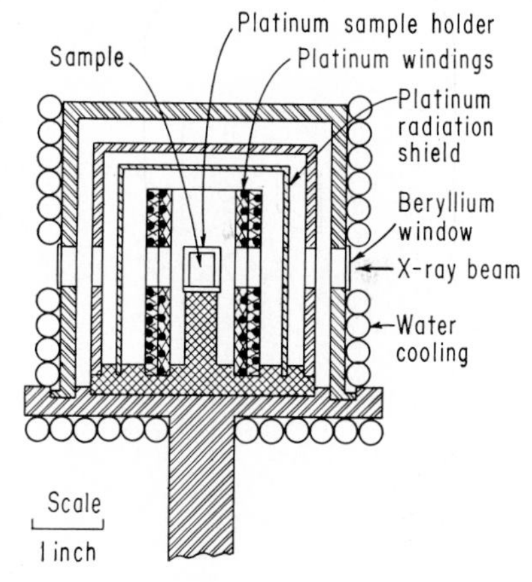

Fig. 5. Wirewound double-core furnace. (*Van Valkenburg and McMurdie.*[17])

Kennedy and Calvert[19] developed a tube-type furnace (see Fig. 6*a*) with the platinum wire wound longitudinally. This furnace was operated only up to 950° C; however, they indicated the furnace, after modification, could be used up to 1600° C.

Tem-Pres, Inc., State College, Pa. (see Fig. 7), initially reported operating temperatures up to 1400° C with their internally wound double-hemisphere platinum alloy wound furnace. A later model, 5X-1B, is capable of extended service up to 1750° C and for short periods at 1850° C in selected atmospheres. Ichikawa[20] presented a detailed discussion on the design of the double-hemisphere furnace constructed at Alfred University.

A furnace designed by Skinner, Stewart, and Morgenstern[21] uses two flat, parallel, radiant windings normal to the sample surface. The heaters extend both above and below the sample surface but do not touch the sample holder. This furnace has been used by the U.S. Geological Survey for a wide variety of mineralogical studies.

Several hot-plate-type heaters have been constructed, all having maximum operating temperatures in the range of 1000° C.

Sample temperatures above 1500 to 1600° C are difficult to achieve with platinum-metal winding because the heat loss through the x-ray gap results in large differences between winding and sample temperatures. The temperatures quoted by Tem-Pres for their model 5X-1B are significantly higher than those for any other furnace in this class.

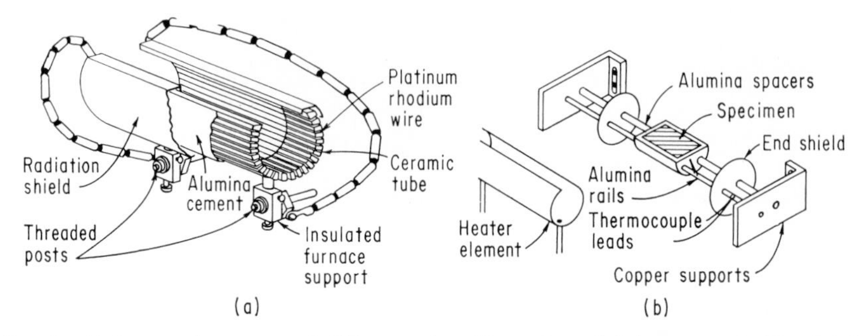

FIG. 6. Tube-type heaters. (*a*) Wirewound. (*Kennedy and Calvert.*[19]) (*b*) Metal foil. (*Spreadborough and Christian.*[40])

Protective Coatings. Use of refractory-metal windings with an oxidation-resistant ceramic coating was considered for use as heating elements. Sherwood[22] reported molybdenum windings protected by a 0.003-in. coating of silicon (primarily as molybdenum disilicide, melting point 2030° C) have resisted oxidation at 1700° C for more than 1,000 hr, at 1800° C for 500 hr, and at 2000° C for 100 hr. Maximum performances found by Wehrmann[23] were 77 hr at 1760° C and 28 hr at 1850° C.

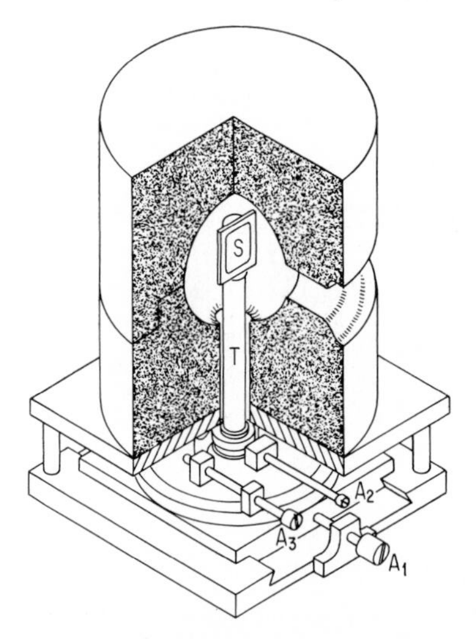

FIG. 7. Internally wound hemispherical heater. (*Tem-Pres, Inc.*) A_1, A_2, A_3 are adjustments for the sample position. S and T indicate location of sample and sample support rod, respectively.

On the basis of these reports, this author concludes molybdenum disilicide–coated windings have about the same maximum temperature as platinum-rhodium alloys. Coated windings can be self-supporting, thus eliminating the need for a ceramic winding core; however, it would be necessary to shape the windings before applying the protective coating.

Silicon Carbide. Perri, Banks, and Post[24] conducted studies in air at temperatures up to 1400° C using a silicon carbide heater. During a test run the platinum sample holder was accidentally melted; therefore, temperatures above 1770° C are possible for short periods.

American Lava Corporation reports a softening temperature of 1800° C and a safe operating temperature of 1450° C for its silicon carbide No. 539. The Carborundum Company quotes a maximum operating temperature of 1650° C for its self-bonded KT silicon carbide in an oxidizing atmosphere.

Silicon carbide heaters can be heated or cooled rapidly and used in either oxidizing or inert atmospheres. However, sample temperatures above 1500° C for extended periods do not seem probable.

Refractory Metals. Four refractory metals that may be used above 1500° C under nonoxidizing conditions are: tungsten, melting point 3410 ± 10° C; rhenium, melting point 3180 ± 20° C; tantalum, melting point 2996 ± 50° C; and molybdenum, melting point 2625 ± 50° C. Molybdenum, tantalum, and tungsten have been used in x-ray diffraction furnaces, but the use of rhenium has not been reported. Rhenium warrants serious consideration because of its high melting point and low vapor pressure at elevated temperatures. Its higher cost does not restrict its use in x-ray diffraction furnaces, as only a small quantity of wire is required.

Mauer and Bolz[12] obtained temperatures up to 1400° C, using self-supported molybdenum windings (see Fig. 8) in a vacuum furnace. Any self-supported winding can be used in this type of furnace with the maximum temperature limited principally

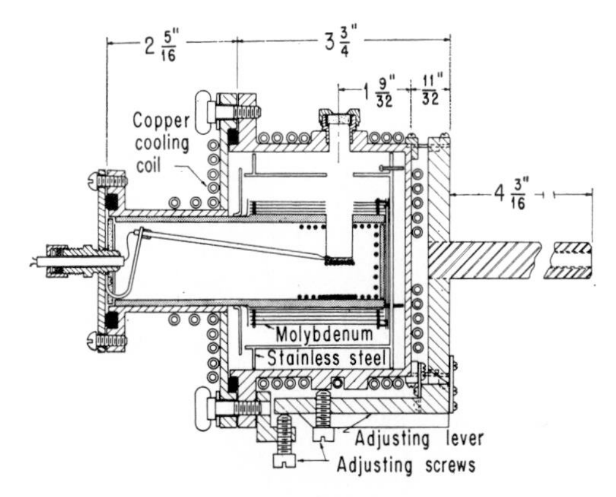

FIG. 8. Self-supported refractory-metal wire heater. (*Mauer and Bolz.*[12])

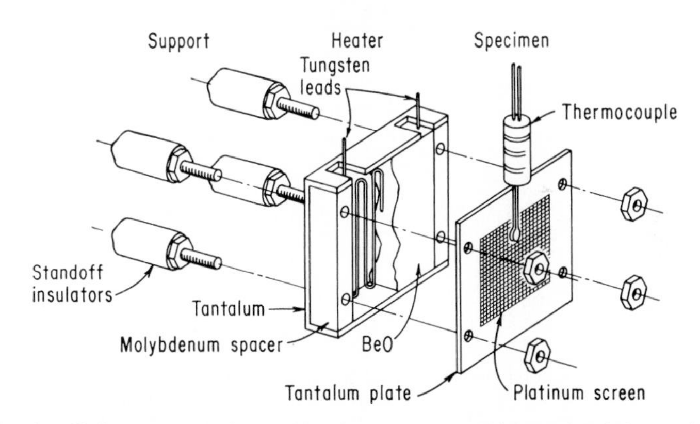

FIG. 9. Refractory-metal wire hot-plate heater. (*Birks and Friedman.*[25])

by the thermal characteristics of the refractory oxide sample-support tube. Dense alumina tubes will not withstand temperatures exceeding 1900° C, and their moderate thermal shock resistance makes slow heating and cooling rates necessary. Higher temperatures require development of superrefractories or the use of a refractory-metal support tube electrically insulated from the windings.

Birks and Friedman[25] developed a hot-plate heater (see Fig. 9) consisting of a tungsten coil embedded in BeO and encased in a tantalum metal box; the maximum temperature reported was 1300° C. Solid metal samples are attached directly to the surface of the box; powders are embedded in a platinum screen fastened on the surface.

A hot-plate heater designed at the Armour Research Foundation[26] uses a Kanthal wire heater embedded in a Lavite block (see Fig. 10). Specimens are brushed onto a ground quartz surface supported on top of the Lavite block. This furnace is capable of attaining 1000° C in an hydrogen atmosphere. Notz, Huntington, and Burkhardt[27] used this type of furnace in their studies on hydrogen reduction of uranium oxides.

McKeand and Hursh[28] reached 1800 to 2000° C with a self-supported tungsten coil heater in a helium atmosphere using a graphite sample support. Considerable reduction of oxide samples by vaporized tungsten metal was observed. They concluded this design was not satisfactory for their proposed study of the ternary system SiO_2-TiO_2-ZrO_2.

Das and Pitman[29] developed a tungsten wire heater wound on thorium oxide insulators in a machined tungsten shell (maximum temperature reported, 2000° C). Sample

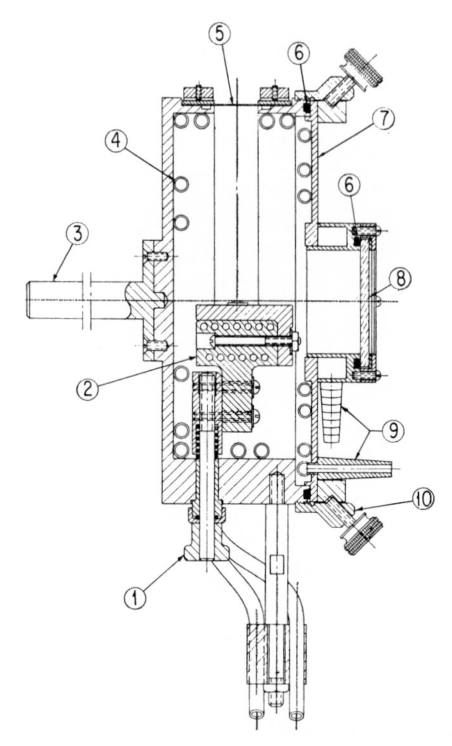

FIG. 10. Kanthal wire hot-plate heater. (*Corvin, Schossberger, and Ticulka.*[26]) (1) Furnace adjustment screw, (2) furnace, (3) goniometer shaft, (4) cooling coils, (5) beryllium window, (6) vacuum seals, (7) removable cover plate, (8) glass window, (9) cooling-hose connections, (10) cover-plate retaining ring.

holders are made from either thorium oxide, tungsten, or a sintered carbide or nitride. By using a cold trap and a large pumping port, operating vacuums of about 10^{-5} mm Hg were obtained at elevated temperatures, thus reducing oxidation of the windings.

Dreikorn[30] achieved temperatures in the range of 2000° C using a tantalum resistance heater. This furnace, designed for a horizontal goniometer, uses samples up to 1.25 in. in diameter and 0.25 in. thick. His power requirements are considerably higher than for other diffractometer furnaces as he requires a 20-kva low-voltage transformer. This furnace has been operated continuously for approximately 8 hr above 1900° C; variations in sample temperature did not exceed 20° C.

Chiotti[31] obtained temperatures up to 1650° C with a low-voltage high-current tantalum foil heater. Johnston, Inc.,[32] was able to go to 1800° C with a similar heater design; however, the furnace was not considered satisfactory by Wright Air Development Center owing to difficulties in temperature measurements, sample alignment, and vacuum failures. Klein[33] (see Fig. 11), by modifying the original design of Chiotti, obtained temperatures up to 2170° C. Power requirements are low with these small furnaces; Klein required only 11 volts at 60 amp to reach the maximum temperature.

The upper temperature limit of a diffractometer furnace depends on vaporization of the heater element, electrical and thermal characteristics of the refractory insulators, and coating of both the x-ray window and optical pyrometer port with vaporized furnace components. Klein suggests two ways to extend the temperature range: reduce the rate of vaporization by a gas blanket at low pressure and reduce heat loss toward the cold x-ray window by metal radiation shielding. The latter restricts the angular range; however, the complete angular range of 0 to 160° 2θ is not required for most investigations.

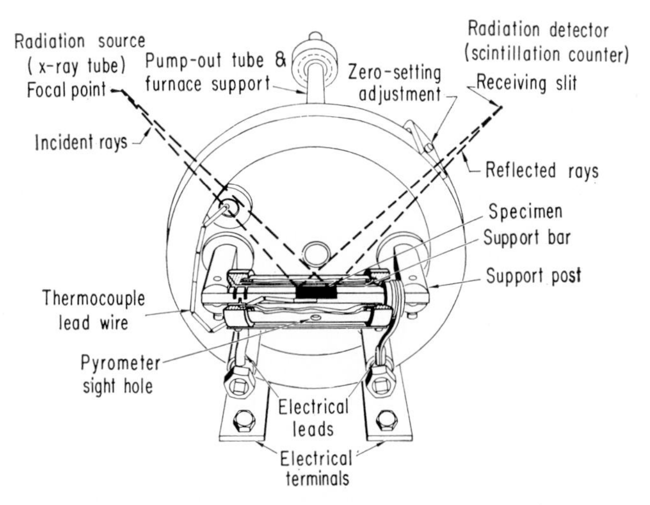

FIG. 11. Refractory-metal foil tube-type heater. (*Klein.*[33])

3. TEMPERATURE CONTROL

Three types of automatic temperature controllers[34] are used: off-on, proportioning with reset, and proportioning with reset and rate action. Simple off-on controllers are not adaptable to these low-heat-capacity furnaces as temperature cycling is excessive. However, modified off-on controls can be used if the power relays are shunted so that the power is decreased by only a small predetermined amount during the off cycle. Mauer and Bolz[12] reduced cycling to $\pm 3°$ C with a power decrease of 10 per cent in the open position.

Proportioning controllers with reset are suitable provided the thermal lag is small. With this type of control, cycling is $\pm 30°$ C for a single controlling and measuring thermocouple positioned on the sample surface, approximately 0.6 cm from the windings.[35,36] When a second thermocouple, for control only, was positioned on the alumina cement covering the windings, temperature fluctuations were reduced to $\pm 3°$ C at 1000° C.

Proportional control, combined with both reset and rate action, reduces the temperature variations to $\pm 3°$ C at 1000° C using a single thermocouple for both controlling and measuring temperature, the rate action correcting for thermal lag.[35,36]

4. TEMPERATURE MEASUREMENTS

Because of conflicting requirements in the design of diffractometer furnaces there are thermal gradients in the sample, which make accurate temperature measurements difficult. Principal factors which affect the accuracy of the temperature measurements are thermocouple errors due to changes in composition or structure, contamination, calibration errors, thermal gradients across and through the sample, heat losses due to thermal conductivity of the thermocouple and its protective tubing, and differences in emissivity between the specimen and the thermocouple.

The ideal furnace design is a small spherical specimen under blackbody conditions in the center of a spherical furnace. However, such conditions cannot be achieved in x-ray diffractometers, owing to the size of the sample, its shape, and the necessity for a 180 to 190° opening for the incident and diffracted x-rays. These conditions reduce the accuracy of temperature determinations on the free surface, as there are thermal gradients both across and through the sample.

Temperature gradients in the sample result in broadened x-ray lines; also the location of the measuring thermocouple is critical. Thermal gradients across the sample are the principal contributors to line broadening, as the temperature difference through the depth viewed by the x-ray beam is usually less than several degrees centigrade. Since x-rays used for diffraction penetrate only about 0.01 cm, temperature measurements must be made on the sample surface if there are large thermal gradients through the sample.

Very low thermal gradients are reported for the furnace developed at Pennsylvania State University.* This furnace uses an internally wound double-hemispherical platinum-rhodium winding (see Fig. 7) somewhat similar in heater design to the B.S.A. Unicam cameras. Using a thermocouple probe, McKinstry (private communication) found temperature differences of less than 2° C from 1 cm in front of the specimen to 1 cm in back for temperatures of 200, 400, 600, and 1000° C. The temperature variation from top to bottom of the sample was less than 0.2° C after a secondary winding was added to compensate for heat loss down the refractory sample support. McKinstry reports this furnace has been used successfully for approximately 50 published studies on ceramics and mineralogical systems.

With a furnace of similar heater design, Ichikawa[20] reported temperature measurements accurate to $\pm 2°$ C at the alpha-quartz inversion temperature (573° C); however, from the variance of his thermal-expansion data his estimate of the accuracy is not justified.

Moore[37] states for hot-plate heaters: "Heating the specimen by conduction through a body of high thermal mass has been used to reduce its thermal differential (the range over which the temperature at a specific point fluctuates during a cycle of the temperature-controlling system) and the thermal gradient across its width. Here, however, the effect of free surface induces a gradient through the specimen which in some cases can be quite severe."

To study thermal gradients in a hot-plate-type heater, Williamson and Moore[37,38] used a copper block 2.5 by 2.5 by 0.5 in. embedded in a refractory oxide and heated by a uniformly wound heating element. Thermal gradients were measured along the diagonal of the exposed surface and through the depth of nickel filings. The filings were compressed into a recess 0.020 in. deep by 1.0 in. diameter machined in the copper block. Nickel filings were used because of their low thermal conductivity and the high emissivity of the oxide which forms at elevated temperatures. The heat loss due to radiation from the exposed surface cannot be replenished rapidly because of the low thermal conductivity of nickel. At 500° C Williamson and Moore found gradients as large as 600° C per centimeter through the sample and 6° C per centimeter along the surface.

For these reasons, Williamson and Moore considered hot-plate heaters unsatisfactory and consequently developed a furnace in which the sample is heated by thermal conduction with a heated gas at a high flow rate. The gas, air or nitrogen, is moved at constant speeds from the heater coils to the sample by fans mounted inside the furnace. The maximum temperature reached was 600° C, but the authors state the use of beryllium windows would increase the range to 900° C. Fluctuations of gas temperature did not exceed $\pm 0.6°$ C with a control period of 15 sec; the fluctuations of specimen temperature are even less.

* Commercially available from Tem-Pres, Inc., 1526 William St., State College, Pa.

At 800° C, Birks and Friedman[25] found gradients less than 5° C per centimeter across metallurgical samples with their hot-plate-type heater, the thermocouple being welded adjacent to the area being irradiated (see Fig. 9). Most metallurgical samples have high thermal conductivity (relative to oxides), minimizing thermal gradients. A phase-transformation temperature of 715° C was observed for a sample reported to have a phase inversion at 720° C. Birks and Friedman stated their lower transition value was partly due to the presence of an impurity which depresses the inversion temperature.

Bassett and Lapham,[39] also using a hot-plate heater, consider their temperature measurements were accurate to ±4° C between 0 and 800° C and about ±8° C for higher temperatures. Their furnace was calibrated from the linear expansion of platinum-rhodium alloys between 20 and 1000° C.

Samples are heated principally by radiation with modified tube furnaces described by Kennedy and Calvert,[19] using platinum wire heaters (see Fig. 6*a*), or Spreadborough and Christian[40] (see Fig. 6*b*), using a tantalum foil heater. Spreadborough and

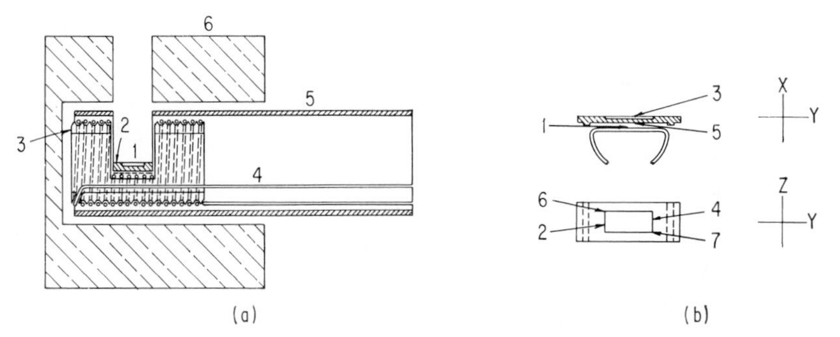

FIG. 12. Cutaway view of furnace showing heater and thermocouple locations. (*Campbell, Stecura, and Grain.*[1]) Part *a*: (1) Sample, (2) sample holder, (3) winding core, (4) platinum-20 per cent rhodium winding, (5) sample-holder support tube, (6) insulating brick. Part *b*: Numbers 1 to 7 indicate thermocouple locations.

Christian found silver diffraction lines were sharp at all temperatures, indicating the absence of appreciable temperature gradients. Also, their expansion data for silver were in close agreement with those published by Reynolds and Hume-Rothery.[41]

In the furnace designed by Mauer and Bolz[12,13] (see Fig. 8), the sample is heated by a combination of conduction and radiation, this design having features of both a tube and a hot-plate heater. Using a powdered specimen pressed into a 1/16-in. cavity in a 1/8-in. alumina slab, Mauer and Bolz observed, at 1200° C in a vacuum, a temperature differential of 30° C across the specimen holder in the direction of the furnace axis and a similar variation from the center of the sample toward both ends in the direction perpendicular to the furnace axis.

There is a temperature differential which may be as high as 200° C through the specimen slab. If the thermocouple is mounted on the alumina holder, temperature measurements will be in error, the magnitude and direction of which depend on the difference in thermal conductivity between the alumina and the sample. Mauer and Bolz state that this is the principal source of error and suggest elimination by calibration.

Using furnaces similar in design to Mauer and Bolz, the following thermal characteristics were determined for oxidizing-atmosphere furnaces at the author's laboratory[1,36] using thin platinum-platinum-10 per cent rhodium thermocouples (0.005 in. thick) positioned as shown in Fig. 12. Precautions were taken to minimize heat losses down both the thermocouple wire and its protective tubing.

At 1000° C there is a thermal gradient of 30 to 40° C per centimeter from the center of the sample toward each end (along Y axis). The length of the sample in the x-ray beam varies with both the Bragg angle and the angular aperture of the divergence slits as expressed in the following equation:

$$L = \frac{l\gamma}{57.3 \sin \theta} \tag{1}$$

where L = length of sample in x-ray beam, cm
l = radius of goniometer, cm
γ = divergence angle, normally 1° in front reflection and 4° for back reflection

At 30° 2θ, with 1° divergence slits, L equals 1.15 cm. For a temperature gradient of 30° C per centimeter, the gradient across the portion of the sample in the x-ray beam is 17° C. Mauer and Bolz[12] stated the effective gradient is less than 5° C; however, they must have used 1° divergence slits in the back-reflection region.

It should be possible to reduce this gradient by slightly lowering the windings in the middle along the Y axis. This will increase the amount of heat to the ends relative to the middle and also compensate for heat losses due to conduction from the ends.

The magnitude and direction of the thermal gradients across the width of the sample, Z axis, vary with the ratio of turns on either side of the holder and by the type and amount of insulation used to prevent heat loss down the ceramic sample support tube. On the side opposite the thermocouple leads, the maximum number of turns possible is 5 (the number of turns controlled by the length and pitch of the core); up to 15 turns are possible on the thermocouple side.

For a winding ratio of 10:5 and a secondary insulator of potassium titanate inside the support tube, there was a positive thermal differential of 55° C at 1100° C toward the thermocouple leads as determined by thermocouples 6 and 7 (Fig. 12). With a winding ratio of 6:5 and no insulation down the support tube, the differential was reduced to 10° C, direction remaining the same.

The thermal differential through the 4-mm-thick alumina holder, X axis, was approximately 100° C at 1000° C. The depression for the powdered oxide sample is 0.65 to 0.70 mm deep; so there is a difference of 16 to 18° C through the total depth of sample. As the x-ray beam penetrates only about one-seventh of the sample thickness, a differential of less than 2° C exists in the effective depth of sample viewed by copper $K\alpha$ radiation.

5. TEMPERATURE CALIBRATION

Because of the difficulties in obtaining accurate temperature measurements, calibration of the furnace is recommended. However, even the calibration of these furnaces is subject to error, particularly when accurate data are required. Brand and Goldschmidt's[42] comment on the calibration of high-temperature x-ray cameras is equally applicable to diffractometers: "Reliable data available are still very scarce, and it would seem highly desirable to extend this information; if an incidental suggestion may be permitted, it would be most valuable to all those working in the x-ray high-temperature field, if a small compendium could be organized and published, to cover both standard dilatometric and transformation point data, and to which contributions could be invited."

Four methods of calibration are power input, melting point, transition point, and thermal expansion. Calibration by power input eliminates the need of a measuring thermocouple. However, the technique is inherently inaccurate because of the continuously changing resistance of the heater and variable sample characteristics.

Melting points and transition points have been used extensively in x-ray diffraction cameras and to a more limited extent in x-ray diffractometers. Melting points are observed either visually or by disappearance of a characteristic x-ray line. Transition points are determined either by disappearance of x-ray lines characteristic of the low-temperature phase or by appearance of the high-temperature phase. Both the melting points and transition points will occur over a temperature range, the magnitude of this range depending on the thermal gradients in the sample.

Calibration by thermal expansion of standard materials is widely employed.

Pearson[41] compiled extensive x-ray data on both high-temperature phases and thermal-expansion characteristics of pure metals, alloys, and, to a lesser extent, oxides, carbides, and other nonmetallics. This reference is highly recommended to all employing high-temperature diffraction techniques.

Expansion values of high-purity metals are the most reliable as x-ray, interferometric, and dilatometric measurements are directly comparable; for example, the maxi-

Table 2. Expansion of Platinum from 25 to 1700° C, Per Cent*

Temperature, ° C.	0	100	200	300	400	500	600	700	800
Increment, ° C.:									
0	--	0.0675	0.1599	0.2548	0.3523	0.4525	0.5554	0.6610	0.7693
2	--	.0694	.1617	.2567	.3543	.4546	.5575	.6631	.7715
4	--	.0712	.1636	.2586	.3563	.4566	.5596	.6653	.7737
6	--	.0730	.1655	.2606	.3583	.4586	.5617	.6674	.7759
8	--	.0748	.1674	.2625	.3603	.4607	.5638	.6695	.7780
10	--	.0767	.1692	.2644	.3622	.4627	.5658	.6717	.7802
12	--	.0785	.1711	.2664	.3642	.4647	.5679	.6738	.7824
14	--	.0803	.1730	.2683	.3662	.4668	.5700	.6760	.7846
16	--	.0821	.1749	.2702	.3682	.4688	.5721	.6781	.7868
18	--	.0840	.1768	.2722	.3702	.4709	.5742	.6803	.7891
20	--	.0858	.1786	.2741	.3722	.4729	.5763	.6824	.7913
22	--	.0876	.1805	.2760	.3742	.4749	.5784	.6846	.7935
24	--	.0895	.1824	.2780	.3761	.4770	.5805	.6867	.7957
26	0.0009	.0913	.1843	.2799	.3781	.4790	.5826	.6889	.7979
28	.0027	.0931	.1862	.2818	.3801	.4811	.5847	.6910	.8001
30	.0045	.0950	.1881	.2838	.3821	.4831	.5868	.6932	.8023
32	0.0062	0.0968	0.1900	0.2857	0.3841	0.4852	0.5889	0.6953	0.8045
34	.0080	.0986	.1918	.2877	.3861	.4872	.5910	.6975	.8067
36	.0098	.1005	.1937	.2896	.3881	.4893	.5931	.6996	.8089
38	.0116	.1023	.1956	.2915	.3901	.4913	.5952	.7018	.8111
40	.0134	.1042	.1975	.2935	.3921	.4934	.5973	.7040	.8134
42	.0152	.1060	.1994	.2954	.3941	.4954	.5994	.7061	.8156
44	.0170	.1078	.2013	.2974	.3961	.4975	.6015	.7083	.8178
46	.0188	.1097	.2032	.2993	.3981	.4995	.6036	.7105	.8200
48	.0206	.1115	.2051	.3013	.4001	.5016	.6057	.7126	.8222
50	.0224	.1134	.2070	.3032	.4021	.5036	.6079	.7148	.8244
52	.0242	.1152	.2089	.3052	.4041	.5057	.6100	.7169	.8267
54	.0259	.1171	.2108	.3071	.4061	.5078	.6121	.7191	.8289
56	.0277	.1189	.2127	.3091	.4081	.5098	.6142	.7213	.8311
58	.0295	.1208	.2146	.3110	.4101	.5119	.6163	.7235	.8333
60	.0313	.1226	.2165	.3130	.4121	.5139	.6184	.7256	.8356
62	.0331	.1245	.2184	.3150	.4141	.5160	.6205	.7278	.8378
64	.0349	.1263	.2203	.3169	.4162	.5181	.6227	.7300	.8400
66	.0367	.1282	.2222	.3189	.4182	.5201	.6248	.7321	.8422
68	.0386	.1300	.2241	.3208	.4202	.5222	.6269	.7343	.8445
70	.0404	.1319	.2260	.3228	.4222	.5243	.6290	.7365	.8467
72	.0422	.1338	.2279	.3248	.4242	.5263	.6311	.7387	.8489
74	.0440	.1356	.2299	.3267	.4262	.5284	.6333	.7408	.8512
76	.0458	.1375	.2318	.3287	.4282	.5305	.6354	.7430	.8534
78	.0476	.1393	.2337	.3306	.4303	.5325	.6375	.7452	.8556
80	.0494	.1412	.2356	.3326	.4323	.5346	.6396	.7474	.8579
82	.0512	.1431	.2375	.3346	.4343	.5367	.6418	.7496	.8601
84	.0530	.1449	.2394	.3366	.4363	.5388	.6439	.7518	.8624
86	.0548	.1468	.2413	.3385	.4383	.5408	.6460	.7539	.8646
88	.0566	.1487	.2433	.3405	.4404	.5429	.6482	.7561	.8668
90	.0585	.1505	.2452	.3425	.4424	.5450	.6503	.7583	.8691
92	.0603	.1524	.2471	.3444	.4444	.5471	.6524	.7605	.8713
94	.0621	.1543	.2490	.3464	.4464	.5492	.6546	.7627	.8736
96	.0639	.1561	.2509	.3484	.4485	.5512	.6567	.7649	.8758
98	.0657	.1580	.2529	.3504	.4505	.5533	.6588	.7671	.8781
100	.0675	.1599	.2548	.3523	.4525	.5554	.6610	.7693	.8803

Table 2. Expansion of Platinum from 25 to 1700° C, Per Cent* *(Continued)*

Temperature, ° C.	900	1,000	1,100	1,200	1,300	1,400	1,500	1,600
Increment, ° C.:								
0	0.8803	0.9941	1.1107	1.2301	1.3524	1.4775	1.6055	1.7365
2	.8826	.9964	1.1131	1.2326	1.3549	1.4801	1.6081	1.7391
4	.8848	.9987	1.1154	1.2350	1.3573	1.4826	1.6107	1.7418
6	.8871	1.0010	1.1178	1.2374	1.3598	1.4851	1.6133	1.7444
8	.8893	1.0033	1.1202	1.2398	1.3623	1.4877	1.6159	1.7471
10	.8916	1.0056	1.1225	1.2422	1.3648	1.4902	1.6185	1.7497
12	.8938	1.0080	1.1249	1.2447	1.3673	1.4927	1.6211	1.7524
14	.8961	1.0103	1.1273	1.2471	1.3697	1.4953	1.6237	1.7550
16	.8983	1.0126	1.1296	1.2495	1.3722	1.4978	1.6263	1.7577
18	.9006	1.0149	1.1320	1.2519	1.3747	1.5004	1.6289	1.7604
20	.9028	1.0172	1.1344	1.2544	1.3772	1.5029	1.6315	1.7630
22	.9051	1.0195	1.1367	1.2568	1.3797	1.5054	1.6341	1.7657
24	.9074	1.0218	1.1391	1.2592	1.3822	1.5080	1.6367	1.7683
26	.9096	1.0242	1.1415	1.2616	1.3847	1.5105	1.6393	1.7710
28	.9119	1.0265	1.1439	1.2641	1.3871	1.5131	1.6419	1.7737
30	.9142	1.0288	1.1462	1.2665	1.3896	1.5156	1.6445	1.7763
32	.9164	1.0311	1.1486	1.2689	1.3921	1.5182	1.6471	1.7790
34	.9187	1.0334	1.1510	1.2714	1.3946	1.5207	1.6497	1.7817
36	.9210	1.0358	1.1534	1.2738	1.3971	1.5233	1.6523	1.7843
38	.9232	1.0381	1.1558	1.2763	1.3996	1.5258	1.6550	1.7870
40	.9255	1.0404	1.1581	1.2787	1.4021	1.5284	1.6576	1.7897
42	.9278	1.0427	1.1605	1.2811	1.4046	1.5309	1.6602	1.7923
44	.9300	1.0451	1.1629	1.2836	1.4071	1.5335	1.6628	1.7950
46	.9323	1.0474	1.1653	1.2860	1.4096	1.5361	1.6654	1.7977
48	.9346	1.0497	1.1677	1.2885	1.4121	1.5386	1.6680	1.8004
50	.9369	1.0521	1.1701	1.2909	1.4146	1.5412	1.6706	1.8030
52	.9391	1.0544	1.1725	1.2934	1.4171	1.5437	1.6733	1.8057
54	.9414	1.0567	1.1748	1.2958	1.4196	1.5463	1.6759	1.8084
56	.9437	1.0591	1.1772	1.2982	1.4221	1.5489	1.6785	1.8111
58	.9460	1.0614	1.1796	1.3007	1.4246	1.5514	1.6811	1.8138
60	.9483	1.0637	1.1820	1.3031	1.4271	1.5540	1.6837	1.8164
62	.9505	1.0661	1.1844	1.3056	1.4296	1.5566	1.6864	1.8191
64	.9528	1.0684	1.1868	1.3081	1.4321	1.5591	1.6890	1.8218
66	.9551	1.0708	1.1892	1.3105	1.4347	1.5617	1.6916	1.8245
68	.9574	1.0731	1.1916	1.3130	1.4372	1.5643	1.6943	1.8272
70	.9597	1.0754	1.1940	1.3154	1.4397	1.5668	1.6969	1.8299
72	.9620	1.0778	1.1964	1.3179	1.4422	1.5694	1.6995	1.8326
74	.9643	1.0801	1.1988	1.3203	1.4447	1.5720	1.7021	1.8353
76	.9665	1.0825	1.2012	1.3228	1.4472	1.5746	1.7048	1.8379
78	.9688	1.0848	1.2036	1.3253	1.4497	1.5771	1.7074	1.8406
80	.9711	1.0872	1.2060	1.3277	1.4523	1.5797	1.7101	1.8433
82	0.9734	1.0895	1.2084	1.3302	1.4548	1.5823	1.7127	1.8460
84	.9757	1.0919	1.2108	1.3326	1.4573	1.5849	1.7153	1.8487
86	.9780	1.0942	1.2132	1.3351	1.4598	1.5874	1.7180	1.8514
88	.9803	1.0966	1.2157	1.3376	1.4624	1.5900	1.7206	1.8541
90	.9826	1.0989	1.2181	1.3400	1.4649	1.5926	1.7232	1.8568
92	.9849	1.1013	1.2205	1.3425	1.4674	1.5952	1.7259	1.8595
94	.9872	1.1036	1.2229	1.3450	1.4699	1.5978	1.7285	1.8622
96	.9895	1.1060	1.2253	1.3475	1.4725	1.6004	1.7312	1.8649
98	.9918	1.1084	1.2287	1.3499	1.4750	1.6030	1.7338	1.8676
100	.9941	1.1107	1.2301	1.3524	1.4775	1.6055	1.7365	1.8703

If the reference temperature used for zero expansion differs from 25° C, values in this table must be corrected as follows:

$$t_{\text{correct}} = t_{\text{table}} + (t_{\text{reference}} - 25)$$

For example, if the reference temperature is 20° C, subtract 5° C from temperatures read from the table.

* Reproduced with permission from *U.S. Bur. Mines Inform. Circ.* 8107, 1962.

mum difference between published dilatometric and x-ray diffraction values of aluminum are less than 2° C. Silver has been widely employed as a calibration standard; however, Mauer and Bolz[12] state the disagreement between published values ranges from ±10° C at 600° C to ±25° C at 950° C among accepted data.

For temperatures above the melting point of silver, two metals, platinum and tungsten, have been used. Selected platinum values were concluded by Campbell[43] to

Table 3. Linear Expansion, in Per Cent, of Magnesium Oxide from 25 to 1400° C (Based on X-ray Camera Data)*

	Temperature °C.							
Increments, °C.	0	100	200	300	400	500	600	700
0	--	0.090	0.215	0.346	0.482	0.622	0.763	0.907
2	--	.092	.217	.349	.485	.624	.767	.910
4	--	.094	.220	.351	.487	.627	.769	.913
6	--	.097	.223	.354	.490	.630	.772	.916
8	--	.099	.225	.357	.493	.632	.775	.918
10	--	.102	.228	.359	.496	.636	.778	.922
12	--	.104	.230	.362	.498	.638	.780	.924
14	--	.107	.233	.365	.501	.641	.784	.927
16	--	.109	.235	.367	.504	.644	.786	.930
18	--	.112	.238	.370	.507	.647	.789	.933
20	--	.114	.241	.373	.509	.650	.792	.936
22	-	.116	.243	.376	.512	.652	.795	.939
24	--	.119	.246	.378	.515	.655	.798	.942
26	0.001	.121	.248	.381	.518	.658	.801	.945
28	.003	.124	.251	.383	.520	.661	.803	.947
30	.006	.126	.253	.386	.523	.664	.806	.950
32	.008	.129	.256	.389	.526	.666	.809	.953
34	.011	.131	.259	.392	.529	.670	.812	.956
36	.013	.134	.261	.395	.532	.672	.815	.959
38	.015	.136	.264	.397	.535	.675	.818	.961
40	.018	.139	.267	.400	.537	.678	.821	.965
42	.020	.141	.269	.402	.540	.681	.823	.968
44	.022	.144	.272	.405	.543	.684	.827	.970
46	.025	.146	.274	.408	.546	.686	.829	.973
48	.027	.149	.277	.411	.548	.690	.832	.976
50	.029	.151	.280	.413	.551	.692	.835	.979
52	.032	.154	.282	.416	.554	.695	.838	.982
54	.034	.156	.285	.419	.557	.698	.841	.985
56	.036	.159	.287	.422	.560	.701	.844	.988
58	.039	.161	.290	.424	.562	.703	.847	.991
60	.041	.164	.293	.427	.565	.706	.849	.993
62	.044	.166	.295	.430	.568	.709	.853	.996
64	.046	.169	.298	.432	.571	.712	.855	.999
66	.048	.172	.301	.435	.574	.715	.858	1.002
68	.051	.174	.303	.438	.577	.718	.861	1.005
70	.053	.177	.306	.441	.579	.721	.864	1.008
72	.056	.179	.309	.443	.582	.723	.867	1.010
74	.058	.182	.311	.446	.585	.727	.869	1.014
76	.060	.184	.314	.449	.587	.729	.873	1.016
78	.063	.187	.317	.452	.590	.732	.875	1.019
80	.065	.189	.319	.454	.593	.735	.878	1.022
82	.068	.192	.322	.457	.596	.738	.881	1.025
84	.070	.194	.325	.460	.599	.740	.884	1.028
86	.072	.197	.327	.463	.602	.744	.887	1.031
88	.075	.199	.330	.465	.604	.746	.890	1.033
90	.077	.202	.333	.468	.607	.749	.893	1.036
92	.080	.204	.335	.471	.610	.752	.895	1.040
94	.082	.207	.338	.474	.613	.755	.898	1.042
96	.085	.210	.341	.476	.616	.758	.901	1.045
98	.087	.212	.343	.479	.618	.761	.904	1.048
100	.090	.215	.346	.482	.622	.763	.907	1.051

Table 3. Linear Expansion, in Per Cent, of Magnesium Oxide from 25 to 1400° C (Based on X-ray Camera Data)* *(Continued)*

	Temperature, °C.						
Increments, °C.	800	900	1,000	1,100	1,200	1,300	1,400
0	1.051	1.194	1.335	1.474	1.608	1.737	1.861
2	1.054	1.197	1.338	1.477	1.611	1.740	--
4	1.057	1.199	1.341	1.480	1.613	1.743	--
6	1.059	1.203	1.343	1.483	1.616	1.745	--
8	1.062	1.206	1.346	1.485	1.619	1.748	--
10	1.066	1.208	1.350	1.487	1.622	1.750	--
12	1.068	1.211	1.353	1.490	1.624	1.752	--
14	1.071	1.214	1.355	1.492	1.627	1.755	--
16	1.074	1.217	1.358	1.495	1.630	1.758	--
18	1.076	1.219	1.361	1.498	1.631	1.760	--
20	1.080	1.223	1.364	1.501	1.634	1.763	--
22	1.083	1.226	1.366	1.503	1.637	1.765	--
24	1.085	1.228	1.369	1.506	1.640	1.767	--
26	1.088	1.231	1.372	1.509	1.642	1.770	--
28	1.091	1.234	1.375	1.512	1.645	1.773	--
30	1.094	1.237	1.377	1.514	1.648	1.775	--
32	1.097	1.239	1.380	1.517	1.651	1.778	--
34	1.100	1.242	1.383	1.520	1.653	1.780	--
36	1.103	1.245	1.386	1.523	1.656	1.782	--
38	1.105	1.249	1.388	1.525	1.658	1.785	--
40	1.108	1.251	1.391	1.528	1.660	1.788	--
42	1.112	1.254	1.394	1.531	1.663	1.790	--
44	1.114	1.257	1.397	1.534	1.666	1.792	--
46	1.117	1.259	1.399	1.536	1.668	1.795	--
48	1.120	1.262	1.402	1.539	1.671	1.797	--
50	1.122	1.265	1.405	1.542	1.674	1.800	--
52	1.126	1.268	1.408	1.545	1.677	1.803	--
54	1.129	1.270	1.410	1.547	1.678	1.805	--
56	1.131	1.273	1.413	1.550	1.681	1.807	--
58	1.134	1.277	1.416	1.553	1.684	1.810	--
60	1.137	1.280	1.418	1.556	1.686	1.812	--
62	1.140	1.282	1.421	1.558	1.689	1.815	--
64	1.143	1.285	1.424	1.561	1.692	1.818	--
66	1.146	1.288	1.428	1.563	1.695	1.819	--
68	1.149	1.290	1.430	1.565	1.697	1.822	--
70	1.151	1.293	1.433	1.568	1.699	1.824	--
72	1.154	1.296	1.436	1.571	1.702	1.827	--
74	1.157	1.299	1.439	1.574	1.704	1.830	--
76	1.159	1.301	1.441	1.576	1.707	1.831	--
78	1.163	1.304	1.444	1.579	1.710	1.834	--
80	1.166	1.308	1.447	1.582	1.712	1.837	--
82	1.169	1.311	1.450	1.585	1.715	1.839	--
84	1.171	1.313	1.452	1.587	1.717	1.841	--
86	1.174	1.316	1.455	1.590	1.719	1.843	--
88	1.177	1.319	1.458	1.593	1.722	1.846	--
90	1.180	1.322	1.461	1.595	1.725	1.849	--
92	1.183	1.324	1.463	1.598	1.728	1.852	--
94	1.186	1.327	1.466	1.600	1.730	1.853	--
96	1.188	1.330	1.469	1.603	1.733	1.856	--
98	1.191	1.333	1.472	1.605	1.734	1.858	--
100	1.194	1.335	1.474	1.608	1.737	1.861	--

If the reference temperature used for zero expansion differs from 25° C, values in this table must be corrected as follows:

$$t_{\text{correct}} = t_{\text{table}} + (t_{\text{reference}} - 25)$$

For example, if the reference temperature is 20° C, subtract 5° C from temperatures read from the table.

* Reproduced with permission from *U.S. Bur. Mines Rept. Invest.* 6115, 1962.

be reliable to within 2, 5, and 25° C, over the temperature range 0 to 700° C, 700 to 1000° C, and 1000 to 1700° C, respectively. Tabular expansion values from 25 to 1700° C in 2° C are listed in Table 2. Equations relating expansion to temperature for several metals are summarized by Brand and Goldschmidt.[42]

Expansion characteristics of high-purity magnesium oxide were determined by 21 cooperating laboratories using one or more of the following techniques: x-ray camera, x-ray diffractometer, dilatometer, interferometer, and telemicroscope.[44] Linear expansion was expressed as a power series in the form of the following equation:

$$\text{Expansion, per cent} = [A + B(\Delta t) + C(\Delta t)^2]\,(\Delta t/10^4) \qquad (2)$$

The constants A, B, and C were determined by least-squares techniques for x-ray camera, x-ray diffractometer, and dilatometer data separately, also for combined data by all five techniques. Below 500° C expansion values obtained by dilatometric and interferometric methods are significantly lower than those by x-ray methods; above 500° C this bias decreases rapidly.

Comparison of results within methods showed the least variance for x-ray camera data; dilatometer and x-ray diffractometer results have about the same variance. The average deviations, in per cent, between observed and calculated expansion values among methods were approximately 10 per cent from 100 to 300° C, 5 per cent from 300 to 500° C, and 2 per cent from 500 to 1400° C. Maximum deviations were approximately a factor of 2 larger in most instances. These results for magnesium oxide emphasize the difficulty in selecting the *best expansion values* to use for calibration. Expansion values for magnesium oxide based on x-ray camera data are given in Table 3.

The accuracy of temperatures derived from expansion of an internal standard are limited by the accuracy of the expansion measurements. Platinum expands approximately 0.1 per cent per 100° C; therefore, an error of ± 0.001 per cent in determining Δd or Δa is equivalent to $\pm 1°$ C. Assuming the error in measuring the diffraction angle to be $\pm 0.01° \; 2\theta$, the error in the thermal-expansion measurement limits the precision of the derived temperature to $\pm 5°$ C over the range from room temperature to 1700° C. To obtain a precision of $\pm 1°$ C, diffraction angles must be measured to $\pm 0.002° \; 2\theta$. While this order of precision can be achieved at room temperature, techniques used to compensate for expansion of sample and furnace components limit precision to $\pm 0.01° \; 2\theta$ at elevated temperatures.

6. CONTROLLED ATMOSPHERES

Aluminum foil, aluminum–4 per cent silicon, and beryllium have been used for vacuum-tight windows, beryllium being preferred. Most of the furnace windows consist of beryllium bent by hot-pressing techniques to fit the curvature of the shell. Usually windows are held in place by metal straps and made vacuum-tight with a suitable sealant such as silicone varnish (Dow-Corning DC 996).[12] Removable windows, with O rings or gaskets for vacuum-tightness, can be employed if the furnace shell is cooled adequately.

Several furnaces have flat beryllium windows which extend out from the shell.[29,32] This type of window is easier to fabricate, seal, clean, and replace; however, the angular range of the diffractometer is restricted at both low and high angles.

Contamination of both the x-ray and optical-pyrometer windows is a source of trouble at temperatures where vaporization of the windings is pronounced. Contamination of the x-ray window is significantly reduced by using either a movable inner-metal shield or a replaceable metallic $K\beta$ shield.

Coatings of unknown thickness on the pyrometer window result in large errors in the temperature measurement; for example, Kellett and Steward[6] found a positive correction of 100° C was necessary at 2500° C.

Several furnaces have a movable shutter over the optical-pyrometer sight window.[32,36] In the furnace designed by Johnston[32] the window is protected from condensing vapors by a soft-iron shutter which is moved by an external magnet.

Vacuum systems are connected to the furnace through either a flexible coupling or a rotatory vacuum seal. Several furnaces have metal bellows[25,30] connected normal to the rotation axis of the furnace. Most of the furnaces have either a glass or metal ball and socket on a rotatory O-ring seal. This rotatory seal is connected either to the front of the furnace or through a hollow spindle to the back of the goniometer. Use of a hollow spindle gives maximum working area around the furnace; however, there are two disadvantages to this arrangement: the sample must be adjusted to the focusing circle through vacuum seals, and both the necessarily small diameter of the spindle bore and the long path length significantly reduce the pumping efficiency.

Metals which are strong getters, such as titanium, zirconium, and hafnium, cannot be heated in ordinary dynamically evacuated systems without rapid deterioration of the sample surface by oxygen and nitrogen. To study titanium at elevated temperatures, Willens[45] enclosed the entire diffractometer and monochromator assembly in a large vacuum chamber 6 ft in diameter and 4 ft high (see Fig. 13). This system,

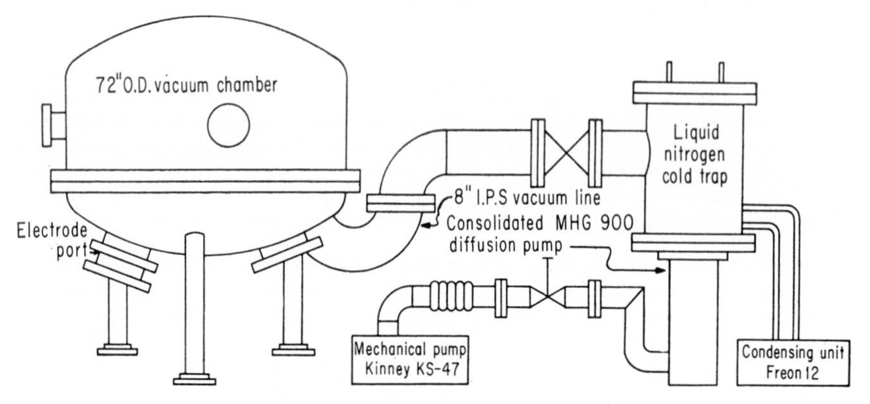

FIG. 13. Schematic of the vacuum system. (*Willens.*[45])

after 2 days of continuous pumping, attained a pressure of 2×10^{-6} mm Hg. Also, all possible sources of air leakage are surrounded by highly purified argon. In this manner it is possible to obtain partial pressures of oxygen and nitrogen several orders of magnitude less than the pressure in the vacuum chamber.

In general, furnaces designed for vacuum operation can also be utilized with selected atmospheres, for example, the very versatile arrangement described by Lang and Franklin.[2] When converting from selected atmospheres to vacuum, or vice versa, the furnace must be thermally calibrated under the conditions to be employed. For example, in vacuum, heat transfer is primarily radiative whereas convection or conduction is important in selected atmospheres.

7. X-RAY OPTICS

For accurate x-ray diffraction measurements the furnace must be mounted on a precision wide-angle goniometer with adjustments provided to both align and maintain the sample on the focusing circle while at elevated temperatures. Supplemental reading of the discussion on sample alignment by Lang and Franklin[2] is strongly recommended.

The initial step is to zero the goniometer accurately, either using the procedure recommended by the manufacturer or with the mechanical alignment device proposed by Parrish and Lowitzsch.[46] The sample surface must be tangent to the focusing circle at O and bisected in the Y direction by the axis of the goniometer (see Fig. 14). On standard diffractometers, the sample is attached directly to the main spindle so the sample is accurately positioned. However, on most furnaces the spindle is connected to the exterior shell; so some means of checking the accuracy of the sample position is necessary. For the Mauer-Bolz furnace the accuracy can be checked by mounting the spindle in a lathe and determining the degree of eccentricity with an indicator gauge. Deviations in the X direction are corrected by the sample-height adjustments; there is no provision for adjustment in the Y direction. However, in the three furnaces constructed for the author's laboratory, the maximum deviation in the Y direction was less than 0.003 in.

The Z axis of the sample must be maintained perpendicular to the X axis. Any tilt about the X axis results in broadened x-ray lines, as part of the sample will be either above or below the focusing circle. Tilt can be determined in several ways: a bubble level across the sample in the Z direction; the target image on photographic film at zero goniometer setting; or the sharpness of the x-ray beam cutoff at zero setting on the goniometer while varying the sample height in the X direction.

For most diffractometer furnaces the sample height is variable, so that it is necessary both to position the sample on the focusing circle and to make the 2:1 alignment. It is essential that the x-ray window extend over an angular range exceeding 180° 2θ in

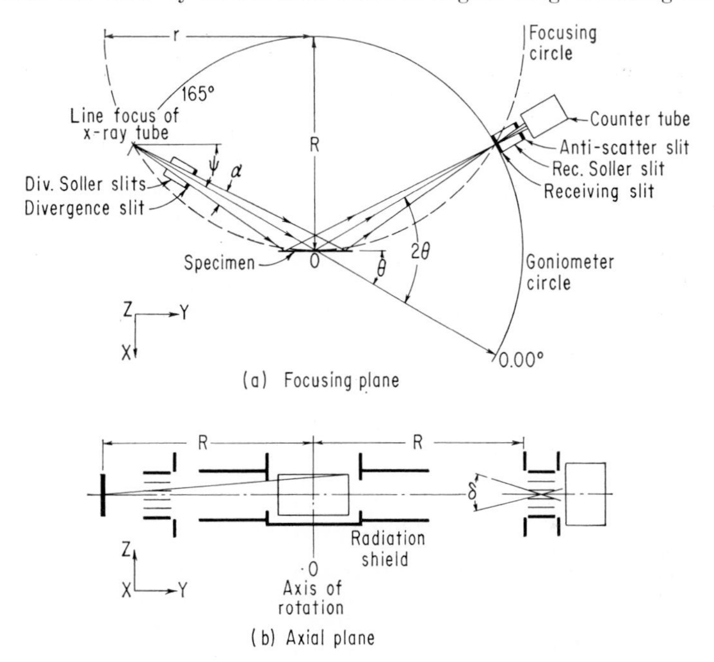

FIG. 14. Focusing conditions for an x-ray diffractometer. (*Parrish and Lowitzsch.*[16])

order to align the sample. With many furnace designs this alignment is not possible. The following procedure used in the author's laboratory is recommended.

First, with the detector arm at zero and using fine slits (1° divergence and 0.003 in. or smaller receiving slits) the sample height is carefully increased while simultaneously varying the 2:1 setting until the intensity is reduced by a factor of 2. This is analogous to using a flat plate setting for the 2:1 setting.

Second, a plate is placed over the sample; this plate has a 0.001-in. recess which forms a long Soller slit (a similar method was described by Corvin et al.[26]); the 2:1 setting and height are then set to maximum intensity. Under these conditions, the 2:1 setting is correct, but the sample will be below the focusing circle by one-half the slit width or 0.0005 in. The height is adjusted accordingly and a standard sample is run to determine the accuracy of alignment.

When accurate x-ray data are required the sample height must be adjusted at each temperature to correct for shrinkage or expansion. Wilson[47] has shown that a displacement of distances from the rotation axis results in an angular error of

$$\Delta\theta_s = -(s/l)\cos\theta \qquad (3)$$

where l = radius of goniometer, cm
s = displacement, cm

Lang and Franklin[2] derived a similar expression for sample displacement from the rotation axis.

Unit-cell determinations are very sensitive to sample displacement in the front-reflection region, with sensitivity decreasing rapidly at higher angles. Since unit-cell dimensions vary with temperature, some means of determining sample displacement without the use of a standard sample of known interplanar spacings is necessary. Mauer and Bolz[12] suggest variation of the sample height until both the front- and back-reflection lines give the same value for the unit cell. A detailed discussion of the accuracy of this method is given in their report.

Because of penetration of x-rays into the sample, the unit-cell determination is angular dependent, particularly for samples having low x-ray absorption properties. Therefore, in the author's laboratory this x-ray absorption dependence is considered in the height adjustment to obtain optimum sample setting. However, it is not necessary to allow for x-ray penetration when thermal-expansion data are required only as differences, rather than as absolute values. With anisotropic samples, diffraction lines should be chosen so that each of the lattice constants can be independently determined ($h00$, $00l$). In many instances these lines are not suitable, and thus simultaneous equations must be used.

To determine unit-cell dimensions accurately when no sample adjustment is available, it is necessary to extrapolate to 180° 2θ, using methods similar to those described by Chiotti.[31]

Most of the furnaces having sample-height adjustment use a precision screw to advance the sample with either a dovetail ways or some similar type of guide to prevent lateral motion (Y direction) of the furnace (see Figs. 3 and 7). With a micrometer screw (40 turns to the inch) each revolution advances the sample 0.025 in., making height adjustment very sensitive to screw position. Mauer and Bolz (see Fig. 8) use a lever arm in combination with a precision screw so that one revolution advances the sample height approximately 0.009 in. Both the precision screw and the combination precision screw–lever arm adjustments are used in the author's laboratory. By using a tripod support, Lang and Franklin[2] combined a tilt adjustment with the elevation adjustment.

8. APPLICATIONS

High-temperature x-ray diffractometry has been employed in a wide variety of problems such as the following: condensation reactions,[11] decomposition,[18] oxidation reduction,[27] phase transformation,[45,48,49,50] effect of stress on phase transformation,[5] eutectoid transformation,[37,38] grain-boundary migration,[51] mineralogical systems,[21,52] thermal expansion,[6,35,43,44,48,49] single-crystal properties,[53] thin films,[26] and atomic vibrations.[54]

This technique can be used for any investigation in which a crystallographic characteristic of the sample varies with temperature, time, etc. For example, thermal expansion is determined by the change in lattice parameter(s) with temperature; for anisotropic materials expansion along each crystallographic axis can be measured. Reactions can be followed dynamically either at selected fixed temperatures or with programmed heating and cooling rates. Operational procedures for these applications are given in the references listed above.

REFERENCES CITED

1. W. J. Campbell, S. Stecura, and C. Grain, High Temperature Furnaces for X-ray Diffractometers, *U.S. Bur. Mines Rept. Invest.* 5738, 1961.
2. S. M. Lang and E. W. Franklin, Research in High-temperature X-ray Diffraction Technology, *ARL* 62-315, Owens-Illinois Technical Center, Toledo, Ohio, March, 1962.
3. H. J. Goldschmidt, High Temperature Methods, chapter in *X-ray Diffraction by Polycrystalline Methods*, pp. 242–264, H. S. Peiser and others (eds.), Institute of Physics, London, 1955.
4. F. Schossberger, High-temperature X-ray Diffraction, chapter in *High Temperature*

Technology, pp. 490–502, I. E. Campbell (ed.), John Wiley & Sons, Inc., New York, 1956.

5. L. S. Birks, Apparatus for X-ray Diffraction Studies of Metals under Controlled Stress at Elevated Temperatures, *Rev. Sci. Instr.*, **25**:963–966 (1954).
6. E. A. Kellett and E. G. Steward, Heating and Cooling Attachments for X-ray Powder Diffractometry, *J. Sci. Instr.*, **39**:306–308 (1962).
7. H. G. Sowman and A. I. Andrews, A Study of the Phase Relations of ZrO_2-TiO_2 and ZrO_2-TiO_2-SiO_2, *J. Am. Ceram. Soc.*, **34**:298–301 (1951).
8. J. Intrater and S. Hurwitt, High Temperature, High Vacuum, Diffractometer Attachment, *Rev. Sci. Instr.*, **32**:905–906 (1961).
9. R. A. Horne, W. J. Croft, and L. B. Smith, Thermoelectric Thermostat for X-ray Diffraction, *Rev. Sci. Instr.*, **30**:1132–1134 (1959).
10. E. Maust Jr. and W. E. Warnke, The Performance and Operating Characteristics of an Image Furnace Having 60-inch Paraboloid Mirrors, *U.S. Bur. Mines Rept. Invest.* 5946, 1962.
11. E. L. Moore and J. S. Metcalf, The Application of X-ray Diffraction at Elevated Temperatures to Study the Mechanism of Formation of Sodium Tripolyphosphate, *Advances in X-ray Analysis*, vol. 5, pp. 276–284, Plenum Press, New York, 1962.
12. F. A. Mauer and L. H. Bolz, Measurement of Thermal Expansion of Cermet Components by High Temperature X-ray Diffraction, *a. Natl. Bur. Std. Rept.*, **3148**: 39 pp., 1953. *b. Natl. Bur. Std. Rept.*, **4685,** 11 pp., 1956. *c. WADC Tech. Rept.*, **55-473,** 57 pp., 1955. *d. WADC Tech. Rept.*, **55-473,** Supplement no. 1, 47 pp., 1957.
13. F. A. Mauer and L. H. Bolz, Problems in the Temperature Calibration of an X-ray Diffractometer Furnace, *Advances in X-ray Analysis*, vol. 5, pp. 229–237, Plenum Press, New York, 1962.
14. Y. Shimura, New Type of High Temperature X-ray Diffractometer, *Rev. Sci. Instr.*, **32**:1404–1405 (1961).
15. J. E. Priddis, The Design of Platinum-wound Electric Resistance Furnaces, *Platinum Metals Rev.*, **2**:38–44 (1958).
16. The Construction of Laboratory Electric Furnaces, Norton Company, Worcester, Mass.
17. A. Van Valkenburg and H. F. McMurdie, High-temperature X-ray Diffraction Apparatus, *J. Natl. Bur. Std.*, **38**:415–418 (1947).
18. J. N. Van Niekerk, Vacuum Furnace for High Temperature X-ray Diffractometry, *J. Sci. Instr.*, **30**:172–175 (1960).
19. S. W. Kennedy and L. D. Calvert, An Oxidizing Atmosphere Furnace for Use with an X-ray Diffractometer, *J. Sci. Instr.*, **35**:61–62 (1958).
20. Y. Ichikawa, Construction of a High Temperature X-ray Diffraction Furnace and Studies of Several Reactions at Elevated Temperatures, *M.S. Thesis*, New York State College of Ceramics, Alfred, N.Y., 1954.
21. B. J. Skinner, D. B. Stewart, and J. C. Morgenstern, A New Heating Stage for the X-ray Diffractometer, *Am. Mineralogist*, **47**:962–967 (1962).
22. E. M. Sherwood, Metals, chapter in *High Temperature Technology*, pp. 17–28, I. E. Campbell (ed.), John Wiley & Sons, Inc., New York, 1956.
23. R. Wehrmann, Oxidation Resistant Coatings for Molybdenum, *Fansteel Met.*, 2 (November, 1956).
24. J. A. Perri, E. Banks, and B. Post, Study of Phase Transitions in WO_3, with a High-temperature X-ray Diffractometer, *J. Appl. Phys.*, **28**:1272–1275 (1957).
25. L. S. Birks and H. A. Friedman, High Temperature X-ray Diffraction Apparatus, *Naval Res. Lab. Rept.* N-3081, 1947.
26. I. Corvin, F. Schossberger, and F. Ticulka, Alignment Device and Thermal-control System for High-temperature X-ray Diffractometry, *Advances in X-ray Analysis*, vol. 5, pp. 221–228, Plenum Press, New York, 1962.
27. K. J. Notz, C. W. Huntington, and W. Burkhardt, Hydrogen Reduction of Uranium Oxides, A Phase Study by Means of a Controlled-atmosphere Diffractometer Hot Stage, *Ind. Eng. Chem. Process Design Develop.*, **1**:213–217 (1962).
28. I. J. McKeand and R. K. Hursh, A Tungsten Coil Furnace for High-temperature X-ray Diffraction Investigations, *J. Am. Ceram. Soc.*, **38**:63–65 (1955).
29. D. K. Das and D. T. Pitman, A Vacuum High Temperature X-ray Diffraction Furnace for the X-ray Diffractometer, *Pittsburgh Diffraction Conf.*, November, 1959.
30. R. E. Dreikorn, A High-temperature X-ray Diffractometer Specimen Holder, *Advances in X-ray Analysis*, vol. 5, pp. 213–220, Plenum Press, New York, 1962.
31. P. Chiotti, Adaptation of a Geiger Counter X-ray Diffractometer for High-temperature Investigations, *Rev. Sci. Instr.*, **25**:683–688 (1954).
32. W. L. Baun, A High Temperature X-ray Diffractometer Specimen Mount, *WADC Tech. Note* 59-139, available as AD 231653.

33. D. J. Klein, Measurement of the Crystallographic Thermal Expansion of Alpha-Alumina and Beryllia to Elevated Temperatures Emphasizing Anisotropic Effects, *NAA-SR* 2542, Atomics International, Canoga Park, Calif., 1958.
34. W. G. Holzbock, *Automatic Control, Principles and Practice*, Reinhold Publishing Corporation, New York, 1958.
35. W. J. Campbell and C. Grain, Thermal Expansion of Alpha Alumina, *U.S. Bur. Mines Rept. Invest.* 5757, 1961.
36. C. F. Grain, Temperature Calibration of a High Temperature X-ray Diffractometer Furnace, *M.S. Thesis*, Georgetown University, June, 1962.
37. A. Moore, The Application of High Temperature X-ray Diffractometer Methods to Solid State Transformations, *Ph.D. Thesis*, University of Birmingham, Birmingham, England, 1955.
38. G. K. Williamson and A. Moore: A Precision High-temperature Specimen Chamber for an X-ray Diffractometer, *J. Sci. Instr.*, **33**:107–110 (1956).
39. W. A. Bassett and D. M. Lapham, A Thermal Increment Diffractometer, *Am. Mineralogist*, **42**:548–555 (1957).
40. J. Spreadborough and J. W. Christian, High Temperature X-ray Diffractometer, *J. Sci. Instr.*, **36**:116–118 (1959).
41. W. B. Pearson, *Handbook of Lattice Spacing and Structures of Metals and Alloys*, Pergamon Press, New York, 1959.
42. J. A. Brand and H. J. Goldschmidt, The Temperature Calibration of a High-temperature X-ray Diffraction Camera, *J. Sci. Instr.*, **33**:41–45 (1956).
43. W. J. Campbell, Platinum Expansion Values for Thermal Calibration of High-temperature X-ray Diffraction Cameras and Diffractometers, *U.S. Bur. Mines Inf. Circ.* 8107, 1962.
44. W. J. Campbell, Thermal Expansion of Magnesium Oxide: An Interlaboratory Study, *U.S. Bur. Mines Rept. Invest.*, 6115, 1962.
45. R. H. Willens, A Vacuum X-ray Diffractometer for High Temperature Studies and an Investigation of the Allotropic Transformation of Titanium (*AFOSR*-1839), California Institute of Technology, Pasadena, Calif., Dec., 1961, available as AD 270632.
46. W. Parrish and K. Lowitzsch, Geometry, Alignment, and Angular Calibration of X-ray Diffractometers, *Am. Mineralogist*, **44**:765–786 (1959).
47. A. J. C. Wilson, Geiger-counter X-ray Spectrometer, Influence of Size and Absorption Coefficient of Specimen on Position and Shape of Powder Diffraction Maxima, *J. Sci. Instr.*, **27**:321–325 (1950).
48. C. F. Grain and W. J. Campbell, Thermal Expansion and Phase Inversion of Six Refractory Oxides, *U.S. Bur. Mines Rept. Invest.* 5982, 1962.
49. S. Stecura and W. J. Campbell, Thermal Expansion and Phase Inversion of Rare-earth Oxides, *U.S. Bur. Mines Rept. Invest.* 5847, 1961.
50. H. T. Sumsion and R. G. Sowman, A High Temperature X-ray Furnace for the General Electric X-ray Spectrometer, *KAPL*-1303, Knolls Atomic Power Laboratory, Schenectady, N. Y., 1955.
51. H. P. Leighly, Jr., Research on the Recrystallization of Aluminum Single Crystals: Quart. Progress Rept., no. 2, Denver Research Institute, Denver, Colo., July–September, 1957, available as AD 145437.
52. F. M. Wahl, Effect of Impurities on Kaolinite Transformations as Examined by High-temperature X-ray Diffraction, *Advances in X-ray Analysis*, vol. 5, pp. 264–275, Plenum Press, New York, 1962.
53. R. Lefker, A. De Bretteville, Jr., and J. S. Dodd, A Single Crystal Temperature Controlled Oven for an X-ray Spectrometer, *Am. Mineralogist*, **39**:976–982 (1954).
54. E. Ryba and P. Chiotti, Use of a High-temperature X-ray Diffractometer to Measure the Temperature Dependence of Reflection Intensities, *Advances in X-ray Analysis*, vol. 5, pp. 257–263, Plenum Press, New York, 1962.

GENERAL REFERENCES

Butters, R. G., and J. G. Parr: A High Temperature X-ray Goniometer, *Can. J. Technol.*, **33**:117–121 (1955).

Johnson, J. R., G. D. White: Note on a High-temperature Attachment for an X-ray Spectrometer, *J. Am. Ceram. Soc.*, **39**:227–228 (1956).

Rowland, R. A., E. J. Weiss, and D. R. Lewis: Apparatus for the Oscillating-Heating Method of X-ray Powder Diffraction, *J. Am. Ceram. Soc.*, **42**:133–138 (1959).

Weiss, E. J., and R. A. Rowland: Oscillating-Heating X-ray Diffractometer Studies of Clay Mineral Dehydroxylation, *Am. Mineralogist*, **41**:117–126 (1956).

Wood, E. A.: Heated Sample Holder for X-ray Diffractometer Work, *Rev. Sci. Instr.*, **27**:60 (1956).

Chapter 14

HIGH-TEMPERATURE CAMERA TECHNIQUES

F. V. Schossberger

IIT Research Institute

1. INTRODUCTION

Before high-temperature x-ray cameras were developed, conditions at high temperatures had to be deduced from quenching experiments or from physical properties such as conductivity and expansion. Such deductions gave no direct information about structural changes and were based on the often unjustified assumption that the high-temperature condition is maintained after the system is quenched.

The high-temperature x-ray diffraction technique is used to investigate structural changes, expansion coefficients of crystals, chemical reactions of solids, and structure of molten substances. The technique was first used to study thermal expansion and phase changes of metal wires. An electric current was passed through the wires, and the diffracted x-rays were recorded on a photographic film. Two different types of apparatus have been developed: the high-temperature powder camera and the high-temperature diffractometer attachment. The latter type of apparatus is discussed in Chap. 13.

The high-temperature powder camera is in principle a Debye-Scherrer camera equipped with a heating device for the sample. The technique requires several hours of exposure, evacuation of the camera or protection of the sample by an inert atmosphere, and shielding to protect the film. Several review articles are available on the subject.[1–3a]

At the present time the x-ray diffractometer is favored over the powder camera because of the ease with which x-ray intensities are recorded by the diffractometer. The high-temperature counter diffractometer method permits transformations to be followed within minutes in contrast to the substantial length of photographic exposure of high-temperature powder diagrams. Early constructors of high-temperature diffractometer equipment expected an additional advantage, namely, a simpler temperature-control system than in powder cameras. But experience has shown that maintaining constant and uniform temperature to $\pm 2°$ C over a 2- by 1-cm area in an x-ray diffractometer is as difficult as controlling the temperature gradient in a high-temperature powder camera with hemispherical furnaces. Of course, specimen rotation is not necessary in diffractometer units, but the difficulties in keeping a diffractometer specimen from warping and in keeping the furnace and specimen from misalignment at high temperatures reduce many of the attractive features. An additional limitation of the diffractometer method is that the pattern to be examined at high temperature must be known, so that a limited range of diffraction angles can be studied.

The x-ray powder photograph has an advantage over the diffractometer unit in its ability to detect weak lines. Faint diffraction lines are easier to detect on photographic films than on diffractometer tracings made at the usual speed. Detection of weak lines by the counter method requires a slower scanning rate at the region of the weakest intensity, and this cancels out one of the prime advantages of the diffractometer method—speed.

In practice it is difficult to satisfy all requirements in one camera. A truly universal camera would have to meet these conflicting requirements: heat a small rotating sample to fairly high temperatures, measure this temperature accurately at the point where the primary x-ray beam hits the sample, maintain the temperature constancy for hours, and keep a photographic film at room temperature when it is only 2 to 3 in.

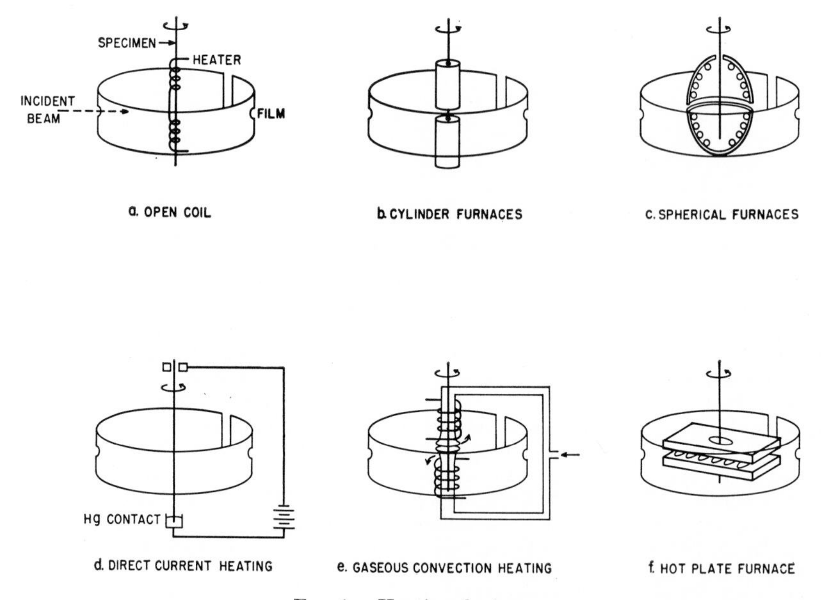

Fig. 1. Heating devices.

away from the furnace. Most cameras were constructed to investigate specific problems, for example, expansion coefficients of metal wires or high-temperature reactions of silicates.

Precision lattice-constant measurements require the same treatment as that developed for room-temperature cameras (see Chaps. 8 and 10).

Figure 1 shows a variety of heating devices for powder cameras. The heating devices developed for Debye-Scherrer cameras range from thermostats heated by liquids or electric bulbs,[4,5] for precision measurements of the lattice constant, to elaborate temperature-controlled resistance furnaces (Unicam camera) with temperatures to 1400° C. If larger temperature gradients can be tolerated and higher temperatures are not required, almost any existing powder camera can be equipped with a simple heating element (Fig. 1*a*). Most high-temperature cameras use external furnaces for heating (Fig. 1*b*, *c*, and *e*). A gap between the two parts of the furnace ensures free passage of the incident and the reflected x-rays. However, the gap is also the cause of a prime difficulty: radiant-heat losses through it cause temperature changes along the sample.

The heater should meet the following requirements: (1) It should maintain uniform temperature over the volume of the specimen exposed to the primary beam. (2) It should maintain a constant temperature of 1000° C ± 2° C for over 5 hr. This constancy cannot be maintained without some form of automatic temperature control. If the furnace is of the wirewound type, ready replacement for burned-out heating elements is an essential feature of design.

Figure 1*b* shows heating by two cylindrical furnaces. The gap between the furnaces should be as small as possible without causing interference with the primary beam. A compromise must be made between minimum heat loss, minimum temperature gradient, minimum exposure time, and suitable length of diffraction lines on the film. By using a 1-mm pinhole system for the primary x-ray beam, the gap between the furnace can be narrowed to about 3 mm. High-melting-point wires, such as platinum or Kanthal A, are used as furnace elements. Cylindrical furnaces of this type can reach temperatures of 1000 to 1100° C at the specimen.

In order to concentrate the heat at the center point of the camera, where the specimen is mounted, opposing hemispheres have been recommended (Fig. 1*c*). If the heating element is wired inside the hemisphere, the furnace temperature is higher. If it is mounted on the outer periphery of the ceramic hemispheres, heat is lost but the temperature distribution in the space between the hemispheres is more uniform. To minimize vaporization, insulated wires on metallic hemispheres are used to support the heating element. Freely suspended wires are seldom used except in the simplest setup (Fig. 1*a*). The metallic backing of the wire can be made as a platinum, molybdenum, or tantalum shell which is cemented to the wire with alumina or zirconia. The cement acts as an insulator. Tungsten, molybdenum, or tantalum heating elements and backing hemispheres allow temperatures up to 1600° C on the specimen but require a protective atmosphere or very high vacuum. The furnace halves are usually run in parallel to adjust the thermal symmetry of the heater and to permit exchange of burned-out heating elements. By using two thermocouples to measure the temperatures of the two furnaces, it is easy to control and adjust their temperatures.

Another way of heating is by an internal current through the specimen or through a metallic wire supporting the specimen (Fig. 1*d*). In a variation of this principle a 0.2-mm platinum wire was used as a support and heating element for the powdered sample. This method has the advantage that the temperature of the specimen can be determined directly from line-shift measurements of the platinum-wire support. Displacement of the platinum lines due to expansion of the lattice is recorded together with the lines of the sample. The temperature of the sample can be calculated by using the expansion coefficient of the platinum support.[6] The advantage of determining expansion coefficients by x-ray diffraction is that the actual coefficients of expansion in the direction of the crystal axes are obtained, not the average coefficient. The average coefficient is derived by conventional dilatometer methods from random polycrystalline agglomerates.

Direct internal-current heating of metallic specimens has been found to be unreliable. Temperature control and measurement are less reliable and accurate than when external-radiation heating elements are used.

Heating by gas convection, shown in Fig. 1*e*, is advantageous because the temperature of the specimen can be changed quickly by varying the flow rate. The temperature gradient in the gap is uniform, but absolute constancy of temperature poses problems with flowing gas systems.

It is important to remember that in all these methods the sample temperature is less than that of the supporting material. Although the temperature of the wire support can be measured directly with a thermocouple or optical pyrometer, the temperature-measuring device has to be calibrated in terms of the actual specimen temperature.

2. REQUIREMENTS FOR A VERSATILE HIGH-TEMPERATURE CAMERA

The requirements for a versatile "ideal" high-temperature camera were substantially laid down by the User Specification on Standard Powder Cameras.[7] The important specifications are as follows:

1. The slit system should be in good contact with the water-cooled vacuum chamber and should preferably not penetrate into the furnace unit. The slit material should be a heat-resistant metal.

2. The film holder should be outside the vacuum chamber.

3. The closed cassette should be light-tight, but on the side facing the specimen it should permit unobstructed entrance of x-rays. For the preparation of these windows, a double layer of carbon paper or a polyethylene film with carbon-black filler is suitable material which gives no visible texture on the photographic film.

4. A very close approach or contact should be provided between the thermocouple and the irradiated portion of the specimen.

5. Provision should be made for full rotation and easy centering of the specimen mounted from above. The motor for this rotation should form an integral part of the camera but should be outside the vacuum chamber. The motor should be nonsynchronous or the rotation slow enough to avoid interference with x-ray tube a-c pulses. The rotational movements can be transmitted through the chamber wall by using magnetic or direct drive and an O-ring seal.

6. The specimen should be at least 3 mm high.

7. The furnace should attain a temperature of at least 1200° C.

8. A constant temperature of $\pm 2°$ C at maximum temperature is required for over 5 hr. This can be achieved only with some form of automatic control and constant circulation of water.

9. The volume of the heat enclosure should be at least 2.5 cc. A spherical shape is recommended, namely, two opposing hemispheres provided with openings for the specimen and a thermocouple. The gap through which the primary and diffracted x-ray beams pass should be as small as possible without fouling the primary beam.

10. Wire or tape heating elements of platinum, rhodium, tungsten, or tantalum are recommended. To minimize vaporization and to provide electrical insulation the wires should be covered with a thin coating of refractory cement such as aluminum oxide or zinc oxide. The wire should have a firm metallic backing, e.g., a platinum, molybdenum, tungsten, or rhodium (for vacuum only) shell to which the wire is cemented.

11. Heat losses toward the outside should be minimized by means of rhodium-plated hemispherical reflectors.

12. The temperature-measuring instrument should measure the specimen temperature directly.

13. Measurement of temperature can depend on one or two thermocouples. These should be as thin as can be reconciled with mechanical strength—0.2 mm in diameter. The two thermocouples are used to measure the specimen and to control the furnace.

14. The weld of a single thermocouple should be capable of being moved momentarily, through a sliding seal, to a position close to the specimen.

15. Outside automatic temperature control should be provided.

16. The gas-evolution rate in the vacuum chamber should cause a pressure rise of not more than 1 micron/min for a volume of approximately 1 liter. The pumping manifold should allow a speed of at least 2 liters/sec at the camera. An ultimate pressure of at least 0.01 micron should be attainable.

17. The suggested diameters of the vacuum chamber are 14 cm in internal diameter, 7 cm in internal height, and 0.3 to 0.6 cm in thickness if wrought metals are used. Castings are unsuitable because absence of porosity is a vital condition. The material should be brass, bronze, or stainless steel.

18. An O-ring seal is recommended at places where demounting is required.

19. The x-ray diffraction slot should be covered by a readily replaceable low-absorbing window consisting of beryllium or aluminum foil 0.001 to 0.002 in. thick. If the highest vacuums are not required, cellophane can be used. The window should be attached to the flanges of the vacuum chamber by wax, shellac, or synthetic resin (see discussion of Vacuum Seal for Thin Beryllium Windows in Sec. 3).

20. The amount of potential gas-absorbing and gas-evolving materials (such as refractories or organic matter) inside the vacuum chamber should be reduced to the absolute minimum.

3. HIGH-TEMPERATURE X-RAY POWDER CAMERAS

Various furnaces and cameras have been described in the literature. The construction of each is summarized below. This compilation is not complete but does cover the more elaborate developments in the field.

High-temperature Adapter.[8] This evacuable adapter can be attached to standard room-temperature cameras. The adapter consists of two parts, the outer envelope and the heater-specimen assembly. The outer envelope (Fig. 2), which surrounds the heater-specimen space, permitting it to be evacuated and protecting the film from radiative heat, consists of a beryllium cylinder 30 mm long, 10 mm in internal diameter, and 1 mm in wall thickness. The tapered ends of the cylinder are sealed, with Glyptal or silicone cement, to two water-cooled copper jackets. The ends of the cooling jackets are ground to form conical joints, so that each end can be connected to either the vacuum system or the heater-specimen assembly. For passage of the direct beam 6- by 1-mm slits are cut in the beryllium cylinder. Cellophane windows cemented with Glyptal over the slits are satisfactory for specimen temperatures up to 900° C and pressures around 10^{-4} mm Hg; no deterioration is observed after several hundred hours of service.

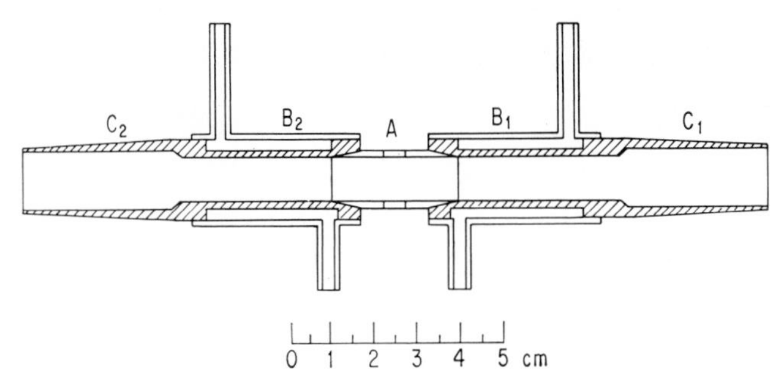

FIG. 2. Outer envelope of adapter.[8] (*a*) Beryllium cylinder. (*b*) Cooling jackets. (*c*) Conical joints.

The specimen-heater assembly is shown in Fig. 3. Two 1-mm nickel rods serve as supports and leads for the current. The leads pass through a closed stainless-steel tube, which forms the shaft for the rocking movement of the specimen, and are insulated by quartz tubing. For a more permanent assembly, metal-to-glass seals are recommended rather than silicone cement.

For heating capillary specimens the heater consists of a closely wound spiral of 4- to 5-mil tungsten or platinum wire, with a gap for passage of the direct beam. The spiral is 0.5 mm in internal diameter and 15 mm long, and the gap is 1 mm wide. For better thermal contact the spiral is covered with an Alundum coating. The heating current is provided by a small transformer, with 10- and 1-ohm variable resistances in secondary circuit for coarse and fine adjustment, respectively. The power consumption of the heater is approximately 10 watts at 900 to 1000° C.

The use of line shifts in the diffraction pattern is recommended as the most dependable means of measuring temperature. With the spiral heater this can be done by adding to the specimen an internal standard such as silver or platinum with a known expansion coefficient. The room-temperature and high-temperature patterns are photographed side by side on the same film. By calculating the line shift of the 422 platinum line and plotting it against temperature, the temperature of the specimen can be read directly. If the line shifts can be measured with an accuracy of ± 0.025 mm, an error of $\pm 5°$ C can be estimated in the temperature determination (when the platinum line 422 and copper $K\alpha$ radiation are used).

Resistance-heated Cameras. *Camera by Johnson.*[9] A top cover (Fig. 4) is mounted to the base of the camera with an O-ring seal, and the film holder slides over the top cover. Cooling coils are used both in the base and in the top cover. The x-rays are diffracted through a beryllium window. Approximately 8° 2θ are cut out on both the entering and emerging sides, and about 20° 2θ is lost in the shadows of the electric and water leads at the 270° position. There is a complete unobstructed picture from 8 to 172°. The cover is made of aluminum, which is sealed tightly to beryllium by using an aluminum–11.6 per cent silicon alloy with an aluminum brazing flux. Copper is used for the cooling coils and electric leads; tantalum for the heaters, radiation shield, and specimen mount; and stainless steel for the collimator and beam stop.

The heaters are two 0.005-in. tantalum strips bent into a shape resembling an old-fashioned keyholder. Their ends fit snugly into slots in two parallel vertical tantalum power leads. The heaters thus protrude in cantilever fashion and encircle the specimen. They are separated by a 1/16-in. space. Most of the heat radiated outward

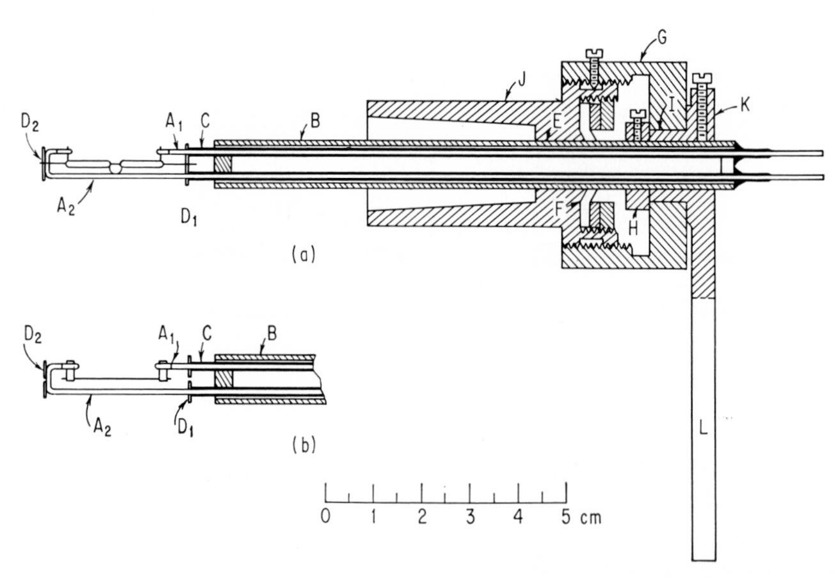

FIG. 3. Heater-specimen assembly.[8] (A) Nickel heater leads. (B) Heater shaft. (C) Quartz tubings. (D) Centering disks. (E) Bearing surface. (F) Seal. (G) Threaded cap for lateral adjustment. (H) Positioning ring. (I) Bearing surface. (J) Mantle of conical joint. (K) Flange with arm L.

is shielded by a tantalum shield, which is a divided cylinder having a 1/4-in. slot cut through 350° of its circumference. The specimen is turned by a magnet with a 3.6-rpm clock motor mounted in the base.

The power source for the heaters consists of three 5-volt 60-amp transformers in parallel fed by a variable transformer, which in turn is fed by a 2-kw electronic voltage regulator. A maximum power of about 900 watts is used at the highest temperature. Constant temperature is maintained within the reading limits of an optical pyrometer (±5° C) by supplying constant power. To obtain the true temperature, each material studied is made into a rod slightly larger in diameter than the corresponding specimen, and a hole is drilled along its axis to the point where the x-rays strike. A blackbody temperature can thus be read and compared with the top-surface temperature normally read on the specimen.

Camera by Austin, Richard, and Schwartz.[10] Heating is accomplished by two resistance-heated 12-mil tantalum strips (Fig. 5). The strips are 3/8 in. wide and are bent to form a cylinder 1/4 in. in diameter with a 1/32-in. gap between the leads. These loops are self-supported in the lead clamps; no ceramic support or insulation is used. A $\frac{1}{16}$-in. gap between the lower and upper heaters permits entry and exit of the x-ray beam.

Radiation baffles are provided to conserve heat. These consist of two concentric tantalum cylinders supported on the camera by a tripod of $\frac{1}{16}$-in. tantalum wire. The camera contains an internal liquid-nitrogen trap, water-cooled vapor baffles, and a shutter that is movable from the exterior through a bellows seal. The shutter is used to check specimen alignment and to check temperature control by an optical

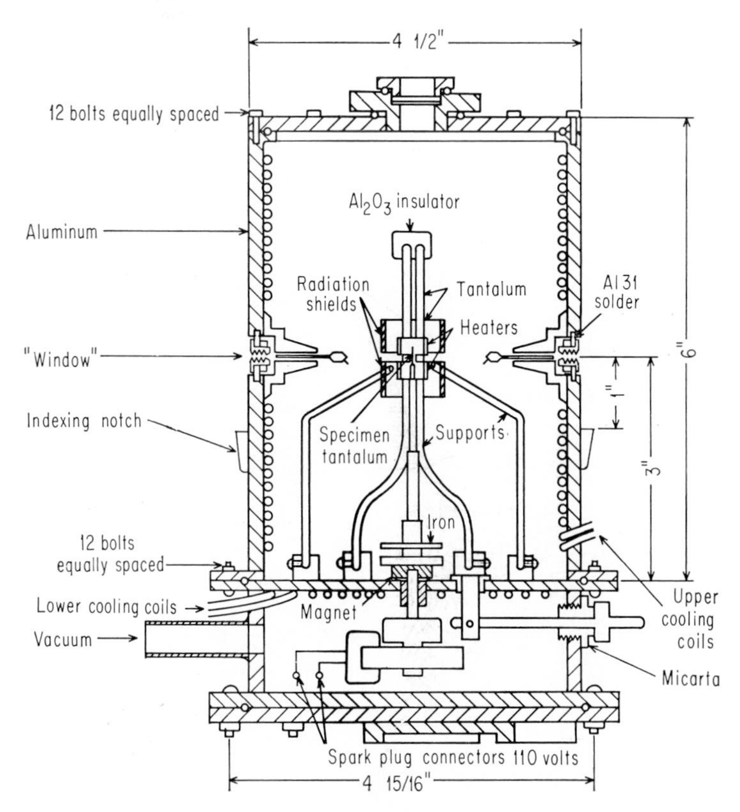

FIG. 4. Johnson's high-temperature camera for 2200° C.[9]

pyrometer for short periods. Water cooling is provided for the power leads, the camera body, the specimen holder, and its bushing.

The film is positioned by the Straumanis method (see Chap. 8). The x-ray beam collimator is machined from tantalum and has a 20-mil defining aperture. The motor rotation is transmitted through the bellows seal. By means of a cam and gear train the supporting shaft for the specimen is oscillated vertically through a $\frac{1}{4}$-in. translation during rotation.

In order to reduce errors (due to eccentricity) in precision measurements of the lattice, it is necessary to align the film cassette so that its inner and upper cylindrical surface has a sliding fit with the outer cylindrical surface of the specimen holder. The tolerance specification of these surfaces is ± 0.0025 in. for a 4-in. diameter.

Induction-heated Camera.[11] The cylindrical sides of the camera (Fig. 6) are machined from a solid piece of brass with channels provided for water cooling. The primary beam passes through a collimator which is made vacuum-tight by means of a beryllium disk seated on a lead washer. The beam is diffracted through a 10-mil beryllium window. A central shaft through the bottom of the camera supports and rotates the specimen and the bottom half of the furnace. The shaft has O-ring seals. A friction-table assembly located on top of the shaft is moved by a vacuum-sealed rod projecting outside the camera in order to align the sample. The top and bottom sections of the furnace are made of tantalum tubing ¼ in. in outside diameter and approximately ¾ in. long. The furnace and the shaft are separated by a zinc oxide spacer in order to reduce conducted heat losses.

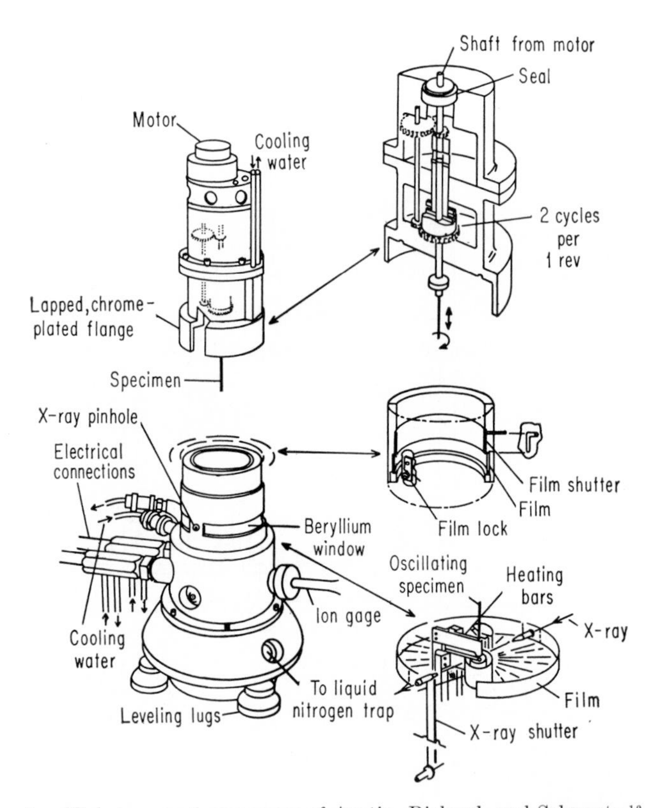

Fig. 5 High-temperature camera of Austin, Richard, and Schwartz.[10]

The work coil surrounding the tantalum heater is formed from $\frac{3}{16}$-in.-diameter copper tubing. A $\frac{1}{16}$-in. spacing is used between the two horizontal turns around each furnace element. A ⅛-in. gap is located between the top and bottom sections of the work coil. A three-phase high-frequency induction heater is used for supplying controlled stepless power to the work coil. The unit operates at 50 kc and has an approximate output of 5 kw. A small tantalum slug is pressed into the lower section of the furnace. A hole drilled in its center provides a means of supporting the specimen, which may be in the form of a wire, a compact, or a capillary. Temperatures above 1500° C can be attained on the specimen.

The cassette consists of a lightweight ring which fits snugly around the camera. The film is loaded by the Straumanis method. By using a large opening at the base of the camera, a vacuum of 1×10^{-5} mm Hg is easily obtained.

The camera possesses two thermocouples. One, of Chromel-Alumel, is embedded in a small Nichrome slug located between the work-coil leads near the bottom section of the camera and is heated by a small amount of radio-frequency power intended primarily for the furnace. Chromel-Alumel is used because the change in emf per degree is relatively high. It was found that the temperature of the furnace is approximately four times that of the Nichrome slug. The mass ratio of the thermocouple to furnace is low. Hence the thermocouple time constant is not a limiting factor in controlling the furnace temperature. The other thermocouple is located in the top

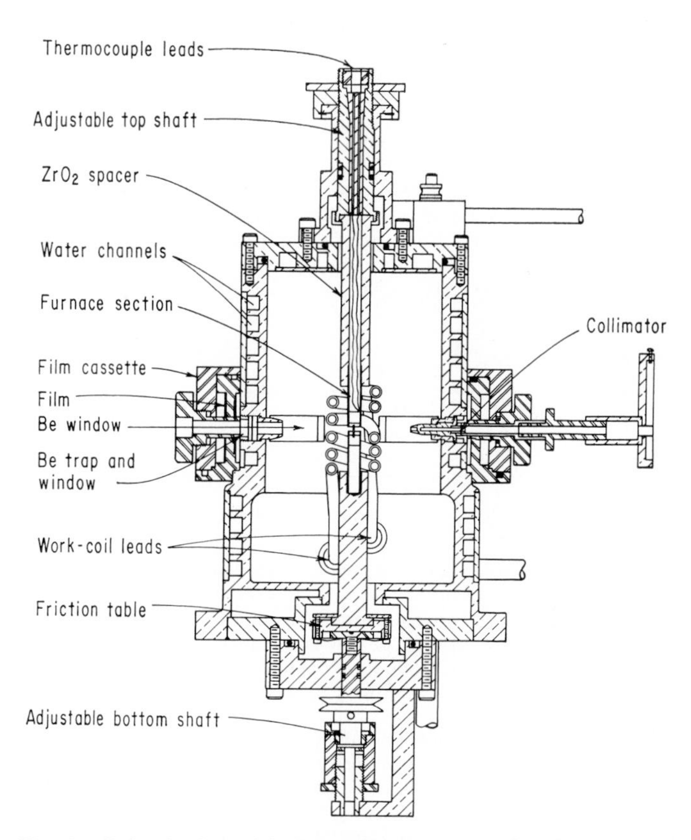

Fig. 6. Induction-heated high-temperature x-ray diffraction camera.[11]

section of the furnace and can also be used for temperature control. The furnace temperature, however, is limited to the operating range of this thermocouple.

The emf output of the controlling thermocouple is electronically compared with a constant d-c reference voltage (Fig. 7), which can be changed manually by means of a potentiometer. If there is a difference between the thermocouple voltage and the reference voltage, this difference is amplified by a Brown high-gain d-c chopper amplifier and an additional d-c amplifier. The amplified voltage error appears as a bias on the grids of the induction-heater thyratrons, which supply the direct current to the radio-frequency heater. The primary circuits of the Variacs in the induction heater are manually adjusted to maintain sufficient radio-frequency power to obtain a balance between the thermocouple voltage and the reference voltage, as indicated by a null galvanometer. With this method of control, temperatures in the furnace are kept constant to ±0.2 per cent. Since temperature measurements are not absolute, the actual temperature of the specimen must be determined by calibration with the optical pyrometer and materials of known melting points.

High-vacuum Glass Camera. If a temperature of 1000° C and a vacuum of 10^{-6} mm Hg must be maintained, as is required for the investigation of titanium and zirconium alloys, ease of outgassing the specimen and interior of the camera becomes a major problem. The special features of the design shown in Fig. 8 are the construction of the camera in glass and the location of the radiant heater outside the camera.[12] The clean smooth interior glass walls simplify outgassing problems, and the outside location eliminates the contamination which occurs in a conventional furnace assembly. The camera has been used for studying the β-to-α phase transformation in titanium-chromium and titanium-zirconium alloys.

The camera consists of a Pyrex envelope joined directly to a liquid-air trap which is attached to the pumping system. Two circular windows allow passage of incident and diffracted x-ray beams. The windows are made of aluminum-silicon alloy,[13] are 0.0015 in. thick, and are permanently bonded by borosilicate cement.[14] Vacuums of 10^{-7} mm Hg can be obtained after outgassing at about 400° C for several hours. Zirconium getters can be operated to remove oxygen and hydrogen. The specimen is rotated about a vertical axis by means of an external magnet.

One method of heating consists of focusing an intense beam of light onto the specimen.[15] The source is a 1,000 watt projection bulb which is situated at one focus of a

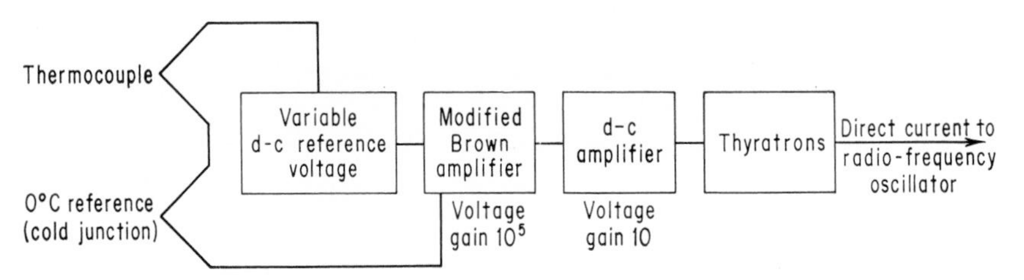

FIG. 7. Control servo for induction-heated high-temperature x-ray camera.[11]

semiellipsoidal aluminum reflector with minor and major axes of 8 and 13 in., respectively. Temperatures up to 1000° C can be achieved. The specimen is at the second focus. If the specimen is to be rotated more than a few degrees on either side of this position, a second reflector, suitably placed, is required to minimize thermal fluctuation.

A second method of heating consists of bombarding the specimen with electrons emitted from a heated filament. Temperatures higher than 1000° C are obtained. The filament consists of a few turns of tungsten wire situated some 3 cm from the specimen. With a filament temperature of 2000° C and a voltage difference of 1,000 volts, a specimen of tantalum attained temperatures of 1500° C.

Temperature is measured by a thermocouple. A 0.010-in. platinum–platinum–13 per cent rhodium thermocouple is spot-welded to a small slug of the specimen. The leads are taken out of the camera through a glass-to-metal seal.

Pressurized High-temperature Camera.[16] The use of x-ray methods for direct determination of the structure of γ and δ manganese in the range of 1100 to 1245° C involves several experimental difficulties. The metal is too reactive to be enclosed in a silica capillary tube and too volatile to be photographed in vacuum. The problem has been solved by the construction of a high-temperature camera designed to study specimens under pressures of several atmospheres of purified hydrogen. The camera withstands a pressure of 20 atm and operates up to 1500° C at pressures of 3 or 4 atm. Pressures of about 2 atm are sufficient to reduce volatilization of manganese specimens to a reasonably small rate.

A sectional view of the camera is shown in Fig. 9. Each hemispherical furnace has a resistance of 7.5 ohms and consists of a noninductively wound element embedded in an alumina shell 0.1 in. thick. The element is made from 0.008-in.-diameter tungsten molybdenum wire formed into a 0.04-in.-diameter coil. The furnaces are separated by a 5-mm gap and are mounted in water-cooled hollow brass holders which are nickel-plated on the furnace side. Temperatures are measured by symmetrical ring thermocouples, mounted at the mouth of the furnaces (Fig. 9).

The specimen is mounted on an alumina tube attached to the end of the motor shaft by a short length of platinum wire. The motor is free to slide in its housing so that the specimen can be introduced into the x-ray beam or withdrawn into the cold well without disturbing conditions inside the camera. The cassette is included in the pressure chamber to eliminate the need for mechanically strong windows between the

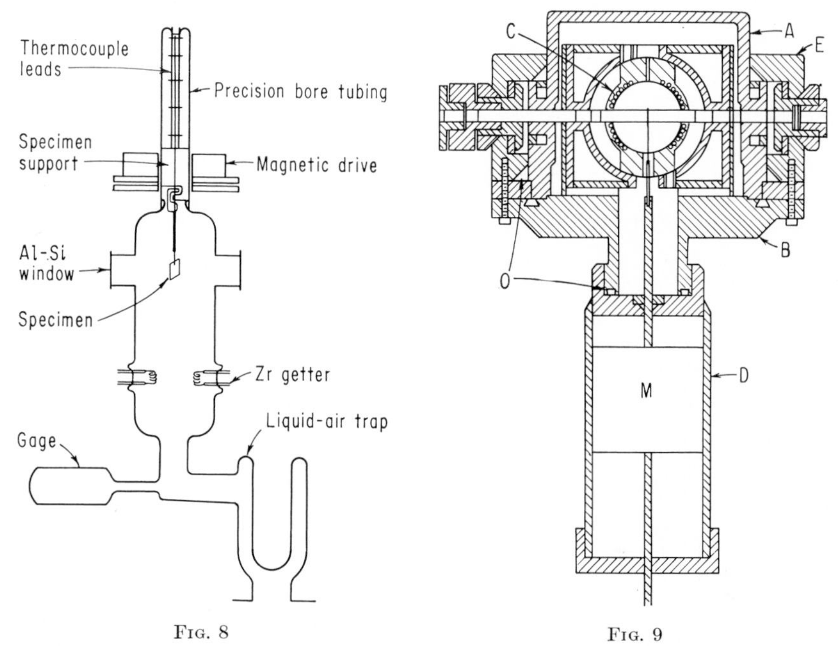

FIG. 8 FIG. 9

FIG. 8. High-vacuum high-temperature camera of Hatt, Kent, and Williams.[12]
FIG. 9. Section through a pressurized high-temperature camera. Thermocouple and power-supply leads, vacuum pumping line, hydrogen inlet tube, and water connections are not shown in this section.[16] (A) Water-cooled body. (B) Base. (C) Furnaces. (D) Specimen-holder assembly. (E) Cassette. (M) Synchronous motor. (O) O rings.

specimen and the film. The x-ray beam enters through a 0.01-in.-thick beryllium window. The exit window is made of $\frac{1}{16}$-in. Perspex and permits visual observation of the interior of the camera when hot. The film is protected from radiation by 0.005-in. aluminum foil. The diameter of the cassette is 12 cm.

Photographs obtained show that γ manganese has a face-centered cubic structure and δ manganese a body-centered cubic structure. When very slight traces of oxygen were introduced into the specimens, a steep rise of the $\gamma \rightleftharpoons \delta$ transition temperature occurred, so that only γ-phase photographs were obtained. The lattice spacing vs. temperature curves of γ and δ manganese are shown in Figs. 10 and 11. The accuracy of lattice-spacing measurements is probably 0.0005 Å and that of temperature measurements $\pm 3°$ C.

Heating of the Specimen with Thermocouple Wires.[17] The essential feature of this setup is the direct mounting of the specimen at the tip of a small thermocouple which registers its own temperature (Fig. 12). The specimen is heated by passing a current through the thermocouple. A synchronous switch that supplies voltage also isolates the thermoelectric current from the heating current by allowing unidirectional pulses of heating current to flow only during alternate half cycles. In the intervening half cycles the thermocouple is connected to the temperature-measurement circuit.

The thermocouple is 0.2 mm in diameter and is made from an alloy composed of 5 per cent rhodium-platinum and 70 per cent rhodium-platinum. This alloy is used because it gives almost linear output of μv/° C between 1300 and 1800° C. The

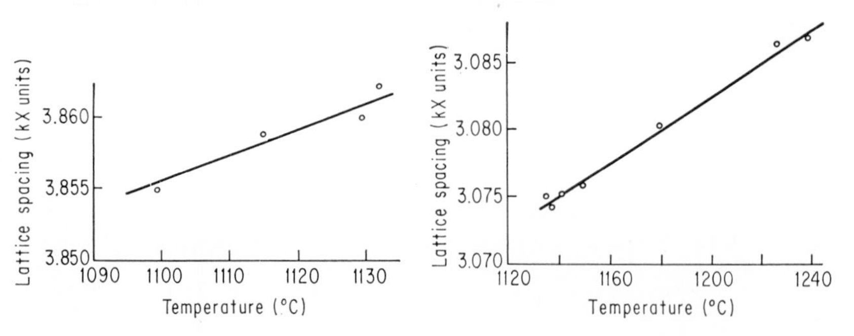

FIG. 10. Curve of lattice spacing vs. temperature for γ manganese (face-centered cubic).[16]

FIG. 11. Curve of lattice spacing vs. temperature of δ manganese (body-centered cubic).[16]

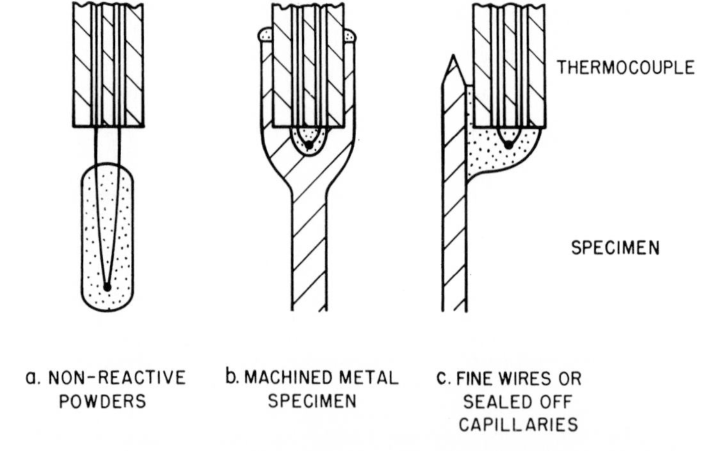

FIG. 12. Specimen supported by thermocouples.[17]

maximum working temperature is 1700° C. The welded junction is maintained at a constant thickness of 0.2 mm by a special, guillotine-type knife. Uniform 0.2-mm spacing between the wires of the junction is achieved by a slip gauge; the specimen is embedded between the wires. The presence of the wires on either side of the specimen partially screens the diffracted lines by absorption.

Oxygen-free nitrogen is dried by passage through magnesium perchlorate and serves as the inert atmosphere. The power supply uses a voltage stabilizer at 3.2 amp and 1.1 volts. Temperature fluctuation is reduced to ±12° C in 5 hr at 1800° C. The technique is not especially suitable for precision measurements of the lattice constant because of the shape of the specimen and the screening effect of the heating wires.

Graphite-tube Heater. The heater shown in Fig. 13 has been used to investigate graphite at high temperatures.[18] The diffraction pattern of Ceylon graphite at 1800° C was recorded, and the shift of the 0004 line found to be the largest. This shift corresponds to the large expansion in the direction normal to the basal plane of graphite.

Ceylon graphite	
c dimension	*a dimension*
28.09×10^{-6}	0.95×10^{-6}
1000–1800° C	1000–1800° C

The furnace consists of a carbon tube 6 cm in length, 6 mm in diameter, and 3 mm in bore. Siemens arc carbon is used; it is homogeneous and has little ash content. Both ends of the carbon tube are electroplated to ensure good electrical contact. The collimated incident x-rays enter from one end of the tube and pass through it without striking the inner surface. The specimen, an 0.5-mm-diameter rod, is inserted vertically in the middle of the tube through a drilled hole which provides a sliding fit. The x-rays scattered from the specimen pass through a horizontal slot 4 mm in breadth. A cylinder of nickel plate (not shown in the figure) wound on a fused silica tube 2 cm

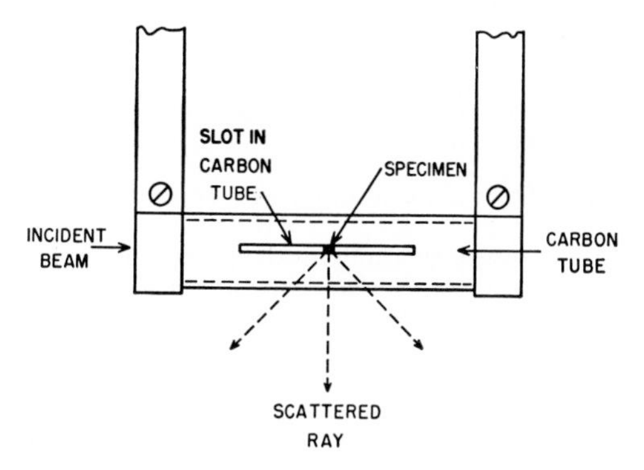

FIG. 13. Carbon-tube heater.[18]

in diameter is attached around the carbon tube for use as a radiation shield, but it is not needed at temperatures up to 1300° C. The power consumption of the furnace is 450 watts at 1800° C. The heating current is supplied by a 2.5-kw 100-volt stabilizer.

Small-radius High-temperature Camera.[19] High-temperature x-ray diffraction of alloys containing alkali metals requires short exposure times because the alkali metal reacts strongly with the glass or quartz capillary. The camera constructed for this purpose has a film radius of about 3 cm and requires exposure times of 40 to 70 min for lithium-cadmium at 500° C. The furnace (Fig. 14) consists of an inner and outer part. The inner part contains a 240-watt (500° C) heating element of Megapyr wire.

To avoid an abrupt temperature gradient in the gap, a second additional heating coil is attached to the surface of the lower furnace. The temperature is maintained at ±1° C by keeping the current constant to ±0.002 amp. However, incorrect centering as well as inconstancy of the water flow rate, the voltage, and the heat conductivity of the sample can raise the total error to ±4° C. The horizontal temperature distribution obtained in the gap is shown in Fig. 15.

Vacuum Seal for Thin Beryllium Windows.[20] Window openings ⅜ in. wide are machined in the cylindrical brass body, as shown in Fig. 16, and cuts are milled to form a shoulder $\frac{5}{16}$ in. wide completely around each window. Small grooves $\frac{3}{32}$ in. wide and $\frac{5}{64}$ in. deep with a small radius at each corner are machined on the shoulder.

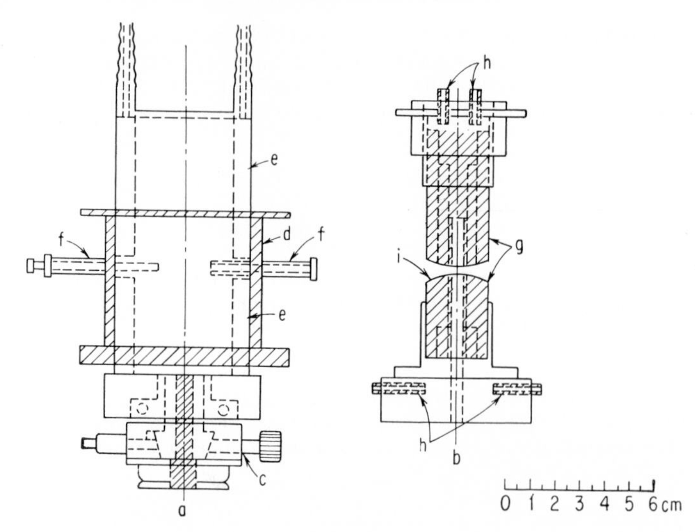

FIG. 14. Small-radius high-temperature camera.[19] (*a*) Camera. (*b*) Furnace assembly. (*c*) Centering of specimen. (*d*) Film carrier for five exposures. (*e*) Water cooling. (*f*) Pinholes. (*g*) Furnaces. (*h*) Power leads. (*i*) Additional heating element.

A continuous O ring is fitted to each groove by cementing the ends together on a tapered joint.

On each window a stainless-steel clamp in the form of a curved "picture frame" ⅛ in. thick holds the beryllium foil against the O ring. Holes are drilled ⅜ in. apart in the top and bottom edges of the frame. Matching holes are drilled and tapped for No. 2-56 screws in the main brass body. Since beryllium is hard and brittle, it is desirable to preform the strip.

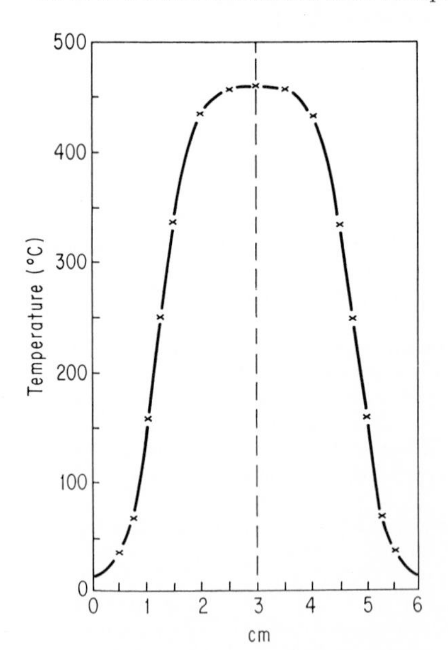

FIG. 15. Horizontal temperature distribution in the gap between pinhole and beam stop of the small-radius high-temperature camera.[19]

High-temperature Camera for Back-reflection Measurements.[21,22] This camera contains a water-cooled plat-

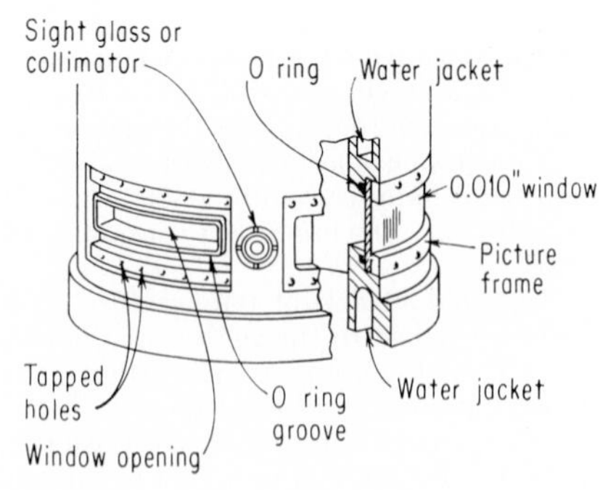

FIG. 16. O-ring seals for beryllium windows.[20]

inum-wound furnace (Fig. 17).[23,24] The x-ray beam impinges upon the sample at 90°, and back reflection from the specimen passes through a horizontal 0.005-in.-thick beryllium window 0.25 in. high and covering an angle of 45°. A curved back-reflection camera is used to avoid the lateral displacement of lines which results when an x-ray beam strikes a two-coated film in a flat camera. The radius of the curved back-reflection camera is precisely determined by measuring the known d values of sodium chloride.

Fiducial marks placed on the film before exposure are used to correct for film-shrinkage errors. The specimen is powdered material of −200 to +325 mesh. It is packed in the platinum holder.

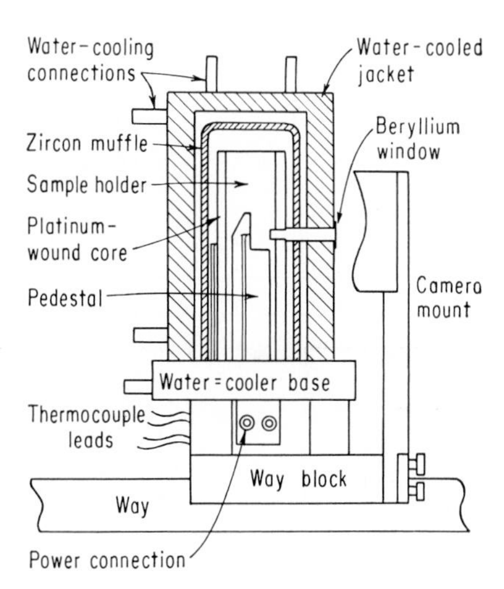

Fig. 17. Sectional view of furnace-camera assembly for high-temperature back-reflection measurements (3/8 in. = 1 in.).[23,24]

For cubic material the thermal expansion coefficient is derived by dividing $\Delta d/d$ by the difference in temperatures. For tetragonal, hexagonal, and rhombic crystals, the relationships are more complex (cf. Chap. 4).

For tetragonal:
$$\frac{\Delta d}{d} = \frac{1}{1 + (h'c')^2}\left[\frac{\Delta a}{a}(h'c')^2 + \frac{\Delta c}{c}\right]$$

where $c' = c/a$
$h'^2 = (h^2 + k^2/l^2)$

For hexagonal:
$$\frac{\Delta d}{d} = \frac{1}{1 + (h'c)^2}\left[\frac{\Delta a}{a}(h'c')^2 + \frac{\Delta c}{c}\right]$$

where $c' = c/a$
$h'^2 = \frac{4}{3}(h^2 + hk + k^2)/l^2$

For rhombic:
$$\frac{\Delta d}{d} = \frac{1}{h^2/a^2 + k^2/b^2 + l^2/c^2}\left(\frac{h^2}{a^2}\frac{\Delta a}{a} + \frac{k^2}{b^2}\frac{\Delta b}{b} + \frac{l^2}{c^2}\frac{\Delta c}{c}\right)$$

where a, b, c = unit cell dimensions
$\Delta a, \Delta b, \Delta c$ = expansions of a, b, c

By knowing $\Delta d/d$ for several indexed planes, it is possible to solve for the axial expansion.

The back-reflection patterns obtained for the (420) plane of magnesium oxide were analyzed. The results are shown in Table 1 ($\phi = 90 - \theta$) and Fig. 18. The expansion coefficient was found to be 14.45×10^{-6} in the range of 20 to 1200° C. As a representative of a hexagonal-rhombohedral system, Fig. 18 also shows the changes in Δd for the (531) plane of alumina (expansion coefficient = 9.50×10^{-6}). The following equation relating interplanar spacings with lattice dimensions can be used to

Table 1. Analysis of Back-reflection Patterns of Magnesium Oxide

Pattern No.	Temp, ° C	ϕ	cos ϕ	d_{420}	Δd	Expansion, %
1	20	18.425	0.9487	0.94087	0.00000	0.000
2	210	18.872	0.9462	0.94335	0.00248	0.264
3	405	19.270	0.9440	0.94555	0.00468	0.497
4	600	19.693	0.9415	0.94806	0.00719	0.764
5	800	20.116	0.9390	0.95058	0.00971	1.032
6	995	20.564	0.9363	0.95333	0.01246	1.324
7	1199	20.900	0.9342	0.95545	0.01458	1.550

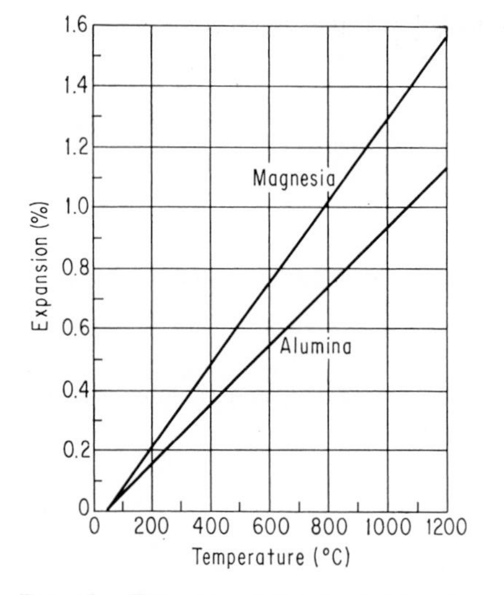

FIG. 18. Thermal expansion of magnesia and alumina.[22]

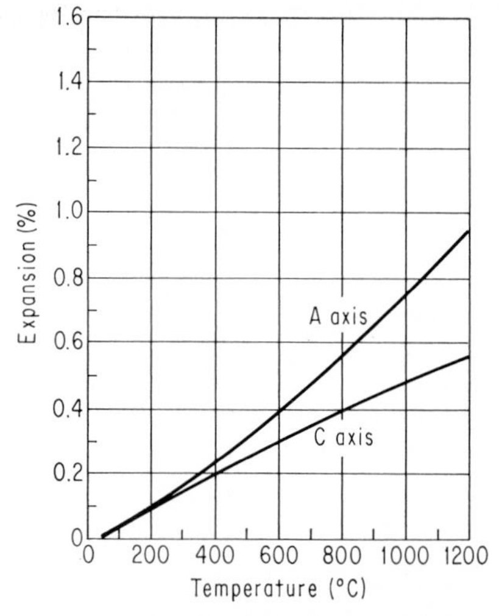

FIG. 19. Thermal expansion of zinc oxide.[22]

index the rhombohedral pattern:

$$d = \frac{a\sqrt{1 + 2\cos^3\alpha - 3\cos^2\alpha}}{\sqrt{(h^2 + k^2 + l^2)\sin 2\alpha + 2(hk + hl + kl)(\cos^2\alpha - \cos\alpha)}}$$

In Fig. 19 the thermal expansion of the a and c axes of hexagonal zinc oxide is shown. Since there are two axes, the lattices expand anisotropically and two sets of planes must be indexed to determine the expansion of the parameters. This is done by measuring $\Delta d/d$ for (105) and (123) zinc oxide. The linear expansion coefficients of zinc oxide are 8.10×10^{-6} cm/cm/°C for the a axis and 4.71×10^{-6} for the c axis.

Heater for Transmission Patterns. An elevated-temperature specimen holder for transmission x-ray photographs has been developed (Fig. 20).[25] It consists of a metal washer, the center of which is filled with the substance to be analyzed. Powders, waxes, or other materials are tamped or melted into the center, and the specimen

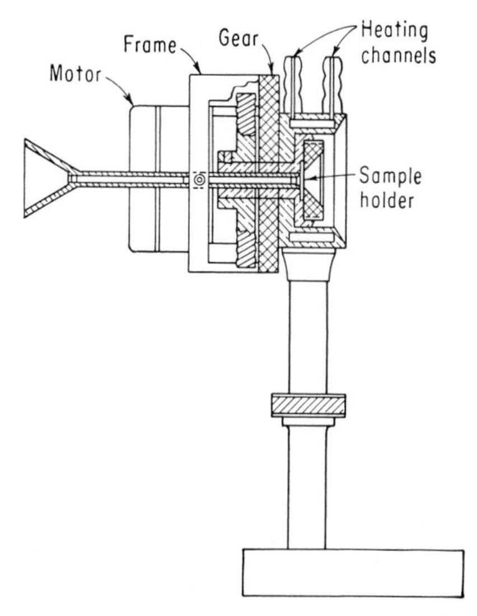

Fig. 20. Rotating specimen holder for transmission patterns at elevated temperatures.[25]

Fig. 21. Camera for transmission patterns at elevated temperatures.[25]

thickness is adjusted to conform to the thickness of the washer. The specimen thickness can be reproduced easily, so that the intensities are comparable on different patterns.

The washer is in thermal contact with a constant-temperature body, through which a heating liquid is circulated. The constant-temperature liquid is supplied by a thermostatically controlled bath and a circulating pump. The inlet and outlet for the circulating liquid are above the metal rod. To avoid temperature fluctuations of the specimen by room air, thin foil is placed over the end of the holder.

The camera is shown in Fig. 21. With metal tubings attached to the heating chamber, oil-bath temperatures can be reached at the specimen.

Continuous High-temperature X-ray Diffraction Analysis.[26,27] Continuous registration of the phase changes in a specimen with temperature has some advantages over conventional methods of taking high-temperature diagrams by separate film exposures. The continuous technique reproduces phase transition, lattice expansion, and recrystallization processes on one film. This is achieved by slowly moving the film cylinder parallel to the axis of the heated specimen and shielding all the diffracted circles except a small part of the equator of the Debye-Scherrer diagram (Fig. 22). The result is a diagram in which the powder reflections appear as more or less parallel straight lines.

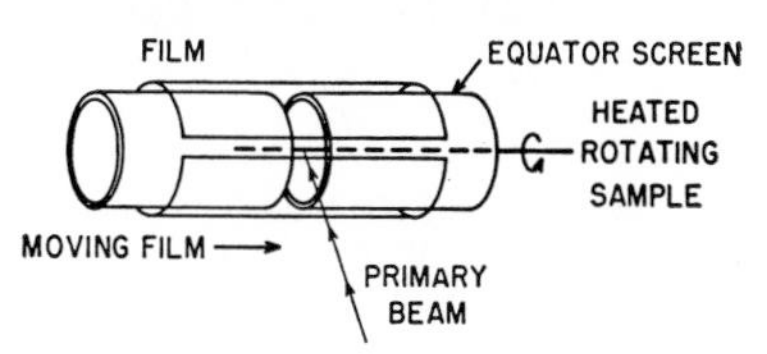

Fig. 22. Principle of continuous registration of Debye-Scherrer lines.[26,27]

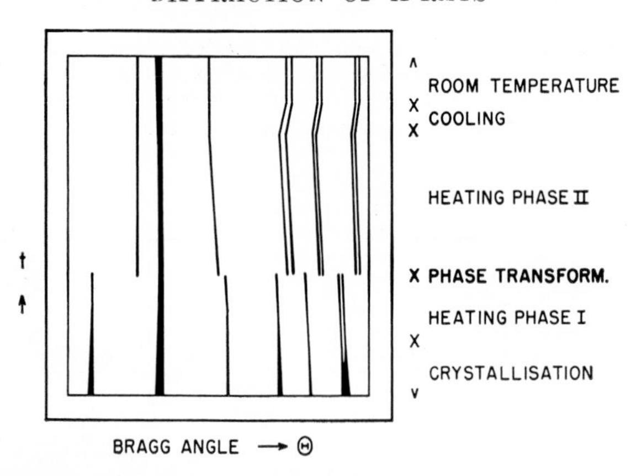

Fig. 23. Continuous registration of crystallization, lattice expansion, phase transformation, and lattice shrinking on a moving-film cylinder.[26]

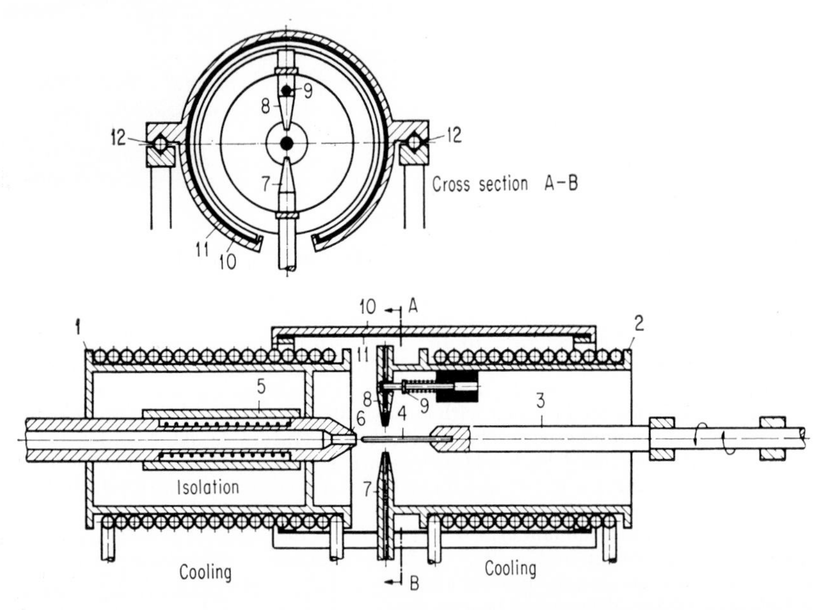

Fig. 24. Schematic drawing of a camera for continuous high-temperature x-ray diffraction.[26] (1, 2) Water-cooled cylinders. (3) Specimen support. (4) Specimen. (5) Furnace. (6) Exit of hot gases. (7) Pinhole, primary beam. (8) Beam stop. (9) Magnetic shutter. (10) Film cassette. (11) Film. (12) Cassette guide.

A schematic drawing of the observations which can be made on a single diagram is shown in Fig. 23. During the first part of the heating a recrystallization process takes place. Next lattice expansion is observable, until a phase change occurs, with only the strongest line of the starting material remaining in the diagram. Cooling to room temperature is accompanied by lattice shrinkage of the new phase.

The furnace and the film cylinder for continuous heating and recording of the diffracted lines are shown in Fig. 24. The specimen is heated by a stream of hot nitrogen. A thermocouple is placed into the specimen capillary, which oscillates around a 300°

angle. The beam stop contains a magnetic shutter which is used to make time marks on the unexposed part of the film. The film cassette is moved by a synchronous motor at a speed of 0.2 mm/min,[27] and the temperature change is 0.5°/min.

Expansion coefficients are determined by making two exposures on the same film, one with a standard substance at room temperature and one with the specimen at increasing or decreasing temperature. The displacement of the diffracted lines in the back-reflection region is determined by measuring the distance to the next available line of the room-temperature standard. The advantage of the method lies in saving the time required to obtain high-temperature recordings of x-ray diagrams. High-precision measurements by this technique probably require further development of the method.

Other applications of the method include thermal-expansion measurements on gold, gold-cadmium, and ζ-silver-zinc, and observations of phase transformation in the gold-vanadium system, of superstructure formation in gold-copper, and of segregation phenomena in copper-silver and gold-platinum alloys.

4. COMMERCIAL HIGH-TEMPERATURE POWDER CAMERAS

In addition to the Unicam camera, described below, commercial high-temperature cameras have been manufactured by the Plessey Company, Ilford, Essex, England; Central Research Laboratories, Red Wing, Minn.; Otto von der Heyde, Maynard, Mass.; Seemann Laboratorium, Freiburg im Breisgau, Germany; and Rigaku-Denki Company, Ltd., Tokyo, Japan, distributed in America by Erb and Gray, Los Angeles, Calif.

Description of the Unicam Camera.* The object of this design was to comply as nearly as possible with the User Specification on Standard Powder Cameras (Sec. 2). The camera was developed from a model built by Goldschmidt and Cunningham.[28]

The furnace consists of two opposing hemispherical platinum shells. The top half is removable for easy access to the specimen chamber. The shells are wound internally with platinum-rhodium wire supported by a thin coating of alumina (Fig. 25). The windings are bare toward the inside to give higher temperatures and to prevent local hot spots. Two platinum reflector bowls are fitted and the whole assembly is mounted in a water-cooled jacket with a polished inner surface.

An x-ray gap of 5/16 in. is left between the furnace sections. A movable platinum–platinum-rhodium thermocouple allows examination of the temperature distribution along the axis of the gap. Neoprene rubber seals are used between the two sections. Wilson seals are used for the drive shafts. A clutch couples the thermocouple drive to the scanning motor of the lower section.

A pump is connected to the camera by a 1-in.-diameter tube. A preformed window of 0.001-in. aluminum foil is fitted around the x-ray window, and similar aluminum disks are located in the entrance and exit apertures. The camera maintains a vacuum of 1×10^{-5} mm Hg or better. The synchronous motor rotates the sample at 4 rpm. Two synchronous motors provide either 11° oscillation or vertical scanning. The camera also takes back-reflection or glancing-angle photographs. The camera and the control unit are shown in Fig. 26.

A standard 10-cm ring-type cassette is used. It is entirely independent of the vacuum chamber and can be removed and reloaded without interference with the vacuum or heating. Knife-edge calibration is used for measuring lattice parameters.

By starting at room temperature and slowly increasing the current (to avoid cracking the alumina), it is possible to reach constancy at any temperature up to 1400° C within 30 min. The constancy of temperature with time is such that only current control is required to maintain a constant furnace temperature within ±2° C. Current consumption at 1450° C is 14 amp. The temperature distribution across the furnace gap at three typical temperatures with no specimen present is shown in Fig. 27. The average cooling time from 1000 to 100° C is 31 min.

* Unicam Instruments, Ltd., Cambridge, England. American distributor: Jarrell-Ash Company, Newtonville, Mass.

Applications of the Unicam Camera. The thermal expansion of silicon carbide of exceptionally high purity has been measured.[29] The cubic β form consists of pale yellow octahedral crystals, while the hexagonal Mod II variety is almost water-white.

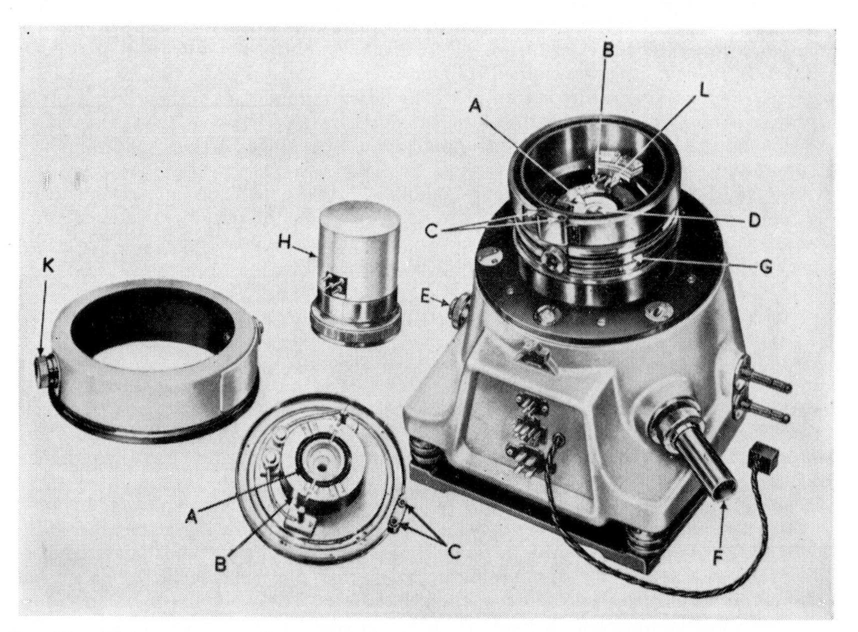

Fig. 25. Unicam camera dismantled for loading of block specimens. (A) Hemispherical furnace. (B) Polished cooling jacket. (C) Nonspilling, self-sealing water valves. (D) Thermocouple. (E) Clutch. (F) Vacuum-pump connection. (G) Aluminum-foil window. (H) Motor. (K) Beam trap. (L) Slits.

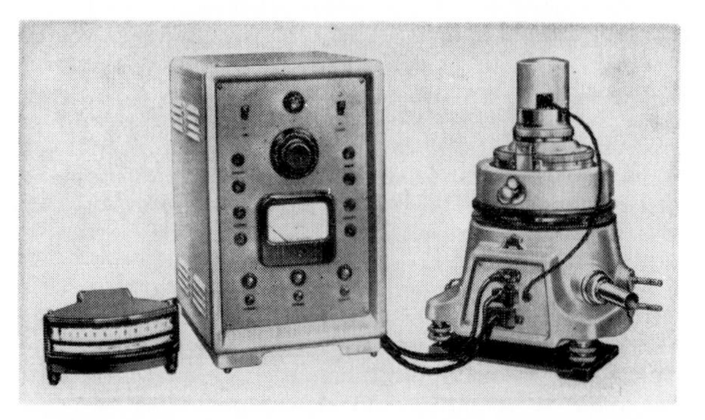

Fig. 26. The Unicam camera with control unit and temperature indicator.

The crystals were ground and sealed in a fused silica tube of ⅓ mm diameter for examination from −195° C to 1500° K. A 19-cm Unicam camera was used for the high-temperature work. The diffraction patterns were taken with iron $K\alpha$ radiation from a demountable high-intensity rotating anode tube; the exposure was 40 to 45 min at 70 ma and 50 kv peak. The temperatures were measured with a 10 per cent rhodium–platinum–platinum thermocouple which was calibrated against the thermal

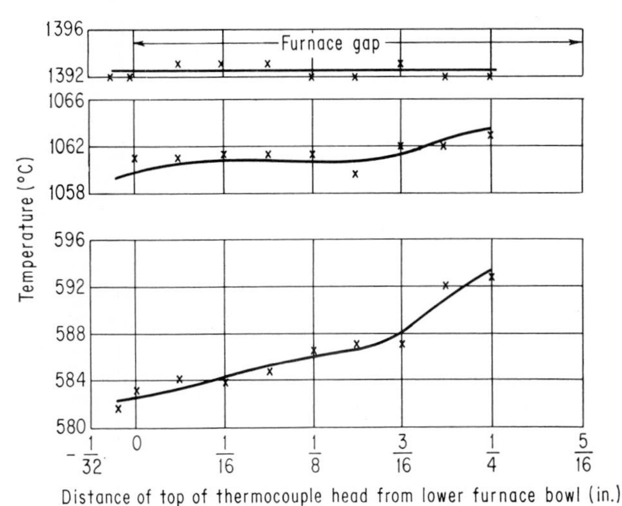

Fig. 27. Temperature distribution across the furnace gap of the Unicam camera.

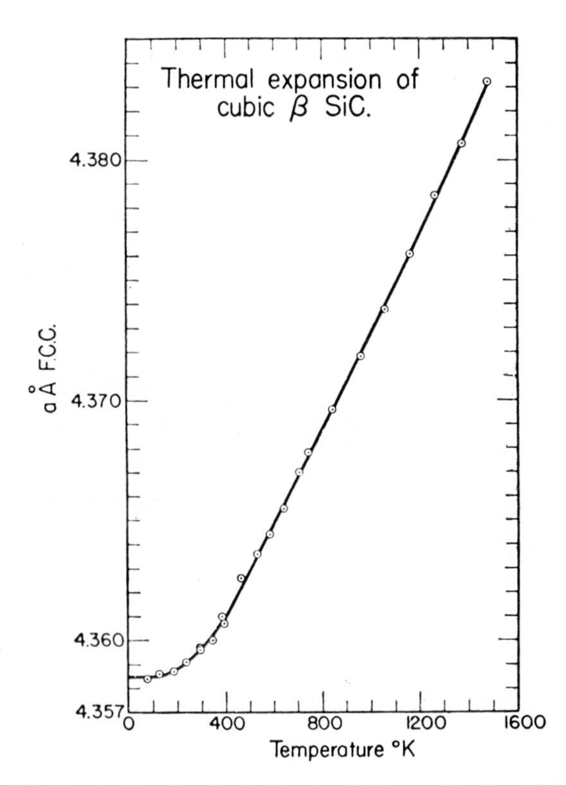

Fig. 28. Lattice parameter of cubic β silicon carbide as a function of temperature.[29]

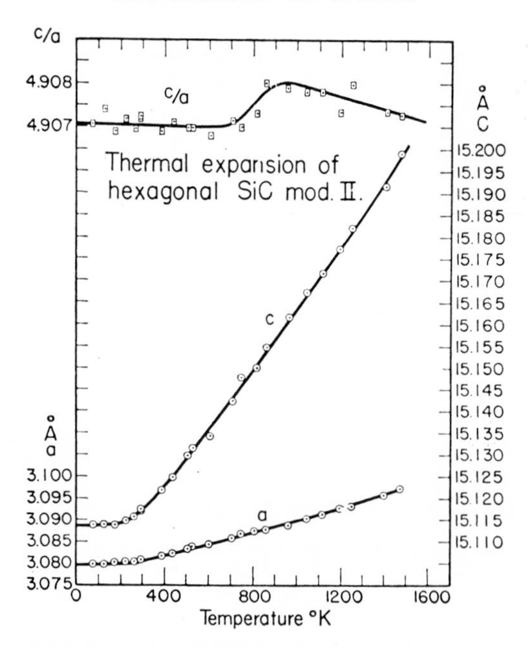

FIG. 29. Lattice parameters and axial ratio of hexagonal silicon carbide Mod II-6H as a function of temperature.[29]

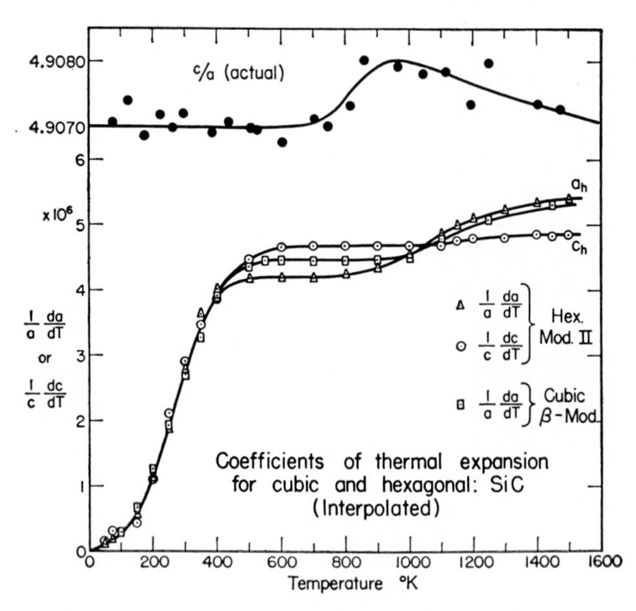

FIG. 30. Coefficients of thermal expansion of cubic and hexagonal silicon carbide Mod II.[29]

expansion of high-purity platinum and aluminum. The temperatures are probably accurate to $\pm 1°$ C. Iron $K\alpha$ radiation yields high-order reflections in the Bragg-angle region $\theta = 83°$ and thus enables lattice parameters to be determined with an accuracy of approximately 0.0001.

Lattice-parameter data for cubic and hexagonal polymorphs are illustrated graphically in Figs. 28 and 29. The axial ratio of the hexagonal form shows an interesting inflection in the 800 to 900° K region. Figure 30 illustrates the variations with temperature of the expansion coefficients $(1/a)(da/dT)$ for cubic and hexagonal forms derived from the lattice-parameter data.

5. HIGH-TEMPERATURE X-RAY CAMERAS FOR MOLTEN SUBSTANCES

The identity and disposition of the molecular and ionic species in molten salts and of the atoms in liquid metals and alloys are of considerable interest. Early work on the diffraction of x-rays by liquids and noncrystalline substances dates back to 1916, when Debye and Scherrer[30] obtained diffraction patterns of benzene and Debye[31] laid the theoretical groundwork for radial-distribution analysis (cf. Chap. 22).

The mathematical treatments of this development can be found in the literature.[32–40] The process of calculation is essentially that of harmonic analysis. The results can be portrayed as a radial-distribution function, which specifies the density of atoms or electrons as a function of the radial distance from any reference atom in the system. The radial-distribution function usually reproduced is $4\pi r^2\rho(r)$, which is easily derived from the differential function. ρr is the effective radial atomic density in atoms per cubic angstrom in a distance r of a given central atom. The areas under the peaks in the distribution curve give a measure of the average number of atoms occurring at various distances from any given reference atom, i.e., the average coordination number.

Three methods have been developed to photograph the scattered intensity of liquids: liquid enclosed in heated capillaries, cuvette-heated specimens, and transmission photographs of molten salt droplets. A fourth method uses a Geiger counter and focusing conditions to register the scattered rays of molten surfaces.

The transmission method and photographic registration of intensities have been used most frequently. Since the function $4\pi r^2\rho(r)$ applies to the coherent or unmodified scattering of the specimen, it is necessary to separate the coherent scatter of wavelength λ from other types of scatter contributing to the observed intensity. These include incoherent (modified) scatter and scatter due to the general radiation, air, and possibly the materials (glass) used to support the specimen.

To eliminate the undesired radiation, a high-temperature camera must be used in conjunction with a crystal monochromator. Otherwise errors are introduced in the interpretation of the scattering curve. Most workers use plane-crystal monochromators such as sodium chloride, quartz, and urea nitrate. These require excessive exposure time, up to 200 hr, and are therefore difficult to use with high-melting salts, which are eventually subjected to selective evaporation or attack the specimen support.[41] Bent-crystal monochromators have been suggested to alleviate this condition.[12] Curved-crystal monochromators are less suitable for the monochromatization of short-wavelength x-rays because of the necessarily short distances involved. It is good practice to use high $\sin\theta/\lambda$ values, since the resolution of the radial-distribution analysis increases with $\sin\theta/\lambda$.

There is an optimum thickness of the specimen. A specimen which is too thin has insufficient scattering matter, and one which is too thick absorbs too strongly. For scattering at small angles, the optimum thickness is the reciprocal of the linear absorption coefficient $1/\mu$.[37] Experience shows that for a cylindrical specimen completely bathed in the beam a cylinder whose diameter is two or three times $1/\mu$ gives more intense patterns than a diameter of $1/\mu$. This is probably due to the fact that the diffractions pattern at points considerably removed from the incident beam are generally of most interest.

Samples of molten salts or alloys are usually enclosed in glass capillary tubes under partial vacuum and sealed at both ends. Because of the high vapor pressure of some of the liquids investigated, such as NH_4Cl,[41] it is necessary to enclose them in tubes unusually thick for x-ray work (0.41 mm inside diameter and 0.13-mm-thick walls). Since the glass diffracts much of the x-ray beam, the glass pattern must be subtracted from the total diffraction pattern. Accordingly, exposures under the same total x-ray flux must be made both filled and empty. It is not permissible simply to subtract the pattern due to the glass tube alone from the total pattern. The blank pattern is affected only by self-absorption, while the glass contribution to the total is affected by absorption in the sample as well.

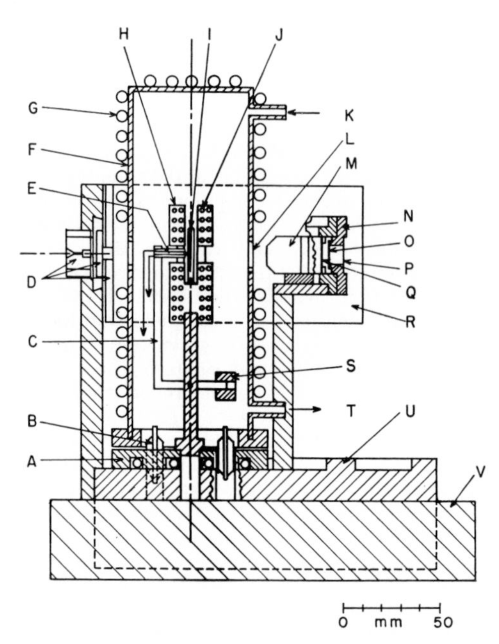

FIG. 31. Heater for molten substances (cuvette specimen).[45] (A) Base plate. (B) Electrical leads. (C) Tilting lever. (D) Pinholes. (E) Thermocouple. (F) Copper cover. (G) Water cooling. (H) Furnace element. (I) Cuvette. (J) Alumina capillaries containing the heating element. (K) Hydrogen. (L) Aluminum foils. (M) Beam stop. (N) Cassette. (O) Film. (P) Foil. (Q) Iron filter. (R) Lead shield. (S) Weight. (T) Hydrogen. (U) Movable furnace support. (V) Prism.

A method for handling this correction is described by Ritter, Harris, and Wood.[43] The correction for absorption in a cylindrical sample bathed by a uniform beam is a complicated operation, but the literature contains tabulated factors and curves for applying this correction.[44] For organic substances and penetrating radiation like molybdenum $K\alpha$, the correction is likely to show negligible variation with angle and can be ignored.

A second type of sample used in high-temperature x-ray diffraction of molten substances is a flat sample upon which a narrow beam is normally incident. When the beam penetrates a flat specimen at perpendicular incidence, the correction factor is

$$\frac{I_{2\theta} = 0}{I_{2\theta}} = \frac{\mu t(\sec 2\theta - 1)}{1 - \exp\left[-\mu t(\sec 2\theta - 1)\right]}$$

t is the thickness of the sample.

Figures 31 and 32 show the experimental setup employing a heated cuvette containing the specimen. If high-absorbing liquids are investigated, short-wavelength x-ray tubes must be used. For example, tungsten radiation from a microfocus tube has been used to obtain the scattering curve of liquid antimony.[45] The optimum thickness of the specimen for antimony is 0.2 mm. The W radiation can be monochromatized by reflection of the tungsten $K\alpha$ line on $(10\bar{1}1)$ of a flat quartz crystal ($\vartheta = 1.8°$); a sharp doublet tungsten $K\alpha_1$-α_2 is obtained. Curved monochromators are not recommended for short-wavelength x-rays because of the small aperture and because of the presence of other, hard-to-eliminate Laue reflections in the vicinity of the α_1-α_2 reflections.

The cuvette consists of two 30- by 0.3-mm quartz glass plates. The temperature is measured by a thermocouple in close contact with the wall of the cuvette. The contact is kept by means of the tilting lever and counterweight. The temperature is controlled to $\pm 0.5°$ C at 650° C. The film cassette (Fig. 32) consists of two film

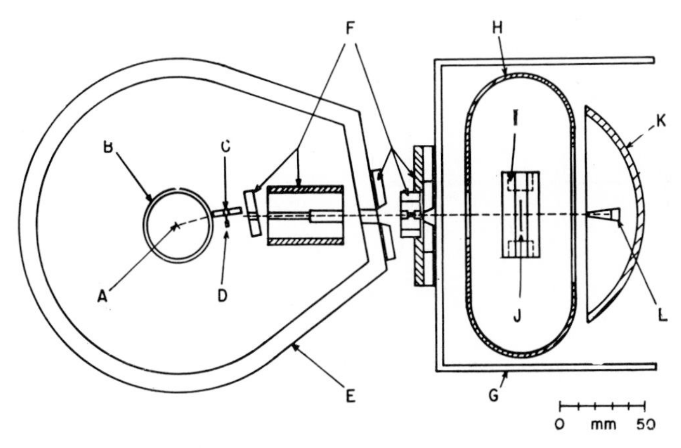

FIG. 32. Experimental setup for high-temperature x-ray diffraction of molten substances (cuvette specimen).[45] (A) X-ray target. (B) X-ray tube. (C) Monochromator. (D) Lead slit. (E) Lead covering. (F) Slit system. (G) Lead shield. (H) Furnace covering. (I) Furnace. (J) Cuvette. (K) Cassette. (L) Beam stop.

cylinders (radius = 70 mm), one inserted in the other, so that two film strips can be exposed simultaneously.

As an example of the results obtainable by this technique, the atomic distribution of liquid antimony obtained at 665° C is shown in Figs. 33 and 34. A useful representation of the data was introduced by Debye and Menke.[46] They used the probability function of the atomic distribution, which is given by

$$W(r) = 4\pi r^2 \rho(r)/4\pi r^2 \rho_0$$

where ρ is the density in the case of uniform distribution of the atomic mass. Figure 35 shows the results of this calculation using different processes of approximation.[47–49] The atomic distribution in liquid antimony shows three density maxima at 3.12, 6.3, and above 9 Å, with smaller maxima in between and in about the same sequence (Fig. 33). Comparison of the atomic-distance coordination numbers in the liquid and solid crystalline state (Table 2) shows surprisingly good agreement.

Figures 36 and 37 show a high-temperature camera in which the specimen is in the form of a molten droplet held by capillary forces over the orifice of a heated metallic plate.[42] This system avoids heating coils and specimen enclosures. The Geiger-counter recorder only serves as a control instrument for the primary beam and is also used to determine the corrections required for air scattering and for absorption in the specimen. A curved quartz monochromator of the Guinier type is used. The heating element consists of a 0.2-mm-thick platinum–20 per cent rhodium alloy strip, shown in Fig. 37. Temperatures up to 1600° C are attainable. The specimen is located on the periphery of the film cylinder, which is 76 mm in diameter.

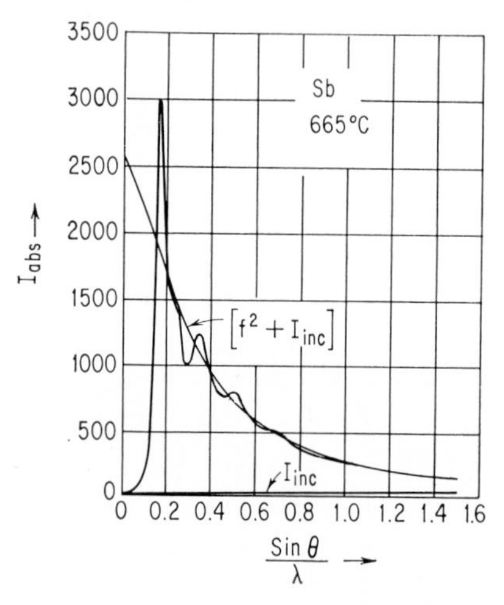

Fig. 33. Intensity curve of liquid antimony.[45]

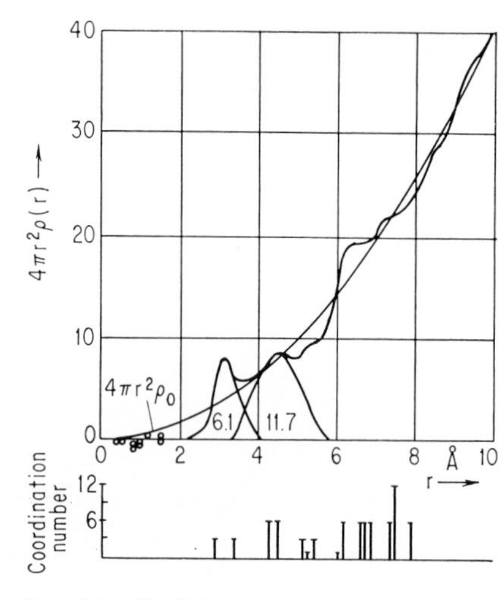

Fig. 34. Radial atomic density in liquid antimony.[45]

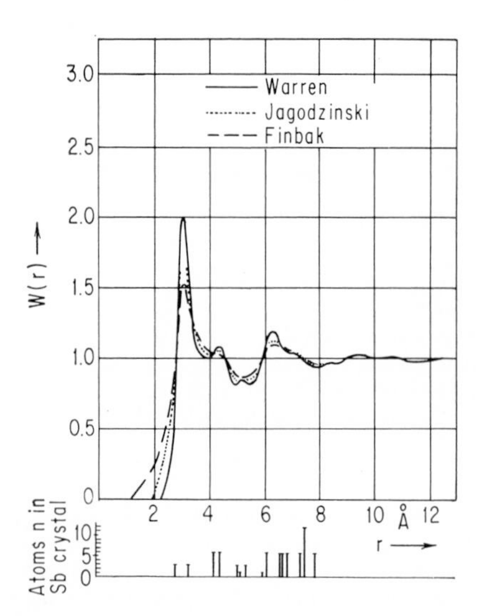

Fig. 35. Probability function W(r) of the atomic distances in liquid antimony.[45]

There are several advantages in this method of investigating liquids. The specimen is in the form of a liquid film supported by its own surface tension, and therefore the absorption can be calculated with precision. The method is useful for investigating molten oxides and silicates which do not react with air at high temperatures, have a relatively low vapor pressure, and do not decompose on heating.

Table 2. Atomic Distances and Coordination Numbers in Crystalline and Liquid Antimony

Crystalline antimony		Liquid antimony	
Distance	Coordination No.	Distance	Coordination No.
3.127	6	3.12	6.1
4.399	12	4.40	11.7
5.295	7	5.3	
6.539	25	6.3	

A fourth arrangement is the use of a Geiger counter or proportional-counter techniques to register the "reflects" from a molten flat surface. When parafocusing geometry is used, the angle of incidence α must always be equal to the Bragg angle θ at which the scattered radiation is being received from the surface. Under these conditions the absorption factor is independent of angle and the exposure time for registering the intensity curve is considerably shortened, a decided advantage over photographic registrations. However, a complicated setup is necessary. It requires

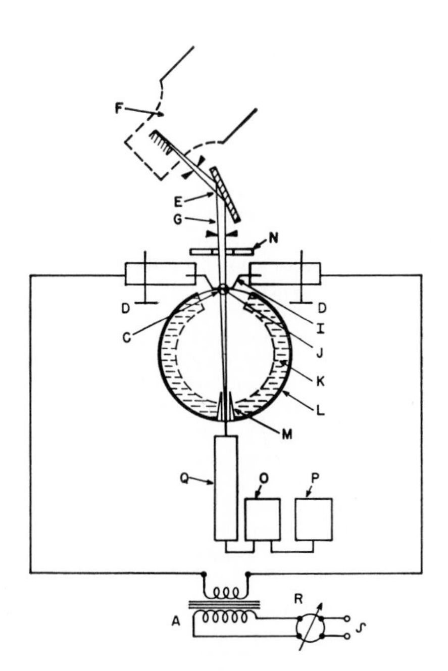

Fig. 36. High-temperature camera for molten substances (droplet specimen).[42] (A) Current supply. (C) Optical reference mark. (D) Resistor alignment. (E) Curved quartz monochromator. (F) X-ray tube. (G) X-rays. (I) Resistance heating element and sample support. (J) Sample. (K) Water-cooled shield. (L) Film. (M) Exit collimator. (N) Water-cooled shield. (O) Integrator. (P) Recorder. (Q) Geiger counter. (R) Variac.

a horizontal, heated flat cuvette containing the liquid with the x-ray tube and the Geiger counter moving in such a way that $\alpha = \theta$ at low angles. An interesting solution of the problem has been reported.[50]

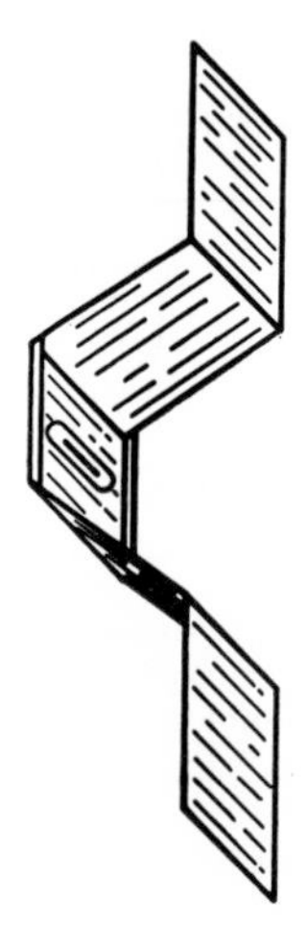

Fig. 37. Heater and specimen support for liquids (droplet specimen).[42]

6. ATTACHMENT FOR HIGH-TEMPERATURE SINGLE-CRYSTAL CAMERA

An attachment built for the Unicam S.25 x-ray goniometer with 6-cm film cassette is suitable for single-crystal or powder work with copper radiation up to 900° C.[51] The heater unit consists of a nickel-foil furnace (0.25 mm thick).

The crystal is cemented to a silicon fiber about 2 mm long and up to 0.4 mm thick. This is cemented to a platinum wire silver-soldered to the pipe which fits on the goniometer head. For the study of transitions of about 200° C, water glass is a suitable cement. It swells at 150 to 200° C and must be heated to 200° C before final setting of the crystal. Organic adhesives carbonize but can usually be relied on to 300° C. A transformer supplies power up to 60 amp at 4 volts through a Variac preceded by a constant-voltage transformer. The element runs at 10 watts at 240° C, 30 watts at 500° C, and 100 watts at 900° C. The thermocouple junction is 1 mm above the crystal. For calibration, crystals of various substances are mounted and their melting points observed with a telescope and collimator light.

Other heaters or attachments[52] for high-temperature single-crystal work are 0.03-mil platinum foil wrapped around the capillary for oscillation photographs,[53] heaters which are removable between exposures of a crystal in a Weissenberg camera,[54] a gas convection cooler and heater for a Weissenberg camera to be used between −150 and 300° C,[55] and a heater for a precession camera.[56] The Nonius Integrating Weissenberg Camera is commercially available with a high-temperature attachment.*

7. TEMPERATURE MEASUREMENT AND CALIBRATION

The difficulty in measuring temperature accurately is due to the temperature difference between the thermocouple bead and the specimen. It is caused by differences in heat loss by thermal conductivity and emissivity of the thermocouple and the specimen. (The thermocouple is connected to the outside by two connecting wires,

* Supplier: N. V. Nederlandsche Röntgen-Apparatenfabriek, Evershed-Enraf, Delft, Holland.

while the specimen is usually mounted on a support.) Other errors arise from contamination of the thermocouple by metallic deposition (rhodium from the furnace elements) and from alteration of its composition by selective evaporation.

The accuracy of temperature measurement is improved by placing the thermocouple inside the specimen and using it as the support.[57] However, thermocouple-supported specimens can hardly be rotated during exposure and an oscillating device must be provided to obtain smooth diffraction lines. The thermocouple should be of fine wire not more than 0.004 in. in diameter. In practice, this is achieved by using fine (0.030 in. in diameter) thermocouple sheathing having two 0.008-in.-diameter holes to carry the wires. Methods of mounting specimens on thermocouples are shown in Fig. 12.

The temperature across the furnace gap of a Unicam Model II camera is constant within a few degrees, and the constancy improves as the temperature is raised (Fig. 27). In order to determine the temperature difference between the specimen and the thermocouple, the camera must be calibrated by comparing the true temperature of the specimen, as derived from the expansion coefficient and measured lattice spacings, with the temperature of the thermocouple.

Berry, Henry, and Raynor[58] have pointed out that, if there is a gap in a furnace, so that blackbody conditions are only approximate, the temperature attained by the specimen depends upon its absorptive power. Blackening tests by Brand and Goldschmidt[59] in the 1400° C Unicam camera showed this effect to be negligible at 500° C. They suggest, however, that artificial blackening be applied when difference in emissivity may be important. They made x-ray high-temperature photographs of silver and tungsten, plotted the spacing-temperature curve, and compared them with data calculated from reliable dilatometric results. The deviation ΔT of the observed from the correct temperature varied from 0 to a maximum of about 40° C near 300° C, thereafter falling to 5° C at 900° C.

Similar results were obtained by Nomura,[60] who calculated quantitatively the temperature deviation as a function of temperature of the thermocouple and specimen holder, their thicknesses, length, emissivity, thermal conductivity, and relative location in the furnace. Nomura found that the temperature deviation is mainly due to the thermal flow through thermocouple wires, while at high temperatures the gap effect becomes predominant. Maximum temperature deviation occurs at about 450° K in vacuum and at about 650° K in air if the gap effect is neglected. Large gap effects produce deviations which increase with temperature, and the calibration curves are strongly affected by the relative position of the thermocouple head and the specimen. Brand and Goldschmidt[59] concluded that the cause of the large corrections required for measured temperatures is essentially the loss of heat along the wires of the thermocouple.

The idealized expression for the temperature deviation ΔT is

$$\Delta T = [C(T - T_0)]/4T^3$$

This equation approaches zero at high values of T and has a maximum value independent of C ($C = Ka/LA\sigma e$, where K is a constant depending on the coefficients of thermal conduction of the thermocouple metals, a is the cross-sectional area, L the effective length of the thermocouple, σ is Stefan's constant, and e the emissivity of the surface). In order to minimize the effect, the constant C must be kept small. By reducing the diameter of the thermocouple wire, increasing the thermocouple head, and blackening the thermocouple with refractory coatings, C can be reduced.

Internal calibration by coating the specimen on a standard platinum wire is an excellent method for ceramic powders. The lattice spacings of the platinum wire give the temperature directly. Metal powders obviously cannot be coated on platinum because of possible alloying. The metals suitable for high-temperature standards are listed in Table 3.

More recent values of the expansion of Pt from 25 to 1700° C for the purpose of calibration were reported by W. J. Campbell,[63] and are given in Chap. 13, Sec. 5. Data on the thermal-expansion characteristics of metals were also reported by Pearson.[64]

According to Vaughan and Schwartz,[65] it is possible to mix silver, platinum, gold, etc., as standards with the specimen of interest, so that the lattice parameter can be determined with considerable confidence. With silver a change of 0.0004 A in lattice parameter is equivalent to a change of 5° C in temperature. Since the thermal expansion of platinum is much less than that of silver, a change in lattice parameter comparable with that would indicate a change of 14° C in temperature.

Errors of specimen-temperature measurement by means of thermocouples were examined theoretically and experimentally by Pease.[66] Thermocouples placed near the ends of the specimen record a temperature different from that of the center of the specimen for two reasons: the radiation temperature of the furnace is not constant from one place to another, and neither the thermocouple heads nor the specimen are at the radiation temperature because of conduction down the leads on the support. In an imperfect vacuum, gaseous conduction also alters the temperatures. In a furnace consisting of coaxial disks, a gap of 0.75 cm, and a thermocouple head above the end of the specimen and near to the upper disk, the two types of errors are of opposite sign and result in a relatively complex calibration curve with a maximum in the region of 200° C and a change of sign at about 600° C.

Table 3. Expansion Equations for Pure Metals Suitable for X-ray High-temperature Work

Metal	Equation*	Ref.
Ag	$l_t = l_0(1 + 19.494 \times 10^{-6}t + 1.038 \times 10^{-9}t^2 + 2.375 \times 10^{-12}t^3)$	61
Pt	$l_t = l_0(1 + 8.988 \times 10^{-6}t + 1.065 \times 10^{-9}t^2 + 0.126 \times 10^{-12}t^3)$	61
Au	$l_t = l_0(1 + 14.146 \times 10^{-6} + 1.585 \times 10^{-9}t^2 + 1.093 \times 10^{-12}t^3)$	61
Cu	$l_t = l_0(1 + 16.733 \times 10^{-6}t + 2.626 \times 10^{-9}t^2 + 0.91 \times 10^{-12}t^3)$	61
Al	$a_t = 4.0392 + 0.00901(t/100) + 0.000432(t/100)^2$	62

* Where l_t and l_0 = length of specimen at t° and 0° C, respectively, and a_t = spacing in kX units.

In order to minimize the errors and to keep them constant from one specimen to another, it is important that (1) the head of the thermocouple be in the gap between the two halves of the furnace, (2) the thermocouple have a large blackened head with thin leads (approximately 0.005 in. in diameter) of maximum length (e.g., by coiling) within the furnace gap, and (3) the specimen be effectively insulated from the higher temperatures in the axial cavity. Spherical furnaces such as used in the Unicam camera should prove more satisfactory than cylindrical furnaces because the axial cavities are removed and thus steep temperature gradients are avoided.

The substance used for calibration of high-temperature cameras should have a large expansion coefficient so that small changes in temperature are readily detected from the change in the Bragg angle. To shorten exposure times there should be a fairly intense x-ray reflection of the Bragg angle at 80°. The low expansion coefficient of aluminum ($\alpha = 18.35 \times 10^{-6}$/° C) means that only a small shift of the reflection is produced for an appreciable temperature interval. Pure lead can be obtained in a high state of purity (99.99 per cent), has a large expansion coefficient ($\alpha = 27 \times 10^{-6}$/° C), and an intense x-ray reflection (620) of Bragg angle 79° with copper $K\alpha$ radiation (22° C).[67] The (620) reflection shifts about 5 mm on a 7-cm-radius camera for a temperature interval of 215° C. Since the position of the reflection can be measured to 0.01 mm by a Hilger photometer, the temperature can be estimated to approximately 0.5° C. For the calculation of the variation of lattice spacings of lead with temperature the following equation can be used:

$$d_{620} = 0.77662 + 0.000021520t$$

t is the temperature in ° K. More sensitive scales, for lower temperatures, can be based on pure resublimed iodine ($\alpha = 84 \times 10^{16}/° C$) or p-nitroaniline

$$(\alpha = 150 \times 10^{-6}/° \text{C})$$

Equality of the temperature in the upper and lower furnaces is essential. In order to be able to adjust this quickly and accurately, two identical Alumel-Chromel thermocouple wires (0.0200 in. in diameter) with their emf's opposed can be mounted[58] as shown in Fig. 38. On heating or cooling, the two furnaces approach equilibrium at different rates, necessitating the use of RH4 to decrease the sensitivity of the galvanometer. R1 is operated electrically upon failure of the current supply to one or both of the furnaces. The furnace rheostats can then be adjusted manually to give a null galvanometer reading, corresponding to equality of temperature within ±0.1° C.

Calibration of cameras by power input to the furnace is difficult when the resistance of the furnace is of the order of 1 ohm at room temperature. The calibration may change gradually because the resistance of the furnace may alter with time (evaporation of wire material).

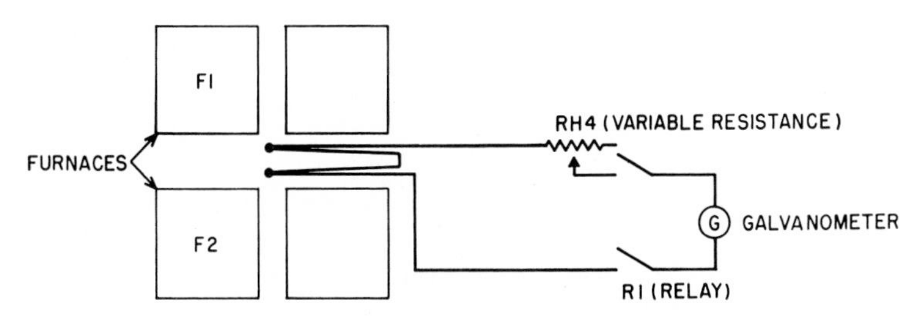

FIG. 38. Furnace-balance indicator circuit.[58]

Calibration of melting points[62] is possible if the melting points are determined by the disappearance of the diffraction pattern. Calibration by transition points is limited, since there are not many suitable materials with reliable transition temperatures. On the whole, these methods appear to be time-consuming.

REFERENCES CITED

1. F. Halla and H. Mark, *Röntgenographische Untersuchung von Kristallen*, J. S. Barth. Leipzig, 1937.
2. H. J. Goldschmidt, High-temperature Methods, in H. S. Peiser, H. P. Rooksby, and A. J. C. Wilson (eds.), *X-ray Diffraction by Polycrystalline Material*, Institute of Physics, London, 1955.
3. F. Schossberger, High-temperature X-ray Diffraction, in I. E. Campbell (ed.), *High-temperature Technology*, John Wiley & Sons, Inc., New York, 1956.

3*a*. F. Schossberger, High Temperature X-ray Diffraction, (I) General Survey
H. Warlimont, (II) Comparison of Instruments and Techniques
W. L. Baun, (III) Review, Illustrations, and Bibliography to Date
in G. L. Clark (ed.), *Encyclopedia of X-rays and Gamma Rays*, Reinhold Publishing Corp., New York, 1963.

4. M. Straumanis and A. Ievins, *Präzisions Bestimmung von Gitter-Konstanten nach der asymmetrischen Methode*, Springer-Verlag, Berlin, 1940.
5. H. Weyerer, *Z. Angew. Phys.*, **7**:536–539 (1955).
6. T. Kubo and H. Akabori, *J. Phys. Colloid Chem.*, **54**:1121 (1950).
7. Courtesy of the Institute of Physics, X-ray Analysis Group, issued under 23/BG/155, London, 1958.
8. J. Fridrichson, *Rev. Sci. Instr.*, **27**:1015–1018 (1956).
9. J. R. Johnson, *J. Am. Ceram. Soc.*, **37**:360–362 (1954).
10. A. E. Austin, N. A. Richard, and C. M. Schwartz, *Rev. Sci. Instr.*, **27**:860–862 (1956).

11. Courtesy of M. H. Mueller and D. H. Zauberis, Argonne National Laboratory, Lemont, Illinois.
12. B. A. Hatt, P. J. C. Kent, and G. I. Williams, *J. Sci. Instr.*, **37**:273–276 (1960).
13. A. G. Provan, B. A. Shaw, and G. I. Williams, *J. Sci. Instr.*, **33**:445 (1956).
14. P. J. C. Kent, *J. Sci. Instr.*, **34**:72 (1957).
15. L. R. Weissberg and G. R. Gunther Mohr, *Rev. Sci. Instr.*, **26**:896 (1955).
16. Z. S. Basinski and J. W. Christian, *Proc. Roy. Soc.* (*London*), **A223**:554–560 (1954).
17. E. Aruja, J. H. Welch, and W. Gutt, *J. Sci. Instr.*, **36**:16–20 (1959).
18. E. Matuyama, *J. Sci. Instr.*, **32**:229–231 (1955).
19. A. Schneider and G. Heymer, *Z. Anorg. Allg. Chem.*, **286**:118–135 (1956).
20. M. H. Mueller, *Rev. Sci. Instr.*, **27**:411 (1956).
21. W. F. Zimmerman and A. W. Allen, *Am. Ceram. Soc. Bull.*, **35**:271–274 (1956).
22. R. J. Beals and R. L. Cook, *J. Am. Ceram. Soc.*, **40**:279–284 (1957).
23. For details of the furnace design see W. F. Zimmerman, Measurement of Lattice Dimensions of Refractory Crystals at Elevated Temperatures, M.S. Thesis, University of Illinois, 1952.
24. H. G. Sowman and A. I. Andrews, *J. Am. Ceram. Soc.*, **34**:298–301 (1951).
25. I. Corvin and F. Schossberger, *Norelco Reptr.*, **5**:62 (1958).
26. F. Endter, *Dechema Monograph*, **38**:21–30 (1960).
27. H. Warlimont, *Z. Metallk.*, **50**:708–716 (1959).
28. H. J. Goldschmidt and J. Cunningham, *J. Sci. Instr.*, **27**:177 (1950).
29. A. Taylor and R. Jones, The Crystal Structure and Thermal Expansion of Cubic and Hexagonal Silicon Carbide, pp. 147–161, in *Silicon Carbide*, J. R. O'Connor and J. Smiltens (eds.), Pergamon Press, London, 1960.
30. P. Debye and P. Scherrer, *Göttinger Nachr.*, vol. 16, 1916.
31. P. Debye, *Ann. Physik*, **46**:809 (1915).
32. F. Zernicke and G. Prins, *Z. Physik*, **41**:184 (1924).
33. B. E. Warren and N. S. Gingrich, *Phys. Rev.*, **46**:368 (1934).
34. K. Lark Horovitz and E. P. Miller, *Phys. Rev.*, **49**:418 (1936).
35. B. E. Warren, H. Krutter, and O. Morningstar, *J. Am. Ceram. Soc.*, **19**:202 (1936).
36. E. E. Bray and N. S. Gingrich, *J. Chem. Phys.*, **11**:351 (1943).
37. N. S. Gingrich, *Rev. Mod. Phys.*, **15**:90 (1943).
38. R. W. James, The Crystalline State, vol. II, *The Optical Principles of the Diffraction of X-rays*, G. Bell & Sons, Ltd., London, 1948.
39. R. F. Kruh, *Chem. Rev.*, **62**:319 (1962).
40. K. Furukawa, *Rept. Prog. Phys.*, **25**:395 (1962).
41. R. L. Harris, R. E. Wood, and H. C. Ritter, *J. Am. Chem. Soc.*, **73**:3151–3155 (1951).
42. J. Zarzycki, *J. Phys. Radium*, **17**(11): 44A-51A (1956).
43. H. L. Ritter, R. L. Harris, and R. E. Wood, *J. Appl. Phys.*, **22**:169 (1951).
44. H. P. Klug and L. E. Alexander, *X-ray Diffraction Procedures*, p. 595, John Wiley & Sons, Inc., New York, 1954.
45. H. K. F. Müller and H. Hendus, *Z. Naturforsch.*, **12a**:102–111 (1957).
46. P. Debye and H. Menke, *Erg. techn. Röntgenkde.*, **2**:1 (1931).
47. B. E. Warren and N. S. Gingrich, *Phys. Z.*, **31**:797 (1930).
48. H. Jagodzinski, *Z. Naturforsch.*, **2a**:465 (1947).
49. Ch. Finbak, *Acta Chem. Scand.*, **3**:1279 and 1293 (1949).
50. P. A. Agron, M. D. Danford, M. A. Bredig, H. A. Levy, and P. C. Sharrah, *Acta Cryst.*, **10**:739 (1957).
51. L. S. Dent and H. F. W. Taylor, *J. Sci. Instr.*, **33**:89–91 (1956).
52. A. Barclay and J. D. Donaldson, *J. Sci. Instr.*, **38**:286–287 (1961).
53. R. L. Wooley, *J. Sci. Instr.*, **25**:321 (1948).
54. L. S. Dent, *J. Sci. Instr.*, **34**:159–160 (1957).
55. A. Kreuger, *Acta Cryst.*, **8**: 348–349 (1955).
56. L. Katz and M. I. Kay, *Rev. Sci. Instr.*, **28**:968–969 (1957).
57. W. Johnson, *J. Sci. Instr.*, **38**:373–374 (1961).
58. R. L. Berry, W. G. Henry, and G. V. Raynor, *J. Inst. Metals*, **78**:643–656 (1951).
59. J. A. Brand and H. J. Goldschmidt, *J. Sci. Instr.*, **33**:41–45 (1956).
60. S. Nomura, *J. Appl. Phys.* (*Japan*), **26**:381–386 (1957).
61. H. Esser and H. Eusterbrock, *Arch. Eisenhüttenw.*, **14**:341 (1941).
62. E. Wilson, *Proc. Phys. Soc.*, **53**:235 (1941).
63. W. J. Campbell, *U.S. Bur. Mines Inform. Circ.* 8107, 1962.
64. W. B. Pearson, *Handbook of Lattice Spacings and Structures of Metals and Alloys*, Pergamon Press, New York, 1958.
65. D. A. Vaughan and C. M. Schwartz, Determination of Thermal Expansion by High-temperature X-ray Diffraction, in *Advances in X-ray Analysis*, vol. 5, p. 238, W. M. Mueller (ed.), Plenum Press, New York, 1962.

66. R. S. Pease, *J. Sci. Instr.*, **32**:476–480 (1955).
67. J. C. McC. Pollock, *Acta Cryst.*, **8**:652–653 (1955).

GENERAL REFERENCES

Basinski, Z. S., W. B. Pearson, and J. W. Christian: Furnace Construction and Thermocouple Arrangements for a High-temperature X-ray Camera, *J. Sci. Instr.*, **29**:154 (1952).

Bond, W. L.: Simple Hot Powder Camera, *Rev. Sci. Instr.*, **29**:654 (1958).

Bridge, J. R., C. M. Schwartz, and D. A. Vaugham: X-ray Diffraction Determination of the Coefficient of Expansion of α-Uranium, *J. Metals*, **8**:1282–1286 (1956).

Connell, L. F., and H. C. Martin: Concerning Reported Discrepancies between X-ray and Macroscopic Measurements of Thermal Expansion of Some Alkali Halides, *Acta Cryst.*, **4**:75 (1951).

Deshpander, V. T., and V. M. Mudholker: Temperature Variation of the Lattice Constant and the Coefficient of Thermal Expansion of Sodium Chlorate, *Acta Cryst.*, **13**:483–486 (1960).

Deshpander, V. T., and D. B. Sirdeshmukh: Thermal Expansion of Tetragonal Tin, *Acta Cryst.*, **14**:355–356 (1961).

Ellinger, F. H.: Crystal Structure of Delta-prime and Epsilon Plutonium, *J. Metals*, **8**:1256–1259 (1956).

Fischmeister, H. F.: Thermal Expansion of NaCl and Some Other Alkali Halides at High Temperatures, *Acta Cryst.*, **9**:416 (1956).

Fischmeister, H. F.: X-ray Measurements of the Thermal Expansion of Trigonal Potassium, Lithium, and Silver Nitrates, *J. Inorg. Nucl. Chem.*, **3**:182–186 (1956).

Goldschmidt, H. J.: A High-temperature X-ray Investigation on Niobium Pentoxide and Some Problems Concerning the Oxidation of Niobium, *J. Inst. Metals*, **87**:235-239 (1959).

Goldschmidt, H. J.: A High-temperature X-ray Study on High-speed Steel, I and II, *J. Iron Steel Inst.*, **186**:68–79 and 79–85 (1957).

Goon, E. J., J. T. Mason, and T. R. P. Gibb: X-ray Powder Diffraction Assembly for Studies at Elevated Temperatures and High Gas Pressures, *Rev. Sci. Instr.*, **28**:342–344 (1957).

Graham, J.: Residual Stresses in Titanium Carbide-Nickel Cermets, Discussion of a paper by H. W. Newkirk and H. H. Sisler, *J. Am. Ceram. Soc.*, **42**:306–309 (1959).

Gubser, R. A., W. Hoffman, and H. U. Nissen: X-ray Diffraction Patterns with Buerger's Precession Interval between 1000 and 2000°C, *Z. Kristallogr.*, **119**:264–272 (1963).

Hall, E. O., and J. Crangle: An X-ray Investigation of the Reported High-temperature Allotropy of Ruthenium, *Acta Cryst.*, **10**:240–241 (1957).

Heal, H. T., E. Williams, and D. G. Cole: Powder Camera Modification for High-temperature Photographs, *J. Sci. Instr.*, **29**:380 (1952).

James, W. J., and M. E. Straumanis: Lattice Parameter and Coefficient of Thermal Expansion of Thorium, *Acta Cryst.*, **9**:376–379 (1956).

James, W. J., and M. E. Straumanis: Lattice Parameter and Coefficient of Thermal Expansion of Vanadium, *Z. Physik. Chem.*, **29**:134–142 (1961).

Johnson, W., and K. W. Andrews: An X-ray Study of the Inversion and Thermal Expansion of Cristobalite, *Trans. Brit. Ceram. Soc.*, **55**:227–236 (1956).

Kempter, C. P., R. O. Elliott, and K. A. Gschneider: Thermal Expansion of Delta and Epsilon Zirconium Hydrides, *J. Chem. Phys.*, **33**:837–840 (1960).

Lefkowitz, I., and H. D. Megaw: A Device for Taking X-ray Photographs of Single Crystals at High Temperatures, *Acta Cryst.*, **16**:453-455 (1963).

Matuyama, E.: Effects of Heating on X-ray Diffraction by Carbons, *Nature*, **184**:544–545 (1959).

Matuyama, E.: Rate of Transformation of Rhombohedral Graphite at High Temperatures, *Nature*, **178**:1459–1460 (1956).

McKeown, P. J. A.: A High-temperature Micro Thermostat for X-ray Studies on Single Crystals of Appreciable Vapor Pressure, *J. Sci. Instr.*, **33**:386 (1956).

Newkirk, N. W., and H. H. Sisler: Determination of Residual Stresses in Titanium Carbide Base Cermets by High-temperature X-ray Diffraction, *J. Am. Ceram. Soc.*, **41**:93–103 (1958).

Robinson, J. M. M., and O. W. Florke: A Simple High-temperature Attachment for the Precession Camera, *Z. Kristallogr.*, **119**:257–263 (1963).

Rowland, R. A., E. J. Weiss, and D. R. Lewis: Apparatus for the Oscillating Heating Method of X-ray Powder Diffraction, *J. Am. Ceram. Soc.*, **42**:133–138 (1959).

Schneider, A., and K. H. Imhagen: Temperature Dependence of the Lattice Constants in the Mixed Crystal Series NiTe-$NiTe_2$, *Naturwiss.*, **44**:324–325 (1957).
Straumanis, M. E., and C. C. Weng: Precise Lattice Constant and Expansion Coefficient of Cr between +10 and +60° C, *Acta Cryst.*, **8**:367–371 (1955).
Trommel, G.: High-temperature X-ray Analyses of Significance to Ceramics, *Ber. Deut. Keram. Ges.*, **29**:2 (1952).
Wilson, W. B.: High-temperature X-ray Diffraction Investigation of the Uranium-Carbon System, *J. Am. Ceram. Soc.*, **43**:77–81 (1960).
Wood, L. J., C. Sweeney, and M. T. Derbes: Reactions between Dry Inorganic Salts, X, The Effect of Rubidium Chloride on the Transition Temperature of Cesium Chloride, *J. Am. Chem. Soc.*, **81**:6148–6152 (1959).

Chapter 15

LOW-TEMPERATURE DIFFRACTION

Charles S. Barrett

The University of Chicago

1. INTRODUCTION

Diffraction with samples at low temperatures has been employed for over 30 years in many laboratories with many different modifications of powder and single-crystal cameras and diffractometers. Since many of the installations have been designed for special purposes they are not presented in detail here, but all the principal types are discussed and selected references are given from which further details may be obtained. Operating suggestions are included when these are particularly critical, and a list is given of the purposes for which diffraction at low temperatures has proved to be of maximum value.

2. APPLICATIONS

The principal uses of diffraction at low temperatures are as follows:

Determining Crystal Structures. Many structures have been determined for substances that are liquid or gaseous at ordinary temperatures, or that yield diffraction patterns too inconveniently weak at ordinary temperatures. The identification of materials by their diffraction patterns is aided by low-temperature diffraction in some instances.

Studying Phase Changes. The crystal-structure changes induced by cooling can be identified and followed as a function of temperature and time. Various phase changes are accelerated and others are made to occur by deforming certain substances at low temperatures. Common ways of accomplishing this are by hammering or scratching a block, sheet, or wire of a material while it is immersed in liquid nitrogen, or by producing filings of the material under liquid nitrogen. Simple devices aid in transferring the sample to the diffraction apparatus without warming it appreciably above 78° K. Some diffraction equipment (mentioned below) permits cold working of the specimen in situ in the diffractometer at temperatures as low as 4.2° K. Retention of the low-temperature phases, and the effect on these of subsequent thermal and mechanical treatments can be readily followed by diffraction. The influence of thermal agitation in causing the onset of rotation of groups of atoms at a certain temperature can be studied.

Determining Thermal Contraction. Diffraction with both powders and single crystals has proved useful for this purpose, and anomalous expansion characteristics have been discovered in some materials that were not expected from work at higher temperatures. Debye temperatures have been determined over wide temperature ranges from precision studies of intensities, as have also vibration amplitudes of individual atoms in a crystal.

Studying Condensed Films. Deposits on substrates maintained at low temperatures have been extensively studied for orientation and structural characteristics by both x-ray and electron diffraction. These deposits have included free radicals and other materials of importance in low-temperature chemistry.

Studying Defects in Crystals. Stacking faults and twin faults are normally produced in metals in much greater quantities when deformation is at temperatures lower than room temperature, and in some metals they cannot be fully retained unless the metal is kept well below room temperature. Point defects also are subject to loss at normal temperatures; hence low-temperature diffraction is of importance in studies of radiation damage.

Aiding the Indexing of Complex Diffraction Patterns. It is frequently an aid in the indexing of powder diffraction patterns if the shifting of individual lines of the pattern is studied as the temperature of the specimen is changed.

Varying the specimen temperature aids the separation of thermal diffuse scattering from disorder diffuse scattering.

3. EQUIPMENT FOR GAS-FLOW COOLING

Most installations for low-temperature diffraction use conventional cameras and diffractometers only slightly modified to provide a stream of cold gas impinging on the specimen. The minimum essentials for this type of equipment are (1) a means of directing a dry-gas stream, at controlled velocity and temperature, at a specimen that is sufficiently insulated from its surroundings so that it can acquire a temperature very near that of the gas stream; and (2) some kind of housing for the specimen that is free from moisture-containing air so that the specimen and all windows through which the x-rays have to pass remain free of ice and moisture condensation.[1–4] The stream of nitrogen (or, less conveniently, air or oxygen) may be supplied from a cylinder of the compressed gas, cooled by passing through a heat-exchanger coil immersed in a refrigerant, and conducted through a lagged tube to a jet placed very near the specimen but outside the x-ray beam. In some designs it is conducted past the specimen in a cellophane tube; in others it is surrounded by a concentric stream of dry gas as it flows past the specimen. Many laboratories prefer to obtain the refrigerating gas by enclosing the liquid nitrogen in a stoppered Dewar vessel and boiling it at a controlled rate by an immersion heater. For operation at temperatures well above 78° K it is often desirable to add a supply of warmer gas to the stream before it reaches the specimen, or to warm the gas by using a heater wire wrapped around the delivery tube. For operation at temperatures near 100° K the consumption of liquid nitrogen can be expected to be in the neighborhood of 2 to 4 liters/hr, according to reports from various laboratories. The accuracy with which the temperature of the specimen can be held constant depends, of course, upon the care with which the apparatus is designed and the stream is monitored, but with simple equipment temperatures can usually be controlled to 1° C or better, and $\pm 0.1°$ is claimed by one laboratory; it is found that the degree of constancy is sufficient to grow crystals in glass capillaries while they are in position in a camera.[5]

It is generally advisable to interpose a cylindrical sheet of plastic between the cold-gas stream and the film of a camera so that the film can be at a temperature near the ambient. One design utilizes a series of concentric cellophane cylinders between the specimen and the film, with the gas circulating alternately up and then down between successive cylinders as it leaves the specimen.[6] To prevent condensation of moisture on the outside of a window, provision can be made for the outflowing dry refrigerating gas to flow continuously over the window; or the warm air from a hair dryer can be directed at it, in which case a double window of thin plastic material is advisable.

In one design, a platinum coil in the gas-delivery tube is used as one arm of an a-c bridge which controls heating current to maintain constant temperature in the stream automatically.[7] In most designs the specimen temperature is measured by a thermocouple made of very fine wire and placed close to the specimen or in contact with it but just outside the x-ray beam; this thermocouple can be made the sensing element of a temperature-controlling system. By avoiding turbulence in the stream as it bathes the specimen and by using larger-diameter streams, thermal gradients are lessened. If the specimen is a metallic wire it must be insulated from the goniometer head or spindle that supports it or its temperature may be as much as 20° C above the temperature of the gas stream; nonconducting samples such as powders in glass capillaries give much less trouble in this respect.

Gas-flow cooling is used in Debye cameras, in special cameras using flat specimens in which the specimen can be rotated in its own plane and oscillated,[8] in various single-crystal cameras,[1,9] and in all types of diffractometers.

If the specimen is clamped to a copper piece (or embedded in a recess in a copper block) it can be transferred from a beaker of liquid nitrogen to an appropriate housing on a diffractometer and immersed in the cold-gas stream without warming more than a few degrees above 78° K.[10] This technique is valuable if it is necessary to carry out operations on the sample while immersed in liquid nitrogen, such as cold-working the specimen to induce phase changes or stacking faults, and then to x-ray the sample without danger of losing the results of the cold work.[11]

Gas-flow cooling can be extended to temperatures near 23° K by the use of hydrogen supplied from a Dewar flask of boiling liquid hydrogen. The heat capacity of hydrogen is much higher than nitrogen, and because its thermal conductivity is also much higher it is more efficient in heat exchange; it also conveniently has very low viscosity. These advantages, plus the low boiling point of liquid hydrogen (20° K), partially compensate for the extra precautions necessary when it is used. Since hydrogen mixed with air is explosive over a tremendous range of concentrations—4 to 96 per cent—a prime necessity with hydrogen-gas cooling is to provide an exhaust system that keeps the gaseous mixtures well below the dangerous range, or a pipe that vents the hydrogen-containing space to the outside of the building. The avoidance of ice and snow at various points in the Dewar vessel and diffraction equipment and the excessive cooling of parts of the diffraction equipment are also much more of a problem than with nitrogen-gas cooling. Details of an installation for a Weissenberg camera have been published by Robertson,[12] and are indicated in Fig. 1. A glass Dewar vessel containing about 3 liters of liquid hydrogen is allowed to boil at a rate governed by its natural heat leak which gives 750 cm^3/hr, and the gas above the liquid is passed through a cooling coil immersed in the liquid, then down through a vacuum-insulated transfer tube to a jet accurately centered about a millimeter from the specimen. The hydrogen-gas strram is surrounded by a stream of carefully dried warm hydrogen which issues from a concentric glass tube. In the published design the equipment is open to the room and explosive mixtures of hydrogen and air are avoided by an exhaust system. This is not a recommended practice from the standpoint of safety, since dangerous concentrations might occur locally. A safer procedure would be to enclose the entire apparatus in a plastic bag (of Mylar, for example) which is vented to the outside of the building. In addition to contributing greatly to the safety of the operation, this would remove danger of ice and also of snow from frozen air, yet would permit manipulation of the equipment by hand; a good forced-ventilation system in the room would be advisable with this arrangement also.

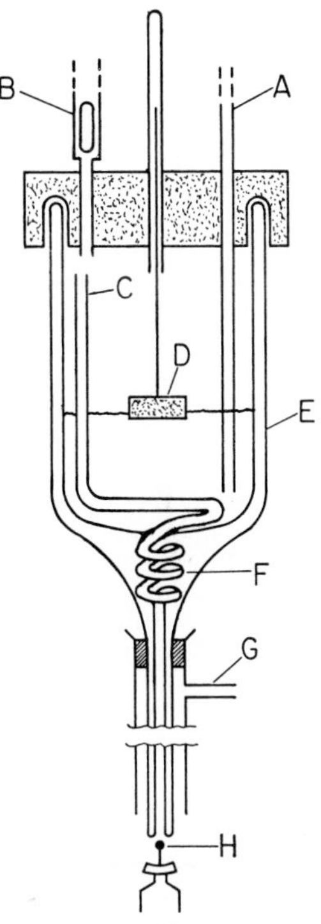

FIG. 1. Cryostat for cooling specimen by hydrogen or nitrogen gas. (*After Robertson.*) (*A*) Inlet for cryogenic liquid. (*B*) Vent. (*C*) Outlet tube for gas to specimen. (*D*) Liquid-level indicator. (*E*) Dewar vessel. (*F*) Coil permitting thermal contraction. (*G*) Inlet for warmer dry gas. (*H*) Specimen.

About 4 hr of operation of this equipment is possible without refilling; the same apparatus when used with liquid nitrogen as a refrigerant evaporates 160 cm^3/hr and operates about 18 hr on one filling with the specimen at 90° K. As a means of testing the temperatures actually obtained in a specimen capillary of glass, one can watch for the liquefaction of a gas sealed in the capillary (oxygen boils at 90° K, neon at 27° K; neon solidifies at 24° K). Many of the advantages of hydrogen over nitrogen are also shared by helium, and this gas is safer to use than hydrogen, but its high cost and limited availability are serious disadvantages.

4. EQUIPMENT COOLED BY STREAMING LIQUID

An effective way to cool a sample is by bathing it continuously in a stream of cold liquid. Apparatus by which liquid nitrogen is dripped over a sample in a camera of a diffractometer has the advantage of extreme simplicity and great constancy of temperature.[10,13] A reasonable rate of flow is obtained if a 0.3-mm-bore tube directs a jet of the liquid at the specimen; the evaporating liquid provides a dry atmosphere for the inside of the camera or specimen housing of a diffractometer.

Use has been made of other liquid coolants for operation at various other temperatures, though these usually have higher viscosity and require delivery tubes of the order of a millimeter in inside diameter. Alcohols have been used for this purpose, for example.[14] In any liquid-flow device it is necessary to keep ice particles from forming in the liquid, for otherwise the flow is quickly hindered or stopped by the crystals lodging in the tube delivering the liquid to the specimen. Thus it is important to exclude all moist air from the liquid container, whether it is a Dewar vessel or merely a metal can insulated by Styrofoam or other convenient insulation. It is easy to keep a specimen at liquid-nitrogen temperature while transferring it from a liquid-nitrogen bath to the diffraction apparatus, by keeping it under a stream of liquid throughout the transfer process.

5. EQUIPMENT COOLED BY CONDUCTION

The widest range of temperatures and the most accurate control at any arbitrary temperature are possible with apparatus in which the specimen is cooled by conduction. If operation is to be limited to a temperature near liquid nitrogen, or ice or solid CO_2, a simple insulated container of liquid can be connected to the specimen by a copper bar or a copper tube containing the liquid; the conductor to the specimen can be wound with a heater to provide a temperature gradient between the bath and the specimen. The principle is frequently used with powder diffractometers[10,15] and with single-crystal devices for x-ray[16] or neutron[17] work.

Among the many designs that permit operation at liquid-hydrogen and liquid-helium temperatures the one developed at the National Bureau of Standards will be described.[18] This is a vertical cryostat, surrounded with a liquid-nitrogen tank, for operation either as a camera or as an attachment to a diffractometer that uses a vertical axis of rotation. Copper radiation shields surround the specimen, and the x-ray window in one of the radiation shields may be covered with 0.00035-in.-thick nickel foil which serves both as a shield and as a beta-radiation filter when copper radiation is used. Beryllium windows 0.025 in. thick are attached to the outside of the evacuated cryostat. Temperatures are measured with a thermocouple of Ag containing 0.37 per cent Au vs. Au containing 2.1 atomic per cent Co, the thermoelectric power of which is approximately 10 μv/° K at 4.2° K. A slide is provided to move the cryostat normal to the specimen face, and the weight of the cryostat is counterbalanced. The specimen may be observed through a glass window. The cryostat provides for the deposition of vapors on the specimen holder and has been used extensively for the study of such deposits. For operation at temperatures above the conventional cryogenic liquids this design has been modified so that the cryogenic liquid can reach the block containing the specimen when desired, or can be kept from touching the block when the block is to be heated to a higher temperature.[19] A carbon resistor in one arm of a Wheatstone bridge is used as the temperature-sensing element in the modified instrument, and temperatures can be held automatically to $\pm 0.1°$ K in the range below 20° K. In addition, a thermocouple of Au plus 2.11 atomic per cent Co vs. Cu is used throughout the range 4.2 to 300° K. The x-ray windows, which in this modification are made of 0.0007-in. Mylar sheet cemented on with epoxy resin, attenuate copper $K\alpha$ radiation by only 8.5 per cent yet are vacuum-tight and withstand the pressure difference of 1 atm.

Many of the features of the Bureau of Standards instrument are found in the somewhat simpler design at the University of Chicago (and duplicated elsewhere), a portion of which is shown in detail in Fig. 2. The outer vacuum container is connected to the upper part of the cryostat with an O-ring seal, and the 1-cm-wide x-ray window

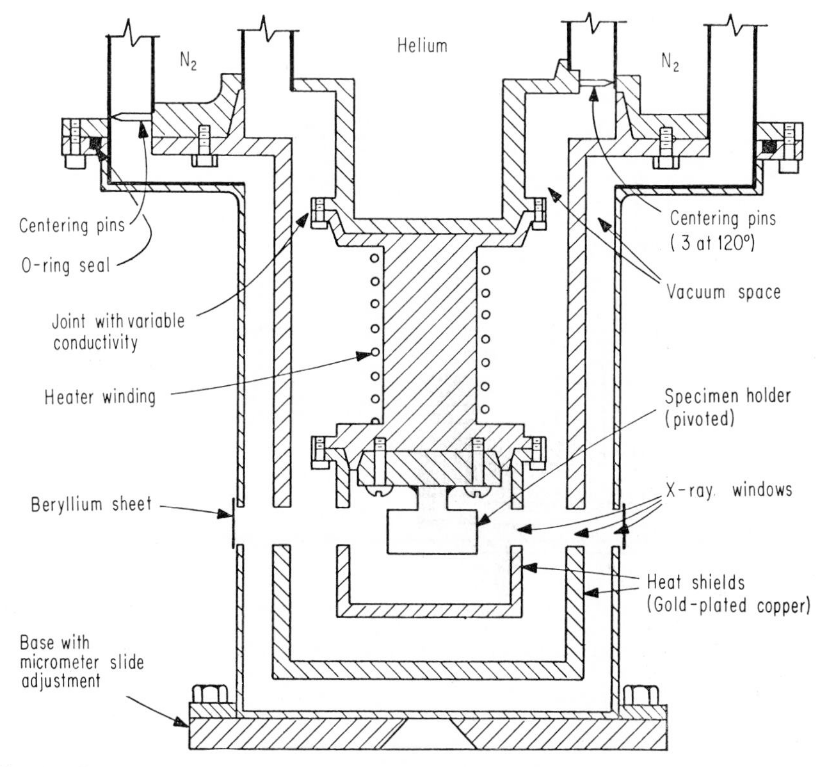

FIG. 2. Lower portion of cryostat for cooling specimen by conduction, used with diffractometer for single-crystal and powder studies at temperatures between 2.7 and 350° K.

in it is covered with 0.006-in. lacquered beryllium sheet throughout its circumferential length of about 200°. Alignment of single crystals and powder specimens is aided by an open framework of dimensions identical with those of the outer container. The heat shields, bolted to the lower ends of the containers for the cryogenic liquids, with conical joints, are of copper. These and walls of the liquid containers are gold-plated to retain good reflectivity with minimum maintenance. Operation above the conventional cryogenic-liquid temperatures either is done during a slow drifting upward in temperature with the inner container empty or is done by applying heat to the specimen holder with the inner container filled but with an insulating shim placed in the joint between the specimen holder and the inner liquid container. With 2 liters of liquid helium in the inner container and about 3 liters of liquid nitrogen in the outer one, operation up to 8 hr has been obtained without helium refilling.

Liquid hydrogen, because of its high heat of evaporation, lasts much longer and is much better suited than helium for operation in the range between 20 and 60° K. A simple crystal holder pivoting about a horizontal axis has proved sufficient for most single-crystal studies undertaken.

An alternate base for the cryostat provides means of cold-working metals in situ at low temperatures.[20] A stainless-steel rod enters the evacuated chamber through a ball-and-socket joint and flexible bellows (Fig. 3). The end of the rod may be shaped and sharpened so that downward strokes cut off oxidized layers from the specimen, in-and-out strokes cold-work the specimen, and upward strokes rub the surface smooth.

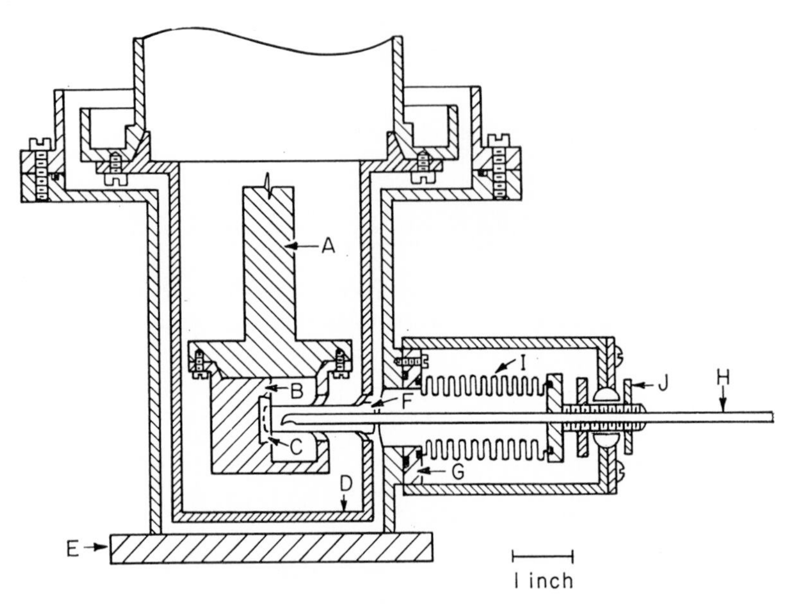

Fig. 3. Lower portion of cryostat for cold-working a sample at low temperatures. (*A*) Copper rod extending down from liquid-helium container. (*B*) Copper specimen holder. (*C*) Cavity for specimen. (*D*) Copper radiation shield bolted to liquid-nitrogen container. (*E*) Base of brass vacuum chamber, provided with slide adjustment. (*F*) X-ray window (Mylar-covered), aligned with windows in *B* and *D*. (*G*) O-ring seal around port for stainless-steel tool *H* which pivots around ball-and-socket assembly with adjusting nuts at *J*. (*I*) Sylphon bellows.

In Germany, many different substances deposited on aluminum-foil substrates at very low temperatures have been studied with powder cameras built into equipment rather similar to that mentioned above.[21,22]

There is a trend in some newer cryostat designs to replace the liquid-nitrogen container that surrounds the helium container by a simple thermal shield of copper, which is attached to the outlet tube from the helium container and is cooled by the gas in this tube.

6. EQUIPMENT WITH IMMERSION COOLING OF THE SPECIMEN

With a specimen completely immersed in a bath of cryogenic liquid, accurate control of specimen temperature is possible and all parts of the specimen are held at the temperature of the surrounding liquid. This principle is used in equipment recently built at Los Alamos.[23] The specimen is placed in a small thin-walled tube extending down from the bottom of the inner chamber of a cryostat; the rays pass through the liquid in reaching the specimen and also after being diffracted by the specimen.

A serious limitation of this type of design is the fact that temperatures are limited to those obtainable with boiling liquids; a continuous variation over a wide range is impossible. On the other hand, the chief advantage of this type is the possibility of accurate knowledge of specimen temperatures even when the specimen is a powder and when the thermal conductivity of the specimen is low (a situation that can cause difficulty in conduction-cooled apparatus). It should be kept in mind that liquid baths under some conditions may have appreciable temperature gradients within them.

The boiling point of a liquid can be reduced by reducing the pressure above the liquid; however, the temperature ranges between the triple point of liquid nitrogen (63.3° K) or liquid oxygen (54.7° K) and the boiling point of hydrogen (20.4° K) are practically inaccessible in this equipment, as is also the range between the triple point of hydrogen (13.9° K) and the boiling point of helium (4.2° K).

7. A SIMPLE THERMAL SWITCH

In various cryogenic experiments including diffraction work it is often desirable to have a thermal switch between the cryogenic liquid and the specimen. A type of thermal switch that is rapidly gaining in popularity because of its simplicity and its ability to control the rate of heat flow uses the principle of the reflux condenser. Suppose an x-ray sample is fastened to the bottom of a stainless-steel tube of $\frac{3}{16}$ in. diameter (or larger); let the top of the tube be fastened to a container holding a cryogenic liquid (H_2 is best) and let the tube be closed except for a capillary tube leading from it through the vacuum space around the sample to a vacuum pump. When the pump is running, relatively little heat will flow along the tube from the specimen to the container of the liquid, but by admitting some gas to the tube the gas can be made to condense at the top of the tube and drip down the inner wall. When it reaches the lower part of the tube it will evaporate and rapidly cool the specimen. The continued condensation and evaporation cycle will very rapidly cool the specimen yet can be stopped quickly by evacuating the tube. Alternately, a slow transfer of heat can be had by maintaining the gas at a reduced pressure in the tube since condensation will not occur but there will then be convection in the gas, and the rate of heat flow can then be altered by altering the gas pressure.

REFERENCES CITED

1. H. S. Kaufman and I. Fankuchen, *Rev. Sci. Instr.*, **20**:733 (1949).
2. H. S. Kaufman and I. Fankuchen, *Anal. Chem.*, **24**:20 (1952).
3. A. R. Ubbelohde and I. Woodward, *Proc. Roy. Soc. (London)*, **185**:488 (1946).
4. J. Thewlis and A. R. Davey, *J. Sci. Instr.*, **32**:79 (1955).
5. T. R. Reed and W. N. Lipscomb, *Acta Cryst.*, **6**:45 (1953).
6. W. Hume-Rothery and D. J. Strawbridge, *J. Sci. Instr.*, **24**:89 (1947).
7. D. E. Henshaw, *J. Sci. Instr.*, **34**: 270 (1957).
8. E. A. Owen and G. I. Williams, *J. Sci. Instr.*, **31**:49 (1954).
9. B. Post, R. S. Schwartz, and I. Fankuchen, *Rev. Sci. Instr.*, **22**:218 (1951).
10. D. F. Clifton, *Rev. Sci. Instr.*, **21**:339 (1950).
11. C. S. Barrett and O. R. Trautz, *Trans. AIME*, **175**:579 (1948).
12. J. H. Robertson, *J. Sci. Instr.*, **37**:41 (1960).
13. K. Lonsdale and H. Smith, *J. Sci. Instr.*, **18**:133 (1941).
14. N. C. Tombs, *J. Sci. Instr.*, **29**:364 (1952).
15. B. A. Calhoun and S. L. Abrahams, *Rev. Sci. Instr.*, **24**:397 (1953).
16. R. Keeling, B. C. Frazer, and R. Pepinsky, *Rev. Sci. Instr.*, **24**:1087–1095 (1953).
17. E. O. Wollan, W. C. Koehler, and M. K. Wilkinson, *Phys. Rev.*, **110**:638 (1958).
18. I. A. Black, L. H. Bolz, F. P. Brooks, F. A. Mauer, and H. S. Peiser, *J. Res. Natl. Bur. Std.*, **61**:367 (1958).
19. F. A. Mauer and L. H. Bolz, *J. Res. Natl. Bur. Std.*, **65C**:225 (1960).
20. C. S. Barrett, *Acta Cryst.*, **9**:621 (1956).
21. W. Ruhl, *Z. Physik*, **138**:121 (1954).
22. H. J. Queisser, *Z. Physik*, **152**:495 (1958).

23. A. F. Schuch, in *Low Temperature Physics and Chemistry*, p. 79, J. R. Dillinger (ed.), University of Wisconsin Press, Madison, Wis., 1958.

GENERAL REFERENCES

Barrett, C. S.: *Structure of Metals*, 2d ed., McGraw-Hill Book Company, New York, 1952.

Peiser, H. S., H. P. Rooksby, and A. J. C. Wilson: *X-ray Diffraction by Polycrystalline Materials*, chap. 10, Institute of Physics, London, 1955.

Ruhemann, M., and B. Ruhemann: *Low Temperature Physics*, Cambridge University Press, London, 1937.

Chapter 16

SMALL-ANGLE SCATTERING OF X-RAYS

J. C. Grosskreutz

Midwest Research Institute

1. INTRODUCTION

The techniques which are described in this chapter and Chap. 17 depend for their success on the behavior of x-rays when they are scattered by inhomogeneous materials or by imperfect crystals. The intelligent use of these methods requires an understanding of the type of "particle" one can measure with a given technique and the relationship of that measurement to one obtained with another method. The following paragraphs will be helpful in selecting a method to fit a particular problem.

Small-angle Scattering. The particles in a sample which are responsible for small-angle x-ray scattering are small microscopic regions which have a different electron density from that of their surroundings. This scattering is produced by the particle as a whole and does not depend in any way on the internal crystal structure which it may possess. In other words, the Bragg condition does not enter into the expressions which describe small-angle scattering. In the ideal case, both the size and shape of the particles can be determined from the scattered intensity expressed as a function of scattering angle. The size range for which the technique is applicable is about 20 to 1,000 Å. Consequently, such things as large molecules in solution, colloidal suspensions, gels, finely divided solids, and precipitates in solid-solution alloys lend themselves to this type of analysis.

Line Broadening (Discussed in Detail in Chap. 17). A large perfect crystal will produce a Bragg diffraction line whose width is determined only by the instrumental broadening. If, however, the dimension perpendicular to the diffracting planes falls below about 0.3 micron, a detectable increase in line width will occur over and above the instrumental factor. Thus, by measuring the width of several diffraction lines from a sample composed of small crystallites, the dimensions of the crystallites may be determined in the directions along the respective reciprocal lattice vectors. The practical range of size determination by this method is about 20 to 3,000 Å. Very fine polycrystalline materials, finely divided crystalline solids, or layered crystals such as graphite lend themselves to the line-broadening technique.

Spotty Diffraction Rings (Discussed in Detail in Chap. 17). Spotty diffraction rings result when the diffracting crystals within a sample are large enough so that the camera geometry will allow resolution of individual reflections. The limiting case is a single crystal in the reflecting position which yields one spot per ring. For a polycrystal, the number of spots in a given ring is proportional to the number of grains which chance to be in the reflecting position. Knowing the total volume irradiated, one can easily calculate the average volume of the reflecting grains. With present-day microbeam x-ray generators, crystallite sizes down to about 0.6 micron can be measured. This technique extends the range of the line-broadening measurement to much larger crystals.

In summary, line broadening and spotty diffraction patterns can be combined to measure the size of *crystallites* down to about 20 Å. Small-angle x-ray scattering techniques can accomplish the same measurement in the size range 20 to 1,000 Å provided the sample can be so dispersed that each crystallite is surrounded by a medium of much lower, or higher, electron density. In addition, the latter technique can be applied to the measurement of particles whose internal structure is *not* periodic, and can therefore be considered a more powerful tool. The major limitation of small-angle x-ray scattering arises when the sample cannot be dispersed to provide the necessary electron-density contrast. For those cases in which both line broadening and small-angle scattering will apply, a choice between the two will be determined largely by the available equipment so long as the crystallite size is less than about 500 Å. Above this value, line broadening can generally be applied with more ease and accuracy.

Other Techniques. Many important non-x-ray methods are also available, of course, for the measurement of particle size. Of these, the most widely used are sedimentation, microscopy, and sieving. Criteria for choosing a technique include state of sample, size range, information desired, and equipment and resources available. Modern electron microscopes, for example, with careful operation, can resolve spacings down to 8 Å so that particle sizes as small as 15 to 20 Å can be measured with accuracy. Thus the entire range of measurement which we have just discussed for x-rays is available to this instrument. For those cases in which the sample is easily prepared for microscopy and the drying and outgassing which occur in the vacuum system of the microscope can be tolerated, there can be no doubt that the electron microscope is superior. A direct measurement of size and shape is obtained, and if a variation in size exists, this is readily apparent and measurable. Only averages can be obtained from the x-ray methods. On the other hand, there are many cases in which a particle-size measurement must be made nondestructively, or under conditions of hydration or pressure which completely eliminate the electron microscope as a possibility. It is these cases which this chapter discusses.

For a general discussion of particle-size techniques, the reader is referred to R. R. Irani and C. F. Callis, *Particle Size: Measurement, Interpretation, and Application* (John Wiley & Sons, Inc., New York, 1963).

2. BASIC PRINCIPLES*

We are primarily interested in the small-angle x-ray scattering ($<5°$) caused by particles whose average electron density differs from that of the medium in which they are dispersed. (The special case of Bragg diffraction at small angles will be treated briefly in Sec. 8.) In the equations that follow, it is assumed that both the incident and scattered waves are monochromatic plane waves, and multiple scattering is neglected.

The scattered intensity from a particle of uniform density averaged over all orientations is

$$I(h) = I_e(h) V \rho^2 \int_0^\infty \gamma_0(r) \left(\frac{\sin hr}{hr}\right) 4\pi r^2 \, dr \qquad (1)$$

where $I_e(h)$ is the scattered intensity from a single electron [essentially constant at small angles and equal to $(7.9 \times 10^{-26} I_0)/d^2$, where d is the distance to the point of observation, and I_0 is the incident intensity], V is the particle volume, ρ represents the difference between the electron densities of the particle and its surrounding medium, $\gamma_0(r)$ is the characteristic function for a particle and represents the probability that

* The reader should also consult the standard works on small-angle scattering given in the General References at the end of this chapter.

two points in the particle will be separated by a distance r, $h = (4\pi \sin \theta)/\lambda$, λ is the x-ray wavelength, and 2θ is the scattering angle.

In principle, one should be able to analyze a given set of scattering data by making a Fourier transformation of Eq. (1) and determining the characteristic function. Unfortunately, no simple method is known for finding the particle size and shape from the characteristic function. A more profitable approach is to assume certain standard particle shapes for which $\gamma_0(r)$ may be derived and to calculate with Eq. (1) the scattered intensity to be expected. These curves are then compared with the experimental data. Some of the more important results of these calculations are listed below.

Standard Single-particle Scattering Functions. It is convenient to write $I(h) = n^2 I_e i(h)$, where n is the number of electrons in a particle and $i(h)$ is called the single-particle scattering function. Note that $i(0) = 1$.

Spheres of Radius a

$$i(h) = \Phi^2(ha) = 3\left(\frac{\sin ha - ha \cos ha}{h^3a^3}\right)^2 = \frac{9\pi}{2}\left[\frac{J_{3/2}(ha)}{(ha)^{3/2}}\right]^2 \tag{2}$$

This function has a maximum at $h = 0$ and a series of subsidiary maxima which decrease rapidly in intensity. Table 1 gives values of $\Phi^2(ha)$.

Table 1. Scattering Function for Uniform Spheres, $\Phi^2(ha)$*

ha	$\phi^2(ha)$	ha	$\phi^2(ha)$	ha	$\phi^2(ha)$	ha	$\phi^2(ha)$
0.5	0.951	5.5	0.00689	10.5	0.000114	15.5	0.000153
1.0	0.816	6.0	0.00704	11.0	0.00000559	16.0	0.000121
1.5	0.628	6.5	0.00449	11.5	0.000161	16.5	0.0000528
2.0	0.427	7.0	0.00163	12.0	0.000342	17.0	0.00000515
2.5	0.249	7.5	0.000140	12.5	0.000371	17.5	0.00000727
3.0	0.119	8.0	0.000159	13.0	0.000241	18.0	0.0000423
3.5	0.0419	8.5	0.000835	13.5	0.0000777	18.5	0.0000705
4.0	0.00758	9.0	0.00126	14.0	0.00000102	19.0	0.0000664
4.5	0.00000	9.5	0.00108	14.5	0.0000358	19.5	0.0000364
5.0	0.00326	10.0	0.000554	15.0	0.000115	20.0	0.00000739

* From Beeman, Kaesberg, Anderegg, and Webb, *Handbuch der Physik*, vol. 32, p. 321, Springer-Verlag OHG, Berlin, 1957.

Ellipsoids of Revolution with Axes 2a, 2a, and v2a

$$i(h) = \int_0^{\pi/2} \Phi^2(ha\sqrt{\cos^2\theta + v^2 \sin^2\theta}) \cos\theta \, d\theta \tag{3}$$

If $R = [(2 + v^2)/5]^{1/2}a$ is the so-called radius of gyration for the particle (defined as the rms distance of the electrons from the center of charge), then Eq. (3) can be tabulated in terms of (hR) for both prolate and oblate ellipsoids of revolution (Tables 2 and 3).

These functions all have a central maximum at $h = 0$ and decrease monotonically with increasing angle. The differences in the curves are best brought out by plotting on log-log paper.

Scattering functions for ellipsoids with three different axes have been published by Mittelbach and Porod.[1]

Right Circular Cylinders of Diameter 2a and Height 2H

$$i(h) = \int_0^{\pi/2} \frac{\sin^2(hH\cos\theta)}{h^2H^2\cos^2\theta} \frac{4J_1^2(ha\sin\theta)}{h^2a^2\sin^2\theta} \sin\theta \, d\theta \tag{4}$$

Table 2. Scattering Functions for Prolate Ellipsoids of Revolution*

hR	$i(h)$						
	v = 1.5	2	3	4	6	10	∞
0.0	1.000	1.000	1.000	1.000	1.000	1.000	1.000
0.5	0.920	0.920	0.921	0.921	0.922	0.922	0.920
1.0	0.713	0.718	0.726	0.730	0.735	0.737	0.738
1.5	0.461	0.477	0.505	0.522	0.537	0.546	0.551
2.0	0.242	0.274	0.327	0.359	0.389	0.407	0.418
2.5	0.0990	0.138	0.206	0.250	0.292	0.318	0.334
3.0	0.0293	0.0616	0.128	0.176	0.225	0.259	0.278
3.5	0.00638	0.0240	0.0760	0.122	0.176	0.214	0.239
4.0	0.00333	0.00789	0.0421	0.0827	0.138	0.180	0.210
4.5	0.00447	0.00294	0.0216	0.0546	0.108	0.153	0.187
5.0	0.00450	0.00270	0.0101	0.0347	0.0836	0.131	0.168

* From Beeman, Kaesberg, Anderegg, and Webb, *Handbuch der Physik*, vol. 32, p. 321, Springer-Verlag OHG, Berlin, 1957.

Table 3. Scattering Functions for Oblate Ellipsoids of Revolution*

hR	$i(h)$						
	v = 1/1.5	½	⅓	¼	⅙	1⁄10	0
0.0	1.000	1.000	1.000	1.000	1.000	1.000	1.000
0.5	0.920	0.920	0.920	0.920	0.920	0.920	0.920
1.0	0.712	0.714	0.716	0.717	0.717	0.718	0.718
1.5	0.457	0.464	0.472	0.475	0.477	0.479	0.479
2.0	0.236	0.250	0.267	0.274	0.278	0.284	0.284
2.5	0.0931	0.112	0.136	0.148	0.154	0.162	0.166
3.0	0.0262	0.0450	0.0714	0.0846	0.0916	0.102	0.106
3.5	0.00688	0.0203	0.0428	0.0555	0.0627	0.0738	
4.0	0.00523	0.0113	0.0274	0.0385	0.0453	0.0562	
4.5	0.00525	0.00625	0.0166	0.0259	0.0320	0.0426	
5.0	0.00369	0.00307	0.00934	0.0170	0.0225	0.0328	

* From Beeman, Kaesberg, Anderegg, and Webb, *Handbuch der Physik*, vol. 32, p. 321, Springer-Verlag OHG, Berlin, 1957.

This expression can be evaluated in closed form for two important limiting cases:
1. Rods ($H \gg a$):

$$i(h) = Si(2hH)/hH - [\sin^2 (hH)]/h^2H^2 \qquad (h \ll 1/a) \tag{5}$$

where $Si(x) = \int_0^x (\sin y)/y \, dy$.

If h is large enough so that $hH \gg 1$, Eq. (5) further reduces to

$$i(h) = \frac{\pi}{2hH} \frac{4J_1{}^2(ha)}{(ha)^2} \cong \frac{\pi}{2hH} e^{-h^2a^2/4} \qquad \begin{cases} h \ll 1/a \\ h \gg 1/H \end{cases} \tag{6}$$

2. Disks ($H \ll a$):

$$i(h) = (2/h^2a^2)[1 - (1/ha)J_1(2Ha)] \qquad (h \ll 1/H) \tag{7}$$

If h is large enough so that $ha \gg 1$, Eq. (7) reduces to

$$i(h) = \frac{2}{h^2a^2}\frac{\sin hH}{(hH)^2} \cong \frac{2}{(ha)^2} e^{-h^2H^2/3} \qquad \begin{cases} h \ll 1/H \\ h \gg 1/a \end{cases} \tag{8}$$

The single-particle scattering function for prolate cylinders has been calculated exactly and is given in Table 4.

Table 4. Scattering Functions for Prolate Cylinders*

hR	$i(h)$						
	$v = 1$	2	3	4	6	8	∞
0.0	1.000	1.000	1.000	1.000	1.000	1.000	1.000
0.5	0.916	0.920	0.921	0.921	0.922	0.922	0.922
1.0	0.704	0.714	0.722	0.732	0.738	0.738	0.738
1.5	0.447	0.482	0.510	0.520	0.533	0.538	0.543
2.0	0.233	0.290	0.340	0.363	0.388	0.399	0.410
2.5	0.0820	0.168	0.235	0.270	0.302	0.314	0.333
3.0	0.0263	0.092	0.162	0.205	0.244	0.258	0.282
3.5	......	0.0463	0.110	0.154	0.198	0.217	0.245
4.0	......	0.0205	0.070	0.113	0.161	0.183	0.217
4.5	......	......	.....	0.0816	0.132	0.155	0.193
5.0	......	......	.....	0.0606	0.108	0.133	0.175

* From Beeman, Kaesberg, Anderegg, and Webb, *Handbuch der Physik*, vol. 32, p. 321, Springer-Verlag OHG, Berlin, 1957.

Table 5. Scattering Functions for Rectangular Prisms*

hR	$i(h)$						
	$v = 1$	2	3	4	6	8	10
0.0	1.000	1.000	1.000	1.000	1.000	1.000	1.000
0.5	0.920	0.920	0.920	0.921	0.921	0.921	0.921
1.0	0.716	0.722	0.728	0.735	0.738	0.738	0.738
1.5	0.462	0.491	0.513	0.525	0.536	0.536	0.536
2.0	0.246	0.308	0.350	0.374	0.393	0.399	0.400
2.5	0.118	0.190	0.348	0.380	0.307	0.320	0.323
3.0	0.055	0.119	0.182	0.218	0.249	0.268	0.273
3.5	0.030	0.077	0.130	0.169	0.206	0.223	0.232
4.0	.....	0.050	0.082	0.128	0.171	0.188	0.199
4.5	.....	0.029	0.063	0.099	0.141	0.160	0.173
5.0	.....	.....	.....	0.076	0.117	0.138	0.151

* From Beeman, Kaesberg, Anderegg, and Webb, *Handbuch der Physik*, vol. 32, p. 321, Springer-Verlag OHG, Berlin, 1957.

Extensive calculations for elliptical cylinders and hollow cylinders may be found in the original literature.[2]

Rectangular Prisims with Sides a, 2a, and 2va. The values of this scattering function are given in Table 5, where $R = [(5 + 4v^2)/3]^{1/2}a$ is the radius of gyration of the particle.

Mittelbach and Porod have also calculated the scattering functions for more general parallelepiped shapes.[3]

General Behavior of Scattering Functions. At very small angles Eq. (1) can be expressed by the Guinier approximation

$$i(h) = e^{-h^2R^2/3} \qquad (h < 1/R) \tag{9}$$

where R is the radius of gyration of the particle. Equation (9) holds for all particles regardless of shape. The slope of a log $i(h)$ vs. h^2 plot in the very small angle region (sometimes called a Guinier plot) will therefore yield a value of R. This measurement is perhaps the most widely used in the application of small-angle techniques. Table 6 lists the radius of gyration of the standard particles in terms of their physical dimensions.

At the large-angle extremity of the small-angle region, Eq. (1) reduces to

$$I(h) = I_e(h)(2\pi\rho^2S/h^4) \qquad (h \gg 1/R) \tag{10}$$

where S is the total surface area contained in the volume irradiated. If one knows the absolute magnitude of the intensity scattered at large angles, the magnitude of S may be determined.

Notice that all small-angle scattering curves from uniform particles will be Gaussian near $h = 0$ and will fall off as the inverse fourth power of the angle at the larger

Table 6. Radius of Gyration R for Various Particle Shapes

Shape	Dimensions	R^2
Sphere	Radius $= a$	$3a^2/5$
Ellipsoid of revolution	Axes $2a$, $2a$, $2va$	$\left(\frac{2 + v^2}{5}\right) a^2$
Right circular cylinder	Diameter $= 2a$; height $= 2va$	$\left(\frac{3 + 2v^2}{6}\right) a^2$
Rectangular prisms	Sides a, $2a$, $2va$	$\left(\frac{5 + 4v^2}{3}\right) a^2$

scattering angles. The behavior in between these angular limits depends on the specific shape of the particles responsible for the scattering.

Scattering by an Assemblage of Particles. In an actual sample there will be many particles within the irradiated volume, all of which will contribute to the experimentally measured scattering curve. The relationship between this curve and the single-particle scattering functions already discussed depends on the properties of the particular sample under study.

Widely Separated Identical Particles. In this case, the total-scattering curve is just N times the single-particle curve, where N is the number of particles in the irradiated volume. As the concentration of particles increases, interference between the individual scattered waves occurs and the scattering curve becomes distorted. The concentration below which interparticle interference can be neglected is usually determined experimentally, and is of the order of a few per cent in most cases.

Closer-packed Identical Particles. The effect of interparticle interference is to decrease the scattering near $h = 0$ and to leave the intensity at larger angles unchanged. As concentration is increased, the scattering curve may actually develop a maximum at very small angles. This maximum has no connection with a Bragg diffraction and should not be interpreted as such. The theory of interparticle interference is complex and the results have not been exploited much in the interpretation of data. The interested reader is referred to more comprehensive treatments of this subject (see General References at end of chapter).

Nonidentical Particles. The theory of scattering from polydisperse samples is extremely complicated, especially if interparticle interference is included. Generally the approach has been to neglect interparticle interference and to treat the problem using various simplifying assumptions.

At very small scattering angles, the Guinier approximation can be used, and the curve will be Gaussian just as for the case of identical particles. However, the radius of gyration which enters in the scattering formula [Eq. (9)] is a weighted mean defined by

$$\overline{R^2} = \sum_m p_m n_m{}^2 R_m{}^2 \Big/ \sum_m p_m n_m{}^2 \tag{11}$$

where p_m is the number of particles with a given size and n_m is the number of electrons in each particle of that size. If the particles are all of similar shape, the larger radii of gyration are weighted heavily in this average.

Another approach is to *assume* a particle-size distribution and to calculate the scattering [using Eq. (9)] from such an assemblage. Maxwellian, Gaussian, and rectangular distributions have been used. The most important result is that nearly identical scattering curves can be obtained by choosing the proper combination of particle shape, type distribution, and width of distribution. Thus, without some prior knowledge of the properties of the sample under study, it is impossible to draw unambiguous conclusions from the small-angle scattering data alone. For further details on the subject, the original literature should be consulted.[4]

For large scattering angles where $I(h)$ is proportional to h^{-4}, the scattered intensity from polydisperse systems, even when densely packed, is proportional to S, the total surface area irradiated.

Other Parameters Obtainable from $I(h)$. In addition to the general size, shape, and surface area of the particle, it is possible to obtain the volume, the characteristic length, and the molecular weight of the particle.

Volume. If the particle has uniform density, then it can be shown that

$$\int_0^\infty h^2 i(h)\, dh = 2\pi^2/V \tag{12}$$

Characteristic Length. We define $\bar{l}$, the characteristic length, as the mean length of all the lines passing through every point of the particle in all directions and ending on the surface of the particle. Then

$$\int_0^\infty h i(h)\, dh = (2\pi/V)\bar{l} \tag{13}$$

Molecular Weight. Finding the molecular weight M involves knowing the absolute intensity of the scattered radiation. Extrapolation of the scattering curve to zero angle then gives M through the relation

$$I(0) = I_e(0) N M^2 (n/M)^2 \tag{14}$$

where N is the total number of particles irradiated and (n/M) is the ratio of the molecular number to the molecular weight.

3. EQUIPMENT

Design. The design of any small-angle scattering device represents a compromise between the two conflicting requirements of intensity and resolution. The incident intensity, for a given angular resolution, is controlled by the choice of the x-ray source. Conventional crystal-diffraction tubes have proved satisfactory, although for the observation of weakly scattering protein and virus solutions, rotating-anode tubes,*

* These tubes are available from Design Incorporated, Madison, Wis. See Chap. 2, Sec. 2, for a discussion of x-ray tubes.

which allow an increase of intensity by about a factor of 3, are desirable. The problem of resolution and its corollary problem, the reduction of parasitic scattering, have been approached by the use of both counter and photographic detection of the scattered radiation. Instruments which utilize each of these methods will be discussed separately.

Counter Detection Instruments

Advantages	*Disadvantages*
1. Quantitative intensity data can be easily and directly obtained.	1. Because of sequential recording, a constant-intensity source is required.
2. A large dynamic range of sensitivity is available. Intensity range of 10^3 over the angular scattering interval is possible.	2. Counter is not sensitive to two dimensional asymmetries in the scattering pattern.
3. Electronic monochromatization (pulse-height selection) is possible.	

Counter detection instruments have been widely used in the study of scattering from proteins and viruses, gels, catalysts, deformed metals, and finely dispersed solids such as carbon black. Either Geiger or proportional counters can be used, but the superiority of the proportional counter, in both its range of counting-rate sensitivity

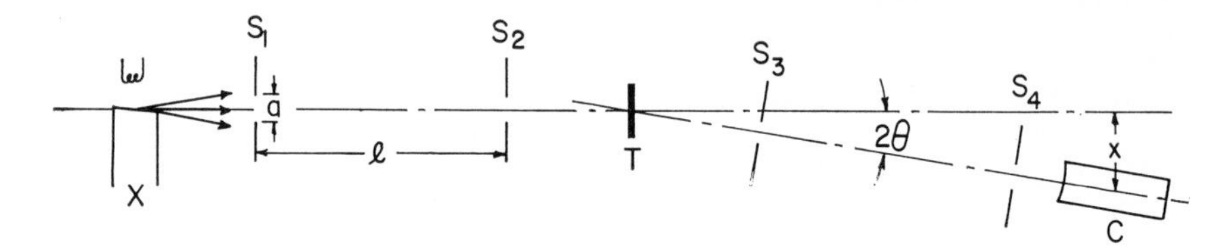

FIG. 1. Four-slit collimating system. X, x-ray source. S_1, S_2, S_3, S_4, collimating slits. l, distance between slits. a, slit width (slit height $b \gg a$). T, sample. 2θ, scattering angle. C, counter detector.

and its ability to discriminate roughly between characteristic and continuous radiation, makes it the better choice. (X-ray detectors are discussed in Chap. 3.) The use of pulse-height selection to provide monochromatic scattering data is extremely simple and useful, and when it is used in conjunction with Ni-filtered Cu radiation, over 99 per cent of the recorded radiation is in the $K\alpha$ lines. Only in cases where the highest precision is desired is it necessary to resort to crystal monochromatization. The loss in intensity which thereby results can be partially regained by using the focusing properties of bent crystals. Typical counter detection instruments are described in the following paragraphs.

1. Four-slit diffractometer: This instrument, originally used by Beeman and his coworkers,[5] is versatile and has been widely copied. The geometry is shown in Fig. 1. All slits are chosen equal in size and the distance between successive slits is the same. The first two slits S_1 and S_2 serve to collimate the incident beam, while slits S_3 and S_4 define the solid angle subtended by the counter at the scatterer, which is placed halfway between slits S_2 and S_3. The second pair of slits and the detecting counter are mounted on a movable arm which can be rotated about an axis through the scatterer. In the small-angle region, the angle of rotation is proportional to the linear distance x traveled by the counter, which provides a simple and convenient measure of the scattering angle. To reduce air scattering, the incident and scattered beam paths should be evacuated to fore-pump pressure. Experimental convenience dictates that the x-ray source, scatterer, and detector be at atmospheric pressure. Therefore, the slits can be mounted in evacuated brass tubes with entrance and exit windows of low-absorbing material placed at the extremities.

The value of the angular resolution $\delta(2\theta)$ in the plane of rotation is obtained by measuring the x-ray intensity vs. angle with no sample in place. Calibrated filters should be used to cut down the direct beam intensity when observing near zero angle. The resulting curve is called a "rocking curve," and the width is equal to $\delta(2\theta)$. The intensity recorded in the wings of this curve is due primarily to slit-edge scattering, sometimes termed "parasitic" scattering. If the slit width (measured in the plane of rotation) is a, and the separation between slits is l, then the direct beam disappears at angle $2a/l$ from the straight-through position, and the parasitic scattering stops at angle $4a/l$. These relations serve to determine the slit size to use in a given application. Typical values of l are 30 to 50 cm; thus a slit width $a = 0.3$ to 0.5 mm will allow data to be taken to within 2 milliradians of the main beam with an angular resolution of 4 milliradians. The slit height b used in this diffractometer is always many times larger than the slit width a. For practical purposes, the slit height is usually taken to be 1 cm.

2. Crystal diffractometers: In addition to monochromatization, reflection of the primary x-ray beam from a crystal set at the Bragg angle also achieves a high degree of collimation. In particular, the bent-crystal collimator gives a monochromatic beam which converges to a very fine line focus and can be so arranged to give an intense

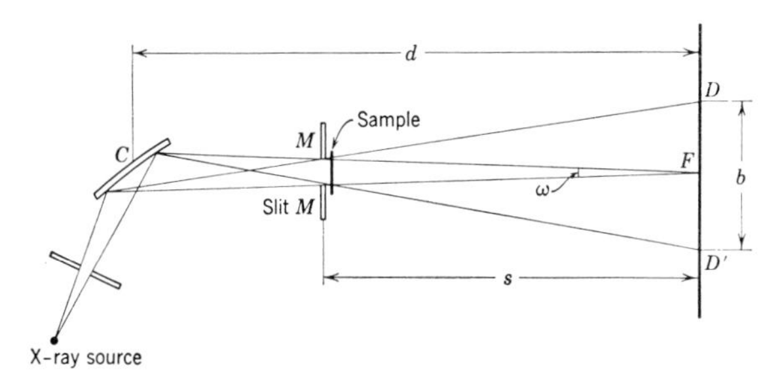

FIG. 2. Bent-crystal (single) collimating system. C, crystal. M, guard slit, ω, beam divergence, F, focus. Either a counter or film is placed at F. (*From A. Guinier and G. Fournet, Small Angle Scattering of X-rays, John Wiley & Sons, Inc., New York*, 1955.)

scattered beam at the point of observation. The geometry of this arrangement is shown in Fig. 2. Parasitic scattering is suppressed by the slit placed just in front of the sample. The edges of this slit are adjusted to approach the beam as closely as possible without actually touching it. The main advantage of this arrangement is that the angular uncertainty $\delta(2\theta)$ at the point of observation is independent of the primary-beam divergence and depends primarily on the separation of the $K\alpha$ doublet. Thus a high degree of resolution can be achieved, but with a sacrifice of intensity over the four-slit arrangement discussed above.

A prime disadvantage of the single-crystal collimator is the high background of diffuse scattering which occurs at the surface of the crystal and seriously limits both the lower limit of scattered intensity which can be observed and the minimum angle at which data can be taken (15 milliradians in a typical instrument). The solution of these difficulties is the use of a second crystal which employs the focus of the first as a source and converges the beam to a new focus (see Fig. 3). Such an arrangement reduces overall intensity by a further factor of $\sim\frac{1}{3}$, but allows data to be obtained down to $\sim$3 milliradians. For more information on this specialized instrument, the reader is referred to a more complete treatment.[6]

The sources employed in the crystal diffractometers discussed above are all line sources, and hence the collimator slit heights are limited only by the size of the crystals in use.*

* Bent-crystal monochromators of the type discussed may be obtained commercially from M. Beaudoin, 3 Rue Rataud, Paris 5, France.

Photographic Detection Cameras

Advantages	*Disadvantages*
1. Constant-intensity source is not required.	1. The dynamic range of sensitivity is limited.
2. Two-dimensional scattering pattern is recorded.	2. Microdensitometry is required for analysis of scattered intensity-curve shape.
3. Arrangement is simple.	

Photographic cameras were the first to be used in the study of low-angle scattering and have been applied to problems in colloids, finely divided solids, metallurgy, and oriented structures. Monochromatization by auxiliary methods is essential, and

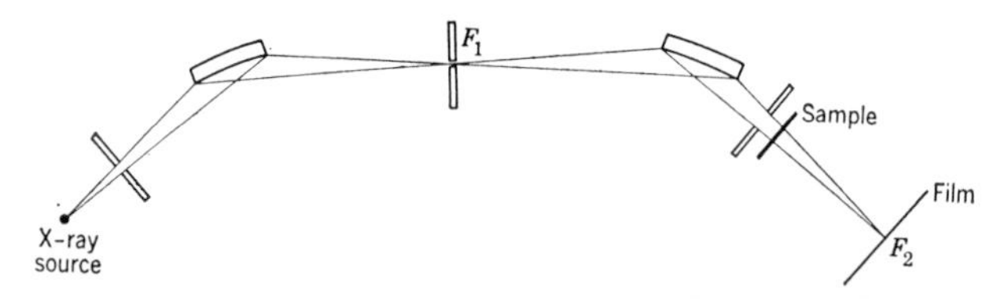

FIG. 3. Double bent-crystal collimating system. F_1, intermediate focus. F_2, final focus. (*From A. Guinier and G. Fournet, Small Angle Scattering of X-rays, John Wiley & Sons, Inc., New York,* 1955.)

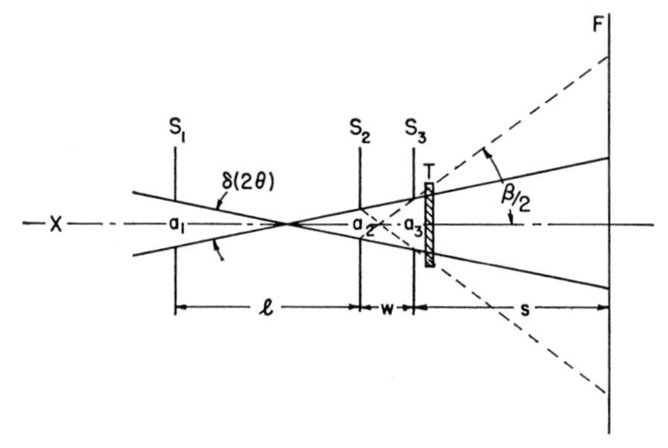

FIG. 4. Standard three-slit collimator. S, slit. a, slit width. F, film. $\delta(2\theta)$, angular resolution. $\beta/2$, maximum angle of parasitic scattering. X, x-ray source.

crystals are usually used. However, the use of filtered radiation is extremely convenient in vacuum cameras and has been applied with success in the determination of the radius of gyration of colloidal particles.[7] Moreover, nickel-filtered Cu radiation has been reported[8] to be 96 per cent $K\alpha$ and is usable in this form for curve-shape analysis. In general, however, caution is advised in the use of mixed radiations because the white radiation which gets through the filter can cause considerable distortions of the theoretically predicted curves. We may mention here that photographic detection using filtered radiation has been extensively used for the determination of long spacings where the detailed shape of the scattering curve is not important. This application will be discussed in Sec. 8.

1. Standard two- or three-slit collimator: The most widely used camera is shown schematically in Fig. 4. Slits S_1 and S_2 serve to define the primary beam, and it is assumed that the x-ray source uniformly illuminates the first slit. Slit S_3, which is sometimes placed in front of the sample, is a guard slit which is just wide enough to allow the primary beam to pass without touching. Its function is to reduce parasitic scattering.

The calculation of slit sizes and spacings is again, as in the case of counter instruments, a compromise between intensity and resolution. Since in most cases intensity considerations require the use of slits with a large height-to-width ratio, these "infinite slits" will be the only ones considered here. (For further details on pinhole slits, the reader is referred to the original literature.[4,7,9])

The design of the camera begins by assigning values to the following parameters which are dictated by the experiment:

$\delta(2\theta)$ = desired angular resolution

$\beta/2$ = angle at which parasitic scattering disappears

p = projected width of x-ray tube focal spot (or crystal monochromator) as viewed along the axis of the collimator

In addition, a convenient value may be chosen for l, the spacing between S_1 and S_2, usually of the order of 50 to 100 mm. The following equations then apply for optimum results:

$$\left.\begin{aligned} a_1 &= p \\ s &\geq \frac{0.1}{\delta(2\theta)} \qquad \text{mm} \\ a_2 &= \frac{s[l\delta(2\theta) - a_1]}{(l+s) + 2a_1/[\beta - \delta(2\theta)]} \\ w &= \frac{2a_2}{\beta - \delta(2\theta)} \\ a_3 &= a_2\left\{1 + \frac{2pa_2}{l[\beta - \delta(2\theta)]}\right\} \end{aligned}\right\} \tag{15}$$

The minimum value of s results in the smallest exposure times but requires the highest resolution in microdensitometry.

A beam stop should be placed in front of the film to absorb the direct beam.

2. Kratky camera: A novel camera[10] which eliminates all slit-edge scattering from one side of the central beam is shown in Fig. 5. The slit separations are all taken equal. The divergence of the beam, and hence the angular error, is determined by the separation of S_1 and S_2 in the vertical direction. Slit S_3 is placed close to, but not touching, the main beam.

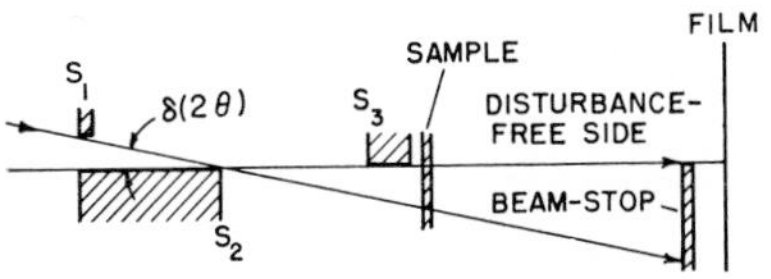

FIG. 5. Kratky camera. [*From O. Kratky, Makromol. Chem.*, **35A**: 12 (1959).]

3. Bent-crystal cameras: The collimating geometries shown in Figs. 2 and 3 can be used equally well with photographic detection. A more elaborate camera which utilizes total reflection of the x-rays from bent optical flats placed at right angles to each other has been described by Franks[11] and is available commercially. By collecting and focusing the radiation in two dimensions, a spot focus of great intensity is obtained.

Commercial Units. At the present time, several of the more elaborate small-angle scattering instruments are available commercially. These include:

Counter and/or Photographic Detection Instruments. Luzatti camera (single bent-crystal monochromator, Fig. 3); distributed by Jarrell-Ash Company, 26 Farwell Street, Newtonville, Mass.

Rigaku small-angle scattering goniometer; distributed by Erb and Gray Scientific Company, 854 South Figuero Street, Los Angeles 17, Calif.

Photographic Cameras Only. Franks low-angle scattering camera; distributed by Jarrell-Ash Company.

4. EXPERIMENTAL CONDITIONS AND PROCEDURES

Monochromatization and Choice of Wavelength. For the measurement of particle size and shape there is no doubt that a high degree of monochromatization is desirable if interpretation of the data is to be unambiguous. Unfortunately, the demands of intensity do not always allow crystal monochromatization to be used. In many applications the use of proportional counters with pulse-height selection is entirely adequate (especially with Cu radiation) and the gain in usable intensity is considerable. With the advent of proportional counters in x-ray work, the use of Ross filters now seems cumbersome and time-consuming. The least desirable condition is the use of filtered radiation without further treatment.

For a fixed value of $\delta(2\theta)$ the recorded intensity is proportional to the square of the wavelength. Thus one should choose to work with the longest practical wavelength. At very long wavelengths, however, the air absorption is large enough to require that the entire path from source to detector be evacuated. Practically speaking, Cu $K\alpha$ (1.54 Å) and Cr $K\alpha$ (2.29 Å) are the longest wavelengths available. Yudowitch[7] has used Al $K\alpha$ (8.32 Å) successfully by working entirely in vacuum. The use of long wavelengths also helps in the monochromatization problem, since the ratio of characteristic to continuous x-ray intensity is inversely proportional to the atomic number.

Slit Construction and Alignment. Tantalum is a highly satisfactory material for constructing slits. It is easily worked, and reasonable thicknesses (0.007 in.) completely absorb most x-rays of interest. Other useful materials are gold, steel, and lead. The slits should be carefully made, and the edges should be independently adjustable to a precision of the order of 0.01 mm. Various slit constructions have been reported ranging from the more conventional knife-edges to parallel cylinders of radius 2 to 3 mm. Slit-width adjustments are best made under a traveling microscope.

Slit alignment is highly important to the successful operation of the small-angle diffractometer or camera. The four-slit instrument of Fig. 1 can be accurately aligned by means of a light source placed before the entrance slit. A fine wire is stretched across the sample position to define the axis of rotation of the movable arm. With the arm at the zero position, a cathetometer is aligned with its optical axis along the collimator axis (defined by the first slit and the rotation axis). The procedure then consists of inserting and aligning the slits S_2, S_3, and S_4 one at a time.

The alignment of the guard slit in the three-slit system of Fig. 5 is extremely critical, and is best carried out with a counter detector which intercepts the main x-ray beam. The slit edges are advanced until the counting rate begins to diminish. The slit is then backed off a fraction of a turn, and the adjustment is complete.

After the alignment of diffractometer slit systems, a rocking curve should be recorded to determine the zero-angle position accurately.

Vacuum Requirements. Evacuation of the x-ray path is useful in reducing both air scattering and absorption. For the case of a strong scatterer and Cu radiation, evacuation is not necessary. For longer wavelengths, evacuation improves the intensity; for weak scatterers (e.g., protein solutions), evacuation is quite necessary. The vacuum attained by a simple mechanical fore pump ($\sim$1 micron) is adequate.

The entrance and exit windows of the evacuated path should have a high transmission and low scattering at small angles. Mica has about the lowest scattered intensity at small angles, and it can be cleaved to give transmissions of the order of 90 per cent. Mylar sheet will give extremely high values of transmission ($\sim$99 per cent), but it contributes a small background scattering[12] which can be easily subtracted out of weak scattering curves. Sintered beryllium sheet, while giving a high value of transmission, gives rise to a strong scattering at small angles, and should be avoided.

Detection Procedures. The usual precautions and procedures discussed in Chaps. 3, 8, and 9 of this handbook for use with photographic film and counters should, of course, be followed. Because of the unusually low intensity associated with small-angle scattering, several additional suggestions are appropriate. First, every effort should be made to reduce background scattering. In counter devices, this means elimination of all possible noise in cables, tubes, and circuit elements. It should be possible, with proportional counters and pulse-height selection, to reduce background counting rates to $\sim$5 counts/min. Second, even at low counting rates, it is not advisable to let the counting statistics fall below about 5 per cent; i.e., at least 400 counts should be recorded at each angular setting. Lastly, it is always good practice to run a background scattering curve without the sample in the scattering position, or with only the solvent normally used in solution samples. When the background amounts to over a few per cent of the total scattering, it should be subtracted out.

Standard Samples. For calibration purposes, several standard scattering samples should be kept in the laboratory and the small-angle diffractometer or camera checked out from time to time. Two good samples are carbon black and SiO_2. The latter is available in the form of aqueous suspensions of spherical particles from Monsanto Company (Syton) or E. I. du Pont de Nemours & Company (Ludox).

Preparation of Samples. Normally, samples are examined in dilute solution for closest approximation to the theory by which the results are interpreted. Above approximately 5 per cent concentration, interparticle interference effects may become troublesome and radius-of-gyration measurements, for example, become meaningless. Solutions are normally handled in thin-walled (Mylar, mica) containers so designed that they can be filled with a hypodermic syringe. In some applications, useful information can be obtained from concentrated samples in either a dry or moist state. Regardless of the state of the sample, optimum thickness is that which gives a transmission of $\sim$38 per cent $(1/e)$. This transmission is easily determined with a counter detection system.

5. CORRECTIONS TO THE DATA

The central problem of the small-angle scattering technique is the determination of the physical structure of the sample which produces the scattering. In principle, one has only to compare the experimental data with the appropriate formula from Sec. 2 to find the radius of gyration, the shape, the surface area, the volume, the characteristic length, or the molecular weight. In practice, however, there are certain corrections which must be made to the data before the basic equations can be used to solve the structure.

Background. The background scattering from the slits, sample-holder windows, and solvent should be subtracted out.

Absorption. It is often of interest to compare the relative scattered intensities from different samples. Therefore, the scattered intensity should be corrected for the absorption of the sample and sample holder. These quantities are easily determined with counter detection instruments.

Finite Slit Size. All the single-particle scattering functions quoted in Sec. 2 were derived assuming perfect collimation of the incident and scattered x-rays. In an actual experiment, an angular divergence exists for the incident ray because of the finite size of the collimating apertures. Moreover, in a counter detection instrument the scattered intensity is integrated over a range of scattering angles because of the size of the detector aperture. The effect of the collimating "errors" on the scattering curves is by no means negligible, and correction for them forms the major task of interpretation.

A detailed discussion of the results of using finite slits is given by Beeman et al.[13] They point out that there are two approaches to the problem. One can calculate the way in which the theoretical curves will be affected by a particular collimation system and compare the experimental data with these "smeared-out" theoretical curves. The other approach is to correct the experimental curves. If the experimental curve is not known accurately, or if it is known only over a small range of angles, the latter procedure can lead to serious errors in interpretation.

Slit-smeared Scattering Functions. In the following, the effects of the slit width a are assumed to be negligible, so that the full correction applies to slit height b. If $b \gg a$, the slits are considered infinite.

If $\mathcal{I}(h)$ is the experimental scattered intensity and $W(z)$ an instrument weighting function, the relation between $\mathcal{I}(h)$ and $I(h)$ is

$$\mathcal{I}(h) = \int_0^\infty W(z) I\left(\sqrt{h^2 + z^2}\right) dz \tag{16}$$

where $z = (4\pi \sin \phi)/\lambda$. $W(z)$ is the probability that a ray will get through the slit system if it is deflected at the sample through an angle ϕ. The angle ϕ is measured in the slit-height plane. Normally, $W(z)$ is Gaussian for finite slits and equal to 1 for infinite slits. [Experimentally, $W(z)$ is equal to the rocking curve taken in the slit-height plane. It should not be confused with the normal rocking curve taken in the slit-width plane, although both their shapes will be approximately Gaussian.] The smearing process for finite slits obviously depends on the magnitude of the height b through the function $W(z)$.

If the slits are infinite the calculations have been carried out to yield the following results.

1. Spheres: Results are shown in Table 7.

Table 7. Maxima and Minima for Uniform Spheres Using Infinite Slits*

ha		Intensity of maxima
Minima	Maxima	
	0	1
4.32	5.31	0.0165
7.52	8.63	0.00383
10.67	11.85	0.00145
13.82	15.04	0.000696
16.96	18.22	0.000282

* From Beeman, Kaesberg, Anderegg, and Webb, *Handbuch der Physik*, vol. 32, p. 321, Springer-Verlag OHG, Berlin, 1957.

2. Ellipsoids of revolution: The following series expansion due to Schmidt[14] gives the infinite-slit particle-scattering function for ellipsoids of revolution with semimajor axis va and equatorial radius a.

$$\mathcal{G}(v,ha) = \sum_{n=0}^{\infty} c_n f_n(v)(ha)^{2n} \tag{17}$$

where
$$f_0(v) = 1 \text{ for all } v$$

$$f_n(v) = [(2n+1)b_n]^{-1}\left[1 + B(v)\sum_{j=0}^{n} b_j v^{2j+1}\right]$$

$$b_j = 2^{2j}(j!)^2/(2j+1)!$$

$$B(v) = (v^2-1)^{1/2}(\cosh^{-1} v)^{-1} \qquad v \geq 1$$

$$B(v) = (1-v^2)^{1/2}(\cos^{-1} v)^{-1} \qquad v \leq 1$$

$$c_n = \frac{30(-1)^n}{(n!)^2(2n+2)(2n+3)(2n+5)}$$

3. Guinier approximation for radius-of-gyration determination: At very small scattering angles where the Guinier approximation is valid, the correction is very simple. The slit-smeared curve is just a constant times the perfect collimation curve regardless of the slit height.

$$\mathcal{G}(h) = \text{const } e^{-h^2R^2/3} \tag{18}$$

4. Infinite slit curves at relatively large angles: Equation (10) for the asymptotic behavior of all scattering functions at large angles becomes

$$\mathcal{G}(h) = (\pi/2)hI(h) = I_e(h)(\pi^2\rho^2S/h^3) \tag{19}$$

Thus the infinite-slit experimental curve falls off as the inverse cube instead of the inverse fourth power of the angle. Similarly, the region of inverse-square dependence for thin platelets discussed in Sec. 2 will become an inverse first-power dependence for infinite slits.

The integrals used in Eqs. (12) and (13) become for infinite slits

$$\int_0^\infty h^2 I(h)\, dh \rightarrow \tfrac{1}{2} \int_0^\infty h \mathcal{I}(h)\, dh \tag{12a}$$

and

$$\int_0^\infty h I(h)\, dh \rightarrow 1/\pi \int_0^\infty \mathcal{I}(h)\, dh \tag{13a}$$

Correction of Experimental Curves. The "unsmearing" process is the inversion of the integral in Eq. (16). The process is difficult and has been carried out only for a few special cases. For infinitely high slits

$$I(h) = \frac{-2}{\pi} \int_0^\infty \frac{\mathcal{I}'(\sqrt{h^2 + z^2})}{\sqrt{h^2 + z^2}}\, dz \tag{20}$$

To use this relation, the derivative of the experimentally determined scattering curve must be determined. Then, for each value of h, a curve of $\mathcal{I}'(\sqrt{h^2 + z^2})/\sqrt{h^2 + z^2}$ is traced and a graphical integration performed. The process is tedious and involves some error in the numerical differentiation of an inexact curve.

If a Gaussian weighting function is assumed, Eq. (16) has been solved to give[15]

$$I(2\theta) = [1/j^2 p \sqrt{\pi}\,(\Delta 2\theta)] \left\{ j(2j+1)^{1/2} \mathcal{I}(j\,\Delta 2\theta) - \sum_{i=1}^{\infty} T_{ij} \mathcal{I}[(i+j)\,\Delta 2\theta] \right\} \tag{21}$$

where $T_{ij} = (j + i)\,[2\sqrt{i^2 + 2ij} - \sqrt{(i-1)^2 + 2(i-1)j}$
$- \sqrt{(i+1)^2 + 2(i+1)j}]\, \exp\,[-(p\,\Delta\theta)^2(2ij + i^2)]$

In these equations, which are in suitable form for numerical calculation, $(\Delta 2\theta)$ is the angular interval, j is a running variable such that a particular value of $2\theta = j(\Delta 2\theta)$, and p is a constant determined by the slit height. For the four-slit diffractometer (Fig. 1), $p = 9\sqrt{\pi}\, l/16b$, where l is the distance between slits and b is the slit height.

6. INTERPRETATION OF THE DATA

It is helpful in the analysis of small-angle scattering curves if one knows in advance whether or not the particles in the sample are monodisperse. Further, the effects of interparticle interference should be checked by running curves from samples of different concentration. If the interference effects are appreciable and further dilution is impossible, then the very small angle portions of the curve should be ignored in the interpretation.

Comparison with Theoretical Scattering Functions. To estimate the shape of a particle in a monodisperse system, the corrected scattering curves should be plotted on log-log paper and compared with the standard single-particle scattering functions. It should be emphasized that several different particle shapes can give rise to nearly identical scattering patterns. Often in those cases where a definite shape is difficult to assign, it can be assumed that the particles are uniform ellipsoids of revolution and the best value for the axial ratio determined. Further evidence about the general shape of the particle can be found by looking for either a $1/h$ (rods) or $1/h^2$ (platelets) dependence in the intermediate angular range.

If the sample is known to be polydisperse, the safest procedure is to compare the experimental curves with the theoretical curves for polydisperse ellipsoids of revolution calculated by Schmidt.[16] In this way, an axial ratio can be determined and the particle described as either flattened or elongated.

Radius-of-gyration Determination. The radius of gyration is the least ambiguous parameter which can be determined from the data. It can be determined accurately, however, only for the cases in which the scattering curve is Gaussian at the very small angles. The slope of a log $I(h)$ vs. h^2 plot will yield the value of R in these cases via Eq. (9). Concentration effects can be eliminated by determining R for several different concentrations c. Extrapolation of the R vs. c curves to infinite dilution then gives the best value for R (see Fig. 7).

Cases will arise in practice where the log $I(h)$ vs. h^2 plot will not be a straight line. If interparticle interference effects have been eliminated, this behavior can only mean that the particles are polydisperse. As stated in Sec. 2, the interpretation of such patterns requires first that a distribution function be assumed for the particle size. Shull and Roess[4] and Hosemann[17] have worked out methods based on a Maxwellian distribution for calculating an average value for R. The interested reader is referred to the original literature for a detailed explanation of these and other methods.[18]

Tail Analysis. When interparticle interference effects cannot be eliminated, or polydispersity renders a calculation of R very difficult, it may still be possible to deduce something about the size and shape of the particles by examination of the scattering curves at relatively large angles. In the region of large scattering angles, all particles scatter as $1/h^4$ regardless of shape [Eq. (10)]. If the particles are spherical, there will be a smooth transition from the Gaussian behavior at small angles directly to the inverse fourth-power dependence. (For uniform spheres, the characteristic maxima and minima oscillate about an inverse fourth-power decrease in average scattered intensity.) For the two limiting cases, flat platelets and long rods, transition regions exist between the Gaussian and $1/h^4$ dependence which are characteristic of the shape and whose angular position allows one to estimate the small dimension of the particle.

A $1/h^2$ transition region indicates the presence of flat platelets [Eq. (8)]. The transition to the $1/h^4$ scattering will occur when $h \approx 1/H$, where $2H$ is the thickness of the platelet.

A $1/h$ transition region indicates the presence of long rods [Eq. (6)], with $1/h^4$ scattering beginning at $h \approx 1/a$, where $2a$ is the diameter of the needlelike rod.

Multiple Scattering. In the case of thick samples containing large particles, the effects of multiple scattering can be appreciable, and the methods described above cannot be used without modification. Dexter and Beeman[19] have determined the scattering function for this case and find that the particle size can be obtained from a series of measurements taken from samples of varying thickness. The slope α of a plot of the scattering-curve width (at $1/e$ of the central maximum) vs. the square root of the mass per unit area of the sample is proportional to the particle radius a,

$$\alpha = 3\sqrt{3}\,\lambda^2 r_0 N_0/4\pi\,\sqrt{a}$$

where N_0 is Avogadro's number, λ the wavelength, and r_0 the classical electron radius.

A somewhat different treatment of multiple scattering at small angles has been given by Luzzati[20] together with some experimental verifications.[21]

Multiple scattering effects of an entirely different nature occur during the irradiation of polygonized metals. Their interpretation is discussed in Sec. 7.

7. APPLICATIONS

Small-angle x-ray scattering techniques can be most successfully applied to the measurement of the size and shape of a collection of identical particles in dilute solution. Particles with a linear dimension (e.g., diameter) in the range 20 to 500 Å will be most amenable to convenient measurement. Samples which are polydisperse, insoluble, and available only in concentrated form raise difficulties in interpretation of the data. The following paragraphs outline briefly the more important applications of small-angle scattering, and where appropriate, examples of data and methods of interpretation are given.

Proteins and Viruses. A variety of both animal and plant proteins as well as viruses consists of identical particles which can be dispersed into solution. The sizes of these particles usually fall into the desirable range, and the particles are therefore well suited for small-angle scattering analysis. Because of the small difference between the electron density of the protein and that of the solvent (usually water), these solutions are weak scatterers. Background scattering must be minimized, and a rotating-anode x-ray source is preferable. Two techniques—radius-of-gyration determination and comparison of data with standard curves—have been used for obtaining the desired information on size and shape. Both these techniques are much easier to apply when counter detection methods are used.

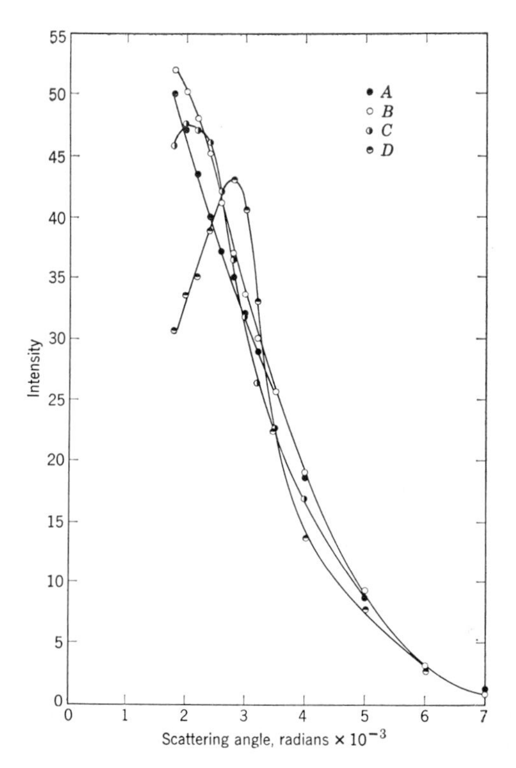

FIG. 6. Interparticle interference effects in the small-angle scattering from turnip yellow-mosaic virus solutions. Curves A, B, C, and D refer to concentrations of 1.6, 3.2, 6.3, and 12.8 per cent, respectively. [*From Schmidt, Kaesberg, and Beeman, Biochim. Biophys. Acta*, **14**: 1 (1954).]

Radius-of-gyration Determination. Regardless of the shape of the protein particle, the radius of gyration R is a definite characteristic of the particle and can be obtained by plotting $\log I(\epsilon)$ vs. ϵ^2, where I is the scattered intensity at angle ϵ. R is obtained from the initial slope of this plot. To obtain reliable values of R, it is necessary to obtain scattering curves from several different concentrations c and extrapolate the R vs. c curve to infinite dilution. Figure 6 shows the effect of interparticle interference on the scattering curve at low angles from solutions of turnip yellow-mosaic virus. Completely erroneous values of R would be derived from curves C and D. Figure 7 displays the R vs. c curve obtained for bovine serum albumin in a series of careful measurements. In addition to concentration, the pH of the solution can also affect the value of R. A good choice is a pH near the isoelectric point.

Comparison with Standard Curves. The form of the scattering curve at larger angles is used to determine whether the particles are essentially spheres, rods, or platelets. This information, together with the value of R, can often lead to a unique model for the size and shape of the particle. Beeman et al.[13] present a good summary of the treatment of several proteins and viruses.

For those cases in which chemical methods do not exist for the separation of naturally occurring protein complexes into their component parts, or in which the known solvents denature the protein, the experimenter must be satisfied with approximate methods. Radius-of-gyration plots for a mixture of particles will not be straight lines but may sometimes be analyzed by the special methods devised for such cases. If dilution is the problem, "tail" analysis will often yield the basic shape of the particle, and sometimes an upper limit on the size can be established. Figure 8 illustrates such a curve for the naturally occurring wheat protein complex and shows that the particles are flat platelets.

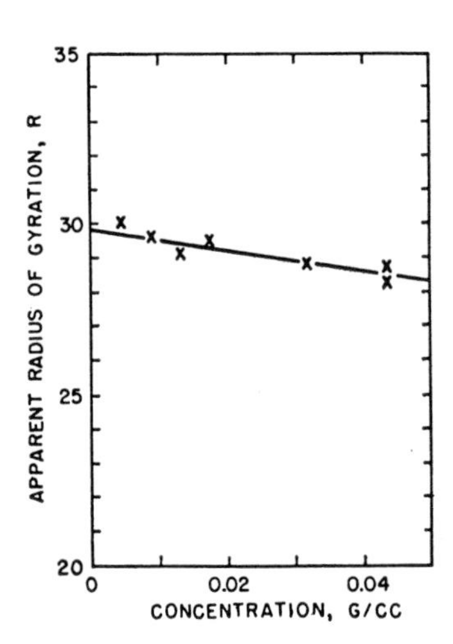

FIG. 7. Radius of gyration vs. concentration in BSA. [*From Anderegg, Beeman, Shulman, and Kaesberg, J. Am. Chem. Soc.,* **77**: 2927 (1955).]

Colloids and Gels. Dilute colloidal solutions are natural subjects for small-angle x-ray scattering measurements, especially if the suspended particles have a high electron density. Gold, silver, xylan, nickel hydroxide, Co_3O_4, and TiO_2 suspensions have all been studied.[7,22] Aluminum hydroxide gels precipitated under various conditions have been investigated,[23] and exhibit scattering typical of platelets.

Finely Divided Solids. Examples of materials which give strong small-angle scattering are carbons and catalyst powders (e.g., Al_2O_3, Fe_2O_3).[4,18] These materials are often polydisperse (possessing a range of sizes) and usually available only in concentrated form. They are strong scatterers, however, and scattering data can be obtained out to 5 to 6°. Because of polydispersity, radius-of-gyration plots will be concave upward and must be interpreted in terms of a size distribution (Sec. 6). The situation at small angles, where the R information is contained, is further complicated by interparticle interference effects, some samples giving the effects, others not. Therefore, the absolute accuracy of size-distribution data so obtained is open to serious question. Nevertheless, good use can often be made of such data to show the comparative effects of various methods of preparation.

Fibers (cf. Chap. 21). Fibers give a small-angle scattering which is very intense in the direction perpendicular to the fiber axis. Hence photographic detection is essential for the proper registration of these patterns. Often the scattering is characterized by peaks, which may sometimes be interpreted by an application of Bragg's law (Sec. 8) as long periodicities in the structure (e.g., collagen). A strict application of particle-size analysis to fiber patterns is not justified in view of the close packing of particles in the fiber. Many attempts have been made to interpret the patterns properly, but at present no well-documented method is available.[24]

Metal Structure. *Work-hardening Substructure.* Many metals divide into subgrains ~1 micron in diameter following cold work. Although these grains are too large and devoid of electron-density "contrast" to register small-angle scattering in the usual sense, an entirely different mechanism leads to a measurable scattering in the low-angle range. Because of the slight misorientation between subgrains, a *double* Bragg scattering occurs which yields a scattered ray at a small angle with respect to the main beam. The interpretation of this scattering proceeds by methods different from those presented in this chapter.[25] Instead of giving the subgrain size, these data provide the distribution of the angles of misorientation among subgrains.

Age-hardening Precipitate Structure. The precipitation of one component of an alloy during age hardening can be detected by small-angle scattering provided the atomic number of the precipitate is considerably different from the host metal (e.g., Al-Ag). The scattering, however, is not of the usual form but gives rise to a strong, circularly symmetric peak at ~2 to 3°. Whether this peak is due to interparticle interference or to an internal structure in the precipitate is not clear. No quantitative method is presently available for calculating precipitate size from the data.

Quenched-in Vacancy Clusters and Radiation Damage. Pure metals which have been quenched from a high temperature or irradiated by neutrons exhibit a small-angle scattering which can be interpreted by the radius-of-gyration technique. Analysis has indicated that the scattering centers are small coherent regions ~100 Å in diameter.[26]

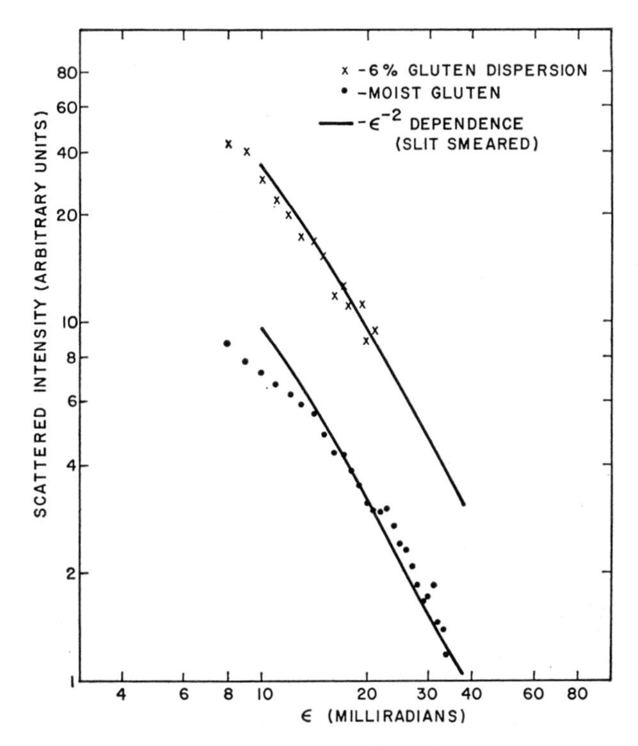

FIG. 8. Small-angle x-ray scattering from wheat gluten showing agreement with theoretical platelet scattering. [*From Grosskreutz, Biochim. Biophys. Acta,* **38**: 400 (1960).]

8. MEASUREMENT OF VERY LONG PERIODICITIES

Crystals and fibers which possess periodicities greater than about 25 Å will produce Bragg diffractions in the "small-angle" region. This diffraction is, of course, in no way related to the scattering produced by the small particles which are the primary subject of this chapter. Nevertheless, the equipment and design considerations are in most cases quite similar. Because of the close spacing of the different orders of diffraction in the small-angle region, the angular-resolution requirement is more stringent for the measurement of long periodicities. Moreover, the consequent sacrifice in intensity effected by this resolution requires that photographic detection be used to reduce operator time. In addition, many materials with long periodicities also produce asymmetric diffraction patterns and make photographic recording even more necessary.

The design of a slit system for measurement of long periodicities requires first a knowledge of the order of magnitude of the period d which is involved. The angular resolution $\delta(2\theta)$ sufficient to just resolve adjacent orders is then

$$\delta(2\theta) = \lambda/d$$

The calculation of slit sizes and separations then follows the procedures outlined in Sec. 3 for photographic cameras. Bolduan and Bear[27] have given typical dimensions for both slit and pinhole cameras capable of resolving various long spacings. Materials which have been studied with such cameras include collagen, keratin, synthetic polyesters, and chrysotiles. See Chap. 21 for a complete discussion of characterization of polymers.

REFERENCES CITED

1. P. Mittelbach and G. Porod, *Acta Phys. Austriaca*, **15**:122 (1962).
2. P. Mittelbach and G. Porod, *Acta Phys. Austriaca*, **14**:405 (1961).
3. P. Mittelbach and G. Porod, *Acta Phys. Austriaca*, **14**:185 (1961).
4. C. G. Shull and L. C. Roess, *J. Appl. Phys.*, **18**:295–313 (1947).
5. H. N. Ritland, P. Kaesberg, and W. W. Beeman, *J. Appl. Phys.*, **21**:838 (1950).
6. A. Guinier and G. Fournet, *Small-angle Scattering of X-rays*, p. 102, John Wiley & Sons, Inc., New York, 1955.
7. K. L. Yudowitch, *Rev. Sci. Instr.*, **23**:83 (1952).
8. U. W. Arndt and D. P. Riley, *Proc. Phys. Soc. (London)*, **A65**:74 (1952).
9. O. E. A. Bolduan and R. S. Bear, *J. Appl. Phys.*, **20**:983 (1949).
10. O. Kratky, *Z. Elektrochem.*, **58**:49 (1954).
11. A. Franks, *Brit. J. Appl. Phys.*, **9**:349 (1958).
12. J. C. Grosskreutz, *Rev. Sci. Instr.*, **30**:744 (1959).
13. Beeman, Kaesberg, Anderegg, and Webb, *Handbuch der Physik*, vol. 32, p. 348, Springer-Verlag OHG, Berlin, 1957.
14. P. Schmidt, *Acta Cryst.*, **8**:772 (1955).
15. P. W. Schmidt and R. Hight, Jr., *Acta Cryst.*, **13**: 480 (1960).
16. P. W. Schmidt, *Acta Cryst.*, **11**:674 (1958).
17. R. Hosemann, *Ergbn. exakt. Naturw.*, **24**:142 (1951).
18. M. H. Jellinek, E. Solomon, and I. Fankuchen, *Ind. Eng. Chem., Anal. Ed.*, **18**:172 (1946). See also p. 151 of Ref. 6.
19. D. L. Dexter and W. W. Beeman, *Phys. Rev.*, **76**:1782 (1949).
20. V. Luzzati, *Acta Cryst.*, **10**:643 (1957).
21. R. Baro and V. Luzzati, *Acta Cryst.*, **12**:144 (1959).
22. L. Kahovec, G. Porod, and H. Ruck, *Kolloid-Z.*, **133**:16 (1953).
23. H. D. Bale and P. W. Schmidt, *J. Phys. Chem.*, **62**:1179 (1958).
24. A. N. J. Heyn, *J. Am. Chem. Soc.*, **72**:5768 (1950).
25. R. H. Neynabor, W. G. Brammer, and W. W. Beeman, *J. Appl. Phys.*, **30**:656 (1959).
26. H. H. Atkinson, R. E. Smallman, and K. H. Westmacott, *J. Appl. Phys.*, **30**:646 (1959).
27. O. E. A. Bolduan and R. S. Bear, *J. Appl. Phys.*, **20**:983 (1949).

GENERAL REFERENCES

Beeman, Kaesberg, Anderegg, and Webb: Size of Particles and Lattice Defects, Part A, *Handbuch der Physik*, vol. 32, p. 348, Springer-Verlag OHG, Berlin, 1957.

Guinier, A., and G. Fournet: *Small-angle Scattering of X-rays*, John Wiley & Sons, Inc., New York, 1955. Appended to this book is a comprehensive bibliography of small-angle x-ray scattering literature.

Klug, H. P., and L. E. Alexander: *X-ray Diffraction Procedures*, John Wiley & Sons, Inc., New York, 1954.

Chapter 17

CRYSTALLITE-SIZE DETERMINATION FROM LINE BROADENING AND SPOTTY PATTERNS

S. F. Bartram

General Electric Company
(with the collaboration of R. C. Rau)

1. INTRODUCTION

The three-dimensional lattice of a crystal diffracts x-rays in a manner analogous to the reflection of visible light from a ruled diffraction grating. The resolution of the optical spectra decreases when the distance between ruled lines is close to the wavelength of the incident radiation. In the case of x-rays, the diffracted beam becomes diffuse when the crystal size is nearly the same as the wavelength of the incident beam. As the crystals decrease in size, the diffracted beam becomes more diffuse until it is lost in the general background. It is this divergence of the x-ray beam which is the basis for the measurement of crystallite size.

The relationship between crystallite size and x-ray line broadening was first derived in 1918 by P. Scherrer.[1] His equation

$$D = K\lambda/\beta \cos \theta \tag{1}$$

states that the average crystallite dimension D is directly proportional to the wavelength λ in angstroms, and inversely proportional to the pure diffraction broadening β and the cosine of the Bragg angle θ. (K equals a constant.) These symbols, along with others used in x-ray line broadening, are defined in Table 1.

The constant K depends largely upon the crystallite shape, the (hkl) indices, and the definitions taken for β and D. Values from 0.70 to 1.70 have been assumed for K by different investigators; many workers arbitrarily set it equal to 1.0 for the sake of uniformity in published results. Calculated values for cubic crystals of different polyhedral shape were reported by Stokes and Wilson.[2,3] An excellent summary of shape-factor determinations is given by Klug and Alexander.[4] Since in most cases the crystallite shape is unknown and may vary from crystal to crystal, it is probably best to define D as the mean dimension of the crystallite perpendicular to the diffracting planes (D_{hkl}). This definition has been shown[5] to give a K value of about 0.9 when β is taken as the half-maximum line breadth. If the integral line breadth is used, K increases to 1.0 or more.

Determination of the pure diffraction breadth β constitutes the major effort associated with crystallite-size analysis. Scherrer's[1] original postulate was that the line breadths are strictly additive so that

$$B = \beta + b \tag{2}$$

This has since been found to be not generally applicable, although it holds quite well for the case of high-angle reflections from a narrow x-ray source (curve I, Fig. 5).

Warren[6] derived the relationship between integral breadths that

$$B^2 = \beta^2 + b^2 \tag{3}$$

where the pure diffraction and instrumental-broadening profiles are both assumed to have a Gaussian shape. This equation can also be used for the half-maximum breadths if the peaks can be described by the function $e^{-k^2x^2}$. However, it has been shown by various other investigators that the instrumental profile more closely follows other functions.

Table 1. Symbols Used for X-ray Diffraction Line Broadening

λ = x-ray wavelength in angstrom units
θ = Bragg angle
K = crystallite shape constant
D = mean crystallite dimension normal to diffracting planes
Δ = angular separation of $K\alpha$ doublet*
B' = observed integral line breadth*
B_0 = observed diffraction peak breadth at half-maximum intensity*
B = B_0 or B' corrected for $K\alpha$-doublet separation*
b' = instrumental integral line breadth*
b_0 = observed diffraction peak breadth at half-maximum intensity for large crystallite-size reference material*
b = b_0 or b' corrected for $K\alpha$-doublet separation = instrumental broadening*
β = B_0 or B' corrected for $K\alpha$-doublet separation and instrumental broadening = pure diffraction breadth due to crystallite-size effect*

* By convention, all angular measurements are in terms of 2θ. The pure diffraction breadth β is then changed to radians to solve the Scherrer equation.

The observed x-ray diffraction-line profiles may be analyzed mathematically by Fourier-transform theory as shown by Shull,[7] Stokes,[8] Paterson,[9] and Alexander.[10] This method was used by Jones,[11] who assumed that the instrumental profile had the Cauchy form $(1 + k^2x^2)^{-1}$. He expressed the instrumental-broadening correction by means of a convenient graph.

Schoening, Van Niekerk, and Haul[12] in 1952 summarized the published data on Fourier analysis of integral line breadths in a very useful table. A thorough mathematical analysis was carried out by Garrod, Brett, and MacDonald.[13] They concluded that, if no assumption is made as to the experimental line profile, the Cauchy function more closely follows the observed peak shape for pure crystallite-size broadening. For a skewed distribution of crystallite size that is often encountered in actual practice, however, the function $(1 + k^2x^2)^{-2}$ was derived and appears to be most satisfactory for integral line breadths. This is the same relationship which Schoening et al. arrived at directly by experiment. It has been verified independently[14] that this function gives a theoretical profile in excellent agreement with observed peaks over a wide range of crystallite sizes. A correction curve of this kind is shown as curve III in Fig. 5.

Although Fourier analysis to obtain the integral half breadth is the most accurate method available, it has several disadvantages. Computing machines are required to handle the Fourier-series summation, the diffracted intensity must be accurately measured at small increments over the whole peak, and the calculations involved are tedious and time-consuming. This approach is therefore not recommended for routine laboratory work.

2. EXPERIMENTAL PROCEDURE

General. Crystal imperfections such as strain, deformation, twinning, composition inhomogeneity, and mosaic structure can also contribute to line breadth. Therefore, the x-ray line-broadening method as a means of crystallite-size determination is strictly applicable only to brittle, well-annealed powdered materials which are free of such defects. The interpretation of broadened line profiles from unannealed metal powders, intermetallic compounds, and solid solutions can provide valuable information as to the nature of the imperfections present. Examples of such measurements are given in Sec. 3.

Sample Preparation. Specimens for line-broadening measurement with the x-ray diffractometer can usually be prepared by packing the sample into a standard holder. For materials of low absorbing power, a thin smooth layer should be spread on a microscope slide. This is readily accomplished by making a slurry of the powder mixed with a binder such as Duco cement diluted with amyl and ethyl acetate or a 2 per cent solution of parlodion in amyl acetate. This technique is to be preferred for such materials as BeO, graphite, or MgO, because penetration of the x-ray beam into thick specimens produces additional asymmetric broadening, leading to erroneous results.[15]

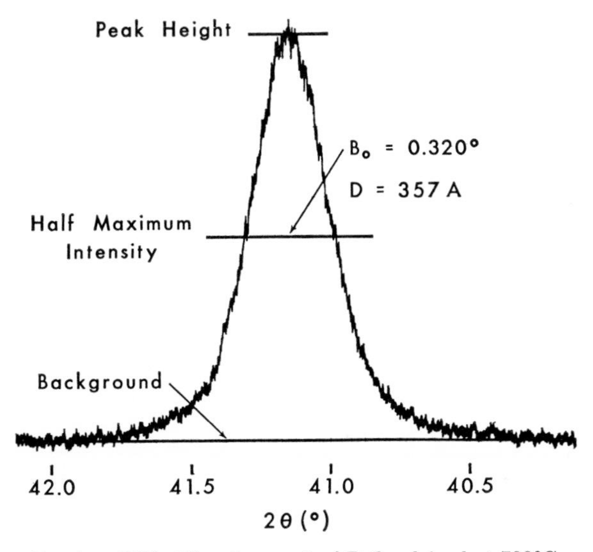

FIG. 1. (002) diffraction peak of BeO calcined at 700°C.

Determination of B_0. Direct measurement of the half-maximum line breadth B_0 can be made on diffraction peaks which are recorded at slow goniometer speeds and fast chart speeds. This combination will generally permit the most precise determination of B_0. Narrow slit systems and linear counting circuits are recommended for such work. The time constant and recorder range should be set to produce a smooth background and nearly full-scale intensity. An example of such a measurement is illustrated in Fig. 1, which shows the (002) reflection of BeO after calcination at 700° C. The half-maximum breadth B_0 is drawn in halfway between the average background level and the peak height.

The integral line breadth B' may be defined as the width in degrees 2θ of a rectangular peak which has the same maximum height and contains the same area as the observed peak. The values of B' may be readily obtained by measuring the integrated intensity under the peak, applying a background correction, dividing by the peak height (maximum counting rate), and converting to degrees. Examples of this calculation are shown in Fig. 2 for BeO lines from the same specimen as above.

Correction of $K\alpha$ Separation. The observed line breadth B_0 or B' must be corrected for $K\alpha$-doublet separation if unresolved radiation is being used. The angular separation of the two wavelengths can be obtained from standard tables or calculated from the equation

$$\Delta = \frac{360}{\pi} \frac{\lambda\alpha_2 - \lambda\alpha_1}{\lambda_{av}} \tan \theta_{av} \tag{4}$$

which reduces to $\Delta = 0.285 \tan \theta_{av}$ for Cu K radiation

derived by Rosauer and Handy.[16] The ratio Δ/B_0 or Δ/B' is then calculated and a graphical correction applied. Curve II of Fig. 3, calculated by Jones[11] from a theoretical basis by assuming two line profiles of the same shape, has been found to agree

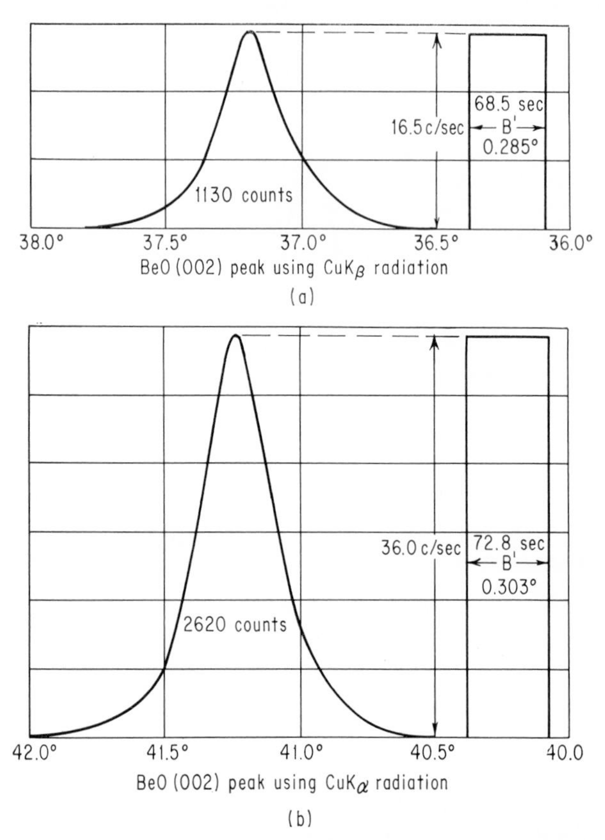

FIG. 2. Determination of integral line breadth B'. Scanning rate = 0.25°/min. (*a*) BeO (002) peak using Cu $K\beta$ radiation. (*b*) BeO (002) peak using Cu $K\alpha$ radiation.

remarkably well with an experimental plot curve I, derived from data on various ceramic oxides of known crystallite dimensions. Using these curves, the ratio B/B_0 or B/B' is read off and the corrected breadth B calculated. If unfiltered $K\beta$ lines or resolved $K\alpha$ reflections are used, this step in the procedure is eliminated, since no such correction is necessary.

Determination of Instrumental Broadening b. Choice of a suitable standard is most important to the determination of crystallite size. Ideally, a powdered strain-free sample of the same material as the unknown should be used. It should consist only of crystallites in the range from 10,000 to 100,000 Å. If such a sample is not available, the reference standard should lie in this crystallite-size range, have similar x-ray absorptivity, and produce x-ray peaks near those in the unknown. For a given set of instrumental conditions, the half-maximum peak breadth b_0 (corrected for $K\alpha$-doublet broadening if necessary) thus obtained can be taken as the true instrumental broadening b. The best approach is to use $K\beta$ lines to avoid the doublet broadening. Then measured $b_0 = b$.

The half-maximum line breadths of the diffraction peaks of the reference standard may then be measured and plotted as a function of diffraction angle 2θ. Such a graph is illustrated in Fig. 4, derived from a specimen of pure BeO containing crystallites of over 10,000 Å average size (as determined by electron microscopy). In this way, the instrumental broadening b at any desired diffraction angle may be readily determined.

The foregoing steps also apply when integral breadths are measured rather than the half-maximum line breadths. Instrumental breadths are measured for $K\beta$ lines

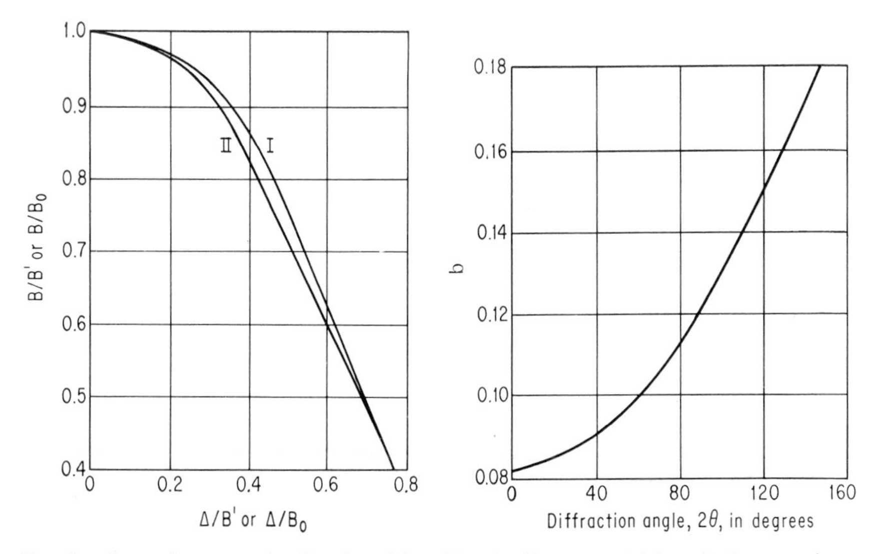

FIG. 3. Curve for correcting line breadths for $K\alpha$-doublet broadening.

FIG. 4. Instrumental broadening as a function of diffraction angle 2θ.

of a well-crystallized standard and plotted in the same way. These results should not differ significantly from the half-breadth values.

Determination of Pure Diffraction Breadth β. After the corrected peak breadth B and the instrumental broadening b have been determined, the pure diffraction breadth β can be obtained by a graphical method from curves calculated by Alexander.[17] These were prepared by convolution analyses of assumed line profiles to obtain the corrections necessary for diffractometers having both wide and narrow x-ray sources. Since most modern x-ray diffractometers are of the latter type, their correction curves are reproduced in Fig. 5. Curve II applies to x-ray lines occurring at 2θ angles less than 90°; its shape is produced by the action of a number of asymmetric factors which have the greatest weight at low angles. For x-ray reflections above 90° (2θ), straight-line curve I can be used. Any error involved in using only curves I and II is negligible compared with the uncertainty in K. Curve III is theoretically and experimentally applicable to integral breadths, as previously discussed.

To obtain β from this graph, calculate the ratio b/B, read off the value of the corresponding ratio β/B, and determine β. The crystallite size is then calculated from the Scherrer equation, converting to radian measure. For Cu $K\alpha$ radiation, assuming

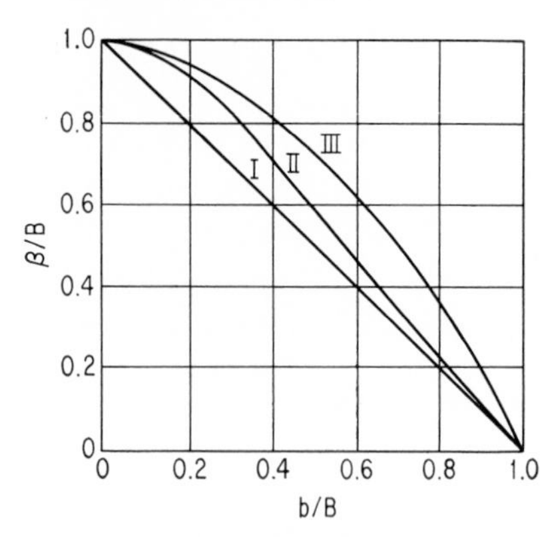

FIG. 5. Curves for correcting x-ray diffractometer line breadths for instrumental broadening.

$K = 0.9$, this equation reduces to

$$D_{hkl} = 79.51/\beta \cos \theta \tag{5}$$

Crystallite-size Calculations. *Half Breadths*

Let $B_0 = 0.320°$ (from Fig. 1)
$2\theta = 41.2°$
$b_0 = 0.092°$ (from Fig. 4)
$\Delta = 0.107$ [from standard tables or by Eq. (4)]
$\lambda = 1.5418$ (Cu $K\alpha$)

1. Calculate $\Delta/B_0 = 0.107/0.320 = 0.334$. Using correction curve I in Fig. 3,

$$B/B_0 = 0.92 \qquad B = 0.294$$

2. In this example, $b_0 = b = 0.092°$. If correction is necessary, follow step 1.
3. Calculate $b/B = 0.092/0.294 = 0.313$. Using correction curve II in Fig. 5,

$$\beta/B = 0.81 \qquad \beta = 0.238$$

4. Convert to radian measure and solve the Scherrer equation

$$D_{hkl} = \frac{K\lambda}{\beta \cos \theta}$$
$$= \frac{(0.9)(1.5418)}{(0.238)(0.936)} \frac{360}{2\pi}$$
$$D_{hkl} = \frac{79.51}{(0.238)(0.936)} = 357 \text{ Å}$$

Warren's Equation (3)

Let $B' = B = 0.285°$ ($K\beta$ peak from Fig. 2)
$b' = b = 0.100°$ (integral breadth for BeO reference standard)
$2\theta = 37.06°$
$\lambda = 1.5443$ (Cu $K\beta$)

1. Calculate

$$\beta^2 = B^2 - b^2 = (0.285)^2 - (0.100)^2$$
$$= 0.0712$$
$$\beta = 0.267$$

2. Convert to radian measure and solve the Scherrer equation

$$D_{hkl} = \frac{(1.0)(1.5443)}{(0.267)(0.948)} \frac{360}{2\pi} = \frac{88.49}{(0.267)(0.948)}$$

$$D_{hkl} = \frac{88.49}{(0.267)(0.948)} = 350 \text{ Å}$$

Integral Breadths

Let $B' = 0.303°$ ($K\alpha$ peak from Fig. 2)
$b' = b = 0.100°$ (integral breadth for BeO reference standard)
$\Delta = 0.107$ [from tables or Equation (4)]
$\lambda = 1.5418$ (Cu $K\alpha$)

1. Calculate $\Delta/B' = 0.107/0.303 = 0.353$. Using correction curve II in Fig. 3,

$$B/B' = 0.88 \qquad B = 0.267$$

2. Calculate $b/B = 0.100/0.267 = 0.375$. Using correction curve III in Fig. 5,

$$\beta/B = 0.84 \qquad \beta = 0.224$$

3. Convert to radian measure and solve the Scherrer equation

$$D_{hkl} = \frac{(1.0)(1.5418)}{(0.224)(0.936)} \frac{360}{2\pi} = \frac{88.35}{(0.224)(0.936)}$$

$$D_{hkl} = \frac{88.35}{(0.224)(0.936)} = 421 \text{ Å}$$

Direct Determination of Crystallite Size. Although the previous procedures may appear to be rather involved, they can be used as a basis for more rapid and direct measurements. All the intermediate steps have been eliminated by one of the modifications suggested by Rau.[18]

A simple computer program may be written to make the necessary corrections shown graphically in Figs. 3 to 5 and to solve the Scherrer equation. Input data required are the observed half-maximum breadth B_0 (or integral breadth B'), the diffraction angle 2θ at which the peak occurs, the instrumental broadening b_0 at this angle, the angular separation Δ (this could be computed), and the wavelength of the radiation used.

The computer program can then proceed stepwise as in the examples given, using the input data to calculate the ratios of Δ/B_0 and b/B. Equations can be written which describe the correction curves; the program then uses these to compute the various corrected peak breadths necessary. The crystallite-size value for each measured diffraction peak is finally printed as output data, along with any desired intermediate computations.

Routine crystallite-size determinations on only one or two kinds of material can best be done by preparing specific crystallite-size curves. Crystallite sizes are calculated for the strongest diffraction lines of the material by assuming various peak breadths. In the examples given previously, only B_0 or B' is varied while the other values are held constant. These calculations are readily carried out with either a desk calculator or the computer program mentioned above. A graph can then be plotted for each peak showing the relationship between observed half-maximum breadth B_0, or integral line breadth B', and the crystallite size. Size determination on samples of this material is then a simple matter of reading the graph. An example of such a set of curves is illustrated in Fig. 6 for use with the (111), (200), and (220) reflections of UO_2 powders in the size range from 80 to 2,000 Å.

This is applicable to laboratory control processes since the time required is only that necessary to scan the diffraction peaks. Each observed peak half breadth obtained using the prescribed standard instrumental conditions is located on the proper crystallite-size curve and the D_{hkl} value read off directly. The utility of this method has been well established. Its rapidity does not decrease the precision of measurement since this depends mainly upon the diffraction-peak breadths.

The preparation of standard curves can readily be extended to yield a completely general direct method for the determination of crystallite size. Such curves can be used for any strain-free material. In this case, a computer program will greatly simplify the task. Assumed values of half-peak breadths or integral breadths together with a series of diffraction angles, in increments of 5 to 10°, are used as input along with the $K\alpha$-doublet separation and instrumental-broadening constants. The crystallite-size values are plotted against half breadths or integral breadths to give a family of curves from which approximate crystallite sizes may be estimated. The observed peak breadth is located on the corresponding diffraction-angle curve, and the crystallite dimension perpendicular to that set of planes is read off. For peaks which fall at intermediate angles, the crystallite size is determined by interpolation. The need for interpolation introduces some error in size estimation, particularly in the larger size range, but this deficiency is not too serious. The conditions applying

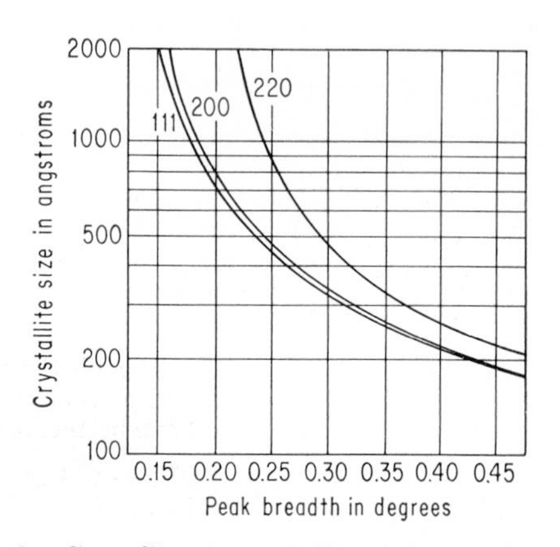

FIG. 6. Crystallite size vs. half peak breadth for UO_2.

to these general curves are similar to those applying to the special curves for specific materials.

Accuracy. It must be pointed out that x-ray line broadening yields relative crystallite sizes; absolute values are not readily obtainable by this method. Relative sizes are very useful in most applications, but if absolute sizes are necessary other methods such as electron microscopy must be used to establish a basis for comparison.

Most powdered materials of interest are composed of crystallites with a wide distribution of sizes. Furthermore, the calculated values are weighted toward the larger crystallites present in the sample, since the intensity of the diffracted beam is a function of the volume irradiated. According to Jones,[11] the volume average crystallite size for cubes can be expressed as

$$D_{hkl} = \Sigma n_i d_i^4 / \Sigma n_i d_i^3 \tag{6}$$

where d_i = cube edge of crystallite, Å

n_i = number of crystallites having the cube edge d_i

In order to find the error introduced by the weighted volume average, calculations were made for two crystallite-size ranges assuming a normal distribution. For a 100- to 1,300-Å sample, the calculated mean crystallite size [using Eq. (6)] amounts to 850 Å, 150 Å greater than the true mean value. Using a wider size distribution from 100 to 2,500 Å, the calculated mean size was 1,600 Å compared with the true value of 1,300 Å. However, if relatively few large crystallites are present with a large number of small crystallites, the measured value will be too high. This has been experimentally demonstrated by Friedman and Birks,[19] who made mechanical mixtures of known crystallite-size fractions of MgO. The average value obtained for such mixtures was correct when the size fractions did not differ in size by more than a factor of 2.

Crystallite-size measurements are limited to the range from about 25 to 5,000 Å. Crystallites smaller than 25 Å do not scatter the primary beam coherently but contribute only to the background radiation. Any material containing ordered regions of this size or less is usually considered to be amorphous.

For crystallites in the upper size range the precision of measurement decreases very rapidly. This can best be demonstrated by Table 2, which shows the marked decrease

Table 2

b/B	B, °	Size, Å	Deviation, Å	% deviation
0.1	1.000	82	±1	1.2
0.3	0.333	290	±12	4.1
0.5	0.200	680	±63	9.3
0.7	0.143	1,612	±313	19.4
0.9	0.111	6,230	±2,990	48.0

in precision of crystallite-size values calculated for a measurement error of $\pm 0.01°(2\theta)$ in B_0. This table shows how essential it is to keep the ratio b/B small, since the precision falls off very rapidly when the measured half breadth B approaches the instrumental broadening b.

In general, crystallite sizes below about 500 Å are measured in the low-angle region but for larger crystallites high-angle reflections should be used. In this case the advantage gained by decreasing the cos θ term in the Scherrer equation is modified somewhat by the increased spectral breadth of the incident radiation.

A recent study by Rau[20] evaluated the reproducibility of crystallite-size measurements between different x-ray diffraction instruments. With identical samples of BeO and similar experimental conditions, a remarkable agreement was obtained. His results show that crystallite-size measurements have a greater validity and are more reliable than has heretofore been supposed.

The influence of various factors upon instrumental line breadth has been summarized by Schoening et al.[12] His data for MgO, various standard substances, and MgO-CaF_2 mixtures are reproduced here as Table 3.

It was concluded that preparation of the specimen is not critical, reproducibility of the method is excellent, and crystallite size shows practically no dependence upon diffraction angle 2θ. Identical results were obtained using internal and external standards. Even the choice of standard substance was found to be immaterial so long as its linear absorption coefficient was not too low and preferred orientation was avoided.

3. APPLICATIONS

Crystallite Growth. In studies of the physical properties of materials, a knowledge of the particle and crystallite size has become increasingly important. This is true because the kinetics of reactions in powders are strongly affected by the crystallite size of the material, particularly in the size range from 25 to 5,000 Å. It is for this reason that x-ray line-broadening techniques are being frequently used to follow sintering processes and crystallite-growth phenomena.

Many investigations have been carried out on the formation of ceramic oxides from various starting materials. One of the first such applications was reported by Friedman and Birks,[19] who followed the growth of MgO crystallites prepared by the decomposition of the basic carbonate at temperatures above 400° C. Electron photomicrographs of the sample were measured, and an excellent check was obtained with

Table 3. Integral Line Breadth in Radians

Substance	Degrees 2θ	Before $\alpha_1\alpha_2$ correction	After $\alpha_1\alpha_2$ correction	Mean integral line breadth	P.E.,† %
MgO	36.9	423×10^{-5}	351×10^{-5}	362×10^{-5}	3
	42.9	474	382		
	62.3	510	362		
	74.7	503	346		
	78.6	538	370		
MgO:					
Normal*	62.3	807	683	700×10^{-5}	2
Tight	....	831	709		
Loose	....	831	709		
LiF	45.0	518	425	378×10^{-5}	3
SiO_2	42.4	472	387		
MgO	42.9	474	382		
NaCl	45.4	498	401		
CaF_2	47.0	482	376		
KI	44.4	468	368		
Ag	44.3	464	364		
W	40.3	450	368		
MgO:					
100%	42.9	465	372	365×10^{-5}	2
75%	....	462	368		
50%	....	450	355		
25%	....	459	365		
CaF_2:					
100%	47.0	482	376	390×10^{-5}	3
75%	....	480	374		
50%	....	512	411		
25%	....	501	398		

* Indicates approximate bulk density of specimen.
† Probable error.

the x-ray measurements. More recently, Quinn and Cherin[21] repeated this study but used the more sophisticated harmonic analysis of Stokes[8] and the Warren[6] method of size distribution to analyze their data.

Fischer[22] studied the growth rate of CaO crystallites from the calcination of $CaCO_3$ by line broadening. As part of an investigation on the properties of ThO_2, Allred, Buxton, and McBride[23] measured the effect of precipitation and calcination temperatures upon the growth of thoria crystallites from thorium oxalate. They observed from the relationship between crystallite size and specific surface area that

$$S = (6/\rho D)(1/F)$$

where $1/F$ is a packing factor indicative of the surface area not available for nitrogen-gas absorption. Growth curves were found to fit an equation of the form

$$D = t^x e^{A-B/T}$$

where D is the crystallite diameter, t is the time, x is a constant for a given precipitate, A and B are constants, and T is the absolute temperature. Log-log plots of their data gave straight lines from which the heat of activation was calculated. This amounted to 10.97 kcal/mole, a value in accord with growth taking place among crystallites.

The crystallite growth of BeO from sulfate, hydroxide, and oxalate source materials has been reported by Bartram[15] as being anisotropic in nature, the degree of elongation along the crystallographic c axis varying with the starting material. His results were compared with particle-size distribution analysis from small-angle scattering as well as surface-area measurements and electron microscopy. It was concluded that individual particles and crystallites were of the same size, although there was a strong tendency for the particles to agglomerate.

Solid Solutions. Mixed crystals formed by solid-state reactions produce anomalous effects, because the x-ray lines are broadened by regions of inhomogeneity as well as the finite size of the crystallites. Interpretation of the results becomes difficult when both factors are contributing. In such cases, true crystallite-size measurements can be applied to such materials only after equilibrium has been established.

Although it is difficult to separate the broadening effects due to crystallite and composition inhomogeneities in a sample, a great deal of worthwhile information may be obtained about solid solutions. For these investigations, an "apparent" crystallite size can be used to follow the course of the reaction.

A study on the stabilization of cubic ZrO_2 by additions of Y_2O_3 is an example of such an application.[24] Growth rates of cubic Y_2O_3 and monoclinic ZrO_2 crystals were first measured separately. Starting materials of from 200 to 500 Å size attained an average crystallite dimension of from 1,500 to 3,000 Å after a 2-hr calcination at 1500° C. Mechanically blended mixtures of these same powders were then reacted under similar conditions. The appearance of the cubic ZrO_2 phase at about 1100° C along with a rapid increase in the apparent size of the Y_2O_3 crystallites indicated that the smaller yttria crystals had reacted with the zirconia. At temperatures above 1300° C, the apparent Y_2O_3 crystallite size decreased gradually; at 1500° C, it approached the value of 500 Å observed for the cubic solid solution and unreacted monoclinic ZrO_2. Surface reaction layers on the yttria and zirconia particles were indicated by the appearance of two intermediate cubic phases. This can be interpreted as a homogenization process occurring by solid-state diffusion. The measured half breadths of such cubic solid solutions producing unresolved peaks are far too large and lead to incorrect crystallite-size values.

The x-ray line-broadening method is ideal for observing the growth of crystallites during heating of an insoluble precipitate. It must, however, be used with caution for studies on coprecipitated materials. This has been found to be especially true in the case of body-centered cubic urania-yttria solid solutions.[25] A $1UO_2$-$7Y_2O_3$ composition was prepared by the decomposition of coprecipitated nitrates. After calcination overnight at 1100° C it was a densely sintered single-phase cubic solid solution. The apparent crystallite size estimated from charts was only 100 to 200 Å. Microscopic examination of this material showed it to be coarse-grained with no "fines"; hence this result should be interpreted as the average dimension of the homogeneous ordered regions within the crystals. This is a particularly interesting result, because it was found that heating at higher temperatures (above 1200° C) caused the cubic solid solution to dissociate into two well-crystallized phases.

Stacking Faults. Another type of line broadening is produced by errors in the order or arrangement of atomic layers in a crystal. If the crystal is made up of close-packed layers of atoms, these may be stacked in various ways. The most common types are a hexagonal *ABABABAB* . . . and a cubic *ABCABC* . . . sequence. Stacking faults are produced in such crystals when mistakes occur in the normal packing order. This is exemplified by cobalt metal, which is well known to exist in both hexagonal and cubic modifications. The hexagonal form often produces a diffraction pattern containing both broadened lines and sharp reflections. An explanation for this has been given by Edwards and Lipson[26] and Wilson[27] as due to faulting. For reflections of the type $(hk0)$, $(00l)$, and (hkl) with $h - k = 3n$ no broadening is observed because there is no change in structure factor on crossing the fault boundary and no extraneous broadening occurs. For all (hkl) reflections with $h - k = 3n \pm 1$ the structure factor changes at each packing mistake and the crystal appears to be broken up into thin layers. The amount of x-ray line broadening will vary with the number of stacking faults and the angle which the (hkl) planes make with the basal plane. Anantharaman and Christian[28] carried out a comprehensive investigation of faulting in hexagonal cobalt by Fourier analysis of broadened line profiles. They were able to differentiate between growth faults and deformation faulting introduced by mechanical stress.

Pyrolytic graphite has been observed[29] to contain stacking faults of this type. The so-called "turbostratic" graphite deposited by gaseous decomposition builds up as layers with the hexagonal graphite *c* axis nearly perpendicular to the substrate surface. Half-breadth measurements of the (004) and (006) lines on a pyrolytic deposit gave an average layer height of 110 Å, while the layer diameter was found to be 230 Å from the (100) and (110) peaks. The (101) diagonal planes showed extreme broadening with D_{101} = 40 Å. This can no doubt be attributed to stacking-fault disorder along the *c* axis.

Noncrystalline carbons produce x-ray diffraction patterns showing only diffuse (00*l*) and (*hk*0) type lines. This two-dimensional order is indicative of a random layered structure and has been analyzed in some detail by Warren.[30] A gradual transformation from the random structure to crystalline graphite can be produced by heating at high temperature, yielding structures which are intermediate in type. This process of graphitization can be followed by careful analysis of the shape and position of the diffraction lines. A series of papers by Franklin[31] give detailed methods for solving this difficult problem.

Other materials which are known to contain stacking faults are SiC, ZnS, and ZnO. Recent observations on BeO by Rau[32] show that it also exhibits faulting.

Table 4. Apparent Crystallite Size of Ni-Al Alloys in Angstroms

Aging time, 1200° C, hr	Matrix (*HKL*)			Superlattice (*hkl*)		
	(111)	(200)	(220)	(100)	(110)	(210)
As solutioned	1,300	. . .	. . .	. . .	120	
9	. . . . .	. . .	. . .	. . .	175	
48	. . . . .	. . .	470	. . .	260	
100	. . . . .	. . .	220	420		
200	580					
415	. . . . .	590	325	690	720	420

Metal Alloys. The heat-treatment of various alloys often produces an ordered arrangement of the metal atoms. X-ray diffraction patterns of such materials show sharp lines from the main lattice which are normally invariant with treatment conditions, while the superlattice lines from ordered domains become progressively sharper as these domains increase in size. When complete order is present, some of the domain boundaries will be out of step. Such "antiphase" domains are analogous to the layering mistakes which produce stacking faults. Hence the breadths of the superlattice lines can be used as a means of determining the size of the ordered antiphase domains, since each domain may be considered as a single crystallite.

Jones and Sykes[33] measured the mean apparent domain size in ordered Cu_3Au by x-ray line broadening. Their results showed a large variation from 100 Å for the (110) line to 200 Å for (100), which was satisfactorily explained by Wilson[34] from a consideration of stacking-fault probability. The Cu_3Au structure contains shifts in alignment of consecutive atomic planes which modify the structure factor of certain reflections.

A recent study of the ordering in Ni_3Al produced by aging at 1200° C has been carried out by Olson, Smith, and Rau.[35] Their results are given in Table 4 showing the apparent crystallite size for the disordered matrix (*HKL*) and the ordered superlattice domains (*hkl*). The domain regions progressively increase in size. The matrix visually contains extremely large grains, although the apparent crystallite size is only 0.1 micron (1,000 Å). The apparent decrease in size of the matrix crystallites can be explained by the tetragonal deformation of the structure to form two phases which differ slightly in lattice parameter.[36] When both these phases are present, the additional line broadening which is observed increases with diffraction angle 2θ, producing a corresponding decrease in the apparent crystallite size. Similar observations have been made on Cu_3Au by Rhines and Newkirk,[37] who found ordered and disordered cubic phases coexisting under equilibrium conditions.

Deformation due to internal stress can also produce x-ray line-broadening effects. This must be taken into account when working with metals and alloys. The mean stress $\bar{\sigma}$ may be expressed by an equation of the form[38]

$$\bar{\sigma} = (E\beta/4) \cot \theta \tag{7}$$

and hence the broadening β will be proportional to $1/\cot \theta$ or $\tan \theta$. Since the crystallite-size breadth β is proportional to $1/\cos \theta$ or $\sec \theta$ (Scherrer equation) it is in theory possible to separate the two effects. If the line breadths plotted against $\tan \theta$ give a straight line, then lattice strain is the major cause of broadening. A straight line through the origin for a plot of β vs. $\sec \theta$ shows that crystallite size is the main factor. In practice, a combination of both effects may be present. Efforts to resolve this problem have been made by several investigators.[39]

Organic Polymers (Cf. Chap. 21). Early work by O. Kratky[40] in 1951 showed the applicability of x-ray line broadening to organic materials. He calculated the lower size limit of the crystalline regions in cellulose hydrate by line-breadth measurements on x-ray patterns. Good agreement was obtained with small-angle scattering results.

Since then x-ray methods have been used extensively to investigate the crystallinity of polymeric substances. A critical examination of such determinations is given by Bonart et al.[41] If the total diffuse scattering is attributed to the amorphous fraction of the material, as is the usual assumption, then at best only the lower limit of crystallinity can be determined. Lattice defects in the crystalline portion of the sample also produce scattered radiation which must be taken into account to determine the true crystallinity of a high polymeric substance.

In spite of these limitations, much valuable information can be derived from x-ray patterns of natural and synthetic polymers. In a study of the melting behavior of polyurethane, broadening of the (002) line from planes of polyurethane molecules at temperatures above 100° C is attributed to loss of long-range order within the crystalline domains prior to actual melting. The (200) line which is assigned to the interlayer hydrogen bonding remains essentially unchanged with temperature nearly to the melting point of 180° C. This anisotropic melting behavior has been explained by the formation of paracrystalline distortions between molecular layers, while the long-range order within a layer is unaffected.

Radiation Damage. The effect of radiation damage by high-energy particles upon inorganic materials is well known. Metals and alloys have been the subject of many studies. Cook and Cushing[42] reported that well-ordered Cu_3Au was rapidly disordered by fast-neutron irradiation while slow neutrons had little effect. When a disordered sample of this alloy was bombarded by thermal neutrons, however, some ordering was produced. These effects are still not clearly understood.

Bombardment of monoclinic ZrO_2 by fast neutrons produces a phase change to the cubic form, according to Wittels and Sherrill.[43] Their measurements of particle sizes in the transformed material indicate that ordered regions are about 200 Å in size, which is only one-fifth the crystallite size of the original monoclinic material. This is attributed to a thermal spike mechanism which produces the transition in localized high-temperature regions.

The effect of fast-neutron irradiation upon BeO is of technical importance because of its nuclear application as a moderating material, and has been studied by Hickman, Sabine, and Coyle.[44] The hexagonal crystalline structure of BeO shows an anisotropic deformation; the $(00l)$ lines exhibit broadening, position shifts, and splitting to a much greater extent than $(hk0)$ type reflections. Extremely high dosages cause so much structural damage that weak diffuse x-ray diffraction patterns are obtained.

Line broadening of the $(hk0)$ lines at intermediate dosages is attributed to anisotropic growth strains since this does not occur in solid specimens which disintegrate during irradiation. The extreme broadening of (hkl) lines (l not equal to zero) after high dosages is believed to be associated with defect clusters.

Recovery of the a parameter begins at temperatures as low as 200° C and is complete at 1000° C, while the c parameter recovers mainly in the temperature range from 800 to 1400° C.

4. GRAIN-SIZE DETERMINATION FROM SPOTTY PATTERNS

Materials containing crystallites larger than about 10 microns in size produce spotty discontinuous rings on Debye-Scherrer powder patterns. Since the size of these spots is in direct proportion to the dimensions of the crystal or grain producing them, x-ray diffraction methods may be used for grain-size determinations.

Filtered $K\alpha$ radiation should be used for measurements of grain size because white radiation will give rise to a confusing background of Laue reflections. Well-annealed specimens of known grain sizes can be used for making a set of standard transmission

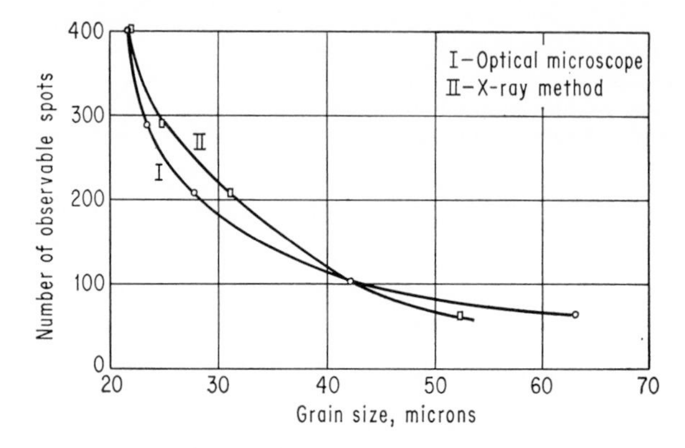

FIG. 7. Relationship between observed spots and grain size.

or back-reflection photographs for the visual estimation of grain sizes in unknown samples. Bass[45] obtained a linear relationship between the grain diameters measured microscopically in the 10- to 100-micron range and the diameters of their x-ray reflections on film. Clark and Zimmer[46] continued this work, obtaining a straight-line relationship between average grain diameter and x-ray spot length for such diverse materials as steel, silicon carbide, and silica.

Instead of measuring the spot sizes, the number of individual reflections can be counted. This gives the actual number of grains which are correctly oriented to produce the particular (hkl) diffraction ring. Although in principle it is possible to calculate the volume of a single grain from the number of observed spots, the total irradiated volume must be accurately known.

Stephen and Barnes[47] determined the empirical relationship between the number of spots observed photographically and the known grain sizes of a standard series of samples. Their data for aluminum metal are reproduced in Fig. 7 showing a comparison between microscopic and x-ray results. A graph of this kind is very useful for repetitive determinations from photographs taken under identical conditions.

Experimentally, the x-ray beam should be kept small to prevent excessive divergence, but at the same time it should irradiate enough grains to provide a representative sampling. Pinhole diameters of about 1.0 mm can generally be used. With $K\alpha$ radiation from Fe, Co, Cr, and Cu targets, a specimen-to-film distance of from 3.0 to 4.0 cm will permit reasonable exposure times for materials of low absorbing power.

It may be necessary to use Mo or Ag $K\alpha$ radiation for specimens containing the heavier elements.

The lower limit for grain-size determinations is generally about 10^{-3} cm (10 microns) using conventional x-ray cameras and slit systems. However, this limit can be extended down to about 0.5 micron by making use of very small beam diameters. Hirsch and Kellar[48] have utilized such a microbeam technique in studies on cold-work deformation of polycrystalline metals. Kelly[49] was able to determine that an electrodeposit of chromium had a crystallite size of 0.8 micron by using a specially collimated x-ray beam only 8 microns in diameter. The maximum beam diameter for a given crystallite size is shown in Table 5, calculated by Hirsch[50] for an angular divergence of 10^{-2} radian.

Table 5. Relation between Crystallite Size and Beam Diameter

Beam diameter, microns	*Crystallite size* $v^{1/3}$, *microns*
0.5	0.1
16.0	1.0
50.0	2.0
170.0	5.0
500.0	10.0
1,500.0	20.0

Both transmission and back-reflection methods are often used conjointly for grain-size measurements. Photographs obtained by transmitted x-radiation require thin sections or slices; they yield information as to the mean grain size of the bulk of material. With this technique, the irradiated volume V is readily calculated from the known cross section of the beam and the thickness of the specimen. It is possible to determine the mean volume v of a single grain according to the following equation:

$$v = VpP/N \tag{8}$$

where N = number of spots on a diffraction ring
V = irradiated volume
p = multiplicity factor
P = $\frac{1}{2} \cos \theta \, d\theta$ = probability that a particular crystal will reflect
$d\theta$ = divergence of beam

Since the volume irradiated is the cross-sectional area A of the beam times the thickness t of the specimen, Eq. (8) can be rewritten

$$v = Atp \cos \theta \, d\theta / 2N \tag{9}$$

If R is the specimen-to-film distance and r the radius of the x-ray beam, $d\theta$ is approximately $2r/R$ and hence

$$v = Atpr \cos \theta / NR \tag{10}$$

which can be solved since the right-hand terms are all known.

Grain-size determination on massive specimens necessitates the use of a back-reflection technique. This method has the advantage of requiring much shorter exposure times than transmission, but the results are characteristic of grains lying in or near the surface of the specimen. The volume irradiated by this method will be unknown since it depends upon the penetration of the x-ray beam. Stephen and Barnes[47] have attacked this problem by making two exposures. The first is for such a short time that only surface crystals produce spots on the film. The second photograph is exposed for a much longer time so that many more reflections are recorded. A comparison of the photographs is made, and from the number of spots in the second exposure having an intensity greater than those in the first exposure the grain size can be calculated.

As an extension of the two-exposure method, Hirsch and Kellar[51] have developed a more general treatment. They expose for long times, take the limiting blackening on the first film as small as practical, and count spots on both photographs. They derived the relationship that

$$\frac{N_1 - N_0}{A \log T_1/T_0} = \frac{2.3p \cos \theta}{2\mu(1 - \sec \theta)} \frac{1}{v} (d\theta + \phi) \tag{11}$$

where A = cross-sectional area irradiated
N_1, N_0 = number of spots for times T_1, T_0
p = multiplicity factor
μ = linear absorption coefficient
Unknown are v = grain volume
ϕ = the angular range of reflection
$d\theta$ = divergence of beam

By taking several photographs at different divergences and plotting

$$\frac{N_1 - N_0}{A \log T_1/T_0}$$

against $d\theta$, a straight line should be obtained whose slope equals v, the mean grain volume.

A novel approach to grain-size determination was suggested by Andrews and Johnson.[52] Their transmission method incorporates a small oscillation about an axis perpendicular to the x-ray beam. This oscillation movement helps to differentiate between Laue reflections and Debye-Scherrer spots. The number of spots on a given ring may be controlled by choosing the collimation diameter and angle of oscillation such that spots do not overlap to any great extent. Exact knowledge of the angular divergence of the x-ray beam is not necessary because the angle of oscillation makes the divergence error insignificant. By making two exposures with different oscillation angles the divergence can be completely eliminated.

According to Hirsch and Kellar,[51] the total divergence D is composed of two parts, one being the actual beam divergence $d\theta$ produced by the experimental geometry and the other an angular divergence ϕ arising from small crystal size, lattice distortions, and wavelength spread. Andrews and Johnson[52] eliminate D by taking two exposures with the same sample at different oscillation angles. If exposure times are adjusted to give equal blackening for equal-sized spots on both films then

$$N_1 - N_2 = (Atp/v\pi)(\psi_1 - \psi_2) \cos \theta \tag{12}$$

where N_1 and N_2 = number of spots on a diffraction ring for oscillation angles ψ_1 and ψ_2, and t = thickness of specimen. Other symbols have same meaning as before.

The probability P that a given crystal will reflect can be expressed as

$$PA = (A/\pi)(\psi_1 - \psi_2) \cos \theta \tag{13}$$

Graphs of PA are plotted against θ for the experimental values of A, ψ_1, and ψ_2. The difference in the number of spots for two different oscillation angles is determined. Division by PAp gives the mean grain volume

$$v = \frac{N_1 - N_2}{\psi_1 - \psi_2} \frac{\pi}{pA \cos \theta} \tag{14}$$

Surface and internal grains of linear dimension l make the following contribution to the mean grain volume:

$$v = l^3/(t + l) \qquad \text{or} \qquad 1/v = t/l^3 + 1/l^2 \tag{15}$$

which can be solved for l.

A graphical solution may be more convenient. Equation (14) can be rewritten

$$(N_1 - N_2)/PAp = t/l^3 + 1/l^2 \tag{16}$$

The function t/l^3 is plotted as abscissa with l as ordinate at different values of t. Using the same origin and ordinate, the function $1/l^2$ is plotted in the negative direction. Their sum then is the horizontal distance between the two curves; this horizontal intercepts the ordinate at the correct linear dimension l. Their graph is reproduced in Fig. 8.

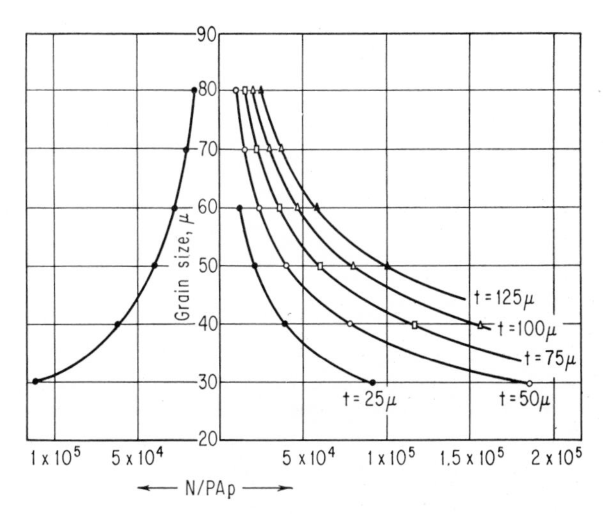

FIG. 8. Plot of $t/l^3 + 1/l^2$ against N/PAp for different values of t.

REFERENCES CITED

1. P. Scherrer, *Göttinger Nachr.*, **2**:98 (1918).
2. A. R. Stokes and A. J. C. Wilson, *Proc. Cambridge Phil. Soc.*, **38**:313 (1942).
3. A. R. Stokes and A. J. C. Wilson, *Proc. Cambridge Phil. Soc.*, **40**:197 (1944).
4. H. P. Klug and L. E. Alexander, *X-ray Diffraction Procedures*, pp. 511–524, John Wiley & Sons, Inc., New York, 1954.
5. L. Bragg, *The Crystalline State*, vol. I, p. 189, G. Bell & Sons, Ltd., London, 1949.
6. B. E. Warren, *J. Appl. Phys.*, **12**:375 (1941).
7. C. G. Shull, *Phys. Rev.*, **70**:679 (1946).
8. A. R. Stokes, *Proc. Phys. Soc. (London)*, **61**:382 (1948).
9. M. S. Paterson, *Proc. Phys. Soc. (London)*, **63A**:477 (1950).
10. L. E. Alexander, *J. Appl. Phys.*, **19**:1068 (1948); **21**:126 (1950); **25**:155 (1954).
11. F. W. Jones, *Proc. Roy. Soc. (London)*, **166A**:16 (1938).
12. F. R. L. Schoening, J. N. Van Niekerk, and R. A. W. Haul, *Proc. Phys. Soc. (London)*, **65B**:528–535 (1952).
13. R. I. Garrod, J. F. Brett, and J. A. MacDonald, *Australian J. Phys.*, **7**(1):77–95 (1954).
14. S. F. Bartram, unpublished work.
15. S. F. Bartram, *Advances in X-ray Analysis*, vol. **4**, pp. 40–63, Plenum Press, Inc., New York, 1961.
16. E. A. Rosauer and R. L. Handy, paper presented at Iowa Academy of Science Meeting, Simpson College, Indianola, Iowa, Apr. 14, 1961.
17. L. E. Alexander, *J. Appl. Phys.*, **25**(2):155–161 (1954).
18. R. C. Rau, *Advances in X-ray Analysis*, vol. 5, pp. 104–116, Plenum Press, Inc., New York, 1962.
19. L. S. Birks and H. Friedman, *J. Appl. Phys.*, **17**:687 (1946).
20. R. C. Rau, *Advances in X-ray Analysis*, vol. 6, pp. 191–201, Plenum Press, Inc., New York, 1963.
21. H. F. Quinn and P. Cherin, *Advances in X-ray Analysis*, vol. 5, pp. 94–103, Plenum Press, Inc., New York, 1962.
22. H. C. Fischer, *J. Am. Ceram. Soc.*, **38**:284 (1955).

23. V. D. Allred, S. R. Buxton, and J. P. McBride, *J. Phys. Chem.*, **61**:117–120 (1957).
24. J. E. Lewis and S. F. Bartram, Repts. DC 61-3-71 and DC 61-7-48, General Electric Co., Aircraft Nuclear Propulsion Dept., Cincinnati, Ohio, Mar. 3, 1961, and June 28, 1961.
25. E. A. Aitken, S. F. Bartram, and E. F. Juenke, *J. Am. Ceram. Soc.*, **47**:171 (1964).
26. O. S. Edwards and H. Lipson, *Proc. Roy. Soc.* (*London*), **180A**:268–277 (1942).
27. A. J. C. Wilson, *Proc. Roy. Soc.* (*London*), **180A**:277–285 (1942).
28. T. R. Anantharaman and J. W. Christian, *Brit. J. Appl. Phys.*, **4** (5):155–156 (1953).
29. S. F. Bartram, unpublished work.
30. B. E. Warren, *Phys. Rev.*, **59**:693 (1941).
31. R. E. Franklin, *Acta Cryst.*, **3**:107 (1950); **4**:253 (1951); *Nature*, **165**:71 (1950).
32. R. C. Rau, *J. Am. Ceram. Soc.*, **47**:179 (1964).
33. F. W. Jones and C. Sykes, *Proc. Roy. Soc.* (*London*), **166A**:376 (1938).
34. A. J. C. Wilson, *Proc. Roy. Soc.* (*London*), **181A**:360 (1943).
35. P. Olson, J. P. Smith, and R. C. Rau, unpublished work.
36. R. O. Williams, *Trans. Met. Soc. AIME*, **215**:1026 (1959).
37. F. N. Rhines and J. B. Newkirk, *Trans. Am. Soc. Metals Preprint No.* 12 (1952).
38. H. D. Megaw and A. R. Stokes, *J. Inst. Metals*, **71**:6 (1945).
39. W. A. Wood and collaborators, *Proc. Roy. Soc.* (*London*), **172A**:231 (1939); **174A**:310 (1940); *J. Inst. Metals*, **75**:571 (1949).
40. O. Kratky, *Kolloid-Z.*, **120**:24–39 (1951).
41. R. Bonart, R. Hosemann, F. Motzkus, and H. Ruck, *Norelco Reptr.*, **7**(3):81–87 (1960).
42. L. G. Cook and R. L. Cushing, *Acta Met.*, **1**:539 (1953).
43. M. C. Wittels and F. A. Sherrill, *J. Appl. Phys.*, **27**(6):643 (1956).
44. B. S. Hickman, T. M. Sabine, and R. A. Coyle, *J. Nucl. Mater.*, **6**(2):190–198 (1962).
45. W. Bass, in Glocker's *Material prüfungen mit Röntgenstrahlen*, Springer-Verlag OHG, Berlin, 1949.
46. G. L. Clark, *Applied X-rays*, p. 507, McGraw-Hill Book Company, New York, 1955.
47. R. A. Stephen and R. T. Barnes, *J. Inst. Metals*, **60**:285 (1937).
48. P. B. Hirsch and J. N. Kellar, *Acta Cryst.*, **5**:162 (1952).
49. A. Kelly, *Proc. Phys. Soc.* (*London*), **66A**:403 (1953).
50. P. B. Hirsch, *X-ray Diffraction by Polycrystalline Materials*, Institute of Physics, London, 1955.
51. P. B. Hirsch and J. N. Kellar, *Proc. Phys. Soc.* (*London*), **64B**:369 (1951).
52. K. W. Andrews and W. Johnson, *Brit. J. Appl. Phys.*, **10**:321–325 (1959).

Chapter 18

DETERMINATION OF PREFERRED ORIENTATION

J. Read Holland

Sandia Laboratory

1. INTRODUCTION

Development of Preferred Orientation. In most polycrystalline bodies preferential crystallographic alignment is exhibited by the individual crystals. Such an alignment is known as a preferred orientation or texture.* Preferred orientation will impart a degree of anisotropy of the physical and mechanical properties depending on the anisotropy in single-crystal properties and extent of preferential crystallographic alignment. If crystals in a polycrystalline material are randomly oriented, the body is isotropic. If, however, the crystals each have very nearly an identical orientation, the anisotropy will approach that of a single crystal.

Thermal and mechanical history of a polycrystalline body determine the preferred orientation developed. Similarity of textures is developed among materials having the same crystal structure for comparable thermal and mechanical histories. From knowledge of crystallographic systems of the slip processes by which crystals deform and the state of stress in a given means of shaping polycrystalline materials, it has been possible, with reasonable success, to predict the preferred orientations that result from plastic deformation.[1–6]

Representation of Preferred Orientations. One of the ways a preferred orientation may be detected is by the Debye diffraction pattern observed when a well-collimated monochromatic x-ray beam impinges upon a polycrystalline sample. If the sample is randomly oriented, the Debye rings viewed on a plane normal to the x-ray beam will be of uniform intensity about the circumference of each diffraction ring. If crystals (the so-called grains in a metal) deviate from the randomly oriented condition, the Debye ring of each family of diffracting planes will exhibit intensity maxima and minima. The diffracted intensity observed in each ring may be correlated with the concentration of crystals in a given orientation. The positions of the changes in diffraction intensity may be defined by an azimuth angle α and by the angle of inclination ϕ of a reference plane in the sample (the rolling plane is most often used for sheet, the cross-section plane for a rod) to the x-ray beam. Since these positions are defined by two angular coordinates, these may be plotted in any projection that utilizes an angular two-coordinate system. The projection most frequently used is a stereographic projection[7] (see Fig. 1), because in this projection, angles are truly represented along any great circle, i.e., line of longitude or equator of the projection.[8]

* A crystallographic texture is a description of the manner in which the overall orientation of the individual crystals composing a polycrystalline body deviates from a random condition.

To describe a preferred orientation completely, the changes in x-ray intensity for a beam diffracted from a given family $\{h,k,l\}$ of planes must be observed and recorded over a range of inclinations, from 0 to 90°, of the specimen to the x-ray beam. Then a plot of the pole distribution, i.e., changes in diffracted intensity for a given family of diffracting planes, over the specimen inclination range, will describe the preferred orientation of the specimen (see Fig. 2).* A stereographic projection of the pole positions for selected $\{h,k,l\}$ families of planes is shown in Fig. 3. The stereographic

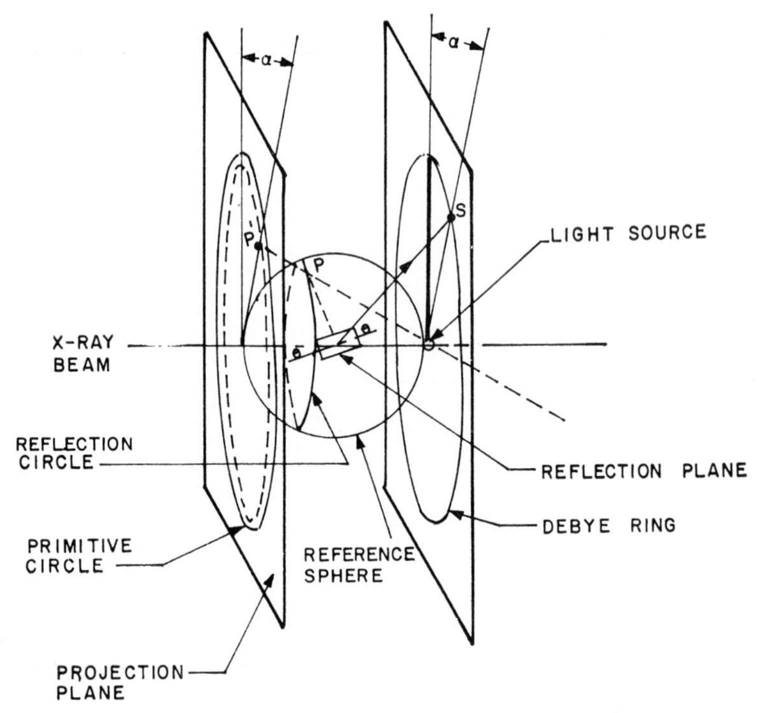

FIG. 1. Schematic of stereographic projection showing relation between incident x-ray beam, reflection plane (i.e., the diffracting planes in a crystal), diffracted beam, and projection. The normal to the reflection plane P, diffracted spot S, projection of the normal P, and incident x-ray beam all lie in a plane. Consider the specimen plane normal to the incident beam; α is the azimuth angle and θ is Bragg angle. The projection of the reflection circle is indicated by a dashed circle on the projection plane and is concentric with the primitive circle of the projection but removed from it by $(90 - \theta)°$. When the specimen is moved from the normal position by $\phi°$ the projected reflection circle shifts a like amount.

projection of the orientation of a single crystal can be represented by the pole position of a given $\{h,k,l\}$ family of planes. Generally speaking, the families of planes that diffract the x-ray beam strongly because of structure-factor considerations are used to obtain preferred-orientation data.

Fiber Textures. When a polycrystalline material is shaped or formed, the crystals tend to rotate into some alignment with the principal stress axis. This rotation takes place by well-known processes of slip, twinning, and kinking. Each crystal must at all times maintain an integral and continuous boundary with the neighboring crystals;

* A more complete description of the properties and uses of a stereographic projection may be found in Chap. 4, Sec. 1, and in Barrett's book (see General References at end of this chapter).

nevertheless, the change in orientation of individual grains can be extensive. If the state of stress in the forming operation is relatively simple, such as in wire drawing, the rotation tends to cause some crystallographic direction(s) to align parallel to the stress axis. The usual case is for one or two directions to align parallel to the fiber or longitudinal axis. Rotational symmetry usually prevails about this axis. Debye patterns obtained, using a collimated monochromatic beam, strongly resemble the diffraction patterns of fibrous materials such as cellulose, asbestos, or the elastomers. Because of this resemblance the terminology "fiber texture" has been applied to preferred orientations developed by wire drawing, extrusion, compression, and similar operations.

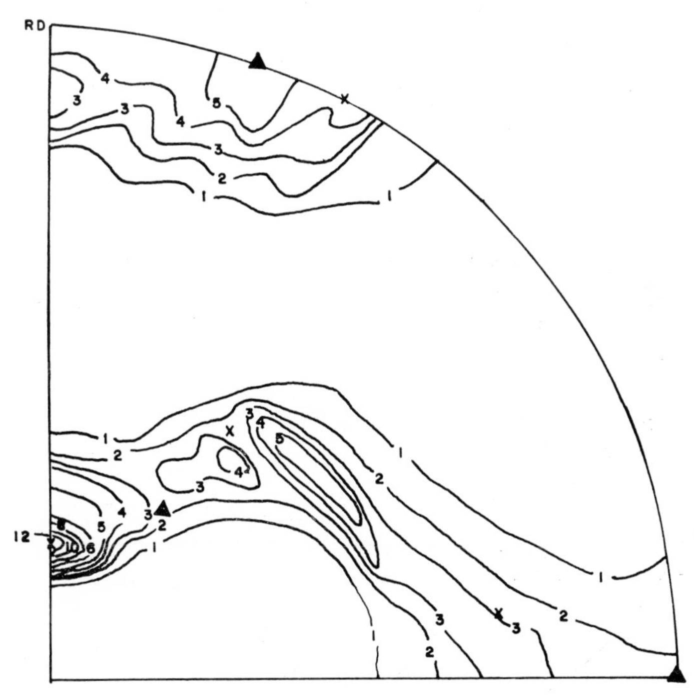

FIG. 2. A normalized 111 pole figure of copper sheet rolled at 150°C. The pole positions of ideal orientations are denoted by × —(123) [41$\bar{2}$]; ▲—(110) [11$\bar{2}$]. The units on the contour lines are multiples of random intensity. The preferred orientation may be described as (123) [41$\bar{2}$].

Fiber Textures in Nonmetals. Knowledge of fiber textures occurring in metals is extensive, but relatively little is known of fiber textures in nonmetallic solids. Recently fiber textures in ionic crystals have been investigated.[9–11] The compression textures of LiF, NaF, NaCl, KCl, and KBr were reported as ⟨100⟩ directions aligned parallel to the compression axis, while MgO exhibited ⟨111⟩ preferred orientation. Since MgO has a rock-salt-type structure, it was expected to develop a texture similar to NaCl. The compression texture of AgCl and AgBr was ⟨110⟩; however, if compression was in a die, the texture was ⟨100⟩ plus an additional ⟨110⟩ component. The compression texture of specimens of cesium chloride–type crystal structure (CsCl, TlCl, and NH_4Cl) was found to be ⟨111⟩.

Fiber Textures in Metals. Textures developed in metals and alloys during wire drawing, extrusion, and compression have been extensively studied. Results of many of these studies are summarized in Table 1. Generally speaking, the texture of swaged or rolled wire is the same as that of drawn wire. On the basis of selected results listed in Table 1 and other results reported in the literature, the textures can be generalized by crystal structure. On this basis the texture of cold-drawn wire of face-centered cubic metals is a duplex ⟨111⟩ and ⟨100⟩ orientation. The ⟨100⟩ orientation decreases in intensity with increasing severity of reduction. Extrusion textures of face-centered cubic metals and alloys are comparable with wire textures. Compression textures are characterized by either a ⟨110⟩ major component with a spread to ⟨113⟩ or ⟨110⟩-⟨111⟩ components with a spread to ⟨113⟩.

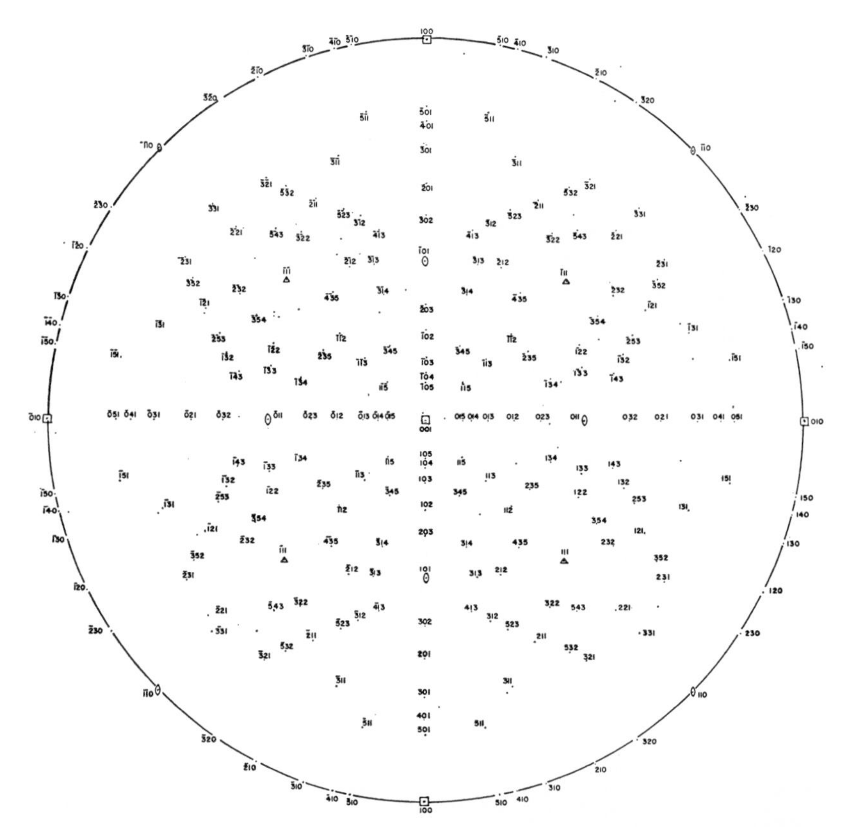

Fig. 3. Standard (001) projection for cubic crystals. This corresponds to stereographic projection of the pole positions for a single cubic crystal.

Wire textures of the body-centered cubic metals and alloys are uniformly a single ⟨110⟩ fiber orientation. Extrusion textures are also simple fiber textures with ⟨110⟩ directions parallel to the extrusion axis. For compression a duplex ⟨111⟩-⟨100⟩ fiber texture is found.

Hexagonal close-packed metals usually have a single fiber texture with $\langle 10\bar{1}0 \rangle$ parallel to the wire axis. For c/a ratios less than $\sqrt{3}$, extrusion textures usually are also single fiber textures of the $\langle 10\bar{1}0 \rangle$ type. Compression textures are generally single fiber textures with (0001) parallel to the compression axis.

Complex Deformation Textures. In more complex textures such as those found in heavily rolled polycrystalline materials there is no simple symmetry element as in fiber textures; hence a more complete crystallographic notation is used to identify the preferential orientation. Common practice is to cite crystallographic plane(s) found parallel to the rolling plane and crystallographic direction(s) found parallel to the rolling direction. Hence the notation (100) $[0\bar{1}1]$ describes a texture where {100} planes are oriented parallel to the rolling plane and ⟨011⟩ directions are parallel to the

Table 1. Fiber Textures Occurring in Face-centered and Body Centered Cubic Metals and Alloys*

	Drawn wire	Ref.	Extrusion	Ref.	Compression	Ref.
Al	⟨111⟩†,‡	12	⟨111⟩ ⟨100⟩	19	⟨110⟩ with spread to ⟨113⟩	23
Ag	⟨111⟩†,‡	12	⟨100⟩ ⟨111⟩	20		
Au	⟨111⟩†	12				
Cu	⟨111⟩†,‡	12, 13	⟨111⟩ ⟨100⟩	20	⟨110⟩ with spread to ⟨113⟩	24
	⟨111⟩ ⟨100⟩	14	⟨111⟩	14		
Ni	⟨111⟩‡	12	....	...	⟨110⟩ with spread to ⟨113⟩	24
Pb	⟨111⟩‡	12				
Pd	⟨111⟩ ⟨100⟩	15				
Cu solid solutions with ≯ 1% Al, 5% Zn, 30% Ni	⟨111⟩ ⟨100⟩	16	....	...	⟨110⟩ with spread to ⟨100⟩ and ⟨113⟩	25
Cu solid solutions with >2% Al, 8% Zn, 85:15 brass, 63:37 brass	⟨111⟩	.....	....	...	⟨110⟩ and ⟨111⟩ with spread to ⟨113⟩	25
72:28 brass	⟨100⟩ ⟨111⟩	17	....	...	70:30 ⟨110⟩ and ⟨111⟩ with spread to ⟨113⟩	24
Cu 30% Ag	⟨111⟩ ⟨100⟩	18				
Al, 4.5% Cu, 1.5% Mg	....	.....	⟨111⟩ ⟨100⟩	21		
Al-Cu-Mg-Zn	....	.....	⟨111⟩ ⟨100⟩	22		
Fe	⟨110⟩	26–28	....	...	⟨111⟩ and ⟨100⟩	31
Mo	⟨110⟩	26				
Nb	⟨110⟩	27				
Ta	⟨110⟩	27				
V	⟨110⟩§	29				
W	⟨110⟩	30				
Fe, 14% Al	⟨110⟩	26				
β brass	⟨110⟩	27				
Fe, 4.6% Si; Fe-V; Fe-Si	⟨110⟩	28	....	...	⟨111⟩ and ⟨100⟩	24

* The results were selected on the basis of the most recent and definite work. Some persistent discrepancies among results have been indicated.

† Freda and Cullity[32] report a duplex ⟨111⟩-⟨100⟩ fiber texture for aluminum, copper, and silver.

‡ Earlier results indicate a duplex ⟨111⟩-⟨100⟩ fiber texture; however, Hibbard[12] has shown that at about 98 per cent reduction in area or less the ⟨100⟩ component disappears.

§ The ratio of ⟨111⟩ to ⟨100⟩ is 3:1 after 50 per cent reduction in area, 9:1 after 80 per cent, and only ⟨111⟩ is present after 96 per cent reduction.

rolling direction. Of course, many individual crystals may deviate considerably from this orientation, but the notation is merely used to locate the ideal situation. Because of such deviations, graphical representation of the pole distribution is necessary to describe a preferred orientation completely.

Complex Deformation Textures in Nonmetals. Recently King and Wilman[11] reported rolling texture of AgCl as (110) $[1\bar{1}2]$, which is similar to that frequently

Table 2. Cold-rolling Textures in Metals and Binary Alloys*

Metal	Solute, atomic %	Primary texture component	Secondary texture component	Ref.
		Face-centered Cubic		
Al	...	(123) $[41\bar{2}]$†	...	34, 35
Al	1.0 Zn	(123) $[41\bar{2}]$	...	34
Al	0.1 Cu	(123) $[41\bar{2}]$	...	34
Al	2.0 Cu	(123) $[41\bar{2}]$	(110) $[1\bar{1}2]$	34
Al	1.25 Si	(123) $[41\bar{2}]$	(110) $[1\bar{1}2]$	34
Al	0.7 Mg	(123) $[41\bar{2}]$	(110) $[1\bar{1}2]$	34
Cu	...	(123) $[41\bar{2}]$†	...	34, 35
Cu	0.6 to 5.7 Al	(123) $[41\bar{2}]$	(110) $[1\bar{1}2]$	34
Cu	8.2 and 12.0 Al	(110) $[1\bar{1}2]$	...	34
Cu	0.35 Au	(123) $[41\bar{2}]$	...	34
Cu	3.0 Au	(123) $[41\bar{2}]$	(110) $[1\bar{1}2]$	34
Cu	6.0 Au	(110) $[1\bar{1}2]$	...	34
Cu	29.6 Ni	(123) $[41\bar{2}]$	...	34
Cu	49.0 Ni	(123) $[41\bar{2}]$	(110) $[1\bar{1}2]$	34
Cu	0.4 and 1.2 Sn	(123) $[41\bar{2}]$	(110) $[1\bar{1}2]$	34
Cu	1.5 Sn	(110) $[1\bar{1}2]$	...	34
Cu	5.0 Zn	(123) $[41\bar{2}]$	(110) $[1\bar{1}2]$	34
Cu	8.1 to 27.4 Zn	(110) $[1\bar{1}2]$	...	34
Au	...	(123) $[41\bar{2}]$†	...	34
Au	10 Cu	(110) $[1\bar{1}2]$	...	34
Ni	...	(123) $[41\bar{2}]$†	...	34
Ni	24.6 Cu	(123) $[41\bar{2}]$	...	34
Ni	48.0 Fe	(123) $[41\bar{2}]$	...	34
Ni	6.0 Mo	(123) $[41\bar{2}]$	(110) $[1\bar{1}2]$	34
Ag	...	(110) $[1\bar{1}2]$	...	34, 36
Ag	1.7 Cu	(110) $[1\bar{1}2]$	...	34
Th	...	(123) $[41\bar{2}]$†	...	34
Th	...	(113) $[12\bar{1}]$	(110) $[1\bar{1}2]$	37
Th	15 to 50 Ce	(123) $[41\bar{2}]$	...	34
Th	12.5 Zr	(123) $[41\bar{2}]$	...	34
		Body-centered Cubic		
Fe	...	(100) $[0\bar{1}1]$	...	38, 39
Cr	...	(100) $[0\bar{1}1]$	...	40
Mo	...	(100) $[0\bar{1}1]$	...	41
Nb	...	(100) $[0\bar{1}1]$	(112) $[1\bar{1}0]$	42
Ta	...	(100) $[0\bar{1}1]$	...	43
V	...	(100) $[0\bar{1}1]$	...	44
W	...	(100) $[0\bar{1}1]$	...	45
Fe	3.9 and 8.7 Si	(100) $[0\bar{1}1]$	...	46
Fe	6.7 Si	(001) $[0\bar{1}0]$	(111) $[1\bar{1}0]$‡ (111) $[11\bar{2}]$	47
		or (001) $[1\bar{1}0]$	(111) $[11\bar{2}]$‡	47
Nb	<8.9 V	(100) $[0\bar{1}1]$	(112) $[1\bar{1}0]$ (111) $[11\bar{2}]$	48
		Hexagonal Close-packed		
Be	...	(0001) $[10\bar{1}0]$	...	49
Hf	...	(0001) $[10\bar{1}0]$	...	49
Ti	...	(0001) $[10\bar{1}0]$	...	50

Table 2. Cold-rolling Textures in Metals and Binary Alloys *(Continued)*

Metal	Solute, atomic %	Primary texture component	Secondary texture component	Ref.
		Hexagonal Close-packed		
Zr.......	....	(0001) [10$\bar{1}$0]	....	51
Mg......	....	(0001) [11$\bar{2}$0]	....	52
Zn.......	....	(0001) [11$\bar{2}$0]	....	53
Mg......	0.33 Ca	{0001} inclined 15° to rolling plane and no directionality	....	54
Ti.......	6.6 Al	(0001) [10$\bar{1}$0]	....	55
Ti.......	11.3 Zn	{0001} inclined 30° to rolling plane and ⟨10$\bar{1}$0⟩ parallel to rolling direction	....	55
Ti.......	4.6 Ta	{0001} inclined 30° to rolling plane and ⟨10$\bar{1}$0⟩ parallel to rolling direction	....	55

* These results were selected as the most recent and definitive. There are some discrepancies between these and earlier, less definitive results. In general, the rolling temperatures were room temperature.

† This texture is sometimes reported as (123) [12$\bar{1}$]; however, this notation is incorrect in terms of common usage. The notation should read (123) [41$\bar{2}$]; see E. R. W. Jones and E. A. Fell, *Acta Met.*, **5**: 689(1957).

‡ These differences appear related to differences in sulfur content; see Ref. 47.

encountered in rolling textures of face-centered cubic metals. This rolling texture is also very similar to textures of abraded surfaces of AgBr and AgCl.[33]

Complex Deformation Textures in Metals. The cold-rolling textures of selected metals and alloys are summarized in Table 2. From these results it appears that face-centered cubic metals and alloys have rolling textures of one of two types: (1) (123) [41$\bar{2}$] or (2) (110) [1$\bar{1}$2]. The body-centered cubic metals rather uniformly have (100) [0$\bar{1}$1] rolling textures. As for the rolling textures of the hexagonal close-packed metals, the usual texture is basal planes aligned parallel to the rolling plane with either the ⟨11$\bar{2}$0⟩ or ⟨10$\bar{1}$0⟩ directions aligning parallel to the rolling direction.

Recrystallization Textures. Recrystallization textures are those preferred orientations that occur as a result of recrystallizing a plastically deformed crystalline body. They are influenced by many variables including prior deformation, deformation texture, impurities present, solute additions, and annealing temperature. This complexity precludes a review of recrystallization textures in this chapter.* As a consequence of deformation followed by recrystallization essentially four texture possibilities exist: (1) the recrystallized structure may be randomly oriented; (2) the deformation texture may be retained, as is often the case in body-centered cubic metals; (3) a new orientation texture may be developed which can persist into the higher-temperature ranges associated with exaggerated grain growth or secondary recrystallization; (4) a new orientation texture developed during primary recrystallization may change upon further annealing, i.e., with the onset of secondary recrystallization.

2. CHOICE OF X-RAY CHARACTERISTICS

In all preferred-orientation methods some means of obtaining a favorable monochromatic x-ray beam is essential. Crystal monochromators are avoided in preferred-

* Reviews of recrystallization textures in metals may be found in C. S. Barrett, *Structure of Metals*, 2d ed., pp. 485–509, McGraw-Hill Book Company, New York, 1952, and A. Taylor, *X-ray Metallography*, pp. 646–653, John Wiley & Sons, Inc., New York, 1961.

orientation studies because of the severe loss of beam intensity experienced. Accordingly, the beam is made nearly monochromatic by selection of a suitable β filter. Ideally such a filter will transmit only the $K\alpha$ and longer-wavelength radiation. These filters may be thin foils of a pure element with suitable K absorption edge or a powder of a compound of the filtering element with an element of low atomic weight such as oxygen. Some suitable filters for reducing the $K\beta$ and shorter wavelengths to low intensity with slight absorption of $K\alpha$ are given in Table 3.

Isolation of a narrow wavelength band can be achieved by differential filtration or the use of so-called balanced filters.[56] In this way the wavelength transmitted can be very nearly limited to $K\alpha$ wavelengths. For example, if Ni and Co are used successively to filter Cu radiation, the difference in wavelengths transmitted corresponds to a narrow band centered near the $K\alpha$ wavelength. Such balanced filters are now commercially available from Tem-Pres Research, Incorporated, State College, Pa., based on a design of McKinstry and Short.[57] The applicability of balanced filters in preferred-orientation studies is limited to the evaluation of spurious diffraction areas in preferred-orientation patterns.

Table 3. $K\beta$ Filters*

Target	Wavelengths, Å			Filters for $\frac{\text{intensity } K\beta}{\text{intensity } K\alpha} = \frac{1}{600}$				
	$K\alpha_2$	$K\alpha_1$	$K\beta$	Material	K edge, Å	Thickness, mm	Material content, g/cm²	Transmission factor for $K\alpha$
Ag........	0.564	0.559	0.497	Rh	0.534	0.079	0.096	0.29
Mo........	0.714	0.709	0.632	Zr	0.688	0.108	0.069	0.31
Cu........	1.544	1.540	1.392	Ni	1.488	0.021	0.019	0.40
Co........	1.793	1.789	1.621	Fe	1.743	0.018	0.014	0.44
Fe........	1.940	1.936	1.757	Mn	1.896	0.016	0.012	0.46
Cr........	2.294	2.290	2.085	V	2.269	0.016	0.009	0.50

* Data taken from Edwards and Lipson.[58] The $K\beta$ absorption for the given conditions is better than 90 per cent.

In addition to problems associated with obtaining a nearly monochromatic x-ray beam, suitable target material must be selected so that fluorescent radiation will not be excited in the specimen. Appreciable fluorescing will occur when the radiation wavelength is just short of the absorption edge of the specimen. For example, Cu $K\alpha$ (λ = 1.540 Å) will excite iron, which has a K absorption edge at 1.743 Å. Mo $K\alpha$ is a suitable choice for most work while Cu $K\alpha$ is useful for nonferrous materials.* Fe $K\alpha$ is often used for ferrous alloys as no element is capable of exciting its own fluorescence, and Co $K\alpha$ finds applications as well. In principle, where a greater depth of x-ray penetration is needed to minimize surface-texture effects, a shorter-wavelength characteristic radiation should be used. On the basis of penetrating power Ag $K\alpha$ is useful for the more strongly absorbing metals such as Ta and W.

The intensity of characteristic radiation is controllable within limits by selection of operating voltage. In practice one is more concerned about ratio of intensities of the characteristic $K\alpha$ radiation intensity to integrated intensity of the continuous spectrum. Intensity of characteristic radiation increases by a $3/2$ power of excess of impressed voltage across the tube over critical voltage. Intensity of the continuous spectrum increases very nearly linearly with voltage. On a theoretical basis an

* Cu $K\alpha$ is never a satisfactory choice for iron alloys or compounds because of the fluorescent radiation excited.

Table 4. Critical Excitation Voltage for *K* Radiation and Operating Voltage

Target	Critical voltage, kv	Operating voltage, kv
Ag	25.5	60-70
Mo	20.0	50-55
Cu	8.86	35-40
Co	7.71	30-35
Fe	7.10	25-30
Cr	5.98	25

applied a-c voltage of five times the critical excitation voltage[59] would produce the most favorable ratio of intensities of characteristic to continuous radiation. However, lower operating voltages in the range of 2.5 to 3.5 times the critical value are used in the interest of longer tube life. At a value of 2.5 to 3.5 times critical voltage, the ratio of intensity of the $K\alpha$ line to the continuous spectrum approaches the theoretical maximum. Suitable operating voltages for various targets are given in Table 4 (cf. Chap. 1, Sec. 4).

3. FILM METHODS

Early methods developed for determination of preferred orientation were based on film techniques (cf. Chap. 8). These methods are of interest from a historical standpoint and may still be used to advantage. A suitable photographic film (e.g., Kodak no-screen x-ray film) is placed at an appropriate film-to-specimen distance (4 to 6 cm)

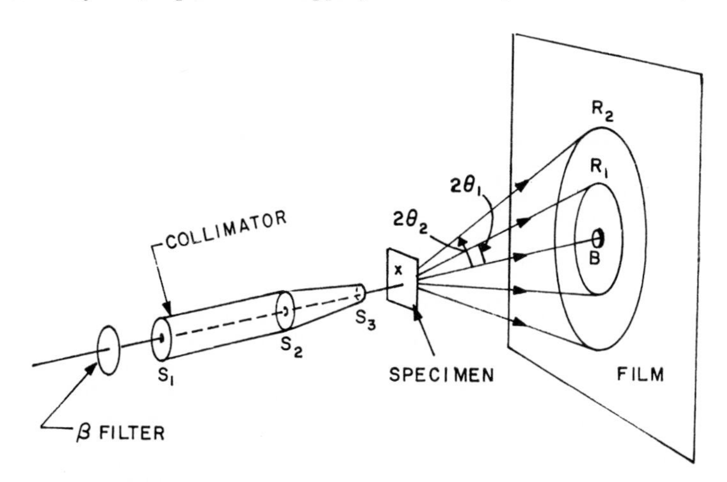

FIG. 4. Transmission or forward-reflection pinhole method used for texture studies. The collimator assembly usually consists of three slits S_1, S_2, and S_3. A lead button is placed at B to absorb the undiffracted beam.

and normal to the x-ray beam so that a Debye pattern is recorded. The method is identical to monochromatic pinhole techniques. The forward-reflection arrangement is shown in Fig. 4. By this arrangement entire Debye diffraction circles are recorded, and circumferential variations in intensity due to preferred orientation or absorption differences can be readily detected. This schematic design is similar to commercial forward-reflection cameras. Precaution should be taken in design so that the exit pinhole, S_3 in Fig. 4, of the collimator traps the scattered radiation from the second pinhole. A lead button, preferably concave, is suspended by a wire from the film holder or glued onto the light shield of the film holder so that undiffracted primary beam transmitted through the specimen is stopped.

A light-tight cassette or film holder is used, and this is mounted on a precision-camera track along with the collimator and specimen holders. The black paper used to exclude light is better replaced by either aluminum foil or some β filter material. The latter will exclude any β radiation that might be excited by the monochromatic incident x-ray beam. If the β filter material is physically removed by approximately ⅛ to ¼ in. from the x-ray film, then fogging, due to fluorescence of the filter by the absorbed β, will be avoided. Both aluminum foils and β filters will reduce the film background and improve the uniformity. White radiation that penetrates through the specimen and is incident upon the film will manifest itself as radial streaks from

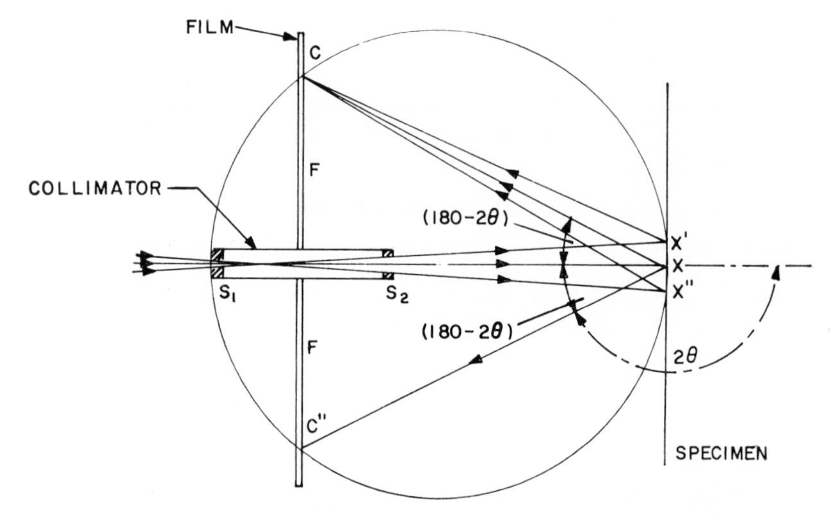

Fig. 5. The back-reflection pinhole technique as applied to texture studies. A monochromating filter is placed between the collimator and the x-ray port. The beam passes through a hole in the film cassette along the lead-shielded collimator and is diffracted from a thick specimen back to the film.

the near center of the film. This characteristic of the film technique can be put to advantage in evaluating the possibility of spurious areas due to white-radiation diffraction in a preferred-orientation pattern determined by electronic counters.

The back-reflection monochromatic pinhole technique is used to determine preferred orientation in thick samples. In this case the x-ray beam is collimated by a pinhole system that passes through the center of the film (see Fig. 5). The beam is incident upon the specimen and a film records diffraction rings at Bragg angles greater than 120° depending on film size and film-to-specimen distance. In this geometry, the Bragg angle θ is related to the apex angle of the diffraction cone ϕ as follows:

$$2\theta = \pi - \phi/2 \tag{1}$$

Beam divergence may be limited by making the pinholes S_1 and S_2 the same size. If only a small area is irradiated then the relationships of S_1 and S_2 to either the film or sample are not critical and all recorded reflections are very nearly equal in sharpness if not in radial breadth. In such a camera, cassette and specimen holders are preferably mounted on the same bracket, and the collimation system is placed flush against a filter holder at the exit x-ray port. Additional lead-foil shielding may be necessary to reduce any scattered radiation that might escape through a gap between the collimator assembly and the filter holder. This scattered radiation could contribute greatly to the background intensity on the film apart from the safety hazard.

When monochromatic pinhole techniques are used to study preferred orientation, pinhole diameters of 0.5 to 1.0 mm diameter are typical. Film-to-specimen distances vary from 3 to 6 cm, but the film is always maintained normal to the beam. Exposure times will vary considerably, depending on many factors, including specimen thickness for transmission patterns, pinhole diameter, tube voltage, tube filament current, film-to-specimen distance, focal-spot size, film sensitivity, monochromating filter material, filter thickness, etc. Exposures may run from one-half to several hours; hence it is usual to make several trial exposures to estimate optimum exposure time for a given set of conditions.

Sometimes a specimen will be encountered that is too coarse-grained to give a satisfactory Debye pattern. This is because the number of grains irradiated is insufficient to be representative of the specimen and to give well-defined intensity maxima. This can readily be detected in film patterns by the spotty appearance of the Debye rings and can often be overcome by some integrating device that translates the specimen back and forth across the beam, thereby increasing the number of grains irradiated. However, integrating the area irradiated may not be sufficient, and in this case optical etch-pit methods or Laue patterns may be used for such very coarse-grained material.

Some considerations regarding specimen thicknesses are of importance in forward- and back-reflection monochromatic pinhole techniques. For forward reflection the specimen must be thin enough to transmit a reasonable number of diffracted x-ray photons in a suitable time period; for example, ½ to 3 hr is normally the time needed to produce a readable pattern on the film. For the back-reflection method the specimen must present an "infinitely long" path to the incident x-ray beam so that the beam does not penetrate through the sample. If the sample is not thick enough to attenuate the beam so that appreciably none of the beam penetrates through, then lead sheet can often be used to attenuate the beam further and prevent spurious intensity peaks caused by diffraction from the specimen holder.

A suitable specimen holder for the monochromatic pinhole techniques is a typical goniometer head with cross slides and arcs, such as that shown schematically in Fig. 6. The specimen is held in place by a mounting device atop the upper cradle Y. The rotary motions about YY' and ZZ' allow one to align the specimen parallel to XX'. The lateral translations along the perpendicular directions AA' and BB' allow one to locate the specimen coincident with XX'. The specimen alignment can be readily accomplished using a low-power telescope with cross hairs. The telescope is placed coincident with the incident x-ray beam path. The vertical cross hair of the telescope is aligned parallel to XX'. Specimens may be mounted on the cradle Y using Apiezon wax, sealing wax, plasticene, etc. Wire specimens are visually aligned parallel to the vertical cross hair. The goniometer is then rotated 180° around XX', and visual alignment of the specimen with the vertical cross hair is repeated. These steps are repeated until the alignment is satisfactory. The goniometer is next rotated 90°, and the alignment procedure given above is repeated until the specimen is parallel to XX'. The specimen is then translated along AA' and BB' and brought into coincidence with XX'. For sheet specimens, the alignment procedure may be modified using the basic steps outlined above.

Film Methods for Fiber Patterns. In order to determine fiber texture of wires, rods, filaments, and similar shapes, a single-pinhole diffraction pattern taken with the fiber axis normal to the incident x-ray beam often suffices. Occasionally a pinhole pattern will be taken with the incident beam parallel to the fiber axis; however, in the case of metals, usually such a pattern will only verify the radial symmetry observed in metal wires, extruded rod, etc.[60]

Fiber texture can be determined by analysis of the fiber patterns such as those in Fig. 7. The similarity of patterns for drawn metallic wire and an organic fiber is readily seen. The fiber patterns observed in metallic wires are analogous to the layer patterns of rotated single crystals when the crystal is rotated completely about an axis perpendicular to the incident x-ray beam. The radial symmetry about the fiber axis observed in fiber texture of metals produces the same effect as rotating a single crystal (see Fig. 8). In Fig. 8 the layer lines equivalent to a rotating single-crystal pattern have been sketched in as dashed lines on the idealized fiber patterns to show the relationship. The diffraction spots lie on the intersections of the Debye rings with the layer lines of a rotated single crystal.

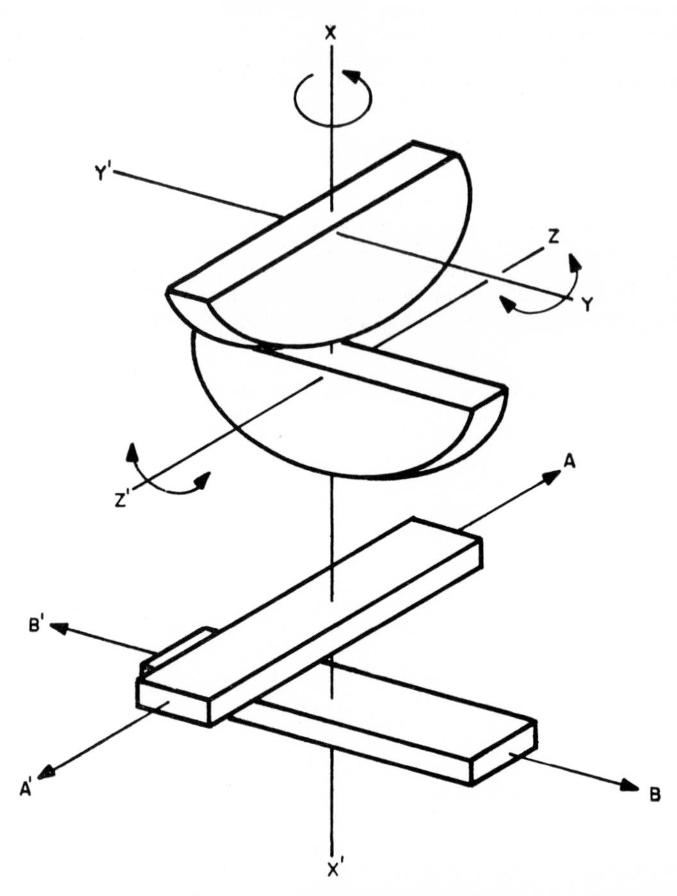

Fig. 6. Schematic diagram of goniometer head suitable for pinhole methods of determining preferred orientation. The specimen is held on the upper cradle YY' and the goniometer is mounted vertically on a post coincident with XX'. Limited rotation ($\pm 30°$) about YY' and ZZ', complete revolution about XX', and translation along AA' and BB' are the goniometer motions.

In analyzing a fiber pattern the first step is to index the diffraction rings (see Chap. 28). This can be done by determining the Bragg angle of the diffraction cone as follows:

$$\tan \theta = r/R \tag{2}$$

where θ is the Bragg angle, r is the radius of the Debye ring, R is film-to-specimen distance. From the θ values, the interplanar spacings or $\sin^2 \theta$ values may be calculated and the indices of reflection determined; however, a pattern may be indexed by inspection if one knows the spectral sequence of lower-order x-ray reflections.

The next step is to determine azimuthal positions of intensity maxima on a given diffraction ring. To do this, the position of the fiber axis is marked on the film. Then the angle α is measured between this reference axis and the intensity maxima. This can be seen in Fig. 9, which represents in an idealized manner the origin of a single diffraction ring in a fiber pattern. The incident beam strikes normal to the

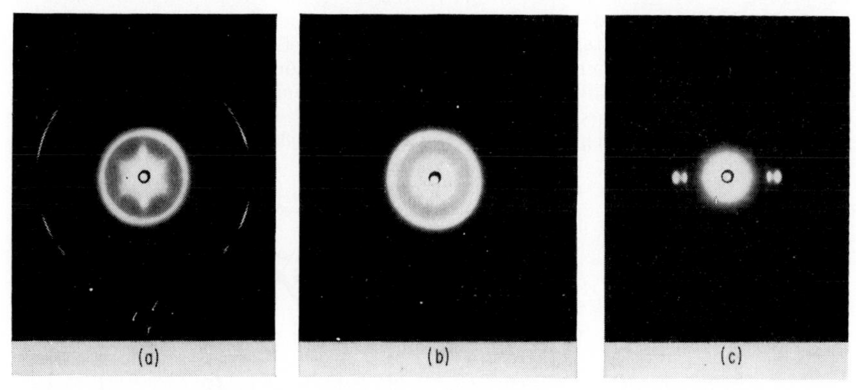

FIG. 7. Typical fiber patterns taken by pinhole transmission using Cu $K\alpha$. (*a*) Drawn copper wire. (*b*) Drawn tungsten wire. (*c*) Monofilament nylon fishing line. The wire axes are in the vertical.

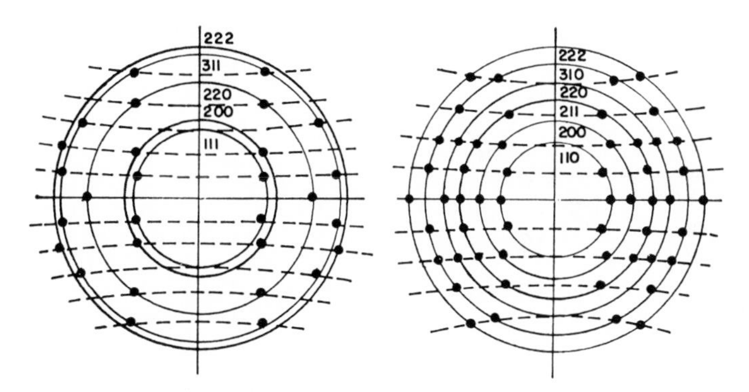

FIG. 8. Relationship between ideal fiber patterns of metals and the layer pattern of rotating single crystals. The beam is normal to the vertical wire axis. Debye rings are represented by solid lines, and layer lines are dashed. (*Left*) Face-centered cubic metal with <111> fiber axis. (*Right*) Body-centered cubic metal with <100> fiber axis.

vertical wire axis at O and is diffracted from the plane represented, producing intensity maxima on the diffraction ring. The wire axis on the film is $O'A$, and O' is the center of the diffraction ring. ON is the normal to the diffracting plane, and δ is the angle ON makes with the fiber axis. The azimuth angle α is related to the Bragg angle θ and the angle δ by the following:

$$\cos \alpha = \cos \delta / \cos \theta \tag{3}$$

This relationship can be readily derived by use of spherical trigonometry.[61] If short-wavelength radiation is used, such as Ag $K\alpha$ or Mo $K\alpha$, then $\cos \theta$ for lower-order reflections will approach unity. Without too great an error the approximation

$$\angle\delta = \angle\alpha \tag{4}$$

may be used. By comparing the values for α on a given ring with inclination angles between plane normals, the normal(s) parallel to the fiber axis can be determined. In this regard the tables of Peavler and Lenusky[62] for the cubic system and those of Lawley[63] and Taylor and Leber[64] for the hexagonal metals are very useful. The solution obtained of crystallographic direction(s) parallel to the fiber axis should be verified by repeating the analysis for at least one additional Deybe ring using either Eq. (3) or the approximation, given by Eq. (4), depending on the value of cos θ.

In case of more complex fiber textures, solutions based on each Debye ring may yield two or more crystallographic directions aligning parallel to the wire axis. In such

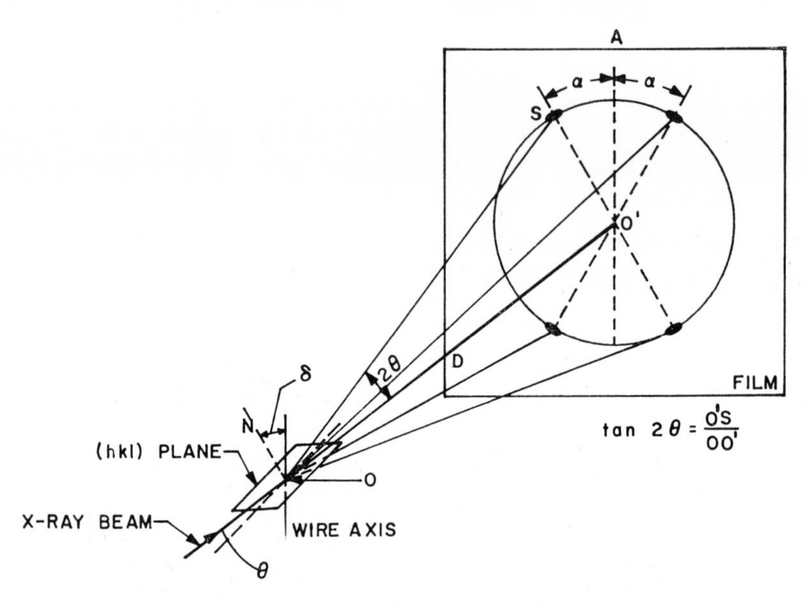

FIG. 9. The origin of a diffracted spot in a fiber pattern. The azimuth angle α is related to the angle δ between the diffracting-plane normal and the wire axis by Eq. (3). The line $O'A$ represents the wire axis on the film.

cases the texture is often represented by plotting the pole-density distribution in a unit stereographic triangle. If this is necessary, relative densities must be assigned to the areas of enhanced intensity either visually or by microdensitometer reading of the film. The circumferential extent for an intensity region corresponding to a given density level is determined in terms of the angle α. If the unit stereographic triangle is oriented so that the fiber axis is normal to the projection plane, then the pole distribution plotted on a unit stereographic triangle can be used to represent density of poles oriented parallel to the fiber axis. This is done by plotting the deviation in terms of $\angle\delta$ of areas of equal relative intensity from an idealized orientation. $\angle\delta_{\text{observed}} - \angle\delta_{\text{ideal}}$ will represent an angular difference from a given pole position and may be laid off as a locus having that angular distance from the pole. For example, a fiber texture having the duplex ⟨100⟩-⟨111⟩ structure often observed in face-centered cubic metals would appear in stereographic projection similar to the fiber texture plotted in Fig. 10.

If, for some reason, it is inconvenient to have the x-ray beam normal to the wire axis or if it is advantageous to tilt the wire axis to reflect from a given (h,k,l) plane, the relationships between δ and α are altered as follows:

$$\cos \delta = \cos \beta \sin \theta + \sin \beta \cos \theta \cos \alpha \tag{5}$$

where β now is angle of inclination of the beam to the fiber axis. Using Eq. (5) a series of δ values can be calculated.

Graphical solutions of fiber axes can be made using a series of δ values. In a stereographic unit triangle the fiber axis can be determined by finding the point that is the proper δ angle from the pole of each diffracting plane. This point then corresponds to a projection of the fiber axis, and the index of direction, corresponding to that crystallographic direction, can be determined. The direction may be identified by comparison with a standard stereographic projection for that crystal system.

Patterns of Molecular Fibers (cf. Chap. 21). There are a number of mineral-silicate, natural organic, and synthetic organic materials that exhibit fibrous properties

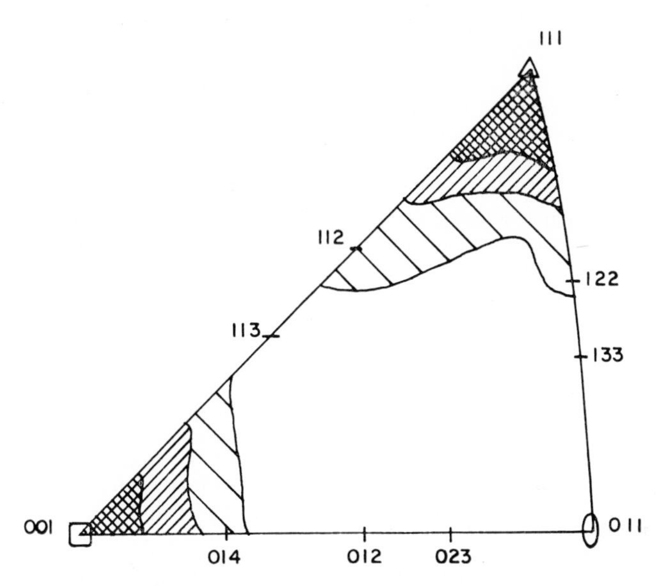

Fig. 10. Typical fiber texture for drawn wire of face-centered cubic metal as represented by a pole figure.

by virtue of their composition of long-chain molecules. Asbestos (chrysotile), for example, is a fibrous mineral composed of elongated bundles of crystals, often called crystallites or micelles in the case of organic fibers, which have their long molecular axis aligned approximately parallel to the fiber axis. The orientation is random in all other respects. The natural polymers such as cellulose, keratin, fibroin, and gutta-percha exhibit fibrous properties while the synthetic polymers such as polyethylene, polyesters, and polyamides can be drawn out to form fibers. In both cases the same type of crystallite orientation results. This orientation is also observed in rubberlike substances which are essentially amorphous unstretched but crystallize when stretched.

When a monochromatic x-ray beam passes through such a fiber, the diffraction pattern produced is essentially the same as a rotating single-crystal pattern since the random orientation of crystallites about the fiber axis produces an effect equivalent to rotating a single crystal. If the fiber is not strongly oriented, the deviation from perfect alignment will be noted by the appearance of arcs on the diffraction rings rather than spots. The angular extent of these arcs can be related directly to the angular spread of those orientations nearly parallel to the fiber axis. Another effect observed in molecular fibers is that the small size of micelles or crystallites causes reflections that are more diffuse than those obtained from large crystals.

These fiber patterns can be used to determine the crystal structure and unit cell dimensions in much the same way that a rotating single-crystal pattern is used in structure determination. Distance from the equatorial line in the fiber pattern to the first layer line corresponds to the identity period and unit cell dimension lying along the fiber axis as follows:

$$I = n\lambda/\cos \alpha_n \tag{6}$$

where I is the identity distance, n is nth layer line used in the determination, λ is the x-ray wavelength, and α_n is the semi-vertical angle of the cone of diffracted x-rays. The relation of α_n to distance of nth layer line from the equatorial line ζ_n and the film-to-specimen distance R is

$$\cot \alpha_n = \zeta_n/R \tag{7}$$

The spots can be related to the reciprocal lattice using ξ and ζ coordinates and a Bernal chart. This method is described in detail by Bunn.[65]

Fiber patterns of organic materials have been useful in determining structure orientation. Analysis of such patterns is similar in many respects to that for inorganic polycrystalline materials. Details of the analysis have been given by Happey.[66] The extent of dispersion from orientation perfection is related to the length of equatorial arcs by

$$\sin \rho = \cos \theta \sin \chi_E \tag{8}$$

where ρ is the semiapex angle of dispersion of crystallites about the fiber axis, θ is the Bragg angle, and χ_E is the semiangle of dispersion of the equatorial arc on the diffraction ring. Meridional reflections occur if the angle of dispersion ρ equals or exceeds the Bragg angle in an orthogonal system. In this case then the semiangle of the polar arc χ_M is related to the semiangle of crystallite dispersion ρ by the relation

$$\cos \rho = \cos \theta \cos \chi_M \tag{9}$$

where χ_M can be measured from the film.

Fiber patterns can also be used to determine the helical angle S for molecules that wind helically around the fiber axis.[66] Such patterns can often be recognized by four nearly equatorial spots symmetrically disposed about the equator. At large helical angles, $\cos S > \sin \theta$ (S is the helical angle and θ is the Bragg angle), the four equatorial spots merge, each pair forming an arc which is characterized by the weakest intensity occurring in the center and the strongest at the arc ends.

Film Methods for Complex Textures. Basic camera arrangements used for determining more complex textures, such as those in rolled sheet, are monochromatic pinhole methods described earlier in this section. However, in the case of complex textures, preferred orientation can be adequately described only by stereographic projection of pole-density distribution data collected for a number of spatial positions, i.e., a pole figure. As noted previously, the pole density is directly related to the intensity of diffracted x-rays. In complex textures, preferred orientations are usually biaxial in the sense that a crystallographic family of planes aligns approximately parallel to a reference plane such as the rolling plane, and equivalent crystallographic directions align approximately parallel to a reference direction such as the rolling direction. In such situations the requisite data are collected by taking a series of photographs of Debye rings as the specimen is rotated stepwise about a vertical axis normal to the incident monochromatic x-ray beam. This vertical axis is usually coincident with the reference direction, and the starting position, i.e., $\phi = 90°$, is with the x-ray beam normal to the reference plane. Increments of rotation depend on degree of filling and detail that is desired for the pole figure; however, 5° steps are usually sufficient for a detailed study. The range of inclinations is from 0 to 90° ϕ. The Debye rings are indexed and positions of circumferential intensity variations are noted as in fiber patterns (see Fig. 9). As before, the approximation $\angle\delta = \angle\alpha$ suffices for low θ angles. The intensity levels noted may be judged visually, or for very careful work microdensitometer readings of the film are required.

Data for the photographic series are plotted as a pole figure with the aid of stereographic nets such as a Wulff net (see Fig. 11). Starting with 0° inclination of the specimen and the plane of the specimen coincident with the plane of projection, the extent of regions of equivalent intensity is determined in terms of the $\angle\alpha$ and plotted on the reflection circle with α corresponding to degrees of latitude (see Fig. 12). The relations of ϕ and α to latitude and longitude are shown in Fig. 12. The reflection circle is concentric with the projection circle (outer circumference of the stereographic net) and lies $(90 - \theta)$ degrees from the center of the projection. If the angle of inclination is rotated counterclockwise 30°, data are plotted at the normal reflection-circle position as before and then are rotated 30° counterclockwise about the north-south axis of the net which corresponds to the vertical axis of rotation of the specimen

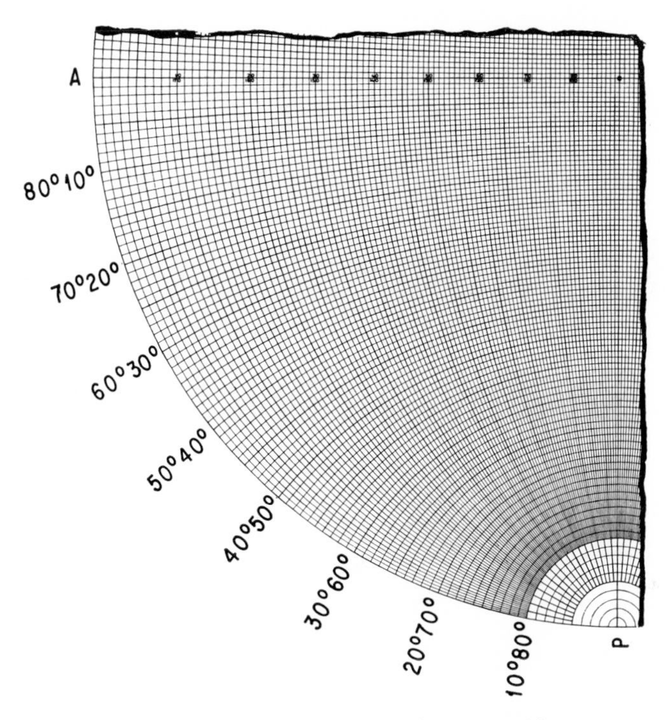

FIG. 11. One quadrant of meridional stereographic net.

(see Fig. 12). Such a rotation is accomplished by moving points along lines of constant angle, i.e., the lines of latitude, through the 30° of longitude. The same thing would be accomplished by plotting the data directly on a reflection circle rotated $90 - (\theta + 30)$ degrees from the projection circle. This process is repeated until either all the data are plotted or the intensity areas of the pole figures are sufficiently well defined. Areas of equal diffraction intensity are connected by isointensity contours or denoted by crosshatching or coloring to give a completed pole figure.

The labor of plotting pole figures from photographically recorded data can be reduced if charts of reflection-circle positions are made up in advance for different θ values encountered depending on specimen material and wavelengths.[7,67] Figure 13 illustrates a chart for molybdenum $K\alpha$ reflecting from $\{110\}$ planes of iron ($\theta = 10°$). Such charts can be constructed with the aid of a Wulff net by rotating the reflection circle from the normal position to an inclined position as noted in the previous paragraph. Decker[67] has given complete instructions for making these charts.

In Fig. 13 it can be seen that the polar areas are not filled. This can readily be accomplished by rotating the specimen 90° about the incident x-ray beam and taking a series of diffraction patterns at appropriate angles of inclination.* The data are plotted with the chart of reflection circles rotated 90° about the center of the projection and are overlaid on the data plotted previously in the usual manner.

As the specimen is rotated about an axis vertical to the incident beam, a change in intensity in the diffraction rings may be observed for transmission patterns. This change is due to absorption of the beam because of the changing x-ray path length as the specimen is inclined to greater angles. As the specimen is rotated the diffracted beam has a shorter path in that portion of the specimen that is brought nearer the x-ray source by the rotation and conversely for that portion of the specimen that

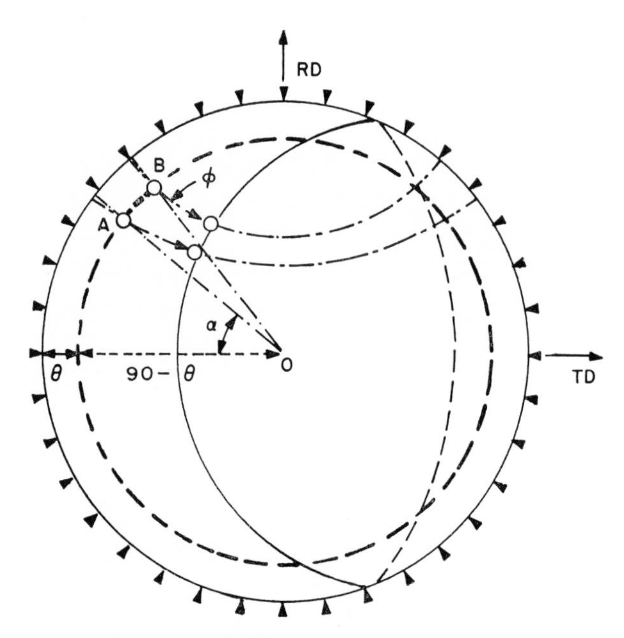

FIG. 12. Method of plotting a pole figure using a meridional stereographic net. The reflection circle with beam normal to specimen plane and projection plane is shown as (— — —), the latitude lines as (— · — · —), and the reflection circle as the specimen plane is rotated φ° (————) and (— — — —). The latter represents the projection on the rear of the reference sphere.

moves away (see Fig. 14). For thin specimens and visual evaluation of intensity levels these intensity changes may be insignificant; however, if microdensitometer measurements are made of the diffraction arcs, it may be necessary to correct for absorption.

The absorption correction is of the form

$$(I_{\pm\phi})_{\text{corr}} = (I_{\pm\phi})_{\text{obs}}(I_0/I_{\pm\phi}) \tag{10}$$

where ϕ is degrees rotation (inclination), the positive sign denoting the specimen portion moving toward the x-ray source (a shorter path) and the negative for the portion moving away from the x-ray source; $I_0/I_{\pm\phi}$ is the ratio of intensities transmitted for a randomly oriented sample at 90° and $\pm\phi°$. A table of $I_0/I_{\pm\phi}$ values has been compiled by Suzanne Beatty[68,69] for absorption factors from 0.1 to 0.9 which is

* For θ = 10°, inclinations from 0 to 20° would suffice.

useful in correcting preferred-orientation data for absorption. The absorption correction becomes severe when the rotation ϕ approaches 90° as shown by Decker.[67] This inaccuracy may be avoided by altering specimen geometry or by using additional specimens which are cut so that the specimen plane and the projection plane are coincident to a cross-section plane.

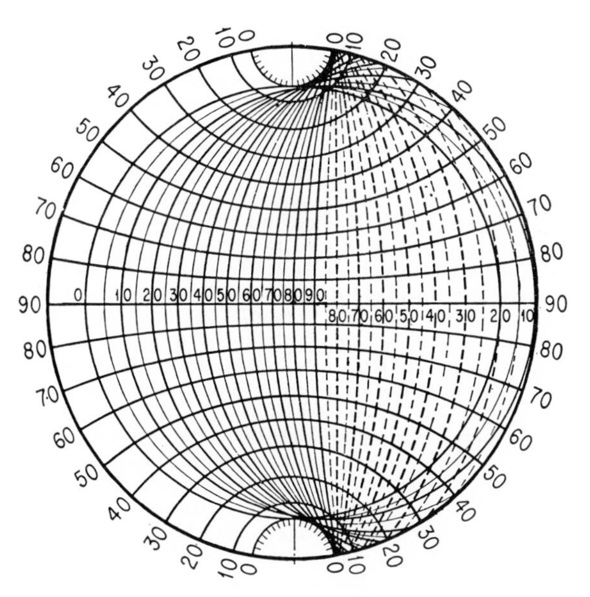

FIG. 13. Pole-figure chart for Mo $K\alpha$ radiation reflecting from (110) planes of iron (θ = 10°). (*From C. S. Barrett, Structure of Metals, 2d ed., McGraw-Hill Book Company, New York,* 1952. *Used by permission.*)

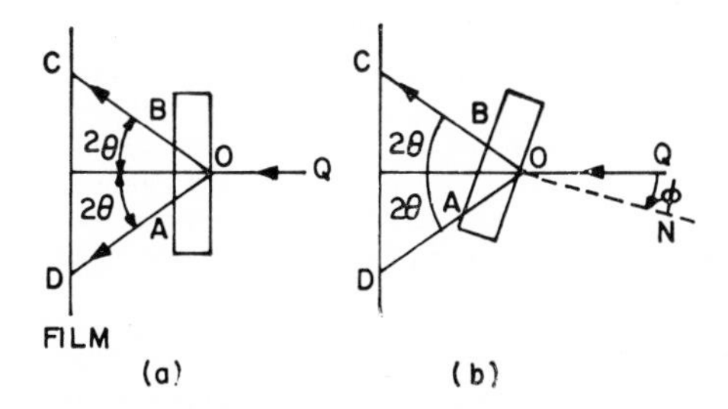

FIG. 14. Absorption path in transmission specimens for preferred-orientation determination. The diffracted x-ray path through the specimen is OA and OB. As the specimen rotates clockwise $\phi°$, OA increases and OB decreases.

It may also be noted in the case of both reflection and transmission methods that, as the angle of inclination ϕ increases, the diffraction pattern becomes increasingly asymmetrical. The reason for this can readily be seen by inspection of Fig. 12. If the specimen is rotated counterclockwise, then the left-hand half of the diffraction pattern is represented by those reflection-circle positions at $90 - (\theta + \phi)$, whereas the right-hand half is represented by positions at $90 - (\theta - \phi)$, i.e., on the negative side of the projection hemisphere.

Because of symmetry relationships frequently occurring in most sheet textures, particularly those of rolled or recrystallized metals, it is usually unnecessary to perform both clockwise and counterclockwise specimen rotations. Therefore, data on the right-hand side of a projection are merely transposed to equivalent positions on the left-hand side and vice versa. If true rolling direction and apparent rolling direction do not coincide, then the symmetry axis will be rotated from the north-south axis of the projection by an amount corresponding to this lack of coincidence. Correction may be required which is accomplished by rotating the pole figure until the apparent and true rolling directions coincide. Symmetry about the cross direction is observed less frequently and may require verification depending on the specimens.

Texture variations are often observed across the thickness of a rolled sheet or across the diameter of a drawn wire. These differences between "surface" and "inside" textures can cause misleading results and interpretation. This can be avoided by averaging the texture across the total thickness of specimen as in offset-reflection methods. Also the outer surface layers may be removed by hand grinding, electropolishing, chemical polishing, chemical etching, etc., or any combination to remove the outer surface layers. For sheet rolled to 0.100 in. thickness removal of 0.005 to 0.010 in. from each surface is usually sufficient to avoid severe surface-texture effects.

Semiquantitative and Special Film Methods. Several efforts have been made with film methods to give a more nearly quantitative representation of pole distribution in an oriented polycrystalline sample than can be achieved by visual evaluation of intensity levels in the diffraction rings. The use of microdensitometers to relate film blackening to x-ray intensity changes certainly yields more nearly quantitative results.

Also, specimen geometry may be altered so that absorption of the x-ray beam is constant.[70] Instead of using a flat sheet a cylindrical stem may be used. This cylinder will present a constant x-ray path as it is rotated about the cylinder axis, and variance in absorption is thereby eliminated. A straightforward method of evaluating the amount of material oriented in a given area of the pole figure was given by Bakarian.[70] A polar stereographic projection divided into 1° units is overlaid on the pole figures, and the number of solid-angle units contained in the various areas is counted so that essentially the pole-figure topography is integrated. The number of area units multiplied by the intensity level of the area is representative of the amount of material oriented in the respective area. The total summed over the entire pole figure of area-intensity units for any given oriented polycrystalline samples corresponds to the intensity of an ideal randomly oriented sample. From this the relative volume in a given orientation can be computed as a percentage or ratio.

If photographic data are to be used in an accurate manner, the photographic-development procedure must be standardized so that changes in development do not introduce changes in observed intensity. Care must be taken to ensure constant developer and fixer strengths, use of the same type of development solutions, equivalent developing times and temperatures, etc. One approach is to develop all films necessary to plot a pole figure in desired detail at the same time, using the same film batch throughout.

Yet another means of deriving semiquantitative data using film methods is to place four to eight film sheets in a cassette and to place between them an absorbing material of known characteristics such as a metal foil. The number of absorbing layers necessary to extinguish a reflection will then be a reasonably accurate measure of the intensity of that reflection.

Several successful efforts have been made to use special scanning cameras to record all the data required for a pole figure on a single film.[71–75] With development of x-ray diffractometers and electronic counting devices, these scanning-camera techniques have been largely replaced by the newer, more accurate and sensitive counter methods. These cameras are merely mentioned because of historical interest.

4. COUNTER-SPECTROMETER METHODS

Fiber Textures. The electronic counter-spectrometer arrangements used for determining fiber textures have generally been those used for more complex textures.

Such techniques will be described in the following section. When applied to study of fiber textures the symmetry of a fiber texture can be used to advantage to reduce greatly the quantity of data required.

A technique was developed by Freda and Cullity[32] that is specific for evaluating fiber textures using a counter-diffractometer arrangement. The method takes advantage of fiber-texture symmetry, and texture data are summarized by means of a pole-density plot along a meridian parallel to the wire axis. The pole distribution along

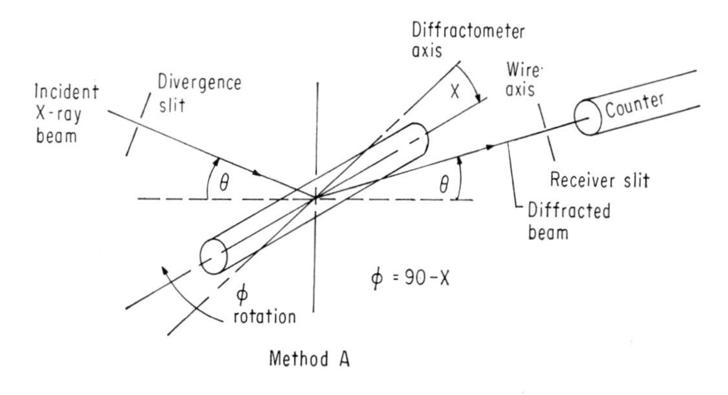

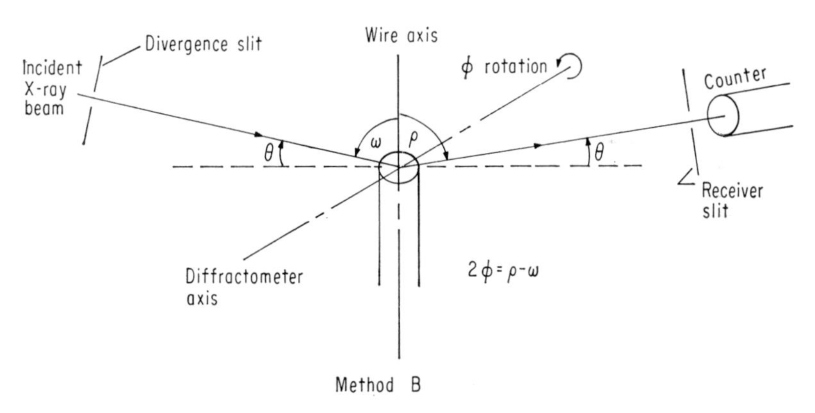

FIG. 15. Schematic representation of the method of Freda and Cullity.[32] In method *A* the ϕ rotation axis is the vertical axis perpendicular to the specimen axis. For method *B* the ϕ rotation axis is the diffractometer axis.

the meridian is plotted as diffracted intensity vs. the angle ϕ between the pole of the diffracting plane and the wire axis. The technique is described schematically in Fig. 15. In method *A* the wire axis is initially coincident to the diffractometer axis ($\phi = 90°$) and is rotated stepwise about an axis lying in the diffractometer plane and perpendicular to the wire axis. Rotation in method *A* has a lower limiting value that is approximately 30 to 40° ϕ. Method *B* permits examination in the lower ϕ regions. Diffraction is from the wire cross section, and ϕ rotation is about the diffractometer axis. The wire axis lies in the plane of the incident and diffracted beam, and $\phi = 0°$

when the wire axis is equi-inclined to the incident and diffracted beams. By combining the two methods a pole-density plot can be obtained from $\phi = 0°$ continuous to $\phi = 90°$ for a given family of planes. Since a variation of effective diffracting volume occurs with ϕ, the observed diffraction intensity must be corrected to make diffraction intensity I_{obs} proportional to pole density.

Complex Textures. Using electronic counter-diffractometer methods, both transmission and reflection techniques are employed to evaluate complex textures. One of the earlier methods was that of Norton,[76] who used cylindrical reflection specimens cut from rolled metal sheets with the rod axis parallel and at selected angles to the rolling direction. This specimen configuration obviates the necessity of making absorption or defocusing corrections. The cylinder axis is perpendicular to the plane of the diffractometer, i.e., the plane defined by the incident x-ray beam and the counter axis. The specimens rotate 180° about the cylinder axis, and diffracted x-ray intensity data are recorded on a strip-chart recorder synchronized with specimen rotation. The intensity recorded is proportional to the electrical pulses counted, which are in turn proportional to the pole concentration. The data recorded correspond to detailed information along a given longitude with the longitude angle equal to the angular difference between the rolling direction and the cylinder axis. As the rotation α corresponds to moving along a longitude, a polar stereographic projection is the most convenient format for plotting these data.

Method of Decker, Asp, and Harker. A quantitative transmission method proposed originally by Decker, Asp, and Harker[77] and subsequently modified[78] is widely used.[79–83] A schematic description of the method is given in Fig. 16. A thin section is mounted in the plane of a ring so its vertical diameter is always perpendicular to the incident beam. A stationary electronic counter is positioned at the proper 2θ angle to monitor reflections from a given family of planes. The specimen is rotated about an axis normal to the specimen plane through 360°. This rotation will be termed α to be consistent with notations used in this chapter. A second rotation is provided by a stem on which the ring is mounted. This ϕ rotation is provided by turning the ring on the mounting stem, which amounts to rotating the specimen about the vertical axis shown in Fig. 16. The relation between the α and ϕ rotations and a stereographic projection is shown also in Fig. 12. The position of a diffracting volume can then be easily located in terms of the ϕ and α angular coordinates.

The normal mode of usage is to set the goniometer at a given ϕ position and rotate α through 90, 180, or 360° depending on whether quarter, half, or full pole figures are desired. The ϕ angle of inclination is then changed 5 to 10° and the α rotation repeated. Thus the usual mode is to stepwise-scan the pole-figure area. The inclusion of an integration movement is due to Suits[80] and extended the useful range to larger grainer sizes. Integration of the specimen surface is accomplished by translating the specimen in a vertical direction parallel to the specimen surface. The integrating frequency is 1 cps, and the integrating path length is 1 in.

In the transmission method, Decker et al.[77] found that the intensity of the diffracted beam varied with the angle of inclination ϕ. A correction may be applied as follows:

$$I_{\pm\phi corr} = I_{\pm\phi obs}(I_0/I_{\pm\phi}) \tag{11}$$

This correction is required because of increasing diffracting volume and increasing absorption as the angle of inclination ϕ decreases. $I_0/I_{\pm\phi}$ is the ratio of intensities at 90° and $\pm\phi°$ for a randomly oriented specimen.* $I_0/I_{\pm\phi}$ is defined as

$$\frac{I_0}{I_{\pm\phi}} = \frac{\mu t \exp(-\mu t/\cos\theta)}{\cos\theta} \; \frac{\cos(\theta \pm \phi)/\cos(\theta \mp \phi) - 1}{\exp[-\mu t/\cos(\theta \pm \phi)] - \exp[-\mu t/\cos(\theta \mp \phi)]} \tag{12}$$

where μ is the coefficient of absorption of the material and t the thickness. μ and t appear only as the product μt; hence μt may be evaluated experimentally. From counter readings of beam intensity with and without the transmission sample placed

* The plus sign refers to counterclockwise and the minus sign to clockwise rotation.

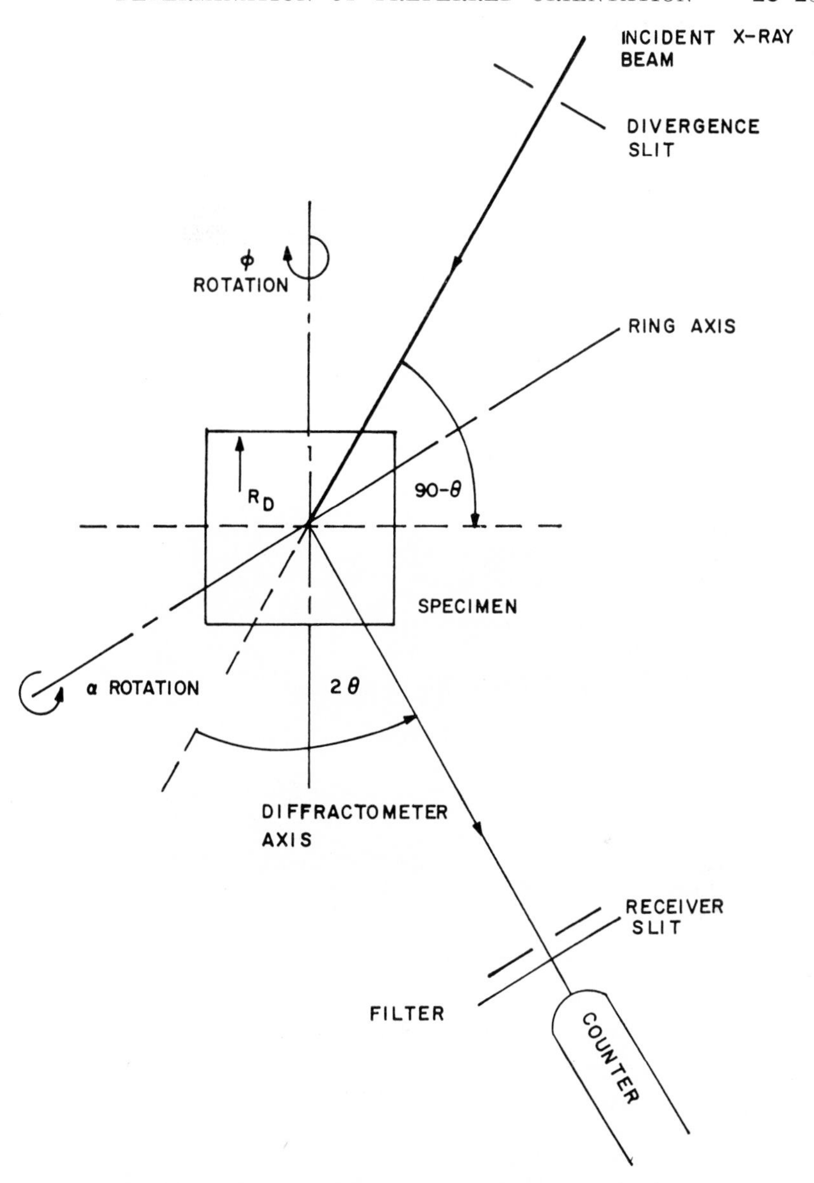

FIG. 16. Transmission method of Decker et al.[77] for determining preferred orientation. The divergent-slit assembly used gives a parallel incident beam. ϕ rotation is about the diffractometer axis and α rotation is about a normal to the specimen plane.

in front of the counter window, μt may be calculated by the formula

$$I_t = I_0 e^{-\mu t} \tag{13}$$

where I_t is the intensity of the transmitted beam and I_0 the intensity of the incident beam. The derivation of Eq. (13) is given by Decker et al.[77]

The correction factor $I_0/I_{\pm\phi}$ for diffracted intensity may be evaluated experimentally as well as calculated using Eq. (11). This can be done by measuring the diffraction intensity of a randomly oriented sample for $\phi = 90°$, i.e., I_0. This value can then be compared with the diffraction intensity of the randomly oriented sample as a function of the angle of inclination ϕ. This experimental determination of $I_0/I_{\pm\phi}$ can be done readily if suitable randomly oriented specimens are available or can be prepared (see Sec. 5).

This transmission pole-figure device is most often used with a strip-chart recorder synchronized to the α rotation. The most elaborate data-recording method is that reported by Geisler.[78,79] An automatic stereographic projection recorder is synchronized with the integrating goniometer. In this instance preselected or standard intensity levels are recorded, using a seven-point recorder pen, directly onto a polar stereographic chart. The data are plotted along the latitude line corresponding to the inclination angle ϕ and the α position of the specimen. The chart rotation is synchronized with the α rotation of the specimen. The α rotation rate is 7.5°/min.

Fig. 17. Photograph of the General Electric pole-figure device. (*Courtesy of General Electric Company.*)

The radial location of the printer is moved as the ϕ angle is changed in 5° increments from 90 to 20°. By use of a 15-rheostat bank the electronic signal corresponding to the diffracted intensity at 85°, 80°, 75°, 70°, . . . , 20° ϕ can be corrected to the same signal level as for 90° ϕ.* For example, using a randomly oriented sample of the material being studied, the intensity signal for a family of diffracting planes is read at 90° ϕ; then the specimen is rotated to 5° ϕ, and using rheostat A the signal is adjusted so that the level indicated is equal to that for 90° ϕ. The procedure is repeated, using a different rheostat to adjust the indicated intensity as described for each of the 15 ϕ positions.[83] In operation each of the preset rheostats switches in as the specimen under study is rotated to the appropriate ϕ position; hence the changes in intensity with ϕ position are compensated for automatically. The integrating goniometer (see

* In the terminology used in this chapter, 90° ϕ is with the incident x-ray beam normal to the reference plane of the specimen. For transmission studies this is the usual starting position when the reference plane and specimen plane are coincident. It is represented in projection by the primitive circle, i.e., outer circle, of the stereographic projection. For reflection methods 0° ϕ is represented by the center point of stereographic net.

Fig. 17) and the automatic pole-figure recorder are sold commercially by General Electric Company as separate units.

The transmission method based on the concept of Decker et al.[77] suffers from the disadvantage that only the outer portion of a pole figure may be determined as ϕ must be greater than θ. Therefore, the lower limiting value of ϕ is the Bragg angle. Beyond this value there is an angular region of beam interference by the specimen and its holder. By using a higher order of diffraction than that used in transmission,

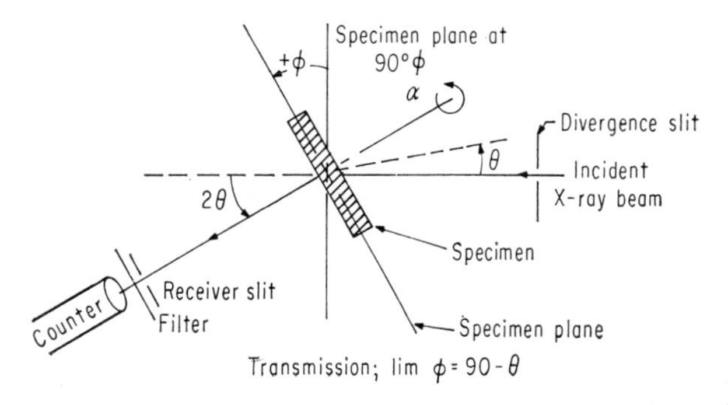

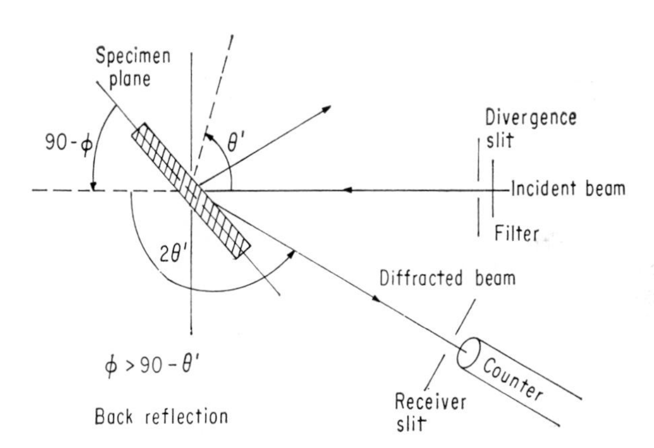

FIG. 18. Transmission technique[77] and back-reflection modification.[81,82] The specimen plane position at 90° ϕ and at 90° − ϕ is shown for the transmission and back-reflection methods, respectively. For back reflection the counter is moved to the back-reflection range on the diffractometer to record a higher-order reflection.

one may obtain useful information in the back-reflection positions.[81,82] A schematic description of the diffraction geometry for such an arrangement* is shown in Fig. 18. The counter is moved to a new position $2\theta'$ where it will receive a higher-order reflection from the same family of planes, e.g., {110} for transmission and {220} for back reflection. As $\theta'_{220} > \theta_{110}$ there will always be a range of ϕ values where the data obtained from back reflection will overlap those for transmission.†

* In back reflection $2\theta > 90°$.

† The upper limiting ϕ for transmission is $\phi = 90 - \theta$; the lower limiting value of ϕ for back reflection is $\phi = 90 - \theta'$. Since θ' is always greater than θ,

$$\phi \text{ (upper limit for transmission)} > \phi \text{ (lower limit for back reflection)}$$

The correction factor for changes in diffraction intensity with inclination angle ϕ for a specimen of "finite" thickness such as that used in the back-reflection method was given by Schwartz.[81] The correction factor is

$$\frac{I_0}{I_\phi} = \frac{\mu t M_\phi \exp(-\mu t/\cos\theta)}{\cos\theta \left\{1 - \exp\left[\frac{\mu t}{\cos(\phi+\theta)} - \frac{\mu t}{\cos(\phi-\theta)}\right]\right\}} \quad (14)^*$$

where

$$M_\phi = 1 - \frac{\cos(\theta+\phi)}{\cos(\theta-\phi)} \quad (15)^*$$

Method of Field and Merchant. A reflection method of determining preferred orientation was devised by Field and Merchant[84] (see Fig. 19). The specimen is mounted on a platform, and the normal to the platform is perpendicular to the diffractometer axis. The α rotation is about this normal. The ϕ rotation is about the

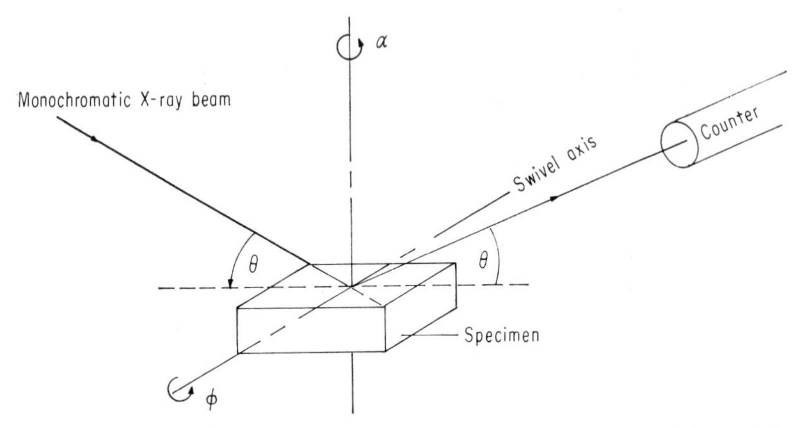

FIG. 19. The method of Field and Merchant[84] described schematically. The swivel axis is coincident with the diffractometer axis; however, the counter position is fixed as the specimen moves through ϕ.

diffractometer axis, thereby changing the angle of inclination of the specimen surface to the incident beam; however, the counter is maintained in its 2θ position as ϕ is changed, i.e., as the specimen surface is moved from the θ position. The correction for the change in intensity of the diffracted beam is given by

$$\frac{I_{\pm\phi}}{I_0} = \frac{2}{1 + \dfrac{\sin(\theta \pm \phi)}{\sin(\theta \mp \phi)}} \quad (16)$$

The specimens used should, as with all reflection methods except the back-reflection method of Schwartz,[81] Newkirk and Bruce,[82] meet the criterion of infinite thickness as regards penetration by the x-ray beam. For an aluminum specimen at a target-to-specimen distance of approximately 17 cm and with Cu $K\alpha$ radiation, a specimen thickness of approximately 3 to 4 mm is sufficient to fulfill the thickness criterion.

* Equations in the form of Eqs. (14) and (15) differ from those of Schwartz as the changes in ϕ are proportional to those in the angle β between the diffracting plane and the specimen surface normal when both are projected onto the plane of the diffractometer. From the law of cosines the relationship of ρ (the angle between the diffracting-plane normal and the normal to the specimen surface) with ϕ and β is $\cos\rho = \cos\phi \sin\beta$.

When the specimen is rotated to an angle of $+\phi = \theta$, the specimen surface cuts off the *reflected* beam, and when rotated to $-\phi = \theta$, the specimen surface cuts off the *incident* beam. Hence rotation is limited to ϕ values of $\pm\theta$. For complex textures the data for angles of inclination from 0 to 90° should be explored, and this limit of ϕ inclination is a severe disadvantage.

This method has been widely used for wire textures by reflecting the beam from the surface of several wires laid side by side. The wire axes are arranged to lie parallel to the diffractometer plane. The beam impinges either on the cross-section plane of the wires or on the wire surface, depending on the nature of the texture. This usefulness for wire textures is derived largely from the enhanced intensity realized by laying several wires side by side in contrast to the weak intensity from using a single wire. Also, generally for wire textures, the deviation of fiber-texture axis from parallelism to the wire axis is within the limits of inclination of the Field and Merchant method.

FIG. 20. Photograph of the Philips pole-figure device and the drive mechanism. (*Courtesy of Philips Electronic Instruments, Inc.*)

Method of Schulz. One of the most widely used reflection methods for determining preferred orientation by diffractometer–electronic-counter means was proposed originally by Schulz.[85] In the past few years both Philips Electronic Instruments, Inc., and Siemens-Halske A. G. have marketed pole-figure devices based on the Schulz reflection method (see Figs. 20 and 21). A definite advantage of the Schulz geometry is the reduction of defocusing and absorption losses that occur as the angle of inclination ϕ of the specimen to the incident beam is increased. In this method the incident-beam divergence angle is limited by divergence and Soller slits at the exit port (see Fig. 22). The beam is then further limited by a main slit located on the goniometer ring and situated at right angles to the divergence slit. The goniometer consists of an outer ring mounted on a stem; this stem is the mounting post and is held coincident with the diffractometer axis.* Rotation of the inner ring of the goniometer allows the specimen to be inclined to the incident beam and by the convention used herein is termed ϕ rotation.† A rotating platform is mounted on the inner ring so that its axis of rotation coincides with a ring diameter. Rotation about this axis is termed

* When such a goniometer is mounted on a Philips diffractometer, the powder-specimen mount is removed and the stem of the goniometer inserted.

† In the Philips goniometer this ϕ rotation is limited to $\pm$ 90°, whereas in the Siemens device 360° ϕ rotation is provided.

α rotation. This rotating platform is the specimen-mounting surface, and the platform height is adjusted until the specimen surface is coincident with the ring diameter and at $\phi = 0°$ with a projection of the mounting-stem axis. Surface integration may be provided by an oscillatory translation of the specimen platform along the ring diameter.*

At $\phi = 0°$ the incident-beam shape on the specimen surface is a rectangle $a \times b$ with a perpendicular to the beam and b parallel to the beam. The a dimension at

FIG. 21. Photograph of the Siemens texture goniometer. (*Courtesy of Siemens New York, Inc.*)

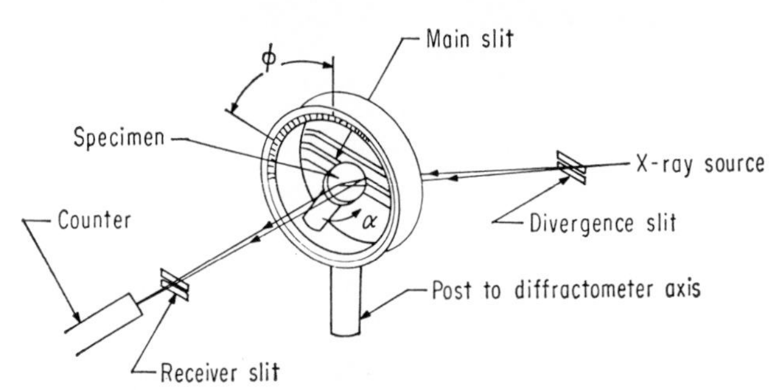

FIG. 22. The Schulz reflection method[85] for determining preferred orientation. The specimen surface is maintained tangent to the diffractometer focusing circle while undergoing ϕ and α rotations. The axis of the mounting post is coincident with the diffractometer axis.

$\phi = 0°$ is limited by the width of the main slit. The b dimension is limited by the θ angle and divergence angle of the beam. As ϕ rotates, the b dimension is constant, as the main-slit width and divergence angle are unchanged. However, a increases as ϕ increases until at some limiting value of ϕ the incident beam has defocused so that the diffracted-beam cross section exceeds the receiver-slit opening because of an increase of effective diffracting volume and diffracted-beam divergence. When this occurs a portion of the diffracted radiation is no longer incident upon the end window

* In the Philips design the length of the translation path can be varied by interchangeable cams, but in the Siemens device the translation distance is fixed.

of the counter tube, and an error is introduced. This effect was originally overlooked by Schulz, and it does impose a limit on the usable extent of ϕ rotation. This and other potential error sources have been analyzed by Chernock et al.[86,87] The useful practical limit of ϕ rotation is about $\pm 60°$.[86–89] Fuller and Vaux[90] assert that the useful ϕ range may be extended to $\pm 90°$ by removing the main slit.*

Correction of the defocusing error inherent in the Schulz reflection technique requires knowledge of the intensity decrease due to defocusing for a randomly oriented standard, preferably of the material under investigation. The decrease in diffracted intensity for ϕ positions over the range where the defocusing error is appreciable is experimentally determined. Correction of the observed intensity from an oriented sample is accomplished by multiplying the I_{obs} times the defocusing factor, i.e., $I_{ran(\phi=0°)}/I_{ran(\phi)}$.

The original Schulz-type pole-figure device was hand-driven, and intensities were read at each ϕ and α position of the specimen. Alterations of the original design to an automatic device were made by Holden,[91] Chernock et al.,[87] and Mueller and Knott.[88] While the details vary, the basis for the changes are similar. Holden[91] suggested a continuous drive of both the ϕ and α rotations by synchronous motor(s). The projected path of such a scan with a continuous, constant rate of change of ϕ and α is a continuous spiral. The ϕ and α rotations are synchronized with a strip-chart recorder. The design of Chernock et al.[87] permits changing ϕ by 5° increments while α is held constant. After stepwise scanning through a predetermined range of ϕ values the goniometer reverses ϕ to the zero position. α position is then changed manually and the ϕ scan repeated. The data are recorded on a printed strip in terms of the elapsed time for a predetermined number of counts for each ϕ position. When the fixed counts are reached and as the print-out is made, the goniometer moves to the next ϕ position.

In addition to these techniques that utilize the basic Schulz reflection geometry, Schulz[92] has described a transmission method to supplement the reflection method (see Fig. 23). The transmission method allows data to be taken to complete the outer portion of the pole figure. In essence the procedure is similar to that of Decker, Asp, and Harker[77] with the modification that a diverging beam, rather than a parallel beam, is used with a narrow receiver slit. When this is done, a plot of I_{obs} (diffracted intensity) vs. angle of inclination, ϕ, is a flat plateau from $\phi = 90°$ to $\phi = 60°$ provided the specimen is sufficiently thin. By controlling sample thickness an optimum μt value can be selected to extend the angle of tilt from the normal position to $\phi = 50°$ without appreciable loss of intensity.[92] When a Schulz goniometer is used in transmission studies, rotation of the inner ring corresponds to α rotation and rotating the goniometer about the axis of the mounting stem corresponds to ϕ rotation (see Fig. 23).

A specimen holder described by Williams and Eppelsheimer[93] incorporates features of both the Decker, Asp, and Harker[77] transmission and the Schulz[85] reflection methods. A similar method was also developed by Bunk et al.[94] However, when one uses both reflection and transmission methods to determine a pole figure, an annulus of data overlay from each method exists. There are some problems associated with equating the intensity level of the data from each method. One method is to normalize the data against an experimental value for the diffraction intensity for that family of planes from a randomly oriented specimen of the same material. Because of the difficulties of mating transmission and reflection data, the problem may be avoided by preparing additional reflection specimens. Complete pole-figure data may be obtained by the Schulz reflection method from rolled metal sheets, for example, by using the rolling plane, transverse cross-section plane, and longitudinal cross-section plane as reflecting specimen surfaces.[88,89]

The Schulz-type goniometer was further modified by Haessner[95] so that an accessory attachment was provided to adapt the goniometer for determination of wire textures. Also, Grewen et al.[96] developed a transmission method similar to that of Schulz[92] specifically for the study of thin metallic foils.

* It has been reported by Mueller and Knott[88] that, when the main slit is removed, loss in intensity due to defocusing is increased and background intensity also increases. This has been confirmed by others.

It should be noted that in many automatic Schulz-type goniometers a precession occurs in the α rotation as the inner ring is driven to provide ϕ rotation. The reason for this is that the drive shaft for the α rotation is usually located on the ϕ ring and connected by flexible shaft or other means to an externally positioned synchronous motor (see Figs. 20 and 21). Hence, as the ϕ ring rotates, the α drive shaft rotates with respect to the external drive. This precession is additive, and its extent varies with the internal gear ratios for the α rotational drive. Typical figures for this are from 6° α precession to 20° α precession for 60° ϕ rotation. As the effect is cumulative the error becomes more serious as ϕ rotation progresses. The data may be corrected for this error if the α precession rate in terms of ϕ rotation is determined.[89]

Offset-reflection Methods. Recently two very similar offset-reflection methods were developed independently[97,98] which utilize Schulz reflection geometry. A specimen reflection surface is prepared so that the reflection-plane normal is approximately centered in the quadrant of a stereographic circle.* From this starting position changing the inclination angle of the reflection surface through approximately 55° ϕ is sufficient to cover all areas of the quadrant. Hence only one reflection specimen is required to obtain data for a pole-figure quadrant. Since fourfold symmetry is frequently observed in pole figures, complete information can often be represented by

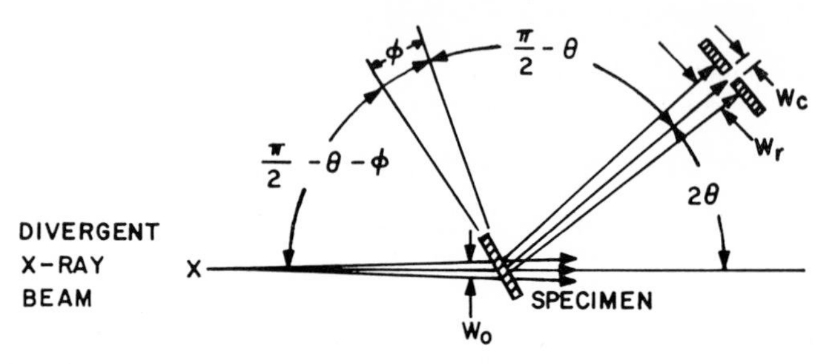

FIG. 23. Schulz transmission method.[92] The incident x-ray beam is diverging while the width of the diffracted beam W_r is greater than the receiver-slit width W_c. The specimen is mounted in the plane of the goniometer ring (see Fig. 22). ϕ rotation is about the mounting axis and α rotation is about the specimen normal.

averaging the data and plotting these in a single quadrant. These offset-reflection methods assume symmetry; however, if asymmetry does exist, additional specimens would be necessary to evaluate the extent of asymmetry.

One distinct advantage of these offset-reflection methods which results from specimen geometry is the averaging of the "surface" and "inside" textures. For example, a cube is laminated from a sheet of the material under investigation. The reflection surface is then exposed by cutting an appropriate cube diagonal. This exposes a cross section of the sheet and allows representation of inside and surface textures in proportion to the volume of material so oriented.

Harris Inverse-pole-figure Method. A method of taking data for so-called inverse pole figures was described by Harris.[99] The technique is useful for materials whose crystal structure is of comparatively low symmetry, e.g., orthorhombic and hexagonal crystal structures, and has been used for α uranium and many hexagonal close-packed metals. When used to evaluate complex textures, specimens are prepared with exposed reflection surfaces normal to two or three reference directions, e.g., rolling, normal, and transverse directions in rolled sheet; however, for fiber textures a cross-section surface normal to the fiber axis suffices. Using an electronic counter-diffractometer, the diffraction lines are recorded by standard spectrometric powder methods. The integrated intensity $I_{\text{obs}, \{hkl\}}$ of each diffraction line is then compared

* Lopata and Kula[98] used specimens whose reflection-plane normal is 54°44′ from the normal, rolling, and transverse directions.

with the calculated or experimental intensities from a randomly oriented sample $I_{\text{ran},\{hkl\}}$. The ratio $I_{\text{obs},\{hkl\}}/I_{\text{ran},\{hkl\}}$ is determined for a number of $\{hkl\}$ lines so that it is possible to represent the pole distribution parallel to a given reference direction. The data are plotted as an inverse pole figure which is a distribution of crystallographic directions perpendicular to the specimen reflection surface. This is done by plotting the $I_{\text{obs}}/I_{\text{ran}}$ ratio for each diffraction line at the corresponding pole position in a stereographic unit triangle of the poles of the diffracting planes. Contours can then be drawn to represent lines of constant value of the ratio $I_{\text{obs}}/I_{\text{ran}}$, and these represent the distribution of crystallographic axes parallel to a reference direction. The projection planes are parallel to the specimen planes; hence an axis concentration in the inverse pole figure represents a concentration of axes parallel to the normal of the specimen reflection surface.

Oak Ridge Inverse-pole-figure Method. The properties of inverse pole figures have been extensively discussed in the literature.[100-105] A widely used inverse-pole-figure

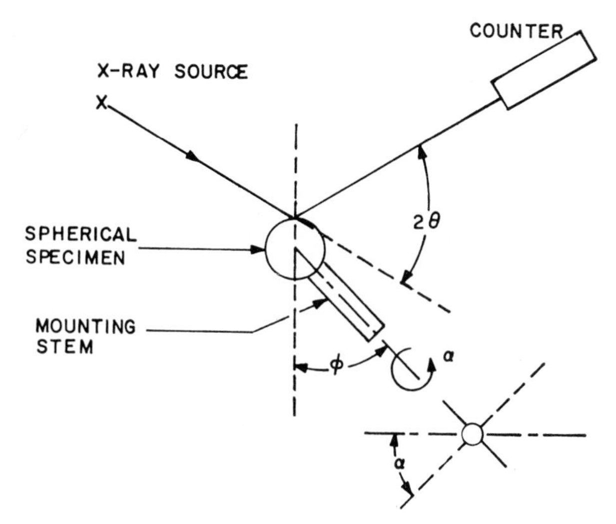

FIG. 24. Reflection method, using a spherical specimen.[100] The ϕ and α rotations are indicated.

method uses a spherical specimen[100-102] which obviates the need for defocusing and absorption corrections. The sphere is typically 5 to 20 mm in diameter and is mounted atop a post which is held in the specimen mount of the goniometer. The initial position of the specimen is with the axis of the mounting post equi-inclined to the incident and diffracted beams* (see Fig. 24). Moving from this position changes the angle of inclination, i.e., ϕ angle, and is provided in the diffractometer plane by the goniometer design. This ϕ rotation is about an axis tangent to the sphere surface and perpendicular to the post axis. The ϕ rotation moves the specimen-mounting axis in the diffractometer plane. Rotation about the post axis corresponds to α rotation. Further details of the specimen mount have been given by Jetter and Borie[100] and Mitchell and Rowland.[101]

When the rates of rotation, ϕ and α, are relatively slow, e.g., 2° ϕ and 50° α per minute, the specimen mount may be used to gather data for conventional pole figures. For inverse pole figures the α rotation rate is very fast while scanning slowly from 0 to 90° ϕ; ϕ rate of 2°/min and α rotation of 250 rpm are typical. The observed intensities of the diffracted beam are recorded as a function of ϕ position and are a plot

* Actually the diffracted beam is cone-shaped; however, the intersection of this cone with the diffractometer plane defines a line which is termed the diffracted beam.

of the pole distribution. These pole-distribution charts are determined experimentally for a number of diffracting planes. Ten families of planes are considered adequate for the cubic system, and those most often used are the following: {111}, {200}, {220}, {113}, {222}, {400}, {133}, {420}, {422}, and {135}. The steps taken hereafter with the data are to invert pole distribution with respect to reference axes into orientation distribution of the reference axes with respect to standard crystallographic axes* (or poles of diffracting planes). As will be seen, the data are normalized without resort to complex calculations or the use of "random" specimens. The axis distribution is deduced from the pole-distribution charts. The axis of the specimen post must be made coincident with the reference axes of interest; i.e., those which are to be used in making axis-distribution charts. Therefore, a specimen has to be prepared for each reference axis of interest.

Table 5. Computation of I_{ran} and Normalized Diffraction Intensity $R(\phi = 0)$*

Diffracting plane {hkl}	Total area A_t†	Diffraction intensity $I_{ran} = \frac{A_t}{90}\frac{\pi}{2}$	Diffraction intensity $I(\phi = 0)$	Normalized diffraction intensity $R(\phi = 0) = \frac{I(\phi = 0)}{I_{ran}}$
{111}	4,148.97	72.41	1,567.11	21.6
{002}	2,906.51	50.72	1,369.44	27.0
{022}	3,087.46	53.87	0.00	0.00
{113}	4,701.86	82.06	21.63	0.26
{222}	1,224.47	21.37	499.62	23.4
{004}	847.73	14.80	410.10	27.7
{133}	2,879.99	50.27	0.00	0.00
{024}	3,034.52	52.96	0.00	0.00
{224}	3,711.41	64.78	9.61	0.15

* From Jetter et al., *J. Appl. Phys.*, **27**:371 (1956). Used by permission.
† Total area in counts/sec × deg under curve of $I \sin \phi$ vs. ϕ.

It has been shown[102] that the random intensity may be obtained by the following integration procedure:

$$\int_0^{\pi/2} I_{(\phi)} \sin \phi \, d\phi = I_{ran} \tag{17}$$

This integration can be carried out graphically using the pole-distribution charts. The I vs. ϕ plots are converted into plots of $I \sin \phi$ vs. ϕ. Integrating the area under this curve from $\phi = 0°$ to $\phi = 90°$ yields the value I_{ran}. From this value and the intensity at a given ϕ position, a normalized diffraction intensity R may be determined by the relation

$$R_{(\phi)} = I_{(\phi)}/I_{ran} \tag{18}$$

$R_{(\phi)}$ then is a representation of the average fiber-axis density.

The values of $R_{\phi=0}$ for the given diffracting planes are plotted on a standard stereographic projection of the associated crystallographic poles. For example, from the $R_{\phi=0}$ values shown in Table 5 the resulting axis-distribution chart is given in Fig. 25.

Details of the axis distribution represented in Fig. 25 were deduced from pole-distribution charts, typically R_ϕ vs. ϕ plots. The contours represent loci of equal axis distribution. It is the placement of these contours that must be deduced from the R_ϕ vs. ϕ charts, and they are typically plotted on a trial-and-error basis. However, a mathematical procedure for checking the accuracy of an inverse plot has been

* It is because of this inversion of orientation distributions that the terminology inverse pole figure was used by Harris.

derived[102] using the following relationship between the normalized intensity R_ϕ and the average normalized axis density $\bar{T}_\phi$:

$$R_\phi = \bar{T}_\phi = \frac{\int_0^{\beta_{\max}} T(\phi,\beta)\, d\beta}{\beta_{\max}} \tag{19}$$

where R_ϕ represents the average of T_ϕ along the path 0–$\beta_{\max}$ for some radius ϕ about the diffracting-plane pole, β is the locus of points at an angle ϕ from the diffracting-plane pole, and T is the fiber-axis density at any given point. Using this relationship R-distribution charts can be calculated based on the assumed axis densities $T_{\phi,\beta}$. These calculated curves may then be compared with the experimental R_ϕ vs. ϕ plots derived as described. Jetter, McHargue, and Williams reported that when R-distribution curves calculated using Eq. (19) for three families of diffracting planes fit the experimental data, the assumed axis densities were accepted as an accurate representation.

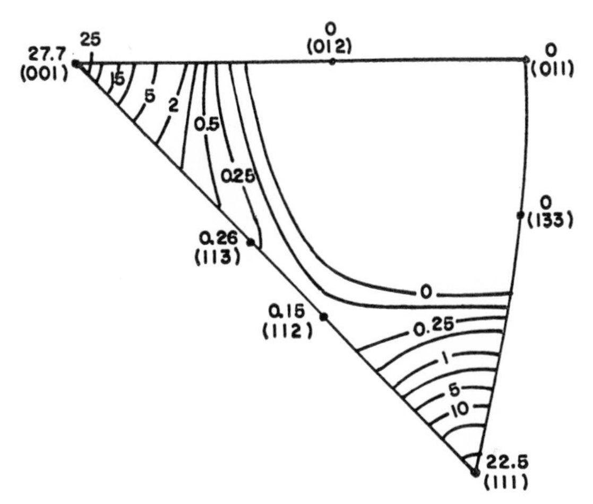

FIG. 25. Fiber-axis-distribution chart for extruded aluminum rod. [*From Jetter et al., J. Appl. Phys.*, **27**: 371 (1956). *Used by permission.*]

The inverse-pole-figure methods offer the advantage that they appear capable of rendering a unique solution of the preferred orientation if the texture is either complicated or not well developed. In other words, they offer improved resolution over the conventional pole figures. Questions arising regarding the extension of inverse pole figures to describe sheet textures as proposed by Mitchell and Rowland[101] and Jetter, McHargue, and Williams[102] are not yet fully resolved;[104] however, reasonably strong experimental evidence exists that supports the validity of the application.[105,106]

Typical Operating Parameters. The operating parameters in terms of x-ray generation, goniometer operation, and diffractometer-counter operation vary from technique to technique and with type of materials being investigated. Hence there is a very broad spectrum of acceptable operating conditions. As a result, the investigator may have to resort to first principles or to trial and error to determine the operating parameters best suited to the problem at hand. A summary, by technique, of typical operating parameters is given below as a guide to the selection of experimental conditions.

Decker, Asp, and Harker. In this transmission technique[77] slits employed are a 1° divergence slit and 0.2° receiver slit; however, the receiver slit may be removed. The General Electric pole-figure device is based on this method, and in this case the α

rotation is continuous through 360° at a rate of 8° α per minute. The ϕ rotation is stepped in 5° increments upon completion of an α revolution. These operating conditions are also applicable to the back-reflection methods[81,82] used with this diffraction geometry.

Schulz Reflection. The slit sizes used in this method[85] are 1° divergence slit, from 0.2 to 2° receiver slits (depending on separation between diffraction peaks and texture definition), and 0.010- to 0.040-in. main slits (0.020 in. is used most frequently). Scatter slits of the same size as the receiver slit or larger are sometimes used. For a Schulz goniometer designed to operate stepwise[87] after a fixed time or count at a spatial position, 10° ϕ increments at a fixed α position are usual. After scanning through the ϕ cycle, a 5° α rotation follows before the ϕ cycle is repeated. For Schulz goniometers designed to operate in a continuous mode the ϕ rotation rates are ½ to 3°/min. Rates of α rotation are 30 to 72°/min. A ratio of ϕ to α rotation rates of 1:60 will give a mean ϕ spacing between α revolutions of 1.5° and a maximum spacing of 3°. This gives more than adequate detail and for routine examination is often more than necessary.

Schulz Transmission. One major operating difference between this method[92] and the previous transmission method is that the beam is allowed to diverge. For a Siemens pole-figure device, used in this fashion, slit sizes may be 2- by 2-mm divergence slit, 2- by 10-mm receiver slit, and 0.5-mm main slit. For transmission studies, the α rotation is usually continuous, with 5 to 60 min required for a complete revolution. For the Siemens device the revolution time is 12 min. The ϕ rotation is often performed manually in 5 to 10° increments upon completion of each α revolution.

Offset Reflection. The slit sizes for this method[97,98] are equivalent to those given for Schulz reflection; however, rotation rates vary. Continuous α rotation at rates of 6 to 20°/min and stepwise ϕ rotation are used by Lopata.* Continuous ϕ and α rotations at rates of ⅙ and 20°/min, respectively, are also used.†

Oak Ridge Method. The method[100,102] normally requires 1° divergence slit and 4° receiver slit without a scatter slit. The rotations are continuous but vary between investigations of fiber and sheet textures. For fiber textures 2° ϕ per minute and 250 rpm of α are the rotation rates used. A ϕ rotation of 2°/min and α of 50°/min are used for sheet textures.

Harris Method. This method[99] is equivalent in operating conditions to standard spectrometric powder techniques. The parameters typical of powder methods in terms of slits, slit sizes, and 2θ scanning rates are usually satisfactory.

General Conditions. With the above techniques any appropriate characteristic radiation may be used. Filtering the radiation to give a monochromatic beam is preferred but in some instances is not used. The selection of the type of radiation depends on several factors, many of which have been previously discussed. However, beam penetration, possibly of fluorescent excitation, separation of diffraction peaks, and absorbing power of the specimen material are all considerations in the selection. The operating-tube voltages and current used can vary considerably, provided strong characteristic radiation is produced. Both voltage and current can be altered to give limited control of intensity of the radiation incident upon the counter.

When maximum diffraction intensity is desired in texture studies the square focal-spot port of the x-ray tube may be used. The Siemens texture diffractometer is the only commercial unit that normally uses square foci. Since most diffractometers are mounted at line-foci ports, using spot foci may necessitate relocating the diffractometer or providing a manually operable diffractometer base for the pole-figure goniometer.

Various alignment procedures have been devised to ensure correct positioning of the specimen. These positions can be critical for reflection methods. Alignment blocks or jigs are often used to ensure proper specimen height for Schulz reflection methods;[87] however, specimen height may be correlated with apparent Bragg-angle value. If the location of the diffraction peak is at a greater 2θ angle than the Bragg angle for that plane this indicates a specimen positioned too high, i.e., above the diffractometer

* Private communication with Dr. S. L. Lopata, Watertown Arsenal.

† Private communication with Prof. D. A. Thomas, Massachusetts Institute of Technology.

axis. The converse relationship is also true. The procedures used to ensure proper diffractometer alignment may also be modified to ensure proper alignment of the texture goniometer in place on the diffractometer.

Sometimes it will be noted that relatively weak intensity maxima are present in a pole-figure plot for a given family of planes without corresponding maxima in a pole-figure plot for a different family of planes for the same specimen. Such spurious diffraction areas[107] may be due to white-radiation diffraction, primarily from x-ray wavelengths shorter than $K\alpha$. Balanced filters or pulse-height analysis with a proportional counter can both be used to evaluate the existence of spurious intensity maxima. Alternatively, the use of different characteristic x-ray radiation will usually suffice to evaluate suspected maxima. True intensity maxima should have the same position in a pole-figure plot regardless of characteristic radiation used; however, spurious maxima will either disappear or shift drastically when x-ray targets are changed.

Counters and Circuits. The standard diffractometer techniques covered in Chap. 9 are applicable when diffractometer-preferred orientation goniometer methods are used to determine preferred orientation. These techniques, particularly with respect to counting devices and circuits, should be considered when selecting counters and circuits. In using electronic circuitry to count diffracted x-ray quanta and record these data, it is essential that sufficient warmup time be allowed for the electronic circuits to stabilize before any attempt is made to take data. Typical warmup times to ensure stability are approximately ½ to 1 hr.

Geiger counters are the most widely used counters for preferred-orientation studies; however, care should be taken to operate these counters approximately 100 volts above the threshold voltage. Also, the counter should be used in its linear counting range, i.e., up to approximately 1,000 counts/sec; otherwise severe counting-rate losses may occur. Proportional counters find application particularly when higher counting rates are encountered as these counters are linear to approximately 10,000 cps. The use of a proportional counter with a pulse-height analyzer allows counter pulses due to selected x-ray wavelengths to be electronically subtracted from the counter output. Hence proportional counters can operate under essentially monochromatic conditions. In this way background contributions due to white radiation and the short-wavelength radiation passed by a β filter may be eliminated. Spurious diffraction maxima may be eliminated using a proportional counter and pulse-height-analyzer circuitry. Scintillation counters are also finding use in preferred-orientation studies, particularly in recent years. Their linear counting rate to 10^5 cps is an advantage, but the relatively high background count may be a disadvantage, particularly when weak or ill-defined preferred orientations are encountered.

As for circuits, counting rate-meter circuits should be used when the pole-figure device is being driven in a continuous or semicontinuous mode. If the mode is stepwise so that the device rotates to a given position and remains until a fixed time or fixed count is reached before moving to the next position, scaler counting circuits should be used. The time constant of rate-meter circuits should be chosen so that the time lag of the circuit compared with the rate of angular motion of the specimen does not seriously displace the data. If short time constants are used, the recorder circuit will detect and record statistical fluctuations of the counter. Therefore, a compromise must be reached between circuit time constant and rate of specimen rotation.

Regardless of the type of counter used, background irradiation cannot be completely eliminated because of the presence of cosmic irradiation. Therefore, it is necessary to subtract the background from the intensity traces. This can readily be done by raising the zero level of the intensity scale to background level. One accepted manner of determining background is to set the pole-figure device at the starting position with the specimen in place and determine the background values on either side of the 2θ position of the diffracting-plane family of interest. If background counts for $(2\theta + d\theta)$ and $(2\theta - d\theta)$ are averaged, a reasonable value for background count is obtained, particularly for a material that exhibits a marked preferred orientation. For a more complete discussion of counters and circuits, see Chap. 3.

Specimen Preparation. Specimens for texture studies must be carefully prepared to ensure that the relation of the specimen to reference plane(s) and direction(s) is maintained. For example, sheet specimens are often cut from a strip with the specimen center line parallel to the rolling direction. If the specimen is out of parallel by a few degrees, then this misalignment is carried over as an inherent data inaccuracy. Therefore, aligning the specimens during preparation and placement on the goniometer is equally as important as having a well-aligned goniometer-diffractometer. Close tolerances on machining operations that might alter specimen alignment are therefore indicated, as well as an alignment procedure with respect to reference directions for the specimen in place on the texture goniometer.

Because of surface-texture effects resulting from machining and deformation it is necessary to remove the outer surface layers. From 0.005 to 0.020 in. is usually removed by hand grinding and/or polishing plus electropolishing or chemical polishing. If 0.002 to 0.003 in. is removed from the surface by electropolishing and chemical polishing an undistorted surface usually results. In some cases this polishing is followed by an etch, but this is generally required only in special situations.

Commercial Pole-figure Devices. At this writing there are three commercially available preferred-orientation goniometers. General Electric Company sells a transmission device that incorporates modifications of the basic design of Decker, Asp, and Harker[77] (see Fig. 17). A goniometer based on the Schulz reflection method[85] is available from Philips Electronic Instruments, Inc. (see Fig. 20). The Schulz reflection and transmission methods[85,92] are the basis of the pole-figure device marketed by Siemens-Halske, A. G. (see Fig. 21). The latter unit is a self-contained device since the goniometer is mounted on its own manually operable diffractometer base. The General Electric Company also sells an automatic pole-figure plotter[78,79] that may be used in conjunction with the GE goniometer and diffraction units.

5. METHODS OF REPRESENTING PREFERRED ORIENTATION

All the preferred-orientation techniques discussed use stereographic projections to give an unprejudiced representation of the texture. The reason for the widespread use of stereographic projections is the ability to measure true angular relations along great circles. As an aid in preparing the projection, meridional stereographic nets (so-called Wulff nets) or polar stereographic nets are useful.* Most pole figures are plotted manually by transferring the data from strip charts or printed tape onto the stereographic projection after appropriate corrections are made. In order to facilitate comparison among pole figures the observed intensity data are often normalized against the intensity for a randomly oriented standard of the same material. These random values may be either experimental or calculated values. If the value is experimental, great care must be exercised to assure that the supposed randomly oriented standard is truly "random."

Two methods are available for reducing the labor involved in preparing pole figures from raw pole-distribution data. One is to use the automatic pole-figure plotter[78,79] sold by General Electric Company, which is limited to use with the GE pole-figure device. A somewhat more versatile method utilizing digital computer and rectilinear plotter techniques was described by Holland et al.[89] The method was applied to the Schulz reflection technique but in principle is adaptable to other techniques. Briefly, the procedure is to transpose the angular-position data for selected intensities from the strip-chart record onto punch cards after defocusing corrections are made and the data are normalized against a random intensity value. These angular positions at the point of attaining preselected intensity levels which correspond to a multiple random intensity level are next corrected for precession by a digital computer. The corrected angular positions are then converted by the computer into rectilinear coordinates that are identical representations of the position in stereographic coordinates. The rectilinear positions in terms of preselected multiples of random intensity are received as computer output. An automatic rectilinear plotter is used to plot the positions rapidly. Through these plotted points contours are drawn to

* Accurate meridional stereographic nets are available through the Hydrographic Office, Department of the Navy, Washington 25, D.C. The chart designation is H.O. 7736-1, and the price is 10 cents for each. The nets are approximately 39 cm in diameter and are a convenient size to use in plotting raw data.

represent loci of equal pole concentration. The result is a rectilinear plot of the data, but plotted so that it is identical with a stereographic projection of the data.

The present methods of plotting data in inverse-pole-figure form are manual, and these have been described earlier, together with the method of gathering the requisite data and the data treatment.

Preferred-orientation Solutions. Pole figures are the only available means of completely describing preferred orientations; however, it is frequently necessary to deduce the important crystallographic elements contributing to the preferred orientation of the aggregate. The components of the preferred orientation may be found by comparing intensity maxima of pole figures (other than inverse) with ideal crystallographic orientations of a single crystal (see Fig. 13). Those idealized orientations which produce a good fit with the experimental data are orientation components of the texture. The relative strength of each component is a function of the volume fraction associated with that orientation.

The idealized orientations used to analyze for the components of a texture are selected on a trial-and-error basis until a solution is achieved. However, the number of attempts necessary to achieve a solution may be considerably reduced if in initial efforts one selects orientations near those texture components previously published for similar material with comparable prior history. If, for example, the pole figure to be analyzed is the {111} pole-distribution plot, the positions of 111 poles for a given ideal orientation are compared with positions of pole-concentration maxima. This is done by plotting in stereographic projection the {111} pole positions for a given ideal orientation represented by (h_i,k_i,l_i) $[u_i,v_i,w_i]$,* e.g., in Fig. 2, the {111} pole positions for the (123) $[41\bar{2}]$ ideal orientation. These {111} pole positions are then compared with pole-concentration maxima. If the pole positions for an ideal orientation are situated within the orientation spread of equivalent concentration maxima, then these maxima can be associated with an orientation component approximated by the ideal orientation. This process is repeated until the concentration maxima in a pole figure are accounted for by ideal-orientation components. However, it frequently happens that the solutions derived on the basis of pole-distribution data for a single (h,k,l) family are not unique solutions. The probability that the solutions are unequivocal is enhanced by comparing the solutions for two or more pole figures, with each figure representing the pole distribution for different $\{h,k,l\}$ families. It is generally considered an adequate test for uniqueness if the solutions fit two sets of pole-distribution data. The likelihood of arriving at unique solutions may be further increased by selecting pole-distribution data of $\{h,k,l\}$ families that exhibit low-order symmetry.

Solution of inverse pole figures, on the other hand, is straightforward as the data are plotted in a manner to suggest the solution directly. Relative concentration of crystallographic axes parallel to given reference axes is plotted in inverse pole figures. This makes the solutions, in terms of planes parallel to reference planes and axes parallel to reference axes, self-evident.

Numerical Indices of Preferred Orientation. The most straightforward method of determining an index of preferred orientation is that recommended by the American Society for Testing and Materials.[108] This requires that the data used to plot the pole figure be replotted as an equal-area projection such as a Lambert azimuthal (or zenithal) equal-area projection.[109] Using a planimeter, the areas of equivalent pole concentrations are integrated. The sum of the products of area A times the mean pole concentration I_{mean} for the area (diffracted intensity) should equal I_{ran}:

$$A^n I^n_{\text{mean}} = I_{\text{ran}} \tag{20}$$

If the projection is now divided into equiangular distances and the corrected intensity I is recorded at each of these angular positions over a large number of positions n,

$$\Sigma I/n = I_{\text{ran}} \tag{21}$$

provided n is sufficiently large.

* The notation $(h_i,k_i,l_i)[u_i,v_i,w_i]$ for an ideal orientation refers to crystallographic plane parallel to a reference plane and direction parallel to a reference axis, e.g., rolling plane and rolling direction in sheets.

The standard deviation from a random condition may be calculated to give an index of the degree of preferred orientation, as follows:

$$\sigma = \sqrt{\frac{\Sigma I^2 - (\Sigma I)^2/n}{n}} \tag{22}$$

If σ is then divided by $\Sigma I/n$ a dimensionless number results that is independent of I and represents an orientation index J as shown by

$$n\sigma/\Sigma I = J \tag{23}$$

An alternate method is that proposed by Jetter, McHargue, and Williams.[102] The volume fraction oriented parallel to a reference axis can be determined as the volume fraction F_c associated with a component whose orientation scatter over the range ϕ_1–ϕ_2 is given by

$$F_c = \frac{p}{2p_c} \frac{\int_{\phi_1}^{\phi_2} I_{(\phi)} \sin \phi \, d\phi}{\int_0^{\pi/2} I_{(\phi)} \sin \phi \, d\phi} \tag{24}$$

where p_c/p is the fraction of the total multiplicity associated with the range ϕ_1–ϕ_2.

An orientation density Q formulation has been derived by Dunn and Walter,[110] as follows:

$$Q_x = c \, d\zeta_x/dv_x \tag{25}$$

where c is a constant, $d\zeta_x$ is the volume fraction associated with an orientation component x, within dv_x, where dv_x is an element of solid volume associated with an orientation range $d\alpha_x \, d\beta_x \, d\gamma_x$ (in spherical-polar-coordinate terminology). The orientation density $Q_{(\alpha,\beta,\gamma)}$ is constant for all orientations in a randomly oriented sample. Setting $Q_{\text{ran}} = 1$, we obtain

$$1 = c(d\zeta)_{\text{ran}}/dv \tag{26}$$

Eliminating the constant c and dv by division gives

$$Q_x = (d\zeta)_x/(d\zeta)_{\text{ran}} \tag{27}$$

which is an expression of Q in multiples of random units. The probability that a given orientation component selected from a randomly oriented group will be within ρ radians of a given position associated with the orientation x is given by

$$(d\zeta)_{\text{ran}} = 1.4\rho^3 \tag{28}$$

provided ρ is not too large, i.e., 10° or less. Therefore, the expression for Q_x becomes

$$Q_x = (d\zeta)_x/1.4\rho^3 \tag{29}$$

This formula may be applied directly to orientation data obtained from a grain-by-grain orientation determination for a polycrystalline specimen. The grain-by-grain orientation determination may be accomplished by taking Laue patterns of individual grains, which is a method often used with coarse-grained material.

Sturcken and Croach have developed a mathematical method of determining an orientation parameter for α uranium from data obtained by the Harris method and have used the orientation parameter to predict physical properties of oriented polycrystalline bodies.*

Determination of Random Values. The means of calculating random intensity developed by Jetter et al.[102] and that recommended by ASTM[108] have been previously

* Private communication with Dr. E. F. Sturcken. The method is described in *Trans. AIME*, **227**: 934 (1963). Other mathematical methods are described by J. R. Holland in *Advances in X-ray Analysis*, vol. 7, Plenum Press, New York, 1964; and by R. H. Bragg and C. M. Packer, *J. Appl. Phys.*, **35**:1322 (1964).

discussed. In addition, Lopata and Kula[98] have developed a means of calculating random intensity from a pole-figure plot. A randomizing net is used that contains 825 points for a complete pole figure, and each point represents an equal area. After a pole figure has been plotted using intensity data expressed in arbitrary intensity units, the intensity at each of the 825 points is tabulated. These intensity values are summed and divided by the number of points to give the random intensity level.

Many means have been employed to produce randomly oriented experimental standards, but regardless of means used, great care must be exercised if the prepared standard is to approximate closely a randomly oriented condition. Consequently, it is not valid to assume that a prepared standard will be randomly oriented; hence each standard prepared must be checked for preferential orientation.

If a transmission standard is required, one of the preferred methods is to prepare a suspension of fine metal powder in glyptal varnish that has been well thinned with acetone. This mixture is evenly sprayed onto paper by suitable means such as a medical atomizer. The choice of powder is important as leaf-shaped pigments like cold-worked flakes tend to develop a preferred orientation when sprayed. Fine powders produced by hydrogen reduction of metal oxides or the very fine spherical metal particles made by a plasma spray should be satisfactory.

Random samples prepared in this manner are not satisfactory for back-reflection measurements as in the method of Schwartz.[81] The incoherent scattering from the paper and varnish binder is excessive. A thick compact is required, and Newkirk and Bruce[82] have described a satisfactory method of preparation. Annealed metal powder is stirred into molten paraffin and allowed to settle into a recessed glass disk placed at the bottom of a beaker. Precaution should be taken to avoid eddy currents in the molten paraffin bath as these will cause uneven distribution of the metal powder. When the powder is sufficiently thick, the glass disk may be removed from the bath, and the wafer of solidified wax impregnated with metal powder is removed from the glass disk. The wafer is then sintered for an appropriate time, temperature, and atmosphere, depending on the metal. This drives off the paraffin and allows densification to occur. The compact can be thinned by hand or power grinding to the desired thickness; a typical thickness is 0.003 in.

Compacts of metal powders have frequently been used for reflection methods. These may be prepared from relatively strain-free metal powder. One method is to mix the powder with thinned epoxy resin to make a very stiff pastelike mixture. The mixture is placed in a die that has been lightly coated with petroleum jelly to prevent the epoxy resin from bonding to the die. The mixture is then pressed to several thousand psi and held under pressure for 5 to 10 min. The pressure is released, and the compact is retained in the die until the epoxy resin has cured. This procedure will produce a compact from 60 to 90 per cent dense, and the compact usually has an orientation near random. Metal compacts of near random orientation have also been made using powder-metallurgical methods such as compacting and sintering as well as slip casting.

If a prepared standard is very weakly oriented, slight variations in intensity are observed as the standard is scanned through ϕ and α. These can be averaged out to give random-intensity data that are useful for normalizing as well as for making defocusing or absorption corrections. When intensity changes in a random standard are used to make defocusing and absorption corrections, a determination of these changes must be made for each different set of diffraction geometry conditions employed. For example, changes in the slit systems will necessitate reevaluation of the correction factors for both absorption and defocusing.

6. OTHER PREFERRED-ORIENTATION TECHNIQUES

Microtechniques for Fibers. While the preferred orientation of fibers may be determined by pinhole methods described earlier, the study of textures in nonmetallic fibers is facilitated by the use of microtechniques.[111] The microcamera of Chesley[112] is particularly useful* in this respect. The camera uses an assortment of capillaries

* The Norelco microcamera is based on the design of Chesley.[112]

⅜ in. long with bores from 100 to 25 microns. This collimation system is readily aligned with the x-ray beam by rotating the camera about horizontal and vertical axes that are provided. Lead apertures are used at the port side of the collimator, and the specimen is positioned flush with the exit end of the collimator, with the specimen held in tension. Translation along and across the specimen axis is accomplished by screw drives with external adjustments. A cassette holds a single frame of 35-mm film in position. The specimen-to-film distance can be adjusted, and the incident x-ray beam is directly observed on a fluorescent screen at the rear of the camera. The cameras may be evacuated to reduce air scattering and exposure times and are widely used in the study of orientation in polymeric materials.

Non-x-ray Methods. A determination of preferred orientation is sometimes difficult, particularly in recrystallized or hot-worked metals, because of large grain size. This becomes very troublesome when the grain diameter exceeds 1 mm. Erratic traces of x-ray intensity will result when diffractometer-counter methods are used and the arcs on Debye rings on films will appear spotty. These difficulties may be overcome by a combination of etch-pit and optical-goniometer techniques.[113–116] Briefly, the metal is etched in a chemical solution known to develop etch pits that are crystallographically well defined. The crystallographic indices of planes parallel to the etch-pit faces are known, and the specimen is mounted in an optical goniometer. From a knowledge of the position at which these etch-pit faces reflect light, the orientation of the individual grains may be determined. The accuracy of this method is limited by the inherent rounding of the sides of the etch pits, and the method is not applicable to deformed or partially recrystallized metals.

Both neutron and electron diffraction may be used to determine preferred orientations. The principles involved are analogous to the x-ray principles used (see Chap. 23). Electron diffraction is useful when surface textures are to be determined and is usually limited to studies of relatively light-element materials because of the shallow depth of penetration of the electron beam.[33] Neutron diffraction[117] is useful in studies of heavy-element materials and may be applied in such cases as determining an averaged texture through a metallic sheet. However, electron and neutron diffraction have not been extensively employed as there is usually no marked advantage over x-ray diffraction.

REFERENCES CITED

1. E. A. Calnan and C. J. B. Clews, *Phil. Mag.*, **41**:1085 (1950).
2. E. A. Calnan and C. J. B. Clews, *Phil. Mag.*, **42**:616 (1951).
3. E. A. Calnan and C. J. B. Clews, *Phil. Mag.*, **42**:919 (1951).
4. E. A. Calnan and C. J. B. Clews, *J. Appl. Phys.*, **22**:1508 (1951).
5. E. A. Calnan and C. J. B. Clews, *Phil. Mag.*, **43**:93 (1952).
6. J. W. F. Bishop, *J. Mech. Phys. Solids*, **3**:130 (1954).
7. F. Wever, *Trans. AIME*, **93**:51 (1931).
8. C. S. Barrett, *Structure of Metals*, 2d ed., pp. 26–44, McGraw-Hill Book Company, New York, 1952.
9. P. S. Dobson and H. Wilman, *Acta Cryst.*, **14**:1275 (1961).
10. P. S. Dobson and H. Wilman, *Acta Cryst.*, **15**:556 (1962).
11. J. N. King and H. Wilman, *Acta Cryst.*, **15**:551 (1962).
12. W. R. Hibbard, *J. Inst. Metals*, **77**:581 (1950).
13. R. Faivre, *Rev. Met.* (*Paris*), **55**:53 (1958).
14. P. G. Bastien and J. Pokorny, *J. Inst. Metals*, **82**:545 (1953–1954).
15. M. Ettisch, M. Polanyi, and K. Weissenberg, *Z. Physik*, **7**:181 (1921).
16. W. R. Hibbard, *Trans. AIME*, **185**:598 (1949).
17. G. Bassi and F. Schuckher, *Z. Metallk.*, **47**:379 (1956).
18. G. v. Göler and G. Sachs, *Z. Physik*, **41**:873, 889 (1927).
19. C. J. McHargue, L. K. Jetter, and J. C. Ogle, *Trans. AIME*, **215**:831 (1959).
20. J. Grewen and G. Wassermann, *Z. Metallk.*, **45**:498 (1954).
21. K. van Horn, *Trans. Am. Soc. Metals*, **47**:38 (1955).
22. H. Kostron and M. Schippers, *Metall.*, **7**:25 (1953).
23. C. S. Barrett and L. H. Levenson, *Trans. AIME*, **137**:112 (1940).
24. C. S. Barrett, *Structure of Metals*, 2d ed., pp. 447–448, McGraw-Hill Book Company, New York, 1952.

25. W. R. Hibbard and D. E. Trout, *Trans. AIME*, **185**:620 (1949).
26. R. A. Swalin and A. H. Geisler, *Trans. AIME*, **206**:1259 (1956).
27. W. R. Hibbard, A. E. Roswell, and A. E. Schuetz, *Trans. AIME*, **191**:808 (1951).
28. C. S. Barrett and L. H. Levenson, *Trans. AIME*, **135**:327 (1939).
29. C. J. McHargue and J. P. Hammond, *Trans. AIME*, **194**:745 (1952).
30. G. D. Rieck, *Philips Res. Rept.*, **12**:423 (1957).
31. C. S. Barrett, *Trans. AIME*, **135**:296 (1939).
32. A. Freda and B. D. Cullity, *Trans. AIME*, **215**:530 (1959).
33. J. N. King and H. Wilman, *Proc. Phys. Soc. (London)*, **78**:979 (1961).
34. R. A. Smallman, *J. Inst. Metals*, **84**:10 (1955–1956).
35. H. Hu, P. R. Sperry, and P. A. Beck, *Trans. AIME*, **194**:76 (1952).
36. H. Hu and R. S. Cline, *J. Appl. Phys.*, **32**:760 (1961).
37. L. K. Jetter and C. J. McHargue, *The Metal Thorium*, pp. 161–185, American Society for Metals, Cleveland, 1959.
38. F. Hassner and H. Weik, *Arch. Eisenhuettenw.*, **87**:153 (1956).
39. M. Gensamer and R. F. Mehl, *Trans. AIME*, **120**:277 (1936).
40. W. H. Smith, *Trans. AIME*, **203**:1064 (1955).
41. M. Semchysen and G. A. Timmons, *Trans. AIME*, **194**:279 (1952).
42. R. T. Begley, *WADC Tech. Rept.* 57-344 (ASTIA Document no. 210258), 180 pp., March, 1959.
43. J. W. Pugh and W. R. Hibbard, *Trans. Am. Soc. Metals*, **48**:526 (1956).
44. C. J. McHargue and J. P. Hammond, *Trans. AIME*, **194**:745 (1952).
45. J. W. Pugh, *Trans. AIME*, **212**:637 (1958).
46. C. S. Barrett, G. Ansel, and R. F. Mehl, *Trans. AIME*, **125**:516 (1937).
47. G. Weiner and R. Corcoran, *Trans. AIME*, **206**:901 (1956).
48. B. S. Shabel, F. W. Kunz, and D. L. Douglass, *Columbium Metallurgy*, pp. 435–458, Interscience Publishers, Inc., New York, 1961.
49. J. H. Keeler, *Trans. AIME*, **212**:781 (1958).
50. C. J. McHargue and J. P. Hammond, *Trans. AIME*, **197**:57 (1953).
51. J. H. Keeler, W. R. Hibbard, and B. F. Decker, *Trans. AIME*, **197**:932 (1953).
52. M. Schwartz, S. K. Nash, and R. Zeman, *Frankford Arsenal Rept.* R-1520 (ASTIA Document no. AD 230-401), 21 pp., August, 1959.
53. V. Caliotti and G. Sachs, *Metall.*, **11**:1 (1932).
54. P. W. Bakarian, *Trans. AIME*, **147**:267 (1942).
55. C. J. McHargue, S. E. Adair, and J. P. Hammond, *Trans. AIME*, **197**:1149 (1953).
56. P. A. Ross, *Phys. Rev.*, **28**:425 (1926).
57. H. A. McKinstry and M. A. Short, *J. Sci. Instr.*, **37**:178 (1960).
58. O. S. Edwards and H. Lipson, *J. Sci. Instr.*, **18**:131 (1941).
59. R. Witty and P. Wood, *Nature*, **163**:323 (1949).
60. J. T. Norton and R. E. Hiller, *Trans. AIME*, **99**:190 (1932).
61. A. Taylor, *X-ray Metallography*, p. 600, John Wiley & Sons, Inc., New York, 1961.
62. R. J. Peavler and J. L. Lenusky, *Angles between Planes in Cubic Crystals*, IMD Spec. Rept. Series no. 8, American Institute of Mining, Metallurgical, and Petroleum Engineers, New York.
63. A. Lawley, *Trans. AIME*, **218**:956 (1960).
64. A. Taylor and S. Leber, *Trans. AIME*, **200**:190 (1954).
65. C. W. Bunn, *Chemical Crystallography*, pp. 147–169, 188–193, 201–203, 348–362, Oxford University Press, Fair Lawn, N.J., 1961.
66. F. Happey, *X-ray Diffraction by Polycrystalline Materials*, H. S. Peiser et al. (eds.), pp. 481–496, Chapman & Hall, Ltd., London, 1960.
67. B. F. Decker, *Proc. Am. Soc. Testing Mater.*, **43**:785 (1943).
68. Suzanne Beatty, *J. Appl. Phys.*, **21**:940 (1951).
69. A. Taylor, *X-ray Metallography*, pp. 947–949, John Wiley & Sons, Inc., New York, 1961.
70. P. A. Bakarian, *Trans. AIME*, **147**:267 (1942).
71. O. Kratky, *Z. Krist.*, **72**:529 (1930).
72. C. S. Barrett, *Trans. AIME*, **93**:75 (1931).
73. A. Guinier and J. Tennevin, *Rev. Met. (Paris)*, **65**:277 (1948).
74. R. Smoluchowski and R. W. Turner, *Physica*, **16**:397 (1950).
75. C. J. Milner and J. A. James, *J. Sci. Instr.*, **30**:388 (1953).
76. J. T. Norton, *J. Appl. Phys.*, **19**:1176 (1948).
77. B. F. Decker, E. T. Asp, and D. Harker, *J. Appl. Phys.*, **19**:388 (1948).
78. A. H. Geisler, *Modern Research Technique in Physical Metallurgy*, pp. 131–153, American Society for Metals, Cleveland, 1953.
79. A. H. Geisler, *Rev. Sci. Instr.*, **25**:727 (1954).

80. C. G. Suits, *Gen. Elec. Rev.*, **54**:32 (1951).
81. M. Schwartz, *J. Appl. Phys.*, **26**:1507 (1955).
82. J. B. Newkirk and L. Bruce, *J. Appl. Phys.*, **29**:151 (1958).
83. E. Acucena and R. Van Kuren, *Gen. Elec. Res. Lab. Rept.* 58-RL-2057, 48 pp., 1958.
84. M. Field and M. E. Merchant, *J. Appl. Phys.*, **20**:741 (1949).
85. L. G. Schulz, *J. Appl. Phys.*, **20**:1030 (1949).
86. W. P. Chernock and P. A. Beck, *J. Appl. Phys.*, **23**:341 (1952).
87. W. P. Chernock et al., *Rev. Sci. Instr.*, **24**:925 (1953).
88. M. H. Mueller and H. W. Knott, *Rev. Sci. Instr.*, **25**:1115 (1954).
89. J. R. Holland et al., *Advances in X-ray Analysis*, vol. 4, pp. 74–84, Plenum Press, Inc., New York, 1961.
90. M. L. Fuller and G. Vaux, *Trans. AIME*, **197**:1038 (1953).
91. A. N. Holden, *Rev. Sci. Instr.*, **24**:10 (1953).
92. L. G. Schulz, *J. Appl. Phys.*, **20**:1033 (1949).
93. D. N. Williams and D. S. Eppelsheimer, *Rev. Sci. Instr.*, **23**:229 (1952).
94. W. Bunk, K. Lücke, and G. Masing, *Z. Metallk.*, **45**:269 (1954).
95. F. Haessner, *Z. Metallk.*, **47**:649 (1956).
96. J. Grewen, A. Segmüller, and G. Wassermann, *Arch. Eisenhuettenw.*, **29**:115 (1958).
97. E. S. Meieran, *Rev. Sci. Instr.*, **33**:319 (1962).
98. S. L. Lopata and E. B. Kula, *Trans. AIME*, **224**:865 (1962).
99. G. B. Harris, *Phil. Mag.*, **43**:113 (1952).
100. L. K. Jetter and B. S. Borie, Jr., *J. Appl. Phys.*, **24**:532 (1953).
101. C. M. Mitchell and J. F. Rowland, *Acta Met.*, **2**:559 (1954).
102. L. K. Jetter, C. J. McHargue, and R. O. Williams, *J. Appl. Phys.*, **27**:368 (1956).
103. W. P. Chernock et al., *J. Appl. Phys.*, **27**:1170 (1956).
104. M. H. Mueller, W. P. Chernock, and P. A. Beck, *Trans. AIME*, **212**:39 (1958).
105. C. J. McHargue and L. K. Jetter, *Trans. AIME*, **218**:550 (1960).
106. C. G. Dunn and C. J. McHargue, *J. Appl. Phys.*, **31**:1767 (1960).
107. A. H. Geisler, *J. Appl. Phys.*, **25**:1245 (1954).
108. ASTM Specification E81-54T.
109. C. H. Deetz and O. S. Adams, Elements of Map Projection, 5th ed., *U.S. Dept. Comm., Coast and Geodetic Surv. Spec. Publ.* 68, pp. 40–41, 73–78, Washington, D.C., 1945.
110. C. G. Dunn and J. L. Walter, *J. Appl. Phys.*, **31**:827 (1960).
111. I. Fankuchen and H. Mark, *J. Appl. Phys.*, **15**:364 (1944).
112. F. G. Chesley, *Rev. Sci. Instr.*, **18**:422 (1947).
113. C. S. Barrett, *Trans. AIME*, **137**:128 (1940).
114. A. Taylor, *J. Sci. Instr.*, **25**:301 (1948).
115. P. A. Beck and H. Hu, *Trans. AIME*, **194**:83 (1952).
116. C. S. Barrett, *Structure of Metals*, 2d ed., pp. 192–195, McGraw-Hill Book Company, New York, 1952.
117. R. A. Swalin and A. H. Geisler, *Trans. AIME*, **206**:1259 (1956).

GENERAL REFERENCES

Barrett, C. S.: *Structure of Metals*, 2d ed., McGraw-Hill Book Company, New York, 1952.
Clark, G. L.: *Applied X-rays*, 4th ed., McGraw-Hill Book Company, New York, 1952.
Cullity, B. D.: *Elements of X-ray Diffraction*, Addison-Wesley Publishing Company, Inc., Reading, Mass., 1956.
Guinier, A.: *Théorie et technique de la radiocrystallographie*, 2d ed., Dunod, Paris, 1956.
Klug, H. P., and L. E. Alexander: *X-ray Diffraction Procedures for Polycrystalline and Amorphous Materials*, John Wiley & Sons, Inc., New York, 1954.
Peiser, H. S., H. P. Rooksby, and A. J. C. Wilson (ed.): *X-ray Diffraction by Polycrystalline Materials*, Chapman & Hall, Ltd., London, 1960.
Taylor, A.: *X-ray Metallography*, John Wiley & Sons, Inc., New York, 1961.

Chapter 19

STRESS MEASUREMENT IN METALS

Macon H. Miller

General Motors Corporation

1. BASIC PRINCIPLES

Unique Advantages. The advantages of the measurement of stresses with x-rays are: it is nondestructive, it is a surface measurement, no special geometries are required, and only elastic strains are detected. In general, x-rays can measure the residual or retained stress in a given direction.

Basic Assumptions. The assumptions on which the x-ray technique is based are: (1) an elastic, homogeneous, isotropic material, and (2) no stress perpendicular to the sample surface. Polycrystalline materials without preferred orientation are a good approximation to the first condition. The shallow penetration of the x-rays effectively ensures a lack of constraint within the diffracting volume, so that the second assumption is satisfied.

Defining Equations. The x-ray measurement of stress is a measurement of strain from which the stress may be calculated. The common procedure is to measure the atomic spacing of two sets of atomic planes which have different orientations with respect to the sample surface. One set is parallel to the surface while the second is oriented at some chosen angle ψ (45 or 60°) with respect to the surface (see Fig. 1). The stress is then calculated from the expression

$$\sigma_\phi = \frac{d_\psi - d_\perp}{d_0} \frac{E}{1 + \nu} \frac{1}{\sin^2 \psi} \tag{1}$$

where σ_ϕ = stress in the sample surface, in the direction ϕ defined by the projection of the diffracted x-ray beam on the sample surface (see Fig. 1*b*)

d_ψ = interplanar spacing of atomic planes at an angle ψ with respect to the surface ($\psi \neq 0°$)

$d_\perp$ = interplanar spacing of atomic planes parallel to surface ($\psi = 0°$)

d_0 = interplanar spacing of stress free sample; replace with $d_\perp$ or calculated value from nominal lattice spacing

E = Young's modulus

ν = Poisson's constant

Examination of Eq. (1) indicates that, for a given σ_ϕ, $d\psi - d_\perp$ is proportional to $\sin^2 \psi$. This indicates that the two ψ angles $\psi = 0$ and $\psi \neq 0$ should be as far apart as possible to increase the sensitivity of the stress measurement. The maximum practical limit is 60° while less than 45° seriously limits the sensitivity. The focusing conditions at 45° will permit measurements on larger samples than will 60° (see Focusing Conditions in Sec. 3).

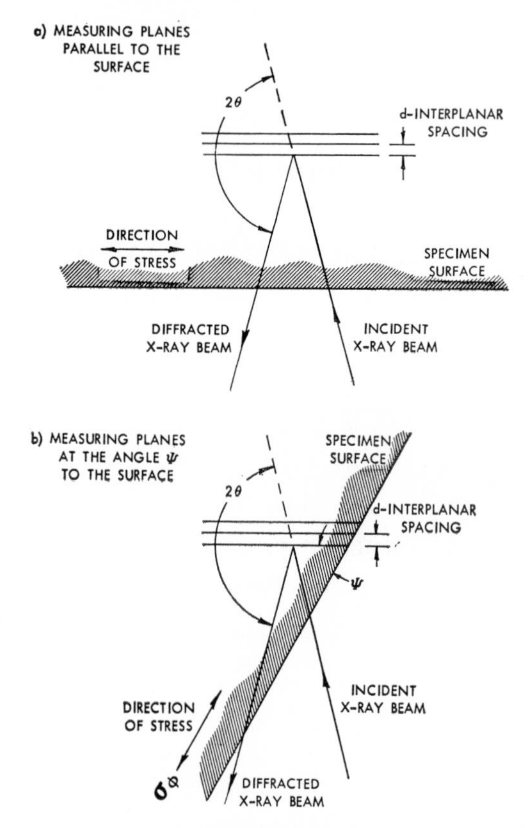

FIG. 1. Orientation of lattice planes measured to direction of stress.

The needed d values of Eq. (1) are obtained from the Bragg expression

$$n\lambda = 2d \sin \theta \tag{2}$$

where n = integer (normally 1)
λ = x-ray wavelength
d = distance between diffracting planes
θ = angle between x-ray beam and diffracting plane

The changes in d will be observed experimentally as changes in θ. The variation in θ is given by

$$\Delta\theta = -(\Delta d/d) \tan \theta \tag{3}$$

Consideration of this equation and Eq. (2) shows that a judicious choice of λ, d, and θ will maximize the measured $\Delta\theta$ associated with a given Δd. Briefly, θ should be as large as the experimental conditions will permit, for tan θ increases steeply as θ approaches 90°.

By rewriting Eq. (3) as

$$\Delta d/d = \Delta(2\theta)/(2 \tan \theta)$$

and substituting into Eq. (1) we can express the stress in terms of the experimentally measured 2θ (or θ):

$$\sigma = K\,(2\theta_{\perp} - 2\theta_{\psi}) \tag{4}$$

Thus the calculated stress is proportional to the shift in the measured diffraction angle (2θ or θ) as the ψ angle is changed from zero to ψ.

The stress constant K, expressed in degrees 2θ, is given by

$$K = \frac{E}{57.3 \times 2(1 + \nu) \tan \theta \sin^2 \psi} \tag{5}$$

and may be evaluated experimentally by measuring the change in 2θ values when a known increment of stress is applied. In most cases the calculated value of K using bulk values of E and ν will be acceptable. The value of $\tan \theta$ is calculated from $2\theta_{\perp}$ or from the nominal lattice constant of the material using the Miller indices of the diffraction line and the wavelength of the x-rays.

The limiting factors of all stress measurements are: (1) control of the effective specimen-to-film (or counter) distance, (2) coarse grain, and (3) preferred orientation.

Choice of Radiation and Filter. The selected radiation should provide a strong line (for good intensity) at a large diffraction angle [for sensitivity, Eq. (3)]. A second criterion is the degree of line contrast available, which is increased by the use of the appropriate filter.

Table 1. Radiation and Diffraction-plane Data for Stress Measurement

Metal	Radiation	Plane	Diffraction angle θ	Filter*
Aluminum	Cu	(511)	81°	Ni
Brass (68% Cu)	Co	(400)	75°30′	Fe
Brass (cartridge)	Ni	(331)	79°	Co
Copper	Co	(400)	81°46.5′	Fe
Magnesium	Fe	(105)	83°	Mn
Iron, steel	Co	(310)	80°37.5′	Fe
Steel (hard)	Cr	(211)	78°	V
Steel (austenitic)	Cr	(220)	64°	V

* Thickness should be 0.0005 to 0.001 in.

The importance of the filter is due to its ability to increase the line contrast by monochromatizing the radiation. The absorption edge of the filter should be slightly on the short-wavelength side of the $K\alpha$ radiation so as to have a minimum effect on the $K\alpha$ radiation and a maximum absorption of the $K\beta$ and white radiation (see Table 1).

Another source of background radiation is fluorescent radiation from the sample. This radiation is absorbed by a filter placed between the sample and the x-ray detector. The filter should be transparent to the primary radiation and opaque to the fluorescent radiation. Placing the $K\beta$ absorbing filter in the diffracted beam rather than in the incident beam will considerably increase the line contrast to the extent that additional filtering is unnecessary. For diffractometers a lithium fluoride crystal is useful in checking the output of the x-ray tube and the effect of the filter.

2. FILM TECHNIQUES

The back-reflection camera is the original instrument technique in measuring residual stress in metals and for some conditions is still the preferred method.

One unique, and sometimes all-important, advantage of the film technique is that portable equipment is available which can be moved to the sample. In addition, small area measurements may require less exposure time because of the integrating effect of the film. The effects of coarse grain, which are increased by reducing the area, can be minimized by oscillating the film.

The first major difficulty of the film technique is to control the sample-to-film distance. This is particularly important when using Eq. (1) as two exposures are needed, one for each set of atomic planes. Two methods are used to solve this problem: (1) some form of collapsible metal gauge[1] or template, or (2) painting the specimen with a powder that gives a sharp reflection from a known d spacing, enabling the operator to calculate the sample-film distance. Each method introduces some error into the stress measurement.

The second difficulty in the film technique arises in measuring the radii of the diffraction rings on the developed film. Samples which give a narrow diffraction line present little trouble. Increasing hardness in the samples results in increasing broadness in the diffracted ring, with the result that the problem of visually assigning a reproducible (and meaningful) position to the diffraction ring soon becomes unmanageable. Aside from the visual difficulties, the increasing diffraction-line width results

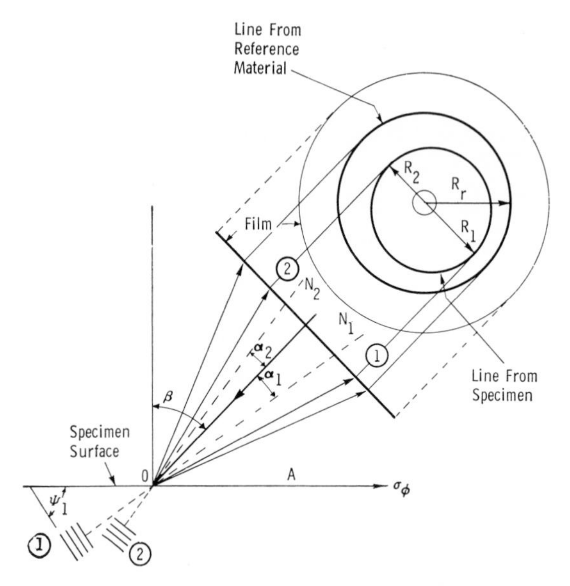

Fig. 2. Back-reflection method at inclined incidence.

in θ- and ψ-dependent factors becoming influential enough to affect the shape, and consequently the position, of the diffraction line (see Correction of Diffraction Data in Sec. 3). The result has been that the film technique has not given useful results when applied to hardened steels in the Rockwell C 45 to 65 range.

The general schematic of the back-reflection technique at an inclined incidence is shown in Fig. 2. Note that the two "sides" of the diffraction "ring" correspond to sets of atomic planes which have different orientations to the sample surface, with the result that the two sides of the "ring" are shifted a different amount with respect to the film center. The reference diffraction ring does not shift since fine powders are stress-free. The different diffraction angles θ from the two sets of planes also cause their normals N_1 and N_2 to have different angles α with respect to the incident x-ray beam. However, α_1 and α_2 are nearly equal to one another and to $90° - \theta$. (Note that the angle β is often referred to as ψ or ψ_0 in the film literature.) Measurements on radii R_1 and R_2 give information about the stresses acting on the planes 1 and 2 at ψ angles of $(\beta + \alpha_1)$ and $(\beta - \alpha_2)$, respectively, to the sample surface. The common practice is to measure only R_1 as it is more sensitive because of the larger ψ angle.

The simplest procedure is a single exposure with the x-ray beam perpendicular to the specimen to give the sum of the two principal stresses in the sample surface

$$\sigma_1 + \sigma_2 = -\frac{E}{\nu}\frac{d_1 - d_0}{d_0} \tag{6}$$

where the d spacing of the unstressed material d_0 is known, and d_1 is calculated from the sample-to-film distance and the diffraction-ring radius. The d_0 value is frequently very difficult to obtain, and the sum of the two principal stresses is of limited usefulness. Nevertheless, there may be occasions when only one orientation of specimen and camera is possible.

If the exposure is made at an angle as indicated in Fig. 2, it is possible to calculate the stress from the difference in d spacing for the two sets of atomic planes 1 and 2. The required relation is

$$\sigma_\phi = \frac{E}{1 + \nu}\frac{1}{\sin 2\beta \sin 2\alpha}\frac{d_1 - d_2}{d_0} \tag{7}$$

assuming $\alpha_1 = \alpha_2 = (90° - \theta)$ and d_1 and d_2 are calculated from R_1 and R_2. The advantage of this equation, aside from only one exposure, is that an accurate value of d_0 is unnecessary. The disadvantage is that the small difference in d_1 and d_2 results in a larger probable error compared with Eq. (1).

The standard method based on Eq. (1) is to make two exposures, one inclined and one normal to the sample surface, in order to maximize the change in d. Actually, an incident x-ray beam normal to the surface will diffract from a set of planes inclined at the angle α to the surface stress. The effect of this is usually small, being proportional to $\sin^2 \alpha$, and can usually be neglected.

Because the experimentally observed variable is the change in radius of the diffraction ring, it is desirable to alter Eq. (1) to relate the calculated stress directly to the observed change in radii. The desired relation (Ref. 2, pp. 439, 440) is

$$\sigma_\phi = \frac{E(R_i - R_n)}{2D(1 + \nu)\sec^2 2\theta \tan\theta \sin^2\psi} \tag{8}$$

where the R's refer to the measured radii from the inclined and normal film exposures, D is the sample-to-film distance, and θ and 2θ can be determined from the relation

$$R = D\tan(180° - 2\theta) \tag{9}$$

Rewriting Eq. (8), we have

$$\sigma_\phi = K_1(R_i - R_n) \tag{10}$$

and

$$K_1 = \frac{E}{2D(1 + \nu)\sec^2 2\theta \tan\theta \sin^2\psi} \tag{11}$$

Average values of θ and 2θ are usually adequate, and the values listed in Table 1 may be used as a first approximation.

3. DIFFRACTOMETER TECHHIQUES

The recent developments in x-ray stress measurements are centered on materials that yield very diffuse diffraction lines, e.g., hardened steel. For these materials, the film technique is inadequate and the diffractometer must be used.

The first advantage in using the diffractometer is due to the combined monochromating effects of filtering the diffracted radiation, the high absorption efficiency of the counter-tube gas, and the discriminating effect of the electronic circuits. The result is good diffraction-line contrast, i.e., peak-to-background ratio, which makes the location of the position of a diffuse line much easier and also more accurate.

The second advantage in using the diffractometer is that the diffracted x-ray intensity as a function of 2θ is immediately available and corrections can easily be made for the θ- and ψ-dependent factors which affect the diffraction-line contour and the resulting apparent position of the diffracted line.

The early workers used cobalt or iron radiation for x-ray stress measurements in steel. Both these radiations provide a diffraction line above 140° 2θ for ferrite or martensite. Both are satisfactory when the hardness is sufficiently low to give fairly sharp diffraction lines but are unsatisfactory for hardened steel with diffuse diffraction lines.

Since the early 1950s, the availability of 0.0005- and 0.001-in. vanadium foil in conjunction with chromium radiation has made it possible to measure stress in steel of Rockwell C 60 to 65. The advantage of chromium radiation is shown in Fig. 3. The martensite {211} planes diffract at about 156° 2θ with a peak-to-background ratio of 3:1 or better for relatively low retained austenite concentrations.

Focusing Conditions. The usual focusing arrangement ($\psi = 0$) of a diffractometer is shown in Fig. 4. The conditions are such that the x-ray source, the sample surface, and receiving slit lie on the arc of a circle. In practice, the sample surface is flat rather than curved, with a resulting loss in maximum sharpness of the diffracted beam.

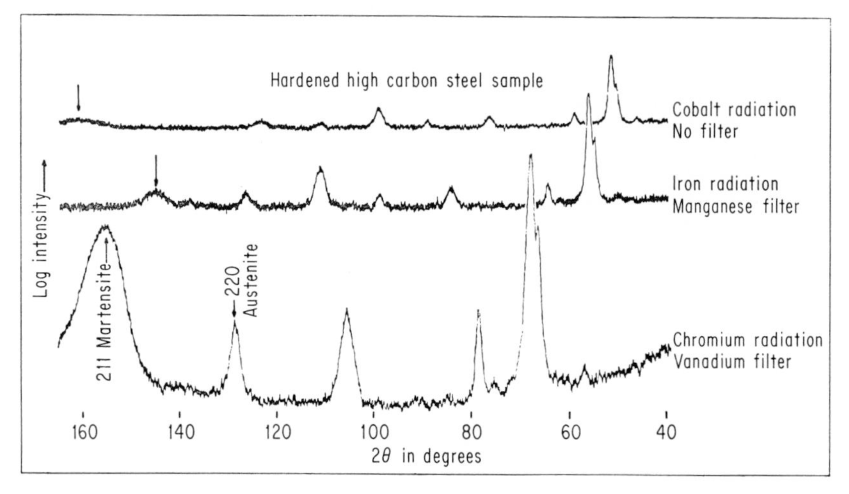

FIG. 3. Diffraction patterns from hardened steel with all traces plotted to same intensity scale.

The rotation of the sample through the angle of ψ destroys the normal focusing arrangement, as shown in Fig. 5. The normal position of the receiving slit no longer lies on the focusing circle which is tangent to the sample surface. The system is refocused by moving the detector system and slit inward to the new point of focus B. The distance the receiving slit must be moved is given by the expression (Ref. 2, p. 445)

$$AB = R_0 - R_0 \frac{\cos [\psi + (90° - \theta)]}{\cos [\psi - (90° - \theta)]}$$

where R_0 = radius of goniometer circle.

In practice, the θ value corresponding to the average position of the diffracted peak is selected and the system is not refocused for other values of θ associated with that particular diffraction line. Refocusing reduces the space available for the specimen on the diffractometer.

It is customary to use the line-focus port on the x-ray tube since it gives higher resolution and better focusing than the spot focus. For a diffuse peak there is no detail to resolve and the spot focus may be found more advantageous, especially when irradiating small areas where the increased counting rate is most useful. The line

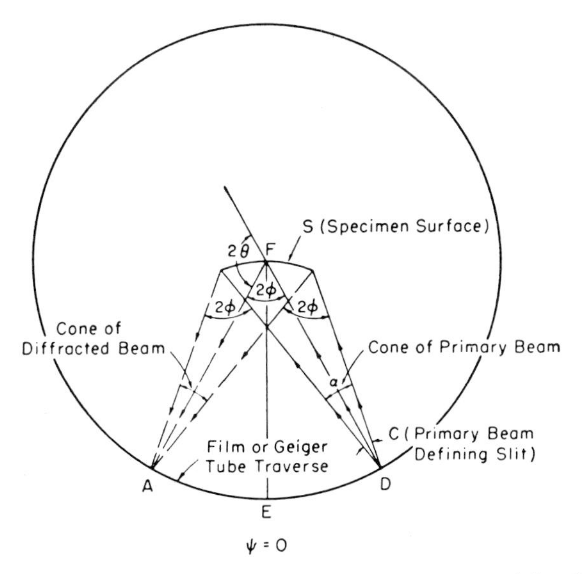

FIG. 4. Diffractometer focusing conditions with sample in normal $\psi = 0°$ position.

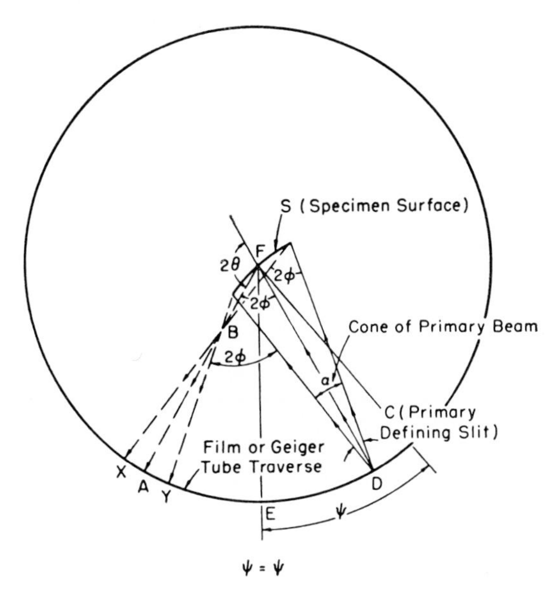

FIG. 5. Diffractometer focusing conditions with sample rotated $\psi°$ from normal position.

focus is used to align the diffractometer and the x-ray tube is then rotated into the spot-focus position, relying on the constructional accuracy of the x-ray tube to maintain the proper alignment.

The "noncritical" focusing requirements of diffuse peaks also permit stress measurements on samples that have poor geometry, i.e., high curvature. A small x-ray beam is used, however, to minimize the effect of sample curvature.

Correction of Diffraction Data. The factors affecting diffraction intensity are well known and are discussed in the literature (Ref. 2, Chap. 4). In the particular case of hardened steel, the diffraction lines are very broad and asymmetrical. Koistinen and Marburger[3] pointed out that these peaks are actually symmetrical after being corrected for θ-dependent intensity factors, including the absorption factor, which they showed to be dependent on the angle ψ.

The polarization-intensity factor $\frac{1}{2}(1 + \cos^2 2\theta)$ arises from the scattering of the x-ray beam by electrons. The Lorentz factor is a geometrical one. For the film

Table 2. Correction Factors for Stress Measurement
(Multiply for fixed time scaling; divide for fixed count)

2θ	$\psi = 0°$	$\psi = 45°$	$\psi = 60°$	2θ	$\psi = 0°$	$\psi = 45°$	$\psi = 60°$
160.0	0.5464	0.4542	0.3570	155.0	0.6920	0.6088	0.5098
159.8	0.5521	0.4600	0.3624	154.8	0.6979	0.6154	0.5169
159.6	0.5579	0.4658	0.3678	154.6	0.7038	0.6221	0.5240
159.4	0.5636	0.4716	0.3733	154.4	0.7098	0.6289	0.5312
159.2	0.5694	0.4775	0.3789	154.2	0.7158	0.6357	0.5385
159.0	0.5751	0.4834	0.3844	154.0	0.7217	0.6425	0.5458
158.8	0.5809	0.4893	0.3901	153.8	0.7277	0.6494	0.5533
158.6	0.5866	0.4953	0.3958	153.6	0.7337	0.6563	0.5608
158.4	0.5924	0.5013	0.4016	153.4	0.7397	0.6632	0.5685
158.2	0.5982	0.5073	0.4074	153.2	0.7457	0.6702	0.5762
158.0	0.6040	0.5134	0.4133	153.0	0.7517	0.6773	0.5840
157.8	0.6098	0.5195	0.4192	152.8	0.7577	0.6844	0.5920
157.6	0.6156	0.5256	0.4253	152.6	0.7638	0.6915	0.6000
157.4	0.6215	0.5318	0.4314	152.4	0.7698	0.6987	0.6081
157.2	0.6273	0.5380	0.4375	152.2	0.7758	0.7059	0.6163
157.0	0.6331	0.5442	0.4437	152.0	0.7819	0.7132	0.6246
156.8	0.6390	0.5505	0.4500	151.8	0.7880	0.7206	0.6331
156.6	0.6448	0.5568	0.4564	151.6	0.7941	0.7279	0.6416
156.4	0.6507	0.5632	0.4629	151.4	0.8001	0.7353	0.6502
156.2	0.6566	0.5696	0.4693	151.2	0.8062	0.7427	0.6590
156.0	0.6624	0.5760	0.4759	151.0	0.8123	0.7502	0.6679
155.8	0.6683	0.5825	0.4825	150.8	0.8185	0.7578	0.6769
155.6	0.6742	0.5890	0.4892	150.6	0.8246	0.7654	0.6860
155.4	0.6801	0.5955	0.4960	150.4	0.8307	0.7730	0.6952
155.2	0.6860	0.6021	0.5029	150.2	0.8369	0.7807	0.7045
155.0	0.6920	0.6088	0.5098	150.0	0.8430	0.7885	0.7140
				145.0*	0.76366	0.52288	0.34661

* Unnormalized.

method and for the diffractometer the Lorentz factor is $\frac{1}{4}\sin^2\theta\cos\theta$. Tabulated values of these functions are usually combined into the Lorentz-polarization factor

$$\frac{1}{8}\frac{1 + \cos^2 2\theta}{\sin^2\theta\cos\theta}$$

Tabulated values usually omit the $\frac{1}{8}$.

The absorption factor $(1 - \tan\psi\cot\theta)$ is geometrical and is of importance when the angle of the diffracted x-ray beam with respect to the sample surface is not the same as that of the incident beam, i.e., a ψ angle other than zero (Fig. 1*b*).

The products of the θ- and ψ-dependent factors are given in Table 2 normalized to unity at 145°. A more complete set of unnormalized factors is available in the literature.[4] Only the Lorentz-polarization factor is applied when $\psi = 0$.

Location of Diffraction Peak. The 2θ diffraction angles (see Fig. 1) must be measured with a precision of 0.02 or 0.03° in order for the variation in calculated stress to be not more than approximately 4,000 psi. Figure 6 indicates the difficulty of the problem since a peak width at half height of 8 to 12° 2θ is common for hardened steel.

The exact d spacing of a broad peak is very difficult to measure. Fortunately, the stress equation requires only the change in d when the sample is rotated through the angle of ψ. Thus relative d values are acceptable provided that they are reproducible. The experimental problem is then to assign reproducible 2θ values to the peaks in question. The general method is that of curve fitting, although other methods have been suggested.[5] The simplest current method is the three-point parabola technique.[3]

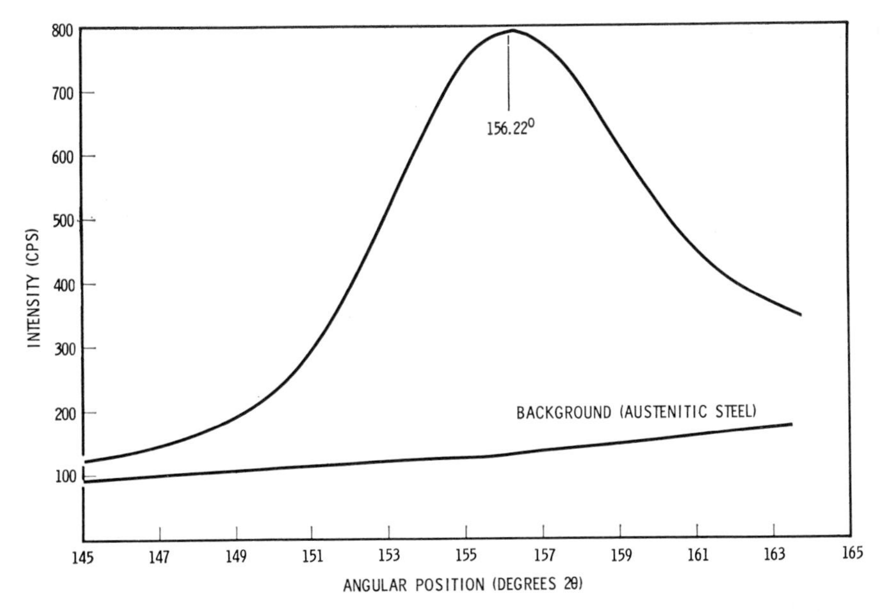

FIG. 6. Typical diffraction peak of hardened steel for normal diffractometer focusing.

Figure 7 indicates a three-point parabola fitted to data that have been corrected for the Lorentz-polarization effect (see Table 2). The original data are indicated by the circles. Three equally spaced points (black circles) are selected and the corrected values are indicated by the black squares. The parabola is fitted to the corrected data and is so indicated. In actual practice the equation of the parabola is not calculated. The position of the peak is defined as the location of the axis of the parabola on the 2θ axis. This 2θ value on the abscissa can be calculated from the values of a and b, the 2θ value of the first experimental point (154.5), and the increments between the 2θ points (1°).

A detailed calculation is shown in Fig. 8. A detailed scan ($\psi = 0$) at 1° (or ½°) intervals was made at low accuracy (10,000 to 15,000 counts) to outline the peak and the data were corrected by multiplying (slide rule) by the appropriate correction factor from Table 2. On the basis of these data, the 2θ values of $2\theta_1 = 153.4°$, $2\theta_2 = 155.2°$, and $2\theta_3 = 157.0°$ were selected. Scaling for 150 sec then gave the total number of counts at each 2θ value, and these are indicated under the heading Intensity, e.g., $I_1(153.4°) = 75{,}580$ counts. These intensities are then multiplied

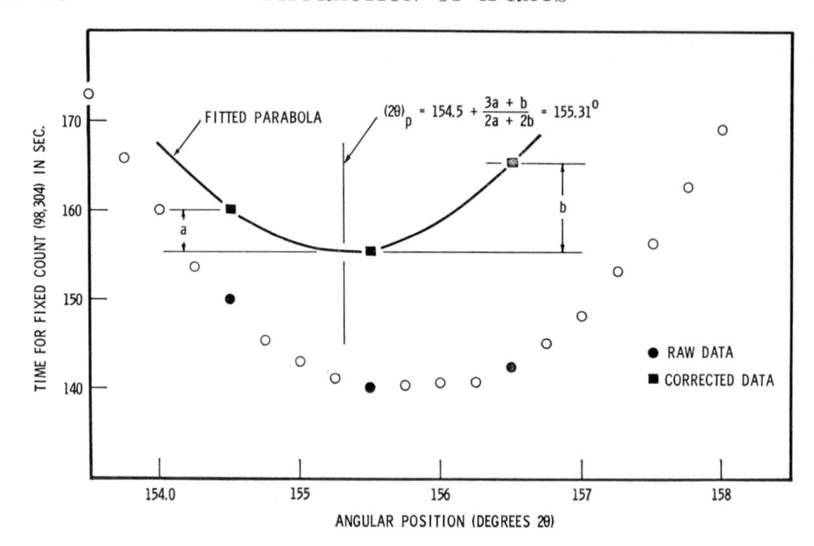

Fig. 7. Peak position as determined from a parabola fitted to corrected x-ray intensity data for $\psi = 0°$.

	ψ 0	ψ 60
Collimator	1°	--
Detector Slit	.3°	.1°
Filter	.0005"	--
Time Fixed Count (Sec.)	150	200

Cr. Tube, 20 ma., 33KV

No.	
Date	
Sample	
Treatment	Etch .005"
Orientation	Tangential

ψ	2θ	Intensity	Corr. Factor	Intensity Corr.	a	b	a + b	3a + b	$\frac{3a+b}{a+b}$	c	$\frac{3a+b}{a+b} - \frac{c}{2}$	$2\theta_1$ + corr.	$2\theta_0 - 2\theta_\psi$	Stress, PSI (calculated)
0	157.0	85,820	.6331	54,333		10,082								
	5.2	93,900	.6860	64,415			18,590	35,606	1.9153	1.8	1.724			
	3.4	75,580	.7397	55,907	8,508		(28.9%)					155.124		
60	157.2	107,660	.4375	47,101		6,913								
	5.4	108,900	.4960	54,014			15,513	32,713	2.1087	1.8	1.898			
	3.6	80,980	.5608	45,414	8,600							155.498	-.374	-22,000

2θ Peak = 155.12
Peak Intensity = 93,900

Background Intensity at 136° = 17,370
Corr. Factor: 1.2
Background Intensity at Peak = 20,840

Correction	
STRESS, PSI (absolute)	

Peak Intensity - Background = 73,060

Corr. Factor .6884

I Corr. = 50,2[illegible]

c^2	a + b	$\frac{Ic^2}{a+b}$
3.24	18,590	8.77

$R_c = 47.9 + 14.85 \log (Ic^2/a + b) = 61.9$

Fig. 8. Calculation of stress and hardness from diffractometer data from hardened steel.

by the correction factors in the adjacent column to give the corrected intensities in the following column [e.g., $I_c(153.4) = 55{,}907$ counts].

Referring to Fig. 7 we see that a and b are the differences in intensity between the two outside 2θ points and the middle point. Thus a is the difference in corrected intensity between 155.2 and 153.4°, or 8,508 counts. The sums of $a + b$ and $3a + b$ are formed and then divided to form the result of 1.9153. This result (1.9153) is multiplied by one-half of the increment C between the equally spaced 2θ points, which is 1.8° 2θ. The result is indicated as 1.724° 2θ. This is the location of the diffraction peak (defined by the parabola axis) measured from the first 2θ point of 153.4°. When measured from zero, the peak position is 2θ, plus the calculated distance from 2θ, or 155.124° from 0° 2θ.

Repeating the procedure for $\psi = 60°$ and subtracting the results gives a shift in peak position of 0.374°. The negative sign indicates that the stress causing this shift is compressive.

Referring to Eq. (5) and assuming $E = 30{,}000{,}000$ psi, $\nu = 0.29$, $\tan \theta = 4.61$ ($2\theta = 155.5$), the calculated value of K is 58,700 psi per degree 2θ (88,000 psi for $\psi = 45°$). Multiplication then gives a calculated compressive stress of 22,000 psi.

Experience with the three-point parabola indicates that diffuse peaks are symmetrical enough to be adequately represented by a parabola and that some lack of symmetry can be tolerated. Reliability of results is best when the three selected points straddle the peak and the two outer points are about 85 per cent of the maximum intensity.

The information that is used to calculate the peak position can also be used, when supplemented by a background measurement, to determine the peak *width*, which is related to the hardness of the diffracting surface layer. The derivation of the hardness calculation in Fig. 8 is discussed in the literature.[6] The particular expression used was derived from a specific calibration based on SAE 52100 specimens of tempered martensite in the hardness range of Rockwell C 29 to 65 using the line focus of the x-ray tube. For good reproducibility, a and b should be approximately equal and their sum approximately 30 per cent of the corrected peak intensity. The background at the peak, based on an austenitic sample, is taken to be 1.2 times that at 136° 2θ, an angle chosen for its freedom from diffraction lines. Smaller collimators and detector slits are needed for the softer samples to avoid broadening of the diffraction line from poor focusing geometry and a resulting hardness value that is too high.

The stress and hardness vs. depth in Fig. 9 are typical of the possibilities inherent in the x-ray measurement of stress to determine the effects of various heat-treatments and processing variables.

A more detailed discussion of the diffractometer technique as applied to steel may be found in the SAE report *Measurement of Stress by X-ray*, SAE TR-182.[4]

Specimen Surface Treatment. The specimen surface should be clean and smooth for the most reliable results. If the stress in the original surface is of prime interest, very little can be done since any mechanical polishing or grinding will introduce significant stress if none is present or change the amount of the stress already present. If possible, the surface should be measured as is, before any treatment is attempted. Surface coatings such as oxides may be removed by electropolishing for a few seconds.

Electropolishing is the most satisfactory method for smoothing the surface or removing thicker layers. When stress measurements are to be made vs. depth, electropolishing is still the best method since a mechanical procedure must be followed by electropolishing to remove the cold-worked layer. The more vigorous the mechanical process, the deeper the disturbed layer formed.

The formulas of two electropolishing baths that have been found quite satisfactory for steels are given in Table 3. Data on other metals may be found in the ASM *Metals Handbook*. Solution No. 1 is five to ten times as fast as No. 2 but does not give so smooth a surface and has a tendency to stain. Most of the metal can be removed in the first bath, followed by a brief polish in the second to give a bright smooth surface. Staining of the sample is minimized by rinsing the specimen promptly upon removal from the bath. An operating temperature of 100 to 120° F is recom-

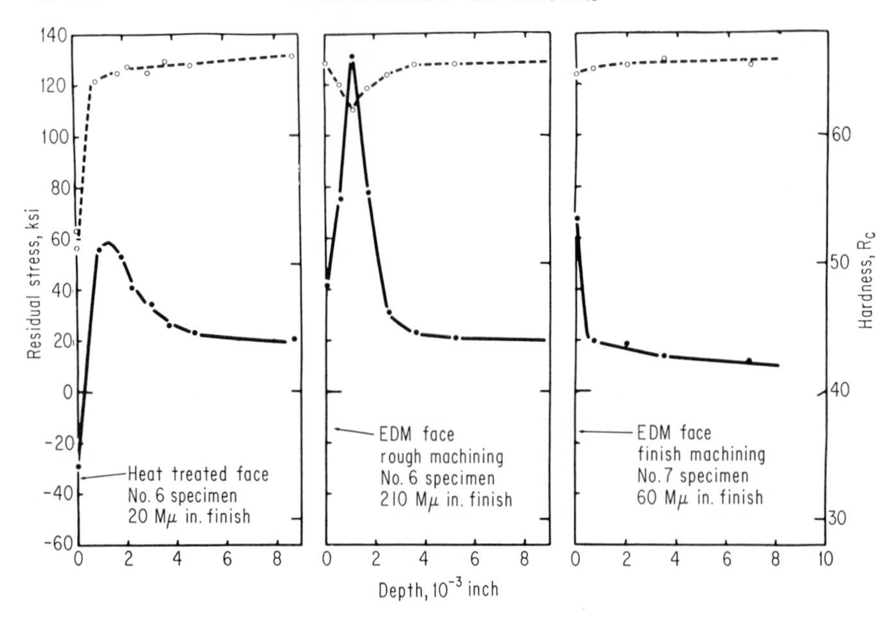

Fig. 9. Residual stress (solid lines) and hardness (dashed lines) in hardened 0-1 tool steel after heat-treatment and after rough and finish machining by electrical-discharge machining (EDM).

mended because metal-removal rate at room temperature is slow. The areas of the specimen which are not to be electropolished may be protected with suitable tapes and stopoff lacquers.

Effect of X-ray Penetration. Although the unique advantage of x-rays is in measuring surface stress, interest in the sample is not always limited to the surface but may extend to the distribution of stress with depth. This information is secured by sacrificing the nondestructive nature of the x-ray method and electropolishing appropriate increments from the specimen, and measuring the stress on each new surface.

The measurement of stress with depth, especially on finished surfaces, frequently reveals a very steep gradient. Under these conditions even the shallow penetration of the x-rays (approximately 0.0002 to 0.0003 in. for $\psi = 0$) is not negligible. The exponential absorption of the x-rays in the specimen means that the diffracted beam represents a weighted average of the diffracting volume of the metal. The result is that the actual surface stress is greater than the measured stress which represents the diffracting volume.

A method for calculating a correction for the penetration of the x-ray beam has been derived by Marburger and Koistinen (Ref. 4, p. 23). The expression given in

Table 3. Electropolishing Baths

Bath	Conc. sulfuric acid	85% phosphoric acid	Water	Chromium trioxide
No. 1 rapid.......	1,500 cm³	1,000 cm³	250 cm³	125 g
No. 2 slow........	....	9 lb	....	1 lb

terms of the experimentally measured 2θ values is

$$F(2\theta) = f(2\theta) - f'(2\theta)/k$$

where $F(2\theta)$ = corrected (i.e., true) function of 2θ
$f(2\theta)$ = experimental function of 2θ (i.e., peak positions vs. depth)
$f'(2\theta)$ = slope of $f(2\theta)$

and
$$k = \mu\left[\frac{1}{\sin(\theta+\psi)} + \frac{1}{\sin(\theta-\psi)}\right]$$

where μ = linear absorption coefficient of the x-rays
θ = diffraction angle
ψ = angle of diffracting planes to sample surface

The values of k for chromium radiation and steel are

$$k(\psi = 0°) = 4.70/0.001 \text{ in.}$$
$$k(\psi = 45°) = 6.96/0.001 \text{ in.}$$
$$k(\psi = 60°) = 11.0/0.001 \text{ in.}$$

An illustration of the method is given in Fig. 10 for the stress measurements (corrected for penetration) given in Fig. 11. A major difficulty in applying the method

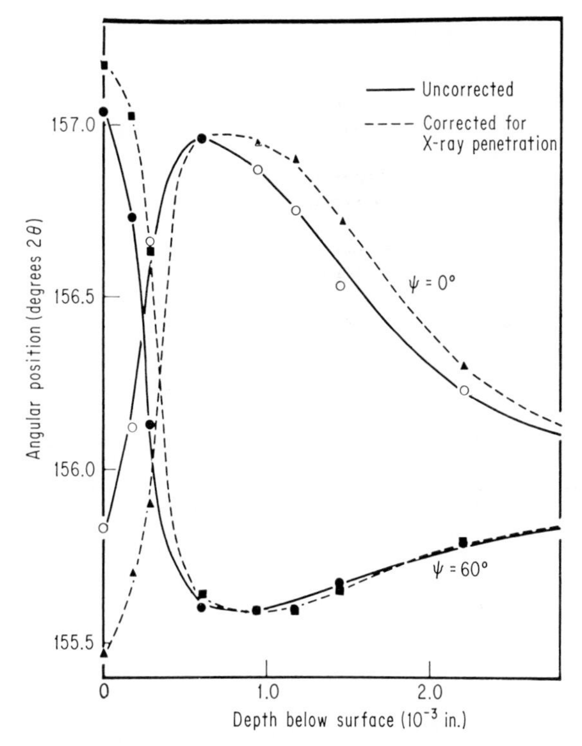

FIG. 10. Correction of 2θ measurements from diffractometer for penetration of x-ray beam.

is accurate determination of the slope $f'(2\theta)$. One solution is to draw straight lines between points and use the slope thus defined. This has the advantage of making the calculated correction independent of the operator's judgment. The difficulty in accurately determining the exact amount of metal removed in the case of very small increments also limits the precision in determining the slope.

The corrected 2θ data are used to calculate corrected stress values (see Fig. 11). The surface stress values thus calculated are sometimes extremely high, well in excess of 300,000 psi, but rapidly decrease to more conventional values away from the surface. This large surface value occurs even when the calculation is based on a conservative estimate of the slope.

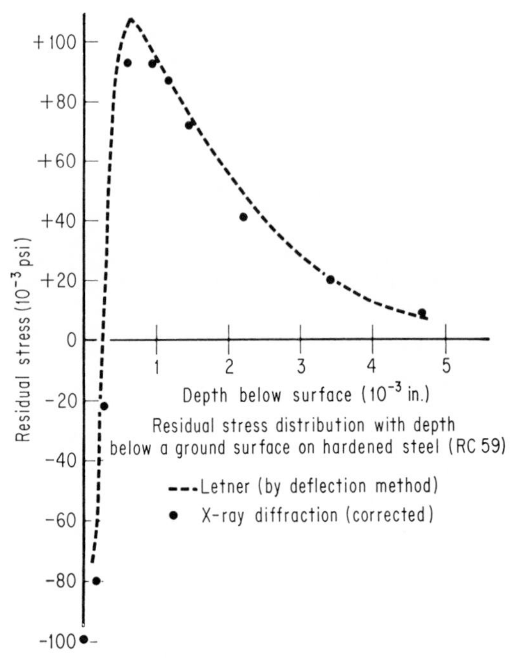

FIG. 11. Comparison of stress measurements by x-ray and Letner's deflection procedure (x-ray measurements corrected for effect of x-ray penetration).

4. ALIGNMENT AND CALIBRATION OF THE DIFFRACTOMETER

Alignment. The specimen holders normally used with diffractometers are inadequate for stress measurements. The holder (or stage) must permit the selected area on the specimen to be placed in the x-ray beam and on the rotation axis of the goniometer. A small amount of dental wax is helpful in holding the specimen in position. In addition, it must be possible to rotate the sample through the desired ψ angle without displacing the specimen surface from the goniometer axis. If the manufacturer cannot supply the required stage, one must be designed and constructed.

After the diffractometer has been mechanically aligned it should be checked for proper geometry on samples having both sharp and diffuse diffraction lines of the materials that are to be measured. The sample should be single-phase and carefully annealed to eliminate macrostresses. Electropolishing several thousandths from the surface will help to assure a low-stress surface. The diffracting angle on the sharp line (low-carbon iron) should not vary as the ψ angle is changed. If the $K\alpha$ doublet is resolved, the intensity corrections will not be necessary. Specimens exhibiting diffuse diffraction lines are more likely to retain some stress, and so the interest is in comparing the peak profiles at different ψ angles when θ corrected data normalized to the same intensity are compared. Except for some shift due to a residual stress that may be present, the peaks should superimpose. The displacement of the detector slit inward to refocus for ψ angles other than zero changes the indicated value of the detector slit, and this must be compensated for by changing to a smaller slit.

Calibration. The question of the proper stress factors E and ν for x-ray stress measurement is still unsettled. Ideally they should be experimentally determined for each sample or at least for each type of sample in the given experimental setup. This being impractical, it is suggested that the conventional values be used until experience indicates they should be changed.

The lack of any method other than x-ray to measure surface residual stress calls for a "boot-strap operation." The measurement of a low stress in a "stress-free" specimen of soft, annealed low-carbon steel is suggestive but not definite. A hard, Rockwell C 60 specimen of stress-free material is much more difficult to produce and is subject to more uncertainty (Ref. 4, p. 20). Low residual stress requires very slow cooling in a protective atmosphere. A simpler approach, but perhaps less certain, is to electropolish 0.020 to 0.030 in. from the surfaces of a suitable sample so as to eliminate all effects of grinding or heat-treatment.

The x-ray stress technique can be checked against strain gauges by using a beam specimen in a suitable fixture. The increment of stress as measured by the x-rays should agree with that indicated by the strain gauges. Agreement would suggest that the bulk values of E and ν are correct. Care must be used, however, to ensure a uniaxial (one-direction) stress and to avoid exceeding the elastic limit.

The sensitive measurement of Letner[7] based on the change in curvature as metal is removed from the specimen is shown in Fig. 11 and compared with x-ray results calculated by using the conventional values of E and ν. The excellent agreement suggests that the conventional values are acceptable for hardened steels.

REFERENCES CITED

1. H. P. Klug and L. E. Alexander, *X-ray Diffraction Procedures*, p. 225, John Wiley & Sons, Inc., New York, 1954.
2. B. D. Cullity, *Elements of X-ray Diffraction*, Addison-Wesley Publishing Company, Inc., Reading, Mass., 1956.
3. D. P. Koistinen and R. E. Marburger, *ASM Trans.*, **51**:537 (1959).
4. A. L. Christenson (ed.), *Measurement of Stress by X-ray*, SAE TR-182.
5. A. L. Christenson and E. S. Rowland, *ASM Trans.*, **45**:638 (1953).
6. R. E. Marburger and D. P. Koistinen, *ASM Trans.*, **53**:743 (1961).
7. H. R. Letner, *Trans. ASME*, **77**:1089 (1955).

Chapter 20

DETERMINATION OF PHASE DIAGRAMS

R. E. Thoma

Oak Ridge National Laboratory

1. INTRODUCTION

A necessary part of any new investigation concerning the properties of materials is a determination of their equilibrium-phase behavior. Basic descriptions of the properties of materials and nature of their interactions as functions of composition, temperature, and pressure are to be found in equilibrium-phase diagrams, sometimes called constitution diagrams. Phase diagrams concisely describe all the reversible interactions which may occur among a group of components in any combination of the physical states vapor, liquid, or solid. In his excellent treatment of the principles of heterogeneous phase equilibria, Ricci[1] has classed investigation of phase equilibria as one of the activities properly called "classical chemistry," that which rests upon the identification and characterization of substances and upon the study of their interaction. Many of the properties of materials which are measured in a wide variety of chemical researches fall in the general category of equilibrium-phase data, such as solubility, vapor pressures, polymorphism, order-disorder characteristics, compound stability as a function of temperature, and nonstoichiometry. Thus limited investigations of phase behavior are often necessary parts of wide varieties of chemical investigations. Less frequently, comprehensive investigations are pursued as subjects of single studies. For this reason, the information available in published phase diagrams varies enormously with respect to the completeness with which phase behavior is described. The evolution of complete phase diagrams often proceeds through several generations of research. It is necessary, therefore, that the most current reports be located if one is to gain a comprehensive appraisal of specific phase behavior.

In application to the construction of phase diagrams, x-ray diffraction analysis has come to serve as the single most significant technique in providing the great detail of information required for elucidating the relationships among solid phases. Qualitative and quantitative analysis derived from x-ray diffraction methods has gradually become so routine that very little formal discussion has arisen emphasizing its application to the construction of phase diagrams. Yet x-ray crystallographic studies proceeding concurrently with the phase investigation are so relevant to the interpretation of equilibrium data that far more precise and detailed equilibrium diagrams may be constructed from the joint investigation than is possible by any single-handed approach. One may find from recent applications of x-ray methods to the investigation of phase equilibria that necessary information, such as identification data, crystallite and unit-cell dimensions, and variation in compound stoichiometry, is often obtainable only from x-ray data. X-ray methods, in fact, sometimes appear to have unique capability in showing phase discontinuities where other methods fail. The rapid evolution of crystal-characterization methods within the last two decades has made possible the definition of equilibrium interactions which would have been impossible prior to that time, an example of Lonsdale's suggestion[2] that within this period there has been greater application of x-ray techniques to chemistry than to all other areas of research.

2. GENERAL EXPERIMENTAL METHODS

Few procedural discussions of the experimental methods for conducting investigations of phase equilibria have been written since the classic works of Roozeboom, Schreinemakers, and Bowen. Since that time, virtually all of the research tools available to the inorganic and physical chemist have been usefully applied in describing phase equilibria. Applications and innovations in experimental methods of investigating phase behavior are discussed occasionally in the *Annual Reviews of Physical Chemistry*. All the methods of obtaining equilibrium-phase data may be classified in two categories: those employing either dynamic methods or static methods.

Dynamic methods employed in measuring discontinuities of properties associated with phase transitions may include such measurements as heat effects associated with these changes, electrical properties, volume changes, and vapor pressures. Such measurements, while very useful, often cannot be interpreted unequivocally and must be supplemented by additional measurements and phase-identification data in order that equilibrium-phase diagrams may be constructed. Results of static-method experiments, entailing equilibration of materials at constant pressure, temperature, and composition, provide the required transition and identification data. Static methods are less commonly employed because they are more time-consuming and expensive than the dynamic methods and because separate experiments are required for each group of fixed composition, temperature, and pressure parameters.

Complete phase diagrams of single- and multicomponent systems designate the character of phase transitions from solid, liquid, and gaseous states and identity of coexisting phases at all composition-temperature-pressure points. For most investigations, determination of equilibrium relations under conditions in which each of these parameters varies widely is impractical and often impossible. Most workers investigating equilibria among several materials choose to deal with no more than two of these variables. As a result, the most common class of phase diagrams is those termed "condensed systems," i.e., those in which the effects of moderate pressure changes are considered to be negligible. The data required for definition of the equilibrium-phase relationships consist entirely of those which lead to an unequivocal establishment of the number and identity of coexisting phases under equilibrium conditions. Recent advances in understanding the association phenomena in liquids have been made in x-ray and neutron-diffraction studies. The fact that such studies are very complex and involve many experimental difficulties obviates their likely application to investigations of phase equilibria in the future. For phase investigations, diffraction data serve primarily to provide identification of crystalline solids, and for this reason the remainder of this discussion concerning x-ray analysis will be confined to solid phases.

Commonly, liquid-solid transition data are obtained from cooling curves. Changes in slope of the temperature of the specimen, when plotted as a function of time, reflect changes which occur on cooling. This technique is generally adequate for determining all except the steepest liquidus curves; steep curves represent small changes in saturation concentrations with temperature and hence small heat effects. Cooling curves also provide information about solidus and subsolidus changes but are prone to give misleading indications because of the impossibility of maintaining equilibrium during cooling. Phase transitions inferred from cooling curves are verified by the quench method, in which phases existing in equilibrium are preserved by quick cooling and identified using microscopic and x-ray diffraction techniques. One infers that the number and identity of phases in the cooled specimens correspond to those in equilibrium at high temperatures. This technique, widely employed in investigations of ceramic materials, has undergone innovations which have made possible wide-ranging investigations of molten-salt systems. Generally, x-ray diffraction experiments provide these data in the greatest number and shortest time of all experimental methods.

In the rapidly developing field of nonmetallic high-temperature equilibrium investigation, transparent crystalline phases predominate. Their identification and characterization are facilitated employing the polarizing-light microscope and x-ray diffraction equipment as complementary identification tools, enabling the investigators to construct detailed phase diagrams of complex systems in a relatively short time. The polarizing-light microscope has unique applicability in the investigation of many oxide and salt systems, arising from the fact that it is frequently not possible to vitrify molten mixtures by quick cooling. Rapidly cooled liquid mixtures of oxides or salts generally crystallize to form a matrix of extremely small crystals, with dimensions less than 1 micron. The presence of larger crystals, e.g., those of an equilibrium primary phase, does not produce significantly different x-ray diffraction patterns. In the presence of microcrystalline quenched materials, well-formed crystalline phases are readily distinguished using the polarizing-light microscope, though not in x-ray diffraction analysis. The microscope technique, therefore, has unique applications in determining liquid-solid transitions in systems where glasses are not formed.

3. X-RAY METHODS

The principal application of x-ray analysis in constructing equilibrium-phase diagrams has been confined in the past chiefly to metal systems. Two general methods are used for locating phase boundaries, the "disappearing-phase method" and the "parametric method." The techniques involved are equally applicable to the investigation of nonmetallic systems.[3,4]

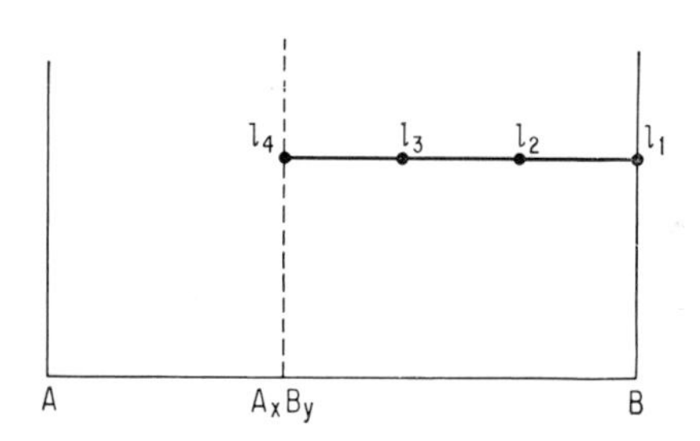

FIG. 1. Application of lever rule for determination of A_xB_y composition.

Disappearing-phase Method. The "disappearing-phase method" is essentially an adaptation of the Schreinemakers method in a restricted sense. In the Schreinemakers method, analyses are obtained for several wet residues separated from a partly crystallized mixture. Extrapolation of a line from the composition of the initial mixture through the compositions of the wet residues terminates with the composition of the dry residue. In x-ray diffraction analysis, as the intensities of the principal lines for one of two coexisting phases disappear, the extrapolation to the composition at which zero intensity is expected indicates the composition of the remaining phase.

If, as shown in Fig. 1, the compound A_xB_y exists only as a pure phase, i.e., does not occur with variable composition as a function of temperature, lever-rule analyses of diffraction data at several composition points between A_xB_y and B and between A and A_xB_y will lead to a determination of the formula of A_xB_y. Assume that the diffraction patterns of equilibrated solids having compositions at l_2 and l_3 indicate the presence of 80 and 60 mole per cent B, respectively, in the presence of the two compounds A_xB_y and B. Assume that the relative intensities of the diffraction lines

I_A and I_B produced by B and A_xB_y are proportional to the lengths of the tie-line fractions

$$l_2l_1/l_4l_1 \quad \text{and} \quad l_3l_1/l_4l_1$$

and that I_B, the per cent intensity of B at composition $l_2 = 67$ per cent, and that likewise at the composition l_3, $I_B = 33$ per cent. Then $I_B = 0$ is expected at a composition containing 40 mole per cent B, or the compound A_xB_y has the formula $3A \cdot 2B$ or A_3B_2. A similar set of computations for compositions between A and A_xB_y can be made for verification. If A_xB_y exists over a significant composition range, the formula estimates derived from mixtures in A-A_xB_y and A_xB_y-B will not be identical. Composition variability at various temperatures may be determined by this method. Quenched specimens in which high-temperature equilibrium phases are preserved may be examined as above for the detection of composition variation. Similar procedures may be applied in high-temperature x-ray diffraction experiments (see Chaps. 13 and 14).

The disappearing-phase method is applicable to the determination of the location of peritectic or "uneven-reaction" boundary curves in ternary systems, i.e., those in which reactions such as A + liquid $\leftrightarrows$ B + liquid occur. Since liquids of original

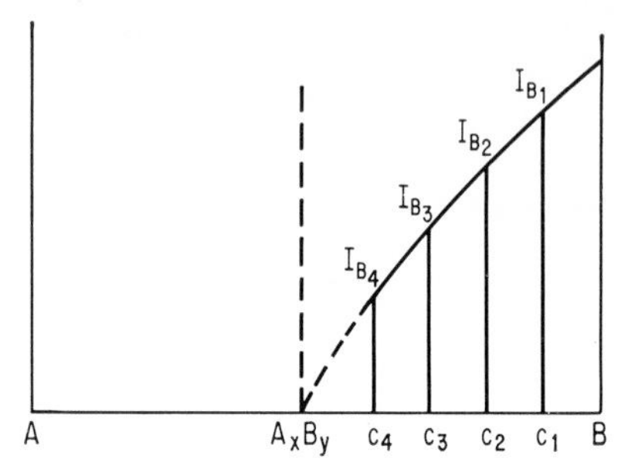

FIG. 2. Relative intensities of x-ray reflections for compositions A_xB_y-B.

compositions in primary phase A cease to crystallize A as the liquid reaches the boundary curve, quenched specimens at various isotherms in the primary-phase field of A are amenable to the disappearing-phase method of analysis for location of the boundary curves separating primary phases A and B.

The disappearing-phase method is suitable for a preliminary estimation of the composition of mixed phases but is chiefly useful in minimizing the number of experiments to be conducted subsequently. The effects of scattering and absorption phenomena may result in a nonlinear extrapolation. Assume that the relative intensity of phase B diffraction lines produced from equilibrated mixtures $c_1 \cdots c_4$ are represented as in Fig. 2 by $I_{B_1} \cdots I_{B_4}$. Then graphical extrapolation through points $I_{B_1} \cdots I_{B_4}$ indicates that phase B disappears at composition A_xB_y and that x and y are not small whole numbers. The composition of the phase A_xB_y must then be verified on the basis of several additional experiments. Otherwise the determination represents a gross estimate of the phase composition or may indicate the existence of a nonstoichiometric phase. The technique may be applied to produce very accurate results if calibration curves are established from a series of synthetic mixtures. However, establishing the calibration curves may require a sufficient amount of effort that the utility of the method in obtaining a preliminary estimate of phase composition by a simple and rapid method is vitiated. Several other factors, such as difficulties in obtaining particle randomization, preferred-orientation effects, and differential-absorption factors, further restrict the useful application of the disappearing-phase method. In application to ternary or more complex systems the disappearing-phase method becomes most useful chiefly by making it possible to reduce the number of experiments required to establish the compositions of some boundary paths and of complex solid compounds in the limiting systems or formed from all the components, e.g., a ternary compound such as $2Li_2O{\cdot}5K_2O{\cdot}7SiO_2$ in the system Li_2O-K_2O-SiO_2.

Parametric Method. According to Barrett,[3] the most precise location of phase boundaries in metal systems involves the use of lattice-spacing measurements. Lattice parameters generally change almost linearly as a function of composition variation within a single-phase region, i.e., according to Vegard's rule. Even if a nonlinear smooth curve of lattice parameters is produced at various compositions in a single-phase region, a correlation of their values can provide very useful information with respect to determination of solubility curves by indicating the composition of phase boundaries. Assume that, as in Fig. 3, specimens of composition R have been annealed and quenched in the temperature interval T_1T_2, so that solid solutions of AC_2 are produced coexisting with solid solutions of AB_2. If the lattice parameters of solid solutions in the composition region $S_1 \cdots S_4$ have been determined for known compositions, then measured lattice parameters of solid solutions $S_1 \cdots S_4$ in quenched specimens at R indicate the compositions of $S_1 \cdots S_4$ and establishment of the equilibrium solubility curve.

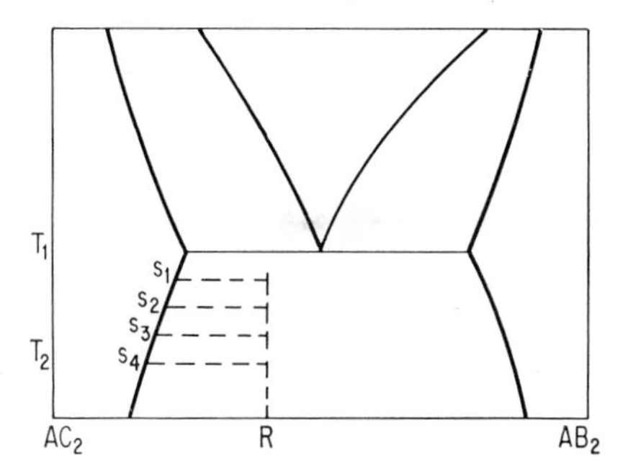

Fig. 3. Determination of equilibrium solubility curve of AB_2 in AC_2.

4. TERNARY AND POLYCOMPONENT SYSTEMS

If, in attempting to employ x-ray diffraction analysis in the investigation of phase behavior in complex multicomponent systems, one can obtain specimens which have crystallized from the liquid state, the task is simplified, for equilibrium will have been achieved in the liquid state. Correlations of thermal and phase-identification data usually indicate whether equilibrium crystal phases were formed from the liquid state or not. Then preliminary estimates regarding the nature of the system will be obtained by identification of the solid phases produced as liquid mixtures crystallize. By judicious choice of the number and variety of compositions investigated, one may, with a minimal number of experiments, establish the identity of the subsystems, often called compatibility triangles. Such information, coupled with tentative estimates regarding the liquidus profiles, is invaluable in planning the experiments required for further detailed description of a system. Static experiments can then be devised for determining the temperatures and compositions of invariant points. From x-ray analyses of solid crystallized mixtures of various compositions, inferences are drawn regarding the character of the subsystems. In an example, let us assume that in system A-B-C (Fig. 4) test specimens having compositions in each of the triangles 1-5 are crystallized from the liquid state. Assume that the products of crystallization in triangle 1 are A, AC, and AB; in triangles 2 and 3 they are AB, AC, and C; and in triangles 4 and 5 they are AB, B, and C. These results indicate that the system A-B-C contains the subsystems A-AB-AC, AB-AC-C, and AB-B-C. They also indicate that the compounds AB and AC probably melt congruently. If, as test compositions in triangle 1 are prepared closer to line AB-AC, phase A disappears, the quasi-binary character of the section AB-AC is suggested, while if in crystallized melts close to AB-AC, phase A persists, one can infer that AB-AC is not quasi-binary and that either or both compounds AC and AB do not melt congruently.

Let us now consider the more complex ternary system shown in Fig. 5 in order to estimate the kind of information which diffraction data can provide in the initial

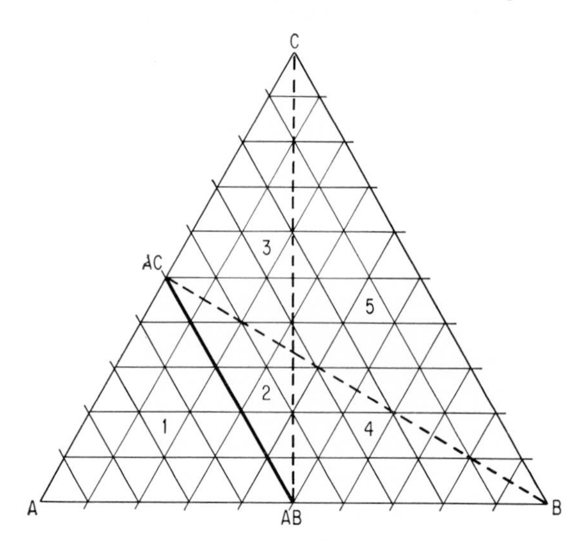

FIG. 4. Possible subsystems in system A-B-C.

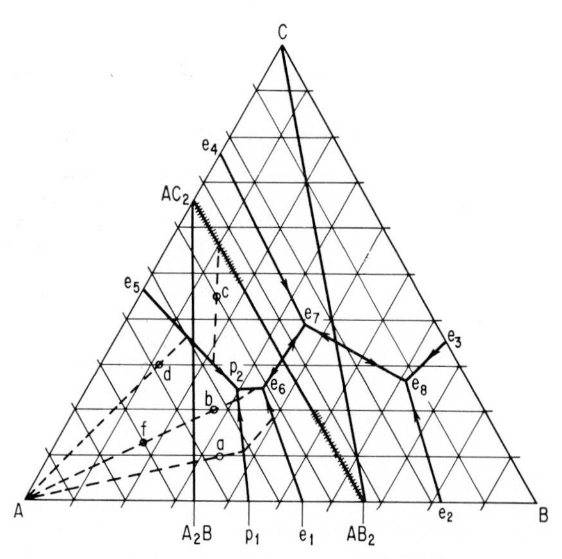

FIG. 5. Tie lines a-d in system A-B-C.

stages of an experimental study. We shall assume that invariant equilibrium points in the phase diagram A-B-C will ultimately be located as shown in Fig. 5. No intermediate compounds are formed from components B and C; a single intermediate compound AC_2, melting congruently, occurs in the system A-C; the congruently melting compound AB_2 and the incongruently melting compound A_2B are formed from components A and B. A careful examination of several crystalline mixtures cooled from the liquid state can be expected to furnish much information about equilibria in the system A-B-C.

Examples. 1. All crystallized specimens having compositions within the triangle AB_2-B-C contain only the pure solid phases AB_2, B, and C. These results indicate that the compounds AB_2, B, and C form a subsystem, that AB_2 probably melts congruently, and that the section AB_2-C is a quasi-binary system. Under these circumstances, a single invariant point, the eutectic e_8, can occur in AB_2-B-C. It may be possible to estimate its approximate composition by examination of the crystallized mixtures. Morphological data, obtained from petrographic or metallographic methods, may reveal the domains of each of the primary phases AB_2, B, and C, as well as the composition of the eutectic.

2. Assume that AC_2 and AB_2 form extensive but limited solid solutions exhibiting maximum solubility at the solidus, as shown in Figs. 3 and 5. In general, lattice constants of AB_2 and AC_2 will change as a function of solute concentration. Therefore, x-ray data obtained from crystallized specimens having compositions intermediate between AB_2 and AC_2 can be examined for lattice-spacing changes and correlated employing the parametric method. Because some exsolution at temperature below T_1 is to be expected when the exsolution curve exhibits considerable slope, one cannot expect to obtain data which indicate concentrations of maximum solubility of AB_2 and AC_2 except by static methods.

3. Occurrence of solid solutions of AB_2 and AC_2 indicates that inferences drawn regarding the subsystem AB_2-AC_2-C can be made from phase analyses of mixtures having compositions in triangle AB_2-B-C in addition to those in AB_2-AC_2-C. Mixtures in triangle AB_2-AC_2-C crystallizing primary-phase AC_2 solid solutions will solidify before the liquid fraction attains the composition e_7 and may not contain detectable concentrations of AB_2 or C. Mixtures crystallizing primary-phase AB_2 solid solutions will behave similarly, producing possibly undetectable amounts of AC_2 or C. The identity of the subsystem AB_2-AC_2-C may thus be equivocal without the conclusion based on other data that AB_2-C is quasi-binary.

4. Much information about phase behavior with the triangles A_2B-AC_2-AB_2 and A-A_2B-AC_2 can be obtained from x-ray analyses of specimens crystallizing with triangle A_2B-AC_2-AB_2. The solid-solution formation along AB_2-AC_2 and the melting relations of A_2B will cause mixtures within A_2B-AB_2-AC_2 to undergo a variety of crystallization reactions. Depending on the character and extent of the solid solution and the melting-freezing behavior of A_2B, x-ray analysis may furnish very informative phase data. Crystallization in polycomponent systems often results in the formation of final products which are in disequilibrium. Identification of the crystalline phases in the final crystallized mixture provides useful inferences as to the nature of the equilibrium-phase diagram. Assume that in the system A-B-C the following crystallization mechanisms occur:

a. Liquids with original composition a reach curve p_1p_2, then e_1e_6, and will solidify before reaching e_6. On examination of the crystallized mixture, one will find present the phases A, A_2B, AB_2 solid solution, and possibly some AC_2 solid solution.

b. Liquids with original compositions of b or f will reach curve p_1p_2, then p_2e_6, and solidify at or near e_6. The final crystalline solid will contain the solid phases A, A_2B, AC_2 solid solution, and AB_2 solid solution.

c. Liquids with original compositions of c may or may not reach curve e_5p_2, depending on the behavior and composition range of the AC_2 solid solution. If the liquid reaches the transition curve e_5p_2, it may or may not reach p_2e_6, again depending on the solid solution. If curve p_2e_6 is reached, solidification will occur before the liquids reach e_6. Solid phases AC_2 solid solution, A, A_2B, and possibly small amounts of AB_2 solid solution will be present in the crystallized mixture.

d. Liquids with original compositions of d will reach curve e_5p_2. Crystallization from that point on will be essentially the same as in c above.

On identification of the solid phases produced during the crystallization of liquids of compositions a, b, c, d, and f, along with rough estimates of the relative quantities of each phase, one could deduce several characteristics of the system:

(1) The presence of compound A in crystallized mixtures within A_2B-AB_2-AC_2 indicates that the compound A_2B melts incongruently to A + liquid and therefore that the section A_2B-AC_2 is not quasi-binary. It also indicates the corollary that no invariant equilibrium points are to be found in the composition triangle A-A_2B-AC_2.

(2) Two invariant points p_2 and e_6 occur in the composition triangle A_2B-AB_2-AC_2.

(3) If it is established that AB_2 and AC_2 exhibit limited mutual solubility and therefore precipitate from liquids in two separate primary-phase domains, the identity of the solid phases present at the invariant points p_2 and e_6 is established. For p_2 they are the solid phases A, A_2B, and AC_2 solid solution, while for e_6 they are A_2B, AB_2 solid solution, and AC_2 solid solution.

This limited discussion demonstrates a few of the ways in which x-ray diffraction analyses may be used in the initial stages of an investigation for rapidly establishing some of the principal features of a system as well as for providing a basis for minimizing the number of experiments to be conducted subsequently.

Reference Standards in X-ray Analysis. While the number of reference patterns for crystalline solid compounds is already very large, phase investigations leading to the construction of new constitution diagrams also frequently lead to the discovery of compounds which have not previously been described. One of the important parts of such investigations consists of defining the crystallographic properties of new compounds. Identification of compounds whose properties are already established is greatly aided with the large reference files now available, such as the ASTM files, Structure Reports, National Bureau of Standards Circulars, the *National Research Council Bulletin* 118, as well as the data collections which may be located with the aid of *Chemical Abstracts* or *Nuclear Science Abstracts*. General analysis methods using the ASTM files, as well as the inherent limitations in the use of such files related to difficulties in making unequivocal identifications because of solid-solution formation, isomorphism, or structural similarities, are discussed by Klug and Alexander,[5] as well as in Chap. 11 of this handbook.

Resolution of x-ray diffraction data can be aided greatly by the use of other analytical tools, particularly with the polarizing-light microscope if transparent crystals are formed, or otherwise with metallographic instruments. The disappearing-phase method described above is useful in leading to an estimate of the stoichiometry of unidentified compounds. On arriving at such an estimate, an investigator should then rely on synthesis methods for preparation of pure single-phase crystals of the new compound. Zachariasen employed a method of estimating the formula of newly discovered crystalline fluoride complex compounds, in which the numbers of cations and anions per unit cell are calculated.[6] For compounds formed from the alkali fluorides and the tetrafluorides, UF_4 or ThF_4,

$$N_A = \frac{V - 4N_XV_F}{V_A + V_F} \qquad N_F = \frac{V + 4N_XV_A}{V_A + V_F}$$

or for the trifluorides, LaF_3 or UF_3,

$$N_A = \frac{V - 3N_XV_F}{V_A + V_F} \qquad N_F = \frac{V + 3N_XV_A}{V_A + V_F}$$

where N_A and N_F are the number of alkali atoms and the number of fluorine atoms per unit cell, N_X the number of heavy-metal atoms per unit cell, V = the volume of the unit cell, and V_A and V_F the volume requirement of the alkali atom and the fluorine atom. Using the results of these equations along with the gross composition of the specimens as prepared, Zachariasen estimated formulas for as many as five intermediate compounds in the fluoride binary systems. This method devised by Zachariasen is limited by the following restrictions: the space group and unit cell of the compound must be known, and the method is applicable chiefly to compounds in which the anions are large with respect to the cations. In the restricted cases where the method is applicable, it is useful in lieu of additional analyses.

5. NONSTOICHIOMETRIC COMPOUNDS

Detailed investigations of phase equilibria often show that many compounds exist whose composition varies as a function of both temperature and composition. Modes of composition variation for such compounds, often referred to as berthollides, were described in three general classes by Anderson:[7]

1. Substitutional solid solution. An excess of one component in a binary compound can be situated on sites vacated by the other.
2. Interstitial solid solution. Atoms of one sort may occupy normally vacant sites which afford them a reasonable environment.
3. Subtractive solid solution. Ions of either sort, or both simultaneously, may be absent from the crystal lattice.

It is obvious that within a nonstoichiometric phase region the structure of the solid phase changes continuously with composition and the variation about a distinct stoichiometric formula may be large or small. In addition, the effect on the measurable crystal properties may or may not be significant. Determination of the actual composition of the compound cannot be obtained from information about the crystal unit cell because x-ray diffraction data are statistical and thus characteristically insensitive to small changes in composition. It is thus apparent that determination of nonstoichiometry is a part of the equilibrium-phase problem and is to be approached in much the same way as the rest of the problem. In determining composition variability of a particular compound good synthesis techniques, accompanied by static methods, must be employed to determine the single-phase composition-temperature limits of the compound. In an interesting system, recently reported by Sturm,[3] a single intermediate compound of undetermined stoichiometry was seen to form from CrF_2 and CrF_3. As single-crystal data became available and crystallographic investigations began, it appeared that the space group and density considerations required that the formula be $CrF_2 \cdot CrF_3$, though phase data indicated that equimolar mixtures of CrF_2 and CrF_3 contained two phases when equilibrated in the solid state. Further detailed examination of solid-state phase relationships finally established that a nonstoichiometric compound of CrF_2 and CrF_3 was formed. The generic formula of the crystalline phase was $CrF_2 \cdot CrF_3$, although the phase was routinely Cr^{3+} deficient and did not exist as a single phase at compositions consisting of greater than 45 mole per cent CrF_3, and further it could exist over a composition range of several mole per cent, varying somewhat as a function of temperature. The results of the phase investigation by Sturm and the crystallographic investigation conducted concurrently by Steinfink and Burns[9] are an example of the interdependence of phase and crystallographic investigations often necessary in obtaining a good understanding of solid-state equilibria.

X-ray diffraction studies of nonstoichiometric solid solutions have recently disclosed that such solids are much less homogeneous than was previously supposed. Examinations of single crystals of nonstoichiometric oxide solid solutions using high-resolution diffraction equipment, as Wadsley has pointed out in two reviews,[10,11] have shown that many of these materials are actually constituted of complex stoichiometric compounds. Such application of x-ray methods to the investigation of solid-state chemistry constitutes a unique method for the study of complex phase equilibria and gives promise of providing much rich detail never before available for many systems. The results of x-ray diffraction analysis of the crystal phases obtained in static-method experiments provide the analytical data required to define the extent of composition variation of a nonstoichiometric compound, especially if high-temperature equilibrium phases are preserved in quenching. The process can be shortened considerably if the number and identity of solid phases in equilibrium at various temperatures are determined in situ at high temperatures. High-temperature diffractometry (cf. Chaps. 13 and 14) has unique application where other experimental methods have been unsuccessful, particularly in two applications: (1) where high-temperature polymorphs are not preserved in either dynamic or static methods of investigation, i.e., a high-temperature form of a crystalline phase cannot be cooled quickly enough to determine its properties; and (2) where metastable phases are so readily formed that it is difficult to prevent their nucleation. In each of these two cases, observation of equilibrated materials at high temperatures via high-temperature x-ray diffractometers provides the equilibrium-property data. Utmost care in maintaining inert atmospheres within the high-temperature diffractometers is necessary for a large group of materials. Small amounts of reactive gases or vapors within the diffractometer can markedly affect the results obtained since so few surface layers of crystalline phases are involved in producing the observed diffraction data.

X-ray Analysis in Solid-state Equilibrium Studies. Achievement of equilibria in solid-state reactions may require very long periods of time for systems constituted of refractory materials, such as refractory metals, oxides, nitrides, and carbides. In attempting to establish the solid-state equilibria in the refractory nonmetal systems, it has become routine to maintain densely packed mixtures of the reactants for some specific time-temperature combination, then examine for evidence of the extent of reaction. On the basis of such an estimate, the partly reacted specimen is reduced to a homogeneous powder, repacked, and the heating process repeated. The operations are repeated until some evidence is observed that equilibrium has been achieved, such as an x-ray analysis showing the absence of the reactants. In such experimental work, phase-identification data, as are available in x-ray and/or petrographic analysis, are invaluable in determining the reaction kinetics. Sintering mechanisms as well as kinetics of solid-state reactions are also demonstrated by such analyses.

A great increase has come in the last few years in the number of equilibrium-phase diagrams reported as well as in the detail with which the investigations were concerned. This is due considerably to the influence of x-ray analysis on such studies. X-ray and optical methods provide reinforcing identification data which, together with the classical thermodynamic methods, make possible highly accurate and detailed descriptions of the equilibrium relationships for a vast group of materials.

REFERENCES CITED

1. John E. Ricci, *The Phase Rule and Heterogeneous Equilibrium*, D. Van Nostrand Company, Inc., Princeton, N.J., 1951.
2. K. Lonsdale, *Crystals and X-rays*, G. Bell & Sons, Ltd., London, 1948.
3. Charles S. Barrett, *Structure of Metals*, 2d ed., p. 196, McGraw-Hill Book Company, New York, 1952.
4. E. A. Owen, chap. 28 in *X-ray Diffraction by Polycrystalline Materials*, H. S. Peiser, H. P. Rooksby and A. J. C. Wilson (eds.), Institute of Physics, London, 1955.
5. Harold P. Klug and Leroy E. Alexander, *X-ray Diffraction Procedures for Polycrystalline and Amorphous Materials*, pp. 391–410, John Wiley & Sons, Inc., New York, 1954.
6. W. H. Zachariasen, *J. Am. Chem. Soc.*, **70**:2147 (1948).
7. J. S. Anderson, *Rept. Progr. Chem.* (*Chem. Soc., London*), **43**:104 (1946).
8. B. J. Sturm, *Inorg. Chem.*, **1**:665 (1962).
9. H. Steinfink and J. H. Burns, *Acta Cryst.*, **17**:828 (1964).
10. A. D. Wadsley, *Rev. Pure Appl. Chem.*, **5**:165 (1955).
11. A. D. Wadsley, "Non-stoichiometric Metal Oxides, Order and Disorder," presented at 141st National Meeting of American Chemical Society, Washington, D.C., Mar. 20–29, 1962.

Chapter 21

CHARACTERIZATION OF POLYMERS

W. O. Statton

E. I. du Pont de Nemours & Company

1. INTRODUCTION

No Best Experimental Method. It is impossible to recommend one particular technique as ideal or most suitable for the study of polymers. There are many variables which govern such a choice. The choice may depend on the form of the sample (bulk, film, or fiber), its state of orientation, its absorption coefficient, one's familiarity with its diffraction characteristics, the nature of the measurements desired, and, of course, the instrumentation available in the laboratory. The following are general statements which may provide a guide in this choice.

For survey purposes and for unfamiliar polymers, film techniques are often preferred. If the sample has molecular orientation with respect to one or more of its axes, film techniques are often preferred in order to record more of the diffraction at one time. For detailed study of a familiar polymer, however, counting techniques are often preferred in order to obtain quantitative data directly and quickly. When the polymer contains heavy atoms, as in polyvinyl chloride, the transmission technique for obtaining the diffraction on films or with counters is not desirable, and reflection with counters is best. For orientation measurements, a special sample rotation is necessary when counters are used; or when film is used, it must be rotated on the photometering instrument. Conversely, when crystallinity studies are desired on oriented material, a sample rotator or randomizer is necessary. Since different polymer laboratories are apt to have many possible combinations of these variables, no fixed rules can be given for laboratory techniques. Instead, this chapter will present suggestions for sample preparation and detailed descriptions of the large variety of measurements which can be obtained. Knowing the type of sample at hand and the measurements which are desired will then usually be sufficient to determine the choice of the preferred technique.

No basic changes in the standard instrumentation are needed for study of polymers. Film techniques are apt to emphasize the use of flat-plate cameras for routine study, and a cylindrical camera is also desirable for measuring layer lines in the patterns for oriented materials. A recording microphotometer is necessary for reducing the film blackening to quantitative intensity readings, and it must be able to provide both radial and azimuthal scans. For rapid survey work using films, emulsions which are fast and large-grained are preferable (e.g., Kodak No-screen or Ilford G). For quantitative measurements from films, slower, fine-grained emulsions are needed (e.g., Kodak type AA or Ilford B). Counting techniques for polymers do not require abnormal procedures except that sample preparation and mounting are sometimes troublesome.

Most polymer studies use x-ray targets of copper since its wavelength of 1.54 Å provides good dispersion of polymer diffractions, which usually have d spacings of about the same size. Copper targets are also used most frequently for small-angle studies, although chromium is sometimes used to give better dispersion of long periods.

Since most organic polymers contain only C, H, N, and O atoms, the absorption coefficient is reasonably low. It turns out that a sample thickness of about 0.020 in. is about ideal for most routine wide-angle transmission studies, and about 0.040 in. is good for small-angle studies.

No Best Interpretation. It is impossible to provide an interpretation of polymer diffraction patterns in terms of exact details of the arrangement of the long molecules for their entire length. There is perhaps no other area of x-ray diffraction study that has so much uncertainty and, at the present moment, so much controversy associated with it as the study of polymers. There are several straightforward reasons for this: (1) High-polymer molecules, by definition, contain hundreds or thousands of atoms connected together by strong covalent bonds into an extra-long chainlike molecule hundreds or thousands of angstroms in length. (2) The diffraction patterns for polymers are always very much poorer in quality than for most other solids since they show broadened peaks and few, if any, higher orders. In addition, they usually contain much diffuse scattering. (3) The character of the diffraction pattern is often quite variable, depending upon the composition and/or history of the polymer. (This variability, of course, is one major reason for wanting to study polymers by x-ray techniques.) (4) Recent experimental findings have caused a serious questioning of the older concepts of polymer aggregation. (5) Recent theoretical interpretations of diffraction have caused a serious questioning of the model which had been based on earlier interpretations of diffraction.

The fact that uncertainties or controversies exist does not rule out any of the importance of the study of polymer x-ray diffraction. On the contrary, it points out the need for doing much more careful and critical work and the need for being alert to the traps or pitfalls of allowing concepts and models to grow beyond their original and proper use until they become "truth." Nor does the existence of the interpretative uncertainties detract in any way from the value of comparing one polymer sample with another by some x-ray criterion or measurement. A great variety of useful measurements can be made on polymer diffraction patterns; the following sections will discuss them and give the modicum of interpretation that is required, fully realizing that the interpretation may be transitory but the measurement is of permanent value as a characterizing technique. The value of these measurements is shown by the simple fact that nearly every laboratory studying polymers in any form relies upon x-ray diffraction techniques to assist in research, development, and sometimes even production control.

2. SAMPLE PREPARATION

Bulk Polymer. If the polymer is a powder, it can be treated by the standard technique of lightly pressing a pellet. No great pressure should be applied which might generate heat or otherwise deform the internal structure of a plastic. Alternatively, thin-walled glass capillaries can be used to contain the powder, or a tiny envelope can be made from thin sheets of cellophane or Mylar* film. As a last resort, rods can be rolled with a noncrystalline adhesive binder like Duco† cement, remembering that the binder will contribute to the diffuse scattering which also arises from the polymer and also remembering that the solvent of the binder may change the polymer and spoil the crystallinity judgment which is sought.

Since many polymers are quite tough and resist breaking or deformation, there are sometimes difficulties in reducing the size of large chunks or objects formed by molding or extrusion. Sometimes a sample can be inserted into a machinist's lathe to obtain thin turnings or sections, taking care to prevent heat rise during the cutting operation.

* Du Pont trademark for polyester film.

† Du Pont trademark.

Another possibility is to chill the chunk in liquid nitrogen and follow with a hammer blow; brittle fracture without distortion can usually be caused by this method.

Polymer Films. When polymer solutions are cast into a thin film, or a polymer melt is extruded or cast into a thin film, the requirements of sampling are made more complex. Because special alignment of the molecules may be present owing to the extrusion or extension (drawing, to be discussed in Sec. 8), special alignment of the sample in the x-ray beam is usually sought.

Since the film is usually quite thin, many layers have to be stacked together in order to have reasonable exposure times or counting rates. A convenient way to cut the film into strips for stacking is shown in Fig. 1.[1] Data can then be obtained and related to the axes of the film. One set of strips is cut parallel to the deformation direction and stacked so that the x-ray beam can be sent either perpendicular or parallel to the plane of the film. Another set of strips is cut perpendicular to the deformation direction and stacked so that the x-ray beam can be sent parallel to the plane of the film. These samples provide three different directional diffraction patterns taken along three mutually perpendicular axes and can be called through, edge, and end patterns. If there is high molecular orientation with respect to the deformation direction, these patterns are somewhat analogous to rotation patterns along the three major axes of a single crystal. If counting techniques are to be used in conjunction with a single-crystal orienter,[2] a convenient procedure of sample preparation consists of cutting a number of ¼- by 1-in. film strips with the long direction normal to the direction of stretch. These pieces are compactly stacked in a vise clamp having a ¼-in.-wide depression to a depth of about 1/16 in. The clamp is closed and the lamination trimmed flush with the surface using a razor blade. Duco cement is applied to the trimmed edge to hold the laminations together, and when dry, a rectangular sample 1/16 by 1/16 by ¼ in. is removed. The long axis of the rectangle is the stretch direction by this technique.

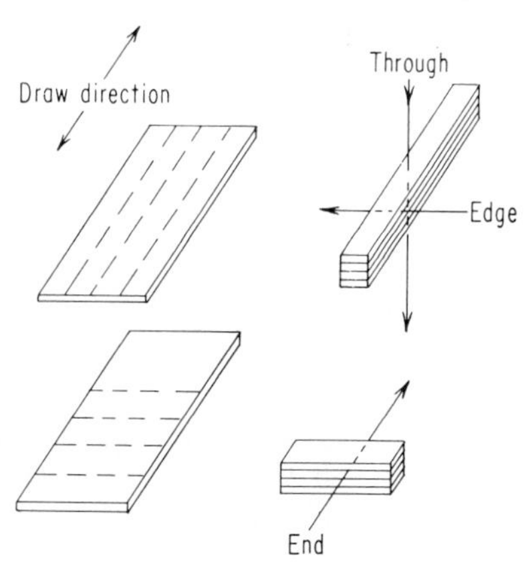

Fig. 1. Stacking of oriented polymer film strips to allow tridirectional diffraction studies.[1]

Fibers. The special shape of a fiber somewhat dictates the way in which it is handled for x-ray study. Since the diameter is usually so very small, many filaments are combined except for the rare studies with a microcamera or when extremely precise orientation measurements are needed (to be discussed later in Sec. 8). Since the amount of the alignment (orientation) of the molecules with respect to the fiber axis is usually sought, effort is made to keep all filaments parallel to each other and perpendicular to the x-ray beam for transmission techniques, or parallel to each other and in a plane if reflection techniques are used.

For counting techniques, continuous filaments can be readily wrapped in a neat and proper fashion around a rectangular wire frame or a card with the center cut out, and if crimp is present, it can be removed by a small restraining force during wrapping. Cut, crimped staple filaments present a real problem for preparation of a proper sample for reflection. Individual filaments must be tediously manipulated and the ends of the fibers glued to the frame to keep them straight and in line.

For photographic techniques, a sample holder-pinhole combination has been devised which has proved to be quite useful.* As pictured in Fig. 2, a thick-walled stainless-steel cylinder has a lead insert through which is drilled or punched a proper-diameter pinhole. The barrel of the cylinder acts as the guard pinhole to remove the diffraction

* W. H. Warhus Co., 406 Rowland Park Blvd., Wilmington, Del.

of the lead. A shelf is placed below the exit of the barrel; the filaments are wound onto the shelf and will automatically place themselves parallel to each other and perpendicular to the x-ray beam if carefully done. The width of the shelf between the barrel and faceplate determines the sample thickness, so reasonable control of sample size and exposure time is available. Crimped staple is sometimes troublesome to straighten out, but it can be handled in this device much more satisfactorily than in preparing a sample for reflection-counting techniques since only a small area in front of the pinhole need be straightened.

Dynamic Diffraction Studies. It is sometimes desirable to obtain diffraction differences in a rapidly varying system, such as changes in crystallinity or orientation in a film or fiber, while it is undergoing formation or deformation. The sample size for such studies may often be too small to produce a proper diffraction pattern in an instantaneous exposure; so a "dynamic diffraction" study is performed in which the moving object is continually passing through the x-ray beam at equivalent places in its process. This provides a continual renewal of the sample, which is always at the x-ray beam at the same moment of its process history. Success with this technique depends, of course, on the validity of the assumptions that (1) the sampling is constant and represents the same state of structure at the point of interest throughout the exposure, and (2) the guidance or manipulation of the moving sample into the path of the x-ray beam does not alter the structure being investigated.

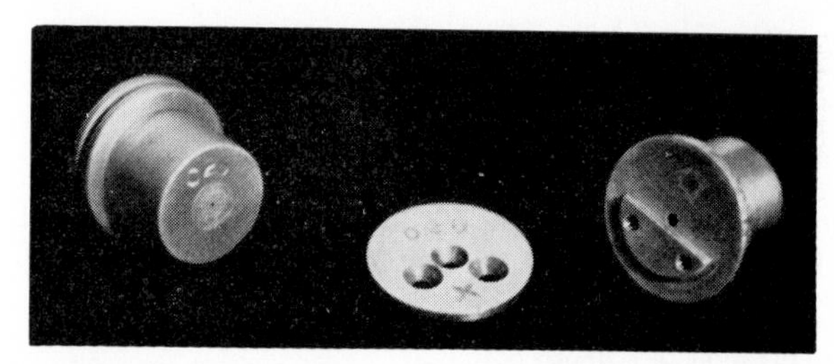

Fig. 2. Photograph of combination yarn holder–pinhole collimator.

3. MEASUREMENTS AND INTERPRETATIONS—WIDE-ANGLE STUDIES

Diffraction patterns are found to be quite variable as the result of different thermal, chemical, or mechanical treatments of the polymer. Any means of measuring this variation is therefore desirable. There are many examples that could be given to show the importance of these variations in relation to physical properties of the polymer; this is the usual motivation for careful study of polymer x-ray patterns. Sections 4 to 10 will not attempt to show these structure-property relationships but will attempt to show the great variety of measurements that can be made on polymer x-ray patterns, with comment on the possible meaning or structural interpretation of the measurements. Table 1 lists the x-ray parameters and observations which can be obtained.

It is helpful to review some of the known facts about polymers and their x-ray patterns which are important in structure interpretation:

1. Polymer molecules are very long, several hundred to several thousand angstroms in length, and are therefore chainlike.

2. Polymer chains are usually aligned by deformation and can often be induced into very high orientation with respect to the deformation direction.

3. Polymer diffraction patterns seldom show the sharpness or higher orders of diffraction that are typical of metals, salts, or low-molecular-weight organic crystals. The polymer crystals are therefore quite small or imperfect. "Crystallites" is the descriptive term used to describe this order.

4. Polymer patterns usually show a diffuse halo in addition to diffractions. This halo is somewhat like (but not so diffuse as) the halo from an amorphous glass. "Amorphous regions" is the usual descriptive term used to describe this disorder.

Many additional facts could be given, but they are of secondary importance to the above basic statements. It is important to remember that nothing is actually known about the exact conformation of molecules along their entire length. Items 3 and 4 above have traditionally been interpreted to mean that the long chains are alternating in and out of regions of order and disorder. This implies the existence of two definite regions or phases having characteristics of crystallinity and amorphousness. This is a model, only, but has been so useful that it has taken on aspects of reality. However, some alternative models have been proposed in recent years and will be mentioned. It is best to realize that the "two-phase model" is just a model which explains much of the data, but not necessarily all.

Table 1

X-ray parameter or observation	*Discussion section*
Amount of diffuse scattering	4. Crystallinity
Amount of sharp diffraction	4. Crystallinity
Changes in Bragg spacings	5. Crystallinity studies at elevated temperatures
Disappearance of sharp diffraction	5. Crystallinity studies at elevated temperatures
Line broadening	6. Crystallite size and perfection
Absence of $(hk0)$ reflections	7. Directional ordering
Absence of $(00l)$ reflections	7. Directional ordering
Arc length	8. Crystallite orientation
Shape of diffuse halo	9. Noncrystalline packing
Radial-intensity distribution	9. Noncrystalline packing

4. CRYSTALLINITY

It has been repeatedly shown that many of the most important properties of polymer systems are directly related to the structural feature called crystallinity, and therefore a measure of it is frequently sought. Crystallinity is a misused word, and it should be pointed out that the crystallinity value determined by x-rays may or may not agree with values obtained by density measurements, infrared absorption, etc. Because of this disagreement, it is urged that a modifying word be used to describe the measurement technique, e.g., x-ray crystallinity, density crystallinity, etc.

X-ray crystallinity can be judged *qualitatively* quite easily by one's eye if the patterns are studied by an experienced observer. A judgment is made of the fraction of the total blackening of the film which is in the sharp diffraction peaks. This visual comparison of intensities of sharp diffraction vs. diffuse scattering is surprisingly good, and a 10-point scale can be used for relative ranking of different samples. Such comparisons may be quite satisfactory for scouting research or routine process modifications using the film technique.

X-ray crystallinity can be judged *quantitatively* by determining the numbers involved in the above comparison. A great many ways have been devised to make these numerical assignments, and much controversy has been noted in the literature regarding the best method for obtaining these quantitative data. Since the procedures are often different for different polymers and are often different in various laboratories, it is risky to try to make comparisons on an *absolute* basis. The following will represent some of the major approaches to x-ray crystallinity measurements. It is not intended to be a complete bibliography of the large amount of work in this area, nor does it pass judgment on relative merits since each approach fulfills an obvious need and may or may not be applicable to other polymers or laboratories. It soon becomes obvious on studying the original literature that every method involves several basic assumptions which are open to question or dispute. This is unfortunate, and the introductory statement must be repeated with application to this measurement: "There is no one best method." What follows, therefore, is not a direct procedure for a novice to follow, but an outline of the various techniques with key references to the literature. The novice will be required to seek out the method most appealing or most applicable for his own situation.

The intensity scan can sometimes be separated into contributions from the sharp diffractions and diffuse halo, as sketched in Fig. 3.[3,4] A comparison of the relative areas under the resolved curves gives the "per cent crystallinity" by the use of an equation which gives the weight ratio of amorphous and crystalline material W_A/W_C:

$$\frac{W_A}{W_C} = K \frac{I_A}{I_{110} + I_{200}}$$

where K is a constant involving the relative scattering efficiencies of unit weight of amorphous and crystalline portions (usually taken to be unity, although the propriety

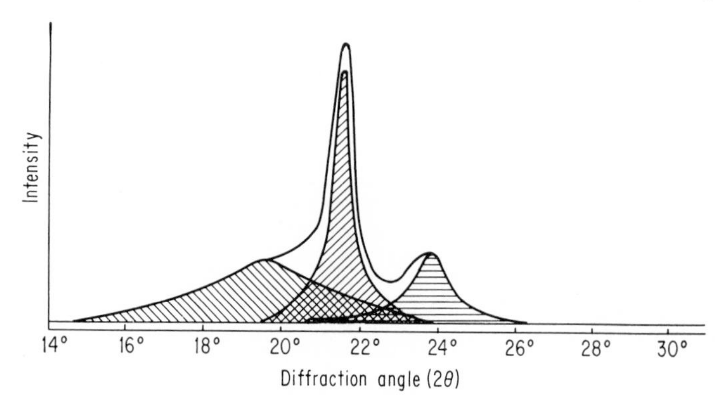

Fig. 3. Resolution of polyethylene diffraction pattern into areas to determine "per cent crystallinity."[3]

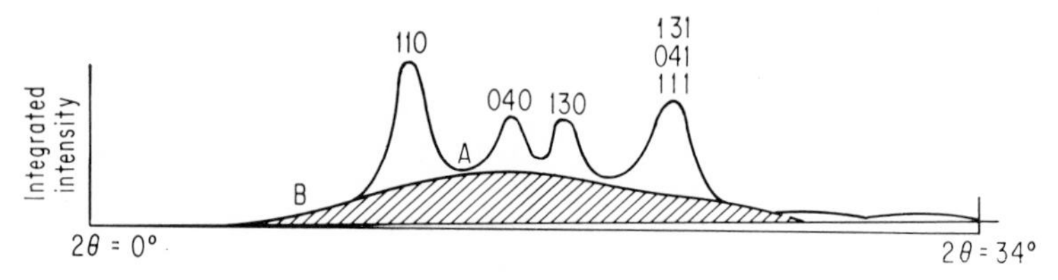

Fig. 4. Resolution of diffraction pattern of drawn polypropylene filaments. Shaded area: noncrystalline background; rise in background: incoherent scatter.[9]

of this has been disputed[5]). I_A is the area under the amorphous curve, and I_{110} and I_{200} are the areas under the 100 and 200 crystalline peaks, respectively, for polyethylene. Refinements have been given[6] to include all crystalline diffractions and revise the choice of background. Both the original and the refined procedures involve several quite important assumptions which are basic in the use of the method. Alternatively, a procedure is given[5,7,8] whereby only the amorphous background is measured in the solid polymer and compared with the molten state, again with several important assumptions involved.

Unfortunately, only a few polymers have their amorphous halo separated from the crystalline diffraction. For polymers with superimposed halo and diffractions, the choice of amorphous background becomes even more arbitrary and obtaining crystallinity values becomes still more complex. Several techniques have been proposed to cope with the situation. Figure 4 shows the drawing in of the noncrystalline background of the pattern from randomized sections of drawn polypropylene filaments.[9] Points A and B are used as reference points for determining the shape of the noncrystalline background, and the crystallinity of the sample is then equal to

$$\frac{\text{Area of crystalline fraction}}{\text{Area of crystalline fraction} + \text{area of amorphous fraction}}$$

(after correction for noncoincidence of the centers of gravity of the amorphous and crystalline reflections). In measurements of this type it is usually assumed that the shape of the noncrystalline background obtained in a high-temperature x-ray photograph of the melt is the same as that which would exist at room temperature for either oriented or unoriented polymers. However, detailed studies of this assumption[10,11] show that in (at least) polyethylene terephthalate and cellulosic fibers there is a

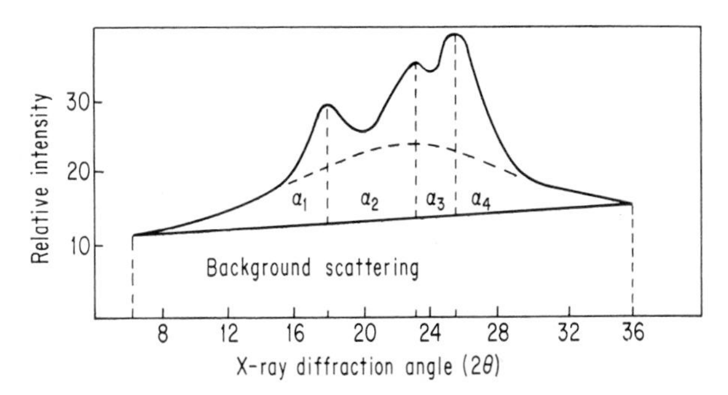

FIG. 5. X-ray diffraction curve of partially crystalline polyethylene terephthalate showing the manner of resolving the crystalline and amorphous scattering effects.[12]

skewed shape for the amorphous halo from drawn fibers and there may be unusual azimuthal intensity distributions, too. Such findings may rule out absolute crystallinity determinations, but they tell us much more about the arrangement of the amorphous segments and the state of aggregation in drawn fibers.

A method was developed which differs from the above graphical method for resolving the crystalline and amorphous diffraction effects.[12] As shown in Fig. 5 for polyethylene terephthalate, the necessity of estimating the amorphous scattering curve is eliminated by the assumption that the shape of this curve is independent of the degree of crystallinity. Lines are extended from the peaks to the background line (the latter is assumed linear between the chosen 2θ limits). These lines define four areas. A scaler-counter is used to totalize the counts within each of these four areas as well as for the background. After correction for absorption, diffraction angles, and temperature variation, these counts (areas) are converted to integrated intensities by the use of four simultaneous equations. Finally, per cent crystallinity is obtained in the usual way by

$$\text{Per cent crystallinity} = \frac{100 I_C}{I_C + K I_A}$$

where K is taken as unity.

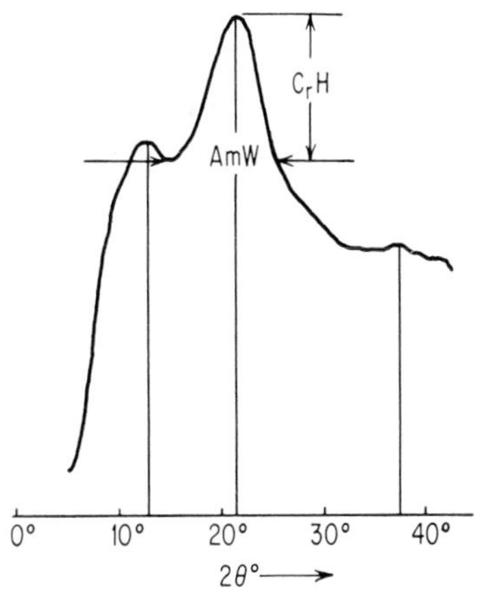

FIG. 6. Densitometer curve of x-ray diffraction from regenerated viscose rayon.[13]

Because the construction of the amorphous background curve is unavoidably arbitrary, successful searches have been made for other ways in which intensity curves could serve as a basis for quantitative crystallinity evaluation. Using the premise that increasing amorphousness tends to broaden the diffraction rings whereas increasing crystallinity increases the blackness of the rings, an index was devised[13] for cellulosics as shown in Fig. 6. The height of the main peak above its adjacent minimum is measured, called *CrH*, and considered to represent the crystallinity of the sample. The width of this main peak at the height of this minimum is also measured, in radians, called *AmW*, and considered to represent the amorphousness of the sample. The x-ray crystallinity *CrI* is then calculated from $CrI = 1 - [t\ (AmW/CrH)]$ where t is

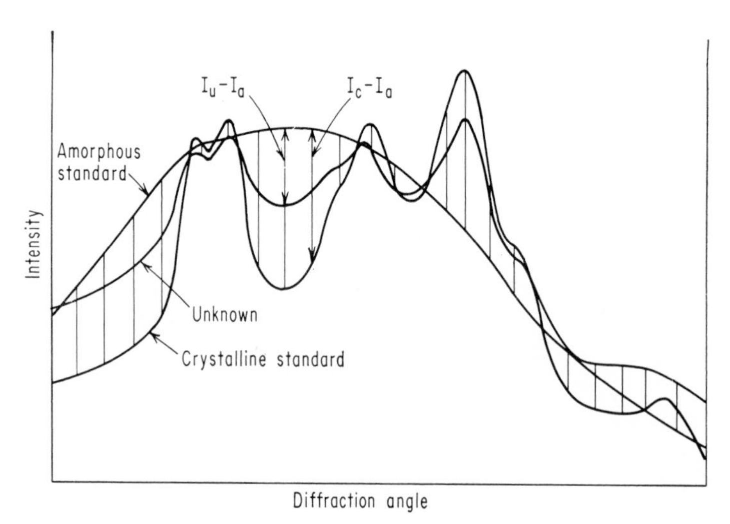

FIG. 7. Radial-intensity distribution of polyethylene terephthalate showing some of the incremental intensity differences used to calculate the crystallinity index.[15]

the scale factor relating the height of *CrH* in millimeters on the scan to full scale (total blackness). *CrI* is put forward as an empirical, dimensionless figure which represents the crystallinity of the cellulose as a whole.

Since every attempt to obtain an exact measure of the x-ray crystallinity is troubled by major assumptions which are not always free from doubt or dispute, there is much difficulty in obtaining an *absolute* x-ray crystallinity. A *relative* x-ray crystallinity value, however, does not have so many serious difficulties as an absolute measurement. All ratings can be compared with the most crystalline sample currently obtainable for a particular polymer. No absolute value need be known for this most crystalline extreme; all ratings are relative to it. Such an approach has been used to study cellulosics[14] and polyethylene terephthalate.[15] An example of the latter is shown in Fig. 7, in which the most extreme amorphous trace and the most extreme crystalline trace are used as standard traces. A sample with unknown crystallinity will fall somewhere between these extremes. Some measure of this difference will give a relative crystallinity index, and in contrast to the previously discussed crystallinity index, a large number of intensity readings are obtained at many increments along the traces. Intensity differences are calculated at each increment for the unknown and the standards and are handled as an xy function of each other, as shown in Fig. 8. Here the ordinate for each data point is the difference $(I_u - I_a)$, at some position i along the intensity

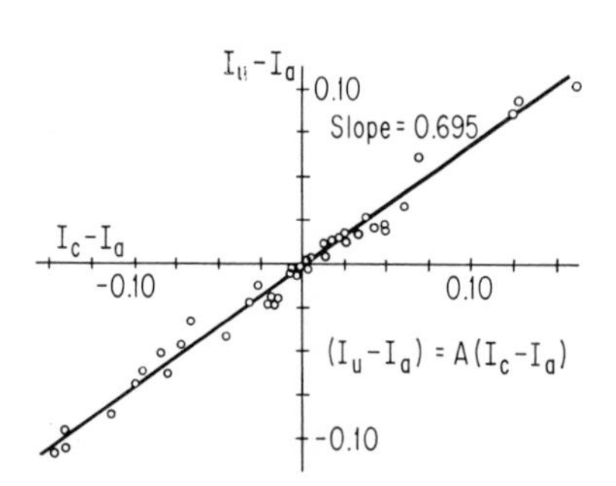

FIG. 8. Plot of incremental intensity differences used to determine a typical crystallinity index by the correlation method.[15]

curve of the unknown compared with the amorphous standard at this same position. The abscissa of the point is the corresponding difference $(I_c - I_a)$ between the intensities of the crystalline and amorphous standards. The equation for the line will be $(I_u - I_a)_i = A(I_c - I_a)_i$. The slope A will be given by

$$A = \frac{(I_u - I_a)_i}{(I_c - I_a)_i}$$

When the values of I_u approach I_c, the value of A will approach 1. On the other hand, if the values of I_u approach I_a, A becomes 0. Use of a small computer greatly simplifies the computation of the differences and best line through the data points. The slope can be converted to a "percentage relative crystallinity" or to some arbitrarily defined "crystallinity index." It is preferable not to use the term "per cent crystallinity" as it is too easily compared with the absolute crystallinities that are so often quoted. Since it is a relative number only, the word "index" is used. Since so few assumptions are involved in this relative method, it has great value in providing rapid, quantitative data in which the primary concern is to compare one sample with another, e.g., determining the effect of a processing variable.

5. CRYSTALLINITY STUDIES AT ELEVATED TEMPERATURES

Since many uses of polymers involve elevated temperatures, there is often a real need to determine the structure at these high temperatures. The only essential requirement is to have a camera or diffractometer attachment which will allow the diffraction pattern to be obtained while the sample is at the desired elevated temperature. These are commercially available* and are discussed in detail in Chaps. 13 and 14.

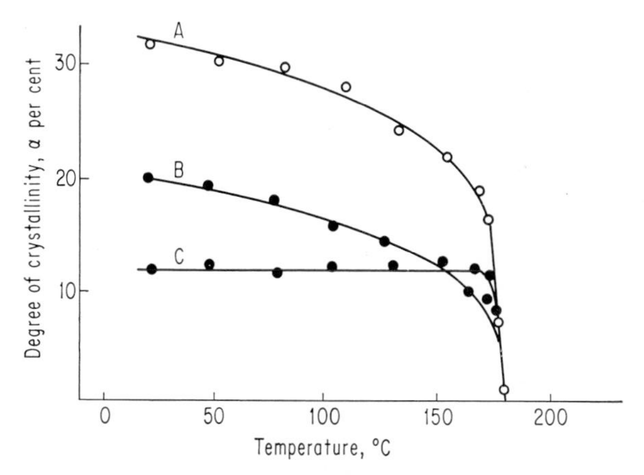

Fig. 9. The degrees of crystallization of a highly annealed polyurethane sample for successive heat-treatments. A = total crystallinity, B = crystallization in the van der Waals direction, C = crystallization in the hydrogen-bond direction.[16]

Any of the crystallinity determinations discussed in the previous section can, in principle, be obtained at elevated temperatures. However, very few such polymer studies have been reported. Typical results are shown in Fig. 9, in which the crystallinity is seen to decrease markedly at temperatures slightly below the melting point, and one direction of the crystal falls apart at lower temperatures than does the other.[16]

* W. H. Warhus Co., 406 Rowland Park Blvd., Wilmington, Del.

This illustrates the possibility of relating property behavior at high temperatures to crystallographic directions in the polymer.

Conversely, as the temperature is lowered for an elastomer,[17] there may be important differences in crystallinity, as shown in Fig. 10.

As the polymer is heated, there is a temperature value at which the last sharp diffraction is still detectable before the entire pattern changes to a halo, as shown in

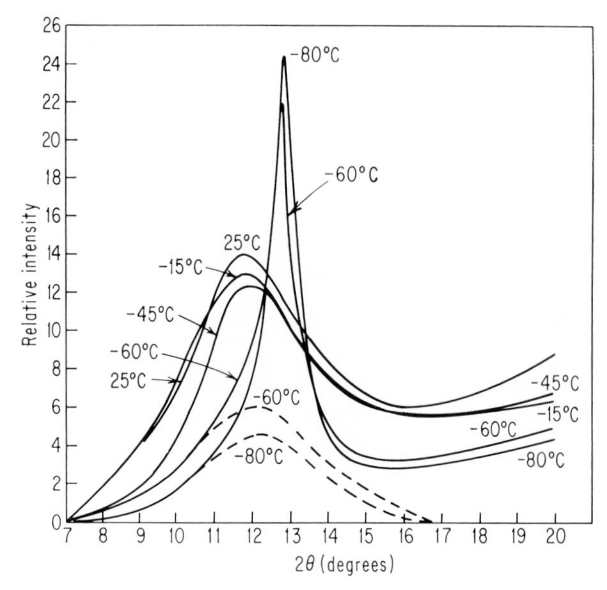

Fig. 10. Radial-intensity profile for unstretched silicone rubber at various temperatures.[17]

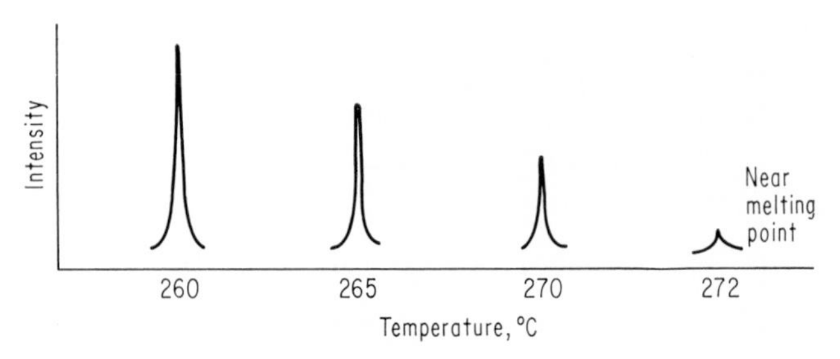

Fig. 11. Determination of "x-ray melting point" by observation of disappearance of diffraction of an experimental polymer. Scans repeated at elevated temperature for fixed angular range, 2θ = 19.0 to 21.0.

Fig. 11. This is a precise method for determining a melting point for the polymer and can be used for routine and precise measurements of $\pm 0.5°$ C. It should be remembered that this technique is *defined* as measuring the "x-ray crystalline melting point"; it may or may not agree with melting-point values obtained by other techniques. As in much other polymer work, the conditions of measurement may affect the outcome since true equilibrium conditions are seldom achieved. The conditions must therefore always be standardized and stated along with results. For instance, the x-ray crystalline melting point can be raised several degrees if a much slower heating rate is used.

As a crystalline polymer is heated, the Bragg spacings usually change. Lattice expansion coefficients can be calculated by measuring these changes and will usually vary with different directions in the crystal lattice, as shown in the results[18] for polycaprolactam in Fig. 12. X-ray expansion coefficients can be compared with dilatometric values as an indirect way to judge crystallinity,[19] but it is seldom done since x-ray data are far easier to obtain than dilatometric data, and both types of data are not often at hand simultaneously.

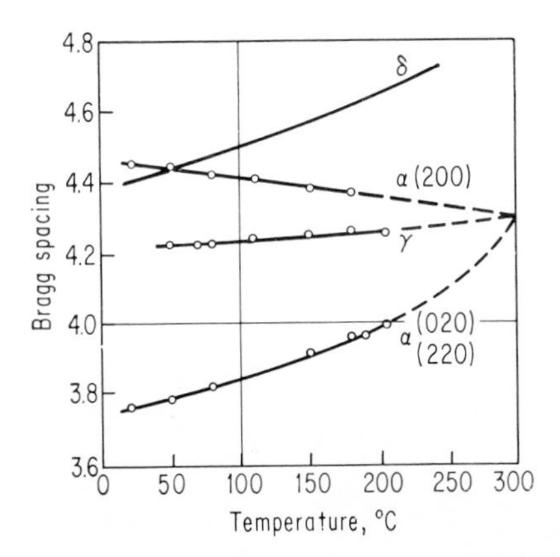

Fig. 12. Bragg spacings of the α, γ, and δ forms of polycaprolactam as a function of temperature.[18]

6. CRYSTALLITE SIZE AND PERFECTION

A measurement which is quite distinct from the previously discussed "amount of crystallinity" is a judgment of how large or how perfect are the crystals that exist in the polymer. These two parameters (commonly called crystallinity and crystallite size) may vary dependently with respect to each other or they may vary completely independently. Since polymer processing usually affects crystallite size, it is of considerable importance to obtain this measurement. The principles of line broadening of polymer diffraction are no different from the traditional approach discussed in Chap. 17. Average crystallite size is usually determined by Warren's correction for Scherrer's line-broadening equation: $B^2 = \beta^2 + b^2$ where β = pure breadth of a diffraction having wavelength λ and Bragg angle θ, B = experimentally observed breadth, and b = breadth due to instrumental conditions. Then $D = K\lambda/\beta \cos \theta$ where D = mean dimension of crystallite in angstroms, and K = constant, 1.0 or 0.9 usually used. Results of measurements using this calculation show that polymer crystallites are quite small, 40 to 100 Å being the typical range of values.

Since such a definite model has evolved of small crystalline and amorphous regions and since this model has been so prominent in the thinking in polymer science, it is often overlooked that the line broadening which gives rise to the measurement of small crystallites could, in principle, be caused by many imperfections in much larger crystals. Such mosaic structures have, of course, been prominent in metallurgical studies and in general solid-state research, but they have been nearly ignored in polymer science. Perhaps crystallite *size* measurements have been preferred because there has not been until recently a good way to handle line broadening in terms of *perfection*. There have now been provided an elegant theory and examples of how polymer diffraction can be analyzed in terms of dislocation domains and disorder parameters of several types.[20] It is shown that the "two-phase concept" of crystalline and amorphous regions is not always needed to explain polymer diffraction but that several types of mosaic crystals with dislocations of different types can also adequately explain the observed diffraction. Details of the mosaic structure or paracrystal theory are complicated and will not be presented here. Other valuable approaches have been suggested[5,21] but have not been used extensively. Instead, it will suffice to emphasize the statement that line broadening in polymers has no single best interpretation and that no single best model exists which adequately explains all the evidence.

7. DIRECTIONAL ORDERING

Some diffraction patterns from oriented polymers do not show sharp diffractions in all directions.[19,22] These patterns indicate that mesomorphic states exist for polymers, as they do for some low-molecular-weight materials. Since polymers have long-chain molecules, it is most useful to describe the polymers which show such patterns as having "directional order" in terms of the chain axis. Thus there is lateral order only (from chain to chain) if the diffraction appears only on the equator of the pattern, as in Fig. 13, where only $(hk0)$ reflections are sharp. Conversely, there is only longitudinal order if the diffraction appears just on the meridian of the pattern, as in Fig. 14 where only $(00l)$ reflections are sharp. This directional-order parameter,

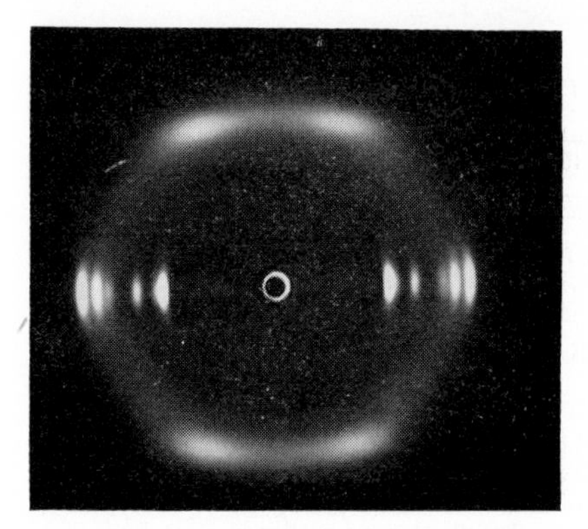

FIG. 13. X-ray diagram of polytrifluorovinylacetate showing absence of longitudinal order. Fiber axis is vertical.[19]

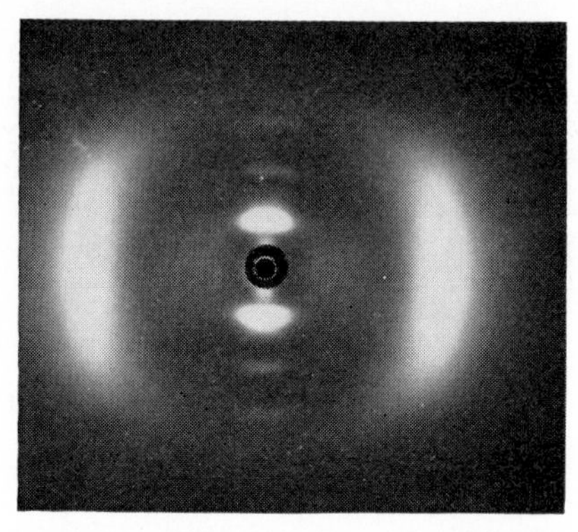

FIG. 14. X-ray diagram of polyheptamethylene terephthalamide. Fiber axis is vertical.[22]

therefore, gives additional information when used for the polymers which show it. To describe it correctly, it may involve both terms designating amount and perfection of order. These can be judged in the usual way except that now individual judgments are made for a particular direction on the pattern. Reliable numbers may be much more difficult to obtain, and qualitative judgment may have to suffice.

The existence of varying directional order adds one more complication to the descriptive model of polymers, and it also can complicate the standard crystallinity measurements and definitions. On the other hand, once directional order has been detected and studied for oriented materials, its existence in bulk polymer or unoriented materials can be detected and studied.[22]

8. CRYSTALLITE ORIENTATION

Diffraction patterns from polymers usually show orientation effects if the material has been subjected to any deforming stress such as extrusion, rolling, calendering, stretching, or drawing. This stress is found to force the molecules into special arrangements and alignments with respect to the stress directions. Since many important physical properties are dependent on the amount of this alignment of polymer chains, some measure of it by x-rays becomes one of the most important reasons for x-ray characterization.

A frequent measurement is to determine the alignment of the crystallites. This is judged by the azimuthal intensity distribution of sharp diffractions, seen in Fig. 15. Several methods can be used to characterize this distribution; the choice will depend upon the laboratory facilities and the needs of the experiment.

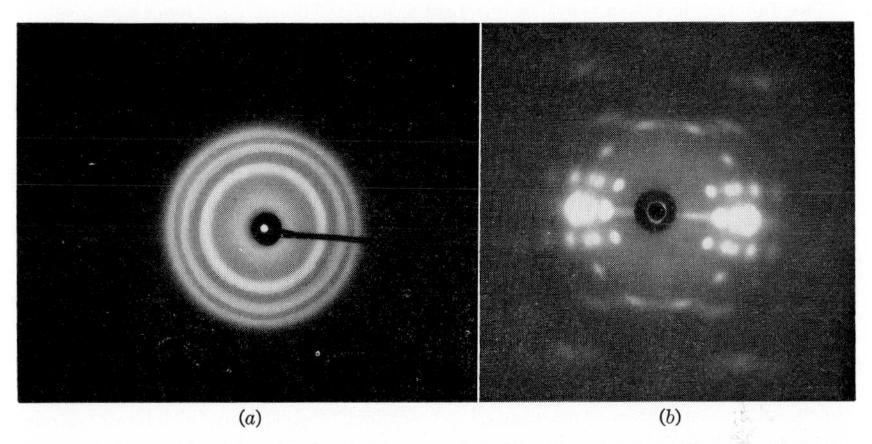

(a) (b)

FIG. 15. X-ray diagrams of polyethylene terephthalate fibers having different orientation of crystallites. (a) Crystalline and unoriented; (b) crystalline and oriented.

For routine characterizations, use of a single measurement to represent the total orientation effect is usually sufficient. Such a measurement is the "orientation angle" for a particular reflection;[23] it is defined as the central angle subtended by the diffraction arc at one-half its maximum intensity, as sketched in Fig. 16. This can be obtained readily by properly rotating the sample with counting techniques or by properly rotating the photographic-film pattern in a densitometer. The arc width at two-thirds peak-intensity value has also been used. Pole figures may be obtained for polymers in an analogous way as for metals (cf. Chap. 18).

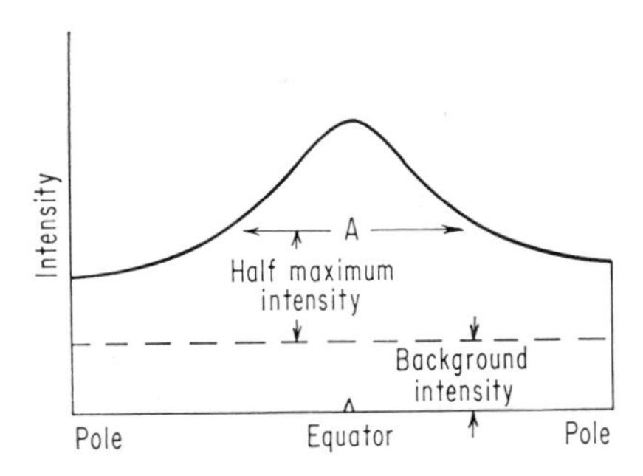

FIG. 16. Azimuthal intensity distribution showing calculation of the orientation angle A.[23]

For more complete knowledge of the orientation effects, a study of the azimuthal intensity *distribution* for a reflection is desirable. A variety of functions have been used to represent the orientation distribution (Ref. 10 with its bibliography). An orientation factor for crystallites f_c has theoretical significance in terms of affine transformation theory and can be thought of as a parameter representing the per cent orientation of crystallites with respect to a deformation direction

$$f_c = 1 - \tfrac{3}{2}\,\overline{\sin^2 \rho}$$

where $\overline{\sin^2 \rho}$ is the average of the squared sine of the angle between the deformation axes and the crystallographic C axis. If possible, a major equatorial reflection is used so that $\overline{\sin^2 \rho}$ is given by

$$\overline{\sin^2 \rho} = \frac{\int_0^{\pi/2} I(\beta) \sin^2 \beta \cos \beta \, d\beta}{\int_0^{\pi/2} I(\beta) \cos \beta \, d\beta}$$

where $I(\beta)$ is the intensity on an azimuthal scan as a function of β, the angle from the equator (assuming it to be for a paratropic plane parallel to the deformation axis and assuming a rodlike orientation). If nonorthogonal unit cells or plateletlike orientation is present, the above must be generalized.[24,25,26]

This function has been especially useful for study of fibers. Extreme care needs to be exercised that the fibers are exactly parallel to each other and perpendicular to the x-ray beam. For extremely high orientation the most ideal sample is a single filament. Even though exposures will be quite long, the increase in accuracy of the orientation determination recommends it, or as an alternative, alignment of individual filaments can be achieved under a binocular microscope.

When the polymer is in the form of a film, there is usually some form of selective alignment of the molecules in the plane of the film, and special attention must be given in sample preparation if understanding of this alignment is sought.[1,2] There may or may not be a preferred alignment in which the molecules lie flat in the plane of the film. There may or may not be further alignment of the molecules with respect to a particular axis of the film. If the film had been extended (drawn) in one direction, there is usually alignment of the chains in this draw direction, i.e., uniaxial orientation. If the film has been drawn in two directions, as is often done, there will be little or no net alignment with respect to the draw directions, as the usual objective is to achieve "balanced" orientation. In this case there may be a high degree of preferred orientation into the plane of the film.[2] If the double drawing is not balanced, biaxial orientation results; this requires complicated geometrical relationships to define crystallographic axes with respect to the plane of the film and draw directions. These have been fully defined,[27,28,29] and a scheme of simultaneous presentations of the various orientations is shown.

9. NONCRYSTALLINE PACKING

Not all important polymers give sharp crystalline diffractions, but some instead show only diffuse halos. The nature of this diffuse scattering, however, can be studied to reveal structural information.

"Degrees of amorphousness" can be determined by obtaining an arbitrary measure of the radial-intensity distribution with the presumption that the more random and "amorphous" the broader will be the halo. The radial width at one-half maximum intensity might be used as a parameter for comparison, but it has no theoretical significance.

Interchain separation R can be measured by the value of 2θ at which the intensity of the diffuse halo is a maximum using the equation

$$R = \tfrac{5}{8}\,(\lambda/\sin\theta)$$

A particularly interesting use of this is the measurement of the glass transition temperature of a polymer by x-rays[30] in terms of a changing expansion coefficient. The value of R at various temperatures shows a definite change in slope, as shown in Fig. 17.

Radial-intensity-distribution analyses, as described in Chap. 22, can be made on the diffuse scattering from polymers (even if the scattering also includes some crystalline diffraction). This technique can have real value in structural interpretations of noncrystalline polymers where there is no opportunity for diffraction analysis.[31]

"Amorphous" polymers can show orientation effects, as in Fig. 18. A measure of this orientation can be obtained via the methods discussed previously, with the simplification that this measure is a *relative* parameter describing molecular orientation and may not be exact in theory as is corresponding crystalline orientation. If, for instance, an orientation-angle parameter is obtained for the equatorial halo of drawn amorphous polyethylene terephthalate fibers, the value will not be the same as the equatorial crystallite orientation angle for the equivalent molecular orientation after this fiber is crystallized. This is due to the complex nature of the halo, which is actually composed of strong nonequatorial scattering maxima from the first layer line. On the other hand, orientation distribution functions can be described accurately for materials which do not crystallize, or which have no strong quadrant diffractions near the equator when they crystallize. Such orientation studies have been made on various amorphous elastomers.[17,32]

Diffuse disorder scattering, even in crystalline polymers, has received study and quantitative measurement.[33] A disorder function takes into account the loss of

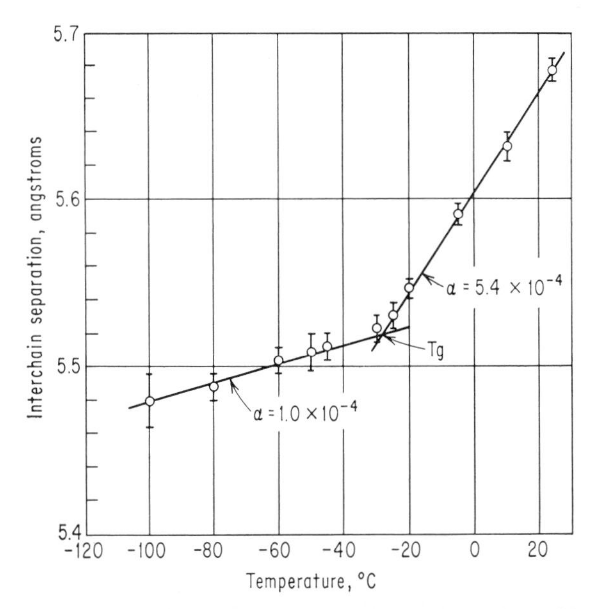

FIG. 17. Variation of interchain separation of amorphous polyethylene with temperature.[30]

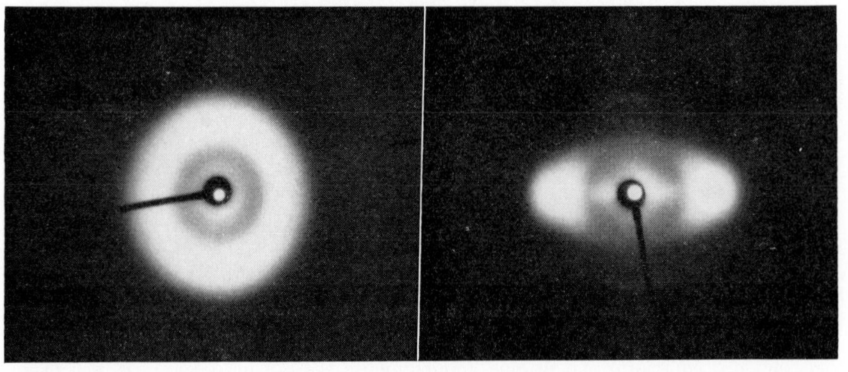

FIG. 18. X-ray diagram of polyethylene terephthalate fibers having different orientation of amorphous halo.

intensity concentrated at the reciprocal lattice point due to deviation of the atoms from their ideal positions. These deviations may be due to thermal vibration and/or lattice imperfections of two kinds. It is shown that it is necessary to take into account the effect of thermal vibrations and disorder phenomena in crystallinity determinations so that the "disorder function" should be determined together with the "crystallinity."

10. ATOMIC ARRANGEMENT

Unit-cell Contents. The packing of polymer molecules with respect to each other is expressed most completely in terms of a unit cell and its contents and symmetry designation. The unit cell has the shape of a parallelepiped with axes a, b, c, and angles α, β, γ. The c axis for polymer crystals is usually designated as the direction of the long axis of the molecule. An example is shown in Fig. 19 for the solution for the complete structure of polyethylene.[34] The mechanics of such full-structure determination are described in Part 3; the manner of solving polymer structures does not differ in principle from standard techniques. However, there are some real differences in the practice of polymer-structure solving. It is difficult or impossible to

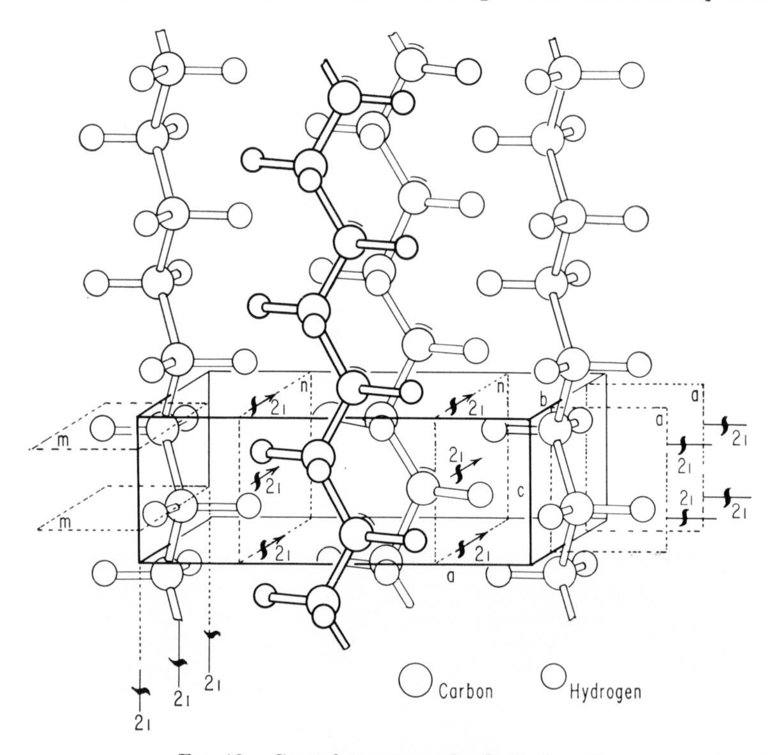

FIG. 19. Crystal structure of polyethylene.[34]

obtain a sufficient number of reflections since disorder is so high. It is usually difficult to obtain satisfactory data from three crystallographic directions. Therefore, only a few satisfactory structures have been fully solved out of the very large number of polymers that have been studied in a cursory manner. For many purposes, however, the exact cell constants and atomic arrangements are not necessary. It will often suffice to obtain one of the following compromise measurements.

Unit-cell Dimensions; Crystalline Density. Following standard procedures described in Part 3, the positions of the x-ray reflections can be measured on oriented polymer diffraction patterns, converted into reciprocal space dimensions, fitted to a three-dimensional point network in reciprocal space, and then converted into a real-space lattice having dimensions of the unit cell.

A very useful quantity determined from unit-cell measurements is the *calculated crystalline density*. This calculated density is the highest value which can be expected for the measured density of a polymer specimen; it is the density corresponding to "100 per cent crystallinity," given by the following equation:

$$\text{Crystalline density} = 1.6598(W/V) = W'/V'$$

where W is the weight in atomic mass units of the contents of the unit cell and V is the volume of the unit cell in cubic angstroms. Alternately, W' is the weight of one chain repeat unit and V' is the volume of the repeat motif, defined below. The constant is equal to 10^{24} divided by Avogadro's number, 6.0248×10^{23}.

A valuable and exhaustive compilation of unit-cell parameters and other crystallographic data for polymers has been given.[35,36]

Repeat Distance; Identity Period. An important and simple measurement to make on oriented polymer diffraction patterns is the repeat distance along the chain axis. This measurement often provides much information about both the configuration and conformation of the molecule (configuration involves chemical structure of a molecule; conformation involves the geometrical arrangement of the atoms along the molecule).

The repeat distance is measured best when the polymer has very high orientation and is well crystallized; efforts to achieve both will be rewarded by much better data

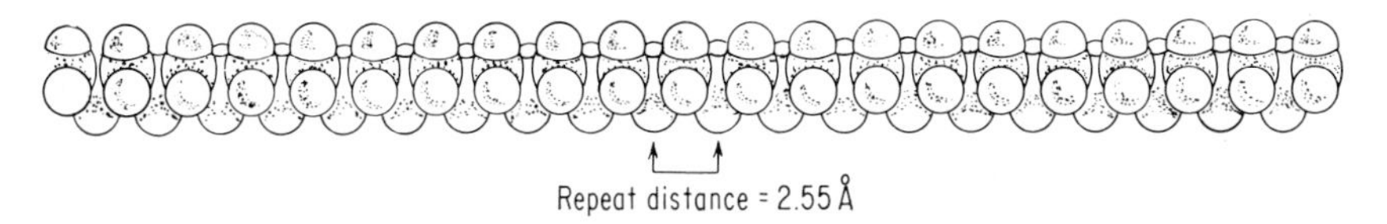

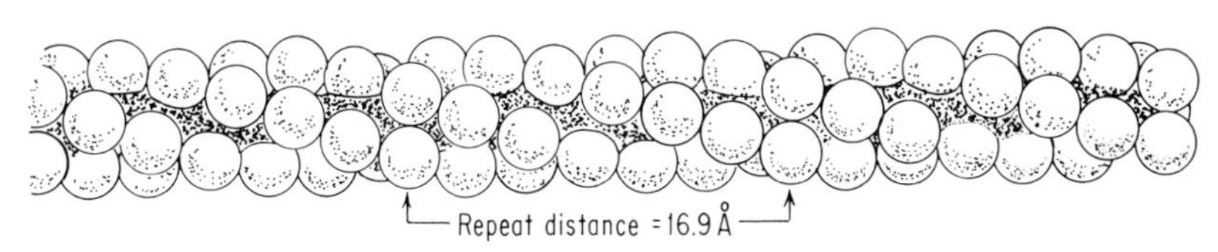

FIG. 20. Conformation and repeat unit for (top) polyethylene and (bottom) polytetrafluoroethylene.[37]

and confidence. Use of a cylindrical camera for obtaining diffraction photographs is perhaps the best and simplest interpretive technique, since a well-developed pattern with straight layer lines is desired. The repeat distance c is determined directly from the distance between the layer lines using the equation

$$c = \frac{n\lambda}{\sin \tan^{-1}(y/r)} \qquad \text{(for cylindrical film)}$$

where n is the layer-line number, λ is the wavelength of the x-rays, y is the distance between the layer line n and the zero layer (equator), and r is the radius of the camera.

Repeat Motif; Helical Structure Analysis. The object of measurement of the above repeat distance is to obtain the repeating motif in terms of the atoms along the molecule. The measurement is most accurate and complete when one determines the unit-cell constants, but this need not always be done, nor can it always be done. Instead, knowing the chemical structure of the molecule and using the accepted values for bond lengths and bond angles, the conformation of the molecule often can be reasoned out. For example, the planar zigzag for polyethylene appears to be the only reasonable arrangement in which C—C bond lengths are 1.54 Å and in which C—C—C bond angles are about tetrahedral; this can give an identity period of 2.55 Å, the same as observed. As sketched in Fig. 20, this is contrasted to polytetrafluoroethylene, which shows an identity period of 16.9 Å, although the expected planar zigzag repeat would give 2.55 Å, as for polyethylene. Therefore, there must be a twist to the molecule, and on further analysis, it is determined that 13 (CF_2) groups are the repeating motif in six turns.[37]

Helical structure analysis has provided an elegant means to short-cut one's way to a knowledge of the repeating motif and some knowledge of the exact conformation of molecules. Many of the polymers that have been intensively investigated in recent years have a helical twist in the main chain: complicated natural polymers such as the nucleic acids, proteins, polypeptides, and less complicated synthetic polymers such as the isotactic polyvinyls, polytetrafluoroethylene, and polyoxymethylene. The novelty of this new approach is that it does not use Bragg's law.

Instead, a mathematical treatment was devised[38] which gave equations for calculating the continuous transform of a helical structure. The application of these equations is rather straightforward, although the full description or use of the principles is quite complicated and beyond the scope of this book. In essence, the continuous-transform calculation tells us approximately where strong spots should be; whether or not spots will actually occur at a particular location depends on the nature of the lattice. This provides us with three new working principles: (1) We can usually deduce *by inspection* whether or not an unknown structure is helical. (2) If it is helical, we can determine the amount of twist and repeat motif. (3) An analysis is provided whereby a structure can often be solved without the usual structure-factor summations.

An oriented diffraction pattern for a helical structure has certain characteristic features which allow it to be readily identified and then measured to learn the motif. In Fig. 21 is shown an optical diffraction analog of a simple helix.[39] The diffraction from the helix has these simple identifying characteristics which are not found in patterns for nonhelical structures: (1) The reflections in the quadrant of the patterns are apt to be as intense as, or even more intense than, the equatorial reflections. (2) The quadrant layer-line reflections usually line up in staggered diagonal lines which form a cross going out from (000). A second such cross may be present which has its center on the meridian above and below the equator. (3) A "clear space" is seen near the meridian for several of the lower layer lines. An example of these helix diffraction characteristics is shown in Fig. 22 for an oriented fiber of polypropylene.

If the above characteristics provide the knowledge that a helix is involved, certain simple measurements on the pattern will provide the repeating motif and the internal conformation:

1. Measurements of the first-layer-line spacing give c, the axial length of repeating motif (the unit-cell c axis length).
2. The measurement of the spacing of the first layer line which has a meridional reflection gives p, the axial distance between successive repeating groups of atoms (monomer unit) in the helix.
3. Determining the layer-line number which gives the first meridional reflection also gives the number of repeating groups of atoms within the repeating motif.
4. Measuring the most intense equatorial spot *may* give the radius of the helix (depending upon the packing geometry of the helix).

These measurements on the pattern in Fig. 22 give much information about the individual chains and their packing.

First layer line = 6.5 Å (unit-cell length, repeat motif length).

Third layer line has a meridional reflection; so there are three monomer units per turn (probably at 120° with respect to each other).

Third layer line = 2.5 Å (axial distance between monomer units in the helix).

Main equatorial spot = 6.2 Å.

Thus a few simple measurements on the pattern of the helix give much useful detailed information without a full-structure determination.

Finding the repeat motif can provide still another important clue about some polymers: their configuration. Configuration is the term used to describe the juxtaposition in space of atoms along the chains. Head-to-head or head-to-tail polymerization, for example, should be distinguishable.

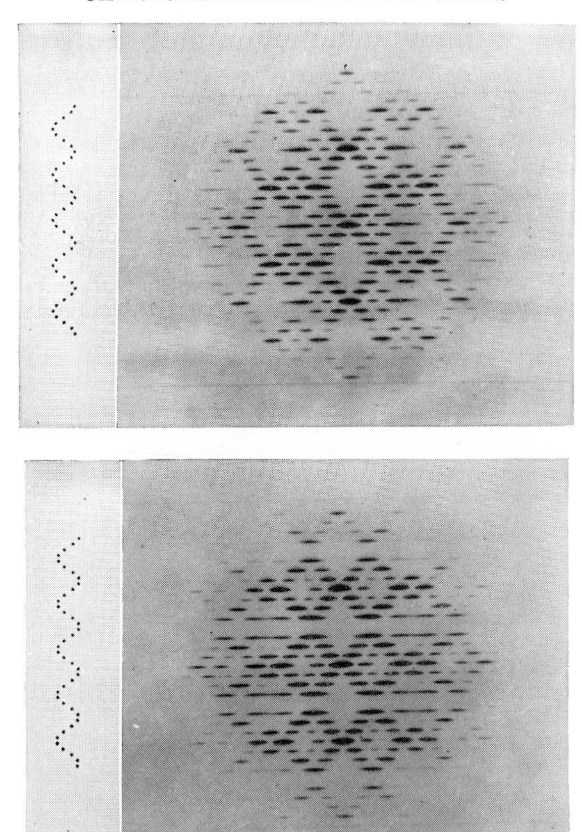

Fig. 21. Optical diffraction analog of a helical structure. Top: two projections of a simple helix; bottom: diffraction patterns of these projections.

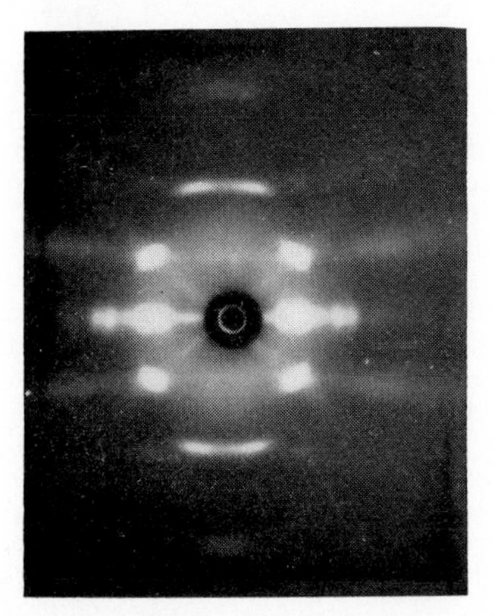

Fig. 22. Oriented x-ray diagram of helical molecule, polypropylene. Fiber axis is vertical.

11. MEASUREMENTS AND INTERPRETATIONS—SMALL-ANGLE STUDIES

Introduction; Experimental Techniques. Polymer studies have used x-ray patterns obtained at small angles with respect to the undiffracted beam. Since these angles are usually less than 2°, the experimental requirements for obtaining small-angle patterns are stringent. Exact interpretations of these patterns are not always possible. In fact, there are some interpretations which are a matter of controversy, and much additional research is required. However, trends and generalities have developed, and this section will highlight the current status of experimentation and interpretation and will show the broad variety of knowledge or parameters that can be gained from small-angle studies of polymers. Three recent reviews[40,41,42] provide detailed descriptions of the interpretative problems and examples.

The major requirement for small-angle studies of any type is for the x-ray beam to be given unusually good collimation as described in Chap. 16. Sketched in Fig. 23 is a

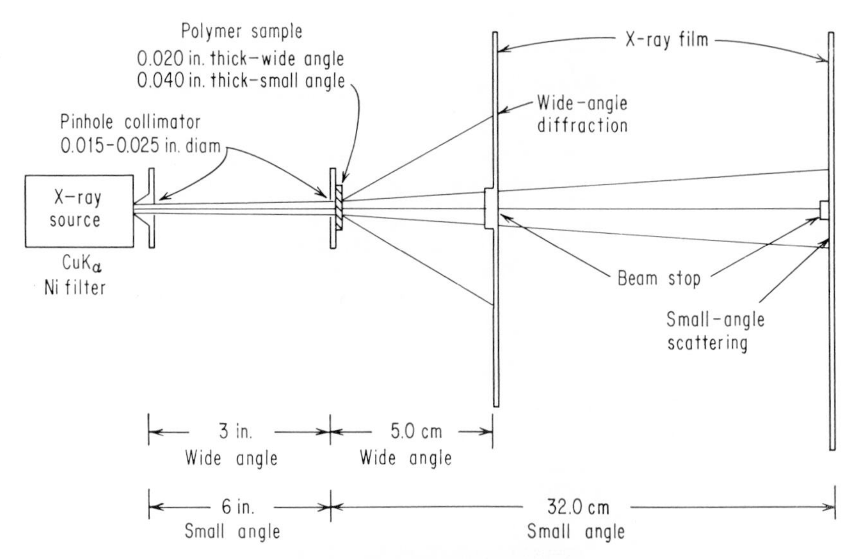

FIG. 23. Comparison of wide-angle and small-angle film arrangement for polymer samples.

typical example of conditions used when a photographic film is the method of recording the pattern. In order to obtain a narrow, nearly parallel beam, several techniques have been used.

The standard procedure for small-angle collimation is to move the edges of slits closer together. When this is combined with Geiger or scintillation counting techniques for detection, relatively rapid data collection is usually possible. This can provide very good resolution (up to 800 Å) combined with relatively good speed in obtaining data. The major disadvantage of slits is their distortion of the scattering pattern due to the rectangular shape of the x-ray beam as it passes through the sample. This can mean loss of information when oriented polymers are studied.

Good collimation of the beam for oriented polymers can be achieved by tiny pinholes placed at proper distances apart.[43] This collimation is usually combined with film to record the scattered x-rays; such cameras are available commercially.* The main advantage of pinhole collimation is the undistorted patterns obtained from oriented

* W. H. Warhus Co., 406 Rowland Park Blvd., Wilmington, Del.

materials. The main disadvantage is the longer exposure time needed for such undistorted patterns.

Unusually high resolution is obtained by a different approach,[44] sketched in Fig. 24. This collimation advantage is somewhat offset by the exacting construction requirements and the distortion of the pattern of oriented materials. The camera has found its greatest value in studying polymer solutions. It is available commercially.*

X-rays can be "focused" by taking advantage of total (specular) reflection when striking solids at small angles. Nearly all the x-rays from the tube can therefore be used; this is a major advantage over all other collimation techniques. A camera has been designed using this principle; it has been successful in producing small-angle patterns rapidly from polymers.[45] The disadvantages of this approach are (1) the exacting requirements of construction, (2) the need for a point source of x-rays, (3) requirements for stability of position of the x-ray source and camera, and (4) some

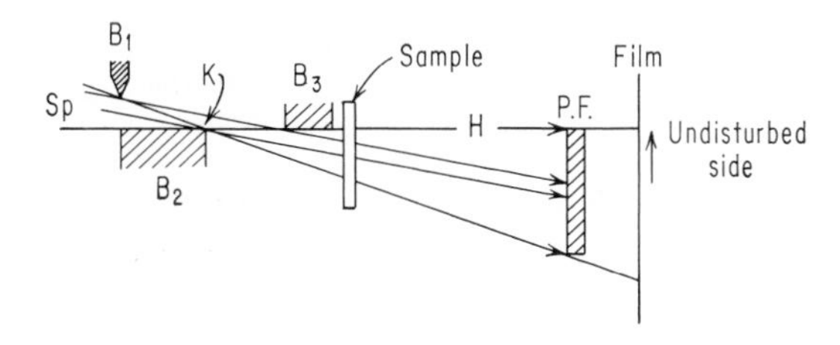

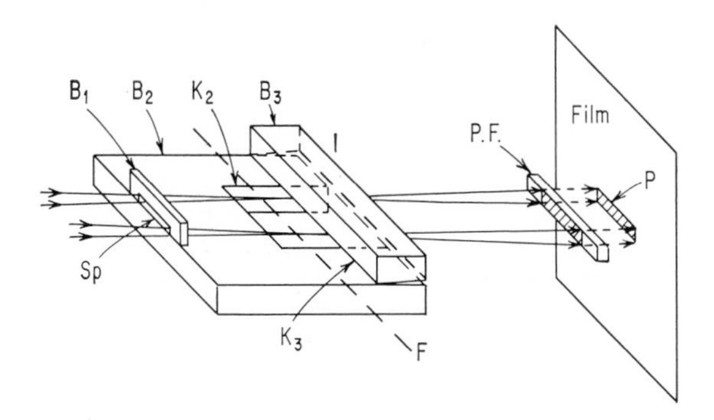

FIG. 24. Sketches of x-ray collimation by the Kratky U-bar method.[44]

distortion of the scattering due to beam shape. The camera and x-ray unit are available commercially.†

The x-ray beam can become focused by using an intense diffracted beam from a crystal as the "source" of the x-rays to be used for the sample. If a thin slab of this crystal is deformed uniformly by bending it to a certain radius of curvature, the diffracted (monochromatic) rays from the various areas of the curved crystal will all converge. Either one or two bent crystals can be used. The advantages of these systems are the more efficient use of the x-ray source, much better resolution, and the production of a monochromatic x-ray beam. The disadvantages are the exacting construction and lineup requirements and the great loss of intensity compared with a normally filtered source. Such cameras are available commercially.‡

* Eastern Scientific Sales Co., P.O. Box 155, Cherry Hill, N.J.

† Jarrell-Ash Co., 26 Farwell St., Newtonville 60, Mass.

‡ Mitchell X-ray Products Co., 354 E. Washington St., Norristown, Pa.; AEG—Export Dept., Berlin-Grunewold, Hohenzallerdamm 150.

The time required for obtaining small-angle scattering data will usually be longer than for conventional wide-angle patterns since the exacting collimation will reduce the intensity of the main x-ray beam. If the photographic technique is used, the sample-to-film distance is also much greater than for wide-angle patterns, so that the scattering intensity is further lowered by a factor involving the square of the distance from the sample to the film. Polymer samples often require exposures for hours or even days in order to obtain a satisfactory film blackening. Even if the most favorable instrumental conditions are used, the sample scattering may be so weak that relatively long exposures are still necessary.

Long exposures have the additional disadvantage of much air scattering in the same angular region where polymers also scatter. It is always necessary, therefore, when using film techniques to evacuate the cameras or otherwise eliminate air scattering.

Large sample size is an obvious way to regain the intensity which is lost by stringent collimation. It is helpful for photographic or transmission techniques to approximately double the thickness of the sample in the beam. As in all wide-angle x-ray techniques, a compromise must be made between desirable exposure time and line broadening or distortion due to using too thick a sample.

Samples can be studied in the same form which is used for wide-angle x-ray studies. If the polymer is oriented, careful alignment of the orientation axis of the sample and the direction of the x-ray beam is usually desired.

The x-ray target most often used for small-angle studies is copper. Chromium has occasionally been used in order to disperse the pattern somewhat to larger angles. For most exacting scattering work, it is necessary to use a monochromatic beam; the Ross-filter difference method is often preferred. Simple filtering of the copper beam with nickel will suffice to remove the bulk of the white radiation for a majority of investigations.

To register the small-angle scattering diagrams either photographic film or a counter tube can be used. There are advantages as well as disadvantages for each technique. Since photographic films can record the entire scattering pattern they can be quite desirable for oriented polymers. Films are also useful to record very weak scattering by lengthening the exposure time. On the other hand, film must still be photometered for quantitative measurements, so that losses in time and precision are likely. Counter tubes have the advantage that the final quantitative result is obtained directly and the counting rate can be used as a measure of intensity. Since counters provide point-by-point measurement, an excessive counting time and manipulation are needed to map an oriented diagram completely.

Two types of x-ray effects at small angles are shown by polymers, diffuse scattering and discrete diffraction. Since there may be no relation at all between these effects, it is important to recognize their distinction and to understand that they are caused by different aspects of the aggregation of polymer molecules.

Polymers can show diffuse scattering in either the solid or liquid states. This scattering usually has a maximum intensity at an angle of 0°, and it decreases in intensity up to 1 to 2° as shown in Fig. 25*a*. Scattering from a polymer solution (and from the melt, which is similar in principle) is usually much weaker than the scattering of the same polymer in the solid state. If the solid polymer has undergone some deformation, the diffuse scattering pattern is usually elongated as in Fig. 25*b*.

Discrete diffraction can be obtained from many solid polymers, but only if they do not appear amorphous in a wide-angle x-ray pattern. The diffraction frequently appears as a single maximum corresponding to a Bragg spacing of 75 to 200 Å, as in Fig. 26*a*. If the polymer has undergone deformation, the discrete ring becomes oriented and is usually found on the meridian of the pattern as in Fig. 26*b*, indicating a structural repeat along the molecular axis of the polymer. The usual pattern of a crystalline polymer shows both diffuse and discrete effects as in Fig. 26*c*.

Diffuse Scattering. If there are inhomogeneities of colloidal dimensions in matter, x-rays will be scattered at very small angles with respect to the primary incident beam. The details of the scattering will depend upon the size, shape, and arrangement of the colloidal inhomogeneities, that is, upon the morphological structure of the system. Learning details about this morphological structure is the reason for studying polymer small-angle scattering, and results have shown that a variety of features can be described.

There are difficulties, however, in interpreting the exact morphological structure from the scattering data. One reason is that Babinet's reciprocity principle of optics also applies to x-rays. This theorem states that the scattering does not change if the electron densities in a two-phase system are interchanged. Therefore, in polymers the small-angle scattering *alone* does not indicate whether the scattering elements are particles or voids; other evidence must be used to distinguish between these possible causes of the scattering.

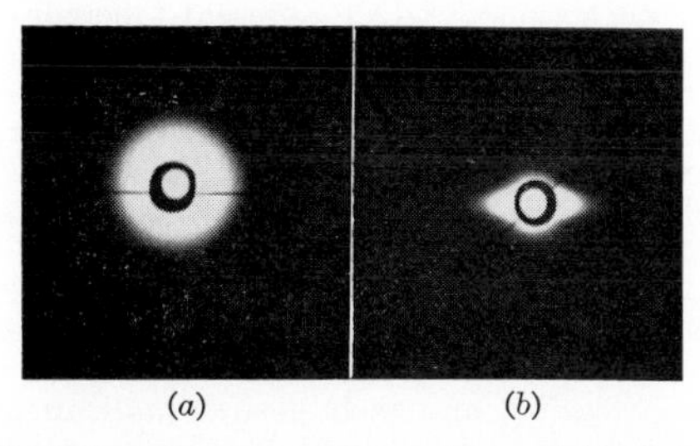

(*a*) (*b*)

FIG. 25. Typical small-angle diffuse scattering. (Central black area is shadow of beam trap; central white spot is main undiffracted x-ray beam registered by removing beam trap momentarily.) (*a*) Unoriented polymer; (*b*) drawn, oriented fiber (fiber axis vertical).

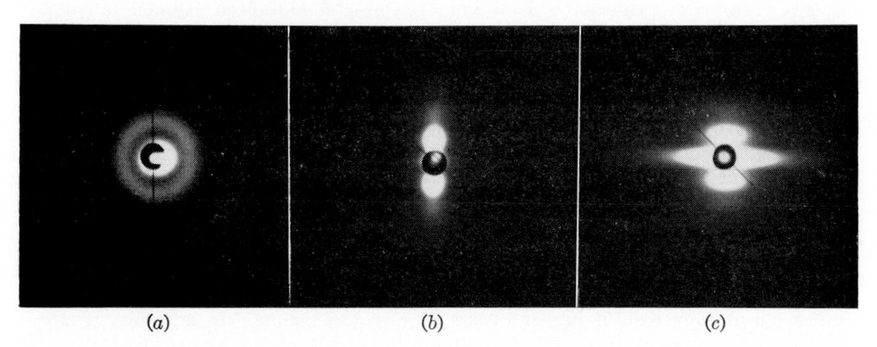

(*a*) (*b*) (*c*)

FIG. 26. Typical small-angle discrete diffraction. (*a*) Annealed, unoriented 6-10 nylon polymer; (*b*) oriented linear polyethylene, showing meridional second order; (*c*) oriented linear polyethylene showing both diffuse scattering and discrete diffraction.

Another reason why the small-angle scattering cannot be evaluated without ambiguity is that the infinite variety of colloidal systems cannot be accurately represented by a family of "typical" scattering curves. Still more difficulty arises from the fact that a scattering curve can sometimes be interpreted in a variety of ways since it cannot be recorded for its entire angular range and the accuracy of measurement is not high. For practical purposes, therefore, if two systems show scattering curves which cannot be distinguished from each other within the experimental error of the scattering measurement, they will be called "scattering equivalent," even though the systems may not be exactly equivalent in actuality.

The angular range of the small-angle scattering is inversely proportional to the magnitude of the inhomogeneity. If a colloidal system is increased linearly by a certain factor, there will be a contraction of the scattering curve by the same factor. This gives rise to the possibility of measuring particle or void sizes from small-angle scattering data. The dimensions of the particle in the scattering direction are obtained.

Since oriented polymers show, as a rule, anisotropic scattering patterns (ovals or streaks), they will be an image of the shape of the scatterer but with all dimensions rotated by 90°. This means that the smallest particle or void dimensions correspond to the largest extension of the small-angle scattering and vice versa.

A distinction must be made between dilute and close-packed systems. That is, the effect of interparticle interference must be determined.

Interaction is less likely to occur the more the particles are separated from each other and the more randomized is their arrangement. In dilute solutions, therefore, the interparticle interference can usually be neglected. The small-angle scattering will then consist of the sum of the scatter due to the individual particles. The scattering is also modified when several sizes are present ("polydispersity") or when there are highly anisotropic particle shapes like rods or lamellae. Thus it should be emphasized that even in dilute solutions detailed information can be expected only if the particles are of uniform size and shape, as sometimes occurs in proteins. In all other cases which have polydispersity of different shapes, only an *average* quantity is obtainable, or possibly some rough approximation of shape or statistical size distribution can be determined.

In the case of close packing of the particles, interparticle interference must be expected. It can take different forms depending upon its extent. The complete description of a close-packed system provides information about the size and shape of particles, their size distribution, and their position and orientation with respect to each other. Unfortunately, such detailed information cannot be obtained from small-angle x-ray scattering alone. The obvious compromise would be to compare observed scattering curves with those calculated from models, but this is not feasible since there is such an infinite variety of colloidal systems and so many difficulties are encountered by any theoretical treatment. However, it is possible and often valuable to compare systems on a *relative* basis, but one should not attempt to go beyond this and give basic interpretations in terms of *actual* sizes, shapes, or size distributions.

The above listing of problems of interpretations of polymer diffuse scattering is not meant to deter future work, but only to warn against improper use of the data. In reality, many interesting and helpful results have been obtained.

The scattering theory, examples of measurements, and examples of results are given in the detailed reviews of Porod,[41] Beeman et al.,[46] Kratky,[40] and Statton.[42]

Discrete Diffraction. The occurrence of discrete maxima in the small-angle pattern is the effect most closely related to the wide-angle diffraction. It is the manifestation of a periodical or at least a quasi-periodical order with a large repeat distance. A clear latticelike arrangement, such as observed for collagen, is seldom observed. The small-angle reflections obtained from polymers are usually rather diffuse, and they exhibit higher orders in rare cases only. In addition, whatever periodicity is present in oriented polymers is usually found in one direction only. The character of the diffraction is more like a statistical interference, and it has been so treated in the literature.[20] The long period usually quoted is obtained as the Bragg spacing corresponding to the mid-point of the diffraction maximum.

Most of the studies of discrete diffraction have been on oriented fibers. It has always been assumed that, when discrete diffraction is found in bulk unoriented polymers, it is due to the same type of structural situation, except that this feature has no orientation.

The distinctness and form of the reflections depend on the size of the regions which cause the scattering. Broadening of the reflections in the meridional direction of the small-angle diagram corresponds in principle to the line broadening in the wide-angle diagrams, which is the result of a small number of periodically recurring elements. This effect, however, is superimposed on the broadening because of the variation of the periodicity; it appears very unlikely that these two factors can be separated.

The lateral shape of the reflections is of importance and can be informative. A periodic series of point elements should lead to layer-line reflections; that is, the intensity should be extended infinitely on a line normal to the periodicity. However, the greater the lateral extent of the elements, the shorter the layer lines. This relationship was used in connection with the reflections of collagen, and their type of measurement has been extended to other fibrous systems[1,47] by comparing fiber wide-angle diagrams and small-angle diagrams and finding a linear relationship of sizes.

The streak often can have strong maxima at its ends in the quadrants, forming the so-called "four-point diagram." A rolled polymer or stretched film can show meridional spots in one direction and quadrant spots when viewed perpendicular to this direction.[1]

It is well established that the long period is not related to the length of the chemical structural repeat period; so it is not some crystallographic superlattice of the type found in metals. It has also been shown that the long period is independent of molecular weight; so it cannot be related to the imperfections caused by the terminal groups on the polymer chains. On the other hand, the long period is definitely associated with the crystalline state, as no long-period diffraction is ever observed in the completely amorphous state (as judged by absence of sharp diffraction in the wide-angle diagram).

The discrete diffraction has an important feature in its variability. Processing conditions of the polymer will determine the type of diagram obtained. The reflections can vary in shape, long-period length, amount of splitting, and radial sharpness. Temperature, tension, plasticization, all have an interplay, but they have not been thoroughly studied. It can be definitely stated, however, that the long period will increase whenever the polymer is annealed to a higher temperature than it has previously encountered.[47,48,49]

The interpretation of the long-period diffraction developed through a well-known "fringe micelle" model which was generally accepted and which originally provided the most plausible explanation.[40,41,42] However, recent results have caused serious doubts whether this model is satisfactory. The completely new concept which has drastically altered much of the thinking about polymer morphology and the cause of the long-period diffraction is the discovery of single crystals of polymers. Instead of the small crystallites embedded in an entangled mass of randomly organized chains, polymers have now been shown to exist as large, orderly arrangements with growth steps, spiral dislocations, dendritic and twinning growth, and other features which are common to the crystal-growth behavior of low-molecular-weight materials.[50] A collection of lamellar polymer crystals shows an intense long-period diffraction which is not basically different from that discussed above for "normal" polymer. This has raised a question as to whether they both have the same general cause for their long-period diffraction.

It was found that the crystals are normally much wider than thick and are usually only about 100 Å thick as grown. It was then found that the axes of the polymer molecules are perpendicular to this thin direction of the crystal. Since the molecules are several thousand angstroms long, this means that the molecules must continuously fold back and forth in the crystal, much as a fire hose is packed into its wall cabinet. If the thickness is 100 Å, the straight portion of the molecule is of this magnitude with sharp folds at the end of this length. If a slurry of these lamellar crystals is sedimented, they will stack like a deck of cards and produce, when x-rays are sent parallel to this stack, an oriented long-period diffraction. Thus the long-period diffraction is caused by the constant thickness of the crystals in close, regular aggregation. Since the chains are regularly folded in these crystals, the long-period diffraction is indirectly caused by the folding of the molecules. It is now generally agreed that the long-period diffraction is the best measure of the fold period, since it is readily and accurately obtained, with several orders usually occurring. This relation of long-period diffraction and fold period has now been shown for many bulk polymers which crystallize in lamellar form from the melt.[50]

Since the small-angle patterns from fibers and single crystals are nearly identical, and since the behavior of the long-period diffraction is identical for heat-treatments to both systems, it is almost necessary, intuitively, to use the same explanation for the cause of the diffractions in the two systems. This would mean, however, that drawn fibers and films contain folded chains. This is a new concept which is novel and interesting but not readily accepted in the light of our previous thinking.

It is thus evident that the interpretation of the cause of the long-period diffraction in polymers is undergoing considerable revision. No general agreement has been reached, nor has it been discussed extensively in the recent literature. This area is the subject of much current research, and this should be considered a report of some current thinking instead of the final word on this subject.

REFERENCES CITED

1. W. O. Statton and G. M. Godard, *J. Appl. Phys.*, **28**:1111 (1957).
2. C. J. Heffelfinger and R. L. Burton, *J. Polymer Sci.*, **42**:289 (1957).
3. J. L. Matthews, H. S. Peiser, and R. B. Richards, *Acta Cryst.*, **2**:85 (1949).
4. S. L. Aggarwal and G. P. Tilley, *J. Polymer Sci.*, **18**:17 (1955).
5. M. Kakudo and R. Ullman, *J. Polymer Sci.*, **45**:91 (1960).
6. P. H. Hermans and A. Weidinger, *Makromol. Chem.*, **44**:24 (1961).
7. P. H. Hermans and A. Weidinger, *J. Polymer Sci.*, **4**:709 (1949).
8. S. Krimm and A. V. Tobolsky, *J. Polymer Sci.*, **7**:57 (1951).
9. G. Farrow, *Polymer*, **2**:409 (1961).
10. P. H. Hermans and A. Weidinger, *Textile Res. J.*, **31**:558 (1961).
11. G. Farrow, *Polymer*, **1**:518 (1960).
12. J. E. Johnson, *J. Appl. Polymer Sci.*, **2**:205 (1959).
13. O. Ant-Wuorinen, *Paperi Puu*, no. 8, 1955.
14. J. H. Wakelin, H. S. Virgin, and E. Crystal, *J. Appl. Phys.*, **30**:1654 (1959).
15. W. O. Statton, *J. Appl. Polymer Sci.*, **7**:803 (1963).
16. H. G. Kilian and E. Jenckel, *Kolloid-Z.*, **165**:25 (1959).
17. S. M. Ohlberg, L. E. Alexander, and E. L. Warrick, *J. Polymer Sci.*, **27**:1 (1959).
18. H. Hendus et al., *Festschr. Carl Wurster* 60 *Geburtstag*, 1960, pp. 293–319.
19. G. T. Bohn, J. R. Schaefgen, and W. O. Statton, *J. Polymer Sci.*, **55**:531 (1961).
20. R. Hosemann and S. N. Bagchi, *Direct Analysis of Diffraction by Matter*, Interscience Publishers, Inc., New York, 1962.
21. A. V. Tobolsky and V. D. Gupta, *J. Chem. Phys.*, **36**:1999 (1962).
22. W. O. Statton, *Ann. N.Y. Acad. Sci.*, **83**:27 (1959).
23. H. G. Ingersoll, *J. Appl. Phys.*, **17**:924 (1946).
24. P. H. Hermans, *Physics and Chemistry of Cellulose Fibres*, Elsevier Publishing Company, Amsterdam, 1949.
25. Z. W. Wilchinsky, *J. Appl. Phys.*, **31**:1969 (1960).
26. M. F. Culpin and K. W. Kemp, *Proc. Phys. Soc.* (*London*), **B69**:1301 (1956).
27. R. S. Stein, *J. Polymer Sci.*, **31**:327 (1958).
28. R. S. Stein, *J. Polymer Sci.*, **31**:335 (1958).
29. C. H. Bamford and H. Tompa, *Acta Cryst.*, **6**:417 (1959).
30. S. M. Ohlberg and S. S. Fenstermaker, *J. Polymer Sci.*, **32**:514 (1958).
31. A. Bjornhaug, O. Ellefsen, and B. A. Tonnesen, *Norsk Skogind.*, **6**:243, 402 (1952); W. Ruland, *Acta Cryst.*, **12**:679 (1959).
32. E. L. Warrick, M. J. Hunter, and A. J. Barry, *Ind. Eng. Chem.*, **44**:2196 (1952).
33. W. Ruland, *Acta Cryst.*, **14**:1180 (1961).
34. C. W. Bunn, *Trans. Faraday Soc.*, **35**:482 (1939).
35. R. L. Miller and L. E. Nielsen, *J. Polymer Sci.*, **44**:391 (1960).
36. R. L. Miller and L. E. Nielsen, *J. Polymer Sci.*, **55**:643 (1961).
37. E. S. Clark and L. T. Muus, *Z. Krist.*, **117**:108, 119 (1962).
38. W. Cochran, F. H. C. Crick, and V. Vand, *Acta Cryst.*, **5**:581 (1952).
39. A. R. Stokes, *Acta Cryst.*, **8**:27 (1955).
40. O. Kratky, *Angew. Chem.*, **72**:467 (1960).
41. G. Porod, *Fortschr. Hochpolymer. Forsch.*, **2**:363 (1961).
42. W. O. Statton in *Newer Methods of Polymer Characterization*, B. Ke (ed.), Interscience Publishers, Inc., New York, 1964.
43. O. E. A. Bolduan and R. S. Bear, *J. Appl. Phys.*, **20**:983 (1949).
44. O. Kratky, G. Porod, A. Sekora, and B. Paletta, *J. Polymer Sci.*, **16**:163 (1955).
45. A. Franks, *Proc. Phys. Soc.* (*London*), **68**:1054 (1955).
46. W. W. Beeman, P. Kaesburg, J. W. Anderegg, and M. B. Webb, Size of Particles and Lattice Defects, in S. Flugge (ed.), *Encyclopedia of Physics*, vol. 32, pp. 321–442, Springer-Verlag OHG, Berlin.
47. W. O. Statton, *J. Polymer Sci.*, **41**:143 (1959).
48. H. A. Stuart, *Kolloid-Z.*, **165**: 3 (1959).
49. R. Eppe, E. W. Fischer, and H. A. Stuart, *J. Polymer Sci.*, **34**:721 (1959).
50. P. H. Geil, *Polymer Morphology*, Interscience Publishers, Inc., New York, 1963.

Chapter 22

RADIAL-DISTRIBUTION ANALYSIS

R. F. Kruh

University of Arkansas

1. INTRODUCTION

In this chapter are outlined techniques for obtaining radial-distribution functions by measurement of the angular dependence of scattered x-ray intensity. The techniques may be applied to systems for which the average radial-distribution function is spherically symmetrical, such as pure liquids, solutions, glasses, and finely divided crystalline powders. Because, for crystalline materials, far more informative methods exist, radial-distribution analysis is used to obtain structural information only as a last resort in, say, a case where it seems impossible to grow crystals suitable for single-crystal study.

For liquids and glasses, however, radial-distribution analysis has afforded a way of acquiring information, often unavailable through any other means, about the geometry of short-range interactions between atoms.

2. PRINCIPLES

The relationships used in radial-distribution analysis are due to Debye,[1] Zernike and Prins,[2] and Debye and Menke.[3] The coherent intensity I_{coh} for a system of identical atoms is usually given[4] as a function of the scattering parameter $s = 4\pi\lambda^{-1} \sin \theta$,

$$I_{\text{coh}} = f^2(s) + f^2(s) \int_0^\infty 4\pi r^2[\rho(r) - \rho_0](\sin sr)(sr)^{-1}\, dr \tag{1}$$

where λ is the wavelength, 2θ is the scattering angle, $f(s)$ is the atomic-form factor, ρ_0 is the macroscopic number density, and $\rho(r)$ is defined as the mean number of atoms per unit volume at a distance r from an atom arbitrarily selected as the origin.

In an actual experiment the x-ray intensity detected at an angle 2θ from the incident beam is, except for background, proportional to

$$I(\theta) = [I_{\text{coh}}(\theta) + I_{\text{inc}}(\theta)]P(\theta)A(\theta) \tag{2}$$

in which I_{coh} = coherent intensity arising from intra- and interatomic phase differences; the interatomic part, $I_{\text{coh}} - f^2(s)$, is the function which provides structural information

I_{inc} = incoherent intensity arising from Compton scattering

$P(\theta)$ = polarization correction

$A(\theta)$ = absorption correction

Fluorescent radiation is not included in Eq. (2) because it is usually eliminated by either filtering or monochromatization of the scattered x-rays. It is desirable to avoid or minimize fluorescence as completely as possible.

The radial-distribution function (RDF) is obtained by applying the Fourier integral theorem to Eq. (1).

$$4\pi r^2\rho(r) = 4\pi r^2\rho_0 + (2r/\pi)\int_0^\infty s(I_{\mathrm{coh}} - f^2)f^{-2}\sin rs\,ds \qquad (3)$$

3. EXPERIMENTAL METHODS

Determination of the intensity $I(\theta)$ with a cylindrical camera or with a commercial diffractometer involves experimental techniques which are the same as those discussed for crystalline powders in Chaps. 8 and 9. Although special diffractometers have also been built for study of amorphous systems their features are not sufficiently uniform to warrant a detailed discussion of their operation.*

Sample Preparation. A cylindrical sample is used for film measurement, either as a freely flowing stream or contained in a thin-walled holder. For a diffractometer, flat samples are generally used, and depending on the design, it may either have a free surface or be contained by thin films or foils of low absorption. A flat sample should have sufficient thickness if used in parafocusing (see Absorption Correction), its width should be great enough to intercept the entire incident beam at low angles, and it should be adjusted so that the diffractometer axis lies accurately in its surface.

An innovation used in transmission is to hold a liquid sample by its own surface tension in a slit cut in a metal sheet.[5]

Detection of Radiation. Although extremes of intensity may vary by a factor of more than several hundred and the exceeding of film linearity requires exposures of varying duration, photographic recording does not require correction for variation in incident intensity. Nevertheless a counter is preferable to film recording because (1) a wide range of intensity may be measured with constant precision, (2) pulse-height discrimination can be used for scintillation or proportional counters, (3) monochromatization of the diffracted beam is possible, and (4) it is more readily adaptable when accessory equipment is needed for controlling temperature. Moreover, stable x-ray sources make a correction for variation of incident intensity virtually unnecessary.

Because of its better energy resolution at x-ray energies a proportional counter is preferable to a scintillation detector. Rate-meter records may be used where there is enough intensity, but counting at fixed angular steps is recommended for low counting rates.

Monochromatization. Essentially monochromatic radiation must be used, and this may be obtained by

1. A crystal monochromator in either the incident or diffracted beam;[6] the latter arrangement discriminates against fluorescent x-rays except when the sample contains the target element.
2. Balanced or Ross filters.[7]
3. Pulse-height discrimination; this is satisfactory if a $K\beta$ filter and proportional counter are used.

It is desirable to use pulse-height discrimination even with a crystal monochromator to suppress the half wavelength which the monochromator will pass in higher order. In order to obtain reasonable structural resolution short wavelengths such as Mo $K\alpha$ or Ag $K\alpha$ are desirable.

* Some of the laboratories at which diffractometers have been built are at the Oak Ridge National Laboratory; the U.S. Bureau of Mines Eastern Experiment Station, College Park, Md.; the University of Missouri; the University of Arkansas; Yale University; and the laboratories of Professors Krebs, University of Bonn; Furukawa, Tohoku University; and Black and Cundall, Birmingham University.

4. TREATMENT OF DATA

Supposing that an intensity record has been made either as a densitometer tracing or as a plot or tabulation of counting rate, the following steps yield the interatomic part of I_{coh}.

The Background Correction. The correction subtracted will usually be independent of angle and is made automatically for a densitometer zeroed with a film from a blank run. In a properly designed diffractometer the background may be taken as the counting rate with sample removed. With pulse-height discrimination it is possible to maintain very low background rates, e.g., 1 to 2 counts/min.

Polarization Correction. The polarization correction is that used for unpolarized incident radiation and is

$$P(\theta) = (1 + \cos^2 2\theta)/2 \tag{4}$$

or if a crystal monochromator is used it is

$$P(\theta) = (1 + \cos^2 2\alpha \cos^2 2\theta)/(1 + \cos^2 2\alpha) \tag{5}$$

where α is the Bragg angle for the crystal.

Absorption Correction. For a reflection technique the absorption correction $A(\theta)$ is approximately constant with angle for specimens of high linear absorption coefficient, say $\mu \gg 10\ \text{cm}^{-1}$. On the other hand, the absorption correction is quite important[8,9] for systems of low atomic number. For a diffractometer with parafocusing geometry the correction is

$$A(\theta) = 1 - (1 - e^{-x})/x \tag{6}$$

where $x = 2W\mu \csc 2\theta$ and W is the vertical width of the beam at the sample. This expression is derived on the basis of parallel incident and detected rays but is found to be quite accurate for reasonably small divergence angles. Here W is taken as the product of the divergence angle and the distance from the anode to the diffractometer axis. The above relation is also restricted to samples whose depths are greater than $(W \sec \theta_{max})/2$. Where this condition is not met or the divergence angles of incidence and viewing are not the same the relationship is more complicated.[8]

Absorption corrections are available for transmission through flat samples,[10] cylindrical samples,[10,11] and cylindrical samples in thin-walled containers.[12]

Scaling. At this stage one has determined $I(\theta)/P(\theta)A(\theta)$ to within a constant k

$$\mathcal{I} \equiv kI(\theta)/P(\theta)A(\theta) = k(I_{coh} + I_{inc}) \tag{7}$$

To determine k use is made of the fact that for large scattering angle I_{coh} approaches the scattering of independent atoms, that is, f^2, or for a polyatomic system $\Sigma x_i f_i^2$ (x_i = mole fraction). Thus with tables of coherent scattering factors,[13] dispersion corrections[14] if needed, and incoherent intensities,[15] $f^2 + I_{inc}$, or $\Sigma x_i f_i^2 + \Sigma x_i I_{inc}$ for a polyatomic system, is calculated, and a value of k is found such that $\mathcal{I}/k$ coincides with $f^2 + I_{inc}$ at high angle. In addition to this arbitrary scale adjustment by eye, two methods have been proposed for analytical determination of the scale constant. The first[16] is that

$$k = \frac{\int s\mathcal{I}\, ds}{\int s(f^2 + I_{inc})\, ds} \tag{8}$$

The second criterion[17] is that

$$k = \frac{\int s^2\mathcal{I}\, ds}{-2\pi^2\rho_0 f^2(0) + \int s^2[f^2(s) + I_{inc}]\, ds} \tag{9}$$

For a polyatomic liquid $f^2(0)$ is replaced by $[\Sigma x_i f_i(0)]^2$.

These integrals are quickly evaluated graphically, but inasmuch as they extend only to s_{max} rather than to infinity, judgment must be applied in selecting the value of

k, and in any event, it is desirable to have data to values of s as great as possible. Empirically it appears possible to select k by combining the three methods so that $I_{coh} + I_{inc}$ oscillates smoothly about $f^2 + I_{inc}$ for large values of s.

In carrying out the above procedure with data obtained with a monochromator in the diffracted beam it may be necessary to correct the tabulated incoherent intensity for the monochromator's discrimination against Compton scattering. This correction can be obtained by comparison of the intensity obtained with a monochromator to that obtained with balanced filters. Table 1 shows the fraction of incoherent intensity from liquid water passed by a DuMond-Johann-Johansson[18] monochromator of rock salt.

Having obtained the scaled intensity one can get the interatomic part of the coherent intensity $I_{coh} - f^2(s)$ by taking the difference

$$\mathcal{I}/k - (f^2 + I_{inc}) = I_{coh} - f^2 \equiv i(s) \tag{10}$$

or for the polyatomic case

$$\mathcal{I}/k - (\Sigma x_i f_i^2 + \Sigma x_i I_{inc}) = I_{coh} - \Sigma x_i f_i^2 \equiv i(s) \tag{11}$$

and can then proceed to the evaluation of the RDF.

The RDF for Monatomic Samples. In Eq. (3), division of the integral by f^2 essentially compensates for the decrease of I_{coh} brought about by the intra-atomic phase differences, and $i(s)f^{-2}$ may be viewed as having been corrected to give an integrand appropriate to point scatterers. The distribution function thus describes the mean distribution of atom centers, and it is much sharper than the distribution function for electronic charge. Accordingly f^{-2} plays the part of a sharpening function

Table 1. Transmission of Incoherent Intensity

s, Å^{-1}	0.0–4.4	5.0	5.5	6.0	7.0	8.0	9.0	10.0–13.0
Fraction of I_{inc} transmitted	1.00	0.94	0.88	0.72	0.66	0.61	0.52	0.50

applied to the interatomic intensity. It can be seen that its inclusion gives increasing weight to $i(s)$ for increasing s. For this reason the distribution function may contain false maxima, and these are discussed later. Finbak[19] has discussed the properties of the density function evaluated so that

$$4\pi r^2\rho(r) = 4\pi r^2\rho_0 + (2r/\pi)\int_0^\infty si(s)f^{-2}(0)\sin rs\,ds \tag{12}$$

in which the maxima are rather broad and less prominent than those given by Eq. (3). Evaluated in this way the function $\rho(r)$ is less likely to contain false maxima but is badly lacking in resolution. A compromise may be obtained by evaluating

$$4\pi r^2\rho(r) = 4\pi r^2\rho_0 + (2r/\pi)\int_0^\infty si(s)f^{-2}\exp(-bs^2)\sin rs\,ds \tag{13}$$

where b is a constant. In actual practice, then, one evaluates

$$4\pi r^2\rho(r) = 4\pi r^2\rho_0 + (2r/\pi)\int_0^\infty si(s)M_1(s)M_2(s)M_3(s)\sin rs\,ds \tag{14}$$

in which $M_1(s) = f^{-2}(s)$, or for the Finbak distribution function the constant $f^{-2}(0)$
$M_2(s) = \exp(-bs^2)$ [in Eq. (3), $b = 0$]
$M_3(s)$ = a step function which equals one up to s_{max} and is zero beyond

The effect of these modification functions M is discussed later.

The RDF for Polyatomic Samples. A distribution function ρ_e may be evaluated with $i(s)$ given by Eq. (11).

$$4\pi r^2\rho_e(r) = 4\pi r^2\rho_{0e} + (2r/\pi)\int_0^\infty si(s)\sin sr\,ds \tag{15}$$

where $\rho_{0e} = \rho_0[\Sigma x_i f_i(0)]^2$. We use the subscript e to call attention to the fact that this density function is indeed an electronic distribution function rather than an atomic distribution function. Its units are usually taken as electron^2 Å^{-3}. Like the function in Eq. (12), this distribution function is quite poorly resolved. As before, this situation can be improved by application of a sharpening function to compensate, at least in part, for the effect of intra-atomic phase differences. In practice one evaluates

$$4\pi r^2\rho_e(r) = 4\pi r^2\rho_{0e} + (2r/\pi)\int_0^\infty si(s)M_1(s)M_2(s)M_3(s)\sin sr\,ds \tag{16}$$

in which $M_1(s)$ = some convenient sharpening function,[20] for example,[21] $[\Sigma x_i f_i(0)/\Sigma x_i f_i(s)]^2$, and $M_2(s)$ and $M_3(s)$ are the same as before. In either the monatomic or polyatomic case one must then evaluate integrals of the form $\int g(s)\sin rs\,ds$.

5. EVALUATION OF THE INTEGRAL $\int g(s)\sin rs\,ds$

The Fourier sine transform of the function $g(s)$ may be obtained in a variety of ways from a graph or tabulation of values of that function at suitable intervals in s. Although special devices, such as the Mader-Ott analyzer, are available, graphical or numerical techniques are most often used.

Graphical Integration. Graphs of $g(s)\sin rs$ vs. s may be drawn from a set of the following master curves (for example): $\pm g(s)$, $\pm g(s)\sin 72°$, $\pm g(s)\sin 54°$, $\pm g(s)\sin 36°$, $\pm g(s)\sin 18°$, $\pm g(s)\sin 9°$. These master curves are all drawn with the same origin and may be distinguished by a color code. A pair of proportional dividers applied to $\pm g(s)$ allows one to draw the remaining curves quickly and easily. Then for each value of r, strips may be prepared on which are indexed the s values for which sr is 0°, 9°, 18°, 36°, and so forth. For large r it is helpful that the strips be several cycles long, and that positive index values be marked in black and negative in red. By covering the plot of master curves with a sheet of tracing paper and then aligning the origin of a strip with the origin of the master curves, one can easily plot the graph of $g(s)\sin sr$. Drawing in a smooth curve of $g(s)\sin sr$ and planimetering its area gives the value of the integral for the r value selected. The procedure is repeated for each r value at which the integral is to be evaluated. It is much more rapid than hand calculation and is valuable in allowing one to see how various parts of $g(s)$ contribute to the value of the integral.

Numerical Integration. The usual procedure involves some interpolation rule for $g(s)\sin rs$ at evenly spaced intervals in s. For a given size of interval the accuracy of a numerical method depends on the value of r and the degree of the interpolation. A treatment of linear interpolation (that is, the trapezoidal rule) follows.

Since $g(0) = g(s_{\max}) = 0$ the integral is approximated by

$$\int_0^{s_{\max}} g(s)\sin rs\,ds \approx \Delta s\sum_1^{N-1} g(s_j)\sin rs_j \tag{17}$$

where $N = s_{\max}/\Delta s$ and the $s_j = 0, s_1, s_2, \ldots, s_N$. This approximation is periodic in r with period $2\pi/\Delta s$, and if the evaluation is to be extended to some value of r, say r_0, then Δs must be chosen so that $2\pi/\Delta s \gg r_0$. This will ensure that Δs will be considerably smaller than the period of $\sin r_0 s$ and that the area under $g(s)\sin r_0 s$ is reasonably approximated by several trapezoidal panels per loop or cycle. If this condition is met for r_0 it applies even more strongly for $r < r_0$.

For hand calculation, or for a computer program which uses a sine table, it is advantageous to evaluate the integral at values of r, say r_k, such that $\Delta s\,\Delta r$ = some fraction of π. A convenient choice is $\Delta s\,\Delta r = \pi/600$, and this gives

$$\sin r_k s_j = \sin jk\,\Delta r\,\Delta s = \sin 2\pi\,jk/1{,}200$$

In actual use, if we take $\Delta s = 0.05$ Å^{-1}, then the integral is evaluated in steps of about 0.1 Å, or exactly $\pi/30$ Å, which gives adequate detail for most purposes.

For computational use this particular choice of $\Delta r\ \Delta s$ requires a sine table containing values over only one-quarter cycle in steps of 1/1,200 cycle, and values may be extracted according to the following scheme for a given jk product. If we label the entries in the table 0, 1, 2, . . . , 300, then the zeroth entry is 0.0000 and the 300th entry is 1.0000. Now determine jk modulo 1,200, that is, find there mainder R for $jk/1{,}200$ (see Fig. 1).

In a more general technique, Filon[22] has shown that one may make a choice of the size of Δs dependent only upon the accuracy of interpolating between values of $g(s)$ rather than between values of $g(s)$ sin rs. This is accomplished by dividing the range $(0,s_{\max})$ into panels in each of which $g(s)$ is represented by an interpolation polynomial of degree n so that

$$\int g(s) \sin rs\, ds \approx \sum_{\text{all panels}} \int_{\substack{\text{single}\\ \text{panel}}} (a_0 + a_1 s^1 + \cdots + a_n s^n) \sin rs\, ds$$

where, of course, the a's are expressed in terms of ordinate values $g(s_j)$ within the

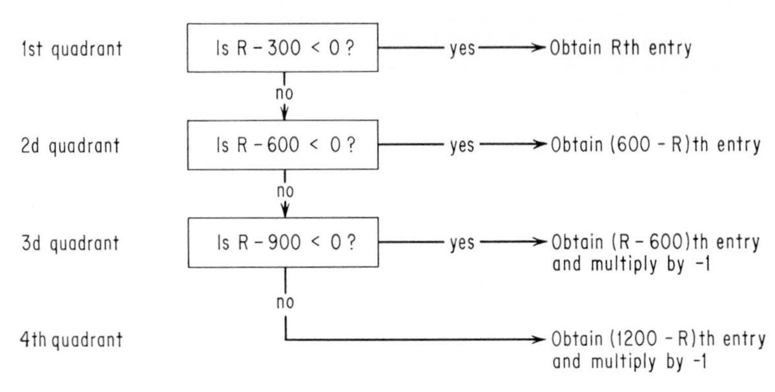

FIG. 1. Logical scheme for selection of sine values.

panel and where the integral is evaluated term by term from analytic expressions for $\int x^n \sin x\, dx$. For a linear-interpolation polynomial one obtains, for example,

$$\int g(s) \sin rs\, ds \approx 2(r\,\Delta s)^{-2}(1 - \cos r\,\Delta s)\,\Delta s \sum_{1}^{N-1} g(s_j) \sin rs_j$$

The result is that for the trapezoidal rule multiplied by a function of $r\,\Delta s$ which partly corrects for the decreasing accuracy of the trapezoidal rule for the larger values of r. More complicated functions arise from interpolations of higher degree, but they have the advantage of constant precision over the entire range of r. To obtain constant precision in interpolation of $g(s)$ sin sr requires a decreasing Δs with increasing r so that $r\,\Delta s$ = constant.

6. INTERPRETATION OF RDFs

The positions of the maxima in the RDF may generally be taken to indicate the most likely mean separations of atom pairs, although the possibility of overlapping unresolved maxima is always present. Areas under resolved maxima indicate the number of atom pairs within a particular range of distance. Together, the number and separation of atom pairs furnish the information for the construction and testing of structural models. This one-dimensional information is similar to the Patterson line projection for crystals, and it is not always possible to deduce a unique three-dimensional geometrical description of structure.

Estimation of Areas. The area under a particular peak, or within a specified range of r, gives, for an atomic RDF, the number of atoms within that range of distance from an atom selected as an origin. Alternatively it gives the number of pairs per atom within that range. For a polyatomic system's electronic distribution

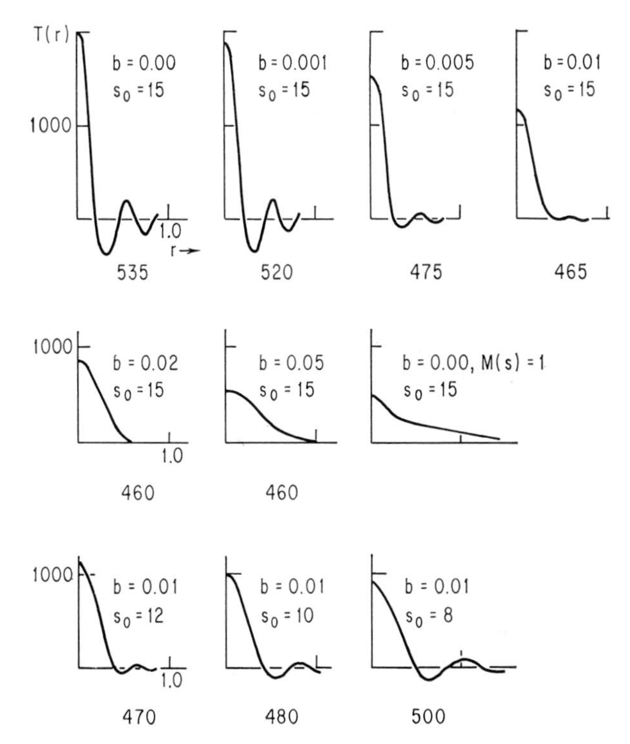

FIG. 2. These curves show the expected shapes of peaks in the RDF for one pair of interacting atoms. The curves were calculated by Eq. (18), and the values of b in $M_2(s)$ and of s_0, the upper limit of integration, are shown. Except for the curve with $M_1(s) = 1$, the sharpening function $M_1(s)$ was taken as f_e^{-2}. The numbers below each curve show the area under the first maximum. The total area under each curve, including ripples, appears to be about 460, however.

function ρ_e it is necessary to know how much area may be associated with a given atom pair. In the Warren-Morningstar-Krutter[21] treatment, that area is $2x_iK_iK_j$ per atom i for unlike and $x_iK_i^2$ for like atoms, where K_i and K_j are effective numbers of electrons. Where atoms of rather different atomic number Z occur, however, the effective electron number is usually reckoned too large for atoms of high Z and too small for low Z.

By making use of Fourier convolution theory it is possible to evaluate the contribution per atom pair making explicit use of individual atomic-form factors. These contributions are given[20,23] as a function of displacement u from the location of the maximum r_0:

$$rT_{ij}(u)/r_0 = (r/r_0\pi) \int_0^\infty f_if_jM_1(s)M_2(s)M_3(s) \cos su \, ds \tag{18}$$

This integral is evaluated by the graphical or numerical methods described before; only a phase shift of $\pi/2$ is required for the trigonometric part.

The value of b in $M_2(s)$ need not be the same as that used in evaluating the sine integral, and its value may be selected to adjust the shape of the calculated to that of the observed maximum. The area under the maximum in T_{ij} remains unchanged by application of a Gaussian damping factor, but larger b values give broader and flatter peaks. This effect is shown in Fig. 2 along with those due to sharpening and the finite upper limit $s_{\max}$. It is apparent that decreasing $s_{\max}$, decreasing the amount of sharpening, and increasing the value of b have comparable effects.

Errors in RDFs. There are a number of discussions[24] of the effects of both experimental error and method of data treatment upon the RDF. Perhaps the most ubiquitous error is that due to finite $s_{\max}$.

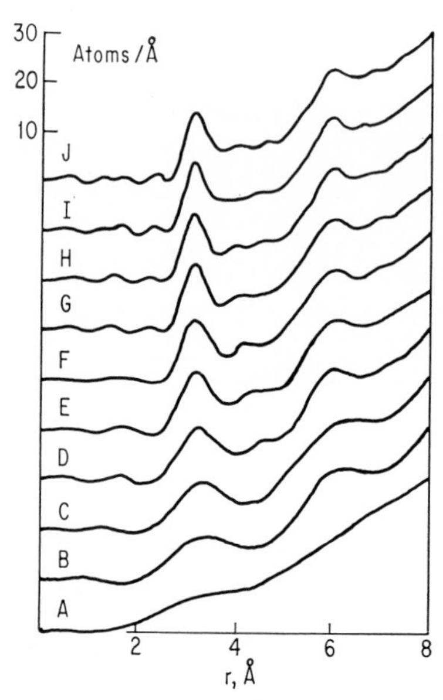

FIG. 3. These radial-distribution curves for liquid mercury were obtained for the following values of $s_{\max}$, in order from A through J: 2.4, 3.1, 4.2, 5.2, 6.3, 7.3, 8.7, 9.4, 10.8, and 12.0 Å^{-1}. These values are the ones at which I_{coh} equals f^2.

Termination Error. The limited resolution arising from a finite upper limit on the Fourier integral produces diffraction ripple which behaves approximately as $(us_{\max})^{-1} \sin us_{\max}$. This effect is shown in Figs. 2 and 3 and can frequently be diagnosed because subsidiary maxima lie at u values for which $us_{\max} = 7.725$, 14.066, and so forth. Figure 2 also indicates how excessive sharpening of the intensity function $i(s)$ may exaggerate ripple. Conversely, Fig. 2 shows how, for a given $M_1(s)$, the amount of sharpening and ripple may be reduced by application of $M_2(s)$.

Peak Position. For a given peak in $\rho(r)$ the value of r at which a maximum occurs increases as we consider, in turn, $\rho(r)$, $4\pi r^2(\rho - \rho_0)$, $4\pi r^2\rho$; and the spread increases the broader the peak in $\rho(r)$. This effect is shown, in exaggerated form, in Fig. 3, where the first peak in $4\pi r^2\rho$ shifts by about 0.3 Å. Scaling error may also have a serious, but less predictable, effect on peak position as well as area.

Oversharpening. Figure 2 shows that excessive sharpening of $i(s)$ may cause negative excursions in the RDF. Moreover the area under the main maximum may be overestimated. A value of b in $M_2(s)$ may be selected which gives a reasonable compromise between false detail and loss of resolution. Extreme oscillation in that part of the RDF between the origin and the first maximum should not occur and may be induced by oversharpening, although scaling and other errors may contribute as well.

7. EXAMPLES

Liquids. Figures 4 and 5 show $si(s)$ and RDFs for liquid mercury and indium and several of their alloys. Although the atomic radii of mercury and indium are

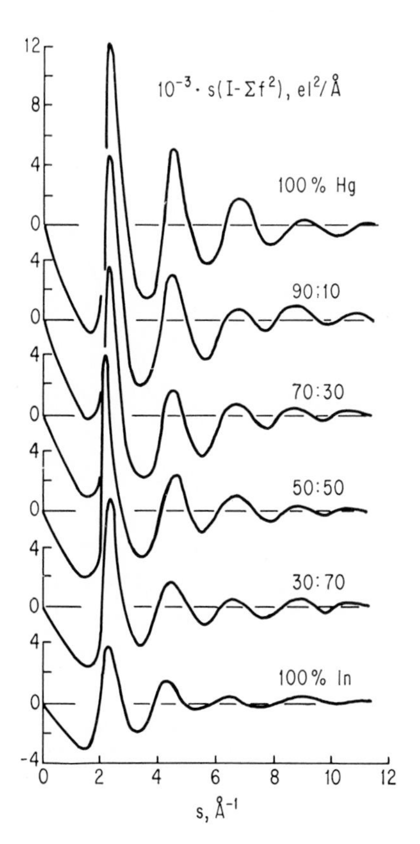

FIG. 4. The function $si(s)$ for the system mercury-indium.

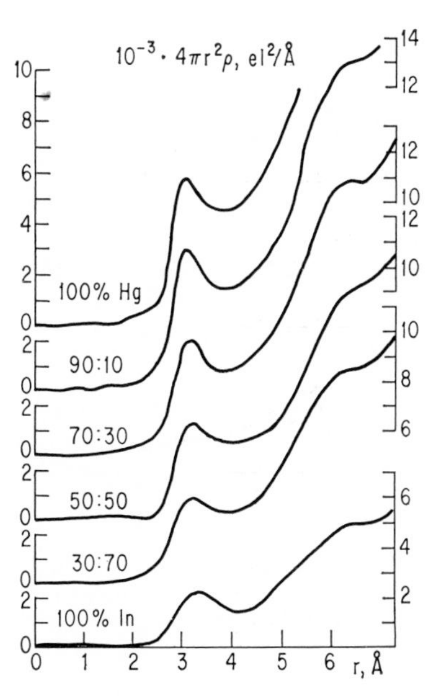

FIG. 5. The radial-distribution functions derived from the functions in Fig. 4.

rather different there is no indication of separately resolved interactions in the alloys. The RDFs have been interpreted[25] in terms of a random participation of atoms in a distribution characterized by a common number of first nearest neighbors. First maxima are at 3.03 and 3.30 Å for mercury and indium, compared with 3.00 and 3.24 to 3.36 Å for nearest-neighbor distances in the crystals.

Glasses. Figures 6, 7, and 8 give results for a series of glasses in the system PbS-As_2S_3. These results show that, in glassy arsenic trisulfide, arsenic retains the coordination it has in the crystalline state, but that the coordination number changes from 3 to 4 as lead sulfide is added. Apparently arsenic adopts tetrahedral and lead octahedral coordination by sulfurs.[26]

Brady has used diffraction techniques to show an unusual distorted octahedral coordination of tellurium in a modified tellurium oxide glass,[27] and also to show that the amorphous material of composition SiO is most probably a mixture of silicon and silica.[28]

Aqueous Solutions. The diffraction method is applicable for reasonably concentrated solutions, but solvent scattering dominates the results if concentrations are too low. To give an example of these limits, we cite Brady's study[29] of aqueous erbium halide solutions. For such a heavy scatterer, usable data were obtained from a solution where only 1.6 per cent of the atoms (not counting hydrogen) were erbium. The results of this study demonstrate nicely the octahedral coordination of Er(III) by water molecules.

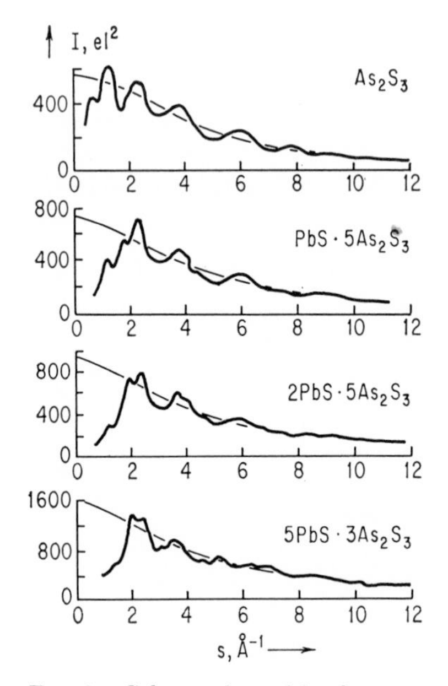

FIG. 6. Coherent intensities for several glasses in the system arsenic sulfide–lead sulfide. The smooth curves are $\Sigma x_i f_i^2$.

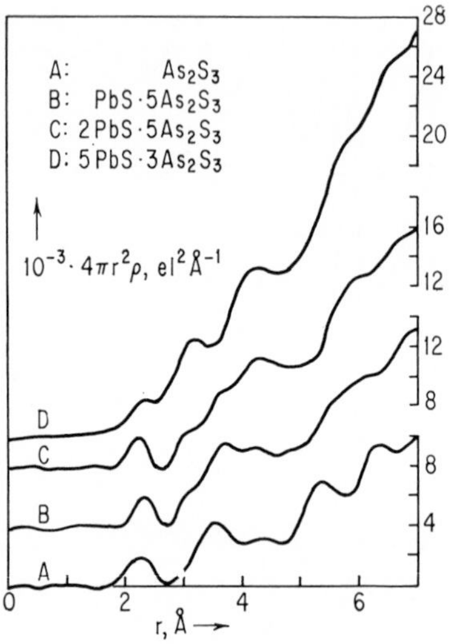

FIG. 7. Radial-distribution functions for glasses in the system arsenic sulfide–lead sulfide.

For solute elements whose atomic numbers are about 30, it is desirable to have a minimum of about 5 per cent of such atoms in the solution. Thus, in a series of measurements[30] on ferric chloride solutions containing added chloride, it was possible to show an average coordination for iron corresponding to $FeCl_4^-$.

In a magnificent study[31] of the silicotungstate ion $SiW_{12}O_{40}^{-4}$ in solution it was shown that the structure obtaining in the solid was retained. This work, done at the Oak Ridge National Laboratory, demonstrates the possibility of verifying structural deductions about monodisperse species by comparing observed and calculated intensities.

Molten Salts. Study[32] of the alkali halides has shown how coordination of ions shifts upon melting, and results[33] for low-melting metal halides give good evidence for the existence of molecules in the liquid state.

Crystalline Powders. The classic study of Warren and Gingrich[34] on orthorhombic sulfur illustrates the application of the RDF technique to a microcrystalline powder. The results show two sulfur neighbors per sulfur, suggesting rings or chains. The method may also be employed for the study of carbon blacks[35] and other poorly defined crystalline systems.

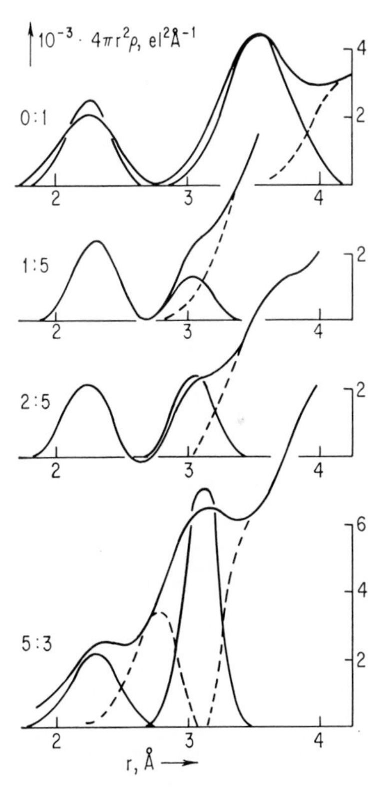

FIG. 8. A comparison of calculated peaks with those occurring in the RDFs shown in Fig. 7. The ratios shown by each curve give the ratio of lead sulfide to arsenic sulfide. For the 1:5 and 2:5 glasses the calculated peak shape for three sulfur neighbors per arsenic at 2.3 Å coincides so closely with that observed that it is not drawn in. A calculated peak shape for three sulfur neighbors per arsenic is indicated for arsenic sulfide, and one for four sulfur neighbors per arsenic is shown for the 5:3 glass. At 3.1 Å calculated peaks are drawn in for six sulfur neighbors per lead, and the calculated peak for arsenic sulfide at about 3.5 Å is for a total of 3 arsenic-arsenic pairs and 14 sulfur-sulfur pairs.

REFERENCES CITED

1. P. Debye, *Z. Physik*, **28**:135 (1927).
2. F. Zernike and J. A. Prins, *Z. Physik*, **41**:184 (1927).
3. P. Debye and H. Menke, *Z. Physik*, **31**:797 (1930).
4. B. E. Warren and N. S. Gingrich, *Phys. Rev.*, **46**:368 (1934).
5. G. Zarzycki, *J. Phys. Radium*, **17**:44A (1956).
6. A. R. Lang, *Rev. Sci. Instr.*, **27**:17 (1956).
7. P. A. Ross, *Phys. Rev.*, **28**:425 (1926); J. A. Soules, W. I. Gordon, and C. H. Shaw, *Rev. Sci. Instr.*, **27**: 12 (1956).
8. M. E. Milberg, *J. Appl. Phys.*, **29**:64 (1958).
9. H. A. Levy, P. A. Agron, and M. D. Danford, *J. Appl. Phys.*, **30**:2012 (1959).
10. K. Sagel, *Tabellen zur Röntgenstrukturanalyse*, sec. B2, Springer-Verlag OHG, Berlin, 1958.

11 *International Tables for X-ray Crystallography*, vol. II, sec. 5.3, Kynoch Press, Birmingham, England, 1959.
12. H. L. Ritter and R. E. Wood, *J. Appl. Phys.*, **22**:169 (1951).
13. K. Sagel, *Tabellen zur Röntgenstrukturanalyse*, p. 106, Springer-Verlag OHG, Berlin, 1958.
14. C. H. Dauben and D. H. Templeton, *Acta Cryst.*, **8**:841 (1955); D. H. Templeton, *Acta Cryst.*, **8**:842 (1955).
15. K. Sagel, *Tabellen zur Röntgenstrukturanalyse*, p. 165, Springer-Verlag OHG, Berlin, 1958. See also A. J. Freeman, *Acta Cryst.*, **12**:274, 929 (1959); *Phys. Rev.*, **113**:169, 176 (1959); *Acta Cryst.*, **13**:190, 618 (1960); **15**:682 (1962).
16. R. Hultgren, N. S. Gingrich, and B. E. Warren, *J. Chem. Phys.*, **3**:351 (1935).
17. J. Krogh-Moe, *Acta Cryst.*, **9**:951 (1956); N. Norman, *Acta Cryst.*, **10**:370 (1957).
18. J. W. M. DuMond and H. A. Kirkpatrick, *Rev. Sci. Instr.*, **1**:88 (1930); N. H. Johann, *Z. Physik*, **69**:185 (1931); T. Johansson, *Naturwiss.*, **20**:758 (1932), *Z. Physik*, **82**:507 (1933).
19. C. Finbak, *Avhandl. Norske Videnskaps-Akad. Oslo. I., Mat. Naturv. Kl.*, no. 3, 14 pp., 1943; *Acta Chem. Scand.*, **3**:1279 (1949).
20. J. Waser and V. Schomaker, *Rev. Mod. Phys.*, **25**: 671 (1953).
21. The expression given is for the function f_e^{-2} utilized by B. E. Warren, H. Krutter, and O. Morningstar, *J. Am. Ceram. Soc.*, **19**:202 (1936).
22. L. N. Filon, *Proc. Roy. Soc. Edinburgh*, **49**:38 (1928–1929).
23. R. F. Kruh, *Chem. Rev.*, **62**:319 (1962).
24. For example, C. Finbak, *Acta Chem. Scand.*, **3**:1279, 1293 (1949); S. Urnes, *Modern Aspects of the Vitreous State*, p. 22, Butterworth & Co. (Publishers), Ltd., London, 1960; J. Waser and V. Schomaker, *Rev. Mod. Phys.*, **25**:671 (1953); A. Bienenstock, *J. Chem. Phys.*, **31**:570 (1959).
25. Y. S. Kim, C. L. Standley, R. F. Kruh, and G. T. Clayton, *J. Chem. Phys.*, **34**:1464 (1961).
26. J. I. Petz, R. F. Kruh, and G. C. Amstutz, *J. Chem. Phys.*, **34**:526 (1961). See T. E. Hopkins, R. A. Pasternak, E. S. Gould, and J. R. Herndon, *J. Chem. Phys.*, **66**:733 (1962), for an interesting study of arsenic trisulfide–iodine glasses.
27. G. W. Brady, *J. Chem. Phys.*, **27**:300 (1957).
28. G. W. Brady, *J. Phys. Chem.*, **63**:1119 (1959).
29. G. W. Brady, *J. Chem. Phys.*, **33**:1079 (1960).
30. C. L. Standley and R. F. Kruh, *J. Chem. Phys.*, **34**:1450 (1961).
31. H. A. Levy, P. A. Agron, and M. D. Danford, *J. Chem. Phys.*, **30**:1486 (1959).
32. H. A. Levy, P. A. Agron, M. A. Bredig, and M. D. Danford, *Ann. N.Y. Acad. Sci.*, **79**:762 (1960).
33. R. L. Harris, R. E. Wood, and H. L. Ritter, *J. Am. Chem. Soc.*, **73**:3251 (1951); R. E. Wood and H. L. Ritter, *J. Am. Chem. Soc.*, **74**:1760, 1963 (1952).
34. B. E. Warren and N. S. Gingrich, *Phys. Rev.*, **46**:368 (1934).
35. R. E. Franklin, *Acta Cryst.*, **3**:107 (1950).

GENERAL REFERENCES

Fournet, G.: *Handbuch der Physik*, vol. XXXII, pp. 238–320, Springer-Verlag OHG, Berlin, 1957.
Furukawa, K.: *Rept. Progr. Phys.*, **25**:395 (1962).
Gingrich, N. S.: *Rev. Mod. Phys.*, **15**:90 (1943).
James, R. W.: *Optical Principles of the Diffraction of X-rays*, chap. IX, G. Bell & Sons, Ltd., London, 1950.
Kruh, R. F.: *Chem. Rev.*, **62**:319 (1962).
Pirenne, M. H.: *The Diffraction of X-rays and Electrons by Free Molecules*, Cambridge University Press, New York, 1946.
Prins, J. A.: *Selected Topics in X-ray Crystallography*, p. 191, North Holland Publishing Company, Amsterdam, 1951.
Riley, D. P.: *X-ray Diffraction by Polycrystalline Materials*, pp. 438–453, Institute of Physics, London, 1955.
Waser, J., and V. Schomaker: *Rev. Mod. Phys.*, **25**:671 (1953).

Chapter 23

RELATED TECHNIQUES

C. M. Schwartz

Battelle Memorial Institute

This chapter provides a brief description of two techniques, electron diffraction and neutron diffraction, each with amply demonstrated ability to supplement x-ray diffraction in analysis of crystal structure. Each of these techniques represents a diffraction phenomenon resulting from the interaction of radiation with crystalline material, and the data provided are, in general, similar to those of x-ray diffraction. However, because of the specific properties of these radiations, their interactions are each sufficiently different to provide unique information not obtainable by x-ray diffraction. In the case of electron diffraction, for example, information is obtainable on the structure and properties of surfaces and surface films and on the identification of microconstituents. Neutron diffraction, because of its special characteristics, is capable of determining the positions of the light elements such as hydrogen, and of providing a wealth of detail concerning magnetic structure, which is superimposed upon the ordinary crystal structure of magnetic compounds and alloys but is not detectable by x-ray diffraction.

It is the objective of this chapter to outline very briefly the theory and physical basis for the unique properties of these two techniques and to point out their applications to structural problems. Detailed descriptions of theory, apparatus, and analytical procedures are available in the cited literature.

1. ELECTRON DIFFRACTION

Wave Motion of Electrons. The dual nature, wave and particulate, of the properties of electromagnetic radiation is well established. The wave properties are evidenced by diffraction effects; corpuscular behavior, by such phenomena as the photoelectric effect and Compton scattering of x-rays. In 1924, L. de Broglie considered whether moving electrons, which are recognized as discrete particles, may exhibit any wave properties. He showed that it was indeed possible to express mathematically the motion of any particle in terms of wave propagation, the wavelength λ being determined by the momentum mv of the particle of mass m and velocity v, according to the relation

$$\lambda = h/mv \tag{1}$$

where h is Planck's constant. Since the velocity v of a stream of electrons is a function of the potential applied to the electrodes of the vacuum tube, for a potential V of a few thousand volts the kinetic energy of the electrons is given by the expression

$$mv^2/2 = eV/300 \tag{2}$$

where m and e are the mass and charge, respectively, of the electron. Substituting in Eq. (1), and with suitable choice of units, it thus follows that

$$\lambda = (150/V)^{1/2}\text{Å}^* \tag{3}$$

Table 1 lists the wavelengths of electron waves for several values of the accelerating potential.

It is important to note that the wavelength associated with 150-volt electrons is 1.0 Å and the wavelength associated with 50,000-volt electrons is approximately 0.05 Å. The former is of the same order of magnitude as the usual wavelengths employed in x-ray diffraction work, whereas the latter is much smaller. At first thought it would appear that low-voltage electrons would be superior for diffraction studies, on the basis of the well-known criterion for diffraction, which specifies that the wavelength of the radiation be of the same order of magnitude as the spacing of the diffracting centers. This would be true, except for the experimental difficulties encountered in this voltage range, owing to (1) the weak penetrating power of slow electrons, resulting in extreme sensitivity to surface contamination and thus requiring use of an ultra-clean high-vacuum system, and (2) the difficulty of detecting the scattered electrons. Furthermore, because of the limited penetration of the surface the information obtained is usually incomplete. It is not surprising, therefore, that high-voltage electron diffraction has been more fully developed.

Table 1. Wavelengths of Electron Waves

Potential, kv	Wavelength	
	Uncorrected λ_u, Å	Relativistic λ_{rel}, Å
20	0.0868	0.0859
30	0.0708	0.0698
40	0.0613	0.0602
50	0.0549	0.0536
60	0.0501	0.0487
70	0.0464	0.0449
80	0.0434	0.0418
90	0.0409	0.0392
100	0.0388	0.0370

Apparatus and Techniques. The first experimental demonstration of the diffraction of electrons was accomplished in 1927 by Davisson and Germer[1] using low-voltage electrons. Although this method is sensitive to the detection of even fractional monolayers on the surface of a specimen, relatively few applications have been reported because of the inherent difficulties just mentioned. However, interest in low-voltage electron diffraction has now been revived owing partly to improvement in methods of detection and in the associated ultra-high vacuum techniques. This method will undoubtedly receive more attention in the near future. The interested reader is referred to the literature.[1-3]

Following the development (1927) of high-voltage electron-diffraction apparatus by G. P. Thomson[4] in England, this technique has been rapidly extended and refined, both in instrumentation and in application.[5-7] Although many laboratory-designed instruments are in existence, it is now possible to purchase apparatus specifically designed for electron diffraction as well as electron microscopes containing electron-

* For higher applied voltages this equation must be corrected for relativistic effects on the mass of the electron.

diffraction accessories. The simplest apparatus usually includes the diffraction camera itself, together with its associated vacuum supply and a generator of constant d-c potential. The camera consists of an electrode structure with electron source and anode across which the accelerating potential is applied, a pinhole aperture to collimate the electron beam into a narrow pencil of the order of $\frac{1}{10}$ mm in diameter, a specimen chamber with a stage capable of orienting the specimen according to the particular technique employed, and a photographic plate chamber and fluorescent screen situated some distance from the specimen. Figure 1*a* shows a schematic diagram of a simple camera of this type. Owing to the short wavelength of the electrons, all the useable diffraction information is obtained within an angle of less than 10°; therefore, in order to obtain adequate dispersion in this type of instrument it is necessary that the specimen-to-plate distance be large, say, of the order of 50 cm. The electron

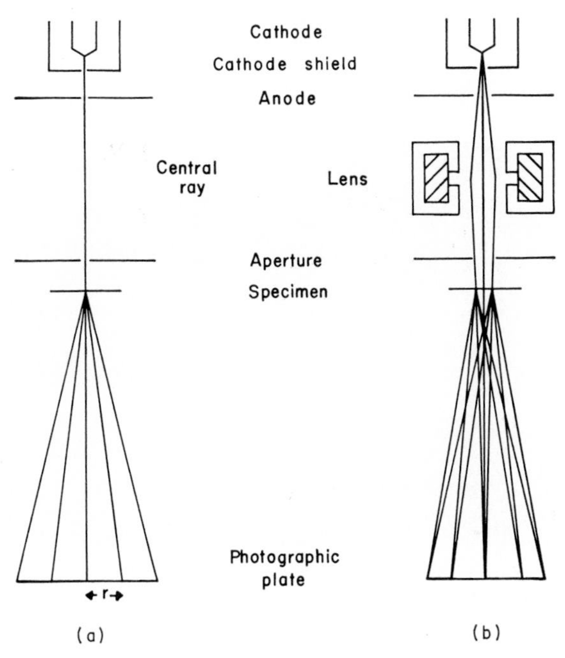

Fig. 1. Electron-diffraction camera schematic and ray diagrams. (*a*) Pinhole collimation, (*b*) magnetic lens focusing.

source may be either a hot filament electron gun or a gaseous discharge tube. The total electron current from the source is rarely over 500 μa, and that in the collimated beam striking the specimen, usually 0.01 to 1 μa. Photographic exposures are very short compared with x-ray exposures, being of the order of seconds to minutes. The entire apparatus must be evacuated to a pressure of at least 0.1 micron except in the case of the gas discharge type of camera, where the source chamber must be held at a somewhat higher pressure to maintain the discharge. The high-voltage generator should develop d-c accelerating potentials of 30 to 100 kv at low current, but the selected voltage must be well stabilized, say, to at least 0.1 per cent.

If, in Fig. 1*a*, the specimen S is a thin film of polycrystalline material through which the electron beam traverses, a typical powder diffraction pattern of concentric rings is seen on the fluorescent screen or recorded on the photographic plate. For a specimen-to-plate distance L and a ring radius r

$$\tan 2\theta = r/L \tag{4}$$

where θ is the Bragg angle. Since the angle θ is very small (short wavelength λ), we have, from Eq. (4) and the Bragg equation, the relation

$$\tan 2\theta \cong \sin 2\theta \cong 2 \sin \theta \cong n\lambda/d$$

to a close approximation. Thus for fast electrons,

$$d/n = \lambda L/r = K/r \tag{5}$$

where $K = \lambda L$ is the camera constant. According to Eq. (5), for example, with $\lambda = 0.05$ Å (= 50-kv electrons) and $L = 50$ cm ($K = 2.5$), the diffraction-ring radius for a 1.0 Å spacing will be 2.5 cm, and the diffraction angle 2θ, about 3°. With pinhole collimation, it is hardly possible to measure diffraction-ring radii to better than 0.1 mm. Adding the uncertainty of about the same magnitude in evaluation of the camera constant K, an overall precision not greater than ½ to 1 per cent is generally attained.

In order to improve on the resolution of the device and thus to increase the precision of lattice-constant measurement, it is possible to employ focusing of the electron beam.

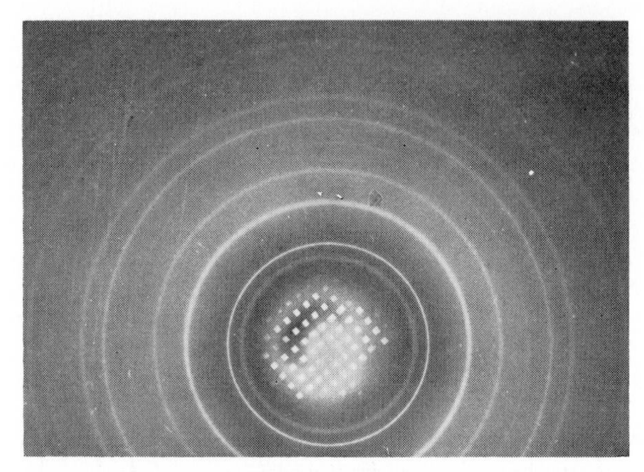

FIG. 2. Transmission pattern of MgO smoke particles. The effect of refraction of electrons traversing cube-shaped particles is evident in the broadening of all reflections except (h00), which are quite sharp.

This has been accomplished by inserting an electromagnetic (or electrostatic) lens between the source and photographic plate (shown schematically in Fig. 1b) and focusing an intense source of small cross section onto the photographic plate. In this way an image spot size of the order of 10 microns on the photographic plate is readily obtained, with corresponding increased sharpness of the diffraction pattern. In a precision camera the sample must be placed between the lens and the photographic plate; with this arrangement, there is no electron optical magnification of the diffraction pattern, and thus distortion of the diffraction image due to lens aberrations is avoided. Figure 1b shows the ray diagram for this arrangement. The diverging electron beam from the source through the anode aperture is focused by the lens onto the photographic plate. The specimen S is placed beyond the lens in the converging beam. The diffraction pattern is in sharp focus and undistorted. The camera constant K is the same as in Eq. (5). Figure 2, a transmission pattern of MgO, is representative of this technique. Using transmission specimens in this type of camera and special techniques to minimize errors, it is possible to measure interplanar spacings to about 0.1 per cent. The precision of measurement of ring radii is improved over that of the pinhole camera by the increased sharpness of the rings; and if λ were known precisely, an accurate value of the camera constant K could be obtained by use of a separate (external) calibrating standard specimen. However, constancy of the accelerating voltage and, therefore, the wavelength cannot be assumed in spite of the usual precautions taken to stabilize it. Thus the common procedure of taking successive exposures of sample and standard, in the hope that the voltage will have remained constant during this time, is not reliable for highest precision. Perhaps the most satisfactory technique is to prepare the specimen with a calibration material (internal standard) combined with it. This can be done, for example, by evaporating a very thin film (25 Å) of pure aluminum onto the specimen. The resulting diffraction photograph is a superposition of the patterns of specimen and standard. Since the voltage is identical for the two patterns, wavelength fluctuation is eliminated as a source of error, and direct comparison of adjacent ring radii of standard and specimen can yield interplanar spacings to the precision specified.

The third type of electron-diffraction instrumentation now available is in the form of accessories supplied with many electron microscopes, in which all the components specified for the simple cameras above are incorporated. In addition to providing for the precision electron-diffraction technique, there is another feature, called selected area diffraction, which combines conventional viewing of the image of the specimen directly in the electron microscope with the ability to obtain diffraction data from a chosen small area of the specimen. The method is as follows: The sample, in the form of a very thin foil or of a layer of fine particles on a thin support, is viewed by normal direct transmission microscopy. A selected portion of the electron optical image may then be chosen for selected area diffraction examination; this is accomplished by providing the electron microscope with an adjustable aperture which can be used to mask off all but the desired portion of the object, as seen in the microscope. Converting from microscopy to diffraction in this type of instrument generally is a simple matter of adjustment of auxiliary lens currents so as to focus the back focal plane of the microscope objective, rather than its image plane, onto the fluorescent screen. Thus the electron optical image and diffraction image can be viewed consecutively in a matter of seconds. The basis for this operation lies in the diffraction theory of image formation, according to which any image is a reconstruction of all the orders of the diffraction pattern. This is illustrated in Fig. 3, where it is seen that the diffraction pattern of the specimen is focused in the back focal plane F of the electron-microscope objective O. For simplicity, only the zero-order and first-order components of the pattern are indicated; their recombination to form the magnified image in image plane I is also shown. The instrument can usually be stopped down to cover objects as small as 1 square micron in area, using the adjustable aperture. If the selected object is a single crystal, single-crystal patterns are readily obtained (Fig. 4). In this technique, the diffraction image has passed through at least two or three lenses, and some distortion of the pattern is unavoidable. In this case also, the effective camera length L in Eq. (5) varies with the current (magnification) in any lens positioned after the specimen, and must be determined for each setting of the controls. This is usually accomplished by employment of "standard" samples. The precision of the measurement is generally quite adequate for phase identification purposes, or for determination of the symmetry of the single-crystal patterns.

Electron Scattering and Interference. The simple theory describing the interaction of electrons with the atomic array of the crystal lattice is quite analogous to the x-ray case, involving classical elastic scattering of electrons by the diffracting centers to produce interference phenomena. The Bragg equation, relating the interplanar spacing, the wavelength, and the incidence angle, holds exactly, and the electron-diffraction pattern of a polycrystalline material appears very similar to its x-ray pattern. However, there are important factors peculiar to electron diffraction which lead to its unique properties and, in turn, limit its range of application. For example, owing to the short wavelength of the radiation, all useable diffraction phenomena occur within a small scattering angle, and it is impossible to obtain the high precision of the x-ray measurement of cell constants. However, sufficient accuracy is usually obtainable for phase-identification purposes. Secondly, the strong interaction between the electrons and the atomic array results in low penetration of the specimen. Thus, in the case of reflection electron diffraction, one must contend with an extreme

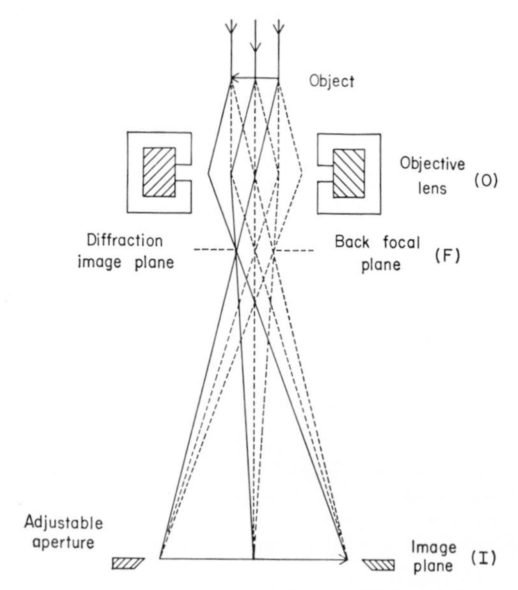

FIG. 3. Selected-area electron-diffraction ray diagram, showing zero-order and first-order ray paths focused by the objective lens *O*. The adjustable aperture in the image plane *I* permits selection of desired portion of object from which diffraction is obtained.

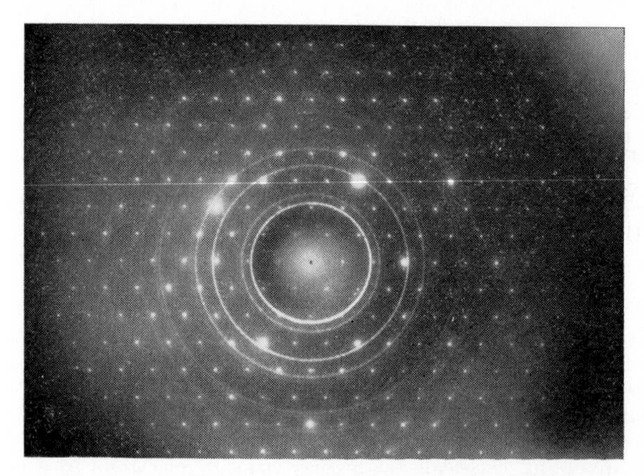

FIG. 4. Selected-area electron-diffraction pattern of pyrophyllite flake, on an evaporated aluminum substrate. The continuous rings of aluminum are used for calibration of the camera constant. The cross-grating pattern is a projection of the reciprocal lattice in the c^* direction.

sensitivity to the presence of surface contaminant, which, since it leads to extra "reflections," must be guarded against continually. Finally, as in the case of x-ray diffraction, the Laue conditions apply to electron-diffraction phenomena. If the crystal size is extremely small, the diffraction ring intensities will be broadened as a result of insufficient periodicity of the lattice and, therefore, relaxation of the Laue conditions (cf. Chap. 15).

Thus the conditions for obtaining typical polycrystalline electron-diffraction patterns are fairly stringent:

1. In order to avoid attenuation of the diffraction pattern due to excessive incoherent scattering, the crystallites of the powder specimen must be less than approximately 3,000 Å thick.

FIG. 5. Reflection electron-diffraction pattern of a Cu_2O film on copper formed by anodic oxidation in an electrolytic bath.

Table 2. Measured Interplanar Spacings and Intensities of Cu_2O Pattern of Fig. 5

r_{cm}	d_{obs}, Å	$d_{x\text{-ray}}$*	I_{obs}	$I_{x\text{-ray}}$*	*hkl*
0.92	3.01	3.020	*m*	9	110
1.12	2.47	2.465	*s*	100	111
1.30	2.13	2.135	*ms*	37	200
1.59	1.74	1.743	*w*	1	211
1.84	1.51	1.510	*ms*	27	220
2.16	1.28	1.287	*ms*	17	311
2.24	1.24	1.233	?	4	222
2.38	1.16	......	*vvw*	...	321
2.60	1.065	1.0674	*vw*	2	400
2.83	0.979	0.9795	*w*	4	331
2.89	0.959	0.9548	*w*	3	420
3.18	0.871	0.8715	*w*	3	422
3.37	0.822	0.8216	*w*	3	511, 333
K = 2.77					

* H. E. Swanson and R. K. Fuyat, NBS Pattern, *National Bureau of Standards Circular* 539, II, p. 24, June 15, 1953.

2. The crystallite dimensions must be greater than about 100 Å; otherwise broadening of the diffraction maxima will be observed (particle-size broadening as in the x-ray case).

3. The orientation of the particles must be random.

Under these conditions a typical "powder" diffraction pattern is usually obtained, as illustrated in Fig. 5, a reflection pattern of Cu_2O. Table 2 lists the measured ring radii of this pattern, the interplanar spacings d/n calculated from the ring radii according to Eq. (5), the visually observed intensities, and the corresponding indices of the diffracting planes.

Other factors, such as refraction, multiple scattering, and dynamic interaction, frequently affect the positions or intensities of the diffraction maxima, increasing the difficulty of interpretation of powder patterns.

Intensity. The scattering intensity is a function of the scattering power of the individual atoms of the crystal. For x-rays, the coherent scattering efficiency or atomic scattering factor f_0 varies with the number of electrons and therefore with the atomic number Z of the scattering atom. On the other hand, electrons are scattered by the nucleus as well as by the electron cloud. Thus the scattering factor for electrons coherently scattered by the atom is

$$f_e = \frac{e^2 m}{2h^2}(Z - f_0)\left(\frac{\lambda}{\sin\theta}\right)^2 \tag{6}$$

where e and m are, respectively, the charge and mass of the electron, and h is Planck's constant. Both f_e and f_0 are inverse functions of $\sin\theta/\lambda$, but f_e is numerically much larger than f_0 at the small angles involved in electron diffraction. Therefore electron scattering efficiencies are much higher than for x-rays.

In computing the intensities of electron-diffraction patterns resulting from the interference of the electron waves scattered by the atoms of the crystal lattice, the factor f_e is substituted for f_0 in the usual expression for the structure amplitude F_{hkl}. The equation for the relative intensities of scattering of electrons by a polycrystalline specimen is of the form

$$I_{hkl} \cong pF^2_{hkl}/\sin^2\theta \tag{7}$$

where p is the usual multiplicity factor. This is simpler than the x-ray analog, since the polarization term $(1 + \cos^2 2\theta)/2$ is omitted, and the term $\cos\theta \cong 1$.

Preparation of Specimens. The two techniques employed in electron diffraction (direct transmission through the specimen and reflection from the surface of the specimen) obviously require different methods of specimen preparation. For transmission electron diffraction, the specimen must be thin enough to permit electrons to traverse the specimen without loss of energy, that is, the thickness must be of the order of 1,000 Å or less, depending upon the applied voltage. Thin specimens for transmission studies have been prepared satisfactorily in a number of ways: by etching, by deposition from the vapor state, by sputtering, or by removal of an oxide film or other thin surface layer from the substrate.

Specimens for reflection electron diffraction can be prepared quite simply. It is necessary that the specimen surface be relatively flat on a macroscopic scale, because of the small incident angle θ. However, to obtain good patterns from a polycrystalline specimen the surface must be somewhat rough on a microscopic scale, thus providing a large number of small asperities. If the tips of these asperities are no thicker than a few hundred angstroms in the direction of the incident beam, the electrons can traverse them as in transmission electron diffraction and yield a satisfactory diffraction pattern. Since reflection electron diffraction is so sensitive to the presence of contaminant on the surface, it is essential that the surface be maintained as clean as possible. To satisfy these conditions, the surface is typically lapped flat, yielding a slightly roughened surface. However, it is usually necessary to remove any mechanically distorted layer. This may frequently be accomplished by light etching, followed by rinsing successively in water and organic solvent, to remove traces of etchant, grease, etc.

Application of Electron Diffraction to Polycrystalline Materials. Most of the important applications of electron diffraction stem from its inherent sensitivity for detection of extremely thin layers of material. Thus it may be employed to detect a wide variety of materials in polycrystalline form deposited on the surface in the form of dust or other particulate material (Fig. 2), oxidation or corrosion products (Fig. 5), many types of grease films (Fig. 6), and reaction products of solids with their environments. Since films as thin as 10 to 20 Å can be detected, it is often possible to detect incipient reaction such as oxidation or corrosion and to follow phase changes (with film growth) due to concentration gradients of the diffusing ion species. As a result, electron diffraction is useful in supplementing the results obtained by x-ray diffraction, primarily in situations where its low penetrating power is an advantage.

The identification of powder patterns is quite analogous to the x-ray case (see Chap. 11, Sec. 2), and it is usually possible to employ the powder diffraction file, due

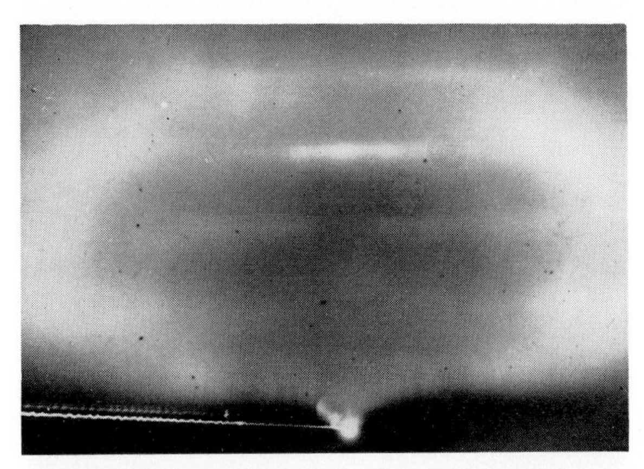

Fig. 6. Reflection electron diffraction pattern of oriented grease, obtained by "rubbing" a hydrocarbon grease film on a metal block. The highly oriented arrangement of straight-chain molecules nearly normal to the surface produces this typical layer-line pattern.

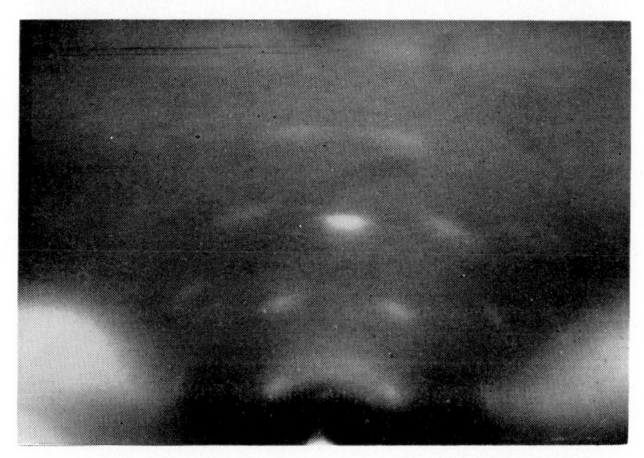

Fig. 7. Reflection pattern of evaporated iron, showing preferred orientation, [111] direction normal to the plane of the deposit.

care being taken to avoid or to account for the presence of "extra" rings, orientation, multiple scattering, refraction, etc.

Preferred orientation in the deposited films may also be detected and analyzed by electron diffraction (Fig. 7). Orientation is detected in the pattern by arcing (that is, a nonuniform distribution of intensity around the ring circumference) or, in some cases, by abnormal intensities or even by the absence of certain reflections. The interpretation of an orientation pattern is similar to the x-ray case (cf. Chap. 18) and will not be discussed further here. Epitaxy, a special case of orientation in which a deposited layer is oriented with respect to its substrate, has been extensively studied by electron diffraction (Fig. 8). Epitaxy is important in current technological applications, specifically in the development of solid-state devices and microcircuitry.

Since the crystallite size of the specimen affects the breadth of the diffraction rings, it is also possible to use the line breadth as a measure of crystallite size, as in the case of x-rays (cf. Chap. 17).

Crystal Structure Determination by Electron Diffraction. The application of electron diffraction to the study of crystal structure requires consideration of a number of factors essential to the proper interpretation of the data; some of these are:

1. The short wavelength of fast electrons
2. The strong interaction between electrons and the scattering atoms, requiring use of very thin specimens
3. Effects of crystal imperfections
4. Dynamic interactions
5. Multiple dynamic scattering

The diffraction of x-rays by crystals of reasonable perfection and periodicity depends upon the simultaneous fulfillment of the three Laue conditions for interference. This criterion is also true for some electron-diffraction patterns, but in many

Fig. 8. Reflection pattern of epitaxially grown iron oxide Fe_3O_4 (or λ-Fe_2O_3) on iron substrate oriented as in Fig. 7. Oxide orientation [110] normal to surface.

cases, the diffraction data must be attributed to one- or two-dimensional scattering. Such effects are produced by the thinness of the crystals required to obtain penetration by the electron beam and by the special geometric conditions imposed by the short wavelength of the electrons.

Diffraction of radiation of wavelength λ from a linear lattice (a straight row of atoms of periodic spacing a) satisfies the Laue condition

$$n\lambda = a(\cos \varphi - \cos \psi) \tag{8}$$

where φ is the conventional angle between incident ray and the row of atoms, and ψ is the angle between lattice row direction and the diffracted ray. The amplitude of the diffracted wave is the result of the superposition of the spherical waves emitted by each atom. For monochromatic radiation λ, the scattered radiation according to Eq. (8) emerges as a set of n ($n = 0, 1, 2, 3, \ldots$) concentric cones with corresponding apex angles $2\psi_n$ and with common cone axis parallel to the lattice row. The intersection of the set of cones with the photographic plate determines the shape of the curves of intensity maxima on the plate. Consider an orthogonal lattice with the electron beam parallel to the c axis. For the c lattice row parallel to the incident beam ($\varphi = 0$) and perpendicular to the plate, the cones intersect in a set of concentric circles centered about the point of intersection of the primary beam on the plate. The diffraction cones from a linear lattice row a or b, placed perpendicular to the incident beam, intersect the plate in a set of hyperbolae with common axis parallel to the plate and to the lattice row. The conditions differ from the x-ray case, however, in that the apex angles $2\psi_n$ for the cones about the c axis are very small ($\varphi \cong 0$) and intersect the plate in small circles, whereas the cones about the a and b axes ($\psi \cong \varphi \cong 90°$) intersect the plate in approximately straight lines. Figure 9 illustrates the superposition of three orthogonal linear-lattice spectra. In the case of diffraction by a three-dimensional lattice, all three interference conditions are fulfilled simultaneously only at the points of mutual intersection of the three spectral sets, the probability of which, in the x-ray case, is very small for a stationary crystal in a monochromatic beam. However, owing to the small electron wavelength, the amount of lattice rotation required for electron diffraction is only one or two degrees over

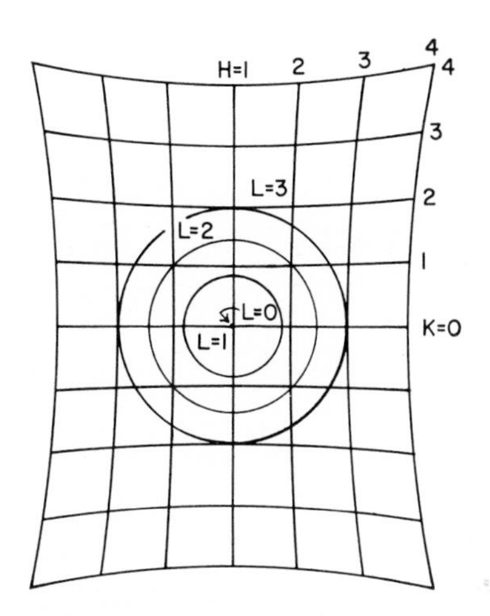

FIG. 9. Superposition of three orthogonal linear-lattice spectra satisfying the Laue conditions for electron diffraction.

several orders of reflection. This small distortion may easily occur in single crystals because of either lattice bending of thin films or "mosaic" structural imperfections. Thus, single-crystal spot patterns of the type shown in Fig. 4 are frequently observed, wherein several orders of reflection appear simultaneously from a set of planes in a single zone whose axis is parallel to the electron beam. This is a pattern of a pyrophyllite platelet with the electron beam oriented in the direction of the pseudohexagonal axis.

This effect of the short wavelength of electrons is illustrated by the reciprocal-lattice† construction in Fig. 10 which is drawn to scale for $\lambda = 0.05$ Å and d spacing $= 20$ Å (the approximate conditions for a mica flake perpendicular to the beam). As $1/\lambda = 20$ Å^{-1} and $c^* = 0.05$ Å^{-1}, the radius of the sphere of reflection is 400 times greater than the reciprocal-lattice spacing, and the curve of the sphere is almost a straight line on the scale of the plot. Since any reciprocal-lattice point in contact with the sphere is in position to diffract, it is evident that slight bending of the sheet or any lattice distortion due to mosaic structure, cleavage, or fracture is sufficient to produce a two-dimensional array of spots.

We shall now consider briefly the effect of specimen thickness on transmission

† For a discussion of the reciprocal lattice, see Chap. 26.

electron-diffraction patterns. It can be shown[8] that the resolving power for diffraction from a row of atoms parallel to the electron beam is much less than for atom rows in the plane of the specimen. As a result, the cones which intersect the photographic plate in concentric circles become diffuse, the diffuseness increasing with decreasing order of diffraction. The effect is represented in reciprocal space by extension of the reciprocal-lattice points into streaks in the thin direction of the crystal, as shown in Fig. 10. Thus, many of the extended points touch the sphere of reflection, and the diffraction pattern consists of an extended two-dimensional array called a cross-grating pattern (Fig. 4). The intensities of the spots are frequently abnormal, and certain reflections appear which are forbidden by extinction in the case of three-dimensional diffraction. As indicated previously, even if the reciprocal-lattice points are not extended because of the thinness of the crystal, bending, distortion, or imperfection of the lattice will result in contact of the reflection sphere with reciprocal-lattice points.

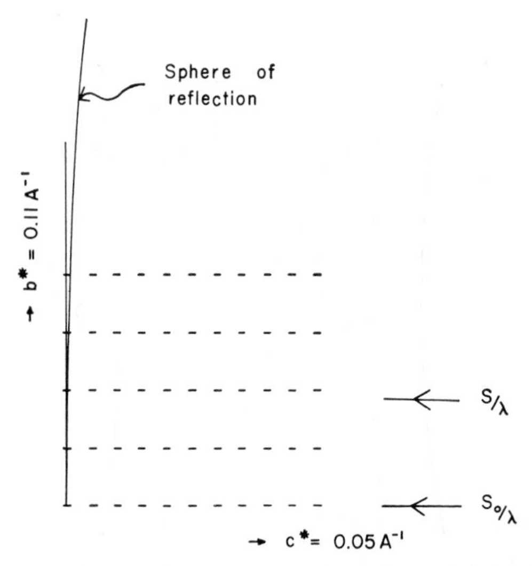

FIG. 10. Reciprocal lattice construction for $c^* = 0.05$ Å^{-1} and $1/\lambda = 20$ Å^{-1}, showing extension of the reciprocal-lattice points in the c^* direction (approximate conditions for a thin mica sheet normal to the electron beam).

Dynamic scattering effects may be observed in the case of thicker specimens ($\cong 10^{-5}$ cm thick), particularly in cases of highly perfect crystals. Because of the strong interaction of electrons with the lattice, considerable scattering takes place within the crystal, both elastic and inelastic. Elastically scattered electrons traveling inthe correct direction for reflection from certain crystal planes will be coherently scattered, enhancing the recorded intensity in corresponding lines on the photographic plate (above the general blackening due to inelastically scattered electrons) and removing energy in the direction of the scattered ray before reflection. Because of the decrease in intensity of elastic scattering with angle of deviation from the direct beam, there is a net enhancement of rays initially scattered at small angles and weakening of those initially scattered at large angles. Thus, the plate will exhibit a pair of black and white lines parallel to and equidistant from the projection of the crystal plane. The series of black and white lines is called a Kikuchi pattern[9] and is similar to Kossel patterns observed with x-rays. The Kikuchi pattern is evidence of high crystal perfection. Dynamic theory of diffraction has been employed successfully to explain the phenomenon.[10]

Dynamic interaction can cause other effects, such as refraction of rays at faces of regularly shaped crystals,[11,12] causing fine structure (multiplicity) of the diffraction spots. Even when the spots overlap, as in a powder pattern, the multiplicity causes broadening of certain diffraction rings, as shown in Fig. 2, where all rings but ($h00$) are broadened by refraction in the cube-shaped particles of MgO. This effect should not be confused with particle-size broadening. Multiple scattering can produce reflections which are "forbidden" by the crystal structure.[13]

Thus, it is evident that considerable care must be employed in interpretation of crystal structure data by electron diffraction. Nevertheless, a great deal of information may be obtained, particularly if one uses precautions in sample preparation to obtain crystals thin enough to yield cross-grating patterns. These may be thought of as essentially plane sections of the reciprocal lattice so that the reciprocal-lattice points may be indexed without difficulty.

2. NEUTRON DIFFRACTION

General Considerations. In accordance with the de Broglie relation, Eq. (1) of the previous section, it is evident that wave properties are associated with the motion of any particle. Therefore, it should be possible to diffract a beam of neutrons by the atomic arrangement of crystals in a manner analogous to x-ray or electron diffraction if the appropriate experimental conditions are established.[14] A necessary criterion for diffraction by a crystalline lattice is that the neutron wavelength be of the same order as the interatomic distances, i.e., approximately 1 Å.

Fortunately, it happens that an intense source of neutrons with velocities equivalent to a wavelength of the order of 1 Å is readily available from many of the research nuclear reactors, specifically of the "thermal" type. In the reactor, the fission neutrons make many collisions with moderator atoms at absolute temperature T and their rms velocity on escape from the reactor is that given by the equation

$$\tfrac{1}{2}mv^2 = \tfrac{3}{2}kT \tag{9}$$

where k is Boltzmann's constant. Fortunately, it happens that for thermal neutrons, that is, neutrons emerging from a moderator at essentially room temperature, the wavelength is close to 1 Å according to Eq. (9). However, the velocities will have a Maxwellian distribution about the rms value, and it is necessary to monochromatize the beam for use in neutron diffractometry of polycrystalline samples. This is generally accomplished by use of a monochromatizing crystal with selected grating constant d placed in the path of the collimated neutron beam emerging from the reactor. The crystal is adjusted at the correct angle θ to diffract neutrons with the selected wavelength λ, according to the Bragg equation. Along the path of the diffracted beam is placed a spectrometer, essentially similar in principle to an x-ray spectrometer, consisting of specimen table and detector arm mounted on a divided circle and usually coupled to provide the necessary θ, 2θ relationship between crystal and detector angle settings. The detector is typically a boron fluoride filled proportional counter, sensitive to the detection of thermal neutrons, placed in a massive shield. For several reasons, however, the neutron diffractometer for powder work must be scaled up in size over the conventional x-ray instrument and is much more massive. First of all, the neutron intensity is extremely low, and it is necessary to use collimator apertures of rather large cross section. For example, in a reactor with central flux 10^{12} n/cm^2/sec, the collimated neutron beam emerging from the exit port of a typical research reactor and incident upon the monochromatizing crystal will have a power of about 10^7 n/sec. The emergent monochromatic neutron beam will be attenuated, becoming the order of 10^4 n/sec, and when this beam, in turn, is diffracted by a polycrystalline specimen placed on the spectrometer table, the diffracted intensity entering the detector will be only a few neutrons per second with the counter set at the peak of a typical strong reflection. Because of the low intensity, neutron beams of large cross section of the order of 10 cm^2 and large specimens with volumes of 5 to 10 cm^3 must be employed. Massive shielding of the spectrometer and the detector tube is required in order to maintain the intensity ratio of peak to background as high as possible. Even so, in order to obtain good counting statistics, it is necessary to record the diffraction pattern very slowly, say, from 12 to 24 hr for a complete angular sweep of the diffractometer. Typical neutron-diffraction patterns are shown in Fig. 11.

It must be pointed out that neutron diffraction is no universal substitute for x-ray diffraction. Because of the large aperture required and the resulting poor geometry, the diffraction peaks are necessarily broad and the resolution between closely spaced peaks is very poor. In spite of this drawback, neutron diffraction possesses unique properties which make it an invaluable tool in certain applications, especially where employed to supplement available x-ray diffraction information. In order to recognize the potential applications of neutron diffraction, it is necessary first to understand the characteristics which determine where it may be used to greater advantage than x-ray diffraction; these characteristics result from the specific properties of neutrons and their interaction with matter. The interactions can be discussed only briefly here.

Neutron scattering occurs mainly by interaction with the nuclei of the atoms rather than by interaction with the extranuclear electrons as for x-rays. An exception to

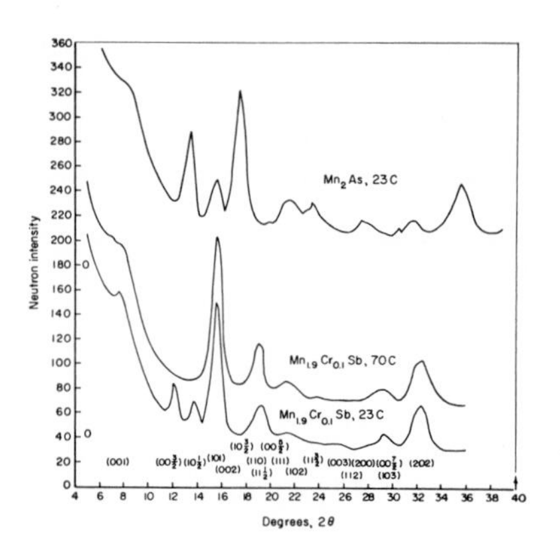

Fig. 11. Powder neutron-diffraction patterns of antiferromagnetic Mn_2As and chromium-substituted Mn_2Sb ($Mn_{1.9}Cr_{0.1}Sb$). The inversion of $Mn_{1.9}Cr_{0.1}Sb$ to the ferrimagnetic state above room temperature is illustrated by the pattern at 70° C, in which the magnetic-cell reflections (fractional l indices based on the chemical cell) are absent.

this rule is found in the case of magnetic materials where electron scattering is also significant, but this will be discussed later. Nuclear scattering of neutrons does not vary with atomic number of the scattering element as does the x-ray scattering amplitude; in fact, the nuclear scattering amplitudes for light and heavy atoms are nearly the same and do not show a regular dependence with atomic number. It is of considerable practical importance that the light nuclei, such as hydrogen and carbon, have large neutron scattering amplitudes in comparison with the heavier elements, thus making it possible to determine their positions in a structure. Furthermore, because of the lack of dependence of scattering on atomic number, adjacent elements or even isotopes of the same element may show large differences in scattering power, again providing unique advantages over x-ray diffraction in these cases. Nuclear scattering is isotropic; that is, it does not diminish rapidly with scattering angle as do the x-ray scattering factors. Finally, neutron scattering by a few of the elements is 180° out of phase with the scattering by most of the elements. Examples of such elements which scatter out of phase are hydrogen, titanium, and manganese.

These differences in interaction for x-rays and neutrons lead naturally to certain specific applications of neutron diffraction wherein the differences are employed to advantage. Such applications will be illustrated later.

Neutron Scattering Principles. According to quantum-mechanical theory, the scattering of low-velocity neutrons by atomic nuclei would be expected to be a function of the "cross section" σ of the nucleus (considered as an impenetrable sphere of radius r) with a value four times that derived from classical hard-sphere collision theory. The measured cross sections of many of the elements, particularly those of high atomic weight, show remarkable agreement with the relation

$$\sigma = 4\pi r^2 \tag{10}$$

where the nuclear radius $r \cong 1.5 \times 10^{-13} A^{1/3}$ cm and A is the atomic mass number. The several cases where the cross section differs markedly from the value of Eq. (10) are explained by the occurrence of a nuclear reaction involving excitation of the nucleus for which the resonance level is close to the energy of the thermal neutrons. The measured scattering cross section, by definition, is the ratio of the emitted neutron current to the incident flux, and is given by

$$\sigma = 4\pi b^2 \tag{11}$$

where b is the scattering length, or amplitude, in centimeters. The amplitude b is the neutron equivalent of the atomic scattering factor f for the x-ray case. Bacon[14] has compiled a table listing values of b and σ for the elements and isotopes, together with the corresponding f values in comparable units. A selection of data from this compilation is shown in Table 3.

Table 3. Neutron and X-ray Scattering Amplitudes

Element	Atomic no.	b (neutrons), 10^{-12} cm	f (x-rays), 10^{-12} cm at $\sin\theta/\lambda$	
			0	0.5 Å^{-1}
H^1	1	−0.38	0.28	0.02
H^2	1	0.65	0.28	0.02
Be^9	4	0.78	1.13	0.39
C^{12}	6	0.66	1.69	0.48
Na^{23}	11	0.35	3.09	1.14
V^{51}	23	−0.05	6.5	2.8
Mn^{55}	25	−0.37	7.0	3.1
As^{75}	33	0.63	9.3	4.4
Cs^{133}	55	0.49	15.5	8.1
Pt^{195}	78	0.95	22.0	12.1

Most of the values of b in the table have a positive sign, corresponding to a phase shift of 180° due to scattering by an impenetrable sphere. The few exceptions of negative sign are a result of an additional phase shift on scattering, associated with a resonance level. Note that the amplitude b of nuclear scattering by the light element carbon is within 50 per cent of the value for platinum, whereas the corresponding x-ray scattering amplitudes differ by more than an order of magnitude. This difference in scattering behavior obviously leads to the application of neutron diffraction to the analysis of structures containing the light elements. Because the nuclear dimensions are small compared with the wavelength of thermal neutrons, neutron scattering of neutrons is isotropic; that is, it is independent of scattering angle, thus differing markedly from the x-ray case.

Other effects must be considered in any rigorous interpretation of neutron-diffraction data. For example, in the case of a scattering nucleus with spin I, combination with the neutron results in formation of two possible compound nuclear states with corresponding amplitudes b_+ and b_- and effective weights $w_+ = (I + 1)/(2I + 1)$ and $w_- = I/(2I + 1)$. Both coherent and incoherent scattering, only the former of which can cause interference, are produced by a nucleus with spin. The cross section for coherent scattering is

$$S = 4\pi(w_+b_+ + w_-b_-)^2$$

In the case of normal hydrogen, with spin = ½ and b_+ and b_- of opposite sign, most of the scattering is incoherent, whereas the isotope deuterium yields a much more favorable ratio of coherent to incoherent scattering. Many elements consist of several isotopes, each with a given abundance and spin, and thus characteristic values of b_+, b_-. These must be summed appropriately[14] to obtain the mean value of coherent scattering cross section $\bar{b}_r$ for the element in a crystal, wherein the various isotopes will be placed at random among the atomic sites for that element. It is $\bar{b}_r$ which is equivalent to f_0, the atomic scattering factor for x-rays, and which determines the Bragg reflection intensities for neutrons. Thus the structure factor for a crystal is given by

$$F^2_{hkl} = \Sigma\bar{b}_r e^{2\pi i(hx+ky+lz)^2} e^{-2W} \qquad (12)$$

per unit cell, including the temperature effect.

The significant applications of neutron diffraction to be considered in this brief survey are concerned with the elucidation of crystal structures.

Applications of Neutron Diffraction. One of the most important applications of neutron diffraction depends upon the much higher scattering amplitudes of the light elements, compared to the x-ray case. Thus, it is possible to determine the atomic positions of carbon and hydrogen in compounds of these elements. For example, although it was known from x-ray studies of LiH that the structure is that of sodium chloride, it was not possible to detect the hydrogen positions in the hydrides of the heavier alkali metals by x-ray analysis. Neutron-diffraction studies[15] of powdered sodium hydride (NaH) and deuteride (NaD) showed that the structure is indeed sodium chloride type. Heavy metal hydrides (such as UH_3, ZrH_2, and ThH_2) and carbides (such as ThC_2) have also been studied by powder neutron diffraction. However, as in the x-ray case, single-crystal techniques provide much more useful data for determination of atomic positions. Thus single-crystal neutron-diffraction studies of compounds such as the ammonium halides, potassium bifluoride, and potassium dihydrogen phosphate have led to determination of their hydrogen positions and other structural details.

The scattering amplitudes of adjacent elements are very similar for x-rays, but may differ considerably for neutrons. This provides another application of neutron diffraction, namely, the study of structures of alloys and compounds of adjacent elements. For example, the superlattice lines from ordered FeCo and Ni_3Mn are readily observed by neutron diffraction,[16] since the scattering amplitudes b are sufficiently different, whereas the corresponding lines in the x-ray patterns of these phases are not readily detected. It is of interest to point out the negative phase of the scattering amplitude of Mn, which must be taken into account in interpreting the neutron-diffraction pattern of Ni_3Mn superlattice and which enhances the intensities of the superlattice lines. On the other hand, the nonsystematic variation of the neutron scattering amplitudes with atomic number does not always work to the advantage of neutron diffraction. Cu_3Au is a representative case in point. The amplitudes b for Cu and Au are identical, so no superlattice lines are observed by neutron diffraction.

Neutron diffraction finds its most significant application in the study of magnetic materials. We must recall that, with magnetic atoms, there is a magnetic scattering in addition to the nuclear scattering, with cross sections of comparable magnitude. Magnetic scattering is caused by interaction between the magnetic moment of the neutron and that of the atom, the latter resulting from orientation of the spins of the extranuclear electrons (3*d* electrons in the case of the transition elements). Therefore, although nuclear scattering is isotropic, magnetic scattering is strongly angle dependent. The scattered intensity is a function of the spin ordering in parallel or antiparallel orientation, as are the magnetic properties. Thus the alignment of magnetic moments, i.e., the magnetic superstructure, may be studied by neutron diffraction. Paramagnetic, ferromagnetic, antiferromagnetic, and ferrimagnetic materials have been studied successfully, some in considerable detail. In many cases, it is possible to explain the changes in magnetic ordering with temperature. For example, the change in magnetic susceptibility of MnO above and below the Curie point (120°K) is caused by a change from thermally disordered spin arrangement above this temperature to an antiferromagnetic (antiparallel) spin ordering of Mn^{+2} ions in a magnetic cell with a cell edge twice that of the chemical (NaCl type) cell, producing characteristic superlattice lines on the neutron-diffraction pattern.[17] When this ordering is complete, the net magnetization is zero. There are other examples of antiparallel ordering in which the antiparallel alignment does not completely cancel, leaving a residual weak magnetism, called ferrimagnetism, as in Fe_3O_4. Figure 11 illustrates the use of neutron diffraction to determine ferrimagnetic and antiferromagnetic structures.[18] The reader is referred to the literature for details.

REFERENCES CITED

1. C. J. Davisson and L. G. Germer, *Phys. Rev.*, **30**:705 (1927).
2. L. H. Germer and C. D. Hartman, *Rev. Sci. Instr.*, **31**:784 (1960).
3. H. E. Farnsworth, R. E. Schlier, T. H. George, and R. M. Burger, *J. Appl. Phys.*, **29**: 1150 (1958).
4. G. P. Thomson, *Proc. Roy. Soc. (London)*, **A117**:600 (1928).
5. G. P. Thomson and W. Cochrane, *Theory and Practice of Electron Diffraction*, Macmillan & Co., Ltd., London, 1939.
6. Z. G. Pinsker, *Electron Diffraction*, translated by J. A. Spink and E. Feigl, Butterworth and Co. (Publishers) Ltd., London, 1953.
7. D. Kay and V. E. Cosslett, *Techniques for Electron Microscopy*, chap. 12, Blackwell Scientific Publications, Ltd., Oxford, 1961.
8. Ref. 6, p. 80.
9. S. Kikuchi, *Proc. Imp. Acad. Japan*, **4**:271, 275, 354 (1928); *Japan J. Phys.*, **5**:83 (1928).
10. M. von Laue, *Materiewellen und ihre Interferenzin*, Akademische Verlagsgesellschaft m.b.H., Leipzig, 1944, and Edwards Bros., Inc., Ann Arbor, Mich.
11. L. Sturkey and L. K. Frevel, *Phys. Rev.*, **68**:56 (1945).
12. J. M. Cowley and A. L. G. Rees, *Proc. Phys. Soc. (London)*, **59**:287 (1947).
13. G. I. Finch and H. Wilman, *Ergeb. Exakt. Naturw.*, **16**:353 (1937).
14. G. E. Bacon, *Neutron Diffraction*, Oxford University Press, London, 1935.
15. C. G. Shull, E. O. Wollan, G. A. Morton, and W. L. Davidson, *Phys. Rev.*, **73**:830 (1948).
16. C. G. Shull and S. Siegel, *Phys. Rev.*, **75**:1008 (1949).
17. G. G. Shull and J. S. Smart, *Phys. Rev.*, **76**:1256 (1949).
18. A. E. Austin, E. Adelson, and W. H. Cloud, *J. Appl. Phys.* (Suppl.), **33**:1356 (1962).

Part 3

DETERMINATION OF CRYSTAL STRUCTURE

Chapter 24

SINGLE-CRYSTAL TECHNIQUES

Howard T. Evans, Jr.

U.S. Geological Survey

In the fifty years following the discovery of the principle of x-ray diffraction in crystals by Max von Laue, techniques making use of the phenomenon have been applied at an ever-increasing pace to seek precise information concerning the solid state through crystal-structure analysis. The basic data for such studies are the geometric dimensions of the crystal lattice and the intensities of its diffraction spectra. While the techniques involved in obtaining these data even today may be considered to be rather involved and difficult, they have for some time been more or less standardized to the point where they may be measured routinely and with high efficiency. In this chapter, some of the most useful methods are described, and procedures are outlined whereby the photographs are prepared for the determination of the geometry and symmetry of a crystal, and a set of intensity data is prepared for its crystal-structure analysis. The special techniques required when intensities are measured by pulse-counter methods are discussed separately in Chap. 25. Further details concerning any of the material covered in this chapter may be found by consulting the general references listed at the end of the chapter.

1. GEOMETRIC BASIS OF X-RAY DIFFRACTION

The Reciprocal Lattice (See also Chap. 26). The concept of the reciprocal lattice is indispensable for the understanding of the principles of the common diffraction methods, and in the development of modifications of them and of new methods. Each point of the reciprocal lattice represents a set of diffracting planes in the crystal, and lies at a distance σ from the origin of coordinates in reciprocal space:

$$\sigma(hkl) = \lambda/d(hkl) \qquad \text{reciprocal-lattice units (rlu)} \tag{1}$$

It will be noted that by Eq. (1) we scale the reciprocal lattice according to the wavelength, and that this lattice is dimensionless. The interaction of the reciprocal lattice with a parallel beam of x-rays is most readily analyzed with Ewald's construction. This geometric device arises from the analogy between Bragg's law

$$\lambda = 2d(hkl) \sin \theta \tag{2}$$

and the expression for the chord C of a great circle of a sphere in terms of arc α and radius R:

$$C = 2R \sin (\alpha/2) \tag{3}$$

wherein C is replaced by σ, the arc angle is the Bragg angle 2θ, and the radius is unity. This geometry is illustrated in Fig. 1. If the incident x-ray beam $\bar{S}_0$ is imagined to be passing through the origin of the reciprocal lattice of the crystal which is immersed in the beam, the crystal will diffract x-rays from the planes hkl according to Eq. (2) only if the reciprocal-lattice point hkl lies on the surface of a sphere of radius 1, whose center at the crystal is the origin of the incident- and diffracted-beam vectors $\bar{S}_0$ and $\bar{S}$. In this case, with the origin of the reciprocal lattice at the intersection of $\bar{S}_0$ and the sphere, the construction, and therefore Bragg's law, is satisfied and diffraction will occur.

If the crystal is stationary and the x-rays monochromatic, there will generally be no diffraction at all, unless by chance one or two lattice points happen to touch the unit sphere. Diffraction effects of the crystal may now be sought in one of two ways:

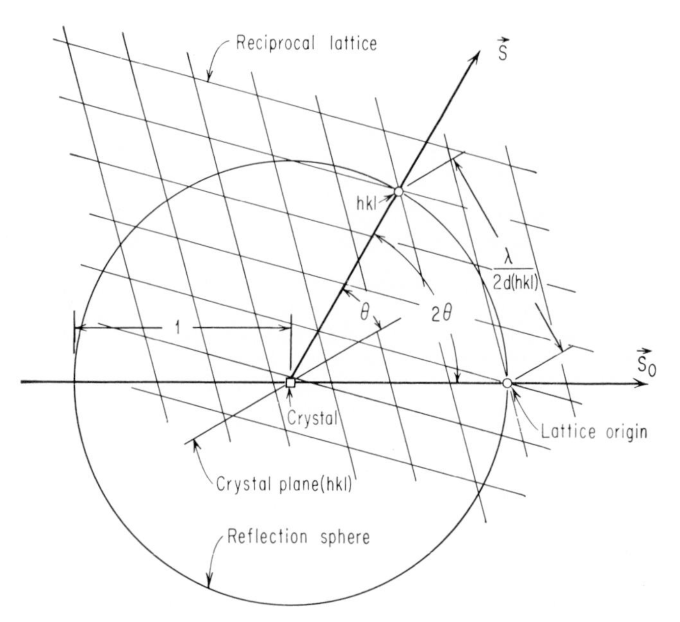

FIG. 1. Relation between the crystal, its reciprocal lattice, and the diffraction phenomenon, illustrating Ewald's construction.

(1) by altering the wavelength of the x-rays so that the reciprocal lattice will shrink or expand [Eq. (1)] and thus bring points to the sphere; or (2) by keeping the wavelength fixed and moving the crystal and with it the reciprocal lattice. The former corresponds to the Laue method, in which "white" x-rays are used to obtain a spread of wavelengths. In the latter case, crystal-orientation changes may be made by means of more or less complex mechanical linkages, or by simply crushing the crystal to a powder. Along these lines the various methods of recording x-ray diffraction effects may be compared in the outline given in the following paragraphs.

Comparison of Diffraction Techniques. The best-known techniques which have been used, emphasizing film methods, are briefly compared in the following outline.

A. Stationary-crystal–stationary-film methods.
  1. White radiation: the Laue method. Offsetting the advantage of simplicity, the method has two serious drawbacks: (*a*) every reflection is recorded with a different unknown wavelength, and (*b*) all orders of a reflection are superimposed in

the same spot. It is used mainly for symmetry and orientation studies, especially for crystal grains embedded in a matrix.

2. Monochromatic radiation. The Laue method is applied in this case to the study of diffuse background in reciprocal space, which can be explored by photographs made with the crystal in a series of successive orientations.

B. Moving-crystal–stationary-film methods, monochromatic radiation.

1. Crystal in wholly random orientation. Only one geometric parameter is measured, the Bragg angle 2θ. The random orientation is generally obtained by grinding the specimen into a powder. The powder method is dealt with extensively in Part 2 of this book.

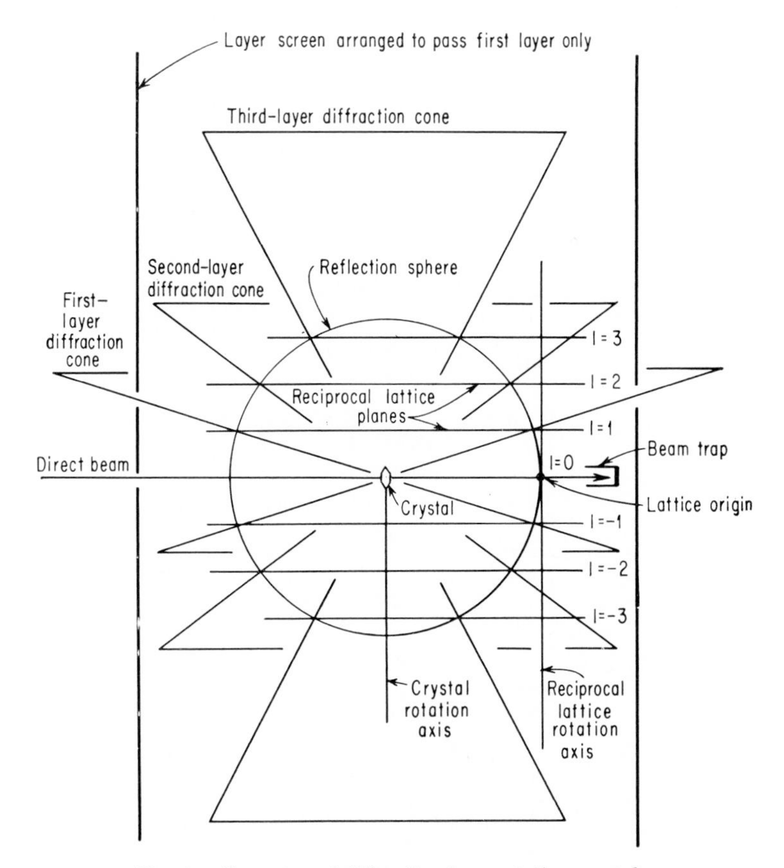

FIG. 2. Geometry of diffraction by a rotating crystal.

2. Random orientation restricted to one or two dimensions. The special techniques used in the study of fibers and textures are described in Chap. 18.

3. Crystal rotated about one axis (see Fig. 2).

   a. The rotation method. One dimension of the crystal lattice is resolved, but the other two are degenerate.

   b. The oscillation method. This technique is similar to the rotation method, but instead of full rotation, the crystal is rocked over a restricted angular range. A knowledge of the crystal lattice then makes it possible to identify the reflections within each layer group, and with a series of patterns made over contiguous rocking ranges a large part of the reciprocal lattice may be resolved and recorded.

C. Moving-crystal–moving-film methods, monochromatic radiation.

1. Crystal rotated about one axis.

a. Weissenberg method. A single layer in the reciprocal lattice is recorded by the use of an appropriate screen between the film and crystal, and the

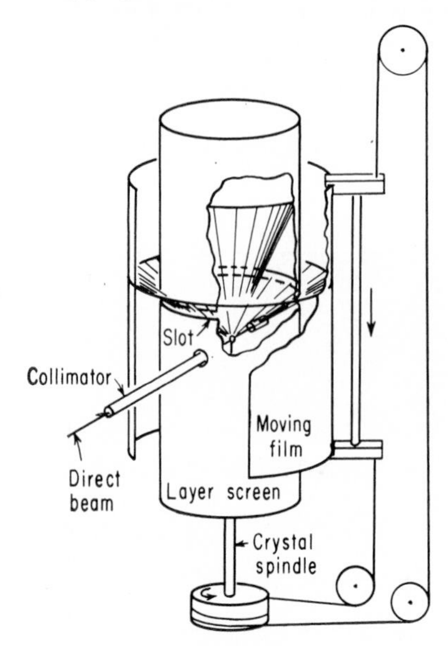

FIG. 3. Geometry of the Weissenberg method.

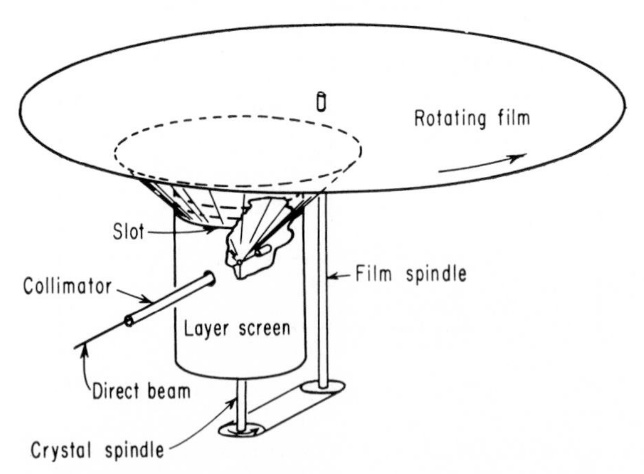

FIG. 4. Geometry of the de Jong and Bouman method.

lateral position of the film is related to the angular position of the crystal (Fig. 3). This method is by far the most widely used, especially for intensity measurements.

b. Sauter and Schiebold methods. In this case, the film is rotated about an axis normal to the crystal-rotation axis, with their angular positions coupled together. These methods, while giving patterns with less distortion of the lattice nets than the Weissenberg method, are much more cumbersome and are little used today.

c. de Jong and Bouman method, also called the retigraphic method. Here, the flat film is rotated about an axis parallel to the crystal-rotation axis (Fig. 4). In this way, an image of the lattice net is obtained in true shape.

2. Crystal rotated about two axes: the Buerger precession method. The crystal is rocked about two perpendicular axes simultaneously and 90° out of phase, so that the lattice-net plane normal sweeps out a cone. The film is made to follow a parallel motion, and thus to record an undistorted image of the lattice net.

Of all the methods referred to above, in the United States two have come to dominate overwhelmingly the technology of single-crystal diffractometry: the Weissenberg and the Buerger precession cameras. In Europe, the Weissenberg camera is also universally used, but the Buerger instrument is not so well known. Instead, the retigraph has recently gained some popularity. All experience shows, nevertheless, that the Weissenberg and Buerger cameras are the most valuable photographic instruments for the crystal-structure laboratory, and are naturally complementary to each other. The reasons for this contention will be set forth in the detailed descriptions of the techniques which follow. Briefer accounts will be given of the rotation, oscillation, and de Jong-Bouman methods.

2. RECORDING OF DIFFRACTION PATTERNS

Rotation Method. A crystal rotated in an x-ray beam around the normal to a set of reciprocal-lattice-net planes will generate diffraction beams in the surface of a series of cones, corresponding to the circles in which the nets intersect the Ewald sphere. These cones are intercepted as straight-line rows of spots by a film rolled into a cylinder coaxial with the rotation axis. A typical pattern is shown in Fig. 5.

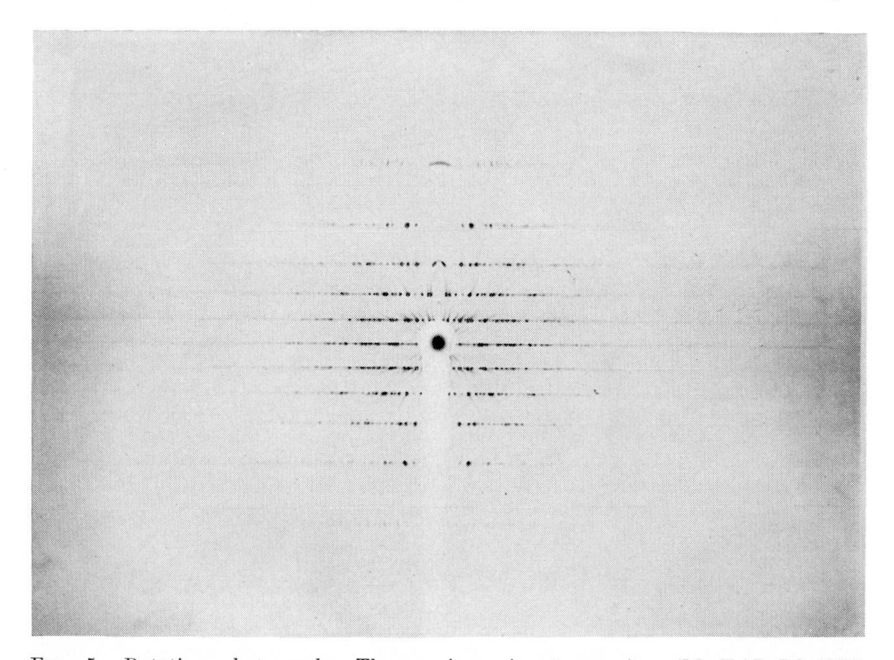

Fig. 5. Rotation photograph. The specimen is väyrynenite, (Mn,Fe)$BePO_4(OH)$, monoclinic, a = 5.41 Å, b = 14.49 Å, c = 4.73 Å, β = 102° 45′, space group $P2_1/a$. Rotation axis is [100], radiation Mo $K\alpha$, Zr filter.

If the rotation axis is the c axis of the crystal (for example), each row of spots will represent diffractions from the planes hkl for which the l index is constant. The reflections on the row through the trace of the direct beam will have $l = 0$, the next will have $l = 1$, then $l = 2$, and so on. These rows are thus commonly referred to as the "zero layer" (or "zero level"), "first layer," "second layer," etc. This terminology is carried over from the rotation method to all the other single-crystal methods.

If the perpendicular distance from the zero-layer row to an upper-layer row is measured on the film as y mm, the corresponding distance between layers of the reciprocal lattice, ζ in rlu, is given by

$$\zeta = y/\sqrt{r^2 + y^2} \tag{4}$$

where r is the radius of the cylindrical film in millimeters. The corresponding value of the c axis (for example) is

$$c = n\lambda/\zeta \tag{5}$$

where λ is the wavelength in Å and n the number of the layer. Thus three rotation photographs, one about each of the crystal axes, will give directly the dimensions of

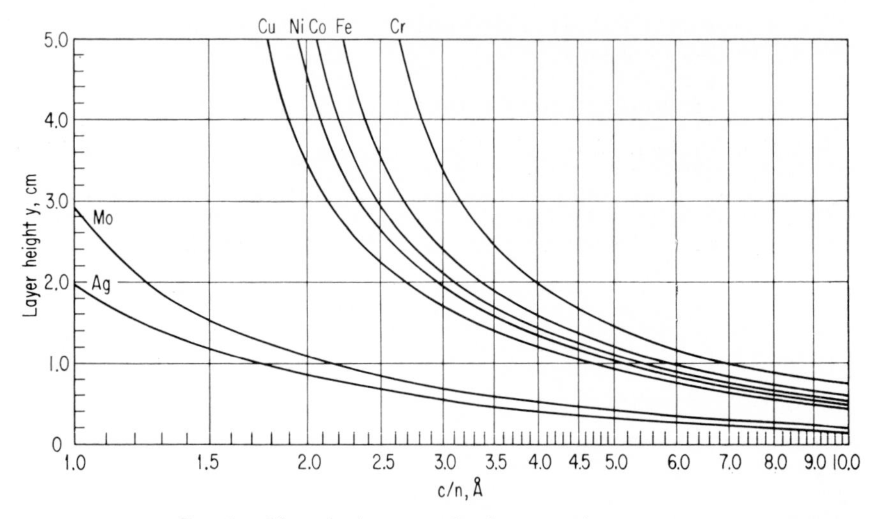

FIG. 6. Chart for layer spacing from rotation patterns.

the unit cell. These measurements will not be accurate because the sine function in Eq. (4) indicates that the diffraction beams for higher layers will be intercepted by the film at very oblique angles.

For rotating-crystal methods, the distribution of lattice points in reciprocal space is best referred to cylindrical coordinates, with the cylindrical axis coincident with the rotation axis. Using Buerger's notation, ξ is the radial coordinate and ζ the axial coordinate in rlu, and ϕ is the angular coordinate. On rotation and oscillation photographs, ζ can be measured directly as a function of y by Eq. (4), ξ is a function of both x and y, but ϕ is degenerate. The radial coordinate is given by

$$\xi^2 = 1 + \frac{r^2}{r^2 + y^2} - 2\sqrt{\frac{r^2}{r^2 + y^2}} \cos\left(\frac{360}{2\pi} x\right) \tag{6}$$

With the advent of the Weissenberg camera, the only measure which is usually of interest is the interlayer spacing ζ. The length of the crystal axis parallel to the spindle can be read directly in terms of the interlayer distances in millimeters from the chart in Fig. 6, which is based on Eqs. (4) and (5), and a camera diameter of 57.3 mm.

Oscillation Method. In order to avoid overlap of spots on the row lines of rotation photographs, it is necessary to restrict the range of rotation of the crystal so that fewer *hkl* nodes enter the sphere of reflection. In this way, using a number of adjacent oscillation ranges of 5, 10, or 15°, depending on the density of the lattice, the whole reciprocal lattice within the range of the sphere may be photographed without serious interference among different reflections. The interpretation, measurement, and geometrical properties of oscillation photographs are the same as those of rotation photographs within the limits imposed by the restricted oscillation range. It will be noted, incidentally, that while rotation patterns always have *mm* symmetry, oscillation photographs may have no symmetry at all, since the two sides of the Ewald sphere penetrate different parts of the reciprocal lattice.

The indexing of oscillation photographs is readily achieved when the unit-cell dimensions and orientation of the crystal are known. In that case, the lattice layers may be drawn carefully to scale, and a circle representing the intersection of the plane of the layer with the Ewald sphere placed over it on transparent film so as to rotate about the axis through the origin of the zero layer. Certain reflections of the zero row at low Bragg angles may be identified on one of the oscillation films by trial,

FIG. 7. Photograph of Buerger precession camera (*left*) and integrating Weissenberg camera (*right*) mounted on a standard water-cooled x-ray generator.

and from these, knowing the angles of oscillation, the remainder of the patterns is easily indexed.

The oscillation method was the first one developed which permits separate registration of all the points of the three-dimensional reciprocal lattice, but it has been largely replaced by more sophisticated techniques which record the lattice layers separately. In certain circumstances it is still useful because of its two great advantages: (1) the camera is mechanically simple, and (2) the time required for recording the whole range of the lattice is relatively very short, comparable with the time required to photograph one lattice layer by other methods.

Weissenberg Method. More widely used to resolve all the reflections of a single crystal is the Weissenberg camera (or goniometer), which produces patterns that are more easily and conveniently interpreted. This apparatus is an adaptation of the rotation camera in which all but one layer line of reflections is stopped by a stationary slotted metal screen, and the cylindrical film holder is arranged to travel parallel to its axis a distance related to the degree of rotation of the crystal. This geometry is illustrated in Fig. 3, and a typical instrument is shown in Fig. 7. Because of the limitation on the travel of the camera, the crystal is generally oscillated through a maximum range of about 220°. The diffraction spots corresponding to one row on the rotation pattern thus become distributed over the whole film. The array of spots is actually a highly distorted image of the reciprocal-lattice net selected by the layer-line screen. In spite of the distortion, the fact that one whole net plane is registered on a single film, rather than scattered over a series of oscillation patterns, offers a tremendous advantage in studying the lattice, especially where intensity distributions are being considered in searching for symmetry. A typical Weissenberg pattern is shown in Figs. 8*a* and 8*b*.

Upper layers are photographed by simply setting the layer-line screen opposite the appropriate rotation row line. If the x-ray beam is kept perpendicular to the rotation axis ("normal-beam" technique), the intersecting circle in the Ewald sphere is displaced from the rotation axis and diminishes in size rapidly at higher layers, so that the

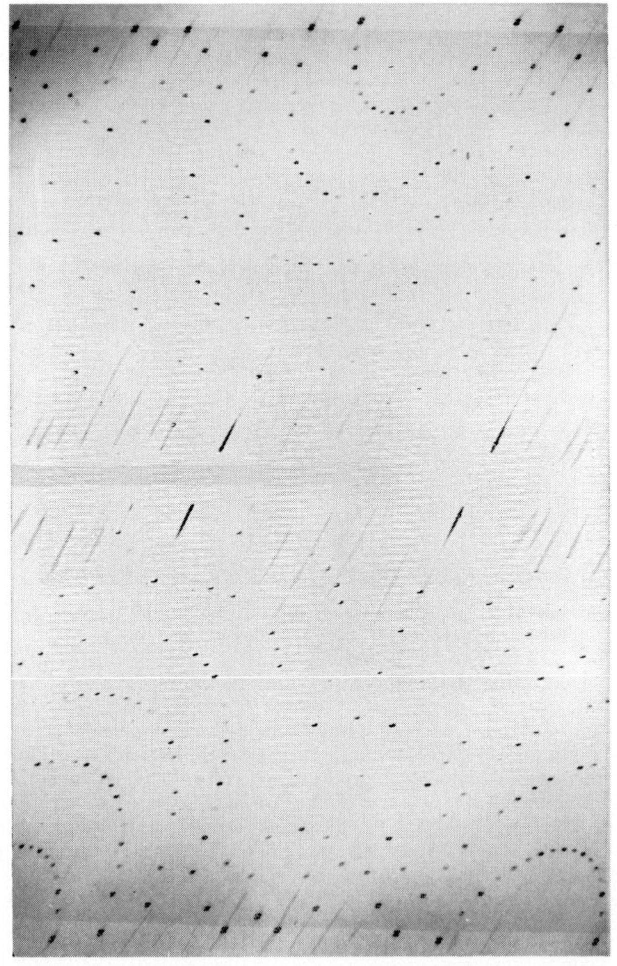

Fig. 8*a*. Weissenberg photograph of 0*kl* net of väyrynenite (for data, see Fig. 5). Cu $K\alpha$ radiation, Ni filter. Notice fogging at top and bottom resulting from fluorescence scattering from Fe and Mn in the specimen; also note the hollow spots near the center resulting from absorption of x-rays by the crystal.

range of the net plane recorded becomes greatly restricted. This effect is greatly ameliorated by tilting the x-ray beam to the rotation axis at an angle such that the beam lies in the surface of the cone of reflections for the layer being photographed. By this technique ("equi-inclination"), the reflecting circle always passes through the rotation axis and its radius is enlarged so that a much larger range of the reciprocal lattice may be recorded.

The Weissenberg method requires a number of mechanical settings to be determined for each photograph. If a satisfactory rotation pattern has been obtained from a crystal mounted on the Weissenberg camera, the appropriate settings may be determined without any knowledge of the crystal-lattice dimensions other than the row-line spacings. For a given Weissenberg photograph, four settings are required:

1. The position of layer-line screen, s in millimeters, translated from the zero-layer position opposite the x-ray beam collimator by an amount s mm.

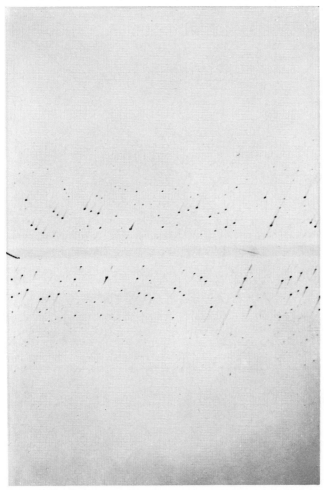

FIG. 8*b*. Same as Fig. 8*a*, but with Mo $K\alpha$ radiation, Zr filter. Notice absence of fluorescence and absorption effects.

2. The angle of inclination μ_E of the x-ray collimator to the rotation axis, for the equi-inclination method.
3. The position of the beam trap, translated in a direction opposite to the layer-line screen on which it is mounted by the amount s for normal beam and $2s$ for equi-inclination techniques.
4. The position of the film holder on its carriage, translated an amount s mm, equal

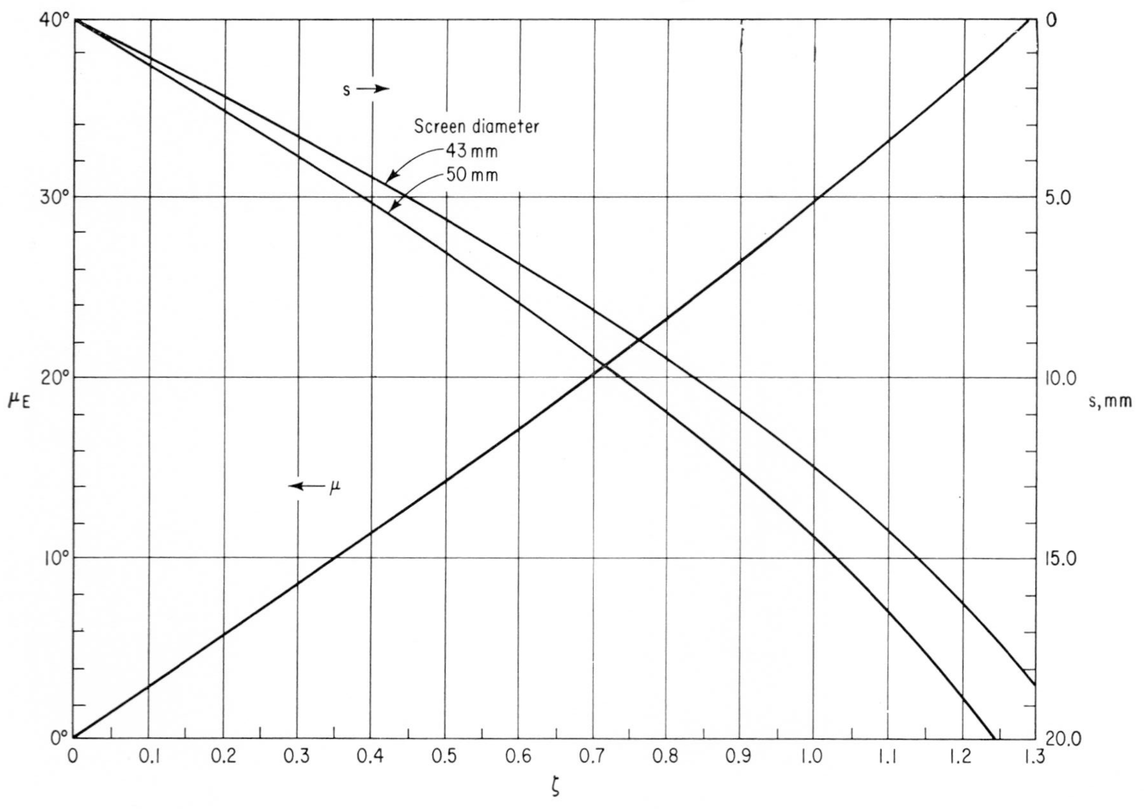

Fig. 9. Chart to determine settings for the equi-inclination Weissenberg method.

to the layer-line screen translation, in order to maintain the pattern centered on the film. These settings are given for the normal-beam method by

$$s = r_s \sqrt{1 - \zeta^2}/\zeta \tag{7}$$

and for the equi-inclination method by

$$\begin{aligned} \sin \mu_E &= \zeta/2 \\ s &= r_s \sqrt{4 - \zeta^2}/\zeta \end{aligned} \tag{8}$$

A chart is shown in Fig. 9 from which the setting constants may be quickly determined from ζ, or from the rotation-photograph measurement y in millimeters, for a camera diameter of 57.3 mm.

de Jong and Bouman Method. In this apparatus, the film is flat and caused to rotate about an axis normal to its center and parallel to the crystal-spindle axis, as shown in Fig. 4. The film is thus kept parallel to the lattice plane of the crystal being photographed, and rotates with it, so that the pattern recorded actually is an undistorted image of the lattice. Mechanical limitations restrict the range of inclination angles available, and the best practice is to make all settings based on a fixed level-cone angle of 45°. The settings required for any exposure are the primary-beam inclination angle μ, the crystal-film-rotation axial displacement Δ, and the screen setting s.

The outstanding advantage of the de Jong-Bouman method over the Weissenberg method is the ability it has to record reciprocal-lattice nets in true shape. It also has one great disadvantage, namely, that the diffraction spots are extremely distorted in shape, being streaked into lines by an unfortunate lack of cooperation in the direction of film motion and the grazing attitude of the reciprocal-lattice point as it passes through the Ewald sphere. Each spot is recorded twice on the film as the point enters and leaves the sphere, and as the direction of smearing is different in the two cases, an x-shaped image is left on the film. The intersection point of the crosslike spot can be used to obtain spacing measurements, but for intensity estimations, one half of the layer-line screen annulus must be covered so that only one arm of the cross is recorded.

Buerger Precession Method. An alternative method of recording the reciprocal-lattice net in true shape was invented by Prof. M. J. Buerger. It is an extension of the oscillation method in which the crystal is made to oscillate about two mutually perpendicular axes both at right angles to the primary x-ray beam. By causing the flat film to follow the same motions as the crystal, an undistorted image is obtained. The two oscillations are produced 90° out of phase to each other, and with equal amplitude, so that a normal to the film plane sweeps out a right circular cone of half angle $\bar{\mu}$ (the inclination angle) coaxial with the x-ray beam. In order to register a crystal-lattice net, its plane must be set parallel to the plane of the film, that is, normal to the x-ray beam when the inclination angle is set at zero. Such a net plane and its parallel upper layers will each intersect the Ewald sphere in a circle subtending a diffraction cone, and the desired layer is selected by means of an annular layer-line screen of appropriate dimensions fixed to the crystal mount. The geometric properties of the precession method are shown with respect to one of the oscillation axes in Fig. 10. A photograph of the common form of the Buerger precession camera is shown in Fig. 7.

In order to make a diffraction pattern, several settings are required, as follows:

1. The inclination (oscillation) angle $\bar{\mu}$
2. The annular layer-line screen radius r_s, usually available in fixed sizes of 15, 20, 25, and 30 mm
3. The layer-line screen-to-film distance s
4. The displacement of the film from the center of precession $M\zeta$ (0 for the zero layer)

For an upper-level pattern the height of the layer above the origin ζ in *rlu* must be known, but otherwise all these quantities are independent of crystal parameters and are given by the relation

$$s = r_s \cot \cos^{-1} (\cos \bar{\mu} - \zeta) \tag{9}$$

For a given lattice plane a variety of camera-setting combinations are possible, but the most important consideration to keep in mind is that the larger the inclination angle $\bar{\mu}$, the larger is the area of the reciprocal-lattice plane covered in roughly square proportion, and the smaller the blind spot at the center for upper-level photographs. On the other hand, the exposure times required are roughly in proportion to $\bar{\mu}^2$. The most favorable combination of setting constants suitable for any situation is readily deduced from the nomogram shown in Fig. 11.

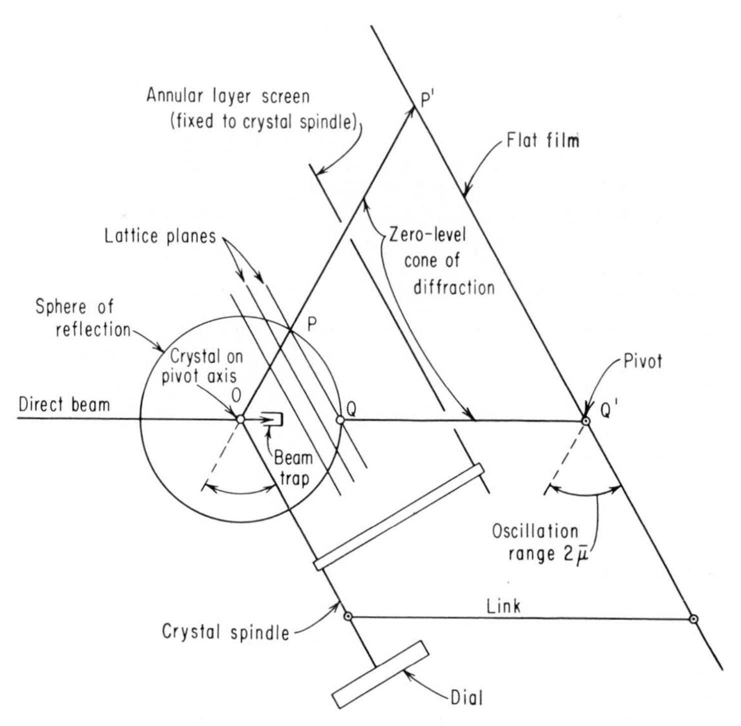

FIG. 10. Geometry of the Buerger precession method. Only one tilt axis is shown; the second coincides with the crystal-spindle axis.

When a set of lattice planes is properly aligned the zero layer can be photographed without any further knowledge of the crystallography of the specimen. The spacing of upper layers can then be measured approximately by placing a flat film in an envelope in place of the layer-line screen for a short exposure, so that the different layers leave their traces as a series of concentric circles. The value of ζ can be determined from the radii of these circles by the relation

$$\zeta = \cos \bar{\mu} - r_l/\sqrt{s^2 - r_l^2} \tag{10}$$

By using the nomogram of Fig. 11 in reverse, entering the circle radii r_l on the r_s scale, this relation is readily solved.

The great limitation of the Buerger precession method is that, because of mechanical limitations, Bragg angles higher than 60° cannot be recorded. This fault is frequently outweighed by its two great advantages, the excellent spot shape recorded on the film, and the ability to record any lattice plane parallel to the crystal-spindle axis. In the

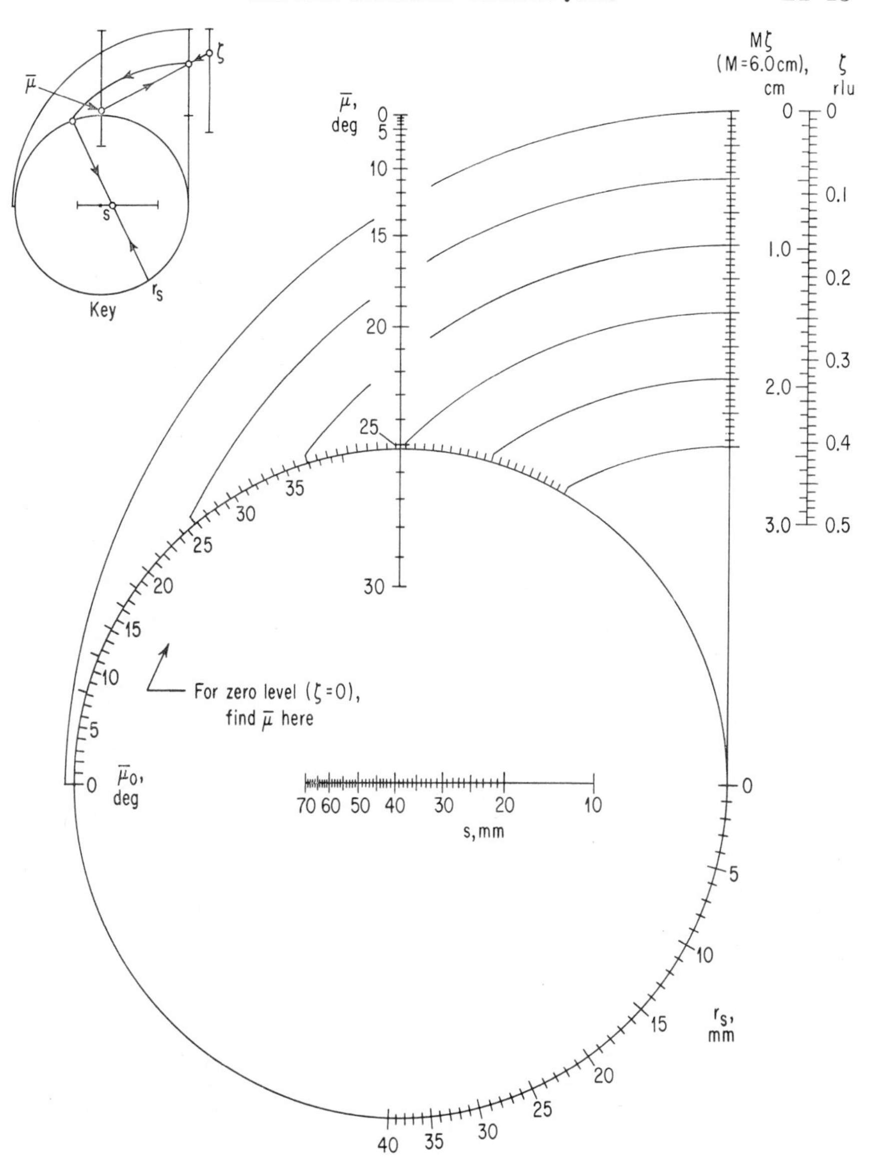

FIG. 11. Chart to determine setting for the Buerger precession method.

precession method, the reciprocal-lattice point always pierces the Ewald sphere at a steep angle (>60°), so that its image is not severely distorted and accurately reflects the shape and texture of the crystal. A good crystal about 0.2 to 0.3 mm in size will give spots in which the Mo $K\alpha_1$ and $K\alpha_2$ components are clearly resolved at the edges of the pattern, permitting reasonably accurate spacing measurements. A typical pattern, made of the same crystal-net plane as Fig. 8, is shown in Fig. 12. The range of the reciprocal lattice that can be recorded for one dial setting, in comparison with the equi-inclination Weissenberg method, is shown in Fig. 13.

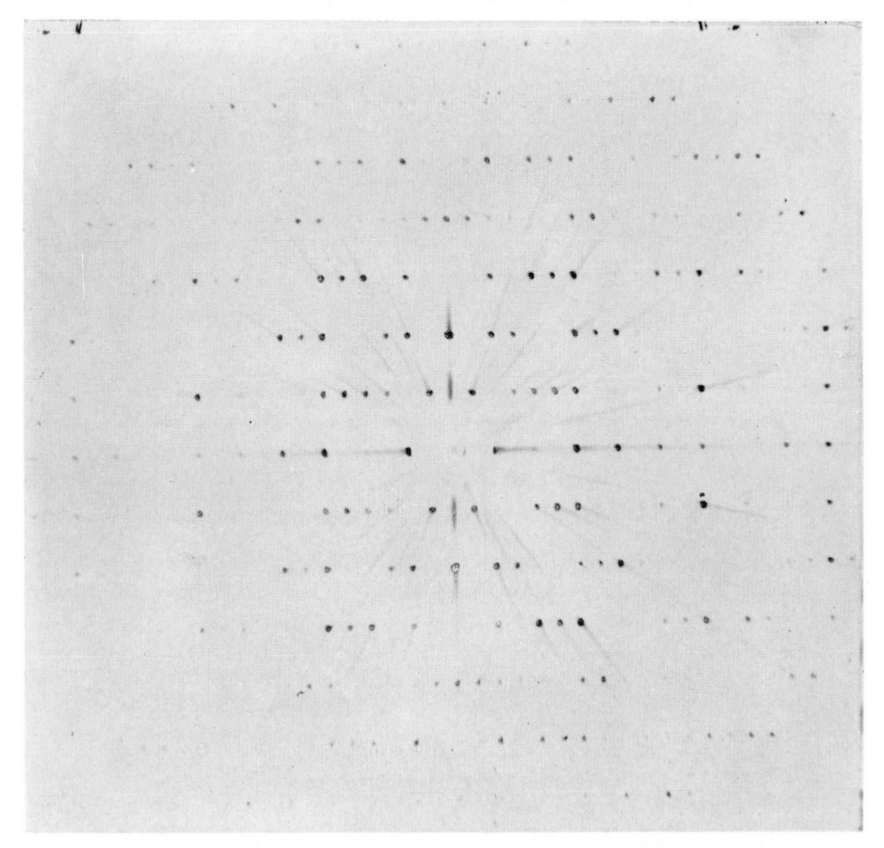

Fig. 12. Buerger precession photograph of the $0kl$ net of väyrynenite (for data, see Fig. 5). Mo $K\alpha$ radiation, Zr filter. The pattern corresponds to Fig. 8, in which the festooned row lines are the same as the horizontal row lines in the precession pattern.

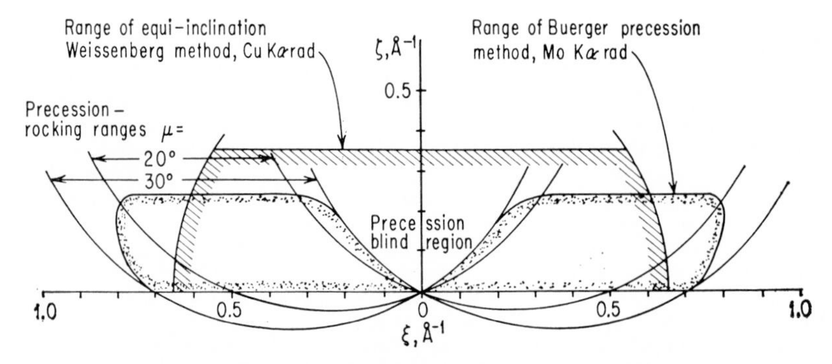

Fig. 13. Relative ranges of the Buerger precession and Weissenberg methods.

The fact that the crystal may be oriented to photograph any set of planes parallel to the axis of the goniometer head gives a great flexibility in exploring the reciprocal lattice. Because of this feature, the entire sphere within the Bragg-angle limitation mentioned above can be photographed. In fact, the range of the Buerger precession camera when used with Mo $K\alpha$ radiation is slightly greater than the equi-inclination Weissenberg method used with Cu $K\alpha$ radiation. Flexibility is enhanced when the Buerger precession method is used in conjunction with the Weissenberg method, because the latter records lattice planes *perpendicular* to the spindle axis.

A third important advantage of the Buerger precession method is the ease with which the patterns can be interpreted for making corrections of preliminary adjustments of crystal orientation on the goniometer head, as described in a later paragraph.

3. PROCEDURES FOR SINGLE-CRYSTAL DIFFRACTION PHOTOGRAPHY

Specimen Selection and Mounting. The selection of a satisfactory crystal specimen is not a straightforward process, but a few generalities can be made as a guide in this process. Large crystals (0.5 to 1.0 mm) will give strong patterns with short exposures useful for exploratory purposes. With the precession camera a corner of a very large crystal may be studied by grazing it with the x-ray beam, since the crystal is not rotated. Sharper patterns and intensity data less affected by absorption are obtained with smaller crystals (0.05 to 0.3 mm). Every effort should be made by optical examination (for complex extinction behavior, reentrant angles, etc.) to detect the presence of twinning. Even when not suspected on preliminary examination, it often becomes apparent from the diffraction patterns. The correct unit-cell symmetry and twin law can usually be worked out from these patterns, but multiple twinning may be difficult to interpret. The accuracy of lattice-constant measurement is reduced, and intensities are almost impossible to measure, on a twinned crystal. Microscopic examination will often lead to an identification of the crystal system, and the subsequent x-ray investigation can then be made with greatly increased efficiency.

A convenient mount consists of a finely drawn glass fiber mounted with a bit of dental wax on a brass pin which has a hole drilled lengthwise through it. A useful mount can also be prepared by soldering a piece of copper wire horizontally on the end of the pin, bending it back, and cementing the glass fiber to it. With this arrangement, very large adjustments of the angular position of the crystal can be made without remounting it. To fasten the crystal to the fiber two cements have proved useful: fresh shellac dissolved in alcohol, and ethyl cellulose dissolved in toluene. The shellac dries slowly and permits easy adjustment of the crystal after it is stuck to the fiber, but it is not a very strong mount and requires 2 or 3 days to dry firmly. It never becomes permanently stable and is not suitable where precise angular measurements are important, as with the counter goniometers. Ethyl cellulose requires more deftness in the mounting process because it dries very rapidly. It is quite strong and dries hard in a few minutes, but it requires some practice to enable one to handle it properly.

Orientation of Crystals. Usually, before any diffraction patterns are recorded, it is possible to learn something about the symmetry of the crystal from its morphological and optical properties. Often, simple examination with a binocular microscope will reveal the probable crystal system and location of the principal axes. The more that can be learned about the crystal at this stage, the more efficiently the x-ray study can be carried out. If a crystal is properly mounted at the outset, a complete unit-cell and space-group determination can sometimes be made with three or four exposures, in as many days.

In order to obtain an accurate registration of a lattice plane by any of the single-crystal methods, the crystal axes must be carefully aligned with the camera axes. On the Weissenberg camera, the lattice-net plane to be photographed must be set normal to the spindle axis, while on the Buerger precession camera it is set parallel to the film, that is, normal to the x-ray collimator when the tilt angle is zero. If the crystal has reflecting faces, a preliminary orientation can be accomplished in a few minutes on an optical two-circle goniometer. Such an instrument, fitted with a standard screw base so that the crystal mounted on a universal goniometer head can be readily transferred from the optical to the x-ray goniometers without disturbing its orientation, can in this way save a great deal of time in x-ray diffraction work, as well as provide valuable additional information about the crystal itself. Another useful instrument consists of a spindle with a graduated circle and standard screw base for the goniometer head, which can be mounted in horizontal position on the stage of a polarizing microscope, so that the optical properties of the crystal as well as its morphology can be used as an aid to preliminary orientation.

The choice of crystal-mounting orientation will depend on the method used. When a new plane in the crystal is sought for, it will be remembered that in the Weissenberg camera the net plane photographed is *perpendicular* to the spindle axis, while in the Buerger precession camera, it is *parallel* to it. If the crystal is elongated strongly in one direction, a dense lattice-net plane may be expected to lie normal to this direction. Therefore, for the Weissenberg camera, the needle should be mounted with its length parallel to the spindle axis, while for the precession camera, it should be mounted across the spindle axis so that it lies in line with the direct x-ray beam when the camera is at $\bar{\mu} = 0$. It is helpful to keep in mind that normal to every crystal edge lies a reciprocal-lattice-net plane.

If optical instruments are not available, or if the crystal is opaque and has no suitable reflecting faces, orientation can be achieved entirely by the interpretation of diffraction patterns. In the Weissenberg case it is important to try to bring the crystal to within about 5° of the correct position. Departures of the net plane from a position normal to the spindle axis are immediately obvious from a spreading of the layer lines of the rotation pattern into fan-shaped streaks. The nature of the misorientation cannot be determined from such a pattern, but if the crystal is allowed to oscillate only ±5° about a fixed position, the adjustments of the goniometer head required can be estimated. Unfiltered radiation is used and exposures for such patterns require only a few minutes. In this case, the lattice plane moves only enough to show its trace around the Ewald sphere as a wavy row line corresponding to the zero row line. The sinuations of this line from the straight equatorial reference line indicate the direction of tilt of the lattice plane with respect to the goniometer-head arcs. When the error is about 1° the deviations of this line are not great, and they are more easily measured if after the first exposure the crystal is turned 180° and the exposure is repeated. In this way a second curved row line is produced whose shape is the reverse of the first, and the separations of the two at any point are easily ascertained. Care must be used to recall which line is which, perhaps by making the second exposure half as long as the first; also, of course, a key must be established to relate the orientation of the film to the position of the goniometer head. Figure 14 shows a typical double oscillation photograph of a misoriented crystal. The angle α between the direction of tilt of the lattice plane and the x-ray beam is given by the position of the intersection of the two sinusoidal curves ($\alpha = x$ in millimeters), and the amount of tilt ϵ (in degrees) by the maximum separation y (in millimeters) between them, according to

$$\epsilon = y/(1 + \sin \alpha) \tag{11}$$

The tilt ϵ must then be resolved between the two goniometer-head arcs. Orientation within 20 min is probably satisfactory for most Weissenberg work.

Refinement of crystal orientation is much more easily accomplished with the Buerger precession camera. To test orientation, photographs are made with unfiltered radiation, no layer screen, and a small angle of tilt (5 to 10°). A correctly oriented lattice plane on such a photograph appears as a radiating set of streaks which terminate approximately in a circle centered on the trace of the direct beam. This circle represents the limit of penetration of the zero-layer net plane into the Ewald sphere, and is moved off center by any missetting of the crystal. A displacement parallel to the spindle axis indicates a misadjustment of one or both of the goniometer-head arcs (it is convenient to mount the crystal so that one arc is parallel to the film), and a perpendicular displacement indicates a misadjustment of the dial axis. Typical patterns indicating the latter situation are shown in Fig. 15. The amount of dis-

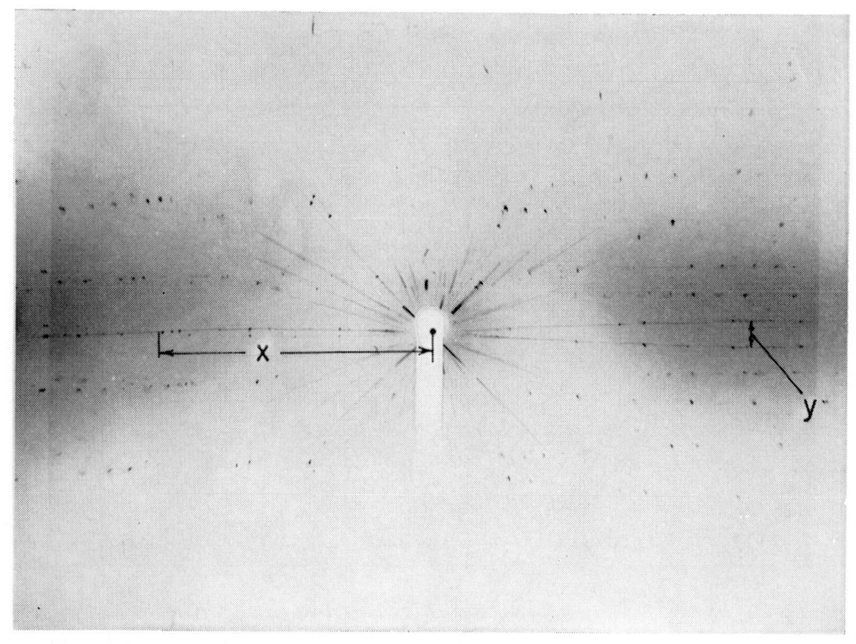

FIG. 14. Oscillation photograph of misoriented crystal of väyrynenite. Cu $K\alpha$ radiation, unfiltered. Double exposure with crystal turned 180° between exposures. Angle of tilt between [100] and rotation axis, 3.0°; tilt axis 27° from direct beam.

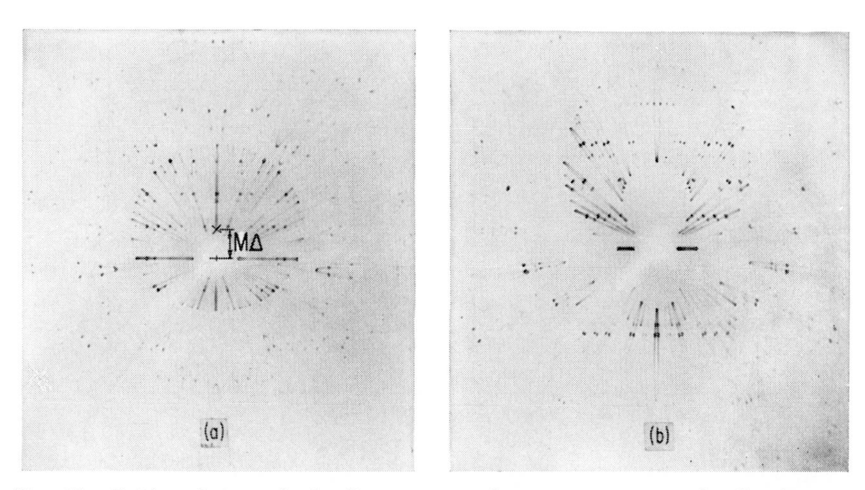

FIG. 15. Setting photographs for Buerger precession camera; väyrynenite (for data see Fig. 5), Mo $K\alpha$ radiation, unfiltered, zero-layer screen. (*a*) $\mu = 10°$, dial axis tilted 4°; (*b*) $\mu = 7.5°$, dial axis tilted 15°. The photograph of this net in true orientation is shown n Fig. 12.

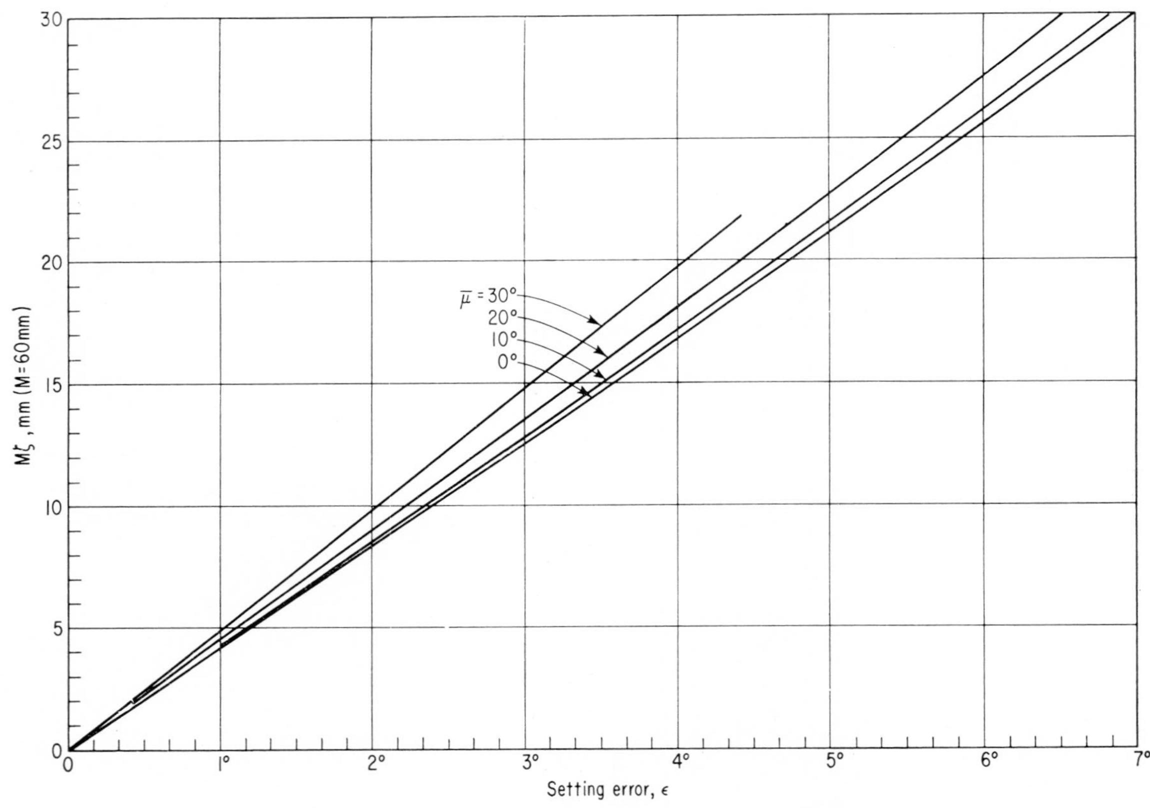

FIG. 16. Chart to determine setting errors for the Buerger precession method.

placement Δ in centimeters is interpreted as angular corrections ϵ on the two sets of arcs and the spindle dial by the relation

$$\Delta = M \frac{\sin 4\epsilon \cos \bar{\mu}}{\cos^2 2\epsilon - \sin^2 \bar{\mu}} \tag{12}$$

where F is the crystal-to-film distance in centimeters. This function is shown plotted in Fig. 16. Whereas oscillation patterns made with a crystal misoriented on the Weissenberg camera by more than 5° are difficult to interpret, the trace of a relatively dense net plane can be detected on precession photographs when tilted well beyond 15°.

Lattice Photography for Unit-cell and Space-group Determinations. For each crystal system, a minimum number of diffraction patterns of certain types are required for a complete unit-cell and space-group determination. These are outlined for the Buerger precession method below.

Triclinic System. Two net-plane Buerger precession photographs are sufficient to measure a^*, c^*, and β^* on one pattern; b^*, c^*, and α^* on the second; and γ as the difference of the spindle-dial angles recorded for the two photographs (c^* parallel to the spindle, common to the two net planes; axial assignments arbitrary). A check should be made with a cone-axis pattern and one first-level photograph to ensure that a truly primitive lattice has been selected. Great care is necessary in interpreting the patterns that the relative positions of the positive and negative directions of the chosen axes are clearly understood, especially in selecting the proper value of γ.

Monoclinic System. If the b axis is set perpendicular to the spindle mount, three patterns will give the necessary information: an $h0l$ net for a^*, c^*, and β^*; an $h1l$ net to determine the lattice type and the glide plane if present; and an $hk0$ net for a^* and b^* and to test for a screw axis. If the b axis is parallel to the spindle axis, the $hk0$ and $0kl$ net planes will give a^*, b^*, c^* (axial assignments arbitrary), and β is determined from the difference of the dial settings. One or more upper levels will then give the necessary information about lattice type and glide plane. It is much better, however, to have a complete $h0l$ pattern in order to be sure of the glide plane.

Orthorhombic System. With one axis parallel to the spindle, four patterns will be required: $h0l$ for a^* and c^*; $h1l$ for lattice type and to detect a glide plane normal to b; $0kl$ for b^* and c^*; $1kl$ to detect a glide plane normal to a (axial assignments arbitrary; c^* parallel to spindle axis). These patterns will give information also about a glide plane normal to c, but to confirm the determination, an $hk0$ pattern may be needed. This may be made most easily on the same crystal by transferring the goniometer head to a Weissenberg camera.

Hexagonal System. With care, it is often possible to mount a hexagonal crystal with one of the a axes tilted about 15° to the spindle axis and the c axis normal to it. Then all necessary information may be obtained from three or four patterns without remounting the crystal: $hk0$ for a^* and to facilitate orientation for the other patterns; $h0l$ for a^*, c^*, to detect rhombohedral centering or glide plane normal to a axis; hhl (goniometer-head arc shifted 30°) for a^*, c^* and to detect glide plane parallel to the a axis.

Tetragonal and Cubic Systems. The requirements are similar to the hexagonal system except that the $h0l$ and hhl net planes are 45° apart and it may not be possible to reach both of them with one crystal mounting.

For most cases, a complete unit cell may be determined from one crystal mount with the Buerger precession method, while several different mounts will be necessary for the Weissenberg camera.

4. THE MEASUREMENT OF DIFFRACTION INTENSITIES

Single-crystal apparatus and techniques have been described in the previous sections mainly with respect to the problem of determining the size, shape, and symmetry of the crystal unit cell. The same apparatus and techniques are readily extended to the second main object of the x-ray diffraction study of crystals, namely, the determination of the arrangement of atoms within the unit cell through a study of the intensity of Bragg reflections produced by a crystal. For this purpose it is necessary to measure the total energy in each of a series of diffraction spectra produced by the crystal. Differences in relative intensity of various reflections are, of course, readily apparent in the various degrees of blackening of spots on diffraction-pattern photographs recorded by the various diffraction cameras, and are used in the geometric study of crystals to determine the symmetry of the crystal. When we become interested in measuring the positions of atoms, we must be concerned in addition with the accurate measurement of these intensities and also with extending the range of Bragg reflections over which they are measured. The parameters which determine a crystal structure are related directly to the diffraction intensities by the structure-factor function

$$F(hkl) = \sum_j t_j f_j e^{-2\pi i(hx_j+ky_j+lz_j)} \tag{13}$$

where x_j, y_j, z_j are the coordinates of the jth atom, f_j is the scattering factor of the jth atom, t_j represents the thermal motion of the jth atom, and $F(hkl)$ is the structure factor. The absolute value of F is derived from the diffraction intensity of the hkl plane. Clearly, the accuracy with which the fundamental chemical information, namely, the x_j, y_j, and z_j values, is known will depend on both the accuracy with which the $F(hkl)$ values are measured and the number of symmetry-independent values that can be collected. The structure factor is related to the intensity of diffraction I by the following expression:

$$|F|^2 = \frac{m^2c^4}{e^4}\frac{1}{\lambda^3N^2V}\frac{1}{ALp}\frac{I}{I_0} = \frac{K^2I}{ALp} \tag{14}$$

where e is the charge and m the mass of the electron, c is the velocity of light, λ the wavelength of the x-rays, N the number of unit cells per unit of volume, V the volume of the crystal, A an absorption factor, L the Lorentz factor, p the polarization factor, I_0 the intensity of the primary beam, and K a scale factor. The quantities m, c, e, λ, N, L, and p are all known with considerable accuracy, but V, A, and I_0 are determined with much greater difficulty. Of these, the absorption effects, including the effects of extinction, are probably the most troublesome. The function [Eq. (14)] is based on the ideal case in which a crystal is assumed to be composed of a collection of slightly misoriented blocks so that coherent scattering acts to produce the diffracted beam but does not subsequently modify this beam by rediffraction. Most crystals, fortunately, conform closely to this ideal case, but some tendency toward the perfect-crystal state is frequently present, and is treated in terms of extinction, which will be considered later together with absorption.

The matter of primary interest in structure analysis is the *relative* values of F, so that I_0 and N^2V assume secondary importance. In the photographic method, the whole diffraction pattern is exposed repeatedly over a relatively long time period so that variations in I_0 are averaged out for the reflections on that pattern, but unless the x-ray source is very well regulated (and also the photographic processing), the relative level of intensity among different patterns must be carefully correlated. When intensities are measured by means of pulse-counter techniques, a high degree of x-ray source regulation is essential. Attempts have been made from time to time to determine the so-called absolute intensity of crystal diffraction by measuring I_0 from the diffraction given by a known crystal (known N^2V, A, and F) and a measurement of N^2V for the unknown crystal, but the results have never proved to be better than those obtained by the much simpler method involving the statistical treatment of the intensity distribution of all the collected relative K^2I/ALp values (e.g., Wilson's method; see Chap. 29).

The Mechanics of Intensity Measurement. The actual measurement of I requires that the diffraction energy be collected from the entire volume of the crystal. Such diffraction, mainly because of the mosaic texture of the crystal referred to above, will not occur in a single angular direction, but rather over a spread of usually about 10 to 30 min of arc. Thus, when the crystal is rotated through the Bragg angle, the profile of intensity vs. angle will be roughly Gaussian in shape, distributed about the

Bragg angle with a width depending on the texture of the crystal. The quantity desired is the area under this profile above the background level, whatever its shape and width, and is therefore referred to as the *integrated intensity*. The two main sources of error in determining $K^2|F|^2$ are errors inherent in the detector system (photographic or pulse-counter technique, integration technique, etc.) and absorption effects. The photographic method is capable of rather poor accuracy at best, so that random errors in $K^2|F|^2$ measured this way seldom are less than 10 per cent and normally range about 15 to 20 per cent. The pulse-counter method, provided integration is properly carried out, can give measurements good to about 1 per cent, so that absorption for such data becomes the dominant source of error. It is astonishing to contemplate that the great majority of the thousands of crystal-structure determinations published, hundreds of which are refined to ± 0.03 Å in atomic position or better, are based on photographic data of quite poor quality by ordinary physical standards. This situation results, of course, from the great superabundance of data available to the crystal-structure analyst, but it also indicates that the full power of the x-ray diffraction method is seldom approached. As the use of counter methods for intensity measurement becomes more common (see Chap. 25) and computers are harnessed to eliminate the tediousness of absorption corrections, crystal-structure determinations in the future will come closer to the extremely high degree of resolution inherent in the x-ray diffraction process.

Calibrated "Intensity Strip." A simple means of intensity measurement consists of preparing a strip of exposures of one reflection varied over a range on one film and using this strip of spots to estimate the unknown spot intensities by direct comparison. Simple as it seems, this method has been used for the majority of crystal structures and is capable of excellent results. The procedure, using a Weissenberg camera, is as follows:

1. Isolate a strong reflection of a zero-layer net of the crystal under study within a 10° oscillation range.
2. Arrange a shutter so that x-rays can be cut off without turning off the high tension. The x-ray unit should be at ambient running temperature and capable of steady, drift-free operation for a period of about 3 hr.
3. Load the camera with two or three films, and arrange the holder so that it may be clamped so that the layer screen slot may be in a position anywhere from one end of the film to the other. A scale with 5-mm intervals marked mounted on the base of the film holder will aid in positioning it.
4. Determine the length of time required for one oscillation by measuring the time of 10 cycles with a stop watch.
5. Plan a series of 15 to 20 exposures varying in time by a factor of $\sqrt{2}$ between one and the next. Exposures may begin with two or three transverses and be increased by counting full traverses up to about 50; beyond that point exposures are best timed with a stop watch or clock.
6. Make each exposure according to the plan, using the shutter, taking care to start and stop at the end of a traverse for the short exposures, and shifting the film holder 5 mm between each exposure.
7. Develop the films after the last exposure in the normal manner.

A typical "intensity strip" made in this way is shown in Fig. 17.

The diffraction patterns themselves must usually be made in five or six graduated exposures, because of the narrow range of density measurable on one film. The intensity strip is useful over a range of about 10 exposure steps, but diffraction intensities may range over 25 or 30 steps, and an appreciable overlap from film to film is necessary in order to obtain adequate scale correlation. Repeated runs are reduced by loading three or four films in a packet in the film holder, sometimes interleaved with absorbing metal foils. The x-ray absorption in the usually available no-screen double-emulsion x-ray film is about 75 per cent for Cu K radiation, and about 50 per cent for such film plus 0.0007-in. Ni foil for Mo K radiation. These factors should be determined by the experimenter for his own established conditions. Intensities are estimated by finding the spot on the intensity strip (numbered 1 to 20) which most nearly matches the spot on the pattern, estimating one-half intervals if possible, and

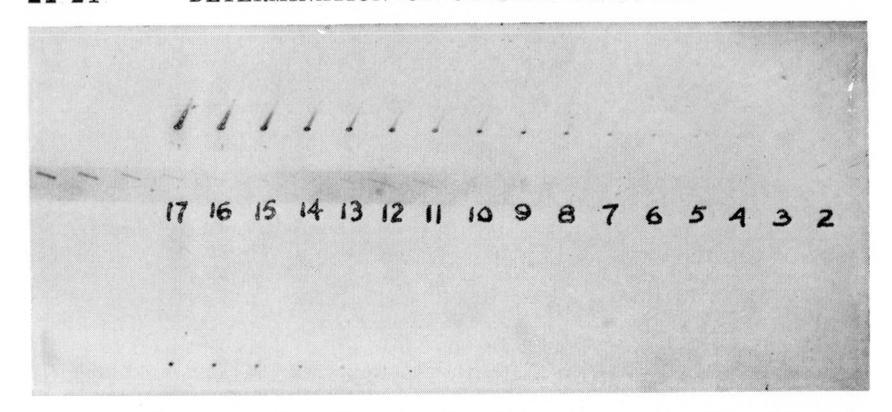

Fig. 17. Calibrated intensity strip made with a Weissenberg camera, using a 10° oscillation about a strong spot.

recording the spot number. Spot numbers recorded for the weaker exposures are brought to the same scale as those of the strongest pattern by adding a constant to the numbers of each film determined by comparing estimates common to two or more films. Thus a constant 3.5 added to the numbers of a weak pattern means that the strongest pattern is $(\sqrt{2})^{3.5} = 3.4$ times stronger.

The scaled spot numbers are then finally converted to intensities by means of a table such as Table 1.

The method of visual estimate with an intensity strip has two great advantages: its great simplicity, and the control over variations in spot shape for different crystals by the use of a spot selected from the same pattern for comparison. Nevertheless, the experimental conditions suggest to the careful worker a wealth of possibilities for error.

Table 1. Intensity Equivalents of Spot Numbers for Which $r = \sqrt{2}$

No.	I	No.	I	No.	I
0	2.00	10	64.0	20	2,048
0.5	2.38	10.5	76.1	20.5	2,436
1	2.83	11	90.5	21	2,896
1.5	3.36	11.5	107.6	21.5	3,445
2	4.00	12	128.0	22	4,096
2.5	4.76	12.5	153.2	22.5	4,872
3	5.66	13	181.0	23	5,792
3.5	6.73	13.5	215.3	23.5	6,891
4	8.00	14	256.0	24	8,192
4.5	9.52	14.5	324.6	24.5	9,745
5	11.3	15	362	25	11,584
5.5	13.5	15.5	431	25.5	13,780
6	16.0	16	512	26	16,380
6.5	19.0	16.5	609	26.5	19,480
7	22.6	17	724	27	23,170
7.5	26.9	17.5	861	27.5	27,550
8	32.0	18	1,024	28	32,770
8.5	38.1	18.5	1,218	28.5	38,970
9	45.3	19	1,448	29	46,340
9.5	53.8	19.5	1,723	29.5	55,110
10	64.0	20	2,048	30	65,540

The fact that estimates are made by eye rather than by some purely artificial detection system introduces a human factor which is often open to suspicion. For this reason, the visual-estimate method is sometimes carried out by two or three different workers independently in order to detect and average out human errors.

Photometric Methods. Much effort has been devoted to the development of techniques of measuring intensity from film density by methods which avoid human factors. One of the most successful and widely used such methods is a mechanical device for scanning the diffraction-pattern spots during exposure so that film density can be measured by means of a photometer over a uniformly exposed area. The integrating mechanism for the Weissenberg camera, invented by Wiebenga, is an ingenious device which shifts the film to a slightly different position between each traverse, so that each spot is spread over a grid about 2 by 2 mm in area, 14 steps in each direction. Thus there is an area at the center to each point of which every part of the diffraction-beam profile has been exposed an equal amount of time, and which therefore corresponds in density to the integrated intensity. This area is uniform and broad enough to cover a 1-mm aperture of a photometer. The Weissenberg camera shown in Fig. 7 is equipped with such a device. A similar mechanism has also been built for the Buerger precession camera.

The film and photometer used with such integrated diffraction patterns must be calibrated with a stepped series of exposures, made either with a crystal reflection as with the visual calibrated strip, or with some special arrangment to expose film uniformly in graduated steps. Unlike ordinary light, x-rays produce a blackening nearly linearly proportional to exposure time and intensity (no reciprocity-law failure), so that these steps should be in constant increments from one to the next, rather than constant ratio. (Constant-ratio steps are used for visual estimate because the eye is accustomed to comparing ratios rather than differences.) In this way, intensity data can be measured whose accuracy depends primarily on the reproducibility of the photographic process.

Another favorable method consists of photometering directly the transmission of a spot on a positive film made from an ordinary (unintegrated) diffraction pattern. By adjusting the photographic-development parameters carefully, the nonlinear character of the positive and negative emulsions can be made to cancel out, so that transmission intensity becomes proportional to the x-ray intensity. This method was first used by Dawton, and developed and described by Buerger.

In spite of the fact that the integrating methods are evidently more advanced and sophisticated than the time-honored visual-estimate method, many crystallographers have found that the results obtained are hardly any better. It is especially surprising because it is well known that the eye, in comparing two complex features such as diffraction spots, tends to match their maximum densities, rather than integrate the total density of each spot. As a matter of fact, the ordinary single-crystal diffraction pattern is integrated by virtue of the convergence of the primary beam, without any mechanical complications. The usual collimator consists of two 0.5-mm-diameter apertures between the x-ray tube target and the crystal, about 50 mm apart, so that if these openings are filled with x-rays (camera set at takeoff angle of about 3°), the convergence angle at the crystal is about 40 min of arc, sufficient to produce a plateau on the diffraction peak whose height is proportional to the integrated intensity. For this reason, visual estimate of peak maximum densities actually results in the measurement of integrated intensities. The main drawback of this method actually lies not so much in the lower quality of the measurements as in the annoyance of eyestrain which prevents the continuation of measurements by one person for more than 1 or 2 hr a day. The photometer methods avoid this difficulty, so that a set of three-dimensional data may be obtained in a shorter time.

The uncertainties of the photographic materials and processes even with well-controlled darkroom conditions, and the "noise" introduced by the coarseness of grain of the high-speed diffraction films, evidently set the limit on the quality of data measured by any photographic method. To improve the quality of intensity measurements significantly, pulse-counter methods must be used. Such methods are nowadays becoming more and more important, and are treated in Chap. 25.

Intensity Corrections. The measurements obtained by the various methods described above must now be transformed to the data needed for crystal-structure analysis, the structure amplitudes. For this purpose allowance must be made for various geometric and physical factors which modify the intensity as predicted by the diffraction process itself, depending on the method by which the intensity is recorded on the one hand, and on the shape and quality of the crystal on the other. The most important modifying factors are summarized in the following paragraphs.

Effect of Spot Shape. The integrated intensity is in principle independent of the shape of the profile of the reflection scan. Thus, if integrating systems such as those mentioned above under Photometric Methods have an integrating aperture large enough to cover the whole scan region, no special corrections are required for profile effects. Otherwise, especially in the case of visually estimated intensities, adjustment of the data may be necessary for two prevalent effects: (1) the varying separation between the components of the $K\alpha_1$-$K\alpha_2$ doublet; and (2) shape distortion due to a "smearing" of the spots on upper-layer Weissenberg patterns.

In the latter case, the mosaic-broadened reciprocal-lattice point passing through the surface of the Ewald sphere at grazing incidence causes the diffraction image to migrate through an appreciable angle in space. The moving cylindrical camera recording these upper-layer reflections will by its motion tend to compensate this migration and thus compress and sharpen the spots on one side of the film, and to enhance the migration and broaden the spots on the other half of the film. Correction functions have been derived to account for the apparent increase or decrease in intensity resulting from this effect, but since the effect is similar for all spots on one half of the film, it is most practical to combine the correction with the ordinary scale factor for the whole level. It is good practice to measure all intensities on the half of the film on which the spots tend to compress, because these spots retain a nearly enough similar shape so that one intensity strip can be used for all levels.

The separation of the $K\alpha_1$-$K\alpha_2$ doublet is more troublesome, especially in intermediate angular ranges where partial overlap occurs. At high angles the intensity of the $K\alpha_1$ spot can be measured separately and the result scaled to the level of the low-angle intensities where $K\alpha_1$ and $K\alpha_2$ are effectively superimposed by multiplying by the ratio of $I(K\alpha_1) + I(K\alpha_2)$ to $I(K\alpha_1)$, which is close to 1.5. This ratio corresponds to one unit on the intensity-strip number scale described above. In the intermediate range, say from 2θ angles of 50 to 70°, a correction of one-half unit may be applied. When photometer methods are used, some sort of empirical calibration curve of the correction ratio against Bragg angle may be set up; but it should be kept in mind that the correction is not far from the limit of accuracy of the photographic process, so that elaborate corrections are probably not worthwhile.

Corrections for Polarization and the Lorentz Factor. Two strictly geometric factors which modify the relative intensities must be accounted for. The first, the polarization factor, is a function of the Bragg angle only and is the same for all methods of measurement. It is easily understood by considering the scattering by one electron in an atom in the crystal, which responds to an impinging x-ray beam. Its oscillations give rise to a secondary x-ray beam of two polarized components, vertical and horizontal, each of intensity one-half relative to the total forward-scattered intensity. At various angles in the horizontal plane, the intensity of the horizontal component as a transverse wave is a maximum at 0 and 180°, parallel to the primary beam, but decreases to zero at 90°, where the transverse electron oscillations have no contribution. The intensity of this wave, then, varies according to $\cos^2 2\theta$. The intensity of the vertical component, on the other hand, remains unchanged at all horizontal scattering angles. Therefore, the scattering intensity from all the electrons in the crystal is reduced by the polarization factor p [see Eq. (14)] according to

$$p = \tfrac{1}{2} + \tfrac{1}{2}\cos^2 2\theta \qquad (15)$$

If a filtered primary beam is taken directly from the x-ray source, this factor is cylindrically symmetrical about the collimated beam. If the beam is first crystal-monochromated, then the coefficients $\frac{1}{2}$ on the right in Eq. (15) may be different and are a function of the diffracting angle of the monochromatizing crystal and its orientation with respect to the camera, so that the function is no longer cylindrically symmetrical. The appropriate modification of Eq. (15) must then be derived for each such case.

A second important geometric factor, known as the Lorentz factor, arises from the fact that the manner in which the various diffracting planes in the crystal pass through the critical diffracting angle is different for different planes. This variation is best understood by considering the angle at which a reciprocal-lattice point passes through the diffracting sphere. If the lattice point were truly a geometric point, the idea of time opportunity that a diffracting plane has while its reciprocal-lattice point passes through the geometric surface of the Ewald sphere would have no meaning; but as a matter of fact, because of the spread of wavelengths in the primary beam, the mosaic character of the crystal, and other factors, the reciprocal-lattice "point" actually has a breadth as it is applied in the practical diffraction problem. Assuming

Table 2. Formulas for the Lorentz Polarization Correction $1/Lp$ for Various Diffraction Methods in Terms of Cylindrical Reciprocal-lattice Coordinates ξ, ζ, and ϕ ($\sigma^2 = \xi^2 + \zeta^2$)

Zero level ($\zeta = 0$)	*Upper levels*
1. Rotation, oscillation, normal-beam, and flat-core Weissenberg methods	
$\dfrac{\sqrt{3}\,\xi}{2(2 - 2\xi + \xi^2)}$	$\dfrac{\sqrt{4\xi^2 - \sigma^2}}{2 + 2(1 - \sigma^2)^2}$
2. Equi-inclination Weissenberg method	
$\dfrac{\xi\sqrt{4 - \xi^2}}{2(2 - 2\xi + \xi^2)}$	$\dfrac{\xi\sqrt{4 - \sigma^2}}{2 + 2(1 - \sigma^2)^2}$
3. Buerger precession method, angle of tilt $\bar{\mu} = 30°$	
$\dfrac{\dfrac{16}{1 + \frac{1}{3}\sin^2(\phi + \cos^{-1}\xi)} + \dfrac{16}{1 + \frac{1}{3}\sin^2(\phi - \cos^{-1}\xi)}}{\sqrt{3}\,\xi(8 - 4\xi^2 + \xi^4)\sqrt{1 - \xi^2}}$	

$$\frac{\dfrac{16}{1 + \frac{1}{3}\sin^2\left[\phi + \cos^{-1}\frac{1}{\xi}(\sigma^2 - \sqrt{3}\,\zeta)\right]} + \dfrac{16}{1 + \frac{1}{3}\sin^2\left[\phi - \cos^{-1}\frac{1}{\xi}(\sigma^2 - \sqrt{3}\,\zeta)\right]}}{\sqrt{3}\,(8 - 4\sigma^2 + \sigma^4)\,[(\frac{1}{4} + \sqrt{3}\,\zeta - \zeta^2) - (\frac{1}{2} + \sqrt{3}\,\zeta - \sigma^2)^2]^{1/2}}$$

(ϕ is the angle between the ξ vector and the spindle axis)

that all the reciprocal-lattice points have the same "spread," it can be seen that a point which passes through the diffracting sphere at a grazing angle will have a longer time to diffract x-rays than one which passes through in a direction nearly normal to the surface. If the angle between the sphere's surface and the direction of movement of the lattice point is ψ, the integrated intensity of the reflection will be increased by the factor

$$L = \sec\psi \tag{16}$$

This factor will depend, in its relation to the crystal-lattice parameters, to a high degree on the geometry of the particular recording method used. In general, because of the Lorentz factor, the intensity of reflections at low Bragg angles, and at angles near the upper limit of diffraction, will be enormously enhanced.

A third geometric factor, the Tunell factor, takes into account the fact that reciprocal-lattice points of a rotating crystal which are farther from the origin move faster with respect to the sphere than those near the origin, and so have less time to diffract x-rays. Thus, reflection intensity is reduced by the amount

$$L_T = 1/\sigma = \tfrac{1}{2}\csc\theta \tag{17}$$

This factor is usually incorporated with the Lorentz factor, to which it is closely related. In fact, we may redefine the Lorentz factor as a function of the projected component of the velocity of a reciprocal-lattice point on the normal to the Ewald sphere at the point of contact.

It is most convenient, finally, to combine all these geometric factors into one algebraic expression which is represented by Lp, the Lorentz polarization factor. The expression may be derived in terms of angular coordinates appropriate to the camera used, such as μ, Υ, and 2θ, or in terms of cylindrical coordinates of the reciprocal lattice

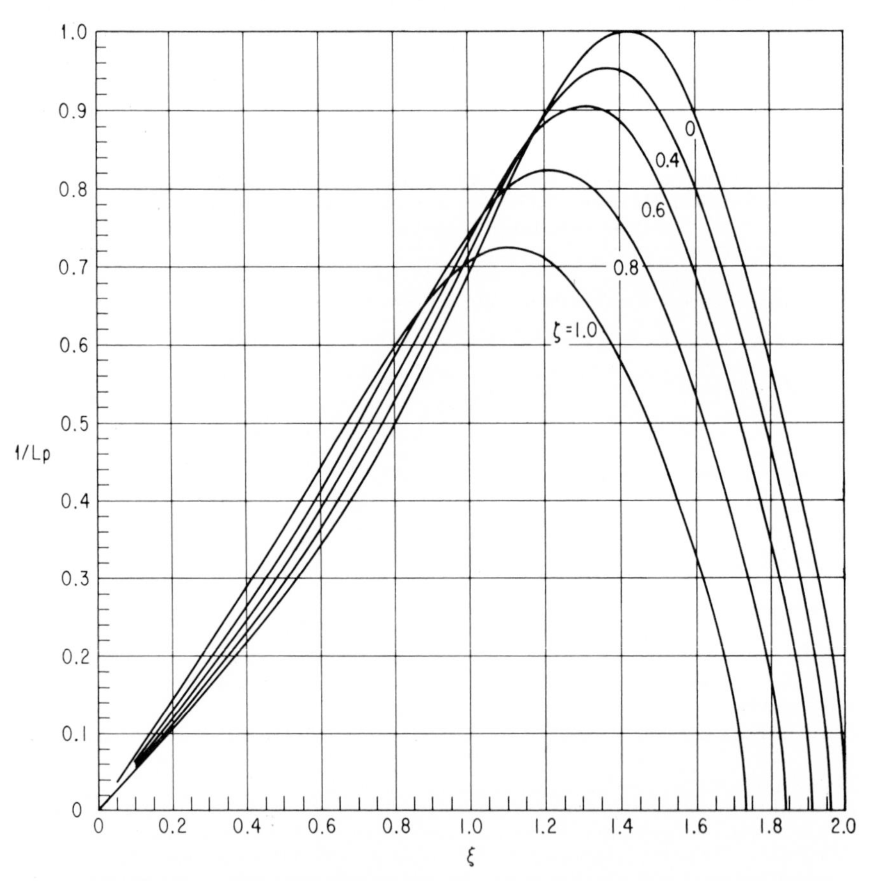

FIG. 18. Lorentz-polarization function for the equi-inclination Weissenberg method.

ζ and ξ. The latter form is the most useful for computer application, and the expressions for several techniques are given in Table 2. In Figs. 18 and 19 are shown graphs of these functions in reciprocal form, which is most convenient to apply as a multiplier correction directly to the measured intensity.

It should be noted that the intensity values should be corrected for the Lorentz polarization effect before groups of data from different layers are compared to derive scaling factors.

Absorption and Extinction. The most troublesome factor which must be accounted for in converting measured intensity values to structure amplitudes results from x-ray absorption in the crystal. If at all possible, conditions are chosen so that the absorption can only cause errors which are less than what it is decided will be tolerated.

The effect can be minimized by using a crystal which is as small as possible and still gives conveniently measurable intensities. Such a crystal may well be somewhat smaller than the so-called optimum crystal size, whose cross section is $2/\mu$ cm (μ is the linear absorption coefficient). Absorption can also generally be considerably reduced by the use of shorter-wavelength x-rays, that is, Mo $K\alpha$ instead of Cu $K\alpha$ radiation. Exceptions to this rule of thumb will occur with crystals which contain an element whose absorption edge approaches the Mo $K\alpha$ wavelength, and can be anticipated by

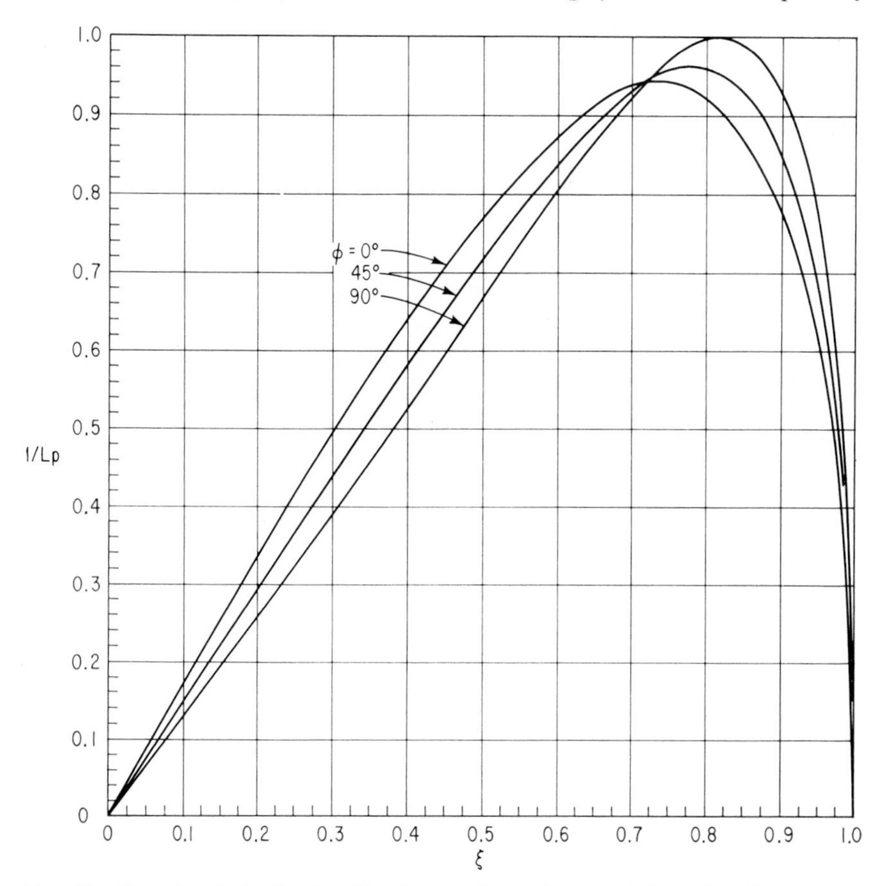

FIG. 19. Lorentz-polarization function for zero-layer photographs from the Buerger precession method.

reference to appropriate tables of linear absorption coefficients (International Tables, vol. III, sec. 3.2).

Certain camera techniques permit the absorption effect to be considerably lessened even when the actual absorption is relatively high. In the Weissenberg method, a cylindrical or spherical crystal will show absorption which is greatest at low diffraction angles and decreases monotonically with increasing angle. If a crystal structure is refined with this type of data which has not been corrected for absorption, abnormally large temperature effects will be derived, but the structure parameters will not be greatly affected. Even a prismatic or needle-shaped crystal may be near enough to a cylinder in absorption properties so that most of the error resulting from neglect of absorption will become associated with the thermal parameters. On the other hand, it may not be possible to obtain useful intensity photographs from such a crystal rotated about any other axis because in that case absorption may be expected to vary greatly among reflections of nearly the same Bragg angle. Thus it occasionally happens that only a limited amount of reliable data can be measured for crystals with a strongly acicular habit.

In the case of the Buerger precession camera, it is easy to show that the path length of any diffraction beam through a crystal plate oriented parallel to the film will be

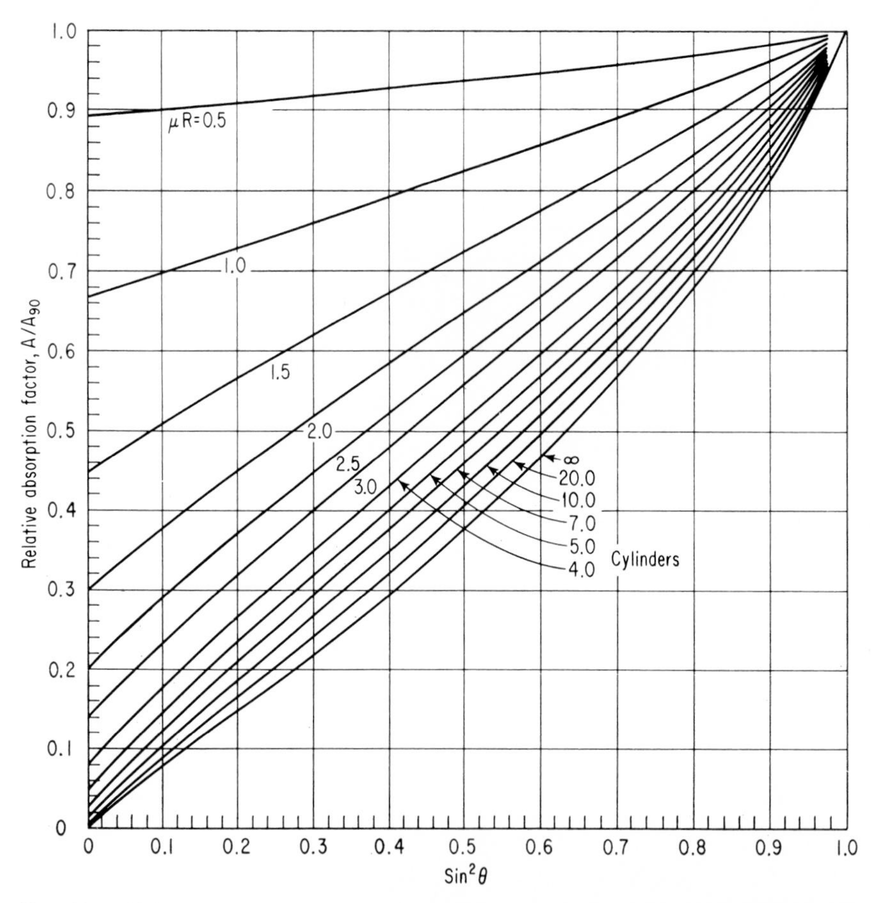

FIG. 20*a*. Relative absorption factor normalized with respect to the factor for $\theta = 90°$ for axially rotated cylinders, plotted in terms of $\sin^2 \theta$.

constant for a given layer. Thus reflections in any net plane parallel to a thin crystal plate recorded on the precession camera will have a nearly constant absorption effect. Even if the plate is tilted somewhat (as with monoclinic or triclinic crystals), the absorption will be compensated for to a considerable extent. The factor will be different for different layers, but it can be included in the scale factor for each level; and so for this type of data, special corrections for absorption can be avoided. Again, however, it may be very difficult to obtain reliable intensity data with any other orientation or method.

If the crystal has a shape such that absorption effects are serious, it can often be converted to a cylinder or sphere by various abrading techniques. Simply by rolling the crystal on a fine abrasive surface with the finger or a piece of wood, it is often possible to obtain rough cylinders or spheres which are good enough to overcome the absorption problem to a large extent. A fine, moist, absorbent surface can be used instead of an abrasive if the crystal is soluble. Excellent spheres down to 0.1 mm in diameter can be obtained with a very simple apparatus consisting of a block of metal about ½ in. thick with a hole bored in it about 1½ in. in diameter, lined with fine abrasive paper. A few crystal fragments are enclosed in this chamber by two plastic

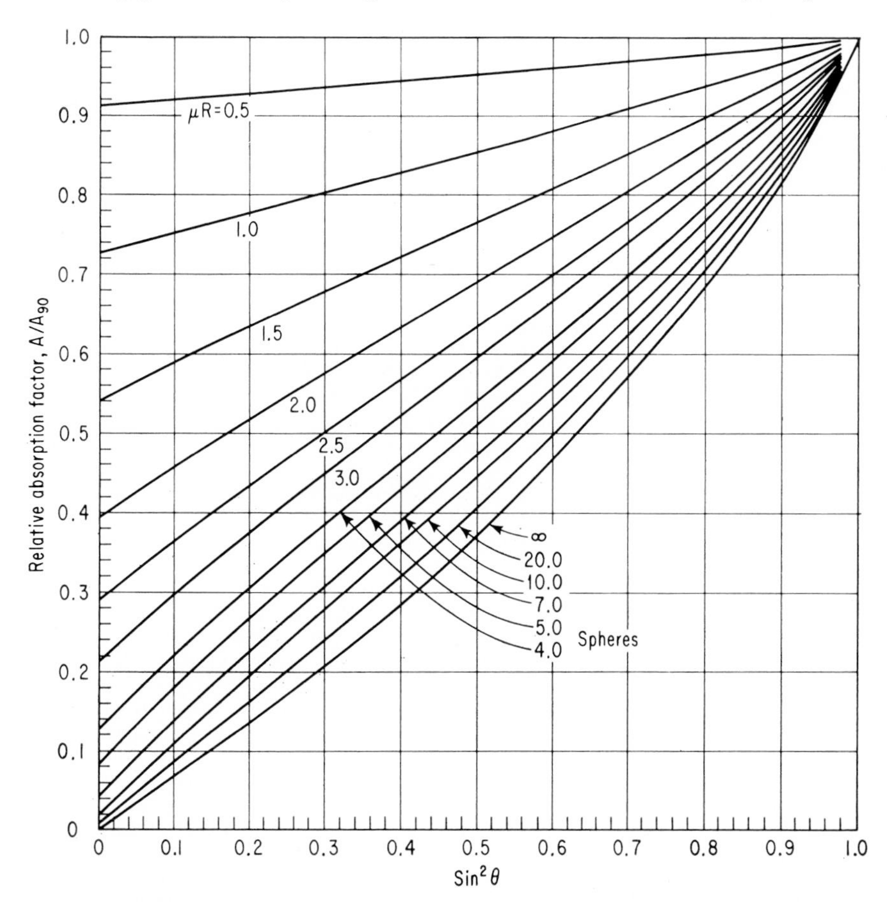

FIG. 20*b*. Relative absorption factor normalized with respect to the factor for $\theta = 90°$ for spheres, plotted in terms of $\sin^2 \theta$.

plates (perforated at the center to allow air to escape) and tumbled by an air jet introduced tangentially to the abrasive wall. Optimum conditions of quality of abrasive, pressure of air jet, and time of treatment must be carefully determined by trial for each new crystal. Sometimes the spheres so produced must be lightly etched to remove plastic deformation which may be produced on the surface.

If a crystal of good cylindrical or spherical shape is available, the absorption effect can be evaluated by means of tables in which the factor A, the ratio of intensity with absorption to that without absorption, has been calculated for various linear absorption coefficients. These functions, normalized so that $A = 1$ at $\theta = 90°$, are illustrated in Figs. 20*a* and 20*b* plotted against $\sin^2 \theta$ so that they become nearly linear.

When the shape of the crystal and the absorption coefficient are accurately known, the absorption factor for any reflection can be evaluated quantitatively, at least by numerical methods. Although the integrals

$$A = \int e^{-\mu(x_1+x_2)}\, dv / \int dv \tag{18}$$

(where x_1 and x_2 are the path lengths to and from the volume element dv) can be exactly evaluated for any volume bounded by plane surfaces, it is usually much easier to carry out the integrations over a grid of volume elements sufficiently closely spaced to give the desired accuracy. This method is well adapted to high-speed digital computers.

When extinction effects become important, they have the effect of increasing the linear absorption coefficient for certain of the stronger reflections. Secondary extinction, which results from a diversion of energy from the direct beam into the diffracted beam, can be accounted for approximately by using an effective linear absorption coefficient

$$\mu_{\text{eff}} = \mu + g(I/I_0) \tag{19}$$

where I/I_0 is the intensity function from Eq. (14). g is usually so small that only half a dozen or so very strong reflections at low Bragg angle are appreciably affected. It will generally be much smaller for Mo $K\alpha$ radiation than for Cu $K\alpha$. The effect can easily be seen when comparing calculated and observed structure factors in late stages of structure refinement, and they are often simply omitted from further refinement calculations. Thus it is seldom necessary to correct intensities for extinction.

Primary extinction occurs when a crystal approaches perfection sufficiently that a diffracted beam is diffracted again parallel to the direct beam 180° out of phase and tends to subtract coherently from its intensity. For some very hard crystals this effect can become quite serious, and there is no convenient analytical way to account for it. Sometimes such a crystal can be thermally shocked by dipping in liquid nitrogen so that enough mosaic texture is introduced to prevent serious coherent coupling of the direct and diffracted beams.

In connection with absorption, mention may be made of the troublesome problem of fluorescent scattering which occasionally occurs when an element in the crystal has an absorption edge near the primary x-ray wavelength. Plane faces on the crystal cast shadows which sometimes produce very characteristic background patterns on the single-crystal diffraction photographs. These patterns are a sure sign of serious absorption and can even be used to estimate its variation from reflection to reflection.

Collecting Intensities for Structure Analysis. The Weissenberg camera is generally more useful for intensity-data collection than the Buerger precession camera, mainly because of its greater range. The strategy for three-dimensional data collection varies with the crystal symmetry as outlined below.

Triclinic System. For each layer except the zero layer two photographs are necessary because the entire layer must be recorded and the Weissenberg oscillation range is only about 200°. If measurements are confined to only one side of the Weissenberg patterns, that on which the spots are concentrated rather than distended, the same calibrated strip can be used for visual estimates on all layers. By extending μ to 30°, if Mo $K\alpha$ radiation is used, layers can be recorded to the top of a sphere of radius $(\sin\theta)/\lambda = 0.7$ Å^{-1}, which is sufficient for most structure determinations. A few layers about another axis will also be necessary in order to scale the first set of films with respect to each other (after correcting for the Lorentz polarization factor) and to register reflections lost in the beam trap on the first set. Two or three additional photographs made with Cu $K\alpha$ may be necessary in addition to record reflections at very low Bragg angles. If Mo $K\alpha$ is not a convenient radiation, as with many organic crystals, a reasonably large sphere cannot be filled out by a set of layers about one axis, and three or more sets may be required about different axes. The indexing of triclinic patterns is facilitated if the oscillation ranges of the Weissenberg patterns are kept uniform for all layers, and by looking for sequences of spots on rows common to Weissenberg patterns made about two different axes. The process is laborious at best, nevertheless, and great vigilance is required to establish the best common scale for all reflections and to avoid indexing errors.

Monoclinic System. One complete set of layers may be made about the b axis, with enough layers about an axis normal to b in addition to scale the b-axis layers and fill out the desired sphere. In recording the latter patterns, care must be taken to ensure that the oscillation range covers all the lattice plane on one side of the mirror plane.

Orthorhombic System. A set of levels recorded about two orthogonal axes up to a layer of $\zeta = 1.00$ will encompass a spherical range of the reciprocal lattice with Mo $K\alpha$ radiation out to $(\sin \theta)/\lambda \sim 1.0$, and with Cu $K\alpha$ to ~ 0.5. If a range of $(\sin \theta)/\lambda \sim 0.7$ is sufficient a set about one axis will suffice, with one or two levels around another axis to provide a basis for correlation of level scales. If greater ranges are desired, a few levels about some diagonal axis such as [110] may be necessary.

Tetragonal and Cubic Systems. Within the range limitations given for the orthorhombic system, a set of level photographs around one a axis will suffice, and further, the fourfold axis will provide symmetry-equivalent reflections on different levels so that scaling can be accomplished internally without the need for photographs taken about another axis.

Hexagonal System. In lower symmetries based on hexagonal axes, it is necessary to record the whole of a 60° sector in the reciprocal lattice, and a set of photographs around both the [10.0] and [11.0] axes may be required. If only a 30° sector is necessary, then a set of photographs around the a axis up to $\zeta = 1.00$ will cover a lattice range out to $(\sin \theta)/\lambda \sim 1.4$ for Mo $K\alpha$ radiation and ~ 0.7 for Cu $K\alpha$, with internal cross checks available for scaling.

GENERAL REFERENCES

Barrett, C. S.: *Structure of Metals*, McGraw-Hill Book Company, New York, 1952.
Buerger, M. J.: *X-ray Crystallography*, John Wiley & Sons, Inc., New York, 1942.
Buerger, M. J.: *The Precession Method*, John Wiley & Sons, Inc., New York, 1964.
Buerger, M. J.: *Crystal Structure Analysis*, John Wiley & Sons, Inc., New York, 1960.
Bunn, C. W.: *Chemical Crystallography*, Oxford University Press, Fair Lawn, N.J., 1945.
Cullity, B. D.: *Elements of X-ray Diffraction*, Addison-Wesley Publishing Company, Inc., Reading, Mass., 1956.
Henry, N. F. M., H. Lipson, and W. A. Wooster: *The Interpretation of X-ray Diffraction Photographs*, The Macmillan Company, New York, 1956.
International Tables for X-ray Crystallography: vol. I, *Symmetry Groups;* vol. II, *Mathematical Tables;* vol. III, *Physical and Chemical Tables*, The International Union of Crystallography, The Kynoch Press, Birmingham, England, 1952–1962.

Chapter 25

DIFFRACTOMETRIC TECHNIQUES FOR SINGLE-CRYSTAL ANALYSIS

Thomas C. Furnas, Jr.

Picker X-ray Corporation

1. OBJECTIVES OF A STRUCTURE DETERMINATION

It is important to distinguish at the outset that there are two distinctly different interests in crystal-structure determinations. They were aptly described by Dr. H. Cole[1] as descending first from the Bragg or English school of investigation which is generally interested in chemically useful structures, and second from von Laue and the German school of investigation which is generally interested in the physics of radiation, matter, and their interactions. The chemically useful structure in many respects is a three-dimensional refinement of the diagrams one draws in an organic chemistry course. Many sophisticated questions are asked by chemists, but their needs often do not require the most precise, the most accurate, or the most complete data. The physicist, the new "solid-state" metallurgist, the electronics engineer, etc., generally are deeply concerned with precision lattice parameters, precision bond lengths, anisotropic electronic configurations, lattice and atomic vibrations, coordination and valence states, etc. To answer questions about these properties, great effort and accuracy are required in all aspects of data collection, correction, and interpretation.

2. TECHNIQUES USED TO DETERMINE A COMPLETE STRUCTURE

There are two general techniques for data collection: photographic and diffractometric. (For a discussion of photographic techniques, see Chap. 24.) These techniques have developed such that in a large measure the first fifty years of x-ray diffraction[2] illustrate much of the progress in chemistry and in physics. The first crystal structures were done by film techniques. The ionization spectrometer spearheaded great strides in x-ray physics during the early decades but was far too tedious and limited an instrument to be much encouragement to doing any but the simplest crystal structures. The invention and development of moving-film cameras such as the Weissenberg and Buerger precession camera made the collection and interpretation of large numbers of reflections a relatively simple photographic task. This was a great period for the exposition of large numbers of chemical structures. In later years came the development of new detector designs, improvements in diffractometers, digital computing equipment, etc., such that chemist and physicist alike have an almost endless array of equipment suited to their respective needs today.

These remarks hint that the general requirements of the chemist may be satisfied by photographic equipment, whereas the general requirements of the physicist demand electronic or diffractometric equipment. This was almost true in the past but is no longer so. Today the two techniques are recognized as being almost ideally complementary to one another. It is especially true that the physicist's interests in crystal structures are most likely to require not only the finest diffractometric equipment but also special photographic equipment to provide the auxiliary data needed for a better understanding of the solid state.

Every investigator, therefore, should be familiar with the properties and limitations of both techniques, to be able to choose the right one for each particular task, to use them together both to avoid missing in one that which to the other is obvious and to attain the required understanding of the phenomena or subject being studied.

3. THEORETICAL BASIS OF THE TECHNIQUES

Toward making the choice of technique, it is important to remember first some of the phenomena or variables that affect a measurement of an x-ray intensity [as illustrated by Eq. (1)] and second some of the basic assumptions in the mathematical formulations for the deduction of crystal structures from x-ray diffraction data.

$$I = KSf(\theta)DI_0\lambda^3LPVAE \tag{1}$$

where I = observed intensity and generally depends upon the method of measurement. It may be expressed in counts per second, blackening of film per unit time, etc.

K = a proportionality constant containing the usual factors which concern the scattering from a single electron

$Sf(\theta)$ includes (1) the geometrical-structure factor (amplitude and phase), (2) the atomic-scattering curves, (3) the temperature diffuse scattering effects

D = response of the detector for the radiation concerned. If the same detector is used to measure both I_0 and I and both measurements contain the same λ range then this term may be dropped from the formula and I_0 expressed in the appropriate relative units

I_0 = true absolute incident intensity, expressed in the same units as I

λ = wavelength of the radiation measured

LP = Lorentz and polarization correction

V = volume of the specimen irradiated and contributing to the measurement

A = absorption correction

E = perfection factor, which includes extinction corrections

An integrated intensity is generally described as the total intensity reflected by a crystal when it is rotated at a constant angular velocity through its reflecting position. The concept of an integrated intensity therefore includes the assumptions that a fixed crystal volume contributes, that the incident intensity remains constant, that each and every part of the crystal contributes fully, that the wavelength content of the measurement is some fixed band (else there would be no uniqueness to "the reflecting position"), etc. In a reverse view of this concept, it is evident that an actual rotation of the crystal is not necessary if one can satisfy the requirements for limiting the spectral range, for holding the incident intensity constant, and for permitting each and every part of the crystal to contribute fully to the measurement. This is described as the stationary crystal–stationary counter method for measuring integrated intensities with a diffractometer.[3]

There are various mathematical expressions and manipulations for obtaining the structure-factor amplitudes and phases from a *set* of integrated intensity measurements. These are explained in Chap. 29. The important feature is that to obtain a valid crystal structure or a valid answer to a structural problem the data used must comprise a very unique *set* in which all members of the *set* have a common basis as described in Eq. (1) above. That is, the data must be collected in such a manner that the only uncontrolled variable in Eq. (1) is the structure-factor term $Sf(\theta)$.

The result is dependent upon the accuracy with which certain corrections, such as those for absorption, are made. The needs for a common incident intensity, for a common spectral content (the equation uses a single value of λ!), and the absence of systematic errors are implicit although often overlooked for one reason: the fortunate happenstance that most crystals yield so much data that the usual parameters required to describe their chemical structures are very much overdetermined. It is for this reason that many crystal structures have been adequately described chemically despite using intensity data expressed on a scale of 10, or even on a scale designating only weak, medium, and strong.

4. COMPARISON OF TECHNIQUE CHARACTERISTICS

The most important single characteristic of photographic techniques is that they record, for subsequent evaluation and study, phenomena that may be totally unexpected. Some features of the photographically recorded x-ray diffraction pattern may be overwhelmingly evident, such as strong diffuse scattering, indistinct spot shape due to cracks or strains in the crystal, "notched" or "accented" portions of spots as caused by multiple scattering, even the shadow of the fiber supporting an improperly mounted crystal, etc.

Diffractometric techniques, on the other hand, are almost totally blind. With them the shapes of reflections, the occurrence of diffuse diffraction streaks and the like, if determinable at all, generally must be sought by techniques quite different from those usually used to collect intensity data for single-crystal-structure determination.

There is, therefore, a serious need for photographs of any crystal studied diffractometrically. There also are some special photographic techniques, such as the recording of individual reflections and their relationship to detector apertures, that are proper companions to diffractometric studies.

As an example of the attention that may be required even in photographic techniques, it may be noted here that the focusing property of the precession camera actually superposes two reflections that occur at different spatial positions of the crystal. It is therefore essentially impossible to ascribe a definite absorption correction, for example, to a given spot measurement. It is possible, however, by displacing the film slightly from its "properly focused" position to cause these two spots to be separated sufficiently to permit their proper individual measurement and correction. The film no longer displays so neatly the reciprocal lattice geometry for which the precession camera is famous, but such is not the intention when this procedure is used.

The second important characteristic of photographic techniques is that they generally collect large numbers of reflections essentially simultaneously on one film. The simultaneity of exposure or the superposition of many incremental exposures as occur in most photographic x-ray diffraction cameras normally is assumed to cancel out the effects of variations in x-ray tube operating conditions (i.e., the kilovolts and milliamperes that affect the incident x-ray intensity) during the exposure. Indeed, with a properly operating unit, this assumption is extended to successive films in the series that is always needed to collect complete sets of data.

The many reflections from a single crystal are individually measured sequentially in diffractometric techniques. Therefore, to produce a set of data that will satisfy the requirements imposed upon Eq. (1) above, it is essential that the incident x-ray intensity and the characteristics of the detecting equipment exhibit both short- and long-term stability commensurate with the quality of data sought.

The third important characteristic of photographic techniques is that they involve certain inherent limitations that are distinctly different from those met in electronic or diffractometric techniques. In particular, the variables of photographic-film manufacture and production, the variables of chemical processing, the measurement of optical densities, and relating these to exposure necessarily impose an ultimate limit of around 1 per cent. The practical limit of photographic precision seems to be in the 2 to 5 per cent range, and even this requires exceptional care.

There is no question but that the most precise data can be collected electronically, because in principle, most of the statistical errors can be reduced to quite insignificant levels if one is willing to go to the required effort and spend the required time.[4] Whereas such precision is an important consideration in many problems, the more probable reason for the limelight enjoyed by diffractometric techniques derives from the obvious usefulness of digital data, since computers are universally used for data reduction and use.

5. EQUIPMENT AND TIME REQUIRED TO DETERMINE A STRUCTURE

The time required to acquire a complete set of x-ray diffraction data on a single crystal often is cited as an important factor in determining the principal technique to be used. This includes the following general activities:

1. To select, mount, and align a crystal
2. To record the diffraction spots (photographically) or to position the crystal for individual assessment of the spots (diffractometrically)
3. To measure the film densities and convert to intensities or to collect the desired number of counts diffractometrically
4. To assess and to apply the corrections appropriate to the technique and equipment used

The selection of a crystal suitable for the collection of data from which a crystal structure may be determined often involves the examination and rejection of many specimens. Dr. E. A. Wood[5] has described in simple yet lucid terms the basic information necessary for the orientation of crystals. For x-ray diffraction experiments, it is important to mount the crystal in such a manner that the crystal will not be shadowed by the mounting fiber, for example. The initial examination should include a diffraction photograph to reveal obvious anomalies and/or a measurement of the mosaicity. Beyond this point, the techniques and equipment strongly affect the time required. Photographic techniques, for example, generally are slow and tedious (many hours are quite common) in achieving a suitable alignment of a crystal. New advances in the use of Polaroid film[6,7,8] with intensifying screens are effecting significant reductions in this time (individual exposures of 1 min instead of 10 to 30 min each).

For a given number of reflections, if judicious choice is made of the crystal settings used, photographic techniques probably provide the most rapid recording of diffraction data.[9,10] Reading the densities, however, has been a very tedious matter only recently subjected to significant time-saving instrumentation.[11,12] All are subject to the inherent limitations of photographic materials and processing.

Diffractometric techniques and instruments now are almost as varied as are the photographic ones; so it is necessary to classify them into two main groups, which may be called *analog* and *digital*,[13] for more detailed consideration. Analog instruments utilize a system of levers and pivots which enable the crystal and detector to be set relative to the incident beam in the orientation required for the measurement of a particular reflection. Examples of these instruments are the linear diffractometers.[14,15,16] They require a minimum of calculations for the settings, and the analog motions permit rapid sequential examination of many reflections with no further setting calculations. Their greatest use[17] to date has been on protein crystals where the amount of data to be collected is extremely large. Some of these instruments are quite cramped regarding space around the crystal; so they are very inconvenient to use during the critical initial crystal-alignment stage. For further discussion below, it is to be noted that these instruments all utilize an inclined detector measurement geometry.

Digital diffractometric techniques may be divided into those using an inclined detector (i.e., equi-inclination or normal-beam nonequatorial)[17,18,19,20] and those utilizing a purely equatorial geometry.[3,21–32] The inclined-detector instruments generally are diffractometric analogs of the Weissenberg camera. They share the same general systematic errors in the upper levels (e.g., the proper measurement of backgrounds is systematically disturbed by the oblique cut of the data measurement through the plane of diffraction; the measurement of properly related integrated intensities is systematically disturbed by the changes in the effective size and shape of the source, by the changes in relative motions of the reflection and of the detector aperture during the measurements, and by the changes in the size and shape of the reflection relative to the detector aperture).

The purely equatorial instruments are characterized by a diffractometer equipped with a goniostat.* These instruments utilize a totally noncamera geometry which emphasizes the concept of the reciprocal lattice and a system of Eulerian axes[33] for orienting the crystal to observe different reflections. These instruments generally provide adequate space around the goniometer head to permit readily the required access during alignment of the crystal. This process is quite direct and often takes much less time (it is not uncommon to align, identify, and determine the space group of a crystal in a few hours) than the processing of films by conventional procedures.

It is to be noted that various of the diffractometric instruments have been automated to free the investigator from the routine and the human error of hand-setting the angular positions and hand-recording the counts collected. (Less than one-half of the total analysis time is required for the hand setting of angles when using the stationary crystal–stationary counter technique with a maximum data-collection rate of perhaps 80 reflections/hr. When scanning techniques are used, the maximum rate is perhaps 20 reflections/hr, although the rate is often as low as 20 per day. The setting time per reflection remains about the same, hence drops to less than 10 per cent of the total time.) The automation has been of two general kinds, the "off-line" installation using paper tape or punched cards for setting angles and for recording observed data, and the "on-line" installation in which a computer is directly linked to the control devices on the diffractometer so they are controlled by the computer. The expected speed and effectiveness of such automatic or computer-controlled operations have yet to be fully demonstrated. The indications are that they may eventually provide the kind of advantage that a slide rule has over longhand multiplication, but current limitations in other facets of the equipment (such as the source and detectors) prevent these systems from being a real break-through for crystallographers. With some of these systems, new developments in sources and detectors, in understanding of systematic errors and corrections, etc., are not likely to obsolete the very expensive automated or computer-controlled portions of the system, and one may benefit by the ability to modernize at a relatively small cost.

The small fraction of the total time generally spent in setting the angular coordinates of the crystal and detector for a measurement, even by hand, makes comparisons of automatic and computer-controlled instruments on the basis of their speed in accomplishing this part of their task somewhat absurd. In general, the extremes in setting speeds already in the literature have their basis on entirely different aspects of the operation of the equipment. For example, an incrementally set system seems to require high-speed capabilities to permit rapid return to a reference datum to check upon the possibility of having lost a count and hence having reached an erroneous angular position. Systems that operate on absolute-position information can do the same job without the need for such high-speed capabilities. The overall time required by either system to obtain a set of three-dimensional crystallographic data, assuming proper performance throughout, should be essentially the same. In other words, this is not the criterion on which to base a selection. Rather, things to look for are ruggedness of design and construction, versatility of arrangement of mechanical components, flexibility of technique, simplicity of alignment and operation, coordination with photographic requirements, and theoretical soundness of design in view of the variety of error sources known to have possible effect upon the data collected.

6. ACCURACY AND PRECISION

These two concepts[34] often are poorly differentiated, with the result that serious confusion has been promulgated by their usage, particularly when they are erroneously

* A goniostat (from the Greek *gonio* meaning angle and *stat* meaning to set) is a device with which the orientation angles (χ and ϕ) of a crystal may be set to allow the three-dimensional diffraction data to be collected (by use of the angle ω and the θ 2θ motion of the diffractometer and detector) in the equatorial plane of diffraction.

used interchangeably. Accuracy concerns the correctness of a measurement, reading, or statement. Precision concerns the reproducibility of a measurement, reading, or statement. A coin counter and packaging device at a bank is a very precise instrument, but if it fails to discriminate against certain types of counterfeits the tally need not be accurate. Events that occur at random, such as the decay of a radioactive isotope, may be measured by several means and the results subjected to statistical analysis to determine the precision of the measurements and to obtain a statement of probability regarding their accuracy. The latter, however, always must be based upon independent measurements or assumptions regarding the nature of systematic and other errors in the measuring equipment. Occasionally a precise instrument can be calibrated against known standards (such as with mirrors and polygons for angle measurements) to obtain a calibration "curve" that relates the observed readings to accurately known entities. One makes gross assumptions, often unwarranted, when interpolating or extrapolating this curve relative to the actual points measured and calibrated. For example, a damaged gear tooth or an error in matching the linear pitch of a worm with the circular pitch of a worm wheel (as a consequence of wear, or manufacturing error or tolerances) may escape detection in some calibration techniques yet produce significant "within-tooth" errors and invalidate a calibration curve. As another example, a synchronous motor may impart a constant angular velocity to a gear mounted upon its shaft. If that gear or any gear in the train is acentric to its shaft then the angular velocity of any subsequent gear will not be constant. Either of these phenomena if present in a diffractometer may adversely affect some individual integrated intensity measurements using scanning techniques. The effect with respect to a whole set of data probably would be random, although avoidable! Within-tooth errors probably would be more important than other kinds of gear errors.

While on the subject of gears, accuracy of setting angles, etc., it is worthwhile to note that a crystal specimen orientation within a few tenths of a degree is quite adequate (and, therefore, rarely surpassed) for photographic data-collecting techniques not only because the sizes, shapes, and positions of the reflections then are reasonable and interpretable but also because the expanse of detector (the film) always encompasses the area wherein the reflection will be recorded. Even the layer-line screens on Weissenberg and precession cameras rarely require much better alignment than this. Such crude orientations, however, are never acceptable in diffractometric techniques not only because of the limited detector aperture, the restricted motion of the detector, and the coupling or relative motions of the detector, specimen, and source, but also because the very much longer lever arms (145 mm or longer is common on a diffractometer whereas 28.7-, 57.3-, or 60-mm radii are most common on cameras) magnify the spatial effects of misorientations without significantly affecting the size of a reflection. This effect plus the lack of spatial discrimination within the detector aperture (i.e., one generally cannot tell that a reflection partially misses the aperture) illustrates the "blindness" of diffractometric techniques. Such "blindness" has tended to cause many investigators to create strict specifications regarding accuracies required of diffractometers in order that they be satisfactory for use in collecting single-crystal intensity data. To put such specifications in their proper perspective, it may be noted that an error of 0.05° in an angular setting will cause the reflection to move a maximum of 0.005 in. on an instrument having a 5.73-in. (145-mm) radius. On the other hand, an error of 0.05° in the initial orientation of a crystal will cause the reflections to oscillate over a total range of 0.010 in. independent of any instrumental errors. It is of extreme importance, therefore, to spend the additional time required to achieve a good initial alignment and to check it with photographs showing the actual relationship of several reflections to the detector aperture. It is correspondingly very poor judgment to so limit the detector aperture, the collimator clearances, the angular range of scan or specimen illumination that *no* tolerance is allowed in crystal position, whether in initial orientation or in instrumental setting.[3,35,36,37]

It is quite evident that the question of accuracy with respect to a set of x-ray or neutron diffraction data is a very subtle one to evaluate and contains some fundamental questions yet unanswered. Among the principal considerations are these:

1. On a film, one can see that a particular reflection does not look the same as others and hence should be discarded, subjected to remeasurement, or otherwise specially handled. Such things as shadow of the mounting fiber, simultaneous (sometimes "forbidden") reflections, and diffuse scattering streaks all are readily identified on photographs but are missed or must be carefully (generally by non-data-collecting procedures)[3] looked for with diffractometric techniques.

2. The systematic errors associated with the several geometrical configurations and schemes[3,13,20,32,38,39,40,41] by which complete sets of three-dimensional data are collected have not yet been subjected to their much-needed scrutiny, comparison, and evaluation toward the elucidation of preferred or minimum-error schemes.[34] We have mentioned the effects of effective source size and shape, etc., in inclined-detector schemes for measurement but no one yet has quantitatively determined their magnitude or effect. Much work is currently under way but the results will be slow in being properly evaluated.

3. Background corrections are necessary, but no one technique or method has been demonstrated to be clearly more satisfactory or valid than others.[3,36,37,38,39,40,41] Instrumental refinements to improve the signal-to-background ratio generally are worthwhile even when some loss in total count rate (intensity) is necessary. The use of balanced filters,[3,42,43,44,45,46,47] for instance, considerably increases the number of readings necessary and hence increases the statistical uncertainty of the net count. Crystal monochromators, on the other hand, very effectively limit the spectral content of a datum[48] but substitute a new class of systematic errors associated with their being directed and not diffuse sources, with their having dispersion of spectral band across the area occupied by the specimen, and a variety of other much less understood problems. The importance of these errors in the most rigorous of crystal-structure determinations has yet to be defined. For most practical purposes, certainly those involving the determination of chemical structures, monochromator errors probably are less serious than those they replace.[49]

4. The variability of a crystal species becomes extremely important when one attempts to obtain a set of data good to 1 per cent, for instance. The tedium of data collection, now on the verge of being appreciably diminished by automatic or computer-controlled devices, has prohibited the collection of sets of data on a statistically significant number of crystals of a given species. Some efforts involving the measurement of crystallographically equivalent reflections (variations of 5 to 20 per cent are not uncommon) from a given crystal have been successful in evaluating a number of the variables in crystal mosaicity, extinction, etc., but one must be cautious in expressing or believing "accuracies of 1 or even a few per cent" where "precision with a single representative of a species" is all that has been demonstrated.

5. The use of radioactive isotopes such as iron-55 for the calibration of pulse-height analyzers, for investigation of the stability of a detector and its associated electronic equipment, and for the comparison of detectors is highly recommended. Other measurements and considerations are necessary to determine the absolute response characteristics of an x-ray quantum detector, but the biggest hurdle is surmounted when its proper operation and stability have been established.

6. About the only way to have a constant crystal volume contributing to the measurements of the many reflections from a single crystal is to have the entire crystal bathed by a uniform incident beam.[3] This requires that the incident-beam collimator provide a radiation beam of suitable size (i.e., appreciably larger than the specimen plus its eccentricity plus the mechanical eccentricity of the instrument) and free from vignetting (penumbra inside the space occupied by the specimen), that the crystal be small from the standpoints both of collimated beam size and of linear-absorption effects so the entire volume of the crystal will be essentially uniformly irradiated, and that the diffracted beam collimator and detector apertures allow the free passage of the entire diffraction spot throughout any angular rotations required during the measurement. (It may be noted that if the latter is true then the net counts measured for any given reflection will be independent—except for air absorption—of the distance between the specimen and the detector.)

There probably are other aspects of data collection and correction that should be scrutinized here, but the above are mentioned to emphasize the fact that one can "get by" with one kind of data when interested in chemical structures, that more care and attention are required when seeking more detailed information regarding a structure, and that in all cases it is possible to "overcompute" a set of data to obtain results that *look like* certain kinds of anisotropic motion or electron-density peaks. The latter situation must be carefully examined since the errors of data collection and sometimes even the systematic errors contained in the method used[34] for collecting said data may produce "interpretable maps or structural features" that are purely artifacts of poor data.

REFERENCES CITED

1. H. Cole, Speculations on Computer-controlled Data Taking, Opening address to the American Crystallographic Association meeting at the T. J. Watson Research Center, I.B.M., Yorktown Heights, N.Y., Mar. 25, 1963.
2. P. P. Ewald et al., *Fifty Years of X-ray Diffraction*, published for the International Union of Crystallography by N.V.A. Oosthoeh's Uitgeversmaatschappij, Utrecht, Holland, 1962.
3. T. C. Furnas, *Single Crystal Orienter Instruction Manual*, Direction 12130A, General Electric Company, X-ray Department, Milwaukee, Wis., 1957. This manual is presently being revised by Dr. Furnas to include full-circle goniostat geometry and other instrumental advances by the Picker X-Ray Corporation.
4. M. Mack and N. Spielberg, Statistical Factors in X-ray Intensity Measurements, *Spectrochim. Acta*, **12**:169–178 (1958).
5. E. A. Wood, *Crystal Orientation Manual*, Columbia University Press, New York, 1963.
6. H. G. Smith, Use of Polaroid Film in Neutron and X-ray Diffraction, *Rev. Sci. Instr.*, **33**:128–129 (1962).
7. H. G. Smith and D. H. Holcomb, Modified Polaroid Film Holder for X-ray and Neutron Diffraction, *Acta Cryst.*, **16**:A149 [18(i)·2] (1963); *Rev. Sci. Instr.*, **34**:1441 (1963).
8. H. K. Herglotz, High Speed in X-ray Diffraction Work by Use of Polaroid Film, *Rev. Sci. Instr.*, **34**:708–709 (1963).
9. H. J. Milledge, A Diffraction Technique for the Study of Crystals in Conditions of Instability, *Acta Cryst.*, **16**:72 (1963).
10. H. J. Milledge and F. E. Ambrose, The Instrumentation and Analysis of Equi-inclination Oscillation Photographs for the Rapid Collection of 3-D Data, *Acta Cryst.*, **16**:A149 [18(i)·7] (1963).
11. O. Kennard, Radioactive Tracer Method for the Measurement of Film Densities, *Acta Cryst.*, **10**:743–744 [1(ii)·8] (1957).
12. S. Abrahamsson, A Fast On-line Intensity Scanner for Single Crystal X-ray Photographs, *Acta Cryst.*, **16**:A147 [18(i)·1] (1963).
13. W. A. Wooster, Geometrical Factors Influencing the Design of Automatic Single-crystal X-ray and Neutron Diffractometers, *J. Sci. Instr.*, **40**:14–19 (1963).
14. U. W. Arndt and D. C. Phillips, X-ray Analysis Group of the Institute of Physics, Manchester Meeting, *Brit. J. Appl. Phys.*, **10**:116 (1959).
15. J. Ladell and K. Lowitzsch, Automatic Single Crystal Diffractometry. I. The Kinematic Problem, *Acta Cryst.*, **13**:205–215 (1960).
16. U. W. Arndt and D. C. Phillips, The Linear Diffractometer, *Acta Cryst.*, **14**:807–818 (1961).
17. H. T. Evans, Use of a Geiger Counter for the Measurement of X-ray Intensities for Small Single Crystals, *Rev. Sci. Instr.*, **24**:156 (1953).
18. W. L. Bond, A Single-crystal Automatic Diffractometer. I, *Acta Cryst.*, **8**:741–747 (1955).
19. S. C. Abrahams, Programmed Electronic X-ray Automatic Diffractometer, *Rev. Sci. Instr.*, **33**:973–977 (1962).
20. S. C. Abrahams, Evaluation of Digital Automatic Diffractometer Systems, *Acta Cryst.*, **16**:A152 [18(i)·15] (1963).
21. W. A. Wooster and A. J. P. Martin, An Automatic Ionization Spectrometer, *Proc. Roy. Soc. (London)*, Sec. A, **155**:150–172 (1936).
22. T. C. Furnas and D. Harker, Apparatus for Measuring Complete Single Crystal X-ray Diffraction Data by Means of a Geiger Counter Diffractometer, *Rev. Sci. Instr.*, **26**:449–453 (1955).
23. W. A. Wooster and A. M. Wooster, X-ray Diffractometer for Automatic Operation, *J. Sci. Instr.*, **38**:477 (1961).

24. W. A. Wooster and A. M. Wooster, Theory of Automatic Setting of Crystals on X-ray Diffractometers Using Punched Tape, *J. Sci. Instr.*, **39**:103 (1962).
25. W. H. Mueller, L. Heaton, and S. S. Sidhu, Full Circle Goniostat for Diffraction Intensity Data, *Rev. Sci. Instr.*, **34**:74–76 (1963).
26. W. H. Mueller, L. Heaton, and S. S. Sidhu, Automatic Single Crystal Neutron Diffractometer, *Acta Cryst.*, **16**:A155 [18(i)·25] (1963).
27. U. W. Arndt and B. T. M. Willis, Automatic Neutron Diffractometer for Three-dimensional Structure-factor Determination, *Rev. Sci. Instr.*, **34**:224–230 (1963).
28. T. C. Furnas, G. V. Patser, and C. Brunnett, An Automatic Goniostat for X-ray and Neutron Single-crystal Diffraction Studies, *Acta Cryst.*, **16**:A154 [18(i)·22] (1963).
29. J. P. Cowan, W. M. MacIntyre, and G. J. Werkema, Cascade: An Automatic Single Crystal X-ray Diffractometer, *Acta Cryst.*, **16**:221–225 (1963).
30. H. Cole, Y. Okaya, and F. A. Chambers, Computer-controlled X-ray Diffractometer, *Acta Cryst.*, **16**:A154 [18(i)·21] (1963); *Rev. Sci. Instr.*, **34**:872–876 (1963).
31. H. A. Levy, Automatic Single-crystal Diffractometers for Neutrons, *Acta Cryst.*, **16**:A152 [18(i)·17] (1963).
32. U. W. Arndt, Analogue and Digital Single-crystal Diffractometers, *Acta Cryst.*, **16**: A151 [18(i)·14] (1963).
33. U. W. Arndt and D. C. Phillips, On the Adoption of Standard Symbols for the Settings of Single-crystal Diffractometers, *Acta Cryst.*, **11**:509–510 (1958).
34. C. Eisenhart, On the Realistic Measurement of Precision and Accuracy, *ISA Proc.*, pp. 75–83, Eighth National Aero-Space Instrumentation Symposium, Washington, D.C., May, 1962.
35. J. Ladell and N. Spielberg, On Minimum Receiving Apertures in Single Crystal Diffractometry, *Acta Cryst.*, **16**:1057–1058 (1963).
36. L. E. Alexander and G. S. Smith, *Single Crystal Intensity Measurements with the Three Circle Counter Diffractometer*, Mellon Institute, Pittsburgh, Pa., June 12, 1961.
37. L. E. Alexander and G. S. Smith, Single Crystal Intensity Measurements with the Three Circle Counter Diffractometer, *Acta Cryst.*, **15**:983 (1962).
38. L. E. Alexander and G. S. Smith, Single Crystal Intensity Measurements with the Three Circle Counter Diffractometer, *Acta Cryst.*, **16**:A152 [18(i)·16] (1963).
39. R. A. Young, Background Intensities in Single Crystal Diffractometry, Georgia Institute of Technology, Engineering Experiment Station, *Tech. Rept.* 2, Project A-389, July 22, 1961.
40. R. D. Burbank, *A Comparison of Omega and Two-theta Scans for Integrated Intensity Measurement*, Bell Telephone Laboratories, Inc., Murray Hill, N.J.
41. H. Cole, F. W. Chambers, and C. G. Wood, Some Geometrical Considerations for X-ray Collimation in Single Crystal Diffraction Work, *Rev. Sci. Instr.*, **33**:435–437 (1962).
42. P. H. Ross, A New Method of Spectroscopy for Faint X-radiation, *J. Opt. Sci. Am.* and *Rev. Sci. Instr.*, **16**:433–437 (1928).
43. P. Kirkpatrick, The Theory and Use of Rose Filters, *Rev. Sci. Instr.*, **10**:186–191 (1939); **15**:223–229 (1944).
44. K. Tanaka, K. Katayama, J. Chikawa, and H. Suita, Use of Balanced Filters for Automatic Recording X-ray Diffractometer, *Rev. Sci. Instr.*, **30**:430–434 (1959).
45. R. A. Young, Balanced Filters for X-ray Diffractometry, Georgia Institute of Technology, Engineering Experiment Station, *Tech. Rept.* 1, Project A-389, June 15, 1961.
46. R. A. Young, Balanced Filters for X-ray Diffractometry, *Z. Krist.*, **118**:3/4, 233–247 (1963).
47. S. C. Abrahams, Automatic Aperture Control for Balanced Filter X-ray Diffractometry, *Rev. Sci. Instr.*, **34**:1279–1280 (1963).
48. J. Ladell and N. Spielberg, Theory of the Measurement of Integrated Intensities Obtained with Single-crystal Counter Diffractometers, *Acta Cryst.*, **16**: A148 [18(i)·5] (1963).
49. S. Miyake, S. Togawa, and S. Hosoya, Polarization Factor for X-ray Monochromator Crystals, *Acta Cryst.*, **17**:1083–1084 (1964).

Chapter 26

THE RECIPROCAL LATTICE

Donald R. Peacor

University of Michigan

1. RELATIONS BETWEEN THE DIRECT AND RECIPROCAL LATTICES

Introduction. It is often difficult to visualize diffraction relations in terms of diffraction of an x-ray beam by a number of sets of planes. The relations are easily interpreted with the aid of the reciprocal lattice, however. The concept of the reciprocal lattice is thus an important tool in the understanding and interpretation of diffraction phenomena. The reciprocal lattice is derived from the direct lattice, to which it is said to be reciprocal. The following relations must be clarified, however, as an introduction to this construction.

A set of parallel and equally spaced planes in the direct lattice

$$h\mathbf{x} + k\mathbf{y} + l\mathbf{z} = N \qquad N = \ldots, -2, -1, 0, 1, 2, \ldots$$

is designated by the indices (hkl). The integers h, k, and l contain no common factor and are the same, of course, for each plane of the set. Here $\mathbf{x}$, $\mathbf{y}$, and $\mathbf{z}$ are the unit translations of the lattice. In diffraction applications planes may be designated by a set of integers $(nh\ nk\ nl)$ which contain the common factor n. Such a set of parallel and equally spaced planes is parallel to the set of planes (hkl). The set with indices $(nh\ nk\ nl)$ contains "n times" as many planes as the set (hkl) and includes all planes of the set (hkl). In addition, the set $(nh\ nk\ nl)$ has an interplanar spacing d, $1/n$th that of the (hkl) planes. These relations are illustrated in Fig. 1 in two dimensions for (101) and (202) planes.

In terms of Bragg's law

$$n\lambda = 2d_{(hkl)} \sin \theta$$

diffraction is usually interpreted as occurring in the nth order from planes with indices (hkl). However, since

$$d_{(nh\ nk\ nl)} = (1/n)d_{(hkl)}$$

Bragg's law may be expressed as

$$\lambda = 2d_{(nh\ nk\ nl)} \sin \theta$$

where the indices nh, nk, and nl contain the common factor n. Thus second-order diffraction from (100) may be interpreted as first-order diffraction from (200). In all further discussion it will be assumed, therefore, that the indices h, k, and l may contain a common factor.

Geometrical Construction of the Reciprocal Lattice. For each crystal lattice there is a corresponding reciprocal lattice which may be derived in the following way. Construct a vector $\boldsymbol{\sigma}$ with base at the origin of coordinates, corresponding to every set of planes (hkl) of the direct lattice. Each vector is directed normal to its corresponding set of planes and has a magnitude

$$\sigma_{(hkl)} = K/d_{(hkl)}$$

Here K is a scale factor conveniently taken as unity, or as the wavelength λ of the characteristic radiation used in a specific application.

The complete set of points at the ends of all such vectors constitutes a lattice and is called the reciprocal lattice. The direct lattice is defined by unit-cell parameters a, b, c, α, β, and γ. The reciprocal lattice is similarly defined by the parameters a^*, b^*, c^*, α^*, β^*, and γ^*, where the superscript asterisk refers, by convention, to reciprocal-lattice parameters. Each lattice point in the reciprocal lattice is designated by the indices of the set of planes (hkl) to which it corresponds. The reciprocal lattice, like the direct lattice, may be considered to be constructed of parallel planes of lattice points, often referred to as levels.

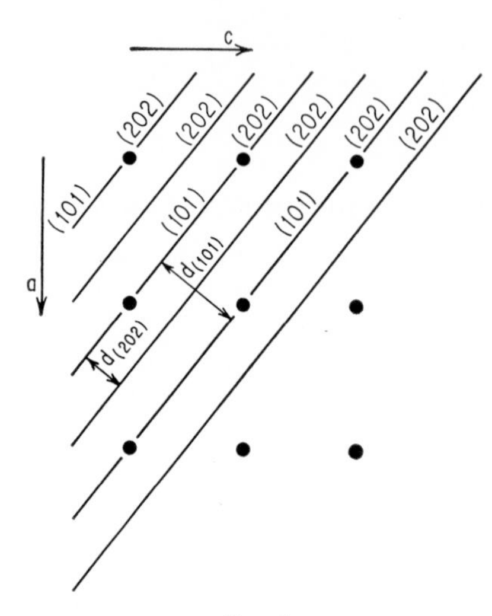

Fig. 1

Construction in Two Dimensions. The relations described above will be illustrated for a two-dimensional example for simplicity. A section of one level of a three-dimensional lattice, with unit-cell translations **a** and **c** in this plane, is shown in Fig. 2*a*. Two adjacent (100) planes are shown, as well as the magnitude and direction of measurement of $d_{(100)}$. In Fig. 2*b* the corresponding reciprocal-lattice vector $\boldsymbol{\sigma}_{(100)}$ is shown, drawn normal to the (100) planes with magnitude $K/d_{(100)}$. The reciprocal-lattice point 100 lies at the end of this vector. The reciprocal-lattice point corresponding to the (200) planes is also shown. As noted above, these have interplanar spacings d of magnitude $\frac{1}{2}d_{(100)}$. Therefore,

$$2\sigma_{(100)} = \sigma_{(200)}$$

Two adjacent (101) planes are also shown in Fig. 2*a*, and the vector $\boldsymbol{\sigma}_{(101)}$ and the reciprocal-lattice points 101 and 202 in Fig. 2*b*. In Fig. 2*c* a more complete section of the plane reciprocal lattice which is reciprocal to the direct lattice of Fig. 2*a* is shown. The elementary unit-cell translations $\mathbf{a}^*$ and $\mathbf{c}^*$ are given by the definition of the reciprocal lattice as

$$a^* = K/d_{(100)} = \sigma_{(100)}$$
$$c^* = K/d_{(001)} = \sigma_{(001)}$$

Three-dimensional Lattice. The three-dimensional reciprocal lattice is constructed from the direct lattice using the principles outlined in the two-dimensional example. Figure 3*a* is a drawing of a monoclinic direct lattice and Fig. 3*b* is the corresponding reciprocal lattice. The second monoclinic setting is used to label

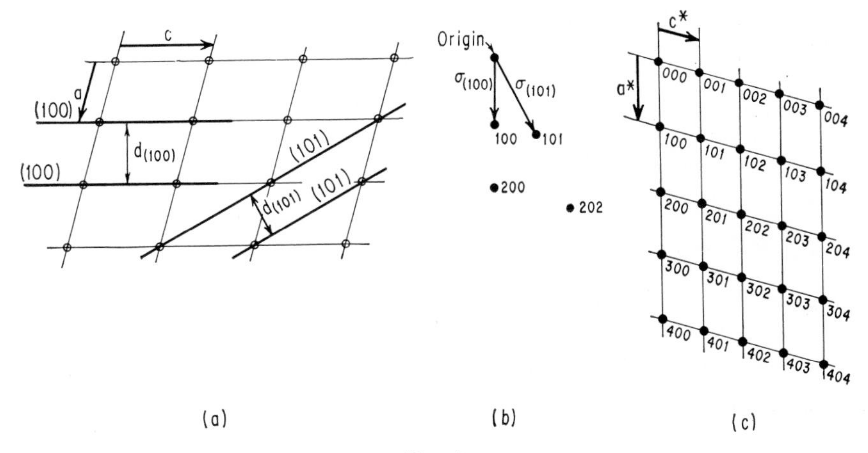

FIG. 2

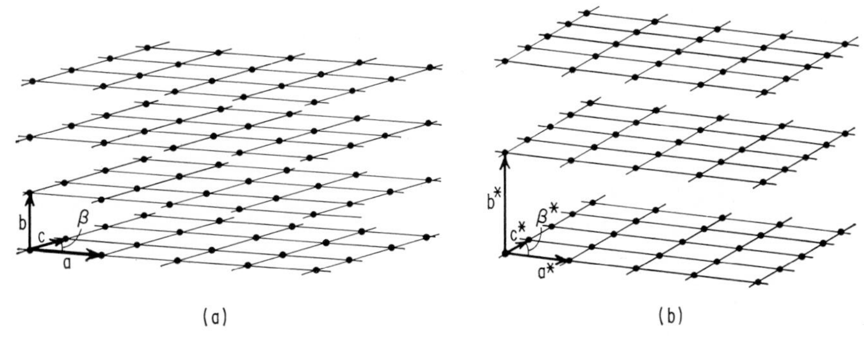

FIG. 3

axes, and thus **b** is the twofold axis of the direct lattice. The magnitudes of the translations defining the reciprocal lattice are given by

$$a^* = K/d_{(100)} \qquad b^* = K/d_{(010)} \qquad c^* = K/d_{(001)}$$

In the general triclinic case **a***, **b***, and **c*** are not in general parallel to **a**, **b**, and **c**, respectively, since **a**, **b**, and **c** are not normal to (100), (010), and (001), respectively. In the monoclinic example shown here **b** and **b*** are parallel since **b** is normal to (010). However, **a** and **a***, and **c** and **c*** are not parallel. These axes are all coplanar, however, and normal to **b** and **b***. These relations are emphasized in Fig. 3*a* and 3*b* by outlining planes of lattice points normal to **b** and **b***, respectively. Each space lattice is thus seen as a stack of lattice planes. Only in the isometric, tetragonal, and orthorhombic systems are **a**, **b**, and **c** all parallel to **a***, **b***, and **c***, respectively.

Relations between the unit-cell parameters a, b, c, α, β, and γ of the direct lattice and the parameters a^*, b^*, c^*, α^*, β^*, and γ^* of the reciprocal lattice may be easily

Table 1. Relations between Direct and Reciprocal Lattice Parameters†

Triclinic system

$$V = abc\,(1 - \cos^2\alpha - \cos^2\beta - \cos^2\gamma + 2\cos\alpha\cos\beta\cos\gamma)^{1/2}$$

$$V^* = \frac{1}{V}$$

$$a^* = \frac{bc\sin\alpha}{V} \qquad b^* = \frac{ac\sin\beta}{V} \qquad c^* = \frac{ab\sin\gamma}{V}$$

$$a^* = \frac{1}{a\sin\beta^*\sin\gamma} = \frac{1}{a\sin\beta\sin\alpha^*}$$

$$b^* = \frac{1}{b\sin\alpha^*\sin\gamma} = \frac{1}{b\sin\alpha\sin\gamma^*}$$

$$c^* = \frac{1}{c\sin\alpha^*\sin\beta} = \frac{1}{c\sin\alpha\sin\beta^*}$$

$$\cos\alpha^* = \frac{\cos\beta\cos\gamma - \cos\alpha}{\sin\beta\sin\gamma} \qquad \cos\beta^* = \frac{\cos\gamma\cos\alpha - \cos\beta}{\sin\gamma\sin\alpha}$$

$$\cos\gamma^* = \frac{\cos\alpha\cos\beta - \cos\gamma}{\sin\alpha\sin\beta}$$

$$\frac{1}{d} = (h^2a^{*2} + k^2b^{*2} + l^2c^{*2} + 2klb^*c^*\cos\alpha^* + 2hla^*c^*\cos\beta^* + 2hka^*b^*\cos\gamma^*)^{1/2}$$

Monoclinic system (second setting)

$$V^* = \frac{1}{abc\sin\beta}$$

$$a^* = \frac{1}{a\sin\beta} \qquad b^* = \frac{1}{b} \qquad c^* = \frac{1}{c\sin\beta}$$

$$\alpha^* = 90^\circ \qquad \beta^* = 180^\circ - \beta \qquad \gamma^* = 90^\circ$$

$$\frac{1}{d} = (h^2a^{*2} + k^2b^{*2} + l^2c^{*2} + 2hla^*c^*\cos\beta^*)^{1/2}$$

Orthorhombic system

$$V^* = \frac{1}{abc}$$

$$a^* = \frac{1}{a} \qquad b^* = \frac{1}{b} \qquad c^* = \frac{1}{c}$$

$$\alpha^* = \beta^* = \gamma^* = 90^\circ$$

$$\frac{1}{d} = (h^2a^{*2} + k^2b^{*2} + l^2c^{*2})^{1/2}$$

Tetragonal system

$$V^* = \frac{1}{a^2c}$$

$$a^* = b^* = \frac{1}{a} \qquad c^* = \frac{1}{c}$$

$$\alpha^* = \beta^* = \gamma^* = 90^\circ$$

$$\frac{1}{d} = [(h^2 + k^2)a^{*2} + l^2c^{*2}]^{1/2}$$

Hexagonal system

$$V^* = \frac{2}{a^2c\sqrt{3}}$$

$$a^* = b^* = \frac{2}{a\sqrt{3}} \qquad c^* = \frac{1}{c}$$

$$\alpha^* = \beta^* = 90^\circ \qquad \gamma^* = 60^\circ$$

$$\frac{1}{d} = [(h^2 + k^2 + hk)a^{*2} + l^2c^{*2}]^{1/2}$$

Table 1. Relations between Direct and Reciprocal Lattice Parameters† *(Continued)*

Isometric system

$$V^* = \frac{1}{a^3}$$

$$a^* = b^* = c^* = \frac{1}{a}$$

$$\alpha^* = \beta^* = \gamma^* = 90°$$

$$\frac{1}{d} = a^*(h^2 + k^2 + l^2)^{1/2}$$

† The constant K of the relation

$$\sigma = K/d$$

is taken as unity.

Relations for transformations from reciprocal- to direct-lattice parameters (or vice versa) may be obtained using the same formulas with direct-lattice parameters replaced by the corresponding reciprocal-lattice parameters and vice versa.

derived for any crystal system. It is easiest to do this for the general triclinic lattice and then derive relations for lattices of higher symmetry merely by introducing the specialized axial relations of a higher-symmetry lattice into the relations for a triclinic lattice. Table 1 is a compilation relating direct and reciprocal unit-cell elements, not only for the general triclinic case but also for crystal systems of higher symmetry. The proportionality constant K of the reciprocal lattice is taken as unity in relations relating axial magnitudes in Table 1. If some particular wavelength λ is employed, all such equations must be multiplied by this constant.

The reciprocal lattice is reciprocal to the direct lattice. The idea of reciprocity is more general, however, and it is also true that the direct lattice is the reciprocal of the reciprocal lattice. Thus each relation of Table 1 has a reciprocal relation. For example, the equation

$$a^* = (bc \sin \alpha)/V$$

is related to a reciprocal relation

$$a = (b^*c^* \sin \alpha^*)/V^*$$

Symmetry in Reciprocal Space. The concept of reciprocity is not confined to the relation that a point in reciprocal space is reciprocal to a set of planes in a direct space lattice. The reciprocal lattice which is so defined consists of a set of dimensionless points, where the location of each point is determined by the translation periodicity of the lattice. However, each reciprocal lattice point *hkl* is related to a set of planes (*hkl*) which has a characteristic electron density. A weight I may be assigned to a reciprocal-lattice point which is a function of this electron density. The reciprocal lattice may therefore be imagined to be constructed of a collection of points *hkl* each of which has a weight I equal to the intensity of the reflection from the set of planes (*hkl*). This collection of points is often referred to as the weighted reciprocal lattice. This is not, in fact, a true lattice since the weight of the points is not consistent with the translation periodicity of the location of the points. The collection of weighted reciprocal-lattice points embodies the more general nature of reciprocity; it is actually the reciprocal of the crystal structure.

Each reciprocal lattice point *hkl* lies on the normal to the set of planes (*hkl*) in direct space and has a weight I which is a function of the arrangement of atoms in this direction. Any symmetry element of the crystal which operates on the crystal structure must similarly transform the set of planes (*hkl*) and their normal. Thus the point-group symmetry of reciprocal space must be the same as the symmetry of direct space.

It can be shown, however, that the symmetry of the "weighted reciprocal lattice," as recorded through x-ray diffraction techniques, must always include a center of symmetry. This effect is known as Friedel's law. The addition of this false center of symmetry by diffraction results in there being only 11 point-group diffraction symmetries. These include all the centrosymmetrical point groups.

Kinds of Reciprocal Unit Cells. In direct space there are 14 unique lattices, called the Bravais lattices, where the unit cell is described as primitive, side-centered, body-centered, face-centered, or rhombohedral. There are also 14 kinds of reciprocal unit cells, which are related to their direct space equivalents as follows:

Direct-unit-cell type	*Reciprocal-unit-cell type*
Primitive	Primitive
A, B, or C centered	A, B, or C centered
Rhombohedral	Rhombohedral
Body-centered	Face-centered
Face-centered	Body-centered

Note that the reciprocal of a primitive, rhombohedral, or end-centered unit cell is a unit cell of the same type, but that the reciprocal of a body-centered unit cell is a face-centered unit cell, and vice versa.

If unit-cell translations $\mathbf{a}^*$, $\mathbf{b}^*$, and $\mathbf{c}^*$ are chosen in the reciprocal lattice which describe a multiple cell, certain reciprocal-lattice points will be found to be absent. The pattern of absences obeys a certain "extinction rule," and the remaining, non-extinct reflections define the lattice with the multiple cell. This is discussed in detail in Chap. 29, under Space-group Determination.

Screw axes and glide planes also cause reflections to be absent according to definite rules. The significance of these "extinct" lattice points is also discussed fully in Chap. 29.

2. APPLICATIONS AND USE OF THE RECIPROCAL-LATTICE CONCEPT

Interpretation of Diffraction Using the Reciprocal Lattice. The concept of the reciprocal lattice is principally used in the interpretation of diffraction relations. It is far more convenient to think of a single point hkl rather than the infinite set of parallel planes. Thus diffraction is interpreted as being caused by a reciprocal-lattice point fulfilling certain conditions, rather than as reflection from a set of parallel planes.

Figure 4a is a diagram illustrating diffraction of an x-ray beam by a plane (hkl) according to Bragg's law

$$\lambda = 2d \sin \theta$$

Here it is assumed that λ, d, and θ exactly satisfy these diffraction conditions. The same geometry is shown in Fig. 4b except that here a circle of radius 1 has been drawn with its center at the intersection of the plane (hkl) and the direct beam. This simple diagram has several interesting properties. Bragg's law may be written

$$\sin \theta = [\lambda/d_{(hkl)}]/2 = \sigma_{(hkl)}/2$$

The following relations found in Fig. 4b are seen to satisfy this equation:

1. $\angle CAD = \theta$
2. $\overline{CB} = \sigma_{(hkl)}/2$
3. $\overline{AB} = 1$

Here the point of exit of the direct beam from the circle of unit radius is chosen as the origin of the reciprocal lattice. Reflection occurs in the direction AB if the reciprocal-lattice point at the end of the vector $\boldsymbol{\sigma}_{(hkl)}$ falls on the circumference of the circle.

In Fig. 4c a plane reciprocal lattice is shown with its origin at the point of exit of the direct x-ray beam from the circle of unit radius. No lattice point falls on the surface of the circle. Therefore, no reflection occurs. However, if the reciprocal lattice is made to go through some motion, say rotation about an axis normal to the plane of the paper, lattice points pass through the circle, as shown in Fig. 4*d*. This motion is brought about by rotating the crystal to which the reciprocal lattice is related. As a reciprocal-lattice point passes through the circle, Bragg's law is satisfied. A reflection occurs in the direction AB, at an angle 2θ from the path of the direct beam. In three dimensions, the plane reciprocal lattice is replaced by the full three-dimensional lattice, and the circle by the "sphere or reflection" of unit radius.

The necessary conditions for reflection from a set of planes can be simply stated in terms of the reciprocal lattice. If a reciprocal-lattice point can be made to fall on the

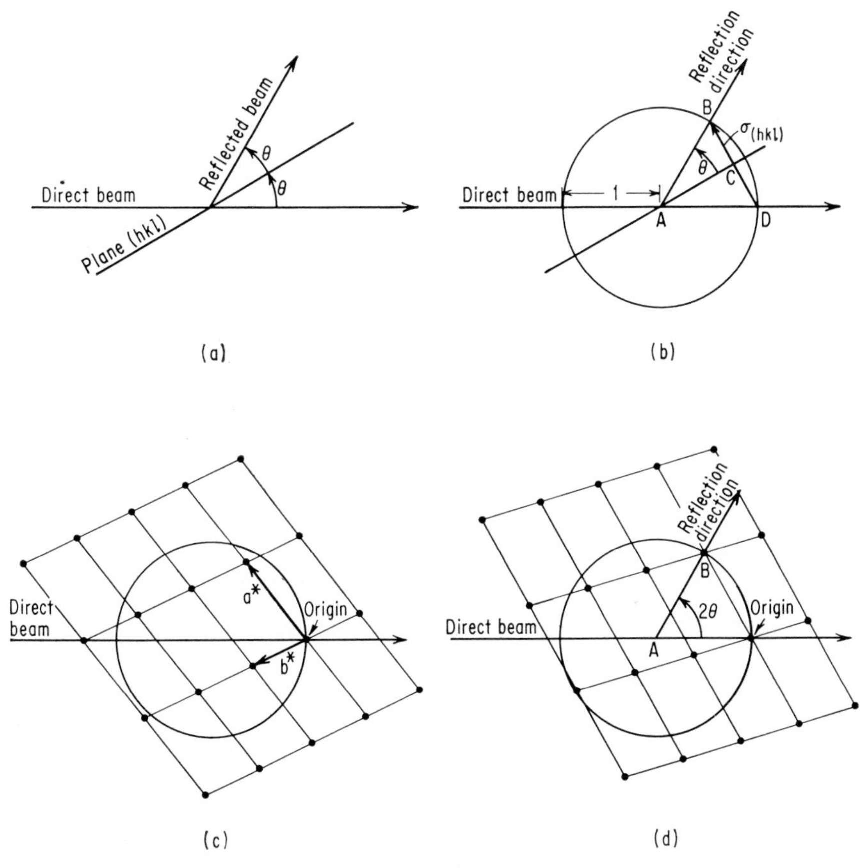

FIG. 4

surface of the sphere of reflection, a reflection occurs at the angle 2θ from the direct beam, along a radius of the sphere of reflection. This is made to occur by imparting some motion to the crystal under investigation. For example, the Weissenberg camera utilizes rotation of the crystal, while the precession camera employs a precessing motion. In the powder technique, the need for rotation is precluded since there are many thousands of randomly oriented grains in a single specimen. Consequently, there are, ideally, grains representing all possible orientations of the lattice.

In the above discussion, it was assumed that the reciprocal lattice is scaled by the proportionality constant K, which is equal to the wavelength of the radiation employed, and that the radius of the sphere of reflection is unity. Exactly the same results may be derived, however, if the proportionality constant is taken as unity and the radius of the sphere of reflection is the wavelength $1/\lambda$.

Determination of Unit-cell Parameters. Since diffraction is very simply interpreted in terms of the reciprocal lattice it is almost always convenient to think in terms of the reciprocal lattice rather than the direct lattice. A reciprocal space lattice may be considered to be constructed of parallel and equally spaced reciprocal plane lattices. In the single-crystal methods described in Chap. 24 and 25, it was shown that reflections are usually recorded in separate "levels" of the reciprocal lattice. Each Weissenberg photograph, for example, is a reproduction of one level of the reciprocal lattice. In this method the actual distribution of reflections on the film represents a systematically "distorted" image of a plane of reciprocal-lattice points, while each precession photograph is an "undistorted" image of such a plane.

The complete three-dimensional lattice is reconstructed from the collection of all such planes. Thus such a series of photographs of adjacent planes of reciprocal-lattice points produces a composite three-dimensional picture of the reciprocal lattice. The direct lattice is then obtained from the known reciprocal lattice with suitable interpretation and transformation. Measurement of relations between reflections provides a determination of the reciprocal-lattice parameters a^*, b^*, c^*, α^*, β^*, and γ^*. These are then transformed easily into direct-lattice parameters with the relations listed in Table 1. In practice a limited number of both direct- and reciprocal-lattice parameters may be easily determined. For instance, a single mounting of a crystal with a translation of the direct lattice as rotation axis, say **b**, would enable the investigator to determine the magnitude of **b** by the rotation method, and a^*, c^*, and β^* by the Weissenberg method. Such cases are easily interpreted with the proper combination of transformations listed in Table 1.

It is difficult, and often impractical, to obtain the reciprocal-lattice parameters in the general triclinic system from powder patterns. However, several methods are available to do this. The reciprocal-lattice parameters may be determined from a powder pattern of a substance of any crystal system, and then transformed to direct-lattice parameters with the equations of Table 1. In cases of high symmetry, however, it may be simpler to determine the unit cell of the direct lattice without first obtaining reciprocal-lattice parameters. Methods for indexing powder patterns are treated in detail in Chap. 28.

General Relations between the Direct and Reciprocal Lattices. Since diffraction is usually interpreted with the reciprocal-lattice concept it is necessary to know the orientation of this lattice relative to a crystal of arbitrary shape when employing a single-crystal technique. Usually the orientation of the direct lattice is easily determined from crystal morphology, since some translations of the direct lattice are always parallel to morphological features such as crystal faces, cleavages, and striations. It was shown above that, in the general triclinic case, reciprocal-lattice translations are not necessarily parallel to direct-lattice translations. However, any plane of reciprocal-lattice points is normal to a translation of the direct lattice. For example, the plane of reciprocal-lattice points defined by $\mathbf{a}^*$ and $\mathbf{b}^*$ is normal to **c**. This is true since $\mathbf{a}^*$ and $\mathbf{b}^*$ are normal to $(h00)$ and $(0k0)$ planes, respectively, which are in turn parallel to **c**. Since any lattice may be thought of as being constructed of parallel planes of lattice points, in this example the reciprocal lattice may be considered to be built up of planes of lattice points normal to **c**. This relation is completely general. If the direction of any direct-lattice translation can be determined in a crystal through examination of its morphology, the orientation of the reciprocal lattice is determined.

This concept is important in single-crystal investigations involving, for instance, the Weissenberg, rotation, or oscillation techniques, where the crystal under investigation is rotated about a translation of the direct lattice. In the precession method, however, the crystal is oriented such that planes of reciprocal-lattice points are normal to the axis of precession and parallel to the plane of the film. Therefore, the precessing axis must be a translation of the direct lattice. The spindle, or dial, axis of the precession instrument is normal to the axis of precession and therefore must be parallel to reciprocal-lattice planes. Ideally it is parallel to a translation in these planes.

Coordinate Systems. The location of a reciprocal-lattice point is usually specified in relation to the axial system of the lattice. That is, a reciprocal-lattice point is located at the end of a vector

$$\boldsymbol{\sigma} = ha^* + kb^* + lc^*$$

h units along a^*, k units along b^*, and l units along c^*. It is often more convenient to use a coordinate system more directly related to the instrumentation being used to investigate the reciprocal lattice. This is especially true of the Weissenberg method where the crystal is made to rotate around a translation of the direct lattice and reciprocal-lattice points occur in planes normal to this axis.

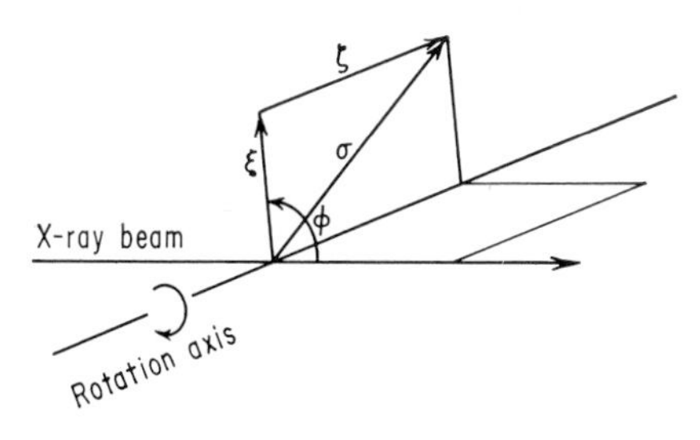

Fig. 5

The relations are illustrated in Fig. 5, where the position of a reciprocal-lattice point is designated by the cylindrical coordinates ζ, ξ, and ϕ. The reference system is the crystal rotation axis and the plane containing this axis and the direct beam. Here ζ is the coordinate parallel to the rotation axis specified in reciprocal-lattice units, ξ the coordinate normal to this axis in reciprocal-lattice units, and ϕ the angle between the plane containing the direct beam and the rotation axis, and the plane defined by the vectors $\boldsymbol{\zeta}$ and $\boldsymbol{\xi}$. The origin of the reciprocal lattice is taken as the intersection of the direct beam and the rotation axis. Note that ζ and ξ may be resolved into the vector $\boldsymbol{\sigma}$, i.e.,

$$\boldsymbol{\sigma} = \boldsymbol{\zeta} + \boldsymbol{\xi}$$

GENERAL REFERENCES

Buerger, Martin J.: *X-ray Crystallography*, John Wiley & Sons, Inc., New York, 1942.

Buerger, Martin J.: *Crystal-structure Analysis*, John Wiley & Sons, Inc., New York, 1960.

Henry, N. F. M., N. Lipson, and W. A. Wooster: *The Interpretation of X-ray Diffraction Photographs*, The Macmillan Company, New York, 1961.

International Tables for X-ray Crystallography, vol. I, Kynoch Press, Birmingham, England, 1952.

Chapter 27

INDEXING SINGLE-CRYSTAL PATTERNS

S. H. Simonsen

The University of Texas

1. ROTATING-CRYSTAL METHODS

Stationary Film. *Rotation Patterns* (See Chap. 24, Sec. 2). In practice a rotation pattern is seldom, if ever, indexed because the indices cannot be determined unequivocally and because in many cases the reflection spots along a layer line are too numerous to permit the resolution required for the measurement of all individual spots. These disadvantages are not applicable to moving-film patterns which, in addition, can be indexed with much less effort. The principal use of a rotation pattern is in the determination of the translation distance along the rotation axis, the camera-inclination angle and layer-line screen settings for upper-level equi-inclination Weissenberg patterns, and the film and layer-line screen settings for precession patterns.

Despite their infrequent use, several methods of indexing rotation patterns will be described, chiefly because of their application to oscillation patterns. Also, the second method can be considered as an exercise in demonstrating the usefulness of the reciprocal-lattice concept (see Chap. 26) in interpreting diffraction data. It is assumed in the following discussion that the crystal system and unit-cell dimensions have been determined by the methods discussed in previous chapters. A flat film holder is rarely used; so the discussion will be limited to rotation patterns obtained using a cylindrical camera.

A rotation pattern can be indexed directly by an analytical method in which the Bragg angle 2θ for each spot is determined from a measurement of the film coordinates of the spot. The corresponding interplanar spacings $d(hkl)$ are computed and the measured spacings are compared with spacings calculated from the unit-cell dimensions. Alternatively, measured 2θ values can be compared with calculated 2θ values.

The geometrical relationship between 2θ and the film coordinates is shown in Fig. 1. The symbols used conform to the notation of Buerger.[1] Υ, the angle ACB, is the azimuth angle of the diffracted beam; χ, the angle SCB, is the inclination angle of the diffracted beam; 2θ, the angle ACS, is the angle between the direct beam and the diffracted beam; x, AB, is the distance from the central axis of the film to the spot; y, SB, is the perpendicular distance of the spot from the equatorial (zero) layer line; and r, BC, is the radius of the camera.

The following trigonometric formulas are applicable:

$$\Upsilon = x/r \text{ radians} = x/r \times 57.30^\circ \tag{1}$$

If the usual camera of radius 28.65 mm is used, Eq. (1) becomes

$$\Upsilon = 2x^\circ \tag{2}$$

when x is measured in millimeters.

$$\tan \chi = y/r \tag{3}$$
$$\cos 2\theta = \cos \Upsilon \cos \chi \tag{4}$$

The interplanar spacing d can then be computed using the Bragg relation

$$d = \lambda/(2 \sin \theta) \tag{5}$$

Several tables[2,3] are available which give the solution of Eq. (5) for the radiations normally used and for small angular intervals of 2θ or θ. Of particular usefulness are the tables of Garrett and Brocklehurst[2] which list separately the unresolved $K\alpha$ doublet, $K\alpha_1$, $K\alpha_2$, and $K\beta$ radiations of copper, molybdenum, iron, chromium, and cobalt.

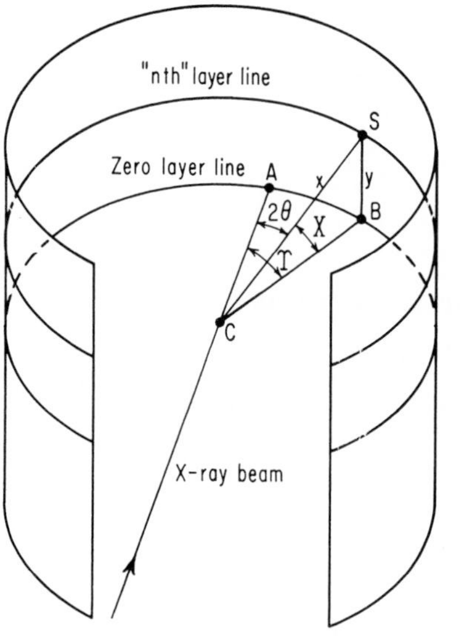

FIG. 1. Geometrical relationship between 2θ and the film coordinates.

The film coordinates x and y are measured on the film using a vernier device capable of reading to the nearest 0.1 or 0.05 mm. Because all spots lying on the same layer line have the same y coordinates, the measurements are reduced essentially to one dimension. The perpendicular distances y between the zero-layer line and the nth-layer lines are measured for each layer. Greater precision can be attained by measuring $2y$, the distance between corresponding layer lines on each side of the zero layer, i.e., between hkn and $hk\bar{n}$. The x values of only one quadrant of the film need be measured because each general (hkl) plane produces four spots on the film as it is rotated through 360°; these spots will have the coordinates x,y; $\bar{x},y$; $x,\bar{y}$; and $\bar{x},\bar{y}$. Again, greater precision results by measuring $2x$, so that on each layer line the distances between corresponding spots x,y and $\bar{x},y$ are measured. These film coordinates are converted to d values by use of Eqs. (2), (3), (4), and (5) and are compared with $d(hkl)$ values computed from the following general equation:

$$\frac{1}{d^2(hkl)} = h^2a^{*2} + k^2b^{*2} + l^2c^{*2} + 2klb^*c^* \cos \alpha^* + 2lhc^*a^* \cos \beta^* + 2hka^*b^* \cos \gamma^* \tag{6}$$

This equation simplifies considerably as the symmetry of the crystal increases. Also, several computer programs[4,5] are available which facilitate the calculation of $d(hkl)$.

To illustrate the above method, the rotation pattern of iodine thiopyrylium about the c axis is shown in Fig. 2. The crystal is rhombohedral, space group $R\bar{3}m$, and the hexagonal unit cell has the dimensions $a_0 = 8.407$ Å and $c_0 = 8.205$ Å. The film coordinates are tabulated in Table 1, together with the measured and calculated interplanar spacings. The tabulation is simplified since $l = 0, 1, 2, 3$, and 4 for all spots on the zero-, first-, second-, third-, and fourth-layer lines, respectively. Only one plane of a form is listed in the table. For a rhombohedral crystal based on hexagonal axes, the four-index symbol is $hkil$, where $i = -(h + k)$; the i is usually omitted in writing the symbol but is used in determining the planes of a form. The condition for nonextinction is $-h + k + l = 3n$. Taking l as positive, there are six planes in the general form (hkl), i.e., (321), ($\bar{3}\bar{2}$1), (2$\bar{5}$1), ($\bar{5}$21), ($\bar{3}$51), (5$\bar{3}$1), all having the same spacing.

Table 1. Analytical Method of Indexing c-axis Rotation Pattern of Iodine Thiopyrylium

Scale readings		$2x = \Upsilon$	2θ	d_{meas}	d_{calc}	(hkl)
Right	Left					
Zero level: ($y = 0$, $\chi = 0$)						
92.25	71.25	21.00	......	4.23	4.20	(110)
100.20	63.35	36.85	......	2.44	2.42	(030)
103.20	60.35	42.85	......	2.11	2.10	(220)
110.50	53.05	57.45	......	1.60	1.59	(140)
114.80	48.65	66.15	......	1.41	1.40	(330)
120.60	42.75	77.85	......	1.23	1.21	(060)
122.60	40.75	81.85	......	1.18	1.16	(250)
128.25	35.05	93.20	......	1.06	1.05	(440)
133.75	29.30	104.45	......	0.98	0.96	(170)
137.70	25.10	112.60	......	0.93	0.92	(360)
First level: ($2y = 10.90$, $\chi = 10°46'$)						
88.00	75.65	12.35	16.30	5.44	5.44	(101)
94.00	69.50	24.50	26.60	3.35	3.33	(021)
98.10	65.40	32.70	34.15	2.63	2.61	(211)
104.30	59.25	45.05	46.00	1.97	1.96	(131)
106.90	56.65	50.25	51.10	1.79	1.78	(401)
109.25	54.25	55.00	55.70	1.65	1.64	(321)
113.80	49.70	64.10	64.60	1.44	1.43	(051)
115.90	47.60	68.30	68.80	1.36	1.36	(241)
117.85	45.60	72.25	72.75	1.30	1.29	(511)
121.80	41.60	80.25	80.35	1.19	1.18	(431)
125.75	37.65	88.10	88.15	1.11	1.10	(161)
129.45	33.85	95.60	95.50	1.04	1.03	(701), (351)
131.35	31.80	99.55	99.40	1.01	1.00	(621)
137.15	25.65	111.50	111.10	0.94	0.93	(541)
139.25	23.65	115.60	115.10	0.91	0.90	(081)
141.35	21.45	119.90	119.30	0.89	0.88	(271)
Second level: ($2y = 23.00$, $\chi = 21°52'$)						
87.60	75.90	11.70	24.65	3.61	3.57	(012)
94.15	69.25	24.90	32.70	2.74	2.72	(202)
98.40	65.00	33.40	39.20	2.30	2.28	(122)
104.90	58.60	46.30	50.10	1.82	1.81	(312)
107.55	55.85	51.70	54.90	1.67	1.66	(042)
110.15	53.35	56.80	59.45	1.55	1.55	(232)
114.75	48.65	66.10	67.90	1.38	1.37	(502)
116.95	46.45	70.50	71.95	1.31	1.30	(422)
119.00	44.30	74.70	75.80	1.25	1.24	(152)
123.15	40.15	83.00	83.50	1.16	1.15	(342)
127.20	35.90	91.30	88.80	1.10	1.07	(612)
131.20	31.70	99.50	98.80	1.02	1.01	(531), (072)
133.25	29.55	103.70	102.70	0.99	0.98	(262)
139.65	23.15	116.50	114.45	0.92	0.91	(452)

Table 1. Analytical Method of Indexing c-axis Rotation Pattern of Iodine Thiopyrylium (Continued)

Scale readings		$2x = \Upsilon$	2θ	d_{meas}	d_{calc}	(hkl)
Right	Left					
Third level: ($2y$ = 38.80, χ = 34°6′)						
91.90	71.60	20.30	39.05	2.31	2.29	(113)
101.35	62.15	39.20	50.10	1.82	1.81	(303)
104.65	58.75	45.90	54.80	1.68	1.67	(223)
113.15	50.25	62.90	67.85	1.38	1.37	(413)
118.10	45.20	72.90	75.90	1.25	1.25	(333)
125.10	38.30	86.80	87.35	1.12	1.11	(603)
127.35	35.75	91.60	88.70	1.10	1.07	(523)
134.15	28.75	105.40	102.70	0.99	0.98	(443)
141.55	21.20	120.35	114.75	0.92	0.91	(713)
Fourth level: ($2y$ = 64.76, χ = 48°30′)						
90.30	73.20	17.10	50.70	1.80	1.78	(024)
97.35	66.00	31.35	55.55	1.65	1.64	(214)
106.50	57.00	49.50	64.50	1.44	1.44	(134)
110.05	53.35	56.70	68.65	1.37	1.36	(404)
113.35	49.90	63.45	72.75	1.30	1.29	(324)
119.60	43.70	75.90	80.70	1.19	1.19	(054)
122.50	40.85	81.65	84.50	1.15	1.14	(244)
125.40	37.80	87.60	88.40	1.11	1.10	(514)
131.10	32.10	99.00	95.95	1.04	1.03	(434)
137.10	25.90	111.20	103.85	0.98	0.98	(164)

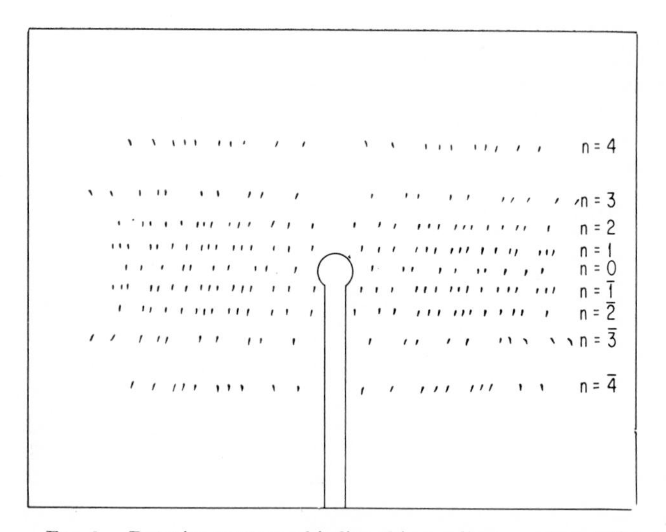

Fig. 2. Rotation pattern of iodine thiopyrylium, c-axis rotation.

The analytical method is accurate and always applicable, but if there are many spots on the pattern it is very time-consuming and tedious. Bernal[6] applied the concept of the reciprocal lattice (Chap. 26) to the interpretation of rotation photographs and developed a graphical method of indexing which is sufficiently accurate and much more rapid than the analytical method.

In terms of the reciprocal lattice, the condition for reflection is that a point of the reciprocal lattice must lie on the surface of the sphere of reflection. Thus diffraction by a rotating crystal can be represented as the rotation of the reciprocal lattice about an axis or, conversely, as the rotation of the sphere through the reciprocal lattice. The origin of the reciprocal lattice is always placed at the point where the incident beam emerges from the sphere of reflection. As each reciprocal-lattice point passes through the surface of the reflection sphere a diffracted beam is produced. The spots on a cylindrical film must then be identified with the corresponding reciprocal-lattice points. To accomplish this it is convenient to define the position of the reciprocal-lattice points using cylindrical coordinates, as in Fig. 3. ζ is the perpendicular distance of the reciprocal-lattice point P from a plane normal to the rotation axis through the reciprocal-lattice origin; ξ is the radius of a cylinder having the rotation axis as axis and passing through P, i.e., the perpendicular distance from the rotation axis to P; ϕ is the angular coordinate of P which acquires all values during a complete rotation and is indeterminate on a rotation photograph; and σ is the reciprocal-lattice-point vector λ/d or d^*. Trigonometric relations have been derived relating the x and y film coordinates to ξ and ζ[1,6,7], but they are very cumbersome, and graphical methods are much more convenient. A chart having contours of equal ξ and ζ can be prepared on transparent paper, the rotation photograph placed on the chart, and the ξ and ζ coordinates read for every spot on the film. A Bernal chart (Fig. 4) suitable for use with films obtained using a cylindrical camera of 57.3 mm diameter can be purchased,[8] prepared from tabulated data,[7] or traced from charts reproduced in various texts.

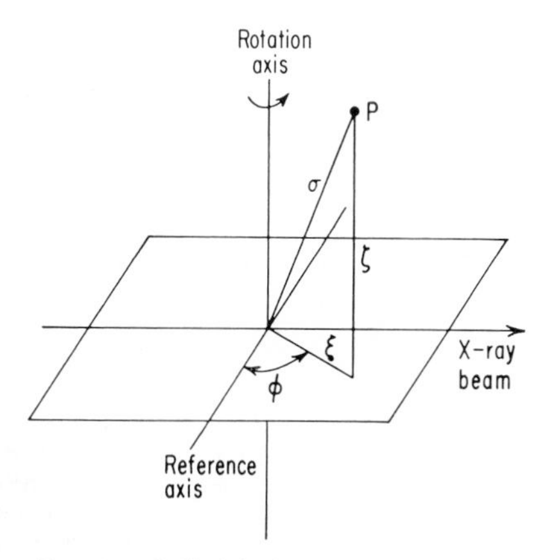

FIG. 3. Cylindrical-coordinate system.

Each pair of spot coordinates must be compared with the coordinates of the reciprocal-lattice points; when coincidence occurs, the indices of the spot and of the point are identical. The coordinates of the reciprocal-lattice points can be determined graphically by drawing the reciprocal-lattice net perpendicular to the rotation axis to a convenient scale, e.g., 10 cm = 1 reciprocal-lattice unit. The extent of the reciprocal net required depends upon the symmetry and the axis of rotation. The number of quadrants is determined by the variation of $d(hkl)$ as the signs of the indices are permuted. For rectangular nets, one quadrant suffices as $d(hk) = d(\bar{h}k) = d(h\bar{k}) = d(\overline{hk})$. Generally, two quadrants are required in the case of nonorthogonal nets. The dimensions of the reciprocal net are expressed generally by

$$a^* = \frac{\lambda}{d(100)} \qquad b^* = \frac{\lambda}{d(010)} \qquad c^* = \frac{\lambda}{d(001)} \qquad \cos a^* = \frac{\cos\beta\cos\gamma - \cos\alpha}{\sin\beta\sin\gamma}$$

$$\cos\beta^* = \frac{\cos\gamma\cos\alpha - \cos\beta}{\sin\gamma\sin\alpha} \qquad \text{and} \qquad \cos\gamma^* = \frac{\cos\alpha\cos\beta - \cos\gamma}{\sin\alpha\sin\beta}$$

The spots are indexed one level at a time; one index is determined by the level (or layer) number. For all zero levels the rotation axis coincides with the origin of the net $\zeta = 0$. It is convenient to plot all values of ξ along a line drawn from the origin, and to place the pivot point of a compass at the origin. Circles are drawn, each having a radius of ξ, through the reciprocal net. When a circle and a net point coincide, within the limits of measurement error, the spot is given the indices of the point, ($hk0$) if the rotation is about the c axis, ($h0l$) if about the b axis, or ($0kl$) if about the a axis.

Indexing of the upper levels is dependent upon the crystal system and upon the axis of rotation. If the rotation axis is parallel with the corresponding reciprocal-lattice axis, the upper-level nets will be directly over the zero-level net and the origins of the upper-level nets will coincide with the rotation axis. In this case, indexing the upper levels is identical to the indexing of the zero level. A radial line is drawn from the origin for each level with the corresponding ξ values plotted on each line and circles

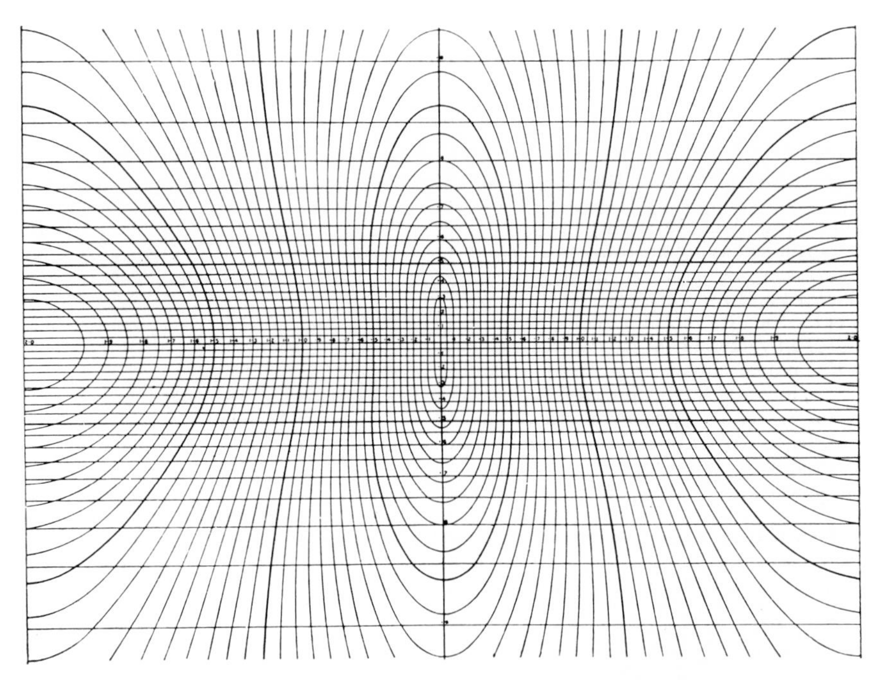

Fig. 4. Bernal chart for camera diameter of 57.3 mm.

drawn through the net. All the spots on each level will have one common index, the level number. It can be seen that all reciprocal-lattice points lying on a row parallel to the rotation axis will have the same ξ value and thus will have two indices in common. These spots appear on the photograph as row lines of constant ξ and are often indicated by the white radiation streak. It is usually necessary to index only the zero level as the other levels can be indexed by inspection of the ξ values. Systematic extinctions due to space-group considerations must be taken into account.

In the case of triclinic crystals rotated about any axis, the reciprocal axis is not parallel to the rotation axis but is inclined to it. The upper levels are parallel to the zero level, but when projected onto it they are displaced from the origin of the zero net by an amount which is dependent upon the projection of the reciprocal axis on the zero level and upon ζ. The zero net can be used for indexing the upper levels by drawing through the origin of the net the projection of the reciprocal axis (which is inclined to the net plane) and marking rotation-axis origins along this line for each level. A line is drawn from each origin with ξ values marked, the pivot point of a compass is placed at the origin, and the ξ values are carried over the zero-level net until each circle and a lattice point coincide. The third index is determined by the level number. The angles between the reciprocal-axis projection and the reciprocal axis of the zero-level net are given by the following relations:

a-axis rotation, δ (delta), the angle between a^* projection and b^*:

$$\tan \delta_a = \frac{\cos \beta^* - \cos \gamma^* \cos \alpha^*}{\cos \gamma \sin \alpha} \tag{7}$$

b-axis rotation, the angle between b^* projection and a^*:

$$\tan \delta_b = \frac{\cos \alpha^* - \cos \gamma^* \cos \beta^*}{\cos \gamma^* \sin \beta^*} \tag{8}$$

c-axis rotation, the angle between c^* projection and a^*:

$$\tan \delta_c = \frac{\cos \alpha^* - \cos \beta^* \cos \gamma^*}{\cos \beta^* \sin \gamma^*} \tag{9}$$

The origin of the *n*th level is then placed at a distance of t_n along the corresponding projection:

a-axis rotation: $t_n = -n[(a^*)^2 - (\lambda/a)^2]^{1/2}$
b-axis rotation: $t_n = -n[(b^*)^2 - (\lambda/b)^2]^{1/2}$
c-axis rotation: $t_n = -n[(c^*)^2 - (\lambda/c)^2]^{1/2}$

Other nonorthogonal crystal systems are special cases of the triclinic case:

A. Monoclinic. $\alpha^* = \gamma^* = 90° \neq \beta^*$.

1. *a*-axis rotation. $\delta = 90°$ [Eq. (7)], or the upper-level nets are displaced in the direction of c^* by $t_n = -na^* \cos \beta^*$.
2. *b*-axis rotation. $\delta = 0°$ [Eq. (8)] and $t_n = 0$; so the upper-level nets are directly over the zero level.
3. *c*-axis rotation. $\delta = 0°$ [Eq. (9)], or the upper-level nets are displaced in the direction of a^* by $t_n = -nc^* \cos \beta^*$.

B. Rhombohedral. $\alpha^* = \beta^* = \gamma^* \neq 90°$. Rotation about a crystallographic axis. Equations (7), (8), and (9) reduce to $\delta = \alpha^*/2$.

$$t_n = -n[(a^*)^2 - (\lambda/a)^2]^{1/2}$$

C. Hexagonal. $\alpha^* = \beta^* = 90°$; $\gamma^* = 60°$; $a^* = b^*$.

1. *a*-axis rotation. $\delta = 0°$; the upper nets are displaced in the direction of b^* by $-n(a^*/2)$.
2. *b*-axis rotation. $\delta = 0°$; the upper nets are displaced in the direction of a^* by $-n(a^*/2)$.
3. *c*-axis rotation. The upper-level nets are directly over the zero level.

The rotation pattern of Fig. 1 is indexed graphically in Fig. 5. The ξ and ζ values read from the film using a Bernal chart are tabulated in Table 2. Notice that for space group $R\bar{3}m$, the requirement for nonextinction is $-h + k + l = 3n$. Thus the common indices in a row line (constant ξ) are interchanged from level to level, i.e., (211), (122), (214).

Because only two of the three cylindrical coordinates required to specify completely the location of a reciprocal-lattice point are measurable on a rotation pattern, the spots cannot be indexed unambiguously. Spots on the same level may have identical or nearly identical ξ values, making it impossible or extremely difficult to choose the reciprocal-lattice point responsible for the spot.

Oscillation Patterns (See Chap. 24, Sec. 2). Oscillation patterns are indexed by the same methods as rotation patterns. The restricted angular rotation produces fewer reflections, which can be assigned indices with a much greater degree of certainty

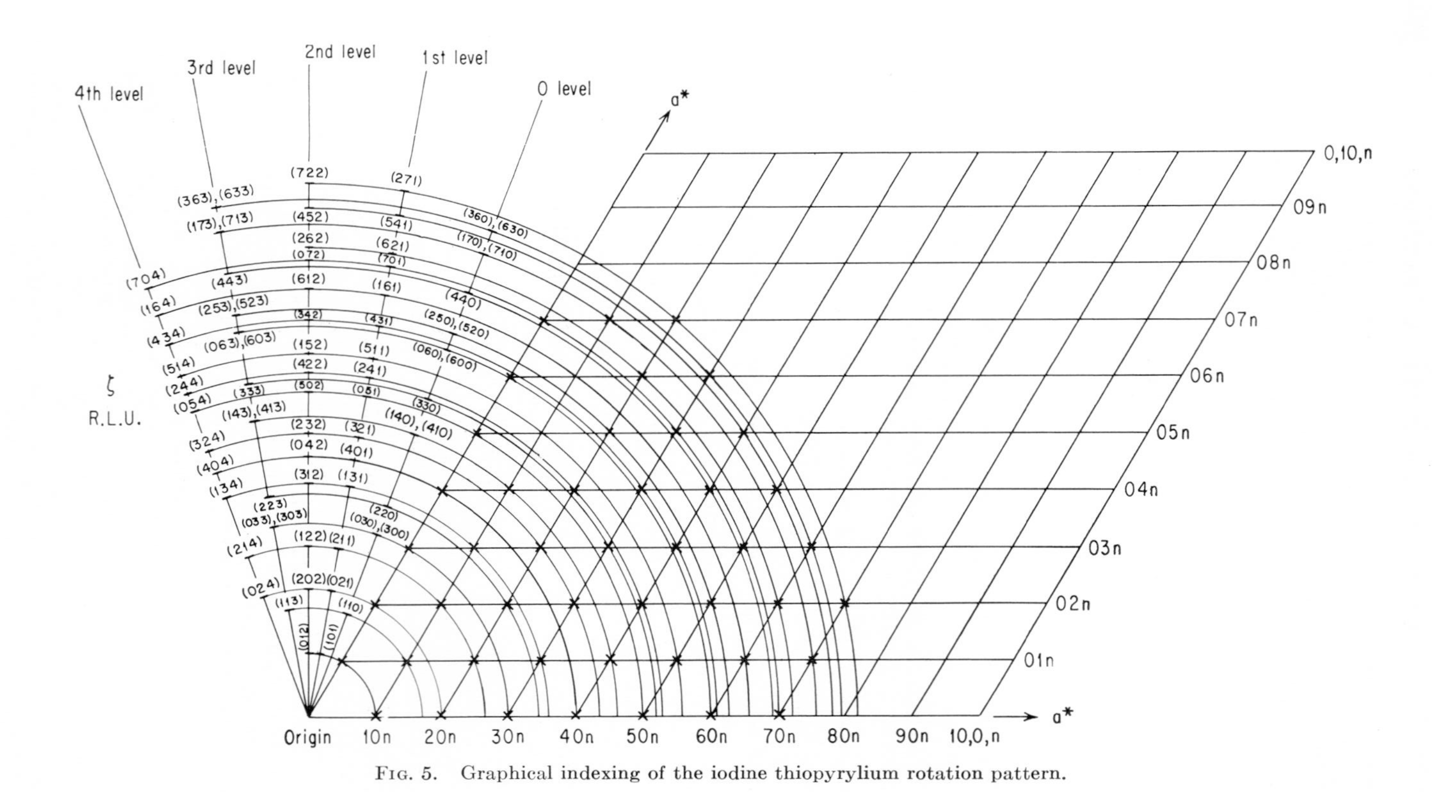

FIG. 5. Graphical indexing of the iodine thiopyrylium rotation pattern.

Table 2. Cylindrical Coordinates of Reflection Spots, Rotation Pattern of Iodine Thiopyrylium

Level									
Zero		First		Second		Third		Fourth	
$\zeta = 0$		$\zeta = 0.19$		$\zeta = 0.38$		$\zeta = 0.57$		$\zeta = 0.76$	
ξ	$(hk0)$	ξ	$(hk1)$	ξ	$(hk2)$	ξ	$(hk3)$	ξ	$(hk4)$
		0.21	(101)	0.21	(012)				
0.36	(110)	....	.....	....	.....	0.36	(113)		
		0.42	(021)	0.42	(202)	....	.....	0.42	(024)
		0.55	(211)	0.55	(122)	....	.....	0.56	(214)
0.64	(030)	....	.....	....	.....	0.63	(033)		
0.73	(220)	....	.....	....	.....	0.73	(223)		
		0.76	(131)	0.76	(312)	....	.....	0.76	(134)
		0.85	(401)	0.85	(042)	....	.....	0.85	(404)
		0.92	(321)	0.92	(232)	....	.....	0.92	(324)
0.97	(140)	....	.....	....	.....	0.97	(143)		
		1.05	(051)	1.05	(502)	....	.....	1.06	(054)
1.09	(330)	....	.....	....	.....	1.09	(333)		
		1.11	(241)	1.12	(422)	....	.....	1.12	(244)
		1.17	(511)	1.18	(152)	....	.....	1.18	(514)
1.26	(060)	....	.....	....	.....	1.26	(063)		
		1.28	(431)	1.28	(342)	....	.....	1.30	(434)
1.32	(250)	....	.....	....	.....	1.32	(253)		
		1.37	(161)	1.38	(612)	....	.....	1.38	(164)
1.45	(440)	....	.....	....	.....	1.45	(443)		
		1.47	(351)	1.47	(532)	....	.....	1.48	(354)
			(701)	....	(072)	....	.....	....	(704)
		1.52	(621)	1.52	(262)				
1.58	(170)	....	.....	....	.....	1.58	(173)		
		1.64	(541)	1.64	(452)				
1.67	(360)	....	.....	....	.....	1.67	(363)		
		1.72	(271)	1.72	(722)				

because the values of ϕ can be determined, within limits, when the orientation of the reciprocal lattice with respect to the oscillation range has been established. The points of the reciprocal lattice which cut the sphere of reflection during the oscillation, and thus produce reflections, can be identified graphically in the following way. Two radial lines, separated angularly by the oscillation range, are drawn from the origin through the reciprocal net. The centers of reflection circles are located on each of these lines one reciprocal-lattice unit from the origin, and circles having radii of $(1 - \zeta^2)^{1/2}$ are drawn. Each level must be considered separately; so it is advantageous to draw the radial lines and reflection circles of each level on separate sheets of transparent paper. Each level can then be laid over the reciprocal net, with the origin of the radial lines placed over the origin of the oscillation axis, and with the oscillation range in correct orientation with respect to the reciprocal net. As in the case of rotation patterns, the origins of the oscillation axis and the zero-level net coincide. For upper levels, the origin of the oscillation axis with respect to the reciprocal net is dependent upon the crystal symmetry; the correct origin must be used for each level.

Consider any one level. The circles represent the angular movement of the reflection circle through the reciprocal net from the initial to the terminal position of the oscillation range. This movement corresponds to the movement of the crystal so that points in the upper right quadrant of the reciprocal net produce spots on the upper right quadrant of the film. The reciprocal points which cut the circumference of the reflection circle during the movement are contained within the areas bounded between arcs of the two circles; these areas are lune- or cusp-shaped. Two lunes are formed, one intersected by each radial line. Figure 6 illustrates the possible reflections of the fourth level of the rotation pattern of Fig. 2; the lunes bounding the reciprocal-lattice points which pass through the reflection circle during oscillation are shaded. The oscillation range is 10°, and the starting point of the oscillation is 10° from the a^* axis.

The zero level is the only level passing through the equator of the reflection sphere, and its reflection circle has a radius of one reciprocal-lattice unit. The upper levels

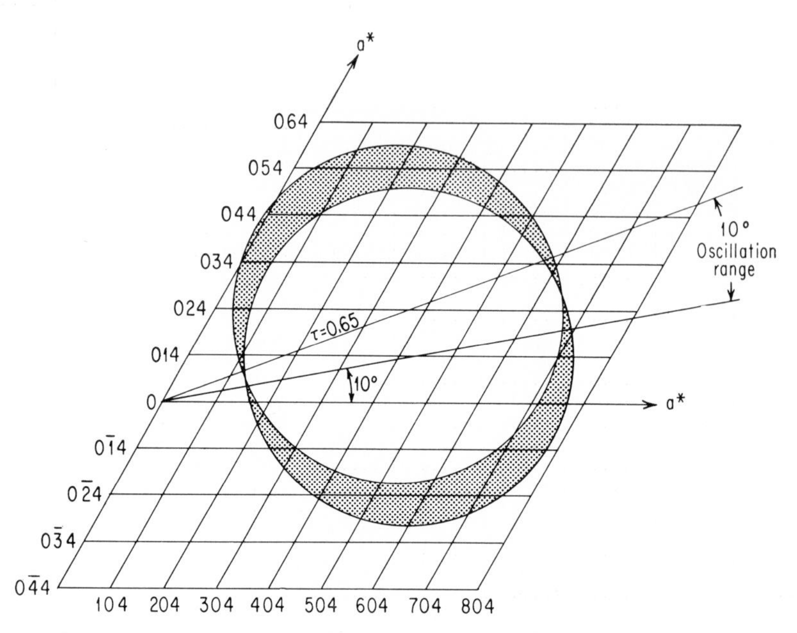

FIG. 6. Graphical indexing of an oscillation pattern. Fourth level of iodine thiopyrylium, 10° oscillation range about c axis, starting point of oscillation 10° from a^* axis.

sweep through great circles of the sphere parallel to the equatorial plane, resulting in progressively smaller lunes as the level number increases. Also, the smaller the oscillation range, the smaller the lunes and the fewer the resulting reflection spots.

If the orientation of the crystal, and accordingly of the reciprocal net, is not known with respect to the oscillation range, it can be found by rotating the overlaid sheet around the origin until the cylindrical coordinates of the reciprocal-net points within the limiting lunes are in agreement with the coordinates of the spots on the oscillation pattern.

Besides having fewer spots, oscillation patterns are different in that the symmetry of the pattern is not necessarily, and indeed not generally, the full C_{2l} (twofold rotation axis at the intersection of vertical and horizontal reflection lines) of a rotation pattern. Depending upon the crystal symmetry, oscillation patterns may have the following symmetries: (1) C_{2l}, (2) C_l (horizontal reflection line), (3) C_l (vertical reflection line), (4) C_2 (twofold rotation axis), or (5) C_1 (no symmetry). In general, then, the cylindrical coordinates of all the spots on an oscillation pattern must be measured.

Moving Film. *Equi-inclination Weissenberg Patterns* (See Chap. 24, Sec. 2). Since Weissenberg patterns are photographed one level at a time, all spots on a given level have the same ζ value. The spots are spread over the two dimensions of the film, making it possible to fix uniquely the other two cylindrical coordinates ξ and ϕ and, accordingly, to index each spot unambiguously. As in the case of rotation patterns x is the distance of a spot to the center line of the film and is proportional to Υ. The distance z of a spot to an arbitrary zero, measured parallel to the center line, is proportional to the angle the crystal has turned ϕ (or ω according to Buerger) in going from the zero point to the spot. It is convenient to use a camera of 57.30 mm diameter so that $\Upsilon = 2x$ (mm)° and to couple the rotation of the crystal and the translation of the film in such a way that $\phi = 2z$ (mm)°.

The spots form a distorted reciprocal-lattice net in which the straight lattice lines are recorded as curved lines. The problem of indexing is reduced to identifying the curved lines on the film with the corresponding straight lines of the reciprocal net.

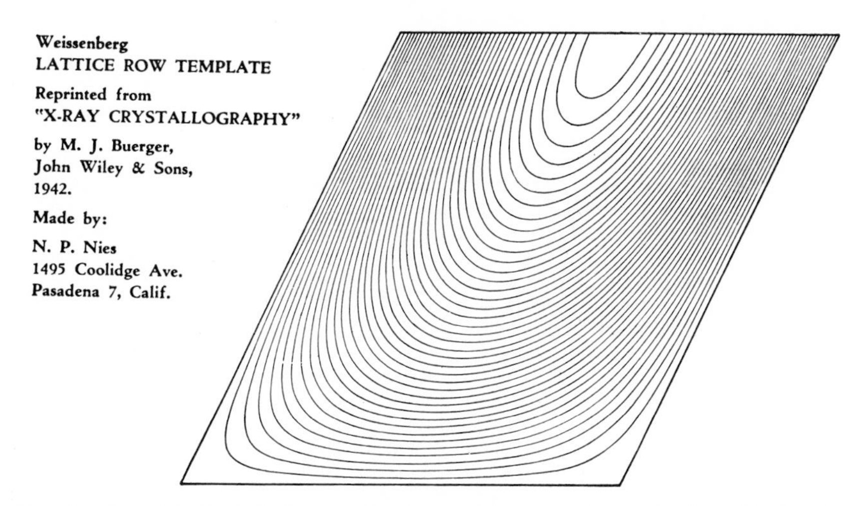

Weissenberg
LATTICE ROW TEMPLATE
Reprinted from
"X-RAY CRYSTALLOGRAPHY"
by M. J. Buerger,
John Wiley & Sons,
1942.
Made by:
N. P. Nies
1495 Coolidge Ave.
Pasadena 7, Calif.

Fig. 7. Template for indexing zero-level normal beam and upper-level equi-inclination Weissenberg patterns.

This can be accomplished easily and rapidly by a graphical procedure on the pattern or a copy of the pattern. A central line of the reciprocal net (a line of reciprocal points passing through the origin of the net) produces a straight line of spots on the film having a constant slope of $\Upsilon/\phi = 2$, i.e., a line making an angle of 63°26′ with the center line of the film. A line of reciprocal points parallel to a central line (a noncentral line) does not pass through the origin during rotation and is recorded as a curved line of spots which is always within the bounds of a parallelogram defined by the central lattice line and the center line of film. The shape of the curve of a noncentral line can be calculated from the geometry of the recording method, and a template prepared which represents the projection of a set of parallel lattice lines upon a Weissenberg film. The left edge is a central lattice line of slope $= 2$, the right edge is the negative side of the same central lattice line appearing after a rotation of 180° (90 mm on the template), and the bottom line corresponds to the center line of the film. Curves are drawn within this parallelogram representing a set of lattice lines, spaced 0.05 reciprocal-lattice unit apart, parallel to the central line. Data for preparing such a template are given in Buerger[1] and in the *International Tables for X-ray Crystallography*,[7] and templates on plastic sheets can be purchased from Nies.[8] Figure 7 illustrates such a template. The great advantage of the equi-inclination method is that the shape of a lattice line is identical for all levels and only one template is required for patterns of all levels.

A pattern can be indexed on the basis of any two central lattice lines chosen as the reciprocal-net axial rows because the reciprocal net can be described in terms of any two central lines, chosen arbitrarily, but with the condition that each unit parallelogram is primitive and the lattice lines are parallel to each of the two central lines. All parallel lines of a set are separated by the same repeat distance. Stated in another way, the reciprocal net consists of a set of points through which may be drawn a grid of equidistant and parallel lines. The grid may be drawn in a variety of ways, each of which represents the distribution of points located at the intersections of the lines.

In practice, however, the central lines selected as axial rows should be consistent with the symmetry of the crystal. Buerger's[1] discussion of the projection patterns of the plane point groups in equi-inclination Weissenberg patterns furnishes invaluable help in this connection and should be consulted. In any case, the central lattice line having the densest array of spots is always a good candidate for a reciprocal-axis row as it represents the longest spacings in the direct lattice. Care must be exercised, however, as systematic extinctions may be present and the axial rows not recognized because they are not the most densely populated. Screw axes and glide planes cause extinctions on the zero level and lattice centerings on the odd upper levels; so it is advantageous to index the second-level pattern first. The extinctions can be readily detected by superimposing several consecutive levels.

To index a pattern a dot copy is made by placing a transparent sheet over the film on a viewing box and marking each reflection spot with an ink dot. This procedure has the advantages of clearly indicating the location of the weak reflections as well as the strong ones, and of enabling one to draw the curved reciprocal-lattice lines through the dots on the copy and to place the indices beside each dot. Tracing paper can be used for the copy, but a material such as Kodak Topographic Sheet, type B, is superior because it has about the same thickness and rigidity as photographic film, making handling easier. One side is roughened so that it can be easily written upon with pen or pencil, and it is quite transparent.

The dot copy is placed over a template on a view box with the central line of the film (the ϕ axis) in coincidence with the bottom line of the template. The central lattice line chosen as a reciprocal-axis row is centered over the left or right margin of the template. All the other dots on the copy will fall on or between the curved lines of the template, and using these lines as a guide, the curves are drawn on the copy with pencil. The curves will be spaced an equal number of reciprocal-lattice units apart; so lines missing because of extinction can be drawn in. The copy is then shifted so that the central line chosen as the second axial row is centered over the margin of the template. Again, all dots will fall on curves parallel to template curves and the curves are marked on the copy. Each dot will now be at the intersection of two curves, and the curves represent the distorted reciprocal net. One index is always the level number n and the other two indices are obtained from the lattice-line numbers. Each curve intersects one of the axial rows at a point ha^*, kb^*, or lc^* and is assigned the appropriate h, k, or l value. For example, if the first-level equi-inclination Weissenberg pattern of a crystal rotated about the c axis is being indexed, the dot at the intersection of a curve passing through the $2a^*$ point and a curve through the $5b^*$ point has the indices (251).

To illustrate the procedure, the ($hk0$) pattern of bis(3-hydroxyl-1,3-diphenyltriazine) palladium(II) is shown in Fig. 8 and its indexed dot copy in Fig. 9; the ($hk2$) pattern is shown in Fig. 10 and its indexed dot copy in Fig. 11. The unit cell is monoclinic, space group $P\ 2/c$, $a_0 = 12.20$, $b_0 = 12.58$; $c_0 = 7.10$; $\beta = 95.0°$.

The shapes of the curved lines of spots on the upper- and zero-level patterns are identical; and the patterns differ only in the following ways: (1) the intensities of the spots are different, (2) systematic extinctions vary from level to level, and (3) the axial rows of the nth reciprocal net may appear as noncentral curves on the nth level, whereas the axial rows of a zero-level pattern always appear as straight central lines.

If the rotation axis does not coincide with the corresponding reciprocal-lattice axis, the origins of the upper-level nets are displaced from the origin of the rotation axis and one or both of the axial rows will be noncentral with respect to the rotation-axis origin. For example, a triclinic crystal, or a rhombohedral crystal rotated about a crystallographic axis, will give upper-level patterns in which both nth axial rows are noncentral. The axial-row curves can be recognized by superimposing the zero- and upper-level patterns. The upper-level pattern must be displaced parallel to the center line of the film by the amount $r \tan \mu$, where r is the radius of the camera and μ the anti-inclination angle, to take into account the displacement of the spots caused

FIG. 8. Weissenberg pattern, bis(3-hydroxyl-1,3-diphenyltriazine) palladium(II), zero-level c-axis rotation.

by the rotation of the upper-level reciprocal net with respect to the zero level resulting from the anti-inclination geometry. The superimposed patterns will show an exact coincidence of spots except for the axial rows, which are straight lines on the zero-level and curved lines on the upper-level pattern. The indexing procedure for the upper-level pattern is the same as that used for the zero level except that the axial row is aligned over a curve on the template instead of over a margin line. All other dots will fall on curves parallel to the axial curve. The copy is then shifted so that the second noncentral axial curve fits a curve of the template. Again all dots will fall on parallel curves and will be at the intersections of two curves which give the values of two indices; the third index is given by the level number. If a monoclinic crystal is rotated

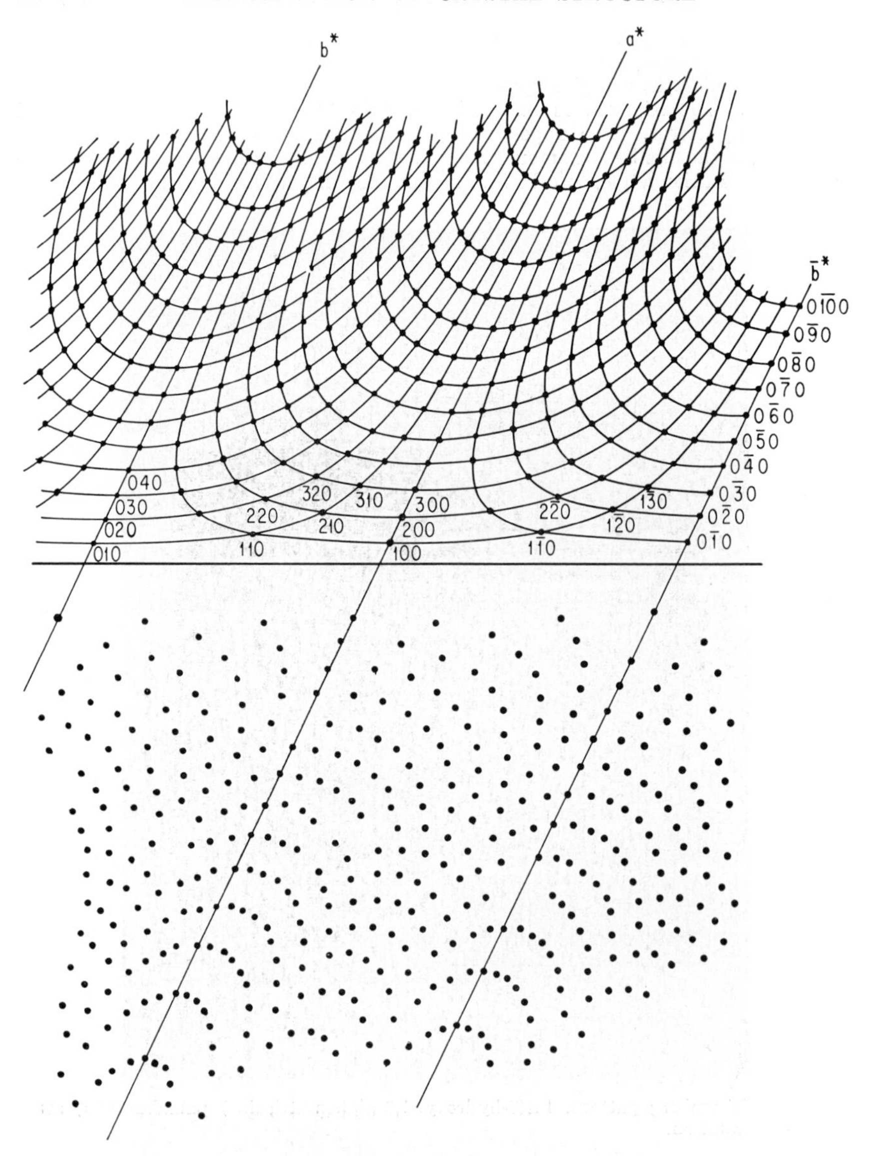

FIG. 9. Indexed dot copy of pattern in Fig. 8.

about the a or c axis (the b axis taken as unique) the c^* or a^* axial row appears as a straight central line, but the b^* axial row is noncentral and appears as a curved line on the pattern. The straight axial row is readily recognized and is aligned over the margin of the template and the curves drawn. The b^* row is aligned over a curve of the template and the parallel curves are drawn (see Fig. 11).

A second method of indexing equi-inclination patterns consists in plotting the measured cylindrical coordinates ξ and ϕ of each spot. The plotting is most conveniently done on polar-coordinate paper as all ξ values having the same ϕ can be placed on the same radial line of the paper. When all the points have been plotted, a unit parallelogram is chosen and the reciprocal net is drawn. The spots are assigned indices corresponding to the indices of the net intersections. Special scales, described by Buerger,[1] can be used for reading the ξ and ϕ values directly from the film. The same ξ scale can be used for all zero-level patterns, but a different scale must be prepared for each upper-level pattern. The same ϕ scale is used for all patterns, 1 mm = 2°. This method offers no advantages with respect to the first method described and is much more time-consuming.

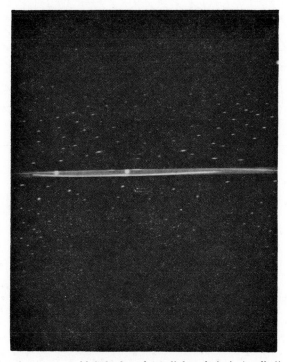

Fig. 10. Weissenberg pattern, bis(3-hydroxyl-1,3-diphenyltriazine) palladium(II), second-level c-axis rotation.

Normal-beam Weissenberg Patterns (See Chap. 24, Sec. 2). The zero level is the same as the zero level of the equi-inclination pattern, but the shapes of the curves of the upper-level lattice rows are dependent upon ζ. Graphical indexing therefore requires that a different template be prepared for each upper-level pattern and for each crystal studied. For this reason the normal-beam method is infrequently used, and upper-level photographs are taken using the equi-inclination geometry. For details of indexing upper-level normal-beam patterns, consult Buerger.[1]

Buerger Precession Patterns (See Chap. 24, Sec. 2). The precession camera projects a layer of the reciprocal lattice without distortion on a flat film; so the pattern is simply indexed by inspection. Care must be taken to account for systematic extinctions. The a^*c^* and a^*b^* nets of bis(3-hydroxyl-1,3-diphenyltriazine) palladium(II) are given in Figs. 12 and 13 (zero levels). The origin of the lattice is at the center of the film, and four quadrants are recorded. On upper levels, the portion of the net

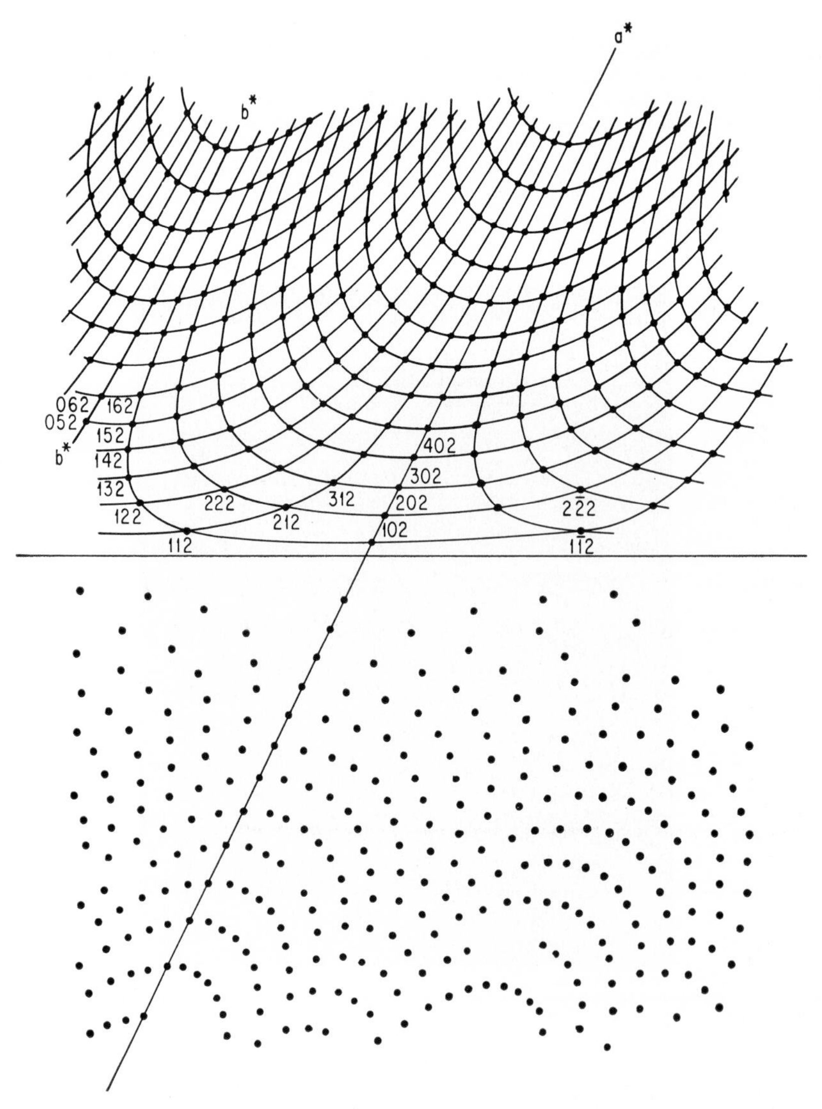

FIG. 11. Indexed dot copy of pattern in Fig. 10.

close to the origin never cuts the sphere of reflection; so that there is always a circle around the origin without spots.

Other Methods. The de Jong and Bouman rotation retigraph (see Chap. 24, Sec. 2) also projects a reciprocal-lattice net without distortion, and the resulting pattern can be indexed by inspection.

2. THE LAUE METHOD

Laue patterns are usually indexed graphically by transforming the reflection spots to gnomonic poles, which are the intersections of the normals of the reflecting planes with the plane of projection, and plotting these poles to form a gnomonic projection. In the case of patterns taken with the incident beam parallel to a crystallographic axis and perpendicular to a flat film (symmetrical pattern), the gnomonic net corresponds to a plane net of the reciprocal lattice and is indexed accordingly. Henry, Lipson, and Wooster[9] represent the poles as the intersection of lines, constructed by joining the origin of the reciprocal lattice to each lattice point, with the projection plane. If the projection plane is taken to coincide with the first level of the reciprocal lattice, the

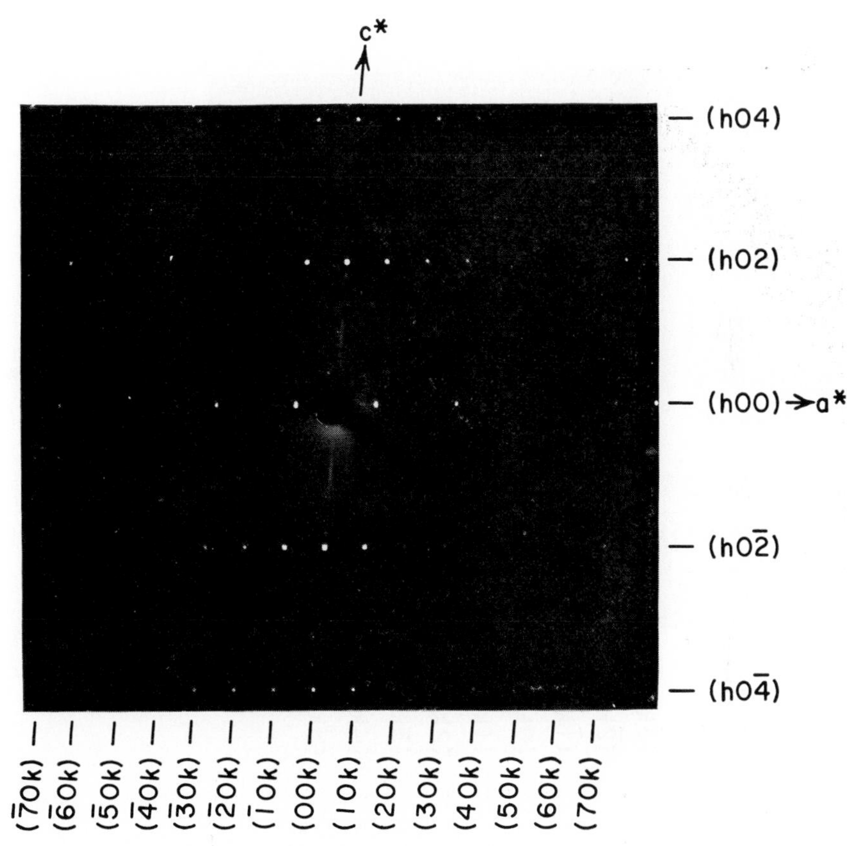

FIG. 12. a^*c^* Buerger precession pattern of bis(3-hydroxyl-1,3-diphenyltriazine) palladium(II), zero level.

lattice points of the first level project so that the poles are located at the intersections of net lines and have one index equal to unity. The other two indices are determined by the coordinates of the intersecting net lines. Points on upper reciprocal-lattice levels project so that the poles are located within the grids defined by the net lines. Their indices are determined by expressing the coordinates as fractions and then clearing the fractions to obtain the lowest possible corresponding integers. For example, a pole having coordinates $2\frac{1}{3}$, $1\frac{1}{3}$, 1 would be assigned the indices (743). Note that the sphere of reflection is tangent to the zero level, so that none of the planes of the zero level can reflect and they therefore do not appear on Laue pattern.

The geometry of the projection is given in Fig. 14. *COO′* is the direction of the incident beam, *CS* is the diffracted beam which intersects the film at point *S*, *OS* is the distance of the spot from the center of the film, OC is the film-to-crystal distance, CP is the normal of the (hkl) plane which intersects the projection plane $O'P$ at point P, $O'C$ is the distance of the crystal from the projection plane, and $O'P$ is the distance of the projected pole from the origin of the projection. CP is coplanar with the plane defined by the incident and diffracted beams.

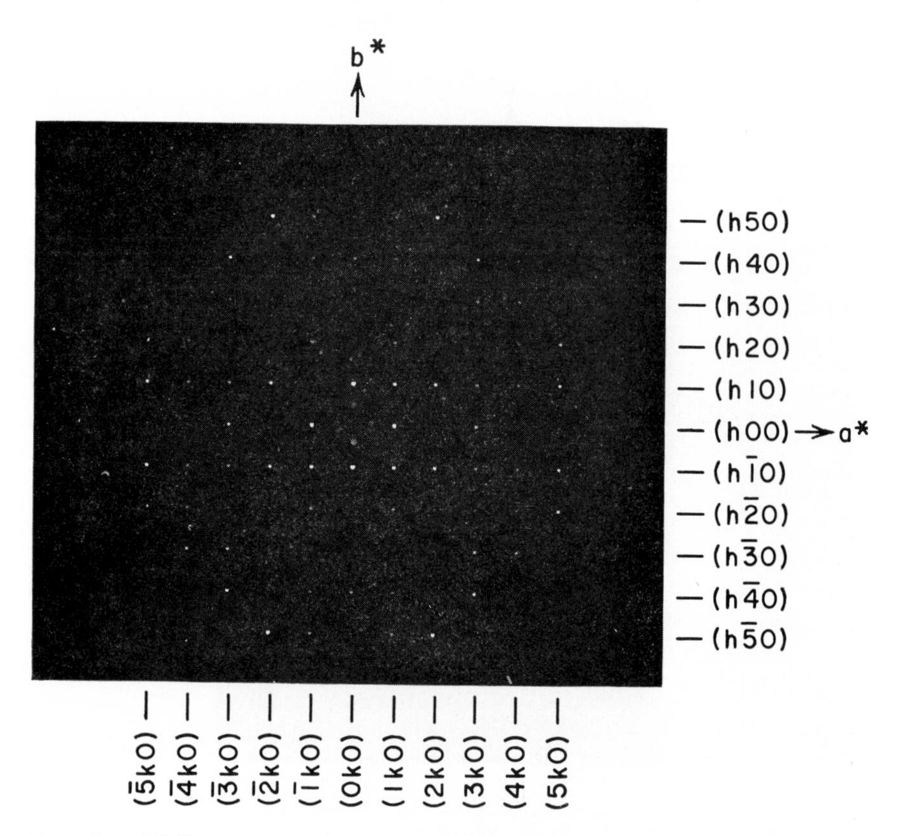

FIG. 13. a^*b^* Buerger precession pattern of bis(3-hydroxyl-1,3-diphenyltriazine) palladium(II), zero level.

The following relations apply:

$$OS = OC \tan 2\theta \qquad (10)$$

$$O'P = O'C \cot \theta \qquad (11)$$

Using the measured value of OS, $O'P$ can be computed.

The most convenient method of making the projection is to construct a special ruler (Wyckoff[10]) relating the distance of the Laue spot from the center of the film OS to the corresponding projection distance $O'P$. The left side of the ruler is calibrated in millimeters, measured from a center point, and the right side gives the corresponding projection distance for each millimeter mark and is labeled accordingly. If the ruler is made using a transparent material, such as topographic sheet, type B, it is easier to observe the spot positions on the pattern. The gnomonic pole and the diffraction spot always lie on the same line passing through the origin of the film; so the Laue

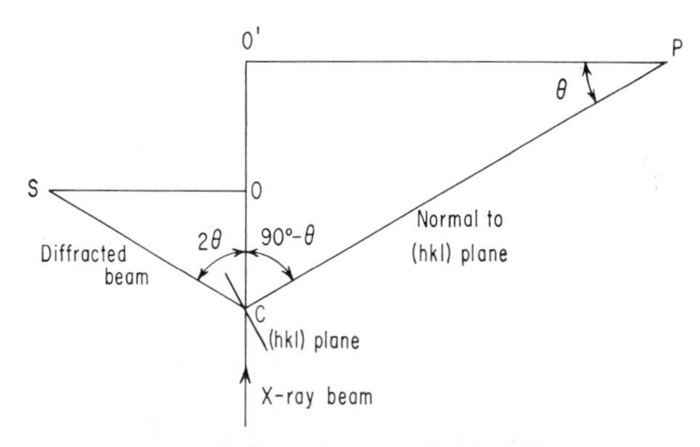

Fig. 14. Geometrical relationships of gnomonic projection of a Laue spot.

Fig. 15*a*. Laue pattern of potassium bromide. Crystal-to-film distance = 3.0 cm.

OC = O'C = 3.0 cm.

7 6 5 4 3 2 1 0 6.00 5.00 4.00 3.50 3.00 2.50 2.30 2.10 2.00 1.90 1.80 1.70 1.60 1.50 1.40 1.30 1.25 1.20 1.15 1.10

Fig. 15*b*. Wyckoff ruler.

pattern is fastened to a large sheet of paper, the center of the ruler is placed over the center of the incident-beam spot, and a pin is placed through the centers. The ruler is pivoted around until the center of a reflection spot falls under the left side and the projection pole is marked on the paper along the right side at the corresponding distance. When all the poles have been marked, appropriate grid lines are drawn and the spots indexed. Tables for constructing the ruler for common crystal-to-film and crystal-to-projection plane distances are found in the *International Tables for X-ray Crystallography*,[7] Davey,[11] and other references. For uncommon distances, the data for constructing the ruler must be computed using Eqs. (10) and (11).

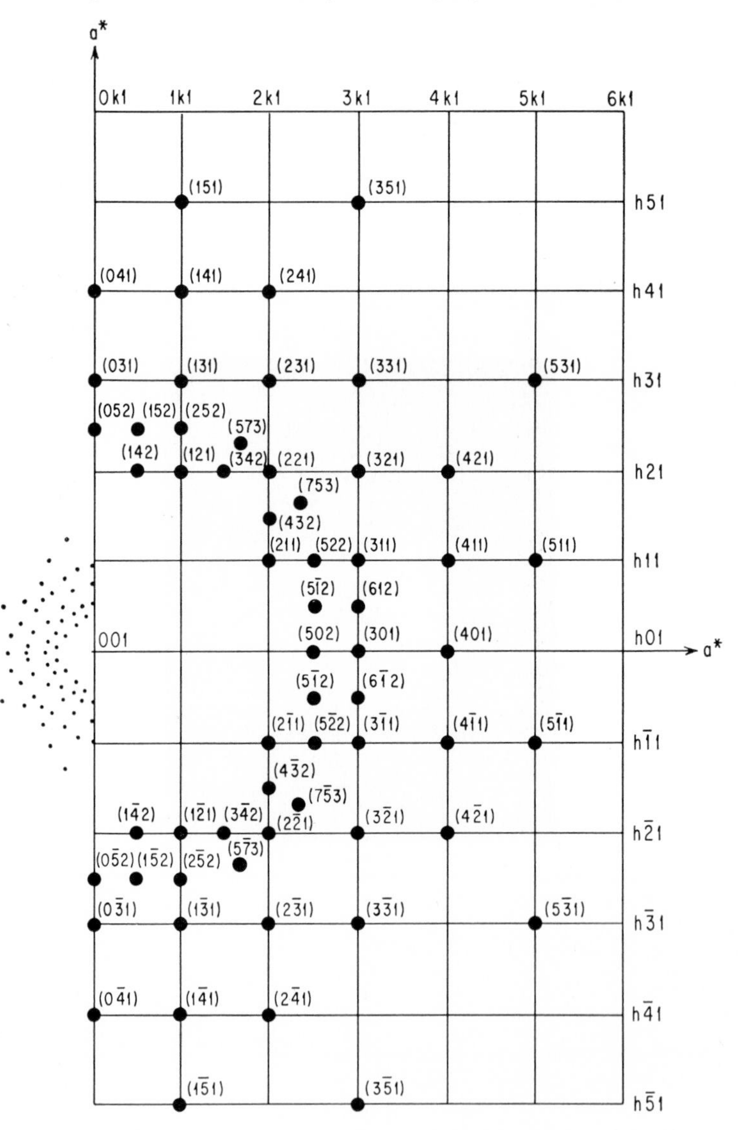

FIG. 15*c*. Gnomonic projection of Laue pattern of potassium bromide.

Figures 15*a*,*b*,*c* illustrate the indexing of a potassium bromide crystal using a Wyckoff ruler.

The grid lines of the projection of a cubic crystal form a square net whose sides are equal to the distance from the crystal to the projection plane *O′C*. Tetragonal and orthorhombic crystals yield orthogonal nets in which the sides have the same ratio to each other as the reciprocals of the corresponding axial ratios of the crystal. For example, an orthorhombic crystal with the incident beam along the a axis will give a rectangular net having the dimensions $(O'C)$ (a/b) in the direction of the b axis and $(O'C)$ (a/c) in the direction of the c axis. The net of a monoclinic crystal with the beam along the twofold axis consists of parallelograms; with the beam along one of the other axes, the net is rectangular, but the origin is displaced from the center of the film. The net of a triclinic crystal, with the beam along any axis, is made up of parallelograms and the origin of the net is displaced from the center of the film. The sides of the parallelograms are related as in the orthorhombic case, and the angle is the angle between the crystallographic axes.

If the crystal is not perfectly oriented with the beam along an axis the net lines are not parallel but are converging. If the misorientation is not severe (less than 10°), the pattern can still be indexed; otherwise the crystal must be reset and a new pattern taken, or the projection rotated using a gnomonic rotation net.[10]

Back-reflection Laue patterns can also be indexed graphically by a gnomonic projection, but a different ruler must be prepared.[7]

REFERENCES CITED

1. M. J. Buerger, *X-ray Crystallography*, John Wiley & Sons, Inc., New York, 1942.
2. H. J. Garrett and R. E. Brocklehurst, Tables of Interplanar Spacings Computed for the Characteristic Radiations of Copper, Molybdenum, Iron, Chromium, and Cobalt, WADC *Tech. Rept.* 57-381, ASTIA Document AD 142344, Wright Air Development Center, February, 1958.
3. National Bureau of Standards, Applied Mathematics Series 10, *Tables for Conversion of X-ray Diffraction Angles to Interplanar Spacing*, Government Printing Office, Washington, D.C., 1950.
4. *International Union of Crystallography World List of Crystallographic Computer Programs*, September, 1962. Copies may be obtained on request from D. P. Shoemaker (editor), Massachusetts Institute of Technology, Cambridge 39, Mass.; or G. A. Jeffrey, Crystallographic Laboratory, University of Pittsburgh, Pittsburgh, Pa.
5. M. H. Mueller, E. F. H. Meyer, and S. H. Simonsen, *Crystallographic D-space Computer Program*, ANL-6519, Argonne National Laboratory, 9700 South Cass Ave., Argonne, Ill., April, 1962.
6. J. D. Bernal, *Proc. Roy. Soc.* (*London*), **A**, **113**: 117-160 (1926).
7. *International Tables for X-ray Crystallography*, vol. II, The Kynoch Press, Birmingham, England, 1959.
8. N. P. Nies, 969 Skyline Drive, Laguna Beach, Calif. 92651.
9. N. F. M. Henry, H. Lipson, and W. A. Wooster, *The Interpretation of X-ray Diffraction Photographs*, The Macmillan Company, New York, 1st ed., 1951; 2d ed., 1960.
10. R. W. G. Wyckoff, *Am. J. Sci.*, **50**: 317 (1920).
11. W. P. Davey, *A Study of Crystal Structure and Its Applications*, McGraw-Hill Book Company, New York, 1934 (out of print).

GENERAL REFERENCES

Barrett, C. S.: *Structure of Metals*, McGraw-Hill Book Company, New York, 1952.
Bunn, C. W.: *Chemical Crystallography*, Oxford University Press, Fair Lawn, N.J., 1946.
McLachlan, Dan, Jr.: *X-ray Crystal Structure*, McGraw-Hill Book Company, New York, 1957.
Wood, Elizabeth A.: *Crystal Orientation Manual*, Columbia University Press, New York, 1963.

Chapter 28

INDEXING OF POWDER PATTERNS

Irving R. Tannenbaum

Chematics Research

1. INTRODUCTION

X-ray diffraction powder patterns may be used either as a means of identification of known materials or to determine the symmetry elements of hitherto uncatalogued materials. The former technique is straightforward and can be very simply accomplished by use of the standard compendia.[1,2]

When the object is to determine the unit cell of a previously uncatalogued material, the problem is more complex. Certainly, any information which can be obtained from other considerations (e.g., symmetry of chemical analogs, observed geometric morphology of the crystals) could point out a logical approach to an attempt to index a pattern.

When, however, the powder pattern arises from a sample of unknown symmetry, a systematic approach to the indexing is mandatory. In such a case, the recommended procedure is to attempt to index the pattern on the basis of the isometric system. If this attempt fails, the process is repeated using, consecutively, systems in order of decreasing symmetry.

The question of which general approach, viz., analytical, graphical, or numerical, is best used in any particular problem is largely a personal choice. If the data are sufficiently precise and a suitable code and computer are available, a numerical procedure is to be recommended (see Sec. 4).

The graphical approaches (Sec. 3) are quite popular, but their area of practical applicability is restricted to patterns of crystals of uniaxial symmetry (isometric, hexagonal, or tetragonal). However, when the proper charts are available, fast checks for these symmetries may possibly be found, although the application of this technique does generally require both patience and good fortune.

The slide-rule technique for cubic patterns (given in detail under Cubic Symmetry in Sec. 3) is a very rapid and often successful test for this symmetry and is highly recommended.

In using the analytical approach (Sec. 2), a question arises if a powder diffraction pattern cannot be indexed satisfactorily on the basis of cubic, tetragonal, or hexagonal symmetry. If the crystal is not uniaxial, the selection of a method to be used is largely a matter of personal preference. The method of Lipson[3] for orthorhombic crystals may be tried, and if this fails, the method of Ito[4] can be applied. This method is laborious but should, in principle, lead to the solution irrespective of the symmetry. It is questionable whether indexing on the basis of an orthorhombic lattice should be attempted prior to use of Ito's general method. Because of the arithmetic difficulty of handling approximate data for crystals of low symmetry, these methods have not been used often, and are largely untried. Certainly no attempt should be made to index patterns known to be of low symmetry, unless they possess high resolution and many lines in the back-reflection region. Certainly no attempt to index powder patterns arising from materials of low symmetry should be made unless the data are precise.

When two or more phases are present, it is often possible to index a portion of the pattern first on the basis of the phase with higher symmetry. The lines remaining unindexed can then be treated as a new pattern in the attempt to complete the indexing. In so doing, however, it must be noted that any given line could, conceivably, arise from both phases.

One special method, not covered in this work, applies to the problem of indexing patterns arising from materials with unit cells much larger in one dimension than in the other two. Vand[5] presents a technique based upon the fact that the long spacing should lead to a banded structure in the pattern. In each band the values for two of the indices should remain constant while the individual lines should vary only in the third index so that the values of the square of the reciprocal-lattice vector ($1/d^2$) should vary as the squares of integers (1, 4, 9, . . .). Further details of this method are not given here since the applicability is limited.

2. ANALYTICAL METHODS

Cubic Symmetry. For a cubic crystal*

$$Q_i = 1/d_i^2 = M_i/a^2 \tag{1}$$

where M_i is given by

$$M_i = h_i^2 + k_i^2 + l_i^2 \tag{2}$$

The simplest analytical method for determining whether a given pattern arises from a crystal of cubic symmetry is to tabulate both the Q_i, in increasing order, and the differences between successive Q_i. The appearance of a common factor

Table 1. Analysis of Powder Pattern of Nickel†

i	Q_i	$Q_i - Q_{i-1}$	$\dfrac{Q_i}{0.0803}$	M	hkl
1	0.24171		3.01	3	111
2	0.32210	0.08039	4.01	4	200
3	0.64411	0.03220	8.02	8	220
4	0.88598	0.24187	11.03	11	311
5	0.96646	0.08048	12.03	12	222
6	1.28839	0.32193	16.04	16	400
7	1.53020	0.24181	19.05	19	331
8	1.61045	0.08025	20.05	20	420

† Data of Swanson and Tatge.[6]

(usually the smallest difference) in $Q_i - Q_{i-1}$ indicates cubic symmetry; the common factor is, of course, $1/a^2$ since the smallest possible change in successive values of $M_i = h_i^2 + k_i^2 + l_i^2$ is one. When the common factor is determined, division into the Q_i gives the values of M_i, and a value of the cell constant can be obtained for each line. If no common factor can be found, the pattern is not cubic.

Table 1 gives the diffraction data for nickel as reported by Swanson and Tatge.[6] The column listing the successive differences $Q_i - Q_{i-1}$ possesses as a common

* Single subscripts designate tabulated values; triple subscripts refer to crystallographic indices.

factor 0.0804. Division of this number into the Q_i gives the values for M_i, in this case characteristic of a face-centered cubic lattice. A primitive cubic lattice gives $M = 1, 2, 3, 4, 5, 6, 8, \ldots$ while a body-centered cubic lattice yields $M = 2, 4, 6, 8, 10, 12, 14, \ldots$. This latter lattice may often be distinguished from primitive by the apparent presence of the forbidden M values 7, 15, etc.

Tetragonal Symmetry. The square of the reciprocal-lattice vector Q for tetragonal crystals is given by

$$Q_{hkl} = M/a^2 + l^2/c^2 \tag{3}$$

in which

$$M = h^2 + k^2 \tag{4}$$

The analytical test for tetragonality rests upon the fact that the values of Q for the successive $(hk0)$ lines should be in the ratio of 1:2:4:5:8:9:10:13:16:17: . . . . The ratio of 2:1 between many of the lines can occur only in the tetragonal or cubic systems, except by happenstance. Therefore, if the possibility of a cubic pattern has already been eliminated, the appearance of factors of 2 in the Q's is an indication of a tetragonal pattern. When this situation is found to apply, it can be assumed that these are the $(hk0)$ lines, and values of a can be calculated by assuming that the first

Table 2. Analysis of Powder Pattern of Indium*

	Q_i	$Q_i - Q_3$	$Q_i - 2Q_3$	$Q_i - 4Q_3$	$Q_i - 5Q_3$
1	0.13565				
2	16855				
3	18937				
4	35310	16373			
5	37870	18933			
6	46281	27344	08407		
7	51404	32467	13530		
8	54234	35297	16360		
9	65377	46440	27503		
10	75707	56770	37833		
11	84108	65171	46234	08360	
12	89207	70270	51333	13459	

* Date of Swanson, Fuyat, and Ugrinic.[8]

of these lines is the $M = 1, 2, 4, 5$, or 8 line and computing the best value of a. The value of c can then be found through trial and error by assuming the first line of the non-$(hk0)$ type to be the 001, 101, or 111 line. The validity of this assumption must then be checked by computing, on the basis of the calculated a and c, the values of all the other lines, which should agree with the observed values.

A more systematic method of determining the second parameter has been described by Henry, Lipson, and Wooster,[7] in which the values of M/a^2 are subtracted from the non-$(hk0)$ Q_i. The differences Δ_{ij} can be represented by

$$\Delta_{ij} = Q_i - M_j/a^2 = (h_i^2 + k_i^2)/a^2 + l_i^2/c^2 - M_j/a^2 \tag{5}$$

For some of the lines, $h_i^2 + k_i^2 = M_j$ so that

$$\Delta_{ij} = l_i^2/c^2 \tag{6}$$

Hence, values of Δ_{ij} can be expected to be in the ratios of 1:4:9:16: . . . . This fully indexes the line and permits the calculation of a and c. An illustration of this type of computation is given in Table 2, which gives the first 12 Q values observed in the diffraction pattern of indium.[8] Note that Q_5 is approximately twice Q_3 and $Q_{10} \approx 4\,Q_3$ so that a good start would be to assume Q_3 to be 100, Q_5 to be 110, and Q_{10} to be 200. Thus, $1/a^2 = 0.18939$, and Table 2 is completed by successive subtraction of $1/a^2$, $2/a^2$, $4/a^2$, and $5/a^2$ from all the remaining lines, including those assumed to be fully indexed. If the original guess is correct, each line should have a value of l^2/c^2; hence, this table is searched for entries in the ratio of squares of integers, i.e., 1, 4, 9, ... Although the number 1355 ± 2 appears three times in the table it can be correlated only to line number 8, which has $Q_8 \approx 4 \times 0.1355$. Therefore, the original guess must be in error.

Next, choose $M_3 = 2$ so that $Q_3 = 2/a^2$ and $1/a^2 = 0.09468$. On this basis $M_5 = 4$ and $M_{10} = 8$. For the sake of brevity, only the first 6 lines are tabulated in Table 3 along with their remainders after successive values of $1/a^2$ are subtracted. The value 0.04097 which appears as $Q_1 - 0.09468$ is a good choice for $1/c^2$ because $4 \times 0.0409 = 0.1637$ and this appears as $Q_4 - 2/a^2$, making $M_4 = 2$ and $l_4 = 2$. The value for $Q_2 \approx 4 \times 1/c^2$, making this the 002 line. Although this fit is only fair, reasonable allowance for experimental error must be made. It is now found that all lines can be indexed on this basis, but accuracy is improved if the values for $1/a^2$ and $1/c^2$ are adjusted to give closer agreement with the inherently more precise high-angle lines.

Table 3. Indexing of Powder Pattern of Indium*

i	$Q_i - 0/a^2$	$Q_i - 1/a^2$	$Q_i - 2/a^2$	$Q_i - 4/a^2$	$Q_i - 5/a^2$	Ml	hkl
1	0.13565	04097				1 1	101
2	16855	07387				0 2	002
3	18937	09469	0			2 0	110
4	35310	25842	16374			2 2	112
5	37870	28402	18934			4 0	200
6	46281	36813	27345	08409		1 3	103

* Data of Swanson, Fuyat, and Ugrinic.[8]

Hexagonal Symmetry. For hexagonal crystals, Eq. (7) applies,

$$Q_{hkl} = \tfrac{4}{3} M/a^2 + l^2/c^2 \qquad (7)$$

in which M is defined as

$$M = h^2 + k^2 + hk \qquad (8)$$

The method used in testing for hexagonal symmetry is identical to that for tetragonal symmetry, except that the ratios of successive ($hk0$) lines, if *all* were to appear, would be 1:3:4:7:9:12:13:16:19:21: . . . , so that the appearance of ratios of 3 for some of the lines indicates the presence of a hexagonal lattice. The indexing is carried out analogously to the tetragonal-crystal case.

Rhombohedral Symmetry. Crystals possessing rhombohedral (trigonal) symmetry can be indexed as hexagonal; the indices, relative to the rhombohedral lattice ($h_R k_R l_R$), are related to the hexagonal indices ($h_H k_H l_H$) by the relations

$$\begin{aligned} h_R &= (h_H - k_H - l_H)/3 \\ k_R &= (h_H + 2k_H + l_H)/3 \\ l_R &= (-2h_H - k_H + l_H)/3 \end{aligned} \qquad (9)$$

Hence, if each line of a hexagonal pattern has indices such that $(h - k + l)$ are all divisible by 3, the crystal can also be indexed as rhombohedral and the cell parameters a_R and α can be obtained from the hexagonal parameters a_H and c_H, as given by Eqs. (10) and (11).

$$a_R = (a_H{}^2/3 + c_H{}^2/9)^{1/2} \qquad (10)$$

$$\alpha = 2 \sin^{-1} \left[\frac{4}{3} + (2c_H/3a_H)^2 \right]^{-1/2} \qquad (11)$$

Orthorhombic Symmetry. For orthorhombic crystals, the square of the reciprocal lattice vector is given as follows:

$$Q_{hkl} = 1/d^2_{hkl} = h^2/a^2 + k^2/b^2 + l^2/c^2 \tag{12}$$

It is clear from Eq. (12) that differences of the type $Q_{hkl} - Q_{hk0}$, which equal $1/c^2$, should appear as a repeating value in a table of differences of the Q_i values. As an initial step in such a table of differences, any recurring value can be tried as $1/a^2$, $1/b^2$, or $1/c^2$. Once a provisional choice is made for a unit-cell parameter, systematic calculation must lead to complete indexing of the pattern, or else inconsistencies must arise which indicate either that a new choice must be made or that the substance is not orthorhombic.

The values of lattice parameters determined directly from the table of differences can be qualitatively checked by use of the direct relationship which exists between the cell parameters and the number of lines appearing on the pattern; i.e., small parameters correspond to few lines and large parameters to numerous lines. For a rough quantitative test, Lipson[3] shows that the approximate values of the cell parameters for an orthorhombic crystal are given by Eq. (13), in which Q_m represents the value of the mth Q.

Table 4. Differences of Values (× 10⁴) for $NiAl_3$

	Q \ $-Q$	1	2	3	4	5	6	7	8	9	10	11	12	13	14	15	16	17	18	19
1	0619																			
2	0661	042																		
3	0738	118	076																	
4	0846	227	185	108																
5	1101	482	439	363	254															
6	1350	731	689	613	504	250														
7	1535	916	874	797	689	434	185													
8	1654	1034	992	916	807	553	303	118												
9	1730	1111	1068	992	883	629	379	195	076											
10	1953			1216	1107	852	603	418	300	223										
11	2087				1240	986	736	552	433	357	134									
12	2142					1041	791	606	488	412	188	055								
13	2319					1218	968	784	665	589	366	232	177							
14	2471						1120	936	817	741	518	384	329	152						
15	2495						1144	960	841	765	542	408	353	176	024					
16	2575						1224	1040	921	845	621	488	433	256	104	080				
17	2691							1156	1037	962	737	604	549	372	220	196	116			
18	2828								1174	1098	875	741	686	509	357	333	253	137		
19	2953									1223	1000	866	811	646	482	458	378	262	125	
20	3229											1142	1087	910	757	734	654	538	401	276

$$1/a^2 \approx 1/b^2 \approx 1/c^2 \approx 0.4\,(Q_m/m^{2/3}) \tag{13}$$

The problem of searching a large table of differences for recurring values can be very tedious; however, this tedium may be relieved by application of the method of Lipson[3] (see also pp. 182ff. of Ref. 7) which is illustrated below using diffraction data for $NiAl_3$. The exercise is carried through in detail because some aspects can be more clearly demonstrated than described. Table 4 gives the Q values for the first 20 lines, along with the values of $Q_i - Q_j < 0.15$ for all values of $i > j$. In order to ascertain which values in this table appear significantly more frequently than others, the values of these differences are plotted as the abscissa vs. the ordinal number i as the ordinate, as shown in Fig. 1. In this plot, the value of the $Q_i - Q_j$ is plotted as a short horizontal line to take into account the experimental error, which in this case is assumed to be ± 0.001.

The frequently recurring differences are then found by scanning the diagram with a vertical line and noting the values where several points are simultaneously cut. In Fig. 1 it will be observed that 0.0738 occurs seven times, and that 0.0546, 0.0256,

0.0191, and 0.0182 each occur five times, with many other values occurring four times each. It will also be noted that the frequently recurring value 0.0182 is approximately $\frac{1}{4} \times 0.0738$, indicating that these differences arise from lines having Miller indices differing, perhaps, by 1 and by 2. This suggests that one might assign the value 0.0184 ($= \frac{1}{4} \times 0.0738$) to one of the required parameters, say $1/a^2$.

Whether this choice is reasonable can be checked by use of Eq. (13). Using the values $Q_{20} = 0.32$ and $m = 20$ gives 0.018 for the very approximate value for $1/a^2$, $1/b^2$, or $1/c^2$, a result in unusually fine agreement with the value assumed from the plot. Hence, the value of $1/a^2 = 0.0184$ is reasonable (being well within a factor of 2 or 3 of the computed approximation) so that the attempt to index can be continued.

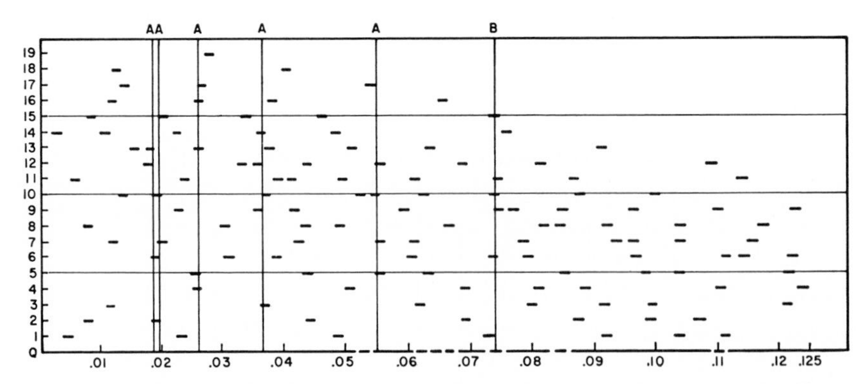

FIG. 1. Diagram of differences of Q values for powder pattern of $NiAl_3$. (*After Henry, Lipson, and Wooster.*[7])

Table 5. Provisional Values of Indices for $NiAl_3$ (Using $1/a^2 = 0.0184$)

Line	h	k	l
1			
2	0	k_2	l_2
3	2	0	0
4	1	k_2	l_2
5			
6	0	k_6	l_6
7	1	k_6	l_6

Noting that $Q_3 = 0.0738 = 4/a^2$ gives an indication that the indices for this line are (200). Further, $Q_4 - Q_2 \approx 1/a^2$ so that $k_2 = k_4$, $l_2 = l_4$ and $h_2 = 0$, $h_4 = 1$. Also, using only the first seven lines for simplicity, it is noted that $Q_7 - Q_6 = 0.0185$ and $Q_{11} - Q_6 = 0.0736$, indicating that $k_6 = k_7 = k_{11}$, $l_6 = l_7 = l_{11}$ and that $h_6 = 0$, $h_7 = 1$, and $h_{11} = 2$.

At this point, of the first seven lines, one is fully indexed (number 3), some information is known about four lines (numbers 2, 4, 6, 7), and nothing is known about two lines (numbers 1 and 5), as summarized in Table 5.

Since the number 0.018 does not appear as a difference $Q_j - Q_i$, the inference may be drawn that $h_1 \neq 0$. ($Q_6 - Q_1 = 0.0731 \approx 4 \times 0.0184$ might be ascribed to a zero value for h_1 so that h_6 would have to be 2, which creates an inconsistency with the already assigned values of h_6, h_7, and h_{11}.) Now simple indices for line 1 are tried; line 1 cannot be (100) for this would require $1/a^2 = 0.0619$, at variance with the previously assigned value. Hence, try (110), making $1/b^2 = Q_1 - 1/a^2 = 0.0435$, which is good since the value 0.0435 appears four times in the table of differences. Also, $4 \times 0.0435 = 0.1740$, which is quite close to the value for Q_9, making that reflection (020). It is further seen that $Q_5 - Q_2 \approx 1/b^2$, so that $k_2 = 0$, $k_5 = 1$, with $h_5 = h_2$ and $l_5 = l_2$; however, $h_2 = 0$, so that line 2 is either (001), (002), or (003), with $1/c^2$ equal, respectively, to 0.0662, 0.0165, or 0.0073. The first two of these numbers are nonrepetitive and the third value appears only twice, so that the indexing based upon $k_2 = 0$ and $k_5 = 1$ must be invalid. The next most simple guess would be to assign, provisionally, the indices (011) to line 2. If this is done, $1/c^2 = Q_2 - 1/b^2 = 0.0227$, a very encouraging result since this value occurs four times in the table of differences.

Now, we have the values for the parameters, $1/a^2 = 0.0184$, $1/b^2 = 0.0435$, and $1/c^2 = 0.0227$, and if these values can reproduce all the lines, the problem is solved, although the naming of the axes may not be conventional. Table 6 shows indexing of the first eight lines based upon the values above.

Obviously, the parameters must be adjusted to give better precision as higher orders are computed. This method may not work with very complex orthorhombic structures but perhaps is worth trying prior to the use either of Zachariasen's method for monoclinic symmetry or of the more general Ito's method.

Table 6. Indexing of First Eight Lines of $NiAl_3$

Line	*hkl*	Calculated	Observed
1	110	0.0620	0.0619
2	011	0.0662	0.0661
3	200	0.0737	0.0738
4	111	0.0847	0.0846
5	102	0.1094	0.1101
6	012	0.1344	0.1350
7	112	0.1529	0.1535
8	{300, 202	{0.1659, 0.1646	0.1654

Monoclinic Symmetry. Indexing powder patterns with low symmetry is, at best, laborious. A recent numerical method, which has been reported by Zachariasen,[9] is easily adaptable to computer techniques and permits the indexing of monoclinic patterns without the use of elegant computational aids. Zachariasen's method determines the unique axis and its lattice parameter b by means of the assumption that in any extensive set of data there will be many pairs (Q_i,Q_j) having the same values of h and l but differing in the value of the index k.

Q_{hkl} for monoclinic crystals is given by Eq. (14),

$$Q_{hkl} = h^2a^{*2} + k^2b^{*2} + l^2c^{*2} + 2hl\, a^*c^* \cos \beta^* \tag{14}$$

or, for the ith line by Eq. (15),

$$Q_i = T_i + k_i^2\, b^{*2} \tag{15}$$

in which the special symbols are defined in Eq. (16).

$$T_i = h_i^2\, a^{*2} + l_i^2\, c^{*2} + 2h_il_i\, a^*c^* \cos \beta^* \tag{16}$$

(The reciprocal-lattice notation is described in Chap. 26.)

For lines having the same values of h and l, but differing in k, Eq. (17) applies

$$Q_i - Q_j = (k_i^2 - k_j^2)b^{*2} \tag{17}$$

The formation of a table of differences should give rise to numbers having recurring values whose ratios are the differences in the squares of integers. For primitive lattices, these ratios are 1:3:4:5:7: . . ., and for centered lattices the ratios are differences in the squares of the even integers, 4:8:12:16: . . . . The table of differences thus clearly permits ready discrimination between centered and primitive lattices. However, in the application of this method or other methods for indexing patterns of materials with low symmetry, precision of measured data is of great importance in order to avoid merely fortuitous recurrences in the values of the table of differences. Since this method should be applied only when the pattern has been tested and found to possess symmetry lower than that of orthorhombic, it serves also to distinguish between monoclinic and triclinic since patterns arising from the latter will give no recurring differences except purely by chance.

If particular values exhibiting the proper ratios are found to occur numerous times in the table of differences, the value of b^{*2} and, hence, b can be computed, and the problem is thereby reduced to a two-dimensional one.

Knowing b^{*2}, it is possible to assign the proper value of k_i to each line and so find the value of $T_i = Q_i - k_i^2 b^{*2}$ representing possible reflections from the $(h0l)$ planes. Since all possible lines are probably not observed, the k_i and T_i values for all lines will not necessarily be determined. However, the determination of the T_i immediately gives the values of k_i.

Furthermore, once a T_i value has been determined, other T values are expected arising from higher-order reflections from the same planes; i.e., $T_j = n^2 T_i$ may exist for each T_i such that $(h_j, k_j, l_j) = (nh_j, nk_j, nl_j)$. In addition to this, if the ith line is not itself first order but rather is mth order, the values for the T_j will be given by

$$T_j = (n^2/m^2)\, T_i \tag{18}$$

so that relationships of the type given by Eq. (18) should be noted in the list of Q_i. The T_i so computed therefore represent the squares of the reciprocal-lattice vectors for many of the $(h0l)$ reflections.

If, from the set of T_i values, subsets of four T_i values can be found which obey Eq. (19) by other than happenstance, then a

$$2(T_i + T_j) = T_m + T_n \tag{19}$$

relationship between the indices exists as given by Eq. (20).

$$\begin{aligned} h_m &= h_i + h_j \qquad & k_m &= k_i + k_j \\ h_n &= h_i - h_j \qquad & k_n &= k_i - k_j \end{aligned} \tag{20}$$

Furthermore, as shown by Zachariasen, if a tetrad is true the indices of the members of the tetrad can be given values arbitrarily as given by

$$\begin{aligned} (h_i,k_i,l_i) &= (p,0,0) \\ (h_j,k_j,l_j) &= (0,0,q) \end{aligned} \tag{21}$$

$$\begin{aligned} (h_m,k_m,l_m) &= (p,0,q) \\ (h_n,k_n,l_n) &= (p,0,\bar{q}) \end{aligned} \tag{22}$$

This is equivalent to a transformation of axes in reciprocal space. If $p = q = 1$, then the primitive order is conserved and all lines can be indexed. If $p > 1$ or $q > 1$, the new cell may not be primitive and indexing based upon the arbitrary assignment of $p = q = 1$ will permit indexing of only $1/n$ of the observed T_i values, where n is the absolute value of the product of the true values of p and q. Hence the procedure to be followed is to try out various combinations of small integers, $p = \pm 1, \pm 2, \pm 3, \ldots, q = \pm 1, \pm 2, \pm 3, \ldots$, until one pair is found which permits indexing the (h_i0l_i) for all the T_i values observed, and a determination of a^*, c^*, and β^*. The unit cell so determined may not be primitive, nor will it in all probability correspond to a conventional choice of axes. However, the transformation to a primitive, conventional coordinate system is easily performed.

An example of this method of indexing is presented below using the data of Zachariasen for the diffraction by α plutonium using Cu $K\alpha$ radiation. The first column of Table 7 shows the observed Q_i values with a precision ± 0.00008 for the first 60 lines of the diffraction pattern. If the differences $Q_i - Q_j$ are formed, the numbers 0.04295, 0.12900, and 0.17190 are found to recur 18, 8, and 12 times, respectively, within the limit of error. The ratio of these repeating differences is 1:3:4, which immediately suggests a primitive monoclinic lattice with $b^{*2} = 0.04300$ and $b = 4.82$ Å. The possible reflections from the $(h0l)$ planes are now sought by searching the table of $Q_i - k^2 b^{*2}$ $(k = 0, 1, 2, \ldots)$ for recurring values and for values obeying Eq. (18). The values of $Q_i - k^2 b^{*2}$ are shown in Table 7, with the sought-for values printed in

Table 7. Diffraction Data for α Plutonium*

Line	Q	$Q - b^{*2}$	$Q - 4b^{*2}$	$Q - 9b^{*2}$	Line	Q	$Q - b^{*2}$	$Q - 4b^{*2}$	$Q - 9b^{*2}$
1	**0.07803**	03508			31	26748 or	22446 or	09545	
2	**10535**	06241			32	**27319**	23017	10116	
3	**10907**	06613			33	**27579**	23277	10376	
4	11747	**07453**			34	27841	**23540**	10639	
5	**11851**	07557			35	28576	**24275**	11374	
6	12093	**07799**			36	28865	**24563**	11662	
7	**12413**	08119			37	29087	24786	**11885**	
8	12940	**08646**			38	29655	25354	**12453**	
9	**13019**	08725			39	**29835**	25534	12633	
10	**13872**	09578			40	30252	25950	**13049**	
11	14814	**10520**			41	30624	**26323**	13422	
12	**14939**	10661			42	31091	26790	**13889**	
13	15198	**10904**			43	31617	**27316**	14415	
14	16155	**11861**			44	31895	**27594**	14693	
15	16696	**12401**			45	32158	27857	**14956**	
16	17182	12888	**00008** ≈ 0		46	34147	**29845**	16941	
17	17315	**13021**	00141		47	**34632**	30331	17430	
18	18163	**13869**	00989		48	35541	**31240**	18338	
19	18382 or	14087 or	01208		49	36337	32035	**19134**	
20	**19102**	14808	01928		50	36967	32665	**19764**	
21	19225	**14930**	02051		51	38031 or	33729 or	20828	
22	**19750**	15455	02576		52	38501	34199	**21298**	
23	21172 or	16877 or	03993		53	**38920**	**34619**	**21718**	00216
24	**21249**	16955	04075		54	40845 or	36544 or	23643 or	02141
25	23423	**19127**	06226		55	41135 or	36834 or	23933 or	02430
26	**23532**	19230	06329		56	41466	37164	**24263**	02761
27	**24270**	19968	07067		57	42037 or	37736 or	24834 or	03332
28	**24580**	20279	07377		58	**42522**	38221	25320	03818
29	26009	**21708**	08807		59	43200	**38899**	25998	04495
30	**26350**	22048	09147		60	43535	39234	**26333**	04831

* Data of Zachariasen.[9]

boldface type. It will be noted that T_4 and T_8 are taken to be 0.07453 and 0.08646, respectively, since four times each number appear as recurring values (i.e., lines 39 and 46, and lines 47 and 53). Line 16 apparently represents the (020) reflection since $Q_{16} \approx 4b^{*2}$. The recurring values of 0.10904 (lines 3 and 13) are, respectively, 4 and 9 times 0.02726, so that this latter number is also a possible T_i. Similarly the T values for lines 6, 18, 29, 48, and 58 all possess the common factor 0.00866, the T values of these lines being the product of this factor with the squares of 3, 4, 5, 6, and 7, respectively. It can be concluded that other possible T values should be 0.00866 and $2^2 \times 0.00866 = 0.03464$ as required by Eq. (18). It will be further noted that no unambiguous assignment of T values or of k values is possible for lines 19, 23, 31,

51, 54, 55, and 57. There are, however, 26 values deduced for the T_i, and these are given in the first two columns in Table 8 in ascending order.

The list of T_i values is now searched to find tetrads obeying Eq. (19) within the prescribed limits of error (in this case ± 0.00032). Many possible tetrads can be found, and the nine having the smallest values for $(T_m + T_n)$ are given in Table 9 along with the dimensions of trial unit cells derived from assuming values of $p = q = 1$. On the basis of these unit cells the attempt is made to index the remaining $(h0l)$ reflections (i.e., in this case the remaining 22 T_i values).

Table 8 shows the indexing of the deduced T_i values for each of the nine possible tetrads of Table 9, from which it can be seen that tetrad number 7 permits indexing all

Table 8. Deduced $(h0l)$ Reflections and Their Possible Indices

Tetrad / i	T_i	1 $(h0l)$	2 $(h0l)$	3 $(h0l)$	4 $(h0l)$	5 $(h0l)$	6 $(h0l)$	7 $(h0l)$	8 $(h0l)$	9 $(h0l)$	Conventional $(h0l)$
1	0.00868				100	100	100	100	100		001
2	02730	100	$10\bar{1}$	$10\bar{0}$				$30\bar{1}$			100
3	03472		100		200	200	200	200	200	100	002
4	07462		001					$10\bar{1}$			102
5	07812	001		$10\bar{1}$	300	300	300	300	300		003
6	08658	$10\bar{1}$		001				$60\bar{1}$	$10\bar{1}$		$10\bar{3}$
7	10538				001	$10\bar{1}$	$10\bar{1}$	$70\bar{2}$		001	$20\bar{1}$
8	10922	200	$20\bar{2}$	200	$10\bar{1}$	001	$20\bar{1}$	$60\bar{2}$			200
9	11881		$30\bar{2}$		101	$20\bar{1}$	001	$80\bar{2}$			$20\bar{2}$
10	12434	101		$20\bar{1}$				001			103
11	13043				$20\bar{1}$	101	$30\bar{1}$	$50\bar{2}$	001	$10\bar{1}$	201
12	13892		200		400	400	400	400	400	200	004
13	14964	$20\bar{1}$		101	201	$30\bar{1}$	101	$90\bar{2}$		101	$20\bar{3}$
14	19131		101					101	101		104
15	19783		$40\bar{2}$		301	$40\bar{1}$	201	$10, 0, \bar{2}$			$20\bar{4}$
16	21285							$80\bar{1}$			$10\bar{5}$
17	21708				500	500	500	500	500		005
18	23540							$10, 0, \bar{3}$			$30\bar{1}$
19	24270							$11, 0, \bar{3}$			$30\bar{2}$
20	24572	300		300				$90\bar{3}$			300
21	26335				401	$50\bar{1}$	301	$11, 0, \bar{2}$		201	$20\bar{5}$
22	27317							$80\bar{3}$			301
23	27587							201			105
24	29841		002		$50\bar{1}$	401	$60\bar{1}$	$20\bar{2}$			204
25	31240	002	300		600	600	600	600	600	300	006
26	34626		$50\bar{2}$	002	501	$60\bar{1}$	401	$12, 0, \bar{2}$	$20\bar{2}$		$20\bar{6}$

26 of the observed T_i values and, of course, all the observed Q_i if the original value of b is utilized.

Hence the problem is solved with the unit cell having the parameters

$$a' = 23.30 \qquad b' = 4.82 \qquad c' = 6.18 \text{ Å} \qquad \beta' = 152.6°$$

This unconventional choice of axes is made conventional by the transformation

$$a_0 = c' \qquad c_0 = a' + 3c'$$

so that the proper lattice parameters become

$$a = 6.18 \qquad b = 4.82 \qquad c = 10.96 \text{ Å} \qquad \beta = 101.8°$$

Simultaneously, the Miller indices undergo the transformation

$$h = l' \qquad l = h' + 3l'$$

to give the conventional indices for the T_i values as shown in the last column of Table 8. Using the conventional lattice parameters all lines of the pattern can be indexed.

In this illustrative example only tetrad number 7 had $p = q = n = 1$, all others having at least one of these parameters greater than unity so that $n = pq > 1$, thereby requiring other alternate values of p and q to be tried for complete indexing in the absence of the observed $n = 1$ tetrad. (It will be noted, e.g., that $p = 1$, $q = 3$ for tetrad number 1 permits indexing of all T_i values, giving a unit cell which yields, upon the transformation of axes, the correct unit cell.) Furthermore, eight of the nine tetrads of Table 9 are correct, with tetrad number 8 fulfilling Eq. (19) only by chance.

Triclinic Symmetry. The triclinic lattice requires the specification of six parameters for the unique description of the substance. The only published method for the indexing of a pattern of such low degree of symmetry is that of Ito (pp. 187ff. of Ref. 4), which, indeed, the originator recommends as a general method to be applied irrespective of the symmetry of the lattice. Ito recommends indexing a pattern on an

Table 9. Smallest Tetrads Such That $2(T_i + T_j) = T_m + T_n$

Tetrad	i	j	m	n	a, Å	c, Å	β, °
1	2	5	6	10	6.18	3.66	101.8
2	3	4	2	14	9.08	6.18	143.7
3	2	6	5	13	6.51	3.65	111.6
4	1	7	8	9	10.78	3.08	94.6
5	1	8	7	11	10.96	3.09	101.7
6	1	9	7	13	11.41	3.09	110.2
7	1	10	4	14	23.30	6.18	152.6
8	1	11	6	14	17.20	4.43	141.3
9	3	7	11	13	5.39	3.08	94.6

arbitrary triclinic lattice followed by a reduction to a lattice of greater symmetry by the method of Delaunay.[10] This cannot, however, be recommended as general procedure, as will be discussed below after the application of the method has been described.

The method of Ito for indexing powder patterns can, in theory at least, be applied irrespective of the symmetry of the compound under investigation. Hence this method should provide a general technique for the interpretation of any powder photograph (cf. Sec. 4). As will be seen below, this method depends primarily upon the presence of all, or nearly all, the possible lines and permits no systematic absences. Furthermore, Ito himself implies that very precise data are required for the successful application of this method.

In broad outline, this method is based upon the fact that any lattice may be represented by an infinite number of unit cells and requires that selected low-angle lines be assumed to be the 100, 010, and 001 lines.

Using the concept and notation of reciprocal space as described in Chap. 26, the square of the reciprocal-lattice vector is given by Eq. (23)

$$Q_{hkl} = h^2a^{*2} + k^2b^{*2} + l^2c^{*2} + 2hka^*b^* \cos \gamma^* + 2hla^*c^* \cos \beta^* + 2klb^*c^* \cos \alpha^* \quad (23)$$

If Q_1, Q_2, and Q_3 are chosen arbitrarily to be Q_{100}, Q_{010}, and Q_{001}, respectively, they will define a lattice, provided that in reciprocal space they are noncoplanar and if they define a primitive cell. The tests for these properties are given below.

If Q_{100}, Q_{010}, and Q_{001} are assumed to be known, a^*, b^*, and c^* are likewise known. The problem then becomes that of assigning values to the angles in reciprocal space: α^*, β^*, and γ^*. This can, conceptually, be easily done by considering the lines $(h0l)$ and $(h0\bar{l})$:

$$Q_{h0l} = h^2a^{*2} + l^2c^{*2} + 2hla^*c^* \cos \beta^* \quad (24)$$

$$Q_{h0\bar{l}} = h^2a^{*2} + l^2c^{*2} - 2hla^*c^* \cos \beta^* \quad (25)$$

whence it is seen that the lines arising from these reciprocal-lattice points are symmetrically placed with respect to the value $h^2a^{*2} + l^2c^{*2}$; that is, their average value is given by Eq. (26):

$$Q'_{h0l} = (Q_{h0l} + Q_{h0\bar{l}})/2 = h^2a^{*2} + l^2c^{*2} \quad (26)$$

The search for lines which are located symmetrically with the real or imaginary lines Q' can be made either analytically or graphically.

In both methods, small values are assigned to h and l; if the graphical method is used, the Q_i values are plotted on a linear scale and the line Q'_{h0l} is drawn where the $h0l$ and $h0\bar{l}$ reflection would appear if the β^* angle were ignored [Eq. (26)]. When the symmetrical reflections are observed, β^* can be obtained from Eqs. (24) and (25) by subtraction to give Eq. (27).

$$\cos \beta^* = (Q_{h0l} - Q_{h0\bar{l}})/4hla^*c^* \quad (27)$$

If a real line occurs at Q'_{h0l}, then $Q_{h0l} - Q_{h0\bar{l}} = 0$ and $\beta^* = 90°$. If no pairs of reflections obeying Eq. (26) can be found with several different choices of h and l, a different set of lines must be chosen as Q_{100}, Q_{010}, and Q_{001} and the process repeated. Ito then suggests that after several sets of lines have been tried if attempts to fit lines are unsuccessful, then new initial guesses should be made for Q_{h00}, Q_{0k0}, and Q_{00l} for various values of h, k, and l.

If successful, this process must be repeated until all angles have been determined. Once all six parameters have been determined, indices can be assigned to all the observed lines and calculated values for the Q_i can be compared with those observed. If the fit is sufficiently good, the pattern is indexed properly.

However, the unit cell so determined may not be the most symmetrical to describe the lattice, and so it must be reduced. By far the easiest method for carrying out this reduction is by use of Ito's algorithm (p.189 of Ref. 4) based upon Delaunay's method.[10]

Since the application of this procedure is quite complex, a complete indexing will not be illustrated; rather, the salient points will be presented to outline the method. Using the data of Byström[11] as given in Table 10, Ito's procedure will be applied to PbF_2.

The first step is to designate arbitrarily lines 1, 2, and 3, respectively, as Q_{100}, Q_{010}, and Q_{001}. The list of Q_i (Table 10) is then searched for values which should index $h00$, $0k0$, or $00l$. Accordingly, it can be noted that

$$2^2Q_1 \approx Q_{11} \qquad 3^2Q_1 \approx Q_{33} \qquad 2^2Q_2 \approx Q_{16} \qquad \text{and} \qquad 2^2Q_3 \approx Q_{19}$$

Using this indexing and Eq. (23), values for the squares of the lengths of the reciprocal-lattice vectors can be obtained. In all cases, the higher-order reflections are used to improve precision. In this case the best values are

$$a^{*2} = 0.0686$$

$$b^{*2} = 0.0833$$

$$c^{*2} = 0.0929$$

Using Eq. (26), an attempt is now made to obtain the remaining three parameters α^*, β^*, γ^*. It is now possible to compute the value for $Q'_{011} = 0.0833 + 0.929$ so that $Q'_{011} = 0.1762$ and note (either analytically or graphically) that Q'_{011} is the mean value between Q_5 and Q_9, i.e.,

$$\frac{Q_5 + Q_9}{2} = \frac{0.1074 + 0.2450}{2} = 0.1762 = Q'_{011}$$

Table 10. Powder Data for PbF_2

n	Q_n	Initial indexing		Indexing of $(0kl)$ lines based upon Eq. (30)		Indexing of $(h0l)$ lines based upon lines 3, 35		Indexing of $(hk0)$ lines based upon lines 10, 27		Corrected values for $(hk0)$ lines
		(hkl)	Q_{calc}	(hkl)	Q_{calc}	(hkl)	Q_{calc}	(hkl)	Q_{calc}	
1	0.0685	100								
2	0836	010						$1\bar{1}0$	0832	0833
3	0934	001				$20\bar{1}$	0928			
4	0967					$\bar{2}02$	0970			
5	1074			$01\bar{1}$	1074					
6	1660					$30\bar{2}$	1655			
7	1804					$30\bar{3}$	2183			
8	2203							$2\bar{1}0$	2202	2205
9	2450			011	2450					
10	2644							$1\bar{2}0$	2643	2646
11	2747	200	2740							
12	2870			$02\bar{1}$	2881	$20\bar{3}$	2870			
13	2985					101, $30\bar{1}$	2987			
14	3011									
15	3177			$01\bar{2}$	3173					
16	3332	020	3344					$2\bar{2}0$	3326	3332
17	3575									
18	3614									
19	3717	002	3736			$40\bar{2}$	3712			
20	3875					404	3880			
21	4307			$02\bar{2}$	4295					
22	4380									
23	4561					$50\bar{4}$	4564			
24	4708									
25	4923					$50\bar{3}$	4924			
26	5195									
27	5394							120	5393	5390
28	5513									
29	5632			021	5637					
30	5913			012	5925					
31	6077					$50\bar{5}$	6063			
32	6125							130	6120	6125
33	6178	300	6165							
34	6360			031	6363					
35	6419					201	6418			
36	6514									
37	6621					$60\bar{4}$	6620			
38	6738					$60\bar{5}$	6746			

Analytically, this would have been observed as

$$Q_9 - Q'_{011} = Q'_{011} - Q_5 = 0.0688$$

Hence Eq. (27) may now be applied to determine α^*, with k and l each equal to 1:

$$\cos \alpha^* = \frac{Q_9 - Q_5}{4 \times 1 \times 1b^*c^*} = \frac{0.2450 - 0.1074}{4b^*c^*} \tag{28}$$

Hence

$$b^*c^* \cos \alpha^* = 0.0344 \tag{29}$$

Using this value, the Q values for the $(0kl)$ lines may be computed, using the previously determined values for b^{*2} and c^{*2}, from the equation

$$Q_{0kl} = k^2b^{*2} + l^2c^{*2} + 2klb^*c^* \cos \alpha^* \tag{30}$$

The results of this computation are given in columns 5 and 6 of Table 10.

To find β^*, Q'_{101} is next computed to be 0.1615 and a search for lines symmetrical with respect to this imaginary line is made. In this particular case, no such lines are found and higher-order Q' values must be tested. Accordingly,

$$Q'_{201} = 2^2a^{*2} + 1^2 \times c^{*2} = 0.3673$$

and a search of the table of Q_i is made to determine the existence of lines meeting the required specifications of symmetry. Three such pairs of lines can be found: $(Q_2 + Q_{36})/2 = 0.3675$, $(Q_3 + Q_{35})/2 = 0.3676$, and $(Q_{10} + Q_{24})/2 = 0.3676$, all of which are equal, within experimental error, to Q'_{201}. The problem of deciding which of these pairs of lines is to be labeled Q_{201} and $Q_{20\bar{1}}$ is resolved by computing, for each value of $a^* c^* \cos \beta^*$, the possible values for various Q_{h0l} to determine which value of β^* best fits the data. By means of such a calculation in the particular application, the value $a^* c^* \cos \beta^*$ is 0.06862, derived from lines 3 and 35 by means of Eq. (27).

In similar fashion, $a^*b^* \cos \gamma^*$ is determined to be 0.03437 from lines Q_{10} and Q_{27} when compared with Q'_{120} (it will be noted, however, that Q_{16} and Q_{24} are also symmetric to Q'_{120} but the former pair of lines gives better agreement with observation). The tentative indexing based upon lines 10 and 27 is shown in Table 10.

At this point, the following determinations have been made:

$$\begin{aligned} a^{*2} &= 0.0686 \\ b^{*2} &= 0.0833 \\ c^{*2} &= 0.0929 \\ b^*c^* \cos \alpha^* &= 0.0344 \\ a^*c^* \cos \beta^* &= 0.06862 \\ a^*b^* \cos \gamma^* &= 0.03437 \end{aligned}$$

All six of the parameters determined above were based upon only one or two observed lines, and so may be in error; hence these parameters could conceivably be improved by comparing the various Q_i computed from them to the observed Q_i and noting the value of $Q_{i(\text{obs})} - Q_{i(\text{calc})}$ for, let us say, the $hk0$ lines as a function of h, k, and $h \times k$. If this be done for the hkl lines, the differences between the calculated and observed values seem to increase with the product $h \times k$ rather than with either h or k alone. From Eq. (23), applied to the $hk0$ lines, as shown in Eq. (31),

$$Q_{hk0} = h^2a^{*2} + k^2b^{*2} + 2hka^*b^* \cos \gamma^* \tag{31}$$

it appears that a better fit would be obtained if the value of $\cos \gamma^*$ were altered slightly, the values of a^{*2} and b^{*2} seemingly being good as evidenced by the apparent independence of the error with respect to h or k separately. Hence, for all $hk0$ lines (columns 9 and 10 of Table 10) the value of $a^*b^* \cos \gamma^*$ which gives agreement with the observed lines is calculated and these results averaged. Using this value, the $hk0$ lines are once more computed and the fit to the observed lines studied. In this case, $a^*b^* \cos \gamma^* = 0.0343$ is obtained and the fit improved as shown in column 11 of Table 10. Similar treatment of the $(0kl)$ and $(h0l)$ reflections leads to small modifications of the other parameters so that the best fit appears to be given by the following constants:

$$
\begin{aligned}
a^{*2} &= 0.0686 \\
b^{*2} &= 0.0833 \\
c^{*2} &= 0.0928 \\
b^*c^* \cos \alpha^* &= 0.0343 \\
a^*c^* \cos \beta^* &= 0.0686 \\
a^*b^* \cos \gamma^* &= 0.0343
\end{aligned}
$$

Using these parameters, each line can be indexed on the basis of the triclinic lattice, as shown in Table 11. The very close approximation of the calculated lines to the observed lines is an indication of the validity of the indexing.

Many processes have been developed to determine the reduced cell from the arbitrary triclinic cell obtained by use of Ito's method of indexing powder patterns. The method recommended by Ito[12] is based upon a reduction process originally described by Delaunay[10] and given in detail by Ito (pp. 189ff. of Ref. 4). The basis of this method is that a unit cell should have sides as nearly equal as possible and obtuse

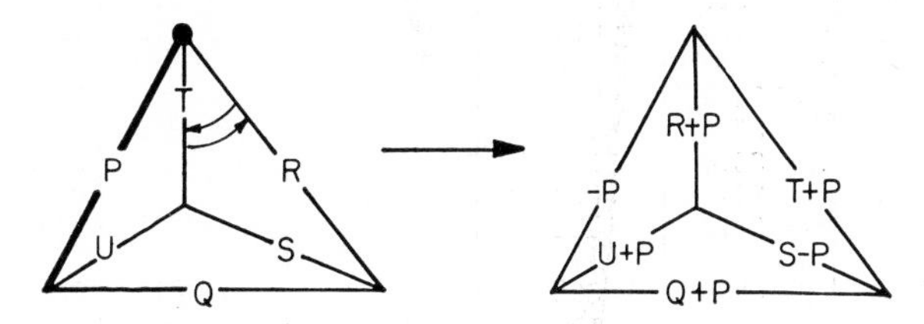

FIG. 2*a*. The Delaunay reduction.

angles least different from 90°.

Hence the parameters P_0, Q_0, R_0, S_0, T_0, and U_0 are computed according to Eqs. (32), in which d_0 is the length of the $(\overline{111})$ vector,

$$
\begin{aligned}
P_0 &= b^*c^* \cos \alpha^* & S_0 &= a^*d^* \cos \varphi_a^* \\
Q_0 &= c^*a^* \cos \beta^* & T_0 &= b^*d^* \cos \varphi_b^* \\
R_0 &= a^*b^* \cos \gamma^* & U_0 &= c^*d^* \cos \varphi_c^*
\end{aligned}
\tag{32}
$$

and φ_a^*, φ_b^*, and φ_c^* are the angles between this diagonal and the a_0^*, b_0^*, and c_0^* vectors, respectively. Geometrical considerations give S_0, T_0, and U_0 in terms of known parameters as given by Eqs. (33).

$$
\begin{aligned}
S_0 &= -(a_0^{*2} + Q_0 + R_0) \\
T_0 &= -(P_0 + b_0^{*2} + R_0) \\
U_0 &= -(P_0 + Q_0 + c_0^{*2})
\end{aligned}
\tag{33}
$$

According to the definition of Delaunay, a cell is said to be reduced when all six parameters P, Q, R, S, T, and U are nonpositive (i.e., zero or negative).

The transformation to the reduced Delaunay cell can most readily be accomplished by arranging the six quantities in a tetrahedral diagram and performing the transformation illustrated in Fig. 2*a*.

This transformation is accomplished by means of the following steps:

1. Start the transformation by marking with a thick line one of the positive edges of the tetrahedron (e.g., P); place a ball on one end of this thick line.

Table 11. Final Indexing of PbF_2

i	Q_{obs}	Q_{calc}	*hkl*			
			Triclinic			Orthorhombic
1	0.0685	0.0686	100			002
2	0836	0833	010	$1\bar{1}0$		101, $\bar{1}01$
3†	0934	0928	001	$20\bar{1}$†		012, $0\bar{1}2$
4	0967	0968	$\bar{2}02$			020
5*	1074	1075	$01\bar{1}$*	$11\bar{1}$	$\bar{1}11$, $\bar{2}11$	$1\bar{1}\bar{1}$, $1\bar{1}1$, $\bar{1}11$, $11\bar{1}$
6	1660	1654	$\bar{1}02$	$30\bar{2}$		$0\bar{2}2$, 022
7	1804	1801	$11\bar{2}$	$21\bar{2}$	$\bar{2}12$, $\bar{1}12$	$1\bar{2}\bar{1}$, $1\bar{2}1$, 121, $12\bar{1}$
8	2203	2205	110	$2\bar{1}0$		103, $\bar{1}03$
9*	2450	2447	011*	$1\bar{1}1$	$21\bar{1}$, $\bar{3}11$	$\bar{1}13$, $1\bar{1}3$, 113, $11\bar{3}$
10‡	2644	2646	$\bar{1}20$‡			200
11	2747	2744	200			004
12	2870	2864	$\bar{2}03$	$40\bar{3}$		032, $0\bar{3}2$
13	2985	2986	101	$30\bar{1}$		014, $0\bar{1}4$
14	3011	3011	$21\bar{3}$	$31\bar{3}$	$\bar{3}13$, $\bar{4}13$	$1\bar{3}\bar{1}$, $1\bar{3}1$, 131, $13\bar{1}$
15	3177	3173	$01\bar{2}$	$\bar{1}12$	$31\bar{2}$, $\bar{4}12$	$1\bar{2}\bar{3}$, 123, $1\bar{2}3$, $12\bar{3}$
16	3332	3332	020	$2\bar{2}0$		202, $\bar{2}02$
17	3575	3574	$12\bar{1}$	$1\bar{2}1$	$\bar{1}21$, $\bar{3}21$	$2\bar{1}2$, $\bar{2}12$, 212, $21\bar{2}$
18	3614	3614	$12\bar{2}$	$\bar{3}22$		$2\bar{2}0$, 220
19	3717	3712	002	$40\bar{2}$		024, $0\bar{2}4$
20	3873	3872	$\bar{4}04$			040
21	4307	4300	$02\bar{2}$	$22\bar{2}$	$\bar{2}22$, $\bar{4}22$	$2\bar{2}\bar{2}$, $2\bar{2}2$, 222, $22\bar{2}$
22	4380	4383	$11\bar{3}$	$\bar{2}13$	$41\bar{3}$, $\bar{5}13$	$1\bar{3}\bar{3}$, 133, $1\bar{3}3$, $13\bar{3}$
23	4561	4558	$\bar{3}04$	$50\bar{4}$		042, $0\bar{4}2$
24	4708	4705	$31\bar{4}$	$41\bar{4}$	$\bar{4}44$, $\bar{5}14$	$1\bar{4}\bar{1}$, $1\bar{4}1$, 141, $14\bar{1}$
25	4925	4922	103	503		034, $0\bar{3}4$
26	5195	5191	111	$2\bar{1}1$	$31\bar{1}$, $\bar{4}11$	115, $\bar{1}15$, $1\bar{1}5$, $11\bar{5}$
27‡	5394	5390	$3\bar{2}0$	120‡		$\bar{2}04$, 204
28	5513	5510	$12\bar{3}$	$\bar{3}23$	$\bar{5}23$, $32\bar{3}$	$2\bar{3}\bar{2}$, 232, $23\bar{2}$, $2\bar{3}2$
29	5632	5632	021	$22\bar{1}$	$2\bar{2}1$, $\bar{4}21$	214, $2\bar{1}4$, $\bar{2}14$, $21\bar{4}$
30	5913	5917	012	$1\bar{1}2$	$41\bar{2}$, $\bar{5}12$	125, $\bar{1}25$, $1\bar{2}5$, $12\bar{5}$
31	6077	6077	$21\bar{4}$	$\bar{3}14$	$51\bar{4}$, $\bar{6}14$	$1\bar{4}\bar{3}$, 143, $1\bar{4}3$, $14\bar{3}$
32	6125	6125	$\bar{1}30$	$2\bar{3}0$		301, $\bar{3}01$
33	6178	6174	300			006
34	6360	6358	$1\bar{2}2$	$\bar{1}22$	$32\bar{2}$, $\bar{5}22$	$\bar{2}24$, 224, $2\bar{2}4$, $22\bar{4}$
35†	6419	6416	$40\bar{1}$	201†		$0\bar{1}6$, 016
36	6514	6518	$32\bar{4}$	$\bar{5}24$		240, $2\bar{4}0$
37	6621	6616	$\bar{2}04$	$60\bar{4}$		044, $0\bar{4}4$
38	6738	6736	$\bar{4}05$	$60\bar{5}$		052, $0\bar{5}2$

The pairs of lines used for the determination of α^*, β^*, γ^* are marked *, †, ‡, respectively.

2. Subtract the original value of the starting edge P from the opposite edge (to give $S - P$).

3. Add the original value of the starting edge P to the other four edges of the tetrahedral diagram and interchange the values of the two edges which meet at the ball.

4. Change the sign on the value of the starting edge.

This process is repeated until all edges of the tetrahedron are negative or zero.

This process must lead to one of the 24 tetrahedral diagrams which are illustrated in Fig. 3 as originally shown by Delaunay.[10] In using this figure it must be noted that, because of experimental errors, numerical values in the tetrahedral diagram may be neither exactly zeros nor exactly equal to each other. Whether the relationships so obtained are real or merely fortuitous is difficult to ascertain. Refinement of the data to give more precise values of the lattice parameters, as described in Chap. 10, will help to resolve this particular ambiguity. Further, it must also be noted that equalities not required by the diagrams of Fig. 3 do not mean that a cell with more symmetry has been encountered, but rather that equalities have occurred beyond that required by symmetry. Note also that a Delaunay reduction step performed on a zero edge serves only to interchange the values of the two edges meeting at the transformation ball, so that a reduced tetrahedral diagram obtained which does not explicitly appear in Fig. 3 may be obtained by an additional final transformation applied to a zero side of the diagram. Further, it will be noted that the interchange of two pairs of edges which oppose each other is equivalent to rotation of the tetrahedron which may lead to one of the standard 24 diagrams. Although the symmetry of the reduced Delaunay cell is that of the Bravais lattice only for primitive cases, there is a unique correspondence between the Delaunay reduced cell and a Bravais cell, and this correspondence is explicitly delineated in the tabulation of Fig. 3; the magnitude and direction of the unit vectors for each of the 24 reduced tetrahedral diagrams are given in Table 12.

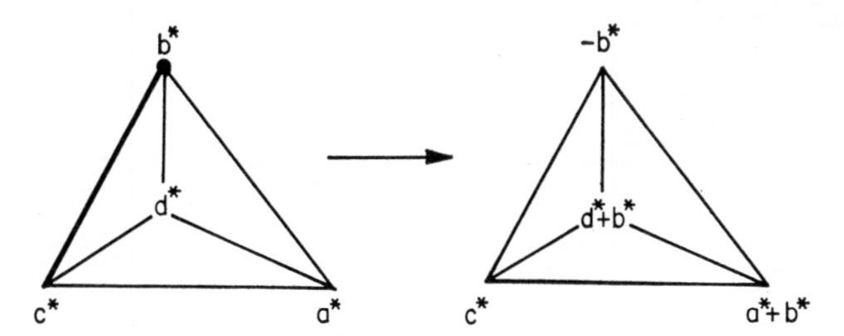

FIG. 2b. The transformation of the axes accompanying the Delaunay reduction.

In theory, this reduction can be applied to either the direct or the reciprocal lattice. Although Ito recommends its application in reciprocal space, current usage[13] calls for its application in direct space to avoid the possibility of ambiguity caused by the periodicity of the cosine function when transforming from reciprocal to direct space.

Accompanying each stage of the transformation is a corresponding transformation of axes as shown in Fig. 2b, in which d^* is defined by Eq. (34).

$$d^* = -(a^* + b^* + c^*) \tag{34}$$

The transformation of axes is accomplished, as shown in Fig. 2b, by means of the following steps:

1. Label a tetrahedral diagram with the symbols a^*, b^*, c^*, and d^* to correspond with the first tetrahedral diagram of Fig. 2a, and draw the corresponding thick line and ball.
2. Change the sign of the symbol at the ball (e.g., $b^* \rightarrow -b^*$).
3. Leave the value of the symbol at the other end of the heavy line unchanged.
4. Add the symbol originally at the ball to the other two symbols.

In the illustrative example, the following values apply:

$$P_0 = 0.0343 \qquad S_0 = -0.0343$$
$$Q_0 = 0.0686 \qquad T_0 = -0.1519$$
$$R_0 = 0.0343 \qquad U_0 = -0.1957$$

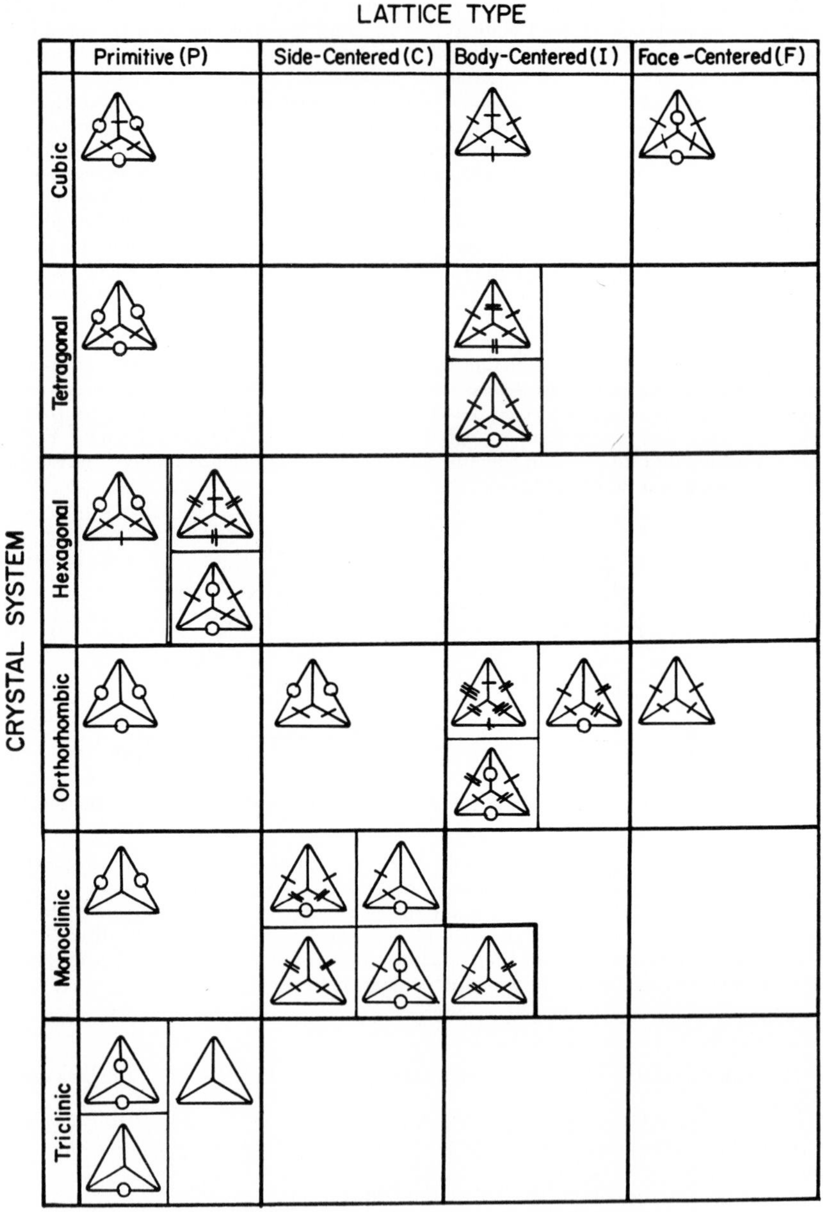

LATTICE TYPE

CRYSTAL SYSTEM

	Primitive (P)	Side-Centered (C)	Body-Centered (I)	Face-Centered (F)
Cubic				
Tetragonal				
Hexagonal				
Orthorhombic				
Monoclinic				
Triclinic				

Fig. 3. The 24 cases of Delaunay reduced tetrahedral diagrams.

Table 12. Transformation Equations* to Convert to Bravais Lattice from Reduced Delaunay Tetrahedral Diagrams of Fig. 3

	Primitive (*P*)	Side-centered (*C*)	Body-centered (*I*)	Face-centered (*F*)
Cubic	$a^2 = b^2 = c^2 = -S$ $\alpha = \beta = \gamma = 90°$		$a^2 = b^2 = c^2 = 4(-P)$ $\alpha = \beta = \gamma = 90°$	$a^2 = b^2 = c^2 = 4(-P)$ $\alpha = \beta = \gamma = 90°$
Tetragonal	$a^2 = b^2 = -S$ $c^2 = -U$ $\alpha = \beta = \gamma = 90°$		$a^2 = b^2 = 2(-R - P)$ $c^2 = 4(-P)$ $\alpha = \beta = \gamma = 90°$ $a^2 = b^2 = 2(-P)$ $c^2 = 4(-T - P)$ $\alpha = \beta = \gamma = 90°$	
Hexagonal	$a^2 = b^2 = 2(-P)$ $c^2 = -S$ $\alpha = \beta = 90°$ $\gamma = 120°$ $a^2 = -S - 2P$ $b = c = a$ $\alpha = \cos^{-1}[P/(-S - 2P)]$ $\beta = \gamma = \alpha$ $a^2 = -S - P$ $b = c = a$ $\alpha = \cos^{-1}[-S/(-S - P)]$ $\beta = \alpha = \gamma$			
Orthorhombic	$a^2 = -S$ $b^2 = -T$ $c^2 = -U$ $\alpha = \beta = \gamma = 90°$	$a^2 = 2(-T - 2P)$ $b^2 = -2T$ $c^2 = -S$ $\alpha = \beta = \gamma = 90°$	$a^2 = 2(-R - P)$ $b^2 = 2(-Q - R)$ $c^2 = 2(-P - Q)$ $\alpha = \beta = \gamma = 90°$ $a^2 = -2P$ $b^2 = -2Q$ $c^2 = -2P - 2Q$ $\alpha = \beta = \gamma = 90°$ $a^2 = -2R$ $b^2 = -2P$ $c^2 = 2(-R - 2T - P)$ $\alpha = \beta = \gamma = 90°$	$a^2 = 4(-Q - P)$ $b^2 = 4(-T - P)$ $c^2 = 4(-P)$ $\alpha = \beta = \gamma = 90°$

Table 12. Transformation Equations* to Convert to Bravais Lattice from Reduced Delaunay Tetrahedral Diagrams of Fig. 3 *(Continued)*

	Primitive (*P*)	Side-centered (*C*)	Body-centered (*I*)	Face-centered (*F*)
Monoclinic†	$a^2 = -Q - S$ $b^2 = -Q - U$ $c^2 = -T$ $\alpha = \beta = 90°$ $\gamma = \cos^{-1}(Q/ab)$	$a^2 = -2S - 2P$ $b^2 = -2P - T$ $c = a$ $\alpha = \beta = 90°$ $\gamma = \cos^{-1}(2P/ab)$		
		$a^2 = -4R - 4T - 2P$ $b^2 = -S - P$ $c^2 = -2P$ $\alpha = \beta = 90°$ $\gamma = \cos^{-1}(2R/ab)$		
		$a^2 = -2S - 2P$ $b^2 = -T - 2P$ $c^2 = -2S - 2P - 4Q$ $\alpha = \beta = 90°$ $\gamma = \cos^{-1}(2P/ab)$	$a^2 = -4Q - 2P - 2R$ $b^2 = -Q - T - 2R$ $c^2 = -2P - 2R$ $\alpha = \beta = 90°$ $\gamma = \cos^{-1}[2(Q + R)/ab]$	
		$a^2 = -4R - 2P$ $b^2 = -R - U$ $c^2 = -2P$ $\alpha = \beta = 90°$ $\gamma = \cos^{-1}(2R/ab)$		
Triclinic	$a^2 = -S - R$ $b^2 = -R - P$ $c^2 = -P - U$ $\alpha = \cos^{-1}(P/bc)$ $\beta = 90°$ $\gamma = \cos^{-1}(R/ab)$			
	$a^2 = -Q - S - R$ $b^2 = -R - T - P$ $c^2 = -P - U - Q$ $\alpha = \cos^{-1}(P/bc)$ $\beta = \cos^{-1}(Q/ca)$ $\gamma = \cos^{-1}(R/ab)$			
	$a^2 = -S - R$ $b^2 = -R - T - P$ $c^2 = -P - U$ $\alpha = \cos^{-1}(P/bc)$ $\beta = 90°$ $\gamma = \cos^{-1}(R/ab)$			

* Note that these equations apply equally well both to the direct lattice and to the reciprocal lattice.

† First setting (*c* unique) is used for monoclinic; second setting (*b* unique) can be obtained by interchanging names of *b* and *c*.

The Delaunay reductions of the parameters and of the axes are shown in Fig. 4*a* and *b*, respectively. [The last step in the transformation (Fig. 4*a*) is merely a rotation of the tetrahedral diagram.]

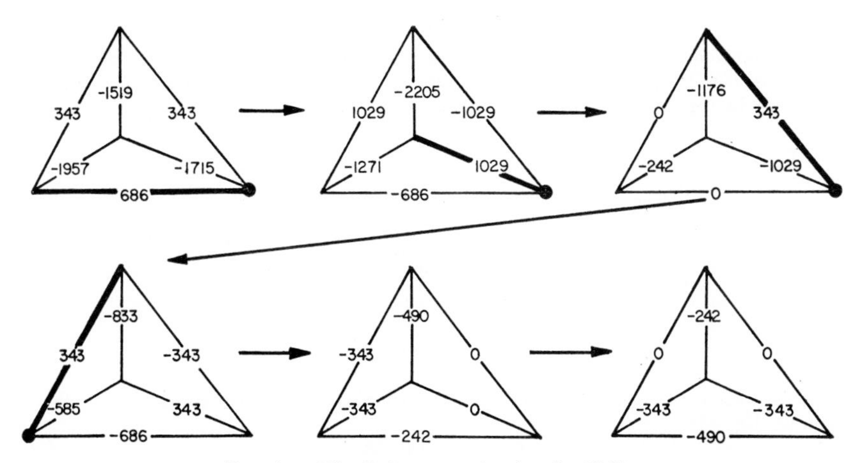

Fig. 4*a*. The Delaunay reduction for PbF_2.

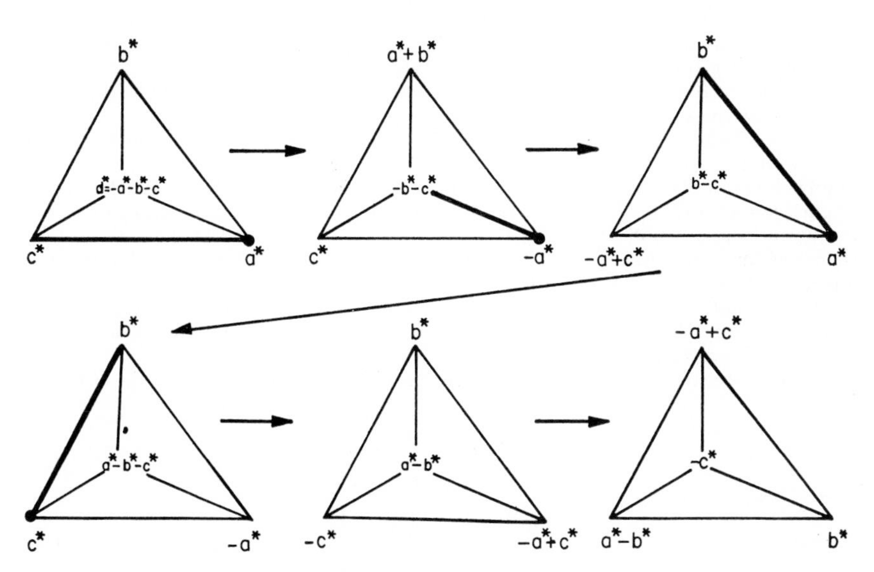

Fig. 4*b*. The transformation of the axes for PbF_2.

The reduced values of the cell parameters are therefore

$$P = 0 \qquad S = -0.343$$
$$Q = -0.0490 \qquad T = -0.0242$$
$$R = 0 \qquad U = -0.0343$$

which is indicative of a base-centered orthorhombic lattice (Fig. 3) with reciprocal-lattice parameters given by

$$\begin{aligned} a^* &= 0.2572 \\ b^* &= 0.1556 \\ c^* &= 0.1309 \\ \alpha^* &= \beta^* = \gamma^* = 90^\circ \end{aligned}$$

The reduction of the axes gives the transformation of the indices from those of the original arbitrary cell to those of the reduced cell. Accordingly, the transformation illustrated in Fig. 4b transforms the axes as follows:

$$\begin{aligned} a^{*\prime} &= b^* \\ b^{*\prime} &= -a^* + c^* \\ c^{*\prime} &= a^* - b^* \end{aligned}$$

in which the primed quantities apply to the reduced Delaunay cell and whence the matrix A for this transformation is given by Eq. (35).

$$A = \begin{pmatrix} 1 & 1 & 0 \\ 0 & \bar{1} & 0 \\ 0 & 0 & 1 \end{pmatrix} \tag{35}$$

Thus the new values for the indices based upon the reduced Delaunay cell would be given by Eq. (36)

$$(h'k'l') = (hkl)A^{-1} \tag{36}$$

for reciprocal space in which the primed quantities represent the new indices and the unprimed quantities the original indices. However, the extension of the transformation of the axes to the Bravais lattice remains incomplete. Each transformation from the reduced Delaunay cell to the Bravais cell should also have a unique transformation of the axes corresponding to it. Unfortunately, no unambiguous tabulation of the matrices for these transformations exists (see pp. 223ff. of Ref. 4). There are, however, two alternate possibilities for obtaining the indices of the observed lines with respect to the Bravais lattice, neither of which is entirely satisfactory. The first approach is to obtain the matrix of the transformation graphically (as Ito does in his original work); calling this matrix B, the matrix for the overall transformation C can be obtained by multiplication of B by A. That is, $C = BA$ so that the indices of the Q_i based upon the Bravais lattice are obtained by rear multiplication of the row matrix (hkl) by C^{-1} [cf. Eq. (36)].

The alternative is to reindex the lines by trial and error using parameters of the Bravais lattice. Computers can easily be programmed to do this computation, and several such programs are available for use.[14,15,16]

In the illustrative example, Ito chose the graphical transformation so the B matrix is given by

$$B = \begin{pmatrix} 1/2 & 0 & \overline{1/2} \\ 0 & 1 & 0 \\ 1/2 & 0 & 1/2 \end{pmatrix} \tag{37}$$

so that

$$C^{-1} = \left[\begin{pmatrix} 1/2 & 0 & \overline{1/2} \\ 0 & 1 & 0 \\ 1/2 & 0 & 1/2 \end{pmatrix} \begin{pmatrix} 0 & 1 & 0 \\ \bar{1} & 0 & 1 \\ 1 & \bar{1} & 0 \end{pmatrix} \right]^{-1} \tag{38}$$

and

$$(h''k''l'') = (hkl) \begin{pmatrix} 0 & 0 & 2 \\ 1 & 0 & \bar{1} \\ 0 & 1 & 2 \end{pmatrix} \tag{39}$$

with the final result being presented in Table 12 after redefinition of the axes to conform to convention.

It is unfortunate that this reduction is not completely and unambiguously described. Many papers[4,13,17,18,19] have appeared over the years since Delaunay first developed his reduction, but none definitely completes the work which Delaunay explicitly states is unfinished.[10] Many of the discussions have given alternate reduction methods, but there is no clear choice that can be recommended as being preferable to those remaining.

3. GRAPHICAL METHODS

Whether graphical or analytical methods are to be used in indexing powder patterns is a matter of personal preference about which there is no unanimity. Certainly, the circumstances under which the indexing is to be done will, in many cases, dictate the final decision. When only a few patterns are to be analyzed and no charts are readily available the patterns usually should be interpreted analytically, since the labor of preparing the charts would, in most cases, be greater than actually indexing the patterns. If, however, a great number of patterns are to be analyzed, it would seem advantageous to have the charts on hand. In many cases, large charts, suitable for laboratory use, are commercially available at nominal cost; a listing of such charts is given following this section.

Only uniaxial lattices are easily amenable to indexing by graphical methods, since lattices of lower symmetry require the simultaneous determination of three or more independent variables, thereby making a graphical solution exceedingly difficult. Only one system for the graphical indexing of low-symmetry lattices is extant,[20] and that is for orthorhombic crystals. The method is quite complex, so that it is deemed to be of little practical value and will not be covered here.

Naturally, in using any graphical method the charts must be sufficiently large to permit easy and relatively accurate readings to be made. Accordingly, any chart made should be larger than 16 in. in its smallest dimension. One inherent shortcoming of the graphical method is that any particular chart can accommodate only those patterns from crystals with cell parameters falling within a given range. This is particularly restrictive if low-order lines are missing. Hence charts must be made to accommodate the crystal sizes generally found in the application sought. In general usage, the vast majority of crystals have lattice parameters smaller than 15 Å, so that, certainly, this range must be covered.

If a pattern is complex, a graphical fit to all lines should not be attempted at once; rather only the low-order lines should be followed until a fit is obtained. Then the fit can be improved by use of the high-order lines.

Cubic Symmetry. Although not strictly graphical, a very simple and fast method using a slide rule may be employed to determine whether a given pattern is derived from a cubic lattice. The equation for a cubic pattern is given by

$$a^2 Q_{hkl} = M_{hkl} \tag{40}$$

If a constant a^2 can be found such that its products with successive Q values for all lines are integral, the constant is the square of the lattice parameter. Thus, if the first line seen on the pattern is assumed to be the (100) line, and Q_i is set on the D scale under the index of the C scale, the observed Q_i on the D scale is opposite the quotient Q_i/Q_{100} on the C scale. This ratio, Q_i/Q_{100}, must always be integral if the crystal is cubic; and if such is the case, the value of a^2 is found on the C scale opposite the index on the D scale. In the event that Q_{100} and other low-order lines are missing, the same test should be done on Q_j, $Q_j/2$, $Q_j/3$, and perhaps $Q_j/4$ for $j = 1, 2,$ and 3. This method is also used as part of a general computer code for all uniaxial patterns.[21]

In the event that charts* are used to obtain d values directly from the films, a different slide-rule scheme may be utilized taking advantage of the explicit $Q = 1/d^2$ relationship which exists between the A scale and the CI scale or the CIF scale. In this case, Eq. (40) may be rewritten in the form

$$a^2/d_{hkl}^2 = M_i \tag{41}$$

To apply the method, remove the slider from the slide rule and invert it; the CI scale is now beneath the A scale and, of course, opposite in sense. If the d_i values on

* Available from N. P. Nies, 969 Skyline Drive, Laguna Beach, Calif.

the CI scale are now moved until all the d_i are opposite integers on the A scale, the value for the lattice parameter a is found on the CI scale under the index of the A scale. That this is indeed the case becomes evident when it is seen that a constant (in reality a^2) is being divided successively by the measured d_i^2, and that the integers so obtained are the M values.

It must be emphasized that the "integers" obtained in these methods will in all probability not be integers, but rather will be integral plus or minus some small amount, say ± 0.05.

Although a truly graphical method is not necessary for the cubic system one will be presented both for the sake of completeness and also to serve as a foundation for the

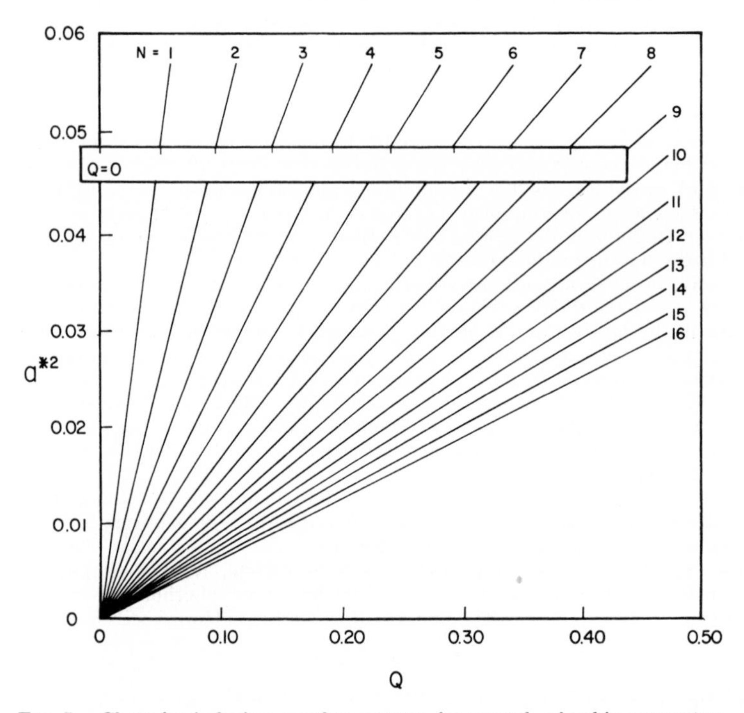

FIG. 5. Chart for indexing powder patterns for crystals of cubic symmetry.

principles involved in graphical indexing of patterns from crystals of lower symmetry. Equation (41) may be rewritten

$$1/a^2 = (1/M_i) \times Q_i \qquad (42)$$

which defines the family of curves giving $1/a^2$ as a function of Q_i with the parameter being M_i. In this case, the curves are straight lines with slope equal to $1/M_i$ and the $(1/a^2)$ intercept of zero, as shown in Fig. 5.

Then plotting the observed values of Q_i on a separate strip of paper to the same scale as the abscissa permits the determination of the lattice parameter, if the pattern arises from a cubic crystal, simply by sliding the paper strip containing the observed Q_i up the chart, keeping the index for $Q = 0$ always on the vertical axis.

This type of chart is very easily constructed since all lines are straight. As previously discussed, one of the limitations of the graphical approach is that the charts being used must be sufficiently large to permit detailed visual observation with sufficient resolution, and the unknown parameters must fall within the limits of the variables plotted on the chart. Most cubic crystals have lattice parameters having values between 3 and 12 Å, although lattice parameters in excess of these values are by no means uncommon. Accordingly, therefore, the values of the ordinate $1/a^2$ should be usable from 0.006 to 0.08. The values of Q_i must extend to numbers sufficiently large as to include most values of the observed Q_i (e.g., with copper radiation the maximum value for Q_i is 1.69). Naturally, in this graphical procedure, as in all others, the fit of the data to the graph should first be carried out using only a few of the low-order lines, and after a reasonable fit is obtained with these lines, attention can be focused on the remainder of the observed lines.

Hexagonal and Tetragonal Symmetry. Graphical interpretation of a cubic pattern is a one-dimensional problem; since hexagonal and tetragonal crystals require the specification of two parameters the problem becomes two-dimensional.

A method similar to that demonstrated for cubic crystals has been described by Bjurström.[22] The equations for tetragonal crystals as given in Eq. (43), and for hexagonal crystals in Eq. (44),

$$Q_{hkl\,(\text{tet})} = (h^2 + k^2)/a^2 + l^2/c^2 \tag{43}$$

$$Q_{hkl\,(\text{hex})} = \tfrac{4}{3}(h^2 + k^2 + hk)/a^2 + l^2/c^2 \tag{44}$$

can be rewritten as shown in Eqs. (45) and (46)

$$Q_{hkl\,(\text{tet})} = (h^2 + k^2 - l^2)/a^2 + l^2(1/a^2 + 1/c^2) \tag{45}$$

and

$$Q_{hkl\,(\text{hex})} = (4/3a^2)\,(h^2 + k^2 + hk - \tfrac{3}{4}l^2) + l^2(1/a^2 + 1/c^2) \tag{46}$$

or as Eqs. (47) and (48)

$$\frac{Q_{hkl\,(\text{tet})}}{1/a^2 + 1/c^2} = (h^2 + k^2 - l^2)\,\frac{1/a^2}{1/a^2 + 1/c^2} + l^2 \tag{47}$$

$$\frac{Q_{hkl\,(\text{hex})}}{1/a^2 + 1/c^2} = \tfrac{4}{3}(h^2 + k^2 + hk - \tfrac{3}{4}l^2)\,\frac{1/a^2}{1/a^2 + 1/c^2} + l^2 \tag{48}$$

both of which are equations of straight lines with the dependent variable being $Q_{hkl}/(1/a^2 + 1/c^2)$ and the independent variable being $(1/a^2)/(1/a^2 + 1/c^2)$. It is clear that the values of the independent variable can range only in the interval (0,1) while those of the dependent variable range in the interval $(l^2,\ h^2 + k^2)$ for tetragonal and $[l^2,\ \tfrac{4}{3}(h^2 + k^2 + hk)]$ for hexagonal. Simultaneously, the value for the ratio c/a has the range $(\infty,0)$, with intermediate values being easily calculated from the definition of the independent variable.

The chart may now be constructed by plotting, on arbitrary scales, the values of $h^2 + k^2$ (for tetragonal) for $c/a = \infty$ (independent variable = 1) and the values of l^2 for $c/a = 0$ (independent variable = 0). Each point on the left-hand ordinate is then connected to each point on the right-hand ordinate so as to obtain a plot of Eq. (47) for all values of h, k, and l as shown in Fig. 6. The horizontal scale connecting the two limiting values (0,1) for the linear independent variable $(1/a^2)/(1/a^2 + 1/c^2)$ can now be calibrated in terms of the more useful function c/a. Thus at

$$(1/a^2)/(1/a^2 + 1/c^2) = 0.1$$

$c/a = \tfrac{1}{3}$, etc.

Now the indexing can be completed by plotting the observed Q_i on a strip of paper and searching for a match. However, since it was chosen arbitrarily, the scale of a and of c is unknown so that the values of Q_i must be drawn on a scale with a continuously varying scale factor. This can easily be accomplished by plotting the observed Q_i values on a suitably expanded scale and joining each of the observed points with a straight line to a common point on the line representing $Q = 0$, shown in Fig. 7. If this "fan diagram" is drawn on tracing paper and superimposed upon the original Bjurström chart, a trial-and-error indexing of the pattern is accomplished when the observed pattern on the fan diagram intercepts the lines on the Bjurström chart on a

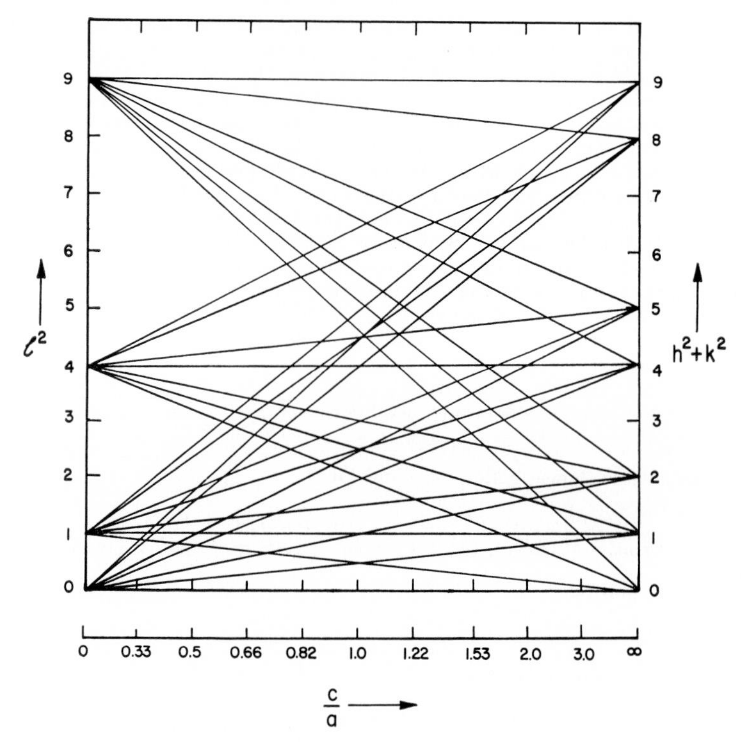

Fig. 6. Bjurström diagram for tetragonal symmetry.

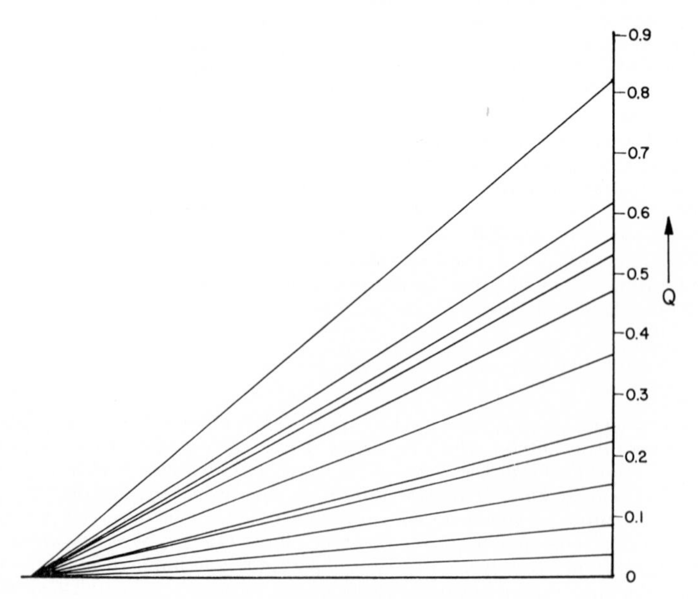

Fig. 7. Bjurström fan diagram.

vertical line, the position of this line determining the ratio c/a. More accuracy, however, can be obtained by using an $(hk0)$ line to determine the value of a and an $(00l)$ line for the determination of c, using, preferably, higher-order lines where possible. Naturally, the simultaneous solution of two equations arising from two lines (h_1,k_1,l_1) and (h_2,k_2,l_2) will also serve to determine the lattice parameters.

Unfortunately, the ease of construction of the Bjurström chart is offset by the difficulty of superimposing two sets of lines to obtain the fit. A mechanical aid in finding a solution by this method is described by Bjurström in his original paper,[22] but the practicability of its use is thought to be so limited as to preclude further discussion here.

This difficulty can be overcome by preparing a logarithmic form of the Bjurström chart by plotting log $(h^2 + k^2)$ on one vertical axis and log l^2 on the other.

The values at intermediate points can be read from the linear Bjurström chart (Fig. 6) for values of $(1/a^2)/(1/a^2 + 1/c^2) = 0.1, 0.2, \ldots, 1.0$, and their logarithms plotted on the new chart. This semilogarithmic chart no longer requires the fan diagram since the absolute value of a (or c) is determined by an additive (logarithmic) constant and the ratio c/a is determined by the location, on the abscissa, of the fit. To use such a chart, the values of the observed Q_i are plotted on a strip of paper using the same logarithmic scale as used for the ordinate, neglecting of course the position of the decimal. The indexing is then accomplished by moving the strip in both dimensions, keeping it at all times perpendicular to the abscissa. When a match of all the observed lines is obtained, the indexing is complete. This chart is essentially a modification of the Hull-Davey chart, the first graphical aid for indexing tetragonal or hexagonal patterns.[23] The original Hull-Davey charts unfortunately require the expenditure of a fair amount of effort to calculate the positions of the various lines, and suffer from the convergence of all lines as the Q_i increase in value; the semilogarithmic Bjurström charts suffer similarly in that the absolute values of the slopes of the $(hk0)$ and $(00l)$ lines increase without bound so that some lines become very steep and crowd together at large and small values of c/a.

These difficulties may be obviated by using the log-log plot of the $(h^2 + k^2)$ and (l^2) vs. c/a as described by Bunn,[24] although somewhat more labor is required in the preparation than for the semilogarithmic charts previously described (see Fig. 8). Large (2 by 4 ft) Bunn charts are commercially available* at modest cost for $0.224 < c/a < 5$ for tetragonal and for $0.1 < c/a < 10$ for hexagonal symmetry. Since the tetragonal systems with $c/a = 1$ become cubic, the same charts at this ratio can be used for indexing isometric patterns.

The methods described above in detail for tetragonal symmetry can also be used for hexagonal by replacing the $h^2 + k^2$ of the tetragonal charts with $h^2 + k^2 + hk$.

Although similar charts can be prepared for rhombohedral symmetry, the hexagonal charts can be used to index these patterns and the transformation to rhombohedral indexing can be made easily, if desired. A rhombohedral crystal referred to hexagonal axes can be easily recognized because for this symmetry all lines obey the criterion of Eq. (49)

$$h + k + l = 3n \qquad n = 0, 1, 2, 3, \ldots \tag{49}$$

The transformation equations are

$$h_R = \tfrac{1}{3}(h_H + 2k_H + l_H) \tag{50}$$
$$k_R = \tfrac{1}{3}(-2h_H - k_H + l_H) \tag{51}$$
$$l_R = \tfrac{1}{3}(h_H - k_H + l_H) \tag{52}$$

NOTE: Harrington charts[25] for uniaxial and orthorhombic crystals are available at no charge from Battelle Memorial Institute, Columbus, Ohio. The charts are in the form of a report entitled Battelle Indexing Charts for Diffraction Patterns of Tetragonal, Hexagonal and Orthorhombic Crystals by J. C. Bell and A. E. Austin.
Box 620, Brooklyn, N.Y., 11202.

* Polycrystal Book Service, GPO, Box 620, Brooklyn, N.Y. 11202.

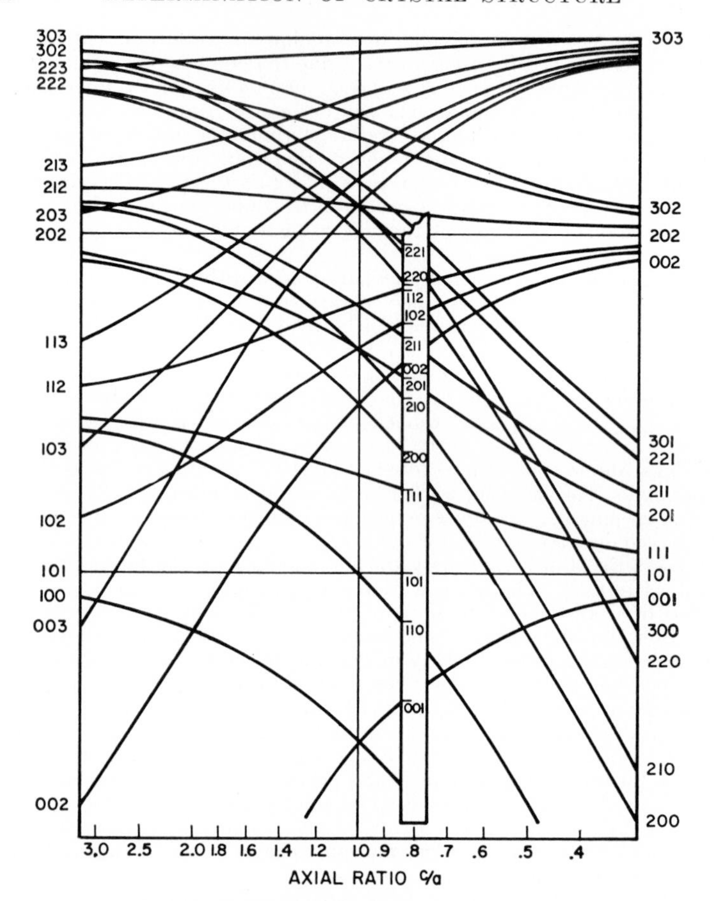

FIG. 8. Bunn chart for tetragonal symmetry.

4. COMPUTER METHODS

Many of the analytical methods described in the preceding sections can, in theory, be programmed for use on electronic computers. However, the complexity of the methods of general applicability, and the large number of subjective judgments which often must be made to index a pattern completely, have thus far discouraged widespread application of this technique to the problem under discussion.

The two general repositories for computer codes, the IBM KWIC listing and SHARE users group, show no listings of checked-out codes for indexing of powder patterns. Both the Commission on Crystallographic Computing of the International Union of Crystallography and the American Crystallographic Association have published lists of programs for the solution of various crystallographic problems. However, at the time of publication of this handbook, no listings were included for application to the indexing of powder patterns.

The most powerful method extant is that of Ito,[4] for with its use, patterns can be indexed regardless of symmetry considerations (see Triclinic Symmetry in Sec. 2). A series of programs to accomplish indexing of powder patterns using the method of Ito has been reported.[26] Subsequent to machine indexing on the basis of an arbitrary triclinic cell, other programs are presented to reduce the triclinic cell to one of higher symmetry using the method of Niggli[27] as listed in Azároff and Buerger (Chaps. 10 and 11 of Ref. 19) and converted to the proper Bravais lattice.

The series of programs continues with a test of the reliability of the unit cell so determined since success in computing a unit cell does not ensure its correctness. The test of reliability used in these programs is a computer version of that introduced by deWolff,[28] and its use should yield some quantitative measure of reliability.

The time required for the calculation is difficult to estimate, but the examples presented required in the range of hours of IBM 1620 time. Presumably, these programs would therefore require minutes in higher-speed machines.

Two other programs for Ito's method have been reported. That of Leidl[29] carries out only the actual indexing, while that of Larsen and McMasters,[30] when complete, will index and carry out the Delaunay reduction and convert to the Bravais lattice.

One of the earliest methods which exploits the ready availability of digital computers has been reported by Tannenbaum, Lemke, and Kramer.[31] This numerical method, of less general applicability, is based upon the analytical treatment by Hesse[32] and is applicable only to uniaxial crystals which give reflections such that

$$Q = AM + l^2/c^2 \tag{53}$$

where $M = h^2 + k^2$, $A = 1/a^2$ for the tetragonal case, and $M = h^2 + k^2 + hk$, $A = 4/3a^2$ for the hexagonal case.

To index a pattern the program computes from the observed Q_i the values of $2Q_i$, $3Q_i$ and all cross sums of the type $Q_i + Q_k$ and $2Q_i + Q_k$ where the i and k range over all the observed lines. The sums are tabulated and each entry in the table of sums is compared with all other entries to obtain all equations of the type

$$\Sigma g_j \sin^2 \theta_j = 0 \pm \epsilon \tag{54}$$

In Eq. (54) the summation is taken over four terms, the g_j have the possible values 0, ± 1, ± 2, ± 3, and ϵ is a previously assigned limit of error.

Since M, l, A, and c are all positive, Eq. (54) implies that the sum of the products of the g_j by the M_j must equal zero and that the sum of the products of the g_j by the l_j^2 must equal zero. These are the working equations.

The trial-and-error solution to these equations is obtained by utilizing a starting combination of permissible M or l numbers in the equation containing the smallest number of variables. The numbers obtained from this starting combination are then substituted into the remaining equations in order of increasing numbers of unknowns. Each value obtained is checked against the list of permitted values for the crystal system under consideration. When a set of numbers is obtained which is internally consistent, the pattern is considered solved.

If a solution is obtained, the highest values of θ for which M_i and l_i were obtained are substituted in Eq. (53), and A and c are obtained by simultaneous solution.

The values of M and l are obtained for the θ_i's which did not appear in the working equations by means of the newly determined approximate values for A and c and Eq. (55).

$$\sin^2 \theta_i = AM_i + l_i^2/c^2 \pm \epsilon \tag{55}$$

The lattice parameters are then computed from the three most reliable high-angle lines by the method of Cohen.[33,34]

This program runs for less than 1 min on an IBM 7094 computer, so that the cost either of indexing a pattern or of determining that it is not uniaxial is minimal when compared with the cost and labor of manual computation. However, the data must have high precision: a practically attainable precision in the Q_i of ± 0.0007 will generally be satisfactory.

With the advent of the widespread distribution and availability of computers, it is anticipated that more codes for powder applications will be reported. The ease of use of such programs will depend upon their being listed at central repositories so that they become accessible.

It must not be inferred that any machine calculation automatically permits determination of unit cells. All such calculations are, of course, subject to the limitations inherent in the method which was programmed and in the precision of the data. Hence many trial runs may often be necessary before successful machine indexing can be accomplished.

ACKNOWLEDGMENT

The author wishes to acknowledge the helpful discussions with Dr. Horace A. Ory of Heliodyne Corporation and Dr. William L. Korst of Atomics International during the preparation of this work and also wishes to thank Gordon Johnson, who did the artwork. He wishes to acknowledge also the cooperation of the secretarial staff of Heliodyne Corporation.

REFERENCES CITED

1. *X-ray Powder Data File*, American Society for Testing Materials, 1916 Race St., Philadelphia 3, Pa.
2. *Fink Inorganic Index to the Powder Diffraction File, ASTM Spec. Tech. Pub.* 48-M3, 1963.
3. H. Lipson, *Acta Cryst.*, **2**:43 (1949).
4. T. Ito, *X-ray Studies on Polymorphism*, Maruzen, Tokyo, 1950.
5. V. Vand, *Acta Cryst.*, **1**:109, 290 (1948).
6. H. E. Swanson and E. Tatge, *Standard X-ray Diffraction Powder Patterns*, vol. 1, *Natl. Bur. Std. (U.S.) Circ.* 539, p. 13, 1953.
7. N. F. M. Henry, H. Lipson, and W. A. Wooster, *The Interpretation of X-ray Diffraction Photographs*, p. 181, The Macmillan Company, New York, 1960.
8. H. E. Swanson, R. K. Fuyat, and G. M. Ugrinic, *Standard X-ray Diffraction Powder Patterns*, vol. 3, *Natl. Bur. Std. (U.S.) Circ.* 539, p. 12, 1954.
9. W. H. Zachariasen, *Acta Cryst.*, **16**:784 (1963).
10. B. Delaunay, *Z. Krist.*, **84**:132 (1933).
11. A. Byström, *Arch. Kemi. Min. Geol.*, **5**:33 (1947).
12. T. Ito, *Nature*, **164**:755 (1949).
13. *International Tables for X-ray Crystallography*, vol. 1, pp. 530ff., Kynoch Press, Birmingham, 1952.
14. I. R. Tannenbaum and W. A. Young, North American Aviation, Inc., Atomics International Division, *Rept.* TDR 5356, 1960.
15. Y. Iitaka, Code no. 8524, IUCr World List of Crystallographic Computer Programs, International Union of Crystallography, Commission on Crystallographic Computing, September, 1962.
16. G. M. Wolten, Code no. 49, IUCr World List of Crystallographic Computer Programs, International Union of Crystallography, Commission on Crystallographic Computing, September, 1962.
17. A. L. Patterson and W. E. Love, *Acta Cryst.*, **10**:111 (1957).
18. M. J. Buerger, *Z. Krist.*, **109**:42 (1957).
19. L. Azároff and M. J. Buerger, *The Powder Method in X-ray Crystallography*, chap. 12, McGraw-Hill Book Company, New York, 1958.
20. C. W. Jacob and B. E. Warren, *J. Am. Chem. Soc.*, **59**:2588 (1937).
21. I. R. Tannenbaum, B. J. Lemke, and D. Kramer, North American Aviation *Rept.* NAA-SR-4710, 1959.
22. T. Bjurström, *Z. Physik*, **69**:346 (1931).
23. A. W. Hull and W. P. Davey, *Phys. Rev.*, **17**:549 (1921).
24. C. W. Bunn, *Chemical Crystallography*, 2d ed., pp. 143ff., Oxford University Press, Fair Lawn, N.J., 1961.
25. R. A. Harrington, *Rev. Sci. Instr.*, **9**:429 (1938).
26. H. M. Haendler and W. A. Cooney, *Acta Cryst.*, **16**:1243 (1963).
27. A. Niggli, *Schweiz. Mineral. Petrog. Mitt.*, **33**:21 (1953).
28. P. M. deWolff, *Acta Cryst.*, **14**:579 (1961).
29. G. L. Leidl, *First Annual Report of Ford Foundation Project on Use of Computers in Engineering and Education*, p. E284, University of Michigan, College of Engineering, 1960.
30. W. L. Larsen and O. D. McMasters, in IS-700, Iowa State University, Annual Summary Report, 1963.
31. I. R. Tannenbaum, B. J. Lemke, and D. Kramer, *Acta Cryst.*, **14**:1287 (1961).
32. R. Hesse, *Acta Cryst.*, **1**:200 (1948).
33. M. V. Cohen, *Rev. Sci. Instr.*, **6**:68 (1935).
34. M. V. Cohen, *Rev. Sci. Instr.*, **7**:155 (1936).

Chapter 29

X-RAY METHODS OF DETERMINING CRYSTAL STRUCTURES

Sri Raman and J. Lawrence Katz

Rensselaer Polytechnic Institute

1. INTRODUCTION

In this chapter, some methods of determining crystal structures from x-ray intensity data will be described. In brief the various steps involved in a crystal-structure analysis might be described as follows: the preliminary determination of the size and space-group symmetry of the unit cell of the crystal, the collection of accurate intensity data, the circumvention of the inherent phase problem and the derivation of the structure therefrom, the refinement of the various independent parameters of the structure, calculation of various functions of the parameters and their standard errors, and a realistic assessment and a reliable interpretation of the results that have been obtained. Our aim, in this chapter, has been only to outline the general principles involved. Detailed discussions may be found in standard textbooks and published papers.

This chapter presupposes that a suitable unit cell has been chosen for the crystal under study, that the various Bragg spectra have been indexed, and that their intensities have been estimated. We shall attempt to describe the subsequent steps involved, laying more emphasis on the principles of the methods of resolving the inherent phase problem than on the other steps listed above.

2. DETERMINATION OF NUMBER OF MOLECULES PER UNIT CELL

The density of a crystal can be determined by the density equation

$$\rho = \text{mass/volume} = NM/V \tag{1}$$

where M is the mass of the atomic ensemble constituting one unit of the chemical formula, N is the number of such chemical units in one unit cell of the crystal, and V is the volume of the crystalline unit cell as determined by x-ray diffraction methods.

Dimensionally, density is generally expressed in grams per cubic centimeter. To convert Eq. (1) to the proper units the following constants are introduced: (1) the mass M, usually expressed in atomic-weight units (AWU), is divided by Avogadro's number, 6.023×10^{23} molecules/mole; (2) the unit-cell volume V, expressed in Å^3, is multiplied by 10^{-24} cm^3/Å^3. After appropriate algebraic manipulations the density equation (1) can be rewritten as

$$\rho\ (\text{g/cm}^3) = \frac{(1.660) \times NM\ (\text{AWU})}{V(\text{Å}^3)} \tag{2}$$

In general the unknown in Eq. (2) is N; the density can be measured experimentally by some method such as flotation; the unit-cell volume is determined directly from x-ray measurements, and M is specified if the chemical composition of the crystal in question corresponds to an ideal chemical formula. Thus N can be determined explicitly from the following equation:

$$N = \frac{\rho\ (\text{g/cm}^3) \times V\ (\text{Å})}{1.660\ M\ (\text{AWU})} \tag{3}$$

Consider the following example: Crystal, N-methylacetamide;[1] chemical formula, $CH_3CONHCH_3$; system orthorhombic; space group, *Pnma*; unit cell, $a = 9.61$ Å, $b = 6.52$ Å, $c = 7.24$ Å; density (flotation), $\rho = 1.02$ g/cm³.

$$\begin{aligned}
V &= (9.61\ \text{Å}) \times (6.52\ \text{Å}) \times (7.24\ \text{Å}) = 453.64\ \text{Å}^3 \\
M &= 7(1.008) + 3(12.011) + 1(14.007) + 1(15.999) \\
M &= 73.095\ \text{AWU} \\
N &= \frac{(1.02) \times (453.64)}{(1.660) \times (73.095)} = 3.81
\end{aligned}$$

The nearest integer, in this case 4, is taken; i.e., there are four molecules of N-methylacetamide in the unit cell. It would be purely fortuitous if such a combination of experimental values led to an integer value of N. If the computed value of N is ambiguous, this may mean that the unit cell has been improperly chosen or the chemical composition has been assigned incorrectly. In the above example, if a value of 4 is substituted for N in Eq. (2), an "x-ray density" $\rho = 1.07$ g/cm³ in good agreement with $\rho = 1.02$ g/cm³ is obtained.

3. DETERMINATION OF SPACE GROUP

In beginning a crystal-structure analysis the knowledge of both unit-cell dimensions and space group is of prime importance. The determination of the shape and size of the unit cell and the assignment of indices to the x-ray reflections have been discussed in Chaps. 26 to 28; space-group theory has been covered in Chap. 4. The following discussion is concerned primarily with the determination of space group by analyzing single-crystal x-ray diffraction data for the systematic absences of certain classes of reflections.

Systematic absences may be defined as a systematic series of reciprocal-lattice points all having diffraction intensities identically zero in magnitude. These reflections with zero intensities are the result of destructive interference between waves scattered into the same angle from planes separated by a path difference $\lambda/2$. Such path differences occur systematically only when symmetry operations involving translation are present. Thus centerings (nonprimitive Bravais lattices), glide planes, and screw axes will give rise to systematic absences, whereas mirror planes, rotation axes, and rotary inversion axes do not. The latter results mean that it is difficult at times to obtain a unique space-group determination based only on x-ray data. In these cases additional information about the crystal such as morphology and physical properties should be investigated.

A summary of the conditions for nonextinction for various classes of reflections and the resulting interpretation in terms of symmetry operations is tabulated along with the appropriate symbols in Table 1. These conditions can be obtained analytically by considering the equation for the amplitude and phase of the radiation (for the order hkl) scattered by the contents of one unit cell. This equation is generally called the *structure-factor equation*.

The Structure Factor. Consider a unit cell containing N atoms, located at positions x_j, y_j, z_j, where $j = 1, 2, \ldots, N$. In order to conform to the usual notation, the positional parameters will be described as fractional coordinates of the unit-cell dimensions. Thus the jth atom in the unit cell is located at

$$\mathbf{r}_j = x_j\mathbf{a} + y_j\mathbf{b} + z_j\mathbf{c} \tag{4}$$

Table 1. Symmetry Interpretations of Extinctions*

Class of reflection	Condition for nonextinction (n = an integer)	Interpretation of extinction	Symbol of symmetry element
hkl	$h + k + l = 2n$	Body-centered lattice	I
	$h + k = 2n$	C-centered lattice	C
	$h + l = 2n$	B-centered lattice	B
	$k + l = 2n$	A-centered lattice	A
	$\left\{\begin{matrix} h + k = 2n \\ h + l = 2n \\ k + l = 2n \end{matrix}\right\}$ $\rightleftharpoons h, k, l$, all even or all odd	Face-centered lattice	F
	$-h + k + l = 3n$	Rhombohedral lattice indexed on hexagonal reference system	R
	$h + k + l = 3n$	Hexagonal lattice indexed on rhombohedral reference system	H
$0kl$	$k = 2n$	(100) glide plane, component $b/2$	$b(P,B,C)$
	$l = 2n$	(100) glide plane, component $c/2$	$c(P,C,I)$
	$k + l = 2n$	(100) glide plane, component $b/2 + c/2$	$n(P)$
	$k + l = 4n$	(100) glide plane, component $b/4 + c/4$	$d(F)$
$h0l$	$h = 2n$	(010) glide plane, component $a/2$	$a(P,A,I)$
	$l = 2n$	(010) glide plane, component $c/2$	$c(P,A,C)$
	$h + l = 2n$	(010) glide plane, component $a/2 + c/2$	$n(P)$
	$h + l = 4n$	(010) glide plane, component $a/4 + c/4$	$d(F)$, (B)
$hk0$	$h = 2n$	(001) glide plane, component $a/2$	$a(P,B,I)$
	$k = 2n$	(001) glide plane, component $b/2$	$b(P,A,B)$
	$h + k = 2n$	(001) glide plane, component $a/2 + b/2$	$n(P)$
	$h + k = 4n$	(001) glide plane, component $a/4 + b/4$	$d(F)$
hhl	$l = 2n$	(110) glide plane, component $c/2$	$c(P,C,F)$
	$h = 2n$	(110) glide plane, component $a/2 + b/c$	$b(C)$
	$h + l = 2n$	(110) glide plane, component $a/4 + b/4 + c/4$	$n(C)$
	$2h + l = 4n$	(110) glide plane, component $a/2 + b/4 + c/4$	$d(I)$
$h00$	$h = 2n$	[100] screw axis, component $a/2$	2_1, 4_2
	$h = 4n$	[100] screw axis, component $a/4$	4_1, 4_3
$0k0$	$k = 2n$	[010] screw axis, component $b/2$	2_1, 4_2
	$k = 4n$	[010] screw axis, component $b/4$	4_1, 4_3
$00l$	$l = 2n$	[001] screw axis, component $c/2$	2_1, 4_2, 6_3
	$l = 3n$	[001] screw axis, component $c/3$	3_1, 3_2, 6_2, 6_4
	$l = 4n$	[001] screw axis, component $c/4$	4_1, 4_3
	$l = 6n$	[001] screw axis, component $c/6$	6_1, 6_5
$hh0$	$h = 2n$	[110] screw axis, component $a/2 + b/2$	2_1

* Table adapted from M. J. Buerger, *X-ray Crystallography*, John Wiley & Sons, Inc., New York, 1942.

as shown in Fig. 1. The difference in path between the waves scattered in the order hkl by the jth atom and one at the origin is given by

$$\lambda(\mathbf{r}_j \cdot \mathbf{d}^*_{hkl}) \tag{5}$$

where

$$\mathbf{d}^*_{hkl} = h\mathbf{a}^* + k\mathbf{b}^* + l\mathbf{c}^*$$

represents the vector in reciprocal space from the origin to the reciprocal-lattice point *hkl*. Because of the reciprocal relationship between the unit-cell vectors **a**, **b**, **c** and the reciprocal-lattice vectors **a***, **b***, **c***, it can be shown that

$$\lambda(\mathbf{d}^*_{hkl} \cdot \mathbf{r}_j) = \lambda(hx_j + ky_j + lz_j) \tag{6}$$

The phase angle $\alpha_j(hkl)$ is obtained by multiplying Eq. (6) by $2\pi/\lambda$, i.e.,

$$\alpha_j(hkl) = 2\pi(hx_j + ky_j + lz_j) \tag{7}$$

The wave scattered by the unit cell is obtained by superposition of the wavelets scattered in the same order by the individual atoms, i.e.,

$$F(hkl) = f_1 \exp i\alpha_1(hkl) + f_2 \exp i\alpha_2(hkl) + \cdots + f_N \exp i\alpha_n(hkl) \tag{8}$$

$$F(hkl) = \sum_{j=1}^{N} f_j(hkl) \exp 2\pi i(hx_j + ky_j + lz_j) \tag{9}$$

where $f_j(hkl)$ represents the scattering factor of the jth atom for the order *hkl*. Numerical values of scattering factors for various atoms are readily available; a rather comprehensive tabulation may be found in vol. 3 of the *International Tables for X-ray Crystallography*.[2]

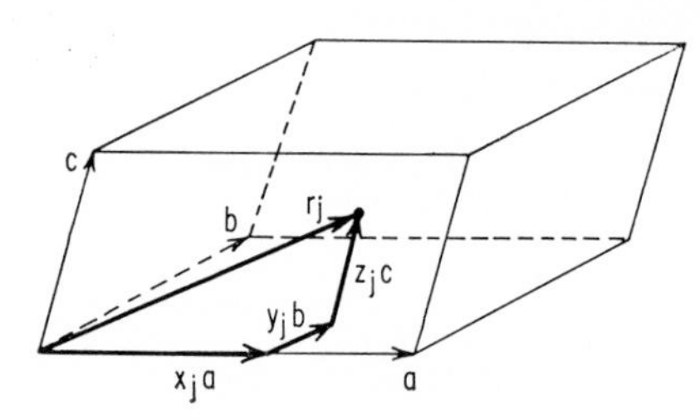

FIG. 1. The location of the jth atom at position $\mathbf{r}_j$ in a unit cell of a crystal belonging to the triclinic system.

Equation (9) is the structure-factor equation. $F(hkl)$, called the *structure factor*, is generally a complex quantity, involving the magnitude $|F(hkl)|$ and phase angle $\alpha(hkl)$:

$$F(hkl) = |F(hkl)| \exp i\alpha(hkl) = A(hkl) + iB(hkl) \tag{10}$$

where

$$A(hkl) = \sum_{j=1}^{N} f_j(hkl) \cos 2\pi(hx_j + ky_j + lz_j) \tag{11}$$

and

$$B(hkl) = \sum_{j=1}^{N} f_j(hkl) \sin 2\pi(hx_j + ky_j + lz_j) \tag{12}$$

The modulus of the structure factor $|F(hkl)|$ is called the structure amplitude and is given by

$$|F(hkl)|^2 = A^2(hkl) + B^2(hkl) \tag{13}$$

The phase $\alpha(hkl)$ is given by

$$\alpha(hkl) = \tan^{-1} [B(hkl)/A(hkl)] \tag{14}$$

Both the scattering power of an atom and the structure factor are expressed in terms of the scattering by a single Thomson electron.

Space-group Absences. Consider now a face-centered Bravais lattice. For each atom at a point x, y, z there are three others at $\frac{1}{2} + x, \frac{1}{2} + y, z$; $\frac{1}{2} + x, y, \frac{1}{2} + z$; $x, \frac{1}{2} + y, \frac{1}{2} + z$. The value of the structure factor will be given by

$$\begin{aligned} F(hkl) &= \sum_{j=1}^{N/4} f_j(hkl)\{\exp 2\pi i[h(\tfrac{1}{2} + x_j) + k(\tfrac{1}{2} + y_j) + lz_j] \\ &\quad + \exp 2\pi i[h(\tfrac{1}{2} + x_j) + ky_j + l(\tfrac{1}{2} + z_j)] + \exp 2\pi i[hx_j + k(\tfrac{1}{2} + y_j) \\ &\quad + l(\tfrac{1}{2} + z_j)] + \exp 2\pi i(hx_j + ky_j + lz_j)\} \\ &= \sum_{j=1}^{N/4} f_j(hkl)\left[\exp 2\pi i(hx_j + ky_j + lz_j)\left(1 + \exp 2\pi i\frac{h+k}{2}\right.\right. \\ &\quad \left.\left. + \exp 2\pi i\frac{h+l}{2} + \exp 2\pi i\frac{k+l}{2}\right)\right] \\ &= \sum_{j=1}^{N/4} f_j(hkl) \exp 2\pi i(hx_j + ky_j + lz_j) \\ &\qquad [1 + (-1)^{h+k} + (-1)^{h+l} + (-1)^{k+l}] \end{aligned} \tag{15}$$

Equation (15) will be nonzero only if h, k, and l have like parity, i.e., the Miller indices are either all odd or all even. In either case, $h + k$, $h + l$, and $k + l$ will all be even so that the last factor in Eq. (15) will have the value 4. Any other combination of h, k, and l, i.e., two odd and one even or two even and one odd, always results in two of the terms in the last factor having the value 1, while the other two have the value -1; the total, therefore, is identically zero. Thus the presence of a face-centered Bravais lattice can be deduced from the absence of all reflections of mixed indices from a set of general (hkl) reflections.

As a second example, consider the n glide which is comprised of an (010) glide plane with translation component $\mathbf{a}/2 + \mathbf{c}/2$. For an atom located at point x, y, z there will be a corresponding atom at $\frac{1}{2} + x, -y, \frac{1}{2} + z$. The structure-factor expression becomes

$$\begin{aligned} F(hkl) &= \sum_{j=1}^{N/2} f_j(hkl)\{\exp 2\pi i(hx_j + ky_j + lz_j) + \exp 2\pi i[h(x_j + \tfrac{1}{2}) - ky_j + l(z_j + \tfrac{1}{2})]\} \\ &= \sum_{j=1}^{N/2} f_j(hkl) \exp 2\pi i(hx_j + lz_j)\left[\exp 2\pi iky_j + \exp(-2\pi iky_j) \exp\left(2\pi i\frac{h+l}{2}\right)\right] \\ &= \sum_{j=1}^{N/2} f_j(hkl) \exp 2\pi i(hx_j + lz_j)[\exp 2\pi iky_j + (-1)^{h+l} \exp(-2\pi iky_j)] \end{aligned} \tag{16}$$

If $k = 0$, Eq. (16) can be written as

$$F(h0l) = \sum_{j=1}^{N/2} f_j(h0l) \exp 2\pi i(hx_j + lz_j)[1 + (-1)^{h+l}] \tag{17}$$

$F(h0l)$ will be nonzero only if $h + l = 2n$ ($n = 1, 2, 3, \ldots$). In this case, the presence of the n glide is deduced from the absences of all $(h0l)$ reflections where

$$h + l = 2n + 1 \quad (n = 0, 1, 2, 3, \ldots)$$

There is an elegant simplicity to be noted in the relationship between the condition for nonextinction and the interpretation thereof. The glide planes present a particularly nice example of this relationship. The presence of the glide operation is deduced by examining the class of reflections having one Miller index = 0, i.e., either $(h0l)$, $(0kl)$, or $(hk0)$ reflections. The glide plane corresponds to the missing index, i.e., (100) plane for absences in $0kl$, (010) for $h0l$, and (001) for $hk0$; the component of the glide depends upon which odd indices are absent, i.e., $\mathbf{a}/2$ for h, $\mathbf{b}/2$ for k, $\mathbf{c}/2$ for l, $(\mathbf{a} + \mathbf{b})/2$ for $h + k$, $(\mathbf{b} + \mathbf{c})/2$ for $k + l$, $(\mathbf{a} + \mathbf{c})/2$ for $h + l$. Similarly relationships for centered lattices and screw axes may be found by studying Table 1.

A close examination of Table 1 shows that it is imperative to collect sufficient x-ray data in order to observe the possibility of absences before assigning unit-cell dimensions. Figure 2*a* represents a zero-layer precession picture of *N*-methylbenzamide taken with Cu $K\alpha$ x-rays parallel to the [001] axis; these data form the $(hk0)$ class of reflection. Figure 2*b* represents a first-layer precession picture with the same orientation, these data thus constituting the $(hk1)$ class of reflections. It is apparent that the

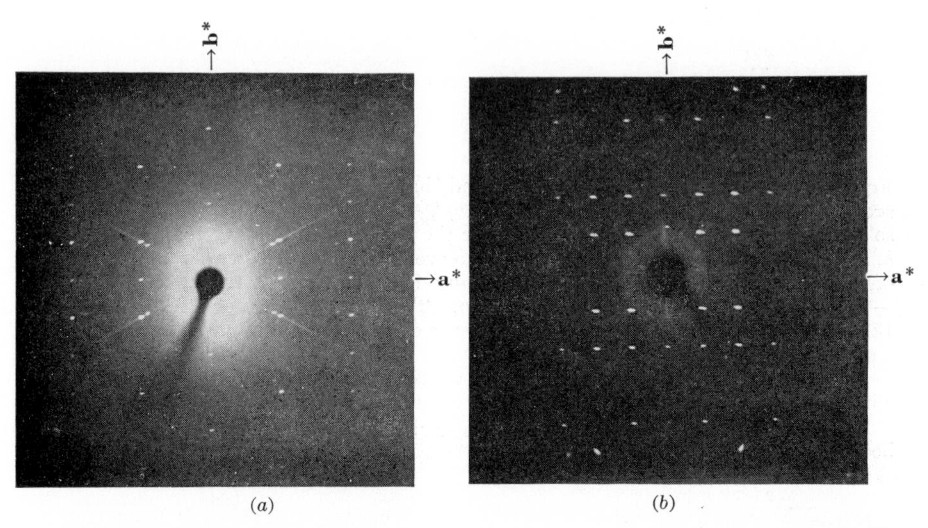

FIG. 2. (*a*) Zero-layer precession photograph of *N*-methylbenzamide taken with Cu K radiation. The incident beam is parallel to the [001] axis. With origin at the center, the $+\mathbf{a}^*$ direction has been chosen to the right and the $+\mathbf{b}^*$ direction is taken vertically up. Note that reflections such as $hk0$, $h = 2n + 1$, are absent because the (001) plane is a glide plane with translation component $a/2$. (*b*) First-layer precession photograph of *N*-methylbenzamide. The setting is the same as that of Fig. 2*a*. Both photographs were obtained through the courtesy of Robert Lanni, Department of Physics, State University at Albany, N.Y.

use of the first picture alone leads to a unit cell with axes $a = 4.83$ Å, $b = 9.23$ Å. The second photograph clearly indicates that the actual cell constants are $a = 9.66$ Å, $b = 9.23$ Å. A (001) glide plane with component $\mathbf{a}/2$ is responsible for the systematic absence of all $(hk0)$ reflections with h odd. Hence choosing the correct unit-cell dimensions is intimately connected with the proper determination of space group.

The assignment of the probable space group (of a given crystal) from considerations of systematic absences is usually a straightforward procedure. However, a final confirmation of the correctness of assigned space group may have to await a successful completion of the structure determination. Further, in some cases, systematic absences alone do not unambiguously determine the space group. For instance, consider the example of *N*-methylacetamide. This crystal (henceforth NMA) undergoes a solid-phase transition at about 10° C. Measurements of Weissenberg and precession photographs indicate that NMA is orthorhombic both above and below the transition temperature. In the low-temperature form the following classes of reflections were not observed: $(hk0)$, h odd, $(0kl)$ $k + l$ odd. Therefore, the symmetry elements present are an (001) glide plane with component $\mathbf{a}/2$ (symbol a) and a (100) glide plane with component $\mathbf{b}/2 + \mathbf{c}/2$ (symbol n). Since there is no systematic absence associated with the (hkl) class of reflections the Bravais lattice is primitive (symbol P). It is true that $(h00)$ h odd, $(0k0)$ k odd, and $(00l)$ l odd reflections also are absent. However, these conditions are already included in the glide-plane absences; i.e., since $(0kl)$ $k + l$ odd are absent, then when $k = 0$, $(00l)$ l odd or when $l = 0$, $(0k0)$ k odd must also be absent. Therefore, it is not clear whether the $(0k0)$ k odd absences are due to an [010] screw axis with component $\mathbf{b}/2$ (symbol 2_1) or are due to the n glide. In the latter case a mirror plane (symbol m) perpendicular to the y axis is possible since mirror planes cannot be detected directly from x-ray data. The space group for NMA is therefore either $Pnma$ or $Pn2_1a$.

An examination of Vol. 1 of the *International Tables for X-ray Crystallography* yields the following information: Space group $Pn2_1a$ (listed in the tables as $Pna2_1$, an interchange of the y and z axes) has only four equivalent positions of point symmetry 1. Space group $Pnma$ contains several possibilities: eight equivalent positions of point symmetry 1 (Wyckoff notation d), four positions of point symmetry m (Wyckoff notation c), or two different arrangements of four equivalent positions of point symmetry $\bar{1}$ (Wyckoff notations b and a).

As shown in Sec. 2, there are four molecules of NMA in the unit cell. Since each molecule constitutes one asymmetric scattering unit, the choice of space group is either $Pn2_1a$ with each molecule in a general position or either of the three latter configurations in $Pnma$ with the molecules in special positions; i.e., one or more positional parameters of each equivalent position are prescribed by symmetry. From data on the simple amides it is evident that while it is likely that the heavier atoms in NMA form a planar molecule (point symmetry m) they cannot have a center of symmetry (point symmetry $\bar{1}$). Thus the four molecules of NMA are located either at $x, y, z; x, \frac{1}{2} + y, -z; \frac{1}{2} - x, \frac{1}{2} + y, \frac{1}{2} + z; \frac{1}{2} + x, y, \frac{1}{2} - z$ in $Pn2_1a$ or at $x, \frac{1}{4}, z; -x, \frac{3}{4}, -z; \frac{1}{2} - x, \frac{3}{4}, \frac{1}{2} + z; \frac{1}{2} + x, \frac{1}{4}, \frac{1}{2} - z$ in $Pnma$. It is apparent that the former positions are equivalent to the latter when $y = \frac{1}{4}$. The final choice of the space group $Pnma$ was made, based on a complete structure determination.

In the above structure it was not possible to assign the space group unambiguously from considerations of systematic absences alone. However, as is often the case when the choice to be made is between centrosymmetric and noncentrosymmetric space groups in a given crystal system, other physical methods may be successful. The presence of pyro- or piezoelectricity in a crystal indicates the absence of a center of symmetry. Unfortunately, the absence of a measurable pyro- or piezoelectric effect does not necessarily warrant the assumption of the presence of a center of symmetry; the effect may be present but is too small to detect. Therefore, if and when the effect is definitely detected, it may be safely assumed that the crystal lacks a center of symmetry.

Statistical Methods. An alternative approach, using x-ray methods directly to distinguish between centrosymmetric and noncentrosymmetric structures, is also available.[3] These methods make use of the differences to be found in the probability distribution of x-ray intensities depending on the presence or absence of a center of symmetry. Each intensity I is expressed as a fraction of the local average intensity $\langle I \rangle$ so that

$$z = I/\langle I \rangle$$

The fractional number of reflections $N(z)$ whose intensities are $\leq z$ is given by the following equations:

Centrosymmetric case, ($\bar{1}$):

$$N(z) = 1 - \exp(-z)$$

Noncentrosymmetric case (1):

$$N(z) = \operatorname{erf}(Z/2)^{1/2}$$

where "erf" represents the error function.[4] A graph of both functions for $N(z)$ vs. z is shown in Fig. 3.

Example. 9:10-anthrahydroquinone Dibenzoate[5]

$a = 8.91,\ b = 12.60,\ c = 5.83$ Å — Triclinic system
$\alpha = 105.2$ Å, $\beta = 106.5$ Å, $\gamma = 58.2$ Å — Chemical formula $C_{28}H_{18}O_4$

ρ (obs) $= 1.314$ g/cm^3, ρ (calc) on the basis of one ($C_{28}H_{18}O_4$) molecule per unit cell $= 1.316$ g/cm^3.

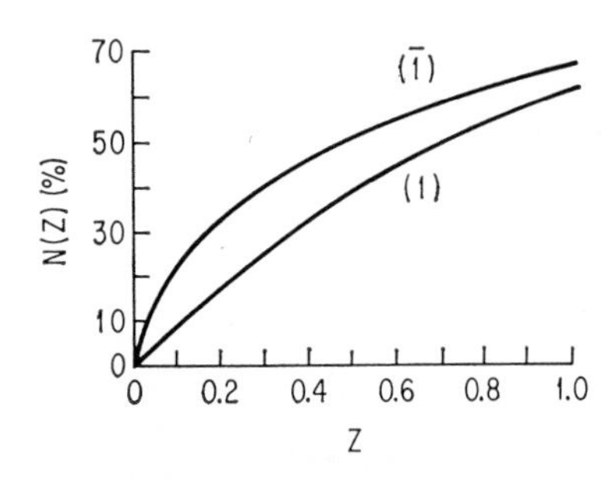

FIG. 3. The theoretical cumulant-distribution curves for an acentric crystal (1) and a centric crystal ($\bar{1}$).

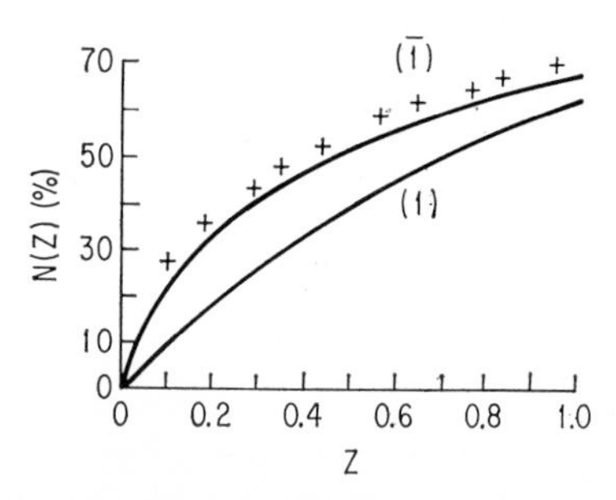

FIG. 4. The cumulant-distribution curve for anthrahydroquinone dibenzoate.[5] The experimental points are shown by the symbols +. The solid curves ($\bar{1}$) and (1) are those which are theoretically expected for a centric and an acentric crystal, respectively.

The choice of space group, i.e., either $P1$ or $P\bar{1}$, was made by applying the above intensity test to the ($hk0$) reflections. The result is shown in Fig. 4; the crosses represent the actual values of $N(z)$ for 10 intervals in z. It is clear that the distribution of intensities of the ($hk0$) reflections is centrosymmetric. This leads to the assignment of $P\bar{1}$ as the probable space group. Since the asymmetric scattering unit for the unit cell is one molecule, the molecule itself must, at least statistically, exhibit a center of symmetry.

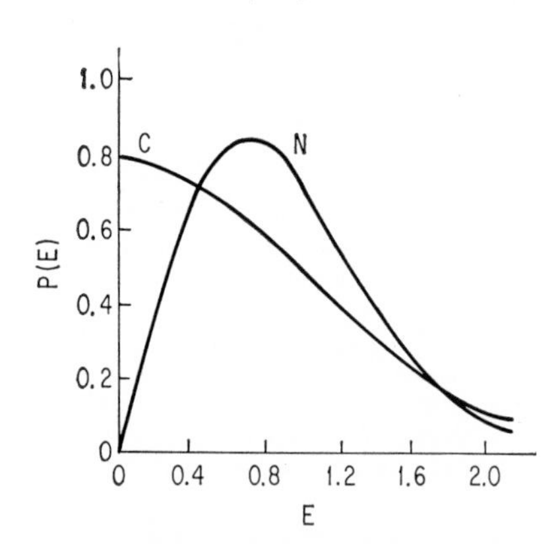

FIG. 5. The probability-distribution curve of a normalized structure amplitude. The solid curves C and N are those which are theoretically expected for a centric and an acentric crystal

A variant of the above method is to draw the probability-distribution function $P(E)\ dE$. A priori distribution functions have been derived for both centric as well as acentric crystals.[6,7,8] The derivation is similar to that of the "random-walk" problem, and the formulas are valid in the case of "equal-atom" structures. In the noncentric case, the theoretical distribution is

$$_NP(E)\ dE = 2E \exp(-E^2)\ dE$$

while in the centric case

$$_CP(E)\ dE = (2/\pi)^{1/2} \exp(-\tfrac{1}{2}E^2)\ dE$$

where $E = |F|/\langle I\rangle^{1/2}$

These theoretical distributions are shown in Fig. 5. It may be seen that while the curve C starts with a maximum value of $(2/\pi)^{1/2} = 0.798$ at $E = 0$, and decreases with increasing E, the curve N starts from 0 at $E = 0$, rapidly increases to a maximum value of $N = 0.857$ at $E = 0.707$, and then decreases with further increase in E. The two distributions have strikingly dissimilar shapes, particularly for values of E less than 0.7. This property may be compared with a corresponding property of the $N(z)$ curves, in which case both cumulant distributions start from the origin. [The parameter $z = E^2$ and $N(z) = \int_0^z P(z)\,dz$.] Therefore, it may be helpful to draw the $P(E)\,dE$ distributions given by the experimental data and attempt to detect the presence or absence of centrosymmetry. The experimental distributions are drawn as follows: the intensities are grouped into suitable ranges of $(\sin\theta)/\lambda$, the local averages $\langle I\rangle$ are computed, and a plot of $\langle I\rangle$ against $(\sin\theta)/\lambda$ is drawn. The value of $\langle I\rangle$ for each reflection is obtained from the plot, and the values $|E|^2$ are derived using the relation $|E|^2 = |F|^2/\langle I\rangle$. The fractional numbers of reflections having $|E|$ values between suitable ranges of $|E|$, such as 0.0 to 0.2, 0.2 to 0.4, are then calculated and plotted against $|E|$ to obtain the experimental $P(E)$ distribution.

There are other methods which may be of use in deducing space-group assignments when the x-ray data alone do not lead to an unambiguous choice. The use of optical methods to determine the crystal class must often be resorted to. In many cases a study of the external shapes of the crystals will distinguish the presence of rotation and rotary-inversion axes and mirror planes; these macroscopic symmetries cannot be directly determined by x-ray methods.

Reduction of Data to Absolute Scale. Among the various mathematical techniques presently applied to crystallographic problems, statistics has been at least as useful as any other. At the very best, direct methods of structure determination have been proposed;[9] at the very least, a highly useful technique is possible for reducing the data to absolute scale. The experimentally derived intensity values are usually corrected for Lorentz polarization and other factors pertinent to the particular experimental method employed. The intensity values of the various Bragg spectra (hkl) constitute a set of numbers which are not squares of the structure amplitudes but are only proportional to them; i.e., we have $I(hkl) = S|F(hkl)|^2$, where S is a constant of proportionality. This equation does not explicitly indicate the role played by the thermal vibrations of the lattice. Under the poor approximation that the thermal vibrations of all the atoms may be taken into account by a single Debye-Waller factor, the intensity values $I(hkl)$ may be related to the squares of the structure amplitudes as follows:

$$I(hkl) = S \exp\left[-2B(\sin^2\theta)/\lambda^2\right]|F(hkl)|^2$$

Therefore, the quantities $|F(hkl)|^2$ may be derived from $I(hkl)$ provided the scale factor S and the Debye-Waller factor B are known. A method commonly used in obtaining preliminary values of S and B is based on the statistical result first derived by Wilson:[6]

$$\langle I(hkl)\rangle = S \sum_{j=1}^{N} f_j^2 \exp - 2B(\sin^2\theta)/\lambda^2 \qquad (18)$$

i.e.,

$$\log_e[\langle I(hkl)\rangle/\Sigma f_j^2] = -2B(\sin^2\theta)/\lambda^2 + \log_e S$$

The averages $\langle I(hkl)\rangle$ are to be taken over small ranges of $(\sin\theta)/\lambda$. The constants S and B may be obtained from a logarithmic plot of the quantities

$$\langle I(hkl)\rangle/\Sigma f_j^2 \text{ against } (\sin^2\theta)/\lambda^2$$

The constant B is to be obtained from the slope, and the factor S is to be obtained from the intercept of the best possible linear plot. The method is applicable to both three- as well as two-dimensional data. The accuracy in S is usually quite good, though there are instances where the values deviate by as much as 50 per cent from the true values. Usually, the method works better with three-dimensional data, because better statistics are then possible. In computing the intensity averages $\langle I\rangle$, certain conditions should be borne in mind. First, the averages are correctly taken only with reflections in whole spherical shells. Usually, people collect data only over segments of the sphere. These segments are hemispheres in the triclinic, quadrants in monoclinic, and octants in orthorhombic cases. Therefore, it is necessary to give proper weights to special reflections such as $hk0$ and $h00$ in relation to general reflections hkl, in order that correct averages may be obtained. As an example, consider the case of an orthorhombic crystal for which one octant of data, i.e., $(+h, +k, +l)$, has been collected. The correct local average over any range is given by $\Sigma\omega I(hkl)/\Sigma\omega$ where $\omega = 1$ if none of the three indices $= 0$; $\omega = \frac{1}{2}$ if one of the three indices $= 0$; $\omega = \frac{1}{4}$ if two of the three indices $= 0$. A second point to be remembered is that systematic absences must be treated on a par with other reflections.

4. FOURIER ANALYSIS OF CRYSTALS

In order to develop the methods of Fourier analysis it is important to obtain the structure factor in terms of the actual electron-density distribution within a unit cell of the crystal. If $\rho(x,y,z)$ is the electron density at a point (x,y,z), then $\rho(x,y,z)$ $V\,dx\,dy\,dz$ represents the amount of scattering material in the volume element $V\,dx\,dy\,dz$. The structure factor can then be found by integrating over a unit cell, i.e.,

$$F(hkl) = V \int_0^{+1} \int_0^{+1} \int_0^{+1} \rho(x,y,z) \exp 2\pi i(hx + ky + lz)\, dx\, dy\, dz \tag{19}$$

A crystal is a three-dimensional periodic array of scattering matter. Thus the electron-density distribution can be represented analytically by a three-dimensional Fourier series, i.e.

$$\rho(x,y,z) = \sum_\alpha \sum_\beta \sum_{\gamma=-\infty}^{\infty} C(\alpha\beta\gamma) \exp 2\pi i(\alpha x + \beta y + \gamma z) \tag{20}$$

Substituting this series for $\rho(x,y,z)$ into Eq. (19) results in an equation for $F(hkl)$ which has a nonzero value if and only if $F(hkl) = VC(\bar{\alpha}\bar{\beta}\bar{\gamma})$. (This result follows from the orthogonality of the exponential functions, which results in a zero value for each integral unless the exponents themselves vanish.) Therefore, the electron-density distribution in a crystal may be expressed in terms of a Fourier series whose coefficients are the structure factors for the waves scattered by the crystal. Thus,

$$\rho(x,y,z) = (1/V) \sum_h \sum_k \sum_{l=-\infty}^{\infty} F(hkl) \exp -2\pi i(hx + ky + lz) \tag{21}$$

The problem of crystal-structure determination then is to determine the appropriate values of all the $F(hkl)$, substitute them into Eq. (21), and compute the values of $\rho(x,y,z)$. This is not a trivial problem! Since the structure factors are complex quantities and only the modulus of the structure factor is directly obtained from the x-ray intensities, it is not possible to calculate $\rho(x,y,z)$ directly. This problem is known as the "phase problem" in x-ray crystallography; it will be discussed in greater detail in Sec. 5.

But here we shall present some further development of mathematical techniques in the utilization of Fourier methods. This development will serve also as the basis for the more sophisticated methods of crystal-structure analysis to be discussed subsequently.

Simplification of the Structure-factor Expression. The structure-factor expression

$$F(hkl) = \sum_{j=1}^{N} f_j(hkl) \exp 2\pi i(hx_j + ky_j + lz_j) \tag{22}$$

where the summation extends over all the atoms in the unit cell, can be simplified considerably for the purposes of numerical computation by introducing the space-group symmetry.

Consider the triclinic space group $P\bar{1}$ (No. 2 in the space-group tables). The origin of the unit cell is conveniently chosen at the center of symmetry $(\bar{1})$. Thus for every atom located at x, y, z there is a centrosymmetrically related atom at $\bar{x}, \bar{y}, \bar{z}$. Equation (22), when summed over such pairs of centrosymmetrically related scattering centers, reduces to a much simpler form, i.e.,

$$F(hkl) = \sum_{j=1}^{N/2} 2f_j(hkl) \cos 2\pi(hx_j + ky_j + lz_j) \tag{23}$$

The sum now extends over only half the unit cell; i.e., only one of each pair of related atoms is included in the summation. In addition the structure factors are no longer complex quantities but are pure real numbers. This considerable reduction in analytical complexity with the attendant computational simplification makes it desirable to locate the origin of the coordinates of a unit cell at a center of symmetry whenever possible.

Volume I of the *International Tables of Crystallography* tabulates the reduced forms for both the structure-factor and electron-density expressions for all 230 space groups. These formulas are derived on the basis of atoms located in general equivalent positions. Following the notation of the International Tables, we have

$$A = \Sigma \cos [2\pi(hx + ky + lz)] \tag{24}$$
$$B = \Sigma \sin [2\pi(hx + ky + lz)] \tag{25}$$

where the functional forms of A and B depend only on the symmetry, i.e., on the equivalent positions. As a further notational simplification in the expressions for the individual space groups, where the actual summation has been performed over all the equivalent positions, the summation signs are omitted. Thus in the case of $P\bar{1}$ treated above the formulas are written

$$A = 2 \cos [2\pi(hx + ky + lz)] \qquad B = 0 \tag{26}$$

By way of further illustration, consider once again space group *Pnma* (origin at $\bar{1}$). There are eight general equivalent positions (four pairs of centrosymmetrically related positions) with coordinates as follows:

$x, y, z;\ \tfrac{1}{2} + x, \tfrac{1}{2} - y, \tfrac{1}{2} - z;\ \bar{x}, \tfrac{1}{2} + y, \bar{z};\ \tfrac{1}{2} - x, \bar{y}, \tfrac{1}{2} + z;\ \bar{x}, \bar{y}, \bar{z};\ \tfrac{1}{2} - x, \tfrac{1}{2} + y, \tfrac{1}{2} + z;\ x, \tfrac{1}{2} - y, z;\ \tfrac{1}{2} + x, y, \tfrac{1}{2} - z$

Substituting these coordinates into the exponential term of the structure-factor expression leads to the following trigonometric expression:

$$\begin{aligned} T = {} & \exp 2\pi i(hx + ky + lz) + \exp -2\pi i(hx + ky + lz) \\ & + (-1)^{h+k+l} \exp 2\pi i(hx - ky - lz) + (-1)^{h+k+l} \\ & \exp -2\pi i(hx - ky - lz) + (-1)^{k} \exp 2\pi i(-hx + ky - lz) \\ & + (-1)^{k} \exp -2\pi i(-hx + ky - lz) + (-1)^{h+l} \\ & \exp 2\pi i(-hx - ky + lz) + (-1)^{h+l} \exp -2\pi i(-hx - ky + lz) \end{aligned} \tag{27}$$

Now since,

$$\exp i\theta + \exp -i\theta = 2 \cos \theta \tag{28}$$

Eq. (27) reduces to the pure real

$$\begin{aligned} A = {} & 2 \cos 2\pi(hx + ky + lz) + 2(-1)^{h+k+l} \cos 2\pi(hx - ky - lz) \\ & + 2(-1)^{k} \cos 2\pi(hx - ky + lz) + 2(-1)^{h+l} \cos 2\pi(hx + ky - lz) \qquad B = 0 \end{aligned} \tag{29}$$

Further simplification using trigonometric identities depends on the parity of the three terms $h + k + l$, k, and $h + l$.

When $h + l = 2n$ and $k = 2n$, $h + k + l$ also is even and Eq. (29) can be simplified to

$$A = 4 \cos (2\pi hx) \cos [2\pi(ky + lz)] + 4 \cos (2\pi hx) \cos [2\pi(ky - lz)] \qquad B = 0$$

which finally can be reduced to

$$A = 8 \cos (2\pi hx) \cos (2\pi ky) \cos (2\pi lz) \qquad B = 0 \tag{30}$$

Similarly, if $h + l = 2n$, $k = 2n + 1$, then $h + k + l$ is odd and Eq. (29) becomes

$$A = -4 \sin 2\pi hx\, [\sin 2\pi(ky + lz) + \sin 2\pi(ky - lz)] \qquad B = 0$$

which reduces to

$$A = -8 \sin (2\pi hx) \sin (2\pi ky) \cos (2\pi lz) \qquad B = 0 \tag{31}$$

For $h + l = 2n + 1$, $k = 2n$, $h + k + l$ is odd and

$$A = -8 \sin (2\pi hx) \cos (2\pi ky) \sin (2\pi lz) \qquad B = 0 \tag{32}$$

Finally, for $h + l = 2n + 1$, $k = 2n + 1$, $h + k + l$ is even again, and

$$A = -8 \cos (2\pi hx) \sin (2\pi ky) \sin (2\pi lz) \qquad B = 0 \tag{33}$$

These equations can be found on page 408 of the International Tables, vol. I.

Since the sine is an odd function, i.e., $\sin(-\theta) = -\sin\theta$, and the cosine is an even function, i.e., $\cos(-\theta) = \cos\theta$, it follows that for $h + l = 2n$ and $k = 2n$ the following relationship among structure factors can be written:

$$F(hkl) = F(\bar{h}\bar{k}\bar{l}) = F(\bar{h}kl) = F(h\bar{k}l) = F(hk\bar{l}) \tag{34}$$

Similarly Eq. (31) leads to

$$F(hkl) = F(\bar{h}\bar{k}\bar{l}) = -F(\bar{h}kl) = -F(h\bar{k}l) = F(hk\bar{l}) \tag{35}$$

for $h + l = 2n$, $k = 2n + 1$. For $h + l = 2n + 1$, $k = 2n$,

$$F(hkl) = F(\bar{h}\bar{k}\bar{l}) = -F(\bar{h}kl) = F(h\bar{k}l) = -F(hk\bar{l}) \tag{36}$$

Lastly, for $h + l = 2n + 1$, $k = 2n + 1$,

$$F(hkl) = F(\bar{h}\bar{k}\bar{l}) = F(\bar{h}kl) = -F(h\bar{k}l) = -F(hk\bar{l}) \tag{37}$$

Similar analytical techniques can be used to obtain corresponding expressions for all the space groups.

Simplification of the Electron-density Expression. The electron-density equation as expressed by Eq. (20) is not in suitable form for the actual quantitative computations of electron densities. In order to reduce this expression to a more usable form, the exponential term is expressed in terms of real and imaginary parts by means of Euler's theorem while the structure factor is expressed in its complex form by Eq. (10). The result is given by the following equation:

$$\rho(x,y,z) = (1/V) \sum_h \sum_k \sum_{l=-\infty}^{\infty} [A(hkl) + iB(hkl)] \times [\cos 2\pi(hx + ky + lz) - i \sin 2\pi(hx + ky + lz)] \tag{38}$$

Consider now the bracketed terms within the summation. Upon multiplying and collecting the real and imaginary terms the following is obtained:

$$A(hkl) \cos 2\pi(hx + ky + lz) + B(hkl) \sin 2\pi(hx + ky + lz) - i[A(hkl) \sin 2\pi(hx + ky + lz) - B(hkl) \cos 2\pi(hx + ky + lz)] \tag{39}$$

Performing the same manipulation of the inverse term $F(\bar{h}\bar{k}\bar{l})$ results in

$$[A(\bar{h}\bar{k}\bar{l}) + iB(\bar{h}\bar{k}\bar{l})][\cos 2\pi(\bar{h}x + \bar{k}y + \bar{l}z) - i \sin 2\pi(\bar{h}x + \bar{k}y + \bar{l}z)] \tag{40}$$

which can be resolved into

$$[A(\bar{h}\bar{k}\bar{l}) \cos 2\pi(\bar{h}x + \bar{k}y + \bar{l}z) - B(\bar{h}\bar{k}\bar{l}) \sin 2\pi(hx + ky + lz)] + i[A(\bar{h}\bar{k}\bar{l}) \sin 2\pi(hx + ky + lz) + B(\bar{h}\bar{k}\bar{l}) \cos 2\pi(hx + ky + lz)] \tag{41}$$

However, since $F(\bar{h}\bar{k}\bar{l})$ is conjugate to $F(hkl)$, $A(\bar{h}\bar{k}\bar{l}) = A(hkl)$ and $B(\bar{h}\bar{k}\bar{l}) = -B(hkl)$.

Thus Eq. (41) can be written as

$$[A(hkl)\cos 2\pi(hx+ky+lz)+B(hkl)\sin 2\pi(hx+ky+lz)] \\ +i[A(hkl)\sin 2\pi(hx+ky+lz)-B(hkl)\cos 2\pi(hx+ky+lz)] \quad (42)$$

Equation (21) can now be summed over pairs of conjugates [with the exception of $F(000)$, which is its own conjugate]. If Eqs. (39) and (42) are added together, the general form of the summation term is obtained as

$$2[A(hkl)\cos 2\pi(hx+ky+lz)+B(hkl)\sin 2\pi(hx+ky+lz)] \quad (43)$$

Hence the electron-density formula, Eq. (20), can be rewritten as

$$\rho(x,y,z)=(1/V)\sum_h\sum_k\sum_{l=-\infty}^{\infty} A(hkl)\cos 2\pi(hx+ky+lz) \\ +B(hkl)\sin 2\pi(hx+ky+lz) \quad (44)$$

It is seen that the electron density is real everywhere. In addition, it is apparent that when all the $B(hkl)=0$, i.e., the structure factors are all purely real, the electron density at x, y, z is equal to the electron density at $\bar{x}$, $\bar{y}$, $\bar{z}$; i.e., the structure has a center of symmetry at the origin. This is nothing more than the inverse statement to Eq. (23), which showed that when a space group had a center of symmetry at the origin of the unit cell, the structure factors were all purely real.

Alternatively Eq. (44) is also written in terms of the structure amplitude $|F(hkl)|$ and the phase angle $\alpha(hkl)$ defined in Eq. (13), i.e.,

$$\rho(x,y,z)=(1/V)\sum_h\sum_k\sum_{l=-\infty}^{\infty} |F(hkl)|\cos[2\pi(hx+ky+lz)-\alpha(hkl)] \quad (45)$$

Additional simplification of either Eq. (44) or Eq. (45) can be accomplished for each of the 230 space groups by using the space-group symmetry as expressed by the structure-factor relationships, e.g., those given by Eqs. (34) through (37) for *Pnma*.

Substituting these relationships into the electron-density expression and simplifying yields the following equation (see International Tables, vol. I, p. 408):

$$\rho(x,y,z)=(8/V)\Big[\sum_h\sum_k\sum_{l=0}^{\infty} F(hkl)\cos(2\pi hx)\cos(2\pi ky)\cos(2\pi lz) \qquad h+l=2n, k=2n$$

$$+\sum_h\sum_k\sum_{l=0}^{\infty} F(hkl)\sin(2\pi hx)\sin(2\pi ky)\cos(2\pi lz) \qquad h+l=2n,\ k=2n+1$$

$$+\sum_h\sum_k\sum_{l=0}^{\infty} F(hkl)\sin(2\pi hx)\cos(2\pi ky)\sin(2\pi lz) \qquad h+l=2n+1,\ k=2n$$

$$+\sum_h\sum_k\sum_{l=0}^{\infty} F(hkl)\cos(2\pi hx)\sin(2\pi ky)\sin(2\pi lz)\Big] \qquad h+l=2n+1,\ k=2n+1$$

(46)

In addition, it is necessary to take into account the number of times a given plane is computed in the electron-density expression; $F(000)$ occurs only once, $F(h00)$ type terms only twice each, $F(hk0)$ terms four times each, and general $F(hkl)$ terms eight times each, i.e., (hkl), $(\bar{h}\bar{k}\bar{l})$, $(\bar{h}kl)$, $(h\bar{k}l)$, $(hk\bar{l})$, $(h\bar{k}\bar{l})$, $(\bar{h}k\bar{l})$, $(\bar{h}\bar{k}l)$.

When the scattering units are located in special rather than in general positions, additional reduction in the trigonometric expressions can be obtained. If the atomic configuration in *Pnma* has point symmetry m coinciding with mirror planes at $y=\frac{1}{4}$ and $\frac{3}{4}$ in the unit cell, the number of equivalent positions reduces to four (see discussion in Sec. 3),

$$x,\tfrac{1}{4},z;\ \bar{x},\tfrac{3}{4},\bar{z};\ \tfrac{1}{2}-x,\tfrac{3}{4},\tfrac{1}{2}+z;\ \tfrac{1}{2}+x,\tfrac{1}{4},\tfrac{1}{2}-z$$

Since the origin is at a center of symmetry, Eq. (24) can be used directly as mentioned above. Therefore,

$$A = \cos 2\pi(hx + k\tfrac{1}{4} + lz) + \cos 2\pi(hx + k\tfrac{3}{4} + lz) \cos 2\pi[h(\tfrac{1}{2} - x) + k\tfrac{3}{4} + l(\tfrac{1}{2} + z)] + \cos 2\pi[h(\tfrac{1}{2} + x) + k\tfrac{1}{4} + l(\tfrac{1}{2} - z)] \qquad B = 0 \quad (47)$$

Using the standard trigonometric identities for the sum and differences of angles Eq. (47) reduces to

$$A = (-1)^k 2 \cos 2\pi(hx + lz - k/4) + 2(-1)^{h+k+l} \cos 2\pi(hx - lz - k/4) \qquad B = 0 \quad (48)$$

Thus when $h + l = 2n$ and $k = 2n$,

$$A = (-1)^{k/2} 4 \cos 2\pi hx \cos 2\pi lz \qquad B = 0 \quad (49)$$

For $h + l = 2n$, $k = 2n + 1$,

$$A = (-1)^{(k+1)/2} 4 \sin 2\pi hx \cos 2\pi lz \qquad B = 0 \quad (50)$$

For $h + l = 2n + 1$, $k = 2n$,

$$A = (-1)^{k/2} 4 \sin 2\pi hx \sin 2\pi lz \qquad B = 0 \quad (51)$$

For $h + l = 2n + 1$, $k = 2n + 1$,

$$A = (-1)^{(k+1)/2} 4 \cos 2\pi hx \sin 2\pi lz \qquad B = 0 \quad (52)$$

The relationships among the structure factors are the same as expressed by Eqs. (34) through (37), respectively.

Fourier Sections and Projections. A full three-dimensional electron-density synthesis using Eq. (21) or a reduced form such as Eq. (44) is generally performed section by section along a specific direction, e.g.,

$$\rho(x,y,z_1) = (1/V) \sum_h \sum_k \sum_{l=-\infty}^{\infty} F(hkl) \exp -2\pi i(hx + ky + lz_1) \quad (53)$$

This has the effect of reducing the triple summation to a computation over only two variables, x and y in this case, since

$$\rho(x,y,z_1) = (1/V) \sum_h \sum_{k=-\infty}^{\infty} \sum_{l=-\infty}^{\infty} F(hkl) \exp(-2\pi i l z_1) \exp -2\pi i(hx + ky) \quad (54)$$

or, in more compact form,

$$\rho(x,y,z_1) = (1/V) \sum_h \sum_{k=-\infty}^{\infty} C(hk) \exp -2\pi i(hx + ky) \quad (55)$$

where

$$C(hk) = \sum_{l=-\infty}^{\infty} F(hkl) \exp(-2\pi i l z_1) \quad (56)$$

These sections, which still require full three-dimensional experimental data, are of course parallel to a rational plane of the unit cell; the computations for nonrational planes are still more complex.

In many cases electron-density calculations involving only one- or two-dimensional summations provide useful information. Such calculations not only require fewer experimental data than do full three-dimensional summations but also prove much easier to perform.

Consider the electron-density distribution along any line within the unit cell parallel to a crystallographic axis. This density can be "projected" onto a point by evaluating an integral of the following kind:

$$\rho(x,y) = c \int_0^1 \rho(x,y,z)\, dz \quad (57)$$

Substituting Eq. (21) for $\rho(x,y,z)$ yields

$$\rho(x,y) = (c/V) \sum_h \sum_k \sum_{l=-\infty}^{\infty} \int_0^1 F(hkl) \exp -2\pi i(hx + ky) \exp(-2\pi ilz)\, dz \tag{58}$$

The integral in Eq. (58) has a nonzero value if and only if $l = 0$. Thus the electron density projected down the [001] axis is given by

$$\rho_0(xy) = (1/A) \sum_h \sum_{k=-\infty}^{\infty} F(hk0) \exp -2\pi i(hx + ky) \tag{59}$$

where only the $hk0$ reflections are needed. This type of calculation proves especially useful if there is little overlap of atoms along the direction of projection. Equation (59) can also be reduced to a more suitable form for computation based on the space-group symmetry by the methods described earlier.

It is to be noted that the synthesis [Eq. (59)] corresponds to the entire density in one unit cell projected onto a plane. In some cases, it may be preferable to project the density within a slab rather than the whole unit cell.[10] For instance, consider the slab bounded by the sections at $z = z_1$ and $z = z_2$. The projected density is

$$\rho(x,y,\Delta z) = c \int_{z_1}^{z_2} \rho(x,y,z)\, dz \tag{60}$$

Again substituting Eq. (21) for $\rho(x,y,z)$ the following is obtained:

$$\rho(x,y,\Delta z) = (c/V) \sum_h \sum_k \sum_{l=-\infty}^{\infty} \int_{z_1}^{z_2} F(hkl) \exp -2\pi i(hx + ky) \exp(-2\pi ilz)\, dz \tag{61}$$

It can be shown that Eq. (61) reduces to

$$\rho(x,y,\Delta z) = (1/A) \sum_h \sum_{k=-\infty}^{\infty} C(hk) \exp -2\pi i(hx + ky) \tag{62}$$

where

$$C(hk) = \sum_{l=-\infty}^{\infty} F(hkl)(\sin \pi l\, \Delta z/\pi l) \exp -2\pi il\, [(z_1 + z_2)/2] \tag{63}$$

Other forms of electron-density projections have proved useful in providing approximate z coordinates as well as the x and y coordinates for each atom in the structure. This kind of projection is called generalized projection, and is particularly useful when only one well-resolved projection (say the xy) is available. The generalized projections are obtained by modifying the electron-density function by some modulating function[11] such as $\sin 2\pi Lz$ or $\cos 2\pi Lz$ or some other suitable sinusoidal term. One such generalized projection is defined as

$$\rho_L(x,y) = c \int_0^1 \rho(xyz) \exp(2\pi iLz)\, dz \tag{64}$$

The same procedure developed for Eq. (57) is used here, $\rho(xyz)$ as defined in Eq. (21) is substituted into Eq. (64), and the resultant integral is evaluated. In this case the critical integral is

$$\int_0^1 \exp 2\pi i(L - l)z\, dz = 1 \quad L = l \tag{65}$$
$$= 0 \quad L \neq l$$

Thus

$$\rho_L(x,y) = (1/A) \sum_h \sum_{k=-\infty}^{\infty} F(hkL) \exp -2\pi i(hx + ky) \tag{66}$$

The ordinary projection $\rho(x,y)$ as given by Eq. (59) is thus seen to be a special case of the generalized projection; i.e., when $L = 0$, Eq. (66) reduces to Eq. (59).

In order to determine the z coordinates by means of generalized projections a recasting of the complex quantities $\rho_L(x,y)$ in terms of its real and imaginary parts is required.

$$\rho_L(x,y) = R_L(x,y) + iI_L(x,y) \tag{67}$$

Using Eq. (10),

$$\rho_L(x,y) = (1/A) \sum_h \sum_{k=-\infty}^{\infty} [A(hkL) + iB(hkL)][\cos 2\pi(hx+ky) - i \sin 2\pi(hx+ky)] \tag{68}$$

so that

$$R_L(x,y) = (1/A) \sum_h \sum_{k=-\infty}^{\infty} A(hkL) \cos 2\pi(hx+ky) + B(hkL) \sin 2\pi(hx+ky) \tag{69}$$

$$I_L(x,y) = (1/A) \sum_h \sum_{k=-\infty}^{\infty} B(hkL) \cos 2\pi(hx+ky) - A(hkL) \sin 2\pi(hx+ky) \tag{70}$$

Now the only difference between the normal projection of an atom and the generalized projection of the same atom is the modulation factor exp $(2\pi iLz_j)$; i.e., the peak location (x_j,y_j) of each atom in the generalized projection is the same as for the zero-layer projection. This is true also for the height z_j which, in addition, has its phase shifted by exp $(2\pi iLz_j)$. Thus

$$\rho_L(x_j,y_j) = \rho_0(x_j,y_j) \exp (2\pi iLz_j) \tag{71}$$

Therefore, the height z_j can be found from the calculation of the real and imaginary parts of the generalized projection by using

$$z_j = \frac{1}{2\pi L} \tan^{-1} \frac{I_L(x_j,y_j)}{R_L(x_j,y_j)} \tag{72}$$

There are limitations to this calculation; z_j values obtained are at best approximate. However, several structures have been solved using varying forms of the generalized projection.

Projections and sections (special, generalized, and/or bounded) are not too tedious, from the point of view of manual computation. Usually, a desk calculator and devices such as Beevers-Lipson strips[12] are sufficient. But a full calculation of the three-dimensional Fourier is too laborious to be attempted manually. Usually these calculations are undertaken only in laboratories having access to high-speed digital computers such as IBM 704, 709, or 7090 or analog (such as XRAC[13]) computers. Examples of programs written for IBM computers are those of Sly and Shoemaker,[14] Zalkin,[15] and Shiono.[16]

5. PATTERSON'S APPROACH TO PHASE PROBLEM

The Phase Problem. The calculation of the electron-density function $\rho(x,y,z)$ by means of Eq. (21) is straightforward, provided the Fourier coefficients $F(h,k,l)$ are known, both in magnitude $|F(h,k,l)|$ and in phase angle $\alpha(h,k,l)$. However, in an attempt to record the intensities of the Bragg spectrum (h,k,l) the information pertaining to $\alpha(h,k,l)$ is lost. In fact, it may appear that the phase angles can be obtained only if the atomic coordinates are known and vice versa. As mentioned earlier, this vicious circle is known as the *phase problem* in x-ray crystallography. The complexity of the problem can be gauged from the fact that, in general, the value of the phase angle, for a given (h,k,l), is some unknown value in the range 0 to 360°. The problem gets somewhat simplified if the crystal belongs to a centrosymmetric space group, in which case α is either 0 or 180°. Even then, for a given number of p structure factors, there are 2^p possibilities, and it is impractical to synthesize $\rho(x,y,z)$ for each possibility and attempt to determine the structure from the synthesized function. It is obvious that some (sensible) method must be attempted to obtain, at least approximately, the phasal portions of the structure factors. The best procedure to be adopted depends on the particular crystal under investigation. However, some general principles may be laid down.

The Patterson Function of Crystallography. *Definition.* In most cases, the first step in the structure analysis is to calculate the Patterson function,[17] a Fourier series whose coefficients are the experimentally measured intensities. This function is

$$P(\mathbf{u}) = (1/V) \sum_{\mathbf{H}=-\infty}^{\mathbf{H}=+\infty} |F(\mathbf{H})|^2 \exp -2\pi i\mathbf{H}\cdot\mathbf{u} \tag{73}$$

i.e.,

$$P(u,v,w) = (1/V) \sum_h \sum_k \sum_{l=-\infty}^{+\infty} |F(h,k,l)|^2 \cos 2\pi(hu + kv + lw) \tag{74}$$

It is to be noted that Eq. (73) is the definition of $P(\mathbf{u})$ and means that $P(\mathbf{u})$ is the inverse Fourier transform of $|F(\mathbf{H})|^2$ where $\mathbf{u}$ is a vector in the crystal space, i.e.,

$$\mathbf{u} = u\mathbf{a} + v\mathbf{b} + w\mathbf{c} \tag{75}$$

while $\mathbf{H}$ is a vector in reciprocal space, i.e.,

$$\mathbf{H} = h\mathbf{a}^* + k\mathbf{b}^* + l\mathbf{c}^* \tag{76}$$

Note that (u,v,w) in Eq. (75) are fractional numbers while (h,k,l) in Eq. (76) is a triplet of integers, i.e., the Miller indices.

Equation (74) is Eq. (73) summed over inverse-related intensities, i.e., $|F(h,k,l)|^2$ and $|F(\bar{h},\bar{k},\bar{l})|^2$. In all cases where $\rho(\mathbf{r})$ is a real function,* the equality

$$|F(h,k,l)|^2 = |F(\bar{h},\bar{k},\bar{l})|^2 \tag{77}$$

holds, and correspondingly Eq. (74) is valid. Equation (77) expresses analytically an experimental relationship known as Friedel's law. It is possible to reduce equation (74) into more simplified expressions, depending on the relations that exist between the various reflection intensities, these relations arising out of the symmetry of the crystal.[2] As it stands, Eq. (74) is for space groups $P1$ and $P\bar{1}$.

It is important to appreciate that the Patterson function is calculated from the experimentally measured intensities and does not require any knowledge of the phases of $F(\mathbf{H})$.

Content of $P(\mathbf{u})$. The peaks contained in $P(\mathbf{u})$ correspond to the interatomic vectors of the structure. This result is elegantly obtained through an application of Fourier-transform theory.[18] Consider the pairs of integrals:

$$F(\mathbf{H}) = \int_0^V \rho(\mathbf{r}) \exp +2\pi i\mathbf{H}\cdot\mathbf{r}\, dV \tag{78}$$

$$\rho(\mathbf{r}) = \int_{-\infty}^{+\infty} F(\mathbf{H}) \exp -2\pi i\mathbf{H}\cdot\mathbf{r}\, d\tau \tag{79}$$

Obviously, $F(\mathbf{H})$ is the F.T. (i.e., Fourier transform) of $\rho(\mathbf{r})$ and $\rho(\mathbf{r})$ is the I.F.T. (i.e., inverse F.T.) of $F(\mathbf{H})$. The fact that $F(\mathbf{H})$ and $\rho(\mathbf{r})$ are a pair of Fourier transforms can be given symbolically by

$$F(\mathbf{H}) \leftrightarrow \rho(\mathbf{r}) \tag{80}$$

Consider a crystal whose unit cell contains P atoms, the Pith of which is at $\mathbf{r}_{Pi}$ and

* $\rho(\mathbf{r})$ is a real function only if the effects of anomalous dispersion of x-rays are negligible for the given x-ray wavelength used in the diffraction experiment.

has a scattering power f_{Pi}.* (Let us assume that f_{Pi} is independent of the scattering angle, i.e., the atoms are point atoms.) The peaks of $\rho_P(\mathbf{r})$ are then symbolically represented by $[f_{Pi}, \mathbf{r}_{Pi}]$ (i.e., the subscript $Pi = 1, P$; location of peak $= \mathbf{r}_{Pi}$ and strength $= f_{Pi}$). Let $\rho_Q(\mathbf{r})$ be a second such function whose peaks are represented by $[f_{Qi}, \mathbf{r}_{Qi}]$ where $Qi = 1, Q$. Then we have

$$F_P(\mathbf{H}) \leftrightarrow \rho_P(\mathbf{r})$$
$$F_Q(\mathbf{H}) \leftrightarrow \rho_Q(\mathbf{r})$$

and

$$F_P F_Q \leftrightarrow \int \rho_P(\mathbf{r})\rho_Q(\mathbf{u} - \mathbf{r})\, dV \tag{81}$$

Equation (81) is the convolution-integral theorem of F.T. theory and expresses the fact that the product of two F.T.'s is the F.T. of the convolution integral of the two corresponding functions. It is to be noted that multiplying the transforms in one space, in this case **H** space, is equivalent to convoluting the functions in the other space, i.e., **r** space and vice versa. The application of this important theorem to the crystallographic case consists in (1) calculating the function $\rho_{PQ}(\mathbf{r})$ (i.e., the convolution integral of ρ_P and ρ_Q) by a Fourier synthesis employing the product $(F_P \cdot F_Q)$ as the coefficient, and (2) evaluating the peaks of $\rho_{PQ}(\mathbf{r})$ which are given symbolically by $[f_{Pi}f_{Qj}, \mathbf{r}_{Pi} + \mathbf{r}_{Qj}]$ where the subscripts Pi and Qj assume values from 1 to P and 1 to Q, respectively; the total number of peaks $= PQ$ and the strength of the peak located at $\mathbf{r}_{Pi} + \mathbf{r}_{Qj}$ is $f_{Pi} \times f_{Qj}$. Note that in forming the peaks, the scattering powers are to be multiplied, but the position coordinates are to be added.

We shall apply the above principle to work out the peaks contained by $P(\mathbf{u})$. Note that

$$P(\mathbf{u}) \leftrightarrow |F(\mathbf{H})|^2$$

i.e.,

$$P(\mathbf{u}) \leftrightarrow F(\mathbf{H})F^*(\mathbf{H})$$

Since we have $F^*(\mathbf{H}) = F(-\mathbf{H})$,† it follows that

$$P(\mathbf{u}) \leftrightarrow F(\mathbf{H})F(-\mathbf{H})$$

where

$$F(\mathbf{H}) \leftrightarrow \rho(\mathbf{r})$$

and

$$F(-\mathbf{H}) \leftrightarrow \rho(-\mathbf{r})$$

whence

$$P(\mathbf{u}) = \int_0^V \rho(\mathbf{r})\rho(\mathbf{u} + \mathbf{r})\, dV \tag{82}$$

Equation (82) expresses the fact that $P(\mathbf{u})$ is the convolution integral of two functions, one of which is the electron density $\rho(\mathbf{r})$, the other $\rho(-\mathbf{r})$. The integral on the right-hand side of Eq. (82) is usually called the self-convolution of $\rho(\mathbf{r})$. It is also called the autocorrelation function of $\rho(\mathbf{r})$. The peaks given by $P(\mathbf{u})$ will then be $[f_i f_j, \mathbf{r}_i - \mathbf{r}_j]$ where $i = 1, N; j = 1, N; N =$ total number of atoms in the unit cell. The positions of the peaks are $\mathbf{u}_{ij} = \mathbf{r}_i - \mathbf{r}_j$, i.e., the interatomic vector between the atoms i and j, and the value of $P(\mathbf{u})$ at the peaks $= f_i f_j$. Both subscripts i and j can assume all values from 1 to N so that $P(\mathbf{u})$ has the following properties: (1) At $\mathbf{u} = 0$, the null-interatomic vectors $(\mathbf{r}_i - \mathbf{r}_i)$, N in number, overlap and produce a strong peak $\sum_{j=1}^{N} f_j^2$, thus giving a convenient origin. (2) The remaining $(N^2 - N)$ interatomic vectors produce peaks at $\mathbf{u} = \mathbf{u}_{ij} = \mathbf{r}_i - \mathbf{r}_j$ with strength $f_i f_j$. (3) Since $\mathbf{u}_{ij} = \mathbf{u}_{ji}$,

* *Convention of subscripts:* Throughout this chapter we have adopted the following convention of subscripts. An actual double subscript will be indicated by two noncapitalized letters such as ij in $\mathbf{u}_{ij}$. Both subscripts i and j assume all allowed values, say 1 to N, and will therefore generate a two-dimensional array. In cases where the first subscript has been capitalized, as is the case with P in $\mathbf{r}_{Pi}$, Pi should be understood as a single subscript which assumes all values from 1 to P, the capitalized letter P, and therefore will generate only a one-dimensional array. The fact that the subscript assumes all values from 1 to P will be represented by the symbol $(Pi = 1,P)$. Clearly a symbol such as $(i, j = 1, N)$ will mean that both i and j will individually assume all values from 1 to N. A specific element of an array will be denoted by a subscript other than the running index, for example, a in $\mathbf{r}_a$. Correspondingly, $\mathbf{u}_{ab}$ will denote a specific element of a two-dimensional array.

† The equality $F^*(\mathbf{H}) = F(-\mathbf{H})$ is valid only if anomalous dispersion is neglected.

the $(N^2 - N)$ peaks become $(N^2 - N)/2$ pairs of peaks, each pair being related by a center of inversion at the origin $\mathbf{u} = 0$. (4) Result (3) shows that $P(\mathbf{u})$ is centrosymmetric irrespective of whether $\rho(\mathbf{r})$ is centrosymmetric or not.

Fundamental Set and the Vector Set. Consider a crystal whose unit cell contains a total number of N atoms, the jth one of which is at $\mathbf{r}_j$. The set of N positions $\{\mathbf{r}_1, \mathbf{r}_2 \cdots \mathbf{r}_N\}$ comprises the fundamental or F set. The F set is referred to an origin, usually the one suggested for the appropriate space group in Vol. I of the *International Tables of Crystallography.* However, the amplitude of scattering is dependent only on the relative phase or path differences between the scattering centers, so that, from the point of view of the intensities, the origin can be chosen on any one of the N atoms. Referring the F set to N such origins, the jth one of which is at $\mathbf{r}_j$, and collecting the resultant F sets, it is possible to generate a square array of N^2 elements. This square array is called the vector set V since each element in the array is an interatomic vector.

$$V = \begin{vmatrix} 0 & \mathbf{r}_2 - \mathbf{r}_1 & \cdots & \mathbf{r}_i - \mathbf{r}_1 & \cdots & \mathbf{r}_N - \mathbf{r}_1 \\ \mathbf{r}_1 - \mathbf{r}_2 & 0 & \cdots & \mathbf{r}_i - \mathbf{r}_2 & \cdots & \mathbf{r}_N - \mathbf{r}_2 \\ \cdot & & \cdot & \cdot & \cdot & \cdot \\ \cdot & & \cdot & \cdot & \cdot & \cdot \\ \cdot & & \cdot & \cdot & \cdot & \cdot \\ \mathbf{r}_1 - \mathbf{r}_N & & \cdots & \mathbf{r}_i - \mathbf{r}_N & \cdots & 0 \end{vmatrix} \tag{83}$$

The diagonal elements of the array are zero and the array is antisymmetric. If $\rho(\mathbf{r})$ corresponds to the F set, $P(\mathbf{u})$ obviously corresponds to the V set. The F set referred to atom j as the origin is also called the image "j" of the structure so that the V set consists of a total number of N "images" of the structure. By its very nature, the V set automatically contains the inverse images "a," the set of N interatomic vectors $\mathbf{r}_a - \mathbf{r}_j$ $(j = 1, N)$. Clearly, the columns of the array V refer to the inverse images, if the rows refer to the direct images "j." Also, the inverse image is simply the enantiomorph of the corresponding direct image.

Patterson Function and Phase Problem. In view of the above discussions, the phase problem can be theoretically formulated in vector space in two ways:

1. The problem is to find the F set, given a poor approximation to the V set.
2. The problem is to identify and pick (any) one image out of a total of N images.

Standard techniques[19] are available to recover the F set from the V set. However, the main problem arises from the simple fact that the Patterson function, which is calculated with a finite number of coefficients, which in turn are derived from an experimental measurement of the intensity data, is really a rather poor approximation to a vector set. In spite of this limitation, crystallographers have developed a good number of methods which attempt to interpret the Patterson function and thus determine the structure. The names given to these methods appear to have depended on the way in which the phase problem was formulated. For instance, formulation 1 has led to methods usually called vector-space methods. Formulation 2 has led to image-seeking methods. A third formulation is possible in terms of Fourier-transform theory. Here the phase problem is the problem of finding that function $\rho(\mathbf{r})$ whose self-convolution is the Patterson function. In other words, the electron density has to be extracted out of the Patterson function. Such a Fourier approach has led to the development of certain Fourier syntheses which are quite helpful in structure determination.

Yet another formulation of the phase problem is as follows: The Patterson function is, after all, only an elegant and convenient way of representing the information contained by the intensity data. The information about the atomic positions, and therefore the phase angles, is present in the data in the form of interatomic vectors. Therefore, one may as well pose the question whether the knowledge of the numerical values of a sufficiently large number of intensities throws any light on the phases of the structure factors. Attempts to find the answer to this question have led to the development of the so-called "direct" methods. However, we should like to point out that there is nothing indirect about Patterson's approach either. Some, if not many, workers, including the authors, are quite partial to Patterson's approach. The main reason for this partiality is not only the very simplicity and elegance of the approach but also the fact that the "direct" methods appear to be, in principle, equivalent to the "Patterson" method, inasmuch as both approaches use the intensity data as the starting point. Most "direct" methods are also simple enough, and they are usually based on useful physical concepts, such as the nonnegativity of the electron-density function. However, the mathematics involved in at least some "direct" methods is camouflaged, though certainly not difficult. These are the very methods which appear to have claims for a routine solution of the phase problem. On the other hand, Patterson's approach is very elegant and simple. It is also much easier to introduce any available information (such as that provided by stereochemistry) into Patterson's approach than into other approaches. In view of these reasons, Patterson's function plays an important role in crystal-structure analysis. Therefore, we shall attempt a fairly detailed discussion.

Symmetry of the Patterson Function. The symmetry of $\rho(\mathbf{r})$ is given by one of the 230 space groups. The symmetry of $P(\mathbf{u})$, however, is given by only one of the 24 space groups[20] and can be obtained from that of $\rho(\mathbf{r})$ by the following rules:

1. Retain the lattice type.
2. Remove all translational parts of symmetry elements.
3. Add a center of inversion.

Some examples are:

(i) $\rho(\mathbf{r})$ in $P2_12_12_1$; $P(\mathbf{u})$ in $P2/m2/m2/m$
(ii) $\rho(\mathbf{r})$ in $Pnma$; $P(\mathbf{u})$ in $P2/m2/m2/m$
(iii) $\rho(\mathbf{r})$ in $C2/c$; $P(\mathbf{u})$ in $C2/m$

Peak Weight, Peak Height, and Peak Density. If the unit cell of volume V contains N atoms, the jth atom having atomic number Z_j and position vector $\mathbf{r}_j$, then the electron density is given by

$$\rho(\mathbf{r}) = \sum_{j=1}^{N} \rho_j(\mathbf{r} - \mathbf{r}_j)$$

where

$$\rho_j(\mathbf{r}) = (1/V) \sum_{\mathbf{H}} f_j(\mathbf{H}) \exp - 2\pi i \mathbf{H} \cdot \mathbf{r}$$

and the weight of the jth atom is defined by

$$\int_0^V \rho_j(\mathbf{r})\, dV = Z_j$$

Correspondingly,

$$P(\mathbf{u}) = \sum_{i=1}^{N} \sum_{j=1}^{N} P_{ij}(\mathbf{u} - \mathbf{u}_{ij})$$

where $\mathbf{u}_{ij} = \mathbf{r}_i - \mathbf{r}_j$ $\quad P_{ij}(\mathbf{u}) = (1/V) \sum_{\mathbf{H}} f_i(\mathbf{H}) f_j(\mathbf{H}) \exp - 2\pi i \mathbf{H} \cdot \mathbf{u}$

The weight of the ijth peak is given by

$$\int_0^V P_{ij}(\mathbf{u})\, dV = Z_i Z_j \tag{84}$$

The height of the peak, however, is

$$P_{ij}(0) = (1/V) \sum_{\mathbf{H}} f_i(\mathbf{H}) f_j(\mathbf{H}) = \int_0^V \rho_i(\mathbf{r}) \rho_j(\mathbf{r})\, dV \tag{85}$$

Note that the peak height and the peak weight are equal only when the electrons are concentrated at a point. In all other cases the peak height is proportional to the peak weight only to the extent that the scattering factor of any given atom j can be represented as $Z_j\hat{f}$ where $\hat{f}$ is a factor dependent on $\mathbf{H}$ (i.e., the scattering angle) and is independent of the atoms. In most cases,

$$\frac{\text{Height of a given peak } ij}{\text{Height of origin peak}} = \frac{Z_i Z_j}{\sum_{j=1}^{N} Z_j^2}$$

The peak density η is approximately the number of interatomic vectors per Å^3, calculated under the assumption that all the $(N^2 - N)$ interatomic vectors are distributed uniformly over the unit cell. The peak density is probably a good measure of the complexity of the particular structure determination. Some examples of fairly difficult structures solved by methods based on $P(\mathbf{r})$ are:

1. Cellobiose:[21] 2 molecules $C_{12}O_{11}H_{22}$ in $P2_1$; N (omitting hydrogen atoms) = 46; η = 2.8 Å^3
2. Harunganin:[22] 8 molecules of $C_{30}H_{36}O_4$ in $C2/c$, $N = 272$; η = 6.8 Å^3

Sharpening of the Patterson Function. The volume occupied by a single atom is of the order of 1 Å^3. The unit-cell volume of structures with one hundred or so atoms is of the order of only 1,000 Å^3. Therefore, the peaks in $P(\mathbf{r})$ usually overlap. In general, the better the resolution of peaks in $P(\mathbf{r})$, the more successful are the methods of determining the structure from $P(\mathbf{r})$. Therefore, it is advisable that the starting point of a structure analysis be a good sharpened Patterson function. Such functions are calculated by Fourier synthesis using $I(h,k,l) \cdot M(S)$ as coefficients where $I(h,k,l)$ are the experimentally measured intensities and $M(S)$ is a suitable modifying function of scattering angle (i.e., $S = \sin\theta/\lambda$). The actual form of the modifying function $M(S)$ depends on how much sharpening is desired.

Patterson Sharpening. In this procedure,[23] the modified coefficients are

$$|F_M(\mathbf{H})|^2 = M(S)I(\mathbf{H}) \tag{86}$$

where

$$M(S) = \left[\frac{\sum_{j=1}^{N} Z_j}{\sum_{j=1}^{N} f_j(\mathbf{H})}\right]^2 \tag{87}$$

and can be calculated, provided that both (1) the chemical composition of the crystal and (2) the curves giving atomic f_j vs. $\sin\theta/\lambda$ are available.[24] The modified intensities correspond to a structure of point atoms of scattering powers Z_j, provided the dependence of f_j on $\sin\theta/\lambda$ is the same for all the atoms (i.e., for values of $j = 1, N$), a proviso which can be seen to hold from the following arguments. If the atoms are point scatterers, all the Z_j scattering electrons are concentrated at a point $\mathbf{r}_j$, the curve of f vs. $\sin\theta/\lambda$ is a straight line, and the structure factor is

$$F_{pt}(\mathbf{H}) = \sum_{j=1}^{N} Z_j \exp 2\pi i\mathbf{H}\cdot\mathbf{r}_j \tag{88}$$

while the intensities are given by

$$|F_{pt}(\mathbf{H})|^2 = \sum_{i=1}^{N}\sum_{j=1}^{N} Z_i Z_j \exp 2\pi i\mathbf{H}\cdot(\mathbf{r}_i - \mathbf{r}_j) \tag{89}$$

In actuality, the scattering atoms are far from being "points." In fact, the Z_j electrons of the jth atom are distributed over the atomic volume so that $f_j(\mathbf{H})$ is now a function of $\sin\theta/\lambda$, provided the electron distribution is isotropic in space. The intensities given by a real crystal are then

$$|F_{rl}(\mathbf{H})|^2 = \sum_{i=1}^{N}\sum_{j=1}^{N} f_i(\mathbf{H})f_j(\mathbf{H}) \exp 2\pi i\mathbf{H}\cdot(\mathbf{r}_i - \mathbf{r}_j) \tag{90}$$

A simple relation between $|F_{rl}|^2$ and $|F_{pt}|^2$ is obtained if

$$f_j(\mathbf{H}) = \hat{f}(\mathbf{H}) \cdot Z_j \tag{91}$$

Equation (91) means that the scattering power of any given atom j can be obtained from the atomic number Z_j provided the $\hat{f}$ vs. $\sin \theta/\lambda$ curve is available. The $\hat{f}$ curve is assumed to be the same for all the atoms (see Fig. 6) and is given by

$$\hat{f}(\mathbf{H}) = \sum_{j=1}^{N} f_j(\mathbf{H}) / \sum_{j=1}^{N} Z_j \tag{92}$$

Under such circumstances [from Eqs. (89) and (90)],

$$|F_{rl}|^2 = (\hat{f})^2 |F_{pt}|^2$$

or

$$|F_{pt}(\mathbf{H})|^2 = \frac{|F_{rl}(\mathbf{H})|^2}{(\hat{f})^2} = |F_{rl}(\mathbf{H})|^2 \left[\frac{\sum_{j=1}^{N} Z_j}{\sum_{j=1}^{N} f_j(\mathbf{H})} \right]^2 \tag{93}$$

The ${}^sP(r)$ function, synthesized with $|F_{pt}(H)|^2$, usually contains peaks sharper than those of the unsharpened function. However, ${}^sP(r)$ does not correspond to the Patter-

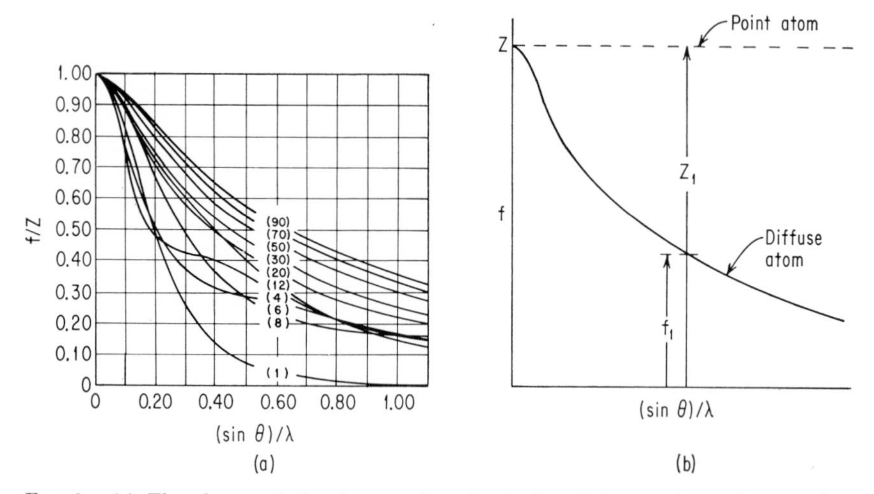

Fig. 6. (*a*) The shapes of the f curves for atoms of various atomic numbers. (*After Harker and Kasper.*) (*b*) The shape of the f curve for a real atom and a point atom. (*Figure adapted from M. J. Buerger, Vector Space and Its Application in Crystal Structure Investigation, John Wiley & Sons, Inc., New York, 1959.*)

son of a point-atom structure. There are two reasons for this. First, one has to consider the thermal motion of the nuclei. The nuclear motion can be corrected for, to the extent that the dynamics of the lattice can be approximated by a factor of the Debye-Waller type. For this,

$$M_t(S) = M(S) \cdot \exp\left(+2B \sin^2 \theta/\lambda^2\right) \tag{94}$$

where B is usually the Debye-Waller factor. But so far as sharpening is concerned, B can be any suitable positive integer, where, as B increases, the degree of sharpening increases. However, it is not advisable to oversharpen the Patterson function because of negative ripples arising from series termination. Secondly, one has to remember that even though one uses point-atom intensities, one does not get back a point-atom Patterson because of the finite nature of the transform.

Normal Sharpening. A second procedure of sharpening involves the use of "normalized" intensities defined by

$$|E(\mathbf{H})|^2 = I(\mathbf{H})/\langle I(\mathbf{H})\rangle \tag{95}$$

where $\langle I(\mathbf{H})\rangle$ is the value of the local average of the intensities at the $\sin\theta/\lambda$ value corresponding to $I(\mathbf{H})$.* The principal advantage is that this method does not require any knowledge of atomic "f curves." Also, the experimental values of $I(\mathbf{H})$ can be placed on a relative scale. In this procedure, the intensities are grouped into ranges of $\sin\theta/\lambda$ (i.e., either spherical shells of equal volume in three-dimensional reciprocal space or circular annuli of equal area in two dimensions, as the case may be) and the average $\langle I(\mathbf{H})\rangle$ of the intensities in each range is computed. The "normalized" intensities [Eq. (95)] can be derived by dividing $I(\mathbf{H})$ by the corresponding $\langle I\rangle$ obtained from a plot of $\langle I\rangle$ vs. $\sin\theta/\lambda$. Note that the local average of $|E(\mathbf{H})|^2$ is unity over the entire range of $\sin\theta/\lambda$. Therefore, $|E(\mathbf{H})|^2$ corresponds to the intensity given by a

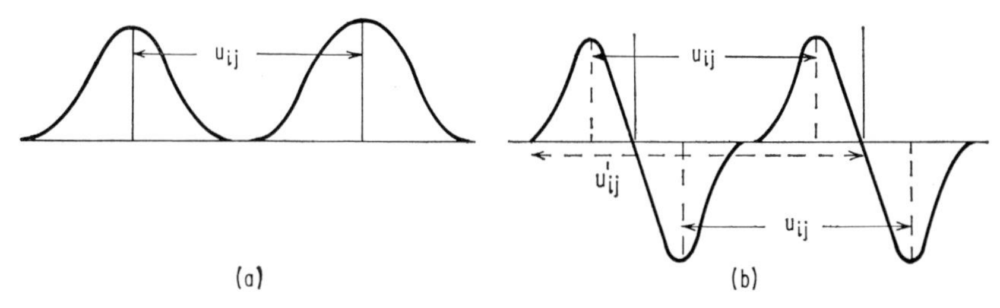

FIG. 7. (*a*) The $\rho(u)$ distribution of two atoms in one dimension. (*b*) The $\nabla\rho(u)$ distribution of the two atoms.

set of point atoms. The synthesized ${}^nP(\mathbf{r})$ is a fairly good approximation to the vector set; any observed deviation is a result of the finiteness of the transform.

Gradient Sharpening. If the modifying function is given by

$$M(S) = \sin^2\theta/\lambda^2 \tag{96}$$

the corresponding ${}^gP(\mathbf{r})$ is synthesized with $|F|^2 \sin^2\theta/\lambda^2$. It is easy to prove that ${}^gP(\mathbf{r})$ is the self-convolution of $\nabla\rho(\mathbf{r})$, where ∇ is the gradient operator. For a general nonorthogonal lattice,†

$$\nabla = a^*(\partial/\partial x) + b^*(\partial/\partial y) + c^*(\partial/\partial z) \tag{97}$$

Inasmuch as the unsharpened $P(\mathbf{r})$ is the self-convolution of $\rho(\mathbf{r})$, the gradient-sharpened $P(\mathbf{r})$ contains, in general, sharper peaks. However, the sharp peaks are accompanied by negative ripples arising from (1) series termination and (2) the inherent nature of ${}^gP(\mathbf{r})$, as is obvious from Fig. 7*a* and *b*. Negative peaks are caused by convolutions that correspond to $u = u'$. Because of such ripples, neighboring peaks may get shifted and in some cases may even get completely suppressed.

* If the scattering factors are known, one may as well use

$$\sum_{j=1}^{N} f_j^2(\mathbf{H})$$

in the place of $\langle I\rangle$, provided $I(\mathbf{H})$ has already been corrected for the Debye-Waller factor B.

† The F.T. of $\int_0^1 \nabla\rho(\mathbf{r})\cdot\nabla\rho(\mathbf{r}+\mathbf{u})\,dv$ is $4\pi^2\mathbf{H}\cdot\mathbf{H} = 16\pi^2\sin^2\theta/\lambda^2$.

A method of offsetting these drastic effects of the negative ripples is to add a small fraction of the unsharpened Patterson function to the gradient Patterson; this fraction could be anywhere between 5 and 20 per cent. A good example of a successful structure determination from a Patterson function sharpened by these procedures is cellobiose.[21]

Removal of Certain Peaks from $P(\mathbf{r})$. The quality of the $P(\mathbf{r})$ can often be improved by eliminating partially or completely some of the interatomic vectors. The big peak at the origin is removed if $P(\mathbf{r})$ is synthesized with the coefficient

$$|F(\mathbf{H})|^2 - \sum_{j=1}^{N} f_j^2(\mathbf{H})$$

When the positions of a certain number (P) of atoms $\mathbf{r}_{Pj}$ are known, the corresponding interatomic vectors $\mathbf{r}_{Pi} - \mathbf{r}_{Pj}$ are suppressed by synthesizing with coefficients

$$|F(\mathbf{H})|^2 - |F_P(\mathbf{H})|^2 \text{ where } F_P = \sum_{j=1}^{P} f_{Pj} \exp 2\pi i \mathbf{H} \cdot \mathbf{r}_{Pj}$$

Summary. Since a number of options are available in calculating $P(\mathbf{r})$, the following summary is given. Let $P(\mathbf{r})$ be a function synthesized with coefficient $C(\mathbf{H}) \cdot M(S)$ where $C(\mathbf{H})$ involves the intensity while $M(S)$ is a modifying function of $\sin \theta/\lambda$.

Case 1. $C(\mathbf{H}) = I(\mathbf{H})$, the experimental values of intensities are on a relative scale and $M(S) = 1$. $P(\mathbf{r})$ is unsharpened. The function values are on a relative scale. In most cases, a good approximation is

$$\frac{\text{Peak height at a given } \mathbf{u}_{ij}}{\text{Peak height at origin } 0} = \frac{Z_i Z_j}{\sum_{j=1}^{N} Z_j^2}$$

Case 2. $C(\mathbf{H}) = I(H)/\langle I(\mathbf{H})\rangle$ (i.e., normalized intensities, $|E(\mathbf{H})|^2$). $M(S) = 1$. $P(\mathbf{r})$ is sharpened.

Case 3. $C(\mathbf{H}) = |E(\mathbf{H})|^2 - 1$. $M(S) = 1$. $P(\mathbf{r})$ corresponds to a sharpened Patterson with origin peak removed.

Case 4. $C(\mathbf{H})$ = same as Case 3. $M(S) = \exp +2B \sin^2 \theta/\lambda^2$. B = any suitable positive integer, not necessarily the Debye-Waller factor. $P(\mathbf{r})$ is further sharpened.

Case 5. $C(H)$ = same as Case 3. $M(S) = \sin^2 \theta/\lambda^2$. $P(\mathbf{r})$ is a gradient Patterson, origin peak removed.

Case 6. $C(\mathbf{H}) = I(\mathbf{H})/\langle I(\mathbf{H})\rangle - a_1 + b_1 I(\mathbf{H})$ where $0 < a_1 < 1$ and $0 < b_1 < 1$. $M(S) = \sin^2 \theta/\lambda^2$. $P(\mathbf{r})$ is the gradient Patterson with suppression of a fraction a_1 of origin peak and addition of fraction b_1 of the unsharpened Patterson. Case 6 is the one commonly used. The following are two possibilities whose potentialities have not yet been completely investigated.

Case 7. $C(\mathbf{H}) = I(\mathbf{H})$. $M(S) = \sum_{j=1}^{P} C_j B_j(\mathbf{H})$ where C_j = a suitable set of constants and $B_j(\mathbf{H}) = (\sin \theta/\lambda)^{2j}$. $P(\mathbf{r})$ is a linear combination of the self-convolutions of different derivatives of $\rho(\mathbf{r})$.

Case 8. $C(\mathbf{H}) = \sum_{j=1}^{P} C_j |E(\mathbf{H})|^{2j}$ where $j = 1, 2, \ldots, P$. $M(S)$ = a suitable function of $\sin \theta/\lambda$. $P(\mathbf{r})$ is a linear combination of different orders of self-convolution of $\rho(\mathbf{r})$.

In both Cases 7 and 8, the coefficients C_j may be chosen in such a fashion as to emphasize the vectors $\mathbf{r}_i - \mathbf{r}_j$ and eliminate the negative ripples. An encouraging feature in Case 8 is the possibility that peaks such as $\mathbf{r}_i - \mathbf{r}_j + \mathbf{r}_k - \mathbf{r}_l \cdots$ that exist in transforms $|E(\mathbf{H})|^{2j}$ (where $j \geq 2$) are uniformly distributed because of their very large number.

Analytical Method of Obtaining Point-atom Pattersons. It appears that, even though one uses sharpened coefficients, one does not get back a Patterson function which is really a good approximation to that of a point-atom structure unless one increases the range of the coefficients used in the summation. An experimental method of extending the range of the coefficients consists in using shorter x-ray wavelengths and in collecting the data at lower temperatures. Further extension may be achieved by means of an analytical method[25,26,27] based on Fourier inversion of the Patterson function. The method appears to make use of properties such as the positivity of the electron-density function and certain information-retrieving properties of the accumulation of minima functions, to be discussed later. A detailed discussion, however, is not given here, in view of the fact that the method appears to be in the early stages of development.

Determination of the Structure from the Patterson Function. *Methods Based on Superpositions of Patterson Functions.* The methods[19] of determining a structure from the $P(\mathbf{r})$ function are, in general, based on the fact that the F set can be recovered from the V set by superimposing two copies of the V set. This is done by shifting the origin of one copy by an interatomic vector $\mathbf{u}_{ab}(= \mathbf{r}_a - \mathbf{r}_b)$ and picking out the peaks which coincide (see Fig. 8). Note that the original copy has peaks at $\mathbf{r}_i - \mathbf{r}_j$, while the shifted copy has peaks at $\mathbf{r}_i - \mathbf{r}_j + \mathbf{r}_b - \mathbf{r}_a$ (where $i = 1, N$; $j = 1, N$).

A peak in the second copy can coincide with a peak in the first copy only if $\mathbf{r}_i - \mathbf{r}_j + \mathbf{r}_b - \mathbf{r}_a = \mathbf{r}_m - \mathbf{r}_n$, i.e., only when subscript $j = b$ or $i = a$. It is clear that a superposition involving a single vector $\mathbf{u}_{ab}$ can provide only the peaks at $\mathbf{r}_i - \mathbf{r}_a$ and $\mathbf{r}_b - \mathbf{r}_j$, i.e., the structure duplicated by its inverse about the midpoint of the shift vector $\mathbf{u}_{ba}$. To pick out the structure alone it is necessary to carry out the superposition with a second interatomic vector, say $\mathbf{u}_{cd}$. The result would be the structure and its inverse about the midpoint of u_{dc}. The output of the first superposition has peaks at $\pm(\mathbf{r}_i - \mathbf{\Delta}_{ab}/2)$, while that of the second has peaks at $\pm(\mathbf{r}_j - \mathbf{\Delta}_{cd}/2)$, where $\mathbf{\Delta}_{ab} = \mathbf{r}_a + \mathbf{r}_b$, $\mathbf{\Delta}_{cd} = \mathbf{r}_c + \mathbf{r}_d$, and $i, j = 1, N$. The structure can be picked out by making a superposition with the two outputs after transforming them to a common origin.

Image-seeking Function. An equivalent way of interpreting the above procedure is in terms of the V set; the V set contains all the images (N in number) of the structure. Note that an image "a" of the structure is the F set referred to $\mathbf{r}_a$ as the origin. The technique of recovering (any) one image from the V set is called image seeking. The basic idea of image seeking is to recover the complete image, knowing a fragment of it. For instance, if a specific interatomic vector $\mathbf{u}_{ab}$ $(= \mathbf{r}_a - \mathbf{r}_b)$ is known, then a line element of the inverse image "a" is available. The image "a" is sought out as follows: The values of $P(\mathbf{r})$ are calculated over a range of $\mathbf{r}$ pertinent to the problem. The function values are examined at two points $\mathbf{r}$ and $\mathbf{r} + \mathbf{u}_{ab}$. If the two values are simultaneously large enough to account for interatomic vectors at both termini of $\mathbf{u}_{ab}$, then a "coincidence" (or a suitable "measure" for a coincidence) is marked at position vector $\mathbf{r}$; the calculation is carried out for all values of $\mathbf{r}$ in one complete unit cell; the function values for $\mathbf{r}$ outside the asymmetric unit are obtained from a knowledge of the symmetry of the vector set. The output of the complete calculation (usually carried out on a digital computer) is a function which is a measure of the coincidence at a given point $\mathbf{r}$.

From considerations under Methods Based on Superpositions of Patterson Functions it is obvious that the output contains peaks at $\pm(\mathbf{r}_i - \mathbf{\Delta}_{ab}/2)$, i.e., the image "$a$" and inverse image "$b$."

To obtain the image "a" alone, it is necessary that the image-seeking fragment be of higher order than a line element $\mathbf{u}_{ab}$. An image-seeking element of order P is defined by a set of P interatomic vectors $\mathbf{u}_{aj}$ $(j = 1, P)$. The calculation of the corresponding Pth-order image function is as follows: for a given $\mathbf{r}$, the values of the Patterson function are examined at the $P + 1$ points $\mathbf{r}$, $\mathbf{r} + \mathbf{u}_{aj}$, . . . , $\mathbf{r} + \mathbf{u}_{aP}$, and if each one of the $(P + 1)$ values is equal to or greater than a certain value, say $Pmin$ (expected for a peak corresponding to an interatomic vector), then the image-seeking function at $\mathbf{r}$ is defined to have some value, say unity; otherwise the function is defined to be zero. It follows that the output function is nonzero only at values of

$$\mathbf{r} = \mathbf{r}_j - \mathbf{r}_a \ (j = 1, N)$$

The reason is that only when $\mathbf{r} = \mathbf{r}_j - \mathbf{r}_a$, each one of $P + 1$ points $\mathbf{r} + \mathbf{u}_{ak}$ becomes $\mathbf{r}_i - \mathbf{r}_k$ so that the corresponding values of the Patterson function will be equal to or greater than *Pmin*.

It is clear that the image "a" can be found provided (1) the order P of the image-seeking fragment is greater than 1, and (2) the fragment is defined by a set of P interatomic vectors all belonging to the same inverse image "a." The second criterion means that the vectors should be of the form $\mathbf{u}_{P_iP_j}$ where one subscript P_i is fixed at a and the other is allowed to take values from $1, P$. The case of $P = 1$ and $P_i = P_j = a$ corresponds to a calculation involving the null vector and yields a new $P(\mathbf{r})$ with values normalized and truncated at *Pmin*. The case $P = 2$ corresponds to picking out image "a" and inverse image (i.e., enantiomorph) "b." For $P > 2$ and P_j fixed at a (instead of P_i fixed at a) the output yields the inverse image "a."

From the above discussion it is also clear that, when a given image-seeking fragment is part of more than one image, the output will yield all those images. Such multiple solutions are of common occurrence in practical structure determination. However, the multiplicity of the solutions decreases as the order of P increases so that in actual cases, a number of iterative cycles of calculations of the image-seeking function may be necessary. The order of P is slowly increased from cycle to cycle, making sure that the new interatomic vectors that are input do really correspond to the image that is being sought. This generally requires judgment and intuition of the investigator, though one may be guided to some extent by considerations of stereochemistry and additional analytical methods such as the *PMA* function, to be discussed later.

An Example. The above principles will be made clear by the following example: Fig. 8*a* shows the positions of four atoms named a, b, c, and d in space group $P1$. Figure 8*b* shows the image "a," which is obtained from Fig. 8*a* by transforming the origin to atom "a." This can be done by subtracting the coordinates of atom "a" from those of a, b, c, and d. Figure 8*c*, *d*, and *e* shows the images "b," "c," and "d," respectively. Figure 8*f* is obtained by putting Fig. 8*b*, *c*, *d*, and *e* together on the common origin, and plotting all 16 peak positions. Clearly, this composite diagram will have a value of 4 at the origin, assuming that the strength of each atom is 1. Figure 8*f* is the vector set and contains the four images. Figure 8*g* is a composite diagram of the four inverse images. (An inverse image is obtained by inverting the direct image about the origin.) Note that Fig. 8*g* is identical with Fig. 8*f*; this only illustrates that the vector set of a fundamental set is identical to the vector set of the inverse of the fundamental set.

Figure 8*h* is a plot of one unit cell of the vector set, with origin on the peak of height value 4. Given the structure, i.e., Fig. 8*a*, it is a trivial problem to obtain the vector set, i.e., Fig. 8*h*. But the problem of crystallography is to obtain Fig. 8*a*, starting with the Patterson function which is not Fig. 8*h* but only an approximation to Fig. 8*h*.

We shall now illustrate the principles of the method of recovering Fig. 8*a* from Fig. 8*h*.

The first step is to choose one of the peak positions from Fig. 8*h*. Let us suppose this to be the peak (0,3). This interatomic vector (0,3) is part of the image "a," as may be seen from Fig. 8*b*. Now we make two copies of Fig. 8*h* and superimpose the second copy on top of the first, after putting the origin of the second copy at the point (0,3) of the first copy. The peak positions are shown by circles on copy 2, while those on copy 1 are shown by the crosses, and the composite diagram is shown in Fig. 8*i*. It may be seen that some circles coincide with some crosses, and others do not. The coincidences have been marked on Fig. 8*j*. The six peaks of Fig. 8*j* describe the structure and its inverse about the point (0,3.5): i.e., the midpoint of the shift vector (0,7). This vector is the interatomic vector between atoms a and b; correspondingly Fig. 8*j* yields the image "b" and the inverse image "a." The remaining problem is to eliminate one of the two and discover either image "b" or the inverse image "a." For this, a copy of Fig. 8*j* is superimposed on Fig. 8*h*, with the origin at the point (2,4)

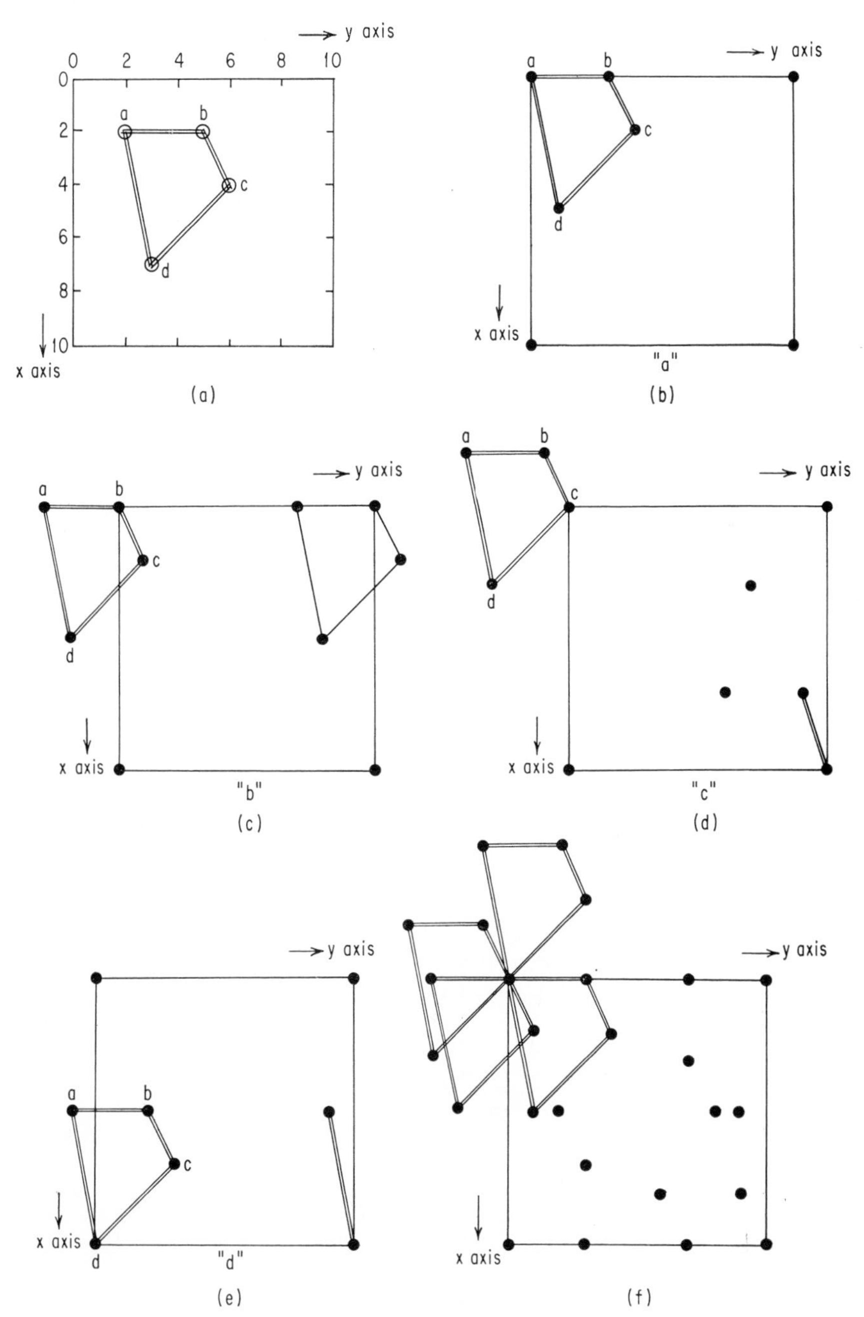

FIG. 8. (*a*) A simulated two-dimensional structure of four point atoms *a*, *b*, *c*, and *d* in space group *P*1. (*b*) The image "*a*" of the simulated structure. (*c*) The image "*b*" of the simulated structure. (*d*) The image "*c*" of the simulated structure. (*e*) The image "*d*" of the simulated structure. (*f*) The assembly of the four images "*a*," "*b*," "*c*," and "*d*" on a common origin.

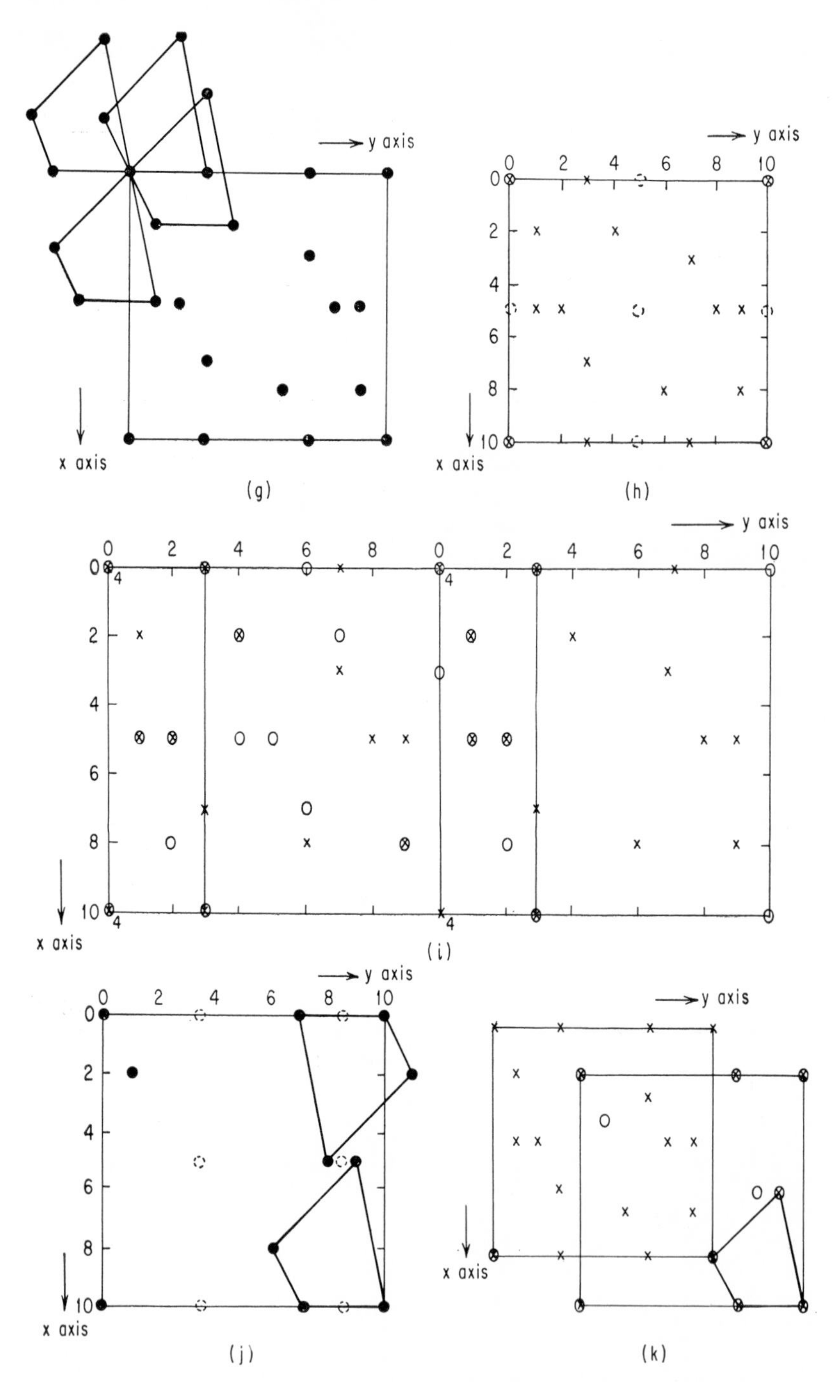

FIG. 8. *(g)* The composite diagram of the four inverse images. *(h)* The Patterson function, theoretically calculated, of the simulated structure. Note the center of symmetry at (0,0), and the accompanying center of symmetry at (5,0), (0,5), and (5,5). The interatomic vectors are shown by crosses on a 10 × 10 grid. *(j)* The output of the procedure of vector shift. This output was obtained by picking out the coincidences between the circles and crosses in Fig. 8*i*. *(k)* The procedure of double vector shift: A copy of Fig. 8*j* was placed with its origin at grid point (2,4) of Fig. 8*h*, and the coincidences were marked.

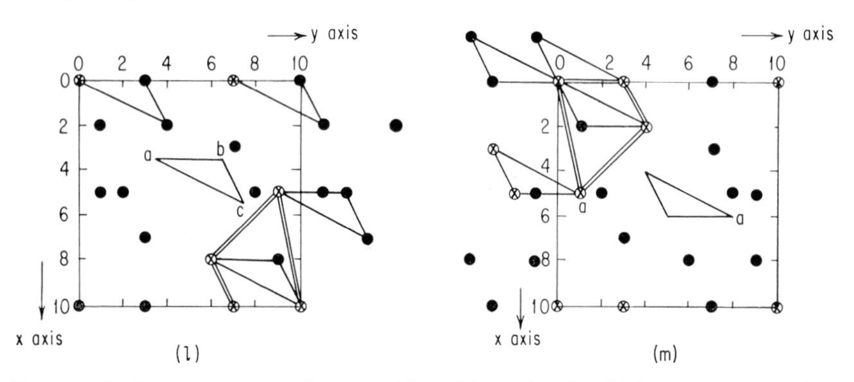

FIG. 8. (*l*) The procedure of image seeking with a triangle which is a fragment of the image "*a*," Fig. 8*b*. (*m*) The procedure of image seeking with a triangle which is a fragment of the inverse image "*a*."

and the coincidences marked (see Fig. 8*k*). There are four coincidences, and these describe the image "*b*."

That this procedure is equivalent to image seeking with two vectors may be seen from Fig. 8*l*. This diagram is obtained by taking a triangle *abc* and allowing it to roam from grid point to grid point of Fig. 8*h*. Coincidences have been marked by crosses whenever all three termini of the triangle end up within circles. There are only four such coincidences, and these describe the inverse image "*a*"; the reason is that the image-seeking triangle, in this case, is part of the direct image "*a*." When the same operation is performed with a triangle which is part of the inverse image "*a*," one discovers the direct image "*a*," as can be seen from Fig. 8*m*.

This example shows that given a vector set, it is possible in principle to discover the structure. However, it must be emphasized that experimental data give only a poor approximation to the vector set. This fact is the most complicating feature in solving the phase problem.

Sum Function. The image-seeking function discussed above is quite general. More specific functions can be developed if specific operations are performed on the values of $P(\mathbf{r})$ at the $(P + 1)$ points $\mathbf{r}$, $\mathbf{r} + \mathbf{u}_{a1}$, etc. . . . These operations may be summation, multiplication, extraction of minima, etc. . . . Let us take the image-seeking element to be defined by the set of vectors $\mathbf{u}_{aj}$ where $j = 1, P + 1$. The value of $j = 1$ corresponds to the null vector $\mathbf{u}_{aa} = 0$.

The sum function is defined by

$$S(\mathbf{r}) = \sum_{j=1}^{P+1} P(\mathbf{r} + \mathbf{u}_{aj})$$

and can be calculated by either manually adding the Patterson-function values, or else by Fourier synthesizing with $|F(\mathbf{H})|^2 F_P$ as coefficients where $|F(H)|^2$ may be the sharpened intensities and F_P is calculated from

$$F_P = \sum_{j=1}^{P+1} \exp + 2\pi i \mathbf{H} \cdot \mathbf{u}_{aj}$$

The major peaks of $S(\mathbf{r})$ correspond to the image "*a*," but such peaks occur against a background of minor and unwanted peaks. The ratio of a wanted structural peak (i.e., $\mathbf{r}_i - \mathbf{r}_a$) to a background peak is of the order of $P + 1$. Note that syntheses such as $S(\mathbf{r})$ presume that a certain number (P) of atoms have been located with respect to the atom a. If the scattering factors f_P are also known, a weighted sum function can be synthesized with coefficient $|F|^2F_P$, where F_P can be calculated from

$$F_P(\mathbf{H}) = \sum_{j=1}^{P} f_{Pi} \exp + 2\pi i\mathbf{H} \cdot \mathbf{r}_{Pj}$$

This weighted sum function has been called the α synthesis. The major peaks of the α synthesis are at $\mathbf{r}_{Pj}$ ($P_j = 1, P$, i.e., input atoms), the second-order peaks are at $\mathbf{r}_{Qj}$ ($j = 1, N - P$) and correspond to the remaining atoms of the image, while the third-order peaks are the unwanted and minor background peaks at $\mathbf{r}_i - \mathbf{r}_j + \mathbf{r}_{Pk}$ ($i \neq j$; $j \neq P_k$). The peak heights are proportional to

$$Z_{Pj} \sum_{j=1}^{N} Z_j^2 \qquad Z_{Qj} \sum_{j=1}^{P} Z_j^2 \qquad \text{and} \qquad Z_iZ_jZ_{Pk}$$

respectively.

The above results are easily obtained by application of the convolution-integral theorem. Each sum function is the convolution of $P(\mathbf{r})$ with $\rho_P(\mathbf{r})$. Therefore, the peak positions and the peak heights can be easily worked out [see content of $P(u)$ above]. There exist a number of sum functions depending on the form of the convoluting functions. In fact, the conventional Fourier itself is one such weighted sum function. The various sum functions proposed so far[28–31] differ from one another with respect to the number and heights of the peaks of the unwanted background.

The advantage of sum functions is the possibility of direct computation from the intensity data [without recourse to $P(\mathbf{r})$] by means of simple Fourier synthesis; the disadvantage is the poor resolution resulting from the unwanted background.[32]

Product Function. The product function[19] is defined as

$$\Pi_P(\mathbf{r}) = \prod_{j=1}^{P+1} P(\mathbf{r} + \mathbf{u}_{aj}) \tag{98}$$

and corresponds to forming the product of values of $P(\mathbf{r})$ at the $(P + 1)$ points $\mathbf{r} + \mathbf{u}_{aa}, \ldots, \mathbf{r} + \mathbf{u}_{aj}, \mathbf{r} + \mathbf{u}_{aP}$. The Π_P function is quite similar to the sum function and is a Fourier synthesis with coefficient $A(\mathbf{H}_1)$ given by

$$A(\mathbf{H}_1) = \sum_{\mathbf{H}_2}\sum_{\mathbf{H}_3} \cdots \sum_{\mathbf{H}_{P+1}} \left[\prod_{j=2}^{P+1} (|F(\mathbf{H}_j)|^2 \exp -2\pi i\mathbf{H}_j \cdot \mathbf{u}_{aj}) \right] \left| F\left(\mathbf{H}_1 - \sum_{j=2}^{P+1} \mathbf{H}_j\right)\right|^2 \tag{99}$$

Minimum Function. Among the various image-seeking functions, the most useful one is probably $M(\mathbf{r})$, the minimum function.[19] For a given image-seeking fragment of order P, the minimum function at $\mathbf{r}$ is defined as the minimum of the values of $P(\mathbf{r})$ at the $(P + 1)$ points $\mathbf{r}, \ldots, \mathbf{r} + \mathbf{u}_{aj}, \ldots, \mathbf{r} + \mathbf{u}_{aP}$. Symbolically

$$PM(\mathbf{r}) = \min\,[P(\mathbf{r}), P(\mathbf{r} + \mathbf{u}_a), \ldots, P(\mathbf{r} + \mathbf{u}_{aP})] \cdots \tag{100}$$

where min is the operation of extracting the minimum of the values within the accompanying square brackets. In principle, the peaks of $M(\mathbf{r})$ correspond to the peaks of the image "a." The peak height at a typical $\mathbf{r}_i - \mathbf{r}_a$ (where $i = 1, N$) is proportional to $Z_a(\min\,\{Z_1,Z_2 \ldots Z_P\})$.

The main advantage of $M(\mathbf{r})$ over the other image functions is the high resolution and smaller background. The reason is the inherent nature of the operation of extracting the minimum.

The quality of the minimum function increases quite rapidly as the order P is increased. However, great care is to be exercised at fairly large values of P. The interatomic vectors should be known to a high degree of accuracy; otherwise the function may be completely washed out. For this reason, some workers[22] prefer to take the sum of the last two or three minima instead of the last minimum of the set of values $P(\mathbf{r} + \mathbf{u}_{aa}), \ldots, P(\mathbf{r} + \mathbf{u}_{aP})$.

The Accumulation Functions. These functions are of recent origin[33,34] and appear to be quite useful. In general, they are integrals of the various image-seeking functions (except the sum function) over the unit-cell volume and give a "measure" of the correctness of the image-seeking fragment in question.

Consider one such fragment of order P defined by a set of P vectors $\mathbf{u}_i (i = 2, P + 1)$ plus the null vector $\mathbf{u}_1 = 0$. The accumulation of minima functions of order P is defined by

$$PMA(\mathbf{u}_1, \mathbf{u}_2, \ldots, \mathbf{u}_P, \mathbf{u}_{P+1}) = \int_V PM(\mathbf{r})\, dV$$

where $PM(r)$ is defined by Eq. (100). From the previous discussion (see Image-seeking Function), it is clear that PMA may have a large value only if the vectors $\mathbf{u}_1, \mathbf{u}_2, \ldots, \mathbf{u}_{P+1}$ are $\mathbf{u}_1 = 0$, $\mathbf{u}_2 = \mathbf{r}_1 - \mathbf{r}_a$, $\mathbf{u}_3 = \mathbf{r}_2 - \mathbf{r}_a, \ldots, \mathbf{u}_{P+1} = \mathbf{r}_P - \mathbf{r}_a$ or else $\mathbf{u}_1 = 0$, $\mathbf{u}_2 = \mathbf{r}_a - \mathbf{r}_1$, $\mathbf{u}_3 = \mathbf{r}_a - \mathbf{r}_2, \ldots, \mathbf{u}_{P+1} = \mathbf{r}_a - \mathbf{r}_P$. As a result, PMA determines whether or not a given set of vectors $\mathbf{u}_i$ belong to the same image "a." This information is very important in image-seeking procedures.

Further, PMA by itself can be used to determine the complete structure. This requires input of an image fragment of order P and calculation of the PMA function for image fragments of order $P + 1$, where P vectors are defined by the input group and the function is calculated for all values of the last vector $\mathbf{u}$ in one unit cell. The result is a function of $\mathbf{u}$ and contains strong peaks at $\mathbf{u} = \mathbf{r}_i - \mathbf{r}_a$. The advantage of PMA over conventional functions is that PMA is not too critical as to the accuracy of the input vectors. Other accumulation functions are integrals of other image functions and have properties similar to PMA but appear to be less useful.

*Generalized Implication Functions.** The methods described so far are quite general, even though the discussion has been specifically for the space group $P1$. The use of any higher space-group symmetry possessed by $\rho(\mathbf{r})$ is of considerable help in the interpretation of the Patterson function.

Consider the simple example of the monoclinic space group $P2_1$. The equivalent points are (x,y,z) and $(\bar{x}, \frac{1}{2} + y, \bar{z})$. The possible interatomic vectors are then of two classes: (1) those between atoms related by the symmetry operation 2_1, and (2) those between other atoms. Vectors of class 1 are of the form $\pm (2X_j, \frac{1}{2}, 2Z_j)$ so that the section of $P(xyz)$ corresponding to $y = \frac{1}{2}$ contains information about symmetry-related atoms. In fact, this section (when drawn to half the scale for this example) contains peaks which correspond to the projection of the structure down the b axis. A Patterson section such as this one is called a Harker[36] section, and can be computed without even computing $P(\mathbf{r})$. For instance, in the above example,

$$H(x,\tfrac{1}{2},z) = (1/V) \sum_h \sum_l A(hl) \exp -2\pi i(hx + lz) \tag{101}$$

where

$$A(hl) = \sum_k |F(hkl)|^2 \exp -i\pi k \tag{102}$$

Note that $H(x,\frac{1}{2},z)$ is only a two-dimensional summation and therefore is easier to calculate than the three-dimensional $P(\mathbf{r})$.

* The basic theory of the implication functions is due to M. J. Buerger.[20] Here we try to present the theory which is generalized into higher dimensions and higher orders. The method is easily adaptable to digital computers. Similar formulations have been given by other workers in the form of symmetry minimum functions, consistency functions, etc. One example of a structure which was solved systematically by the procedure outlined here is that of the mineral pachnolite.[35]

The actual locations of the Harker sections are available from the equivalent points[2] relevant to the space group. Some simple rules to remember are: (1) Axial-symmetry elements such as N_P parallel to a crystallographic axis a_i have Harker sections at $P/N \perp a_i$. For example, $P2_1$ has Harker section at $y = \frac{1}{2}$. $P4_1$ has two (independent) sections, one at $y = \frac{1}{4}$ and the other at $\frac{1}{2}$; $P2$ has the section at 0, and so on. (2) Reflection planes and glide planes have only Harker lines. In general, a symmetry plane with translational components n_1/m_1 and n_2/m_2 parallel to the a and b axes, respectively, has Harker lines of the form

$$H(n_1/m_1,\, n_2/m_2,\, z)$$

For example, if the (001) plane is a "b glide," the translational components are 0 and $\frac{1}{2}$, and the Harker line is $(0,\frac{1}{2},z)$. If the (001) plane is an n glide, the Harker line is $(\frac{1}{2},\frac{1}{2},z)$; if the plane is a simple mirror, "m," the line is $(0,0,z)$; and so on.

Harker sections are useful, in most cases, to the extent that they may provide a good starting point for carrying out subsequent image-seeking procedures. However, overoptimism about their potentialities is not justifiable, for the simple reason that not all the peaks on a given Harker section do really correspond to vectors between symmetry-related atoms. For example, consider the space group $P2_1$. Any two atoms whose y coordinates differ by $\frac{1}{2}$ by sheer accident will also give rise to a peak on the Harker section. In actual cases, in fact, such fake peaks may outnumber the genuine Harker peaks.

If the space group is such that more than one Harker section is available, the information contained by all of them is usefully combined and given by the implication function $IF(\mathbf{r})$. $IF(\mathbf{r})$ can be calculated from $P(\mathbf{r})$ with the a priori information regarding the space-group symmetry as follows: Let the equivalent points for the given space group be $\vec{S_i}(\mathbf{r})$ where $\vec{S_i}$ is a symmetry operator and $i = 1, n$ (the symmetry number). For a given value of $\mathbf{r}$ (in the asymmetric unit of the space of $\rho(\mathbf{r})$) there are n symmetry-equivalent points given by $\vec{S_i}(\mathbf{r})$. The corresponding n^2 interatomic vectors are $\mathbf{u}_{ij} = \vec{S_i}(\mathbf{r}) - \vec{S_j}(\mathbf{r})$. Knowing $\mathbf{r}$ and $\vec{S_i}$, the $\mathbf{u}_{ij}$ are computed and if the value of $P(\mathbf{u}_{ij})$ at each one of n^2 points $\mathbf{u}_{ij}$ is $>$ than $Pmin$ (see Image-seeking function, above) the IF function at $\mathbf{r}$ is defined to be unity. (The IF function can also be (1) the sum, (2) the product, or (3) the minimum* of the $P(\mathbf{u}_{ij})$ values).† The calculations are carried out for values of $\mathbf{r}$ in an asymmetric unit of the unit cell.

Note that peaks in $IF(\mathbf{r})$ are probable atomic positions that are consistent with the Harker sections (i.e., requirements of space-group symmetry). The symmetry of $IF(\mathbf{r})$ is usually much higher than the symmetry of the corresponding $\rho(\mathbf{r})$. The reasons are: (1) Reversals of signs of coordinate axes are allowed. (2) The origin of a space group can be chosen in more than one way. This $IF(\mathbf{r})$ function is the implication function of order 0.

The importance of $IF(\mathbf{r})$ is that the function yields possible atomic positions located with respect to the space-group symmetry elements. Such a location simplifies the problem of recovery of the F set from the V set because it is now sufficient if the asymmetric unit of the F set is recovered rather than the entire F set. But general procedures such as the one outlined above (see Image-seeking Function) purport to locate the entire F set and subsequently locate the origin of the space group from a careful study of the symmetry of the F set.

The next step in the structure analysis by means of $IF(\mathbf{r})$ is to calculate higher-order $IF(\mathbf{r})$ functions. In general the Pth-order function can be calculated by inserting a certain number P of atoms at $\mathbf{r}_{Pi}$, from a preceding calculation of $IF(\mathbf{r})$, and examining the values of $P(\mathbf{r})$ at the n^2P points given by $\mathbf{u}_{ik} = \vec{S_i}(\mathbf{r}_{Pj}) - \vec{S_k}(\mathbf{r})$ where i and $k = 1$,

* The minimum is probably better than others.

† A fourth possibility is to count the number of times the value of $P(\mathbf{r})$ exceeds $Pmin$ and give this count as the value of the implication function at the point $\mathbf{r}$.

$n; j = 1, P$. The calculation is performed for values of $\mathbf{r}$ in one asymmetric unit of the unit cell. The first cycle of calculation is performed with $P = 0$, which means that one makes use of just the known space-group symmetry of the crystal. A careful study yields possible choices for atoms which have been located with respect to the space-group origin of the unit cell. The subsequent iterative cycles start with $P = 1$, and in each cycle, the number of atoms that are input (i.e., value of P) is increased by one or more. The higher symmetry of the $IF(\mathbf{r})$ function of zero order vanishes as the iterations proceed, and after a few cycles it may be possible to obtain the complete structure.

The power of the $IF(\mathbf{r})$ is considerably increased by the imposition of stereochemical requirements, e.g., prescribing a certain minimum and a maximum value possible for the distances between atoms. In fact, it is possible to program the calculation of $IF(\mathbf{r})$ in such a way as to discover chemically meaningful fragments of the structure. Such procedures, in general, give a better starting point than the simplified $IF(\mathbf{r})$ which inputs only $\vec{S}_i$.

With such programs, a model two-dimensional structure with 20 equal atoms per cell of space-group symmetry $P2_12_12_1$ was solved from the two-dimensional Patterson projection by a systematic procedure; the computation took approximately 30 min on an IBM 1620.

So far we have not explicitly considered the Patterson of centrosymmetric structures. For a structure possessing $P\bar{1}$ as a subgroup, the equivalent points are $\pm(\mathbf{r}_i)$ where $i = 1, N/2$. The corresponding vector set has two types of interatomic vectors besides the origin peak. The first type refers to vectors between atoms related by inversion center; these are single interactions. Their number is N and positions are $\pm 2\mathbf{r}_i$. The second type refers to vectors between atoms not related by inversion; these are at $\pm(\mathbf{r}_i \pm \mathbf{r}_j)$ where $i \neq j$. It is obvious that these are double interactions; i.e., their peak heights are twice that of the single interactions. The number of peaks of double interaction is $\frac{1}{2}(N^2 - 2N)$, i.e., there are $\frac{1}{4}(N^2 - 2N)$ pairs of centrosymmetrically related peaks. The importance of the peaks of the single interactions is as follows: The identification and separation of these single-interaction peaks from those of the double interactions implies the solution of the structure. This follows by merely dividing the coordinates of the above single-interaction peaks by 2. It is unfortunate that such an identification is usually not possible because of the large number of double-interaction peaks, as well as the poor peak resolution of the Patterson function. However, even if a few single interactions can be identified, a good image-seeking fragment is available for further iterations.

From this discussion it is seen that the presence of a center of inversion in $\rho(\mathbf{r})$ is an advantage in interpreting $P(\mathbf{r})$. For one thing, the peak density η of $P(\mathbf{r})$ is only half of what it is if $\rho(\mathbf{r})$ is acentric. These are small advantages, and in general, absence of a center of inversion does not seem to be a great handicap.

Some examples of structure determination by techniques based on image seeking are (1) cellobiose,[21] (2) some boron hydrides,[37] (3) harunganin,[22] and (4) pachnolite.[35]

An Example. Our discussion of Patterson methods has so far been theoretical. We shall now describe an example to illustrate one way of determining a structure from the Patterson function. The example is an "equal-atom" structure in space group $P2_12_12_1$, No. 19 in *International Tables for X-ray Crystallography*, vol. I. This space group is noncentrosymmetric but has three centrosymmetric projections down the three twofold screw axes. The symmetry number $n = 4$, and the four equivalent points are (x,y,z); $(\frac{1}{2} + x, \frac{1}{2} - y, \bar{z})$; $(\bar{x}, \frac{1}{2} + y, \frac{1}{2} - z)$; $(\frac{1}{2} - x, \bar{y}, \frac{1}{2} + z)$, where the origin has been chosen midway between three pairs of nonintersecting screw axes. The relations between the structure amplitudes are

$$\begin{aligned} &|F(hkl)| = |F(\bar{h}k\bar{l})| = |F(h\bar{k}\bar{l})| = |F(\bar{h}\bar{k}l)| \\ &= |F(\bar{h}\bar{k}\bar{l})| = |F(h\bar{k}l)| = |F(\bar{h}kl)| = |F(hk\bar{l})| \end{aligned}$$

Using the above relationships, the general expression for the Patterson function reduces to

$$P(xyz) = (2/V) \sum_0^\infty \sum_0^\infty \sum_0^\infty |F(hkl)|^2[\cos 2\pi(hx + ky + lz) + \cos 2\pi(hx - ky + lz) + \cos 2\pi(hx + ky - lz) + \cos 2\pi(-hx + ky + lz)]$$

$$= (8/V) \sum_0^\infty \sum_0^\infty \sum_0^\infty |F(hkl)|^2 \cos (2\pi hx) \cos (2\pi ky) \cos (2\pi lz) \quad (103)$$

The Patterson function may be calculated by performing the triple Fourier summation, Eq. (103).

In the present example, there are five "equal atoms" of scattering power = 1, so that there are 20 atoms per unit cell. Correspondingly, there are 400 interatomic vectors. Of these 400, there are 20 null vectors, which assemble at the origin and produce an origin peak of strength = 20. The remaining 380 interatomic vectors produce 190 pairs of peaks; the two peaks in each pair will be centrosymmetrically related about the origin, and the strength of each peak is unity. The symmetry of the Patterson function will be $P\frac{2}{m}\frac{2}{m}\frac{2}{m}$. The c-axis projection of the Patterson function is shown in Fig. 9*a* on a 20 × 20 grid. The mirror planes at $x = 10$ and $y = 10$ may be noted; the symmetry is $\frac{2}{m}\frac{2}{m}$. The 380 nonorigin peaks are not all resolved but are overlapping to various degrees.

With this as a starting point, the structure may be determined as follows: The first step is to calculate the $IF(x,y)$ function of order 0. Let us suppose that a grid point is denoted by the two coordinates I, J. The four points equivalent to (I,J) are (I,J), $(10 + I, 10 - J)$, $(20 - I, 10 + J)$, and $(10 - I, 20 - J)$. There are 16 interatomic vectors between these 4 points. These interatomic vectors may be obtained by taking each one of the four points and subtracting from it the four equivalent points, one by one. For instance, consider the specific grid point $I = 0$, $J = 1$; i.e., (0,1). The four equivalent points are (0,1), (10,9), (20,11), and (10,19). The interatomic vectors among these four grid points are obtained by subtracting each grid point in turn from all the others. For example, in the case of grid point (0,1) these vectors are (0,0), (10,12), (20,10), and (10,2). In calculating these, one makes use of the translational properties of the lattice. For instance, grid point $(-10, -18) = (10,2)$ and $(-10, -8) = (10,12)$. The interatomic vectors pertaining to the remaining three grid points are obtained in a similar fashion. Then one looks up the map (Fig. 9*a*) and obtains the Patterson function values at these 16 grid points, i.e., at the termini of the 16 vectors. The minimum value among these 16 Patterson function values is then taken as the value of the IF function at the grid point (0,1).

The entire calculation is then repeated in exactly the same manner for other grid points, in fact, for all values of $I, J = 1, 11$. Thus, one obtains the IF function over an asymmetric unit of the cell. This function, whose order is zero, is shown in Fig. 9*b*. Note the extra symmetry of the diagram, in particular, the additional mirror planes at $x = 5$ and $y = 5$ (i.e., $x = 1/4$ and $y = 1/4$).

The second stage is to choose one or more atoms from the IF function of order 0 and calculate IF functions of higher order. An examination of an asymmetric unit of Fig. 9*b* shows that the strongest peaks (in this case of value 8) occur at (0,1) and (0,4). The next strongest peaks (value 4) occur at (1,1), (4,1), (3,4), and (4,4). Usually, it is a good idea to avoid peaks on special lines. At this stage, there is no clear-cut rule as to which peak should be chosen. In principle, any one peak may be chosen so long as it is not a spurious peak; of course, one does not know a priori whether a given peak is a good one or spurious.

In this example, the peak at (4,4) was chosen. The next step is to obtain the coordinates of the atoms equivalent to the one at (4,4). These are four in number, located at (4,4), (14,6), (16,14), and (6,14). The first-order function may then be calculated as follows: As in the case of the zero-order calculation, one obtains the four equivalent grid points of the starting grid point (I,J); the 16 interatomic vectors between the four grid points are then obtained as described before. In addition to this, one also computes the 16 interatomic vectors between the four input atoms and

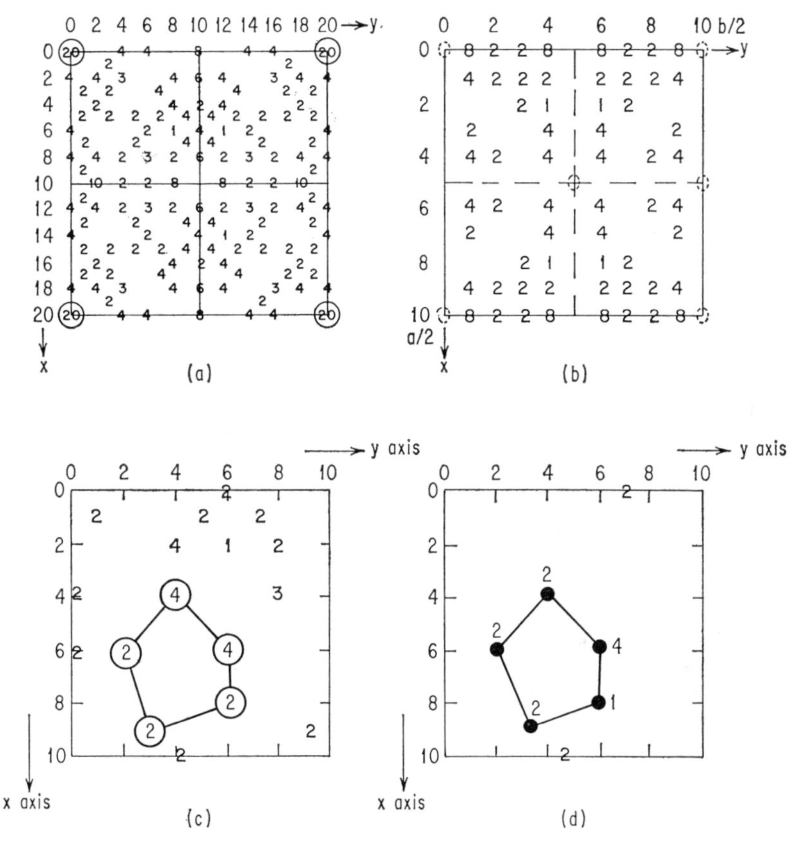

FIG. 9. (*a*) The theoretically computed Patterson function of a simulated model of a structure of point atoms; five atoms per asymmetric unit in space group $P2_12_12_1$. (*b*) The implication function of order 0 of the model. (*c*) The implication function of order 1 of the model. The coordinates of the one atom, which was input, was (4,4). (*d*) The implication function of order 2 of the model. The coordinates of the two atoms, which were input, were (4,4) and (8,6).

the four grid points. The values of the Patterson function at these 32 grid points are obtained from the map shown on Fig. 9*a* and the minimum value among them is the value of the *IF* function of order 1 at grid point (I,J). Upon carrying out the above calculations for all the grid points, one obtains the diagram shown in Fig. 9*c*.

The iterations may be continued by inserting more atoms. In general, the *IF* function of order p can be calculated if the positions of p atoms are known. Basically in such a case one examines the Patterson function at $n^2(p + 1)$ points and finds the minimum value.* Figure 9*d* shows the second-order function calculated on the basis of only two atomic positions known, one at (4,4), the second at (8,6). The structure is clear even at the second-order stage.

Summary. The above description has been given in the minimum-function formulation of the implication theory. As was pointed out earlier, there are other formulations as well. However, one must appreciate the fact that all the various methods are based on the simple fact that the intensity data contain information regarding the interatomic vectors. In forming the Patterson function, one is merely taking the Fourier transform of the data; the aim is clearly to obtain a simple, convenient, and elegant representation of the data. Therefore, the question as to which method should be used might be answered by the following list:

1. The method should be easy to use, at least from the point of view of the computer.
2. The method should aim at full use of the "entire" information contained in the data.
3. It should be possible to introduce useful auxiliary physical and chemical criteria into the formalism of the method.

With this understanding, one may appreciate that what the various image-seeking procedures have in common is the central fact that, in order to obtain the value of the *IF* function at a given grid point, one looks at the values of the Patterson function at $n^2(p + 1)$ points. What is different, among the various methods, is the manner in which one manipulates the values of the Patterson function at these $n^2(p + 1)$ points. In the minimum-function formulation, one takes the minimum of the $n^2(p + 1)$ values and defines it to be the value of the *IF* function. Alternative formulations are as follows:

1. One takes the sum of the last two or three minima.
2. One takes the sum, or a weighted sum, of all the $n^2(p + 1)$ values.
3. One takes the product, or a weighted product, of all the $n^2(p + 1)$ values.
4. A fourth possibility is to accept a certain value of peak height *Pmin* which may be expected for a certain interatomic vector in the Patterson function. Then one may count the number of times the value of the Patterson function equals or exceeds the value *Pmin* and assign this number to be the value of the *IF* function at the grid point in question. Clearly, the maximum possible value of this number, in the case of the *IF* function of order p, of a crystal of symmetry number n, is $n^2(p + 1)$.

Alternatives such as these are usually resorted to in cases where the order of p is very high. They probably assure that no useful information is lost when one is adopting the rather drastic operation of taking the minimum of a large number of values. One must bear in mind that this minimum may conceivably become zero, particularly when one is looking at a large number of points and does not have sufficient accuracy in the coordinates of the input atoms or, for that matter, in the data themselves.

6. DIRECT METHODS OF DETERMINING PHASE ANGLES

So far we have outlined methods of determining a crystal structure from the Patterson function. An alternative procedure is to examine the problem in reciprocal space. In this formalism, the phase problem is the problem of determining the phases of the structure factors, given the intensities $I(\mathbf{H})$; methods aimed at such determinations are called *direct methods*. These methods are "direct" only in the sense that calculation of the Patterson function and the subsequent image-seeking procedures may be bypassed.

* The number $n^2(p + 1)$ has been given for the sake of generality and rigor. In actuality, the number of points is much less than this. At the zero-order stage ($p = 0$), the number is only $\frac{1}{2}(n^2 - n)$, in view of the centrosymmetry and origin peak of the Patterson function. At higher-order stages ($p \neq 0$), the number of points may be just $pn + \frac{1}{2}(n^2 - n)$. The first term pn is the number of cross vectors, i.e., the vectors between the input atoms (i.e., pn in numbers) on one hand and the grid point (I,J) on the other hand. The second term $\frac{1}{2}(n^2 - n)$ is the number of interatomic vectors among the n equivalent points of the grid point (I,J).

The Unitary Structure Factor. The direct methods are best described in terms of certain quantities derivable from the experimentally measured intensities.

The unitary structure factor $U(\mathbf{H})$ is defined by

$$U(\mathbf{H}) = \sum_{j=1}^{N} n_j \exp 2\pi i \mathbf{H} \cdot \mathbf{r}_j \tag{104}$$

where n_j = fractional number of electrons of atom j, i.e.,

$$n_j = Z_j \Big/ \sum_{j=1}^{N} Z_j \tag{105}$$

where Z_j is the atomic number of the atom j. These quantities may be obtained from $F(\mathbf{H})$ by means of the relation

$$U(\mathbf{H}) = F(\mathbf{H})/\hat{f}F(0) \tag{106}$$

where $F(0) = \sum_{j=1}^{N} Z_j$ and $\hat{f}$ is the average-atomic-shape factor. To obtain $|U(\mathbf{H})|^2$ from $I(\mathbf{H})$, it is necessary that (1) the experimental values $I(\mathbf{H})$ must be placed on an absolute scale, (2) the values $I(\mathbf{H})$ must be corrected for thermal motion of the nuclei, (3) the "f_j vs. $\sin\theta/\lambda$" curves are available, and (4) the assumption $f_j = \hat{f}Z_j$ is valid for all atoms in the unit cell. The last condition is obeyed to a large extent by equal-atom structures and to some extent by most structures.

The $|U(\mathbf{H})|^2$ values may be obtained more simply from the normalized intensities $|E(\mathbf{H})|^2$ defined by

$$|E(\mathbf{H})|^2 = I(\mathbf{H})/\langle I(\mathbf{H})\rangle \tag{107}$$

The method of deriving $|E|^2$ from $I(\mathbf{H})$ has been discussed in Sec. 5, under Normal Sharpening. The corresponding $|U(\mathbf{H})|^2$ value is obtained by means of

$$|U(\mathbf{H})|^2 = \left(\sum_{j=1}^{N} n_j^2\right) |E(\mathbf{H})|^2 \tag{108}$$

Note that in this formalism, the $I(\mathbf{H})$ values can be on a relative scale, and no knowledge of either the "f_j curves" or the Debye-Waller factor B is required. Of course, it is necessary to know the atomic numbers Z_j of the atoms in the unit cell, so that the quantity Σn_j^2 can be computed from

$$\sum_{j=1}^{N} n_j^2 = \sum_{j=1}^{N} Z_j^2 \Big/ \left(\sum_{j=1}^{N} Z_j\right)^2 \tag{109}$$

Note also that for equal-atom structures, each $Z_j = Z$ (i.e., subscript j has no meaning), $\Sigma n_j = NZ/NZ = 1$, and $\Sigma n_j^2 = NZ^2/N^2Z^2 = 1/N$.

Both quantities $U(\mathbf{H})$ and $E(\mathbf{H})$ refer to the structure of point atoms. In fact, $U(\mathbf{H})$ refers to the structure factor given by point atoms of strength

$$Z_j \Big/ \left(\sum_{j=1}^{N} Z_j\right) \text{ at } \mathbf{r}_j$$

while $E(\mathbf{H})$ refers to the structure factor given by point atoms of strength

$$Z_j \Big/ \left(\sum_{j=1}^{N} Z_j^2\right)^{1/2} \text{ at } \mathbf{r}_j$$

Note also that

$$\langle|U(\mathbf{H})|^2\rangle = \sum_{j=1}^{N} Z_j^2 \Big/ \Big(\sum_{j=1}^{N} Z_j\Big)^2 = \sum_{j=1}^{N} n_j^2 \tag{110}$$

$$\langle|E(\mathbf{H})|^2\rangle = 1 \tag{111}$$

and

$$\langle|F(\mathbf{H})|^2\rangle = \sum_{j=1}^{N} f_j^2 \tag{112}$$

For an equal-atom structure, $\langle|U(\mathbf{H})|^2\rangle = 1/N$, so that $\langle|E(\mathbf{H})|^2\rangle = N\langle|U(\mathbf{H})|^2\rangle$. Note also that for a structure of N equal atoms, each having the atomic number Z, the maximum value possible for F is $F(000) = NZ$, that for E is $E(000) = \sqrt{N}$, and that for U is $U(000) = 1$. The corresponding averages are

$$\langle|F(\mathbf{H})|^2\rangle = \sum_{j=1}^{N} f_j^2 \qquad \langle|U(\mathbf{H})|^2\rangle = 1/N \qquad \langle|E(\mathbf{H})|^2\rangle = 1$$

The Harker-Kasper Inequalities. Certain inequality relations between the structure factors may be derived through an application of mathematical inequalities, such as Cauchy's inequality and Schwartz's inequality.[38] Cauchy's inequality, valid for two numbers a_j and b_j, can be stated as

$$\Big|\sum_{j=1}^{N} a_j b_j\Big|^2 \leq \Big(\sum_{j=1}^{N} |a_j|^2\Big)\Big(\sum_{j=1}^{N} |b_j|^2\Big) \tag{113}$$

Let us consider an equal-atom structure (i.e., $f_j = 1$, $n_j = 1/N$), in which case

$$U(\mathbf{H}) = (1/N) \sum_{j=1}^{N} \exp +2\pi i \mathbf{H} \cdot \mathbf{r}_j \tag{114}$$

Putting $a_j = 1/N$ and $b_j = \exp +2\pi i \mathbf{H} \cdot \mathbf{r}_j$, in Eq. (113), we obtain

$$\Big|\sum_{j=1}^{N} 1/N \exp +2\pi i \mathbf{H} \cdot \mathbf{r}_j\Big|^2 \leq \Big(\sum_{j=1}^{N} |1/N|^2\Big)\Big(\sum_{j=1}^{N} |\exp +2\pi i \mathbf{H} \cdot \mathbf{r}_j|^2\Big) \tag{115}$$

The left-hand side of Eq. (115) is $|U(\mathbf{H})|^2$ [from Eq. (114)]; the terms on the right-hand side reduce to unity because

$$\sum_{j=1}^{N} |1/N|^2 = N/N^2 = 1/N$$

and

$$\sum_{j=1}^{N} |\exp +2\pi i \mathbf{H} \cdot \mathbf{r}_j|^2 = N$$

The final result is the inequality

$$|U(\mathbf{H})|^2 \leq 1 \tag{116}$$

which is a trivial result. In fact, the maximum value of $|U(\mathbf{H})|^2$ occurs for $\mathbf{H} = 0$, when all the atoms scatter in phase, in the direction of the incident x-ray beam; this maximum value $= 1$.

Inequality (116) cannot be used to determine the phase of $U(\mathbf{H})$. Phase-determining inequalities, however, may be derived by putting in information regarding the space-group symmetry. For instance, consider the case of $P\bar{1}$ whose equivalent points are (x,y,z) and $(\bar{x},\bar{y},\bar{z})$, i.e., $\mathbf{r}_j$ and $-\mathbf{r}_j$. The expression for $U(\mathbf{H})$ is

$$U(\mathbf{H}) = 2 \sum_{j=1}^{N/2} n_j \cos 2\pi\mathbf{H}\cdot\mathbf{r}_j$$

Putting $a_j = n_j^{1/2}$ and $b_j = n_j^{1/2} \cos 2\pi\mathbf{H}\cdot\mathbf{r}_j$ in Cauchy's inequality, we obtain

$$\left|\sum_{j=1}^{N/2} n_j \cos 2\pi\mathbf{H}\cdot\mathbf{r}_j\right|^2 = \left(\sum_{j=1}^{N/2} |n_j^{1/2}|^2\right)\left(\sum_{j=1}^{N/2} |n_j^{1/2} \cos 2\pi\mathbf{H}\cdot\mathbf{r}_j|^2\right)$$

The term on the left-hand side $= \frac{1}{4}|U(\mathbf{H})|^2$.

Since $\sum_{j=1}^{N} n_j = \sum Z_j / \sum Z_j = 1$, the first term on the right-hand side $= \frac{1}{2} \sum_{j=1}^{N} n_j = \frac{1}{2}$.
The second term on the right-hand side is

$$\sum_{j=1}^{N/2} n_j \cos^2 2\pi\mathbf{H}\cdot\mathbf{r}_j = \sum_{j=1}^{N/2} n_j \frac{1+\cos 4\pi\mathbf{H}\cdot\mathbf{r}_j}{2}$$

$$= \tfrac{1}{4} + \tfrac{1}{2}\sum_{j=1}^{N/2} n_j \cos 2\pi(2\mathbf{H}\cdot\mathbf{r}_j) = \tfrac{1}{4} + \tfrac{1}{4}U(2\mathbf{H})$$

so that we obtain the inequality

$$|U(\mathbf{H})|^2 \leq \tfrac{1}{2} + \tfrac{1}{2}U(2\mathbf{H}) \tag{117}$$

The above inequality may be used to determine the sign of $U(2\mathbf{H})$ from the known value of the unitary intensity $|U(\mathbf{H})|^2$ under certain circumstances. In fact, the sign of $U(2\mathbf{H})$ can be determined to be positive if the value of $|U(\mathbf{H})|^2$ is greater than 0.5, or else if both $|U(\mathbf{H})|^2$ and $|U(2\mathbf{H})|^2$ are greater than 0.25. Note the limitation, however, that the inequality (117) cannot be used to determine the sign of $U(2\mathbf{H})$ to be negative.

Inequalities pertaining to other symmetry elements, such as 2, 2_1, etc. . . . , may be derived from Cauchy's inequality, by procedures similar to the above one. These are given in Table 2. Note that these inequalities can be used to determine the phases only of reflections of even order, such as $(2h,2k,2l)$, $(2h,0,2l)$, and $(0,2k,0)$. Information about reflections of other orders may be obtained from other inequalities derivable from Cauchy's inequality. For instance, consider the sum of two reflections $\mathbf{H}_1$ and $\mathbf{H}_2$ (i.e., $h_1k_1l_1$ and $h_2k_2l_2$). We have

$$U(\mathbf{H}_1) + U(\mathbf{H}_2) = \sum_j n_j[\cos 2\pi(\mathbf{H}_1\cdot\mathbf{r}_j) + \cos 2\pi(\mathbf{H}_2\cdot\mathbf{r}_j)]$$

$$= \sum_j n_j \left(2 \cos 2\pi \frac{\mathbf{H}_1+\mathbf{H}_2}{2}\cdot\mathbf{r}_j \cos 2\pi \frac{\mathbf{H}_1-\mathbf{H}_2}{2}\cdot\mathbf{r}_j\right)$$

$$= \sum_j n_j 2 \left[\frac{1+\cos 2\pi(\mathbf{H}_1+\mathbf{H}_2)\cdot\mathbf{r}_j}{2}\right]^{1/2} \times \left[\frac{1+\cos 2\pi(\mathbf{H}_1-\mathrm{H}_2)\cdot\mathbf{r}_j}{2}\right]^{1/2}$$

$$= \sum_j [n_j + n_j \cos 2\pi(\mathbf{H}_1+\mathbf{H}_2)\cdot\mathbf{r}_j]^{1/2} \times [n_j + n_j \cos 2\pi(\mathbf{H}_1-\mathbf{H}_2)\cdot\mathbf{r}_j]^{1/2}$$

Table 2. Harker-Kasper Inequalities: Limitations on Amplitudes Due to Symmetry Elements*

Symmetry element $\|c$	*Limitation*
1	$\|U_{hkl}\|^2 \leq 1$
$\bar{1}$	$U^2_{hkl} \leq \frac{1}{2} + \frac{1}{2} U_{2h2k2l}$
2	$\|U_{hkl}\|^2 \leq \frac{1}{2} + \frac{1}{2} U_{2h2k0}$
2_1	$\|U_{hkl}\|^2 \leq \frac{1}{2} + \frac{1}{2}(-1)^l U_{2h2k0}$
$\bar{2} = m$	$\|U_{hkl}\|^2 \leq \frac{1}{2} + \frac{1}{2} U_{02k0}$
a	$\|U_{hkl}\|^2 \leq \frac{1}{2} + \frac{1}{2}(-1)^h U_{002l}$
3	$\|U_{hkl}\|^2 \leq \frac{1}{3} + \frac{2}{3}\|U_{(h-k)(h+2k)0}\| \cos 2\pi \phi_{(h-k)(h+2k)0}$
3_1, 3_2	$\|U_{hkl}\|^2 \leq \frac{1}{3} + \frac{2}{3}\|U_{(h-k)(h+2k)0}\| \cos 2\pi[\phi_{(h-k)(h+2k)0} + \frac{1}{3}l]$
$\bar{3} = 3 + \bar{1}$	$U^2_{hkl} \leq \frac{1}{6} + \frac{1}{6} U_{2h2k2l} + \frac{1}{3} U_{hk2l} + \frac{1}{3} U_{(h-k)(h+2k)0}$
4	$\|U_{hkl}\|^2 \leq \frac{1}{4} + \frac{1}{4} U_{2h2k0} + \frac{1}{2} U_{(h-k)(h+k)0}$
4_1, 4_3	$\|U_{hkl}\|^2 \leq \frac{1}{4} + \frac{1}{4}(-1)^l U_{2h2k0} + \frac{1}{2}(\cos 2\pi \frac{1}{4} l) U_{(h-k)(h+k)0}$
4_2	$\|U_{hkl}\|^2 \leq \frac{1}{4} + \frac{1}{4} U_{2h2k0} + \frac{1}{2}(-1)^l U_{(h-k)(h+k)0}$
$\bar{4}$	$\|U_{hkl}\|^2 \leq \frac{1}{4} + \frac{1}{4} U_{2h2k0} + \frac{1}{2}\|U_{(h-k)(h+k)2l}\| \cos 2\pi \phi_{(h-k)(h+k)2l}$
6	$\|U_{hkl}\|^2 \leq \frac{1}{6} + \frac{1}{6} U_{2h2k0} + \frac{1}{3} U_{(h-k)(h+2k)0} + \frac{1}{3} U_{hk0}$
6_1, 6_5	$\|U_{hkl}\|^2 \leq \frac{1}{6} + \frac{1}{6}(-1)^l U_{2h2k0} + \frac{1}{3}(\cos 2\pi \frac{1}{3} l) U_{(h-k)(h+2k)0} + \frac{1}{3}(\cos 2\pi \frac{1}{6} l) U_{hk0}$
6_2, 6_4	$\|U_{hkl}\|^2 \leq \frac{1}{6} + \frac{1}{6} U_{2h2k0} + \frac{1}{3}(\cos 2\pi \frac{1}{3} l) U_{(h-k)(h+2k)0} + \frac{1}{3}(\cos 2\pi \frac{1}{3} l) U_{hk0}$
6_3	$\|U_{hkl}\|^2 \leq \frac{1}{6} + \frac{1}{6}(-1)^l U_{2h2k0} + \frac{1}{3} U_{(h-k)(h+2k)0} + \frac{1}{3}(-1)^l U_{hk0}$
$\bar{6} = 3/m$	$\|U_{hkl}\|^2 < \frac{1}{6} + \frac{1}{6} U_{002l} + \frac{1}{3}\|U_{(h-k)(h+2k)0}\| \cos 2\pi \phi_{(h-k)(h+2k)0} + \frac{1}{3}\|U_{(h-k)(h+2k)2l}\| \cos 2\pi \phi_{(h-k)(h+2k)2l}$

* Table adapted from M. J. Buerger, *Crystal Structure Analysis*, John Wiley & Sons, Inc., New York, 1960.

The above reduction is achieved by using trigonometric identities, such as

$$\cos A + \cos B = 2 \cos [(A + B)/2] \cos [(A - B)/2]$$

and $\cos A = 2 \cos^2 A/2 - 1$.

Letting $a_j = [n_j + n_j \cos 2\pi(\mathbf{H}_1 + \mathbf{H}_2) \cdot \mathbf{r}_j]^{1/2}$ and

$$b_j = [n_j + n_j \cos 2\pi(\mathbf{H}_1 - \mathbf{H}_2) \cdot \mathbf{r}_j]^{1/2}$$

in Cauchy's inequality, and using the result $\sum_j n_j = 1$, we can obtain the inequality

$$|U(\mathbf{H}_1) + U(\mathbf{H}_2)|^2 \leq [1 + U(\mathbf{H}_1 + \mathbf{H}_2)][1 + U(\mathbf{H}_1 - \mathbf{H}_2)] \tag{118}$$

Some more inequalities, similar to (118), are given in Table 3. These inequalities, however, refer to specific symmetry elements, such as $\bar{1}$, 2, and 2_1. More powerful

Table 3. Some Inequalities Involving Three Reflections*

Centrosymmetrical structures	*Noncentrosymmetrical structures*
$\|U_H + U_{H'}\|^2 \leq (1 + U_{H+H'})(1 + U_{H-H'})$	$\|U_H + U_{H'}\|^2 \leq 2 + 2 \operatorname{Re} U_{H-H'}$
$\|U_H - U_{H'}\|^2 \leq (1 - U_{H+H'})(1 - U_{H-H'})$	$\|U_H - U_{H'}\|^2 \leq 2 - 2 \operatorname{Re} U_{H-H'}$
$\|U_{H+H'} - U_{H-H'}\|^2 \leq (1 + U_{2H})(1 - U_{2H'})$	

* Table adapted from M. J. Buerger, *Crystal Structure Analysis*, John Wiley & Sons, Inc., New York, 1960.

inequalities may be derived through an application of Cauchy's inequality to the structure-factor equations pertaining to a group of symmetry elements. For a given space group, the general expression for the structure factor can be reduced to a simpler form by summation over the equivalent points. The reduced expression may be expressed, as far as possible, as a product of sines and cosines. The relevant inequalities can then be derived from Cauchy's inequality. For instance, the equivalent points for the space group $P2/m$ are four in number and are given by $\pm\ (x,y,z)$, and $\pm\ (x,\bar{y},z)$. The expression for the structure factor is

$$\begin{aligned} U(\mathbf{H}) = \sum_{j=1}^{N/4} n_j[&\exp 2\pi i(hx_j + ky_j + lz_j) + \exp +2\pi i(-hx_j + ky_j - lz_j) \\ &+ \exp -2\pi i(hx_j + ky_j + lz_j) + \exp + 2\pi i(hx_j - ky_j + lz_j)] \\ = 2 \sum_{j=1}^{N/4} &n_j[\cos 2\pi(hx_j + ky_j + lz_j) + \cos 2\pi(hx_j - ky_j + lz_j)] \\ &= 4 \sum_{j=1}^{N/4} n_j \cos 2\pi(hx_j + lz_j) \cos 2\pi ky_j \end{aligned}$$

In applying Cauchy's inequality to this reduced expression for $U(\mathbf{H})$, the quantities a_j and b_j may be chosen in different ways, and yet the quantity $\left|\sum_{j=1}^{N} a_j b_j\right|^2$ can equal $|U(\mathbf{H})|^2$. For instance, one simple choice is $a_j = n_j^{1/2}$ and

$$b_j = n_j^{1/2} \cos 2\pi(hx_j + lz_j) \cos 2\pi ky_j$$

An equally valid choice is $a_j = n_j^{1/2} \cos 2\pi ky_j$ and $b_j = n_j^{1/2} \cos 2\pi(hx_j + lz_j)$. By inserting each one of such pairs (a_j,b_j) into Cauchy's inequality, it is possible to obtain a corresponding inequality for the structure factors. Some of the inequalities applicable to the space group $P2/m$ are given in Table 4.

Table 4. Inequalities for Space Group $P2/m$*

1. $|U(hkl)|^2 \leq \frac{1}{4}[1 + U(0,2k,0) + U(2h,0,2l) + U(2h,2k,2l)]$
2. $|U(hkl)|^2 \leq \frac{1}{4}[1 + U(0,2k,0)][1 + U(2h,0,2l)]$
3. $[U(h0l) \pm U(hkl)]^2 \leq \frac{1}{2}[1 \pm U(0k0)]\{[1 + U(2h,0,2l)] \pm [U(0k0) + U(2h,k,2l)]\}$
4. $[U(hkl) \pm U(h'kl')]^2 \leq \frac{1}{2}[1 \pm U(h + h', 0, l + l')]\{1 + U(0,2k,0) \pm [U(h - h', 0, l - l') + U(h - h', 2k, l - l')]\}$
5. $[U(hkl) \pm U(h'k'l')]^2 \leq \frac{1}{4}\{2 + U(0,2k,0) + U(2h,0,2l) + U(2h,2k,2l) + U(0,2k',0) + U(2h',0,2l') + U(2h' + 2k' + 2l') \pm 2[U(h - h', k - k', l - l') + U(h - h', k + k', l - l') + U(h + h', k - k', l + l') + U(h + h', k + k', l + l')]\}$

* Table adapted from H. Lipson and W. Cochran, *Crystalline State*, vol. III, G. Bell & Sons, Ltd., London, 1953.

The technique for solving a crystal structure by the method of inequalities is outlined below. In giving this outline, we restrict our discussion to the determination of only the signs of structure factors. Therefore, our discussion is valid for all the centrosymmetric space groups and for any available centrosymmetric projections of noncentrosymmetric space groups, such as the b-axis projection of space group $P2_1$, and the a-axis, b-axis, and c-axis projections of space group $P2_12_12_1$. The reason for this restricted discussion is that the method of inequalities does not appear to be very helpful for phase determination in the case of noncentrosymmetric crystals.

In using the method, the first step is to derive the unitary intensities $|U(\mathbf{H})|^2$ from the experimental intensity values $I(\mathbf{H})$, as outlined above under The Unitary Structure Factor. The second step is to list the unitary intensities in decreasing order of magnitude. The third step is to choose arbitrarily the signs of a prescribed number p of suitable structure factors (see The Direct Method of Hauptman and Karle, below). The fourth step is to determine the signs of as many of the even-order (i.e., $2\mathbf{H}$) reflections as possible, by means of inequalities which aim at the determination of the sign of $U(2\mathbf{H})$, given the intensities of reflections $\mathbf{H}$. After a sufficient number of signs have been determined by such means, other inequalities that involve knowledge of signs besides intensities may be used to obtain signs of additional structure factors. Thus, the signs of a sufficient number of strong reflections of both even and odd orders may be determined. The final step is to calculate Fourier syntheses, based on these signs, using the usual iterative refinement methods described later in Sec. 8.

The main advantage of the method of inequalities is its applicability to solution of equal-atom structures. These generally are the structures that are more difficult to solve. However, the limitation of the method is that its usefulness decreases as the number of atoms per unit cell increases. The reason for this limitation is as follows: The effectiveness with which the inequalities can be used to determine the sign of a particular $U(\mathbf{H})$ depends to a large extent on the possibility of distinguishing $+U(\mathbf{H})$ from $-U(\mathbf{H})$. In other words, the structure factors involved in a given inequality relation must preferably correspond to strong reflections, so that the difference between $+U$ and $-U$ is sufficiently large. However, the average value of $|U|^2$ for an equal-atom structure is only $1/N$, and the rms value is $\sigma = 1/\sqrt{N}$. Assuming that the structure amplitudes are distributed according to a Gaussian law, only 10 per cent of the reflections may have values of U greater than 1.7σ, and 0.1 per cent may be expected to exceed 3.3σ. The presence of higher symmetry improves the situation a little. But then, for a given symmetry number n, the effectiveness of the method depends on p, the number of atoms in the asymmetric unit.

It is therefore clear that as the value of p increases, the number of strong reflections decreases, and very few signs may be determined by the method of inequalities. Some examples of structures solved by this method are oxalic acid dihydrate,[39] with $p = 4$, and decaborane,[40] with $p = 5$. The method seems to be of little value by the time $p = 9$ is reached, as was the case with melamine.[41]

The various inequalities can be systematized and shown to result from the simple physical fact that the electron-density function $\rho(\mathbf{r})$ is a nonnegative function. This attractive theoretical development of the subject is due to Karle and Hauptman.[42] These two workers have derived very general inequalities among the coefficients [i.e., $F(\mathbf{H})$] of the Fourier series representing the electron density $\rho(\mathbf{r})$ in a crystal on the physical basis that the series represents a nonnegative function. No symmetry properties of the crystal space are required for deriving these inequalities, but they may be readily introduced into the inequality relationships. The most important result is that if the magnitudes and phases of a certain number of structure factors are known, the magnitude and phase of an additional structure factor $F(\mathbf{H})$ are limited to specific values calculable from the known data. This is true in the most general case of $P1$. Presence of higher symmetry results in further reduction of the possibilities for the phase of $F(\mathbf{H})$. In this way, the various Harker-Kasper inequalities become special cases of the more general phase-limiting relationships of Karle and Hauptman.

Sayre's Approach and Methods Based on "Squared" Electron-density function. A direct method[43] of sign determination has been developed based on the relationship between the Fourier coefficients $F^{sq}(\mathbf{H})$ and $F(\mathbf{H})$ of the syntheses for $\rho^{sq}(\mathbf{r})$ and $\rho(\mathbf{r})$, respectively. The method is of a range of applicability wider than that of the Harker-Kasper inequalities. To appreciate the principle of the method, consider the function

$$\rho^{sq}(\mathbf{r}) = \rho(\mathbf{r})\rho(\mathbf{r})$$

Clearly, $\rho^{sq}(\mathbf{r})$ is obtained by squaring $\rho(\mathbf{r})$ in the space of $\mathbf{r}$. The F.T. of $\rho^{sq}(\mathbf{r})$ is then the convolution integral of $F(\mathbf{H})$ in the space of $\mathbf{H}$ (see Sec. 5, under The Patterson Function of Crystallography). Thus we obtain

$$F^{sq}(\mathbf{H}) = \int F(\mathbf{K})F(\mathbf{H} - \mathbf{K})\, d\tau$$

In other words,

$$F^{sq}(\mathbf{H}) = (1/V) \sum_{\mathbf{K}} F(\mathbf{K})F(\mathbf{H} - \mathbf{K})$$

Now we have to relate $F^{sq}(\mathbf{H})$ to $F(\mathbf{H})$. Such an exact relation will be very useful but in general cannot be obtained. However, consider the extreme case of an equal-point atom structure whose f_j's are all equal to unity; for such a structure, $F^{sq}(\mathbf{H}) = F(\mathbf{H})$.

For other equal-atom structures, a similar relationship is available, provided "unitary" amplitudes are involved and provided such "unitary" amplitudes have been derived after resetting the quantities n_j to unity.*

We then have

$$V(\mathbf{H}) = \langle V(\mathbf{K})V(\mathbf{H} - \mathbf{K})\rangle_{\mathbf{K}} \tag{119}$$

The above equation (119) relates the phase and magnitude of a specific unitary structure factor $V(\mathbf{H})$ with the phases and magnitudes of a large number of unitary structure factors. In fact, strictly speaking, the series is an infinite series. For this reason, Eq. (119) as such is not very useful from the viewpoint of phase determination. However, certain important conclusions can be derived as follows: Consider the right-hand side of Eq. (119). This average is proportional to a sum of a large number of products such as $V(\mathbf{K}_1)V(\mathbf{K}_2)$ where $\mathbf{K}_2 = \mathbf{H} - \mathbf{K}_1$. Most of the products will usually have small values. A given product can have a large value only if the quantities $V(\mathbf{K}_1)$ and $V(\mathbf{K}_2)$ are both large. Consider the specific case when the linear sum contains only one product of large value, say $V(\mathbf{H}_1)V(\mathbf{H}_2)$, and a large number of small products. One can reasonably expect a mutual cancellation of the small products, provided their number is large. Thus, there is some hope that one might determine the phase of $V(\mathbf{H})$, provided the phases and magnitudes of $V(\mathbf{H}_1)$ and $V(\mathbf{H}_2)$ are known. In other words, knowledge of the phases and magnitudes of two large structure factors $V(\mathbf{H}_1)$ and $V(\mathbf{H}_2)$ may enable one to determine the phase of the reflection $(\mathbf{H}_2 + \mathbf{H}_1.)$

Equation (119) is valid for both centrosymmetric and noncentrosymmetric crystals. However, it has been more commonly used for centrosymmetric crystals. In such cases, the actual relation employed is the following:

$$s(\mathbf{H}) = s(\mathbf{H}')s(\mathbf{H} + \mathbf{H}')$$

i.e.,

$$s(hkl) = s(h'k'l')s(h + h', k + k', l + l') \tag{120}$$

where $s(hkl)$ is the sign of the reflection (hkl) and so on. Equation (120) can be obtained from (119) by making use of an equality $V(h,k,l) = V(\bar{h},\bar{k},\bar{l})$, which is valid for centrosymmetric crystals.

Equation (120) is probably valid provided the three structure factors have sufficiently large values. In other cases, a related expression is

$$s(\mathbf{H}) = s\langle U(\mathbf{H}')U(\mathbf{H} + \mathbf{H}')\rangle_{\mathbf{H}'} \tag{121}$$

The expression on the right-hand side of (121) is an average of products such as $U(\mathbf{H}')U(\mathbf{H} + \mathbf{H}')$, where the running index $\mathbf{H}'$ assumes all possible values. It is interesting to note that one way of calculating the average is to construct a reciprocal lattice in which each reciprocal-lattice point (h',k',l') is weighted with its corresponding $U(h',k',l')$ value. One can then make a duplicate copy of the weighted reciprocal lattice and shift the origin of the copy with respect to the origin of the original by a given vector $\mathbf{H}$ (i.e., hkl). The two weighted lattices are superimposed and the product of their respective weights at the same point $\mathbf{H}'$ is formed. A third lattice is constructed in which the weight at a given lattice point $\mathbf{H}'$ is just this product. The sum of the weights contained by the third lattice can be calculated; the sign of the sum is the sign of the reflection $\mathbf{H}$.

However, note the fact that Eq. (121) can be used only if both the magnitudes and phases of a large number of reflections are known in advance. This must be compared with Eq. (120), which demands knowledge of phases and magnitudes of only two (strong) reflections. Therefore, it is clear that Eq. (121) can be used effectively only after obtaining the phases of a sufficient number of reflections by other methods, such as the method of inequalities, and utilization of Eq. (120).

In actual cases, the sign determination usually proceeds as follows: The first step is to derive the magnitudes of the unitary structure factors and arrange them in decreasing order of magnitude. The second step is to choose arbitrarily the signs of a prescribed number p of structure factors. The third step is to obtain as many signs as

* $V(\mathbf{H}) = \sqrt{N}\,E(\mathbf{H}) = NU(\mathbf{H})$, $V(000) = N$, and $\langle|V|^2\rangle = N$.

possible by the method of inequalities. The fourth step is to extend the range of available signs by means of Eq. (120). The correctness of a particular sign, determined at this stage, may be assessed from the formula[44]

$$P_+[U(\mathbf{H})U(\mathbf{H}')U(\mathbf{H}+\mathbf{H}')] = \tfrac{1}{2} + \tfrac{1}{2}\tan(e_3/e_2^3)|U(\mathbf{H})U(\mathbf{H}')U(\mathbf{H}+\mathbf{H}')| \quad (122)$$

where $e_m = \sum_{j=1}^{N} n_j^m$. When the atoms are equal, $e_m = N^{1-m}$. Equation (122) gives the probability that the sign of $U(\mathbf{H})$ is the same as the sign of the product $U(\mathbf{H}')U(\mathbf{H}+\mathbf{H}')$. Note that unambiguous conclusions regarding a particular sign can be reached only if the value of P_+ deviates significantly from $\frac{1}{2}$.

After the signs of a sufficient number of reflections have been determined in the manner described above, it may be possible to start using Eq. (121) to extend the range of the sign determination. The final step is to calculate a Fourier synthesis, using the signs that have been obtained, together with the known magnitudes. The latter quantities can be the U's, E's, or the F's. The advantage of using U or E is to obtain "sharpened" electron-density syntheses, which may have better resolution, of course, at the expense of errors arising from series termination.

The method described so far is strictly valid for only those structures which contain equal atoms. A further requirement is that the peaks in either function $\rho^{sq}(\mathbf{r})$ or $\rho(\mathbf{r})$ do not overlap. Both conditions are satisfied to a large extent by most equal-atom structures, provided unitary intensities are used in the calculations, and provided a three-dimensional analysis has been undertaken. However, the first condition will not be obeyed even in three dimensions if the structure contains unequal atoms. The second condition may not be obeyed, in most cases, for two-dimensional projections. Attempts have been made[45] to obtain improved formulas by expressing the Fourier coefficient of $\rho(\mathbf{r})$ in terms of the Fourier coefficients of $\rho^{sq}(\mathbf{r})$, and those of higher powers of $\rho(\mathbf{r})$, such as $\rho^3(\mathbf{r})$. In addition, attempts have been made to generalize this procedure of sign determination as well as to automatize with digital computers. In one procedure[45] the signs of a selected set of strong structure factors are obtained, using Eq. (121), in terms of the signs of a small number t of structure factors. The signs of the latter are given by all the possible permutations.

Since the sign of a given structure factor for the centrosymmetric case can only be either plus or minus, there are 2^t sign permutations for the t structure factors, and correspondingly there are 2^t solutions for the signs of all the selected set of reflections. The correct set of signs is probably one of the 2^t sets. A laborious procedure is to synthesize and study each of the 2^t maps of the electron density. A better procedure is probably one which involves a "zero check." In this procedure[46] a quantity R, given below, is calculated for each set of signs, and the set having the lowest R value is taken to be the solution most probably correct. The quantity is

$$R = K \sum_{\mathbf{H}} \sum_{\mathbf{H}'} U(\mathbf{H}')U(\mathbf{H}+\mathbf{H}')$$

where the summation over $\mathbf{H}$ is carried out for those reflections whose U values are close to zero, the summation over $\mathbf{H}'$ is for available $U(\mathbf{H}')$ of the selected set, and K is a factor for scaling purposes. The basic idea of the zero check is that if a given $U(\mathbf{H})$ is zero, the corresponding values of $K \sum_{\mathbf{H}'} U(\mathbf{H}')U(\mathbf{H}+\mathbf{H}')$ should be quite small, if not zero also. Therefore, the correct set of signs is probably that set which has the minimum value of R.

In a second procedure[47] called the symbolic-addition method, the signs of a small number t of structure factors are represented by symbols, such as $a_1, a_2, \ldots, a_t$.*

* There appears to be no clear-cut rule as to which reflections should be assigned symbolic signs. Ideally these reflections should preferably have large $|E|$ values and should have a large number of the "Sayre" type of interaction among themselves and with other strong reflections.

These symbols, together with the prescribed number p of signs, available from origin specifications, are input into equations such as (127). As sign determination proceeds, internal consistency between the symbols is looked for, and the correct values (i.e., + or −) of the symbols are inferred. Both methods are probably quite reliable with three-dimensional data and for equal-atom structures.

Examples of structures solved by methods based on the squared electron density are glutamine,[48] metaboric acid,[49] rubrofusarin,[50] D-xylose,[24] cyclo (hexaglycyl) hemihydrate,[51] and the alkaloid jamine.[52]

The Direct Method of Hauptman and Karle. Routine procedures of phase determination, directly from the intensity data, have been proposed by Karle and Hauptman.[53] The procedures are based on a system of phase-determining formulas. These formulas were first inferred from a statistical approach to the phase problem. These early methods were concerned with probability distribution functions of a real structure factor. They were developed on the basis that the Miller indices were fixed and the atomic coordinates were uniformly distributed over the unit cell. However, the technique is subject to the condition that the magnitudes of a sufficient number of structure factors are known. Typical formulas obtained in this fashion for space group $P\bar{1}$ are

$$\Sigma_1: sE(2\mathbf{H}) \simeq s[|E(\mathbf{H})|^2 - 1] \tag{123}$$

$$\Sigma_4: sE(2\mathbf{H}) \simeq s\left\{\sum_{\mathbf{K}} [|E(\mathbf{H})|^2 - 1][|E(\mathbf{H}+\mathbf{K})|^2 - 1]\right\} \tag{124}$$

$$\Sigma_3: sE(2\mathbf{H}) \simeq s\left\{\sum_{\mathbf{K}} E(2\mathbf{K})[|E(\mathbf{H}+\mathbf{K})|^2 - 1]\right\} \tag{125}$$

$$\Sigma_2: sE(\mathbf{H}) \simeq s\left[\sum_{\mathbf{K}} E(\mathbf{K})E(\mathbf{H}+\mathbf{K})\right] \tag{126}$$

In the above four expressions, $E(\mathbf{H})$ is the normalized structure factor of reflection $\mathbf{H}$, s means "sign of," and the symbol $\simeq$ means "probably is." Analogous formulas have been given for some other space groups.

In the second stage of development of their methods, Karle and Hauptman[54] used an algebraic approach to derive exact relationships such as the following:

$$E(\mathbf{H}) = N^{1/2}\langle E(\mathbf{K})E(\mathbf{H}+\mathbf{K})\rangle_{\mathbf{K}} \tag{127}$$

$$E(2\mathbf{H}) = N\langle E(2\mathbf{K})[|E(\mathbf{H}+\mathbf{K})|^2 - 1]\rangle_{\mathbf{K}} \tag{128}$$

The above two formulas are for the case of N identical point atoms per unit cell in space group $P\bar{1}$.

In the third stage of development,[54] these workers generalized the algebraic formulas to structures containing dissimilar atoms, as well as to all the 230 space groups. The generalized formulas for space group $P1$ are

$$\begin{aligned}|E(\mathbf{H}_1)E(\mathbf{H}_2)E(\mathbf{H}_3)| \cos(\alpha_1+\alpha_2+\alpha_3) &= (w^3/2)\langle[|E(\mathbf{K})|^2 - 1][|E(\mathbf{H}_1+\mathbf{K})|^2 - 1][|E(\mathbf{H}_1+\mathbf{H}_2+\mathbf{K})|^2 - 1]\rangle_{\mathbf{K}} \\ &\quad + w^{-1}[|E(\mathbf{H}_1)|^2 + |E(\mathbf{H}_2)|^2 + |E(\mathbf{H}_3)|^2 - 2]\end{aligned} \tag{129}$$

The formulas for $P\bar{1}$ are

$$\begin{aligned}E(\mathbf{H}_1)E(\mathbf{H}_2)E(\mathbf{H}_3) &= (w^3/8)\langle[|E(\mathbf{K})|^2 - 1][|E(\mathbf{H}_1+\mathbf{K})|^2 - 1][|E(\mathbf{H}_1+\mathbf{H}_2+\mathbf{K})|^2 - 1]\rangle_{\mathbf{K}} \\ &\quad + w^{-1}[|E(\mathbf{H}_1)|^2 + |E(\mathbf{H}_2)|^2 + |E(\mathbf{H}_3)|^2 - 2] \\ &\quad + (w^{-1}/2)[E(\mathbf{H}_1)E(\mathbf{H}_2-\mathbf{H}_3) + E(\mathbf{H}_2)E(\mathbf{H}_3-\mathbf{H}_1) + E(\mathbf{H}_3)E(\mathbf{H}_1-\mathbf{H}_2)] \\ &\quad - w^{-2}[E(2\mathbf{H}_1) + E(2\mathbf{H}_2) + E(2\mathbf{H}_3)]\end{aligned} \tag{130}$$

where α_1 is the phase of $E(\mathbf{H}_1)$, etc., $w = \sqrt{N}$ for an equal-atom structure, and the three indices involved obey the condition $\mathbf{H}_1 + \mathbf{H}_2 + \mathbf{H}_3 = 0$.

In the fourth stage of development, Karle and Hauptman[55] resort to statistical methods. However, this time probability distributions of several structure factors are derived on the basis that the atomic coordinates are fixed, while the Miller indices are allowed to range uniformly, but not independently, over the integers. In this way, the "generalization" of the algebraic formulas has been obtained.

The claim that a routine solution of the phase problem is possible by means of formulas such as the above has been disputed by many workers.[56] One worker[57] in particular has shown that some of the typical algebraic formulas of Karle and Hauptman may be derived very elegantly from an application of Fourier-transform theory in general and the convolution integral theorem in particular. The advantage of such a Fourier approach is that it is now possible to appreciate the physical principles underlying the various formulas. In fact, the different formulas are expressions of the relationships between the function $\rho(\mathbf{r})$ and/or the various powers of the self-convolution of $\rho(\mathbf{r})$, such as $P(\mathbf{r})$ and $\rho(\mathbf{r})P(\mathbf{r})$. By such analytical arguments, it is possible to define an "order" for each one of the algebraic formulas, the "order" being some measure of the range of validity of the formula.[57] For instance, the formula of lowest "order" is the one which purports to equate $\rho(\mathbf{r})$ to $\rho^{sq}(\mathbf{r})$. This equality, when translated into the language of Fourier theory, leads to development of useful methods based on Sayre's relation (discussed above under Sayre's Approach), given in the present formalism by the Σ_2 equation (126). The underlying assumption of the relation is that the peaks in either function $\rho(\mathbf{r})$ or $\rho^{sq}(\mathbf{r})$ are resolved from one another. Analytically, this condition can be expressed as follows:

$$\mathbf{r}_i - \mathbf{r}_j \neq 0 \tag{131}$$

for all values of i and $j = 1, N$. Similar conditions may be obtained for other algebraic relations, and corresponding "orders" may be defined. In general, the value of an "order" is one higher than the number of atomic-position vectors involved in the analytical expression of that condition. For instance, the order of relations such as Eq. (127) is three. The more useful a given phase-determining relation seems to be, the lower its order. These and similar arguments, together with the more important fact that an actual Patterson function is only a poor approximation to the ideal vector set, enable some workers[57] to conclude that equal-atom structures with $N < 100$ may probably be solved by such methods based on relations of order greater than three (N = total number of atoms per unit cell). Possibly, this upper limit of $N = 100$ may be an overoptimistic estimate; a more realistic estimate is probably only $N = 25$.

Some examples of structures solved by the direct methods of Karle and Hauptman are (1) colemanite,[58] (2) p,p'-dimethoxybenzophenone,[59] and (3) spurite.[60]

A rather broad outline of directions for using the method follows. The first step is to derive the normalized intensities from the experimental values. The second step is to arrange the E values in decreasing order of magnitude. The third step is to choose arbitrarily the signs of a prescribed number p of structure factors. This freedom of choice is available because the origin can be chosen on any one of the centers of symmetry, relevant to the particular space group of the crystal under investigation. For this purpose, Karle and Hauptman[53] find it convenient to classify all the structure factors into two classes, namely, structure invariants and semi-invariants. The invariants are those reflections whose phases depend only on the structure (i.e., the set of N atomic positions $\mathbf{r}_j$) and are independent of the choice of origin. For a centrosymmetric crystal, in space group $P\bar{1}$, the origin can be chosen on any one of the eight positions, given by $(x0 + e)$, $(y0 + e)$, and $(z0 + e)$ when $x0 = y0 = z0 = 0$, and e can be either 0 or $\frac{1}{2}$. The sign of even-order reflection (i.e., $\mathbf{H} = 2n$, where n is an integer) is the same, no matter where the origin is chosen. Such reflections are called invariants. For three-dimensional data, the signs of three structure semi-invariants can be arbitrarily chosen. These three reflections should be linearly independent.[61] Such a choice fixes the origin on one of eight possibilities. However, for two-dimensional data only two signs can be arbitrarily chosen. The structure factors, whose signs are arbitrarily chosen, should preferably have large E values.

The fourth step is to employ relevant formulas such as Σ_1 and Σ_4, and determine the signs of as many structure factors as possible, from intensity data alone. The next step is to use formulas such as Σ_2 and Σ_3, and extend the range of the sign determination. The rest of the procedure is similar to other sign-determining methods.

We do not wish to assert, or for that matter deny, the claims of Karle and Hauptman. However, we do wish to stress that the direct methods are equivalent, in principle, to the vector-space methods based on the Patterson function. It is not clear why the direct methods should be preferred to vector-space methods, particularly in view of the fact that there may be structure determinations (for example, cellobiose,[62,21] L-asparagine monohydrate[24,63]) in which the direct methods were not quite useful whereas the vector-space methods did succeed. The methods used depend upon the preferences of the investigator since the phase problem, as of today, has not been completely solved in a rigorous sense.

There are other direct methods, such as the method of Banerjee[64] and that of Ott and Avrami,[65] which we do not propose to discuss because of limited usage.

7. METHODS BASED ON VARIATION OF SCATTERING FACTORS

In Sec. 5 we discussed structure-determination methods based on the Patterson function which contains the minimum amount of information available from the intensity data alone. We shall now describe methods aimed at determination of the phases of $F(\mathbf{H})$ themselves. Such methods are possible under certain special circumstances, which may be better understood by examining the following expression.

$$I(\mathbf{H}) = \sum_{i=1}^{N} \sum_{j=1}^{N} f_i f_j^* \exp +2\pi i \mathbf{H} \cdot (\mathbf{r}_i - \mathbf{r}_j) \tag{132}$$

It is clear that $I(\mathbf{H})$ depends on the atomic-scattering factor f_j. If the value of $f_{Pj}^{(1)}$ at a known point $\mathbf{r}_{Pj}$ in the unit cell can be changed by some technique to $f_{Pj}^{(2)}$, there will be a corresponding change in $I(\mathbf{H})$. Knowing $f_{Pj}^{(2)}$, $f_{Pj}^{(1)}$, $\mathbf{r}_{Pj}$, and measuring the intensity change ΔI, it may be possible to get information regarding the phase angle $\alpha(\mathbf{H})$. Such a change of f_j may be achieved in at least two ways which are theoretically equivalent but procedurally different. The first one is a purely physical method; it is based on the dependence of scattering factors on the wavelength λ of the incident x-rays and leads to the anomalous dispersion method. The second one is a chemical substitution of the atom at $\mathbf{r}_{Pj}$ and leads to the isomorphous replacement method.

The Anomalous Dispersion Method. The scattering power f_j of an atom is independent of the wavelength λ of the incident x-rays only under the assumption that the electrons of the atom scatter as free (Thomson) electrons. This assumption is valid provided λ_K, the K-absorption edge of the atom, is quite far from the incident λ (similarly for λ_L, etc.), so that dispersion effects can be neglected. If the latter effects are also taken into account, the scattering factor of the jth atom must be represented, in general, as

$$f_j = f_j^0 + f_j' + i f_j'' \tag{133}$$

where f_j^0 is the value of f_j for $\lambda \gg \lambda_K$; f_j^0 is independent of λ and dependent on only scattering angle, viz., $\sin \theta/\lambda$.

The second (f_j') and third (f_j'') terms are the correction terms to f_j^0, these terms arising out of dispersion effects. Both terms are dependent on incident λ: f_j' is a small correction to the real part of f_j, and f_j'' is the imaginary component.

The important difference between f_j'' and f_j' is that f_j'' is nonzero only if $\lambda < \lambda_K$. If the various K-, L-, M- absorption edges of an atom are taken into account, f_j, in general, is a complex quantity. The correction terms f_j' and f_j'' have been calculated for different incident wavelengths, by approximate methods, and are available in literature.[66,67]

Formulas for Intensities. Consider a crystal whose unit cell contains a certain number P of atoms at $\mathbf{r}_{Pi}$, for which dispersion effects cannot be neglected for a given incident λ. Let N be the total number of atoms. Then we have a situation where

$$f_{Pi} = f_{Pi}^0 + f_{Pi}' + i f_{Pi}''$$

and

$$f_{Qi} = f_{Qi}^0$$

where $P_i = 1, P$; $Q_j = 1, Q$; and $Q = N - P$. The structure factor of reflection **H** is

$$F_N(\mathbf{H}) = F_N{}^0(\mathbf{H}) + F_P{}'(\mathbf{H}) + F_P{}''(\mathbf{H}) \tag{134}$$

where $$F_N{}^0(\mathbf{H}) = F_P{}^0(\mathbf{H}) + F_Q(\mathbf{H}) = \sum_{j=1}^{P} f_{Pj}{}^0 \exp +2\pi i\mathbf{H}\cdot\mathbf{r}_{Pj} + \sum_{j=1}^{Q} f_{Qj}{}^0 \exp +2\pi i\mathbf{H}\cdot\mathbf{r}_{Qj}$$

i.e.,

$$F_N{}^0(\mathbf{H}) = \sum_{j=1}^{N} f_j{}^0 \exp +2\pi i\mathbf{H}\cdot\mathbf{r}_j \tag{135}$$

$$F_P{}'(\mathbf{H}) = \sum_{j=1}^{P} f_{Pj}{}' \exp +2\pi i\mathbf{H}\cdot\mathbf{r}_{Pj} \tag{136}$$

$$F_P{}''(\mathbf{H}) = \sum_{j=1}^{P} i f_{Pj}{}'' \exp +2\pi i\mathbf{H}\cdot\mathbf{r}_{Pj} \tag{137}$$

The intensity of reflection **H** (i.e., h, k, l) is obtained by multiplying Eq. (134) by its complex conjugate and is given by

$$\begin{aligned}|F_N(\mathbf{H})|^2 = |F_N{}^0(\mathbf{H})|^2 + |F_P{}'(\mathbf{H})|^2 + |F_P{}''(\mathbf{H})|^2 \\ + [F_N{}^0(\mathbf{H})F_P{}'^*(\mathbf{H}) + F_N{}^{0*}(\mathbf{H})F_P{}'(\mathbf{H})] + [F_P{}'(\mathbf{H})F_P{}''^*(\mathbf{H}) + F_P{}'^*(\mathbf{H})F_P{}''(\mathbf{H})] \\ + [F_N{}^0(\mathbf{H})F_P{}''^*(\mathbf{H}) + F_N{}^{0*}(\mathbf{H})F_P{}''(\mathbf{H})]\end{aligned} \tag{138}$$

In terms of the phase angles $\alpha_N{}^0$, $\alpha_P{}'$, and $\alpha_P{}''$ of the corresponding quantities $F_N{}^0$, $F_P{}'$, and $F_P{}''$, Eq. (138) simplifies to

$$\begin{aligned}|F_N(\mathbf{H})|^2 = |F_N{}^0(\mathbf{H})|^2 + |F_P{}'(\mathbf{H})|^2 + |F_P{}''(\mathbf{H})|^2 \\ + 2|F_N{}^0(\mathbf{H})|\,|F_P{}'(\mathbf{H})| \cos(\alpha_N{}^0 - \alpha_P{}') \\ + 2|F_P{}'(\mathbf{H})|\,|F_P{}''(\mathbf{H})| \cos(\alpha_P{}' - \alpha_P{}'') \\ + 2|F_N{}^0(\mathbf{H})|\,|F_P{}''(\mathbf{H})| \cos(\alpha_N{}^0 - \alpha_P{}'')\end{aligned} \tag{139}$$

The intensity of the inverse reflection $-\mathbf{H}$ (i.e., $-h, -k, -l$) can be obtained by replacing **H** with $-\mathbf{H}$ in Eq. (134), multiplying it with the corresponding complex-conjugate equation, and using the relations $F_N{}^{0*}(-\mathbf{H}) = F_N{}^0(\mathbf{H})$, $F_P{}'^*(-\mathbf{H}) = F_P{}'(\mathbf{H})$, and $F_P{}''^*(-\mathbf{H}) = -F_P{}''(\mathbf{H})$, i.e.,

$$\begin{aligned}|F_N(-\mathbf{H})|^2 = |F_N{}^0(\mathbf{H})|^2 + |F_P{}'(\mathbf{H})|^2 + |F_P{}''(\mathbf{H})|^2 \\ + 2|F_N{}^0(\mathbf{H})|\,|F_P{}'(\mathbf{H})| \cos(\alpha_N{}^0 - \alpha_P{}') \\ - 2|F_P{}'(\mathbf{H})|\,|F_P{}''(\mathbf{H})| \cos(\alpha_P{}' - \alpha_P{}'') \\ - 2|F_N{}^0(\mathbf{H})|\,|F_P{}''(\mathbf{H})| \cos(\alpha_N{}^0 - \alpha_P{}'')\end{aligned} \tag{140}$$

From Eqs. (139) and (140) it follows that

$$|F_N(\mathbf{H})|^2 \neq |F_N(-\mathbf{H})|^2 \tag{141}$$

which is a violation of Friedel's law. Friedel's law is given by

$$|F_N(\mathbf{H})|^2 = |F_N(-\mathbf{H})|^2 \tag{142}$$

The condition for Eq. (142) to hold is that $(\alpha_P{}' - \alpha_P{}'')$ and $(\alpha_N{}^0 - \alpha_P{}'')$ must each equal $\pi/2$, i.e., the crystal must possess a center of inversion. Thus, Friedel's law is strictly valid only for a centrosymmetric crystal. For a noncentric crystal, the law is valid only to the extent $f_{Pj}{}''$ may be neglected. Therefore, in general, there is a difference $\Delta(\mathbf{H}, -\mathbf{H})$ between the intensities of inverse related reflections.*

* At least there may be one circumstance under which a noncentrosymmetric crystal containing anomalous scatterers need not violate Friedel's law. This case arises when all the N atoms in the unit cell are equivalent anomalous scatterers, i.e., for all values of $j = 1, N$, $f_j{}'' = f''$.

From Eqs. (139) and (140) we obtain

$$\Delta(\mathbf{H}, -\mathbf{H}) = 4|F_P'|\,|F_P''| \cos(\alpha_P' - \alpha_P'') + 4|F_N{}^0|\,|F_P''| \cos(\alpha_N{}^0 - \alpha_P'') \quad (143)$$

The sum of the two intensities is

$$S(\mathbf{H}, -\mathbf{H}) = 2|F_N{}^0|^2 + 2|F_P'|^2 + 2|F_P''|^2 + 4|F_N{}^0|\,|F_P'| \cos(\alpha_N{}^0 - \alpha_P') \quad (144)$$

Using $F_N' = F_N{}^0 + F_P'$, these expressions can be simplified to

$$\Delta(\mathbf{H}, -\mathbf{H}) = 4|F_N'|\,|F_P''| \cos(\alpha_N' - \alpha_P'') \quad (145)$$
$$S(\mathbf{H}, -\mathbf{H}) = 2|F_N'|^2 + 2|F_P''|^2 \quad (146)$$

In the above expressions, $|F_N(\mathbf{H})|^2$ and $|F_N(-\mathbf{H})|^2$ are intensities of $\mathbf{H}$ and $-\mathbf{H}$ when anomalous dispersion is taken into account. These are the quantities that are actually measured in any given experiment and are not necessarily equal unless the crystal is centrosymmetric. The quantity $|F_N{}^0(\mathbf{H})|^2$ is the intensity obtained if dispersion effects are completely neglected, i.e., if $\lambda \gg \lambda_K$. Also, $|F_N{}^0(\mathbf{H})|^2 = |F_N{}^0(-\mathbf{H})|^2$. The quantity $|F_N'(\mathbf{H})|^2$ is the intensity that will be obtained if the imaginary component f_P'' is zero. Also, $|F_N'(\mathbf{H})|^2 = |F_N'(-\mathbf{H})|^2$.

The above formulas are quite general. They are valid even if the atoms P are not of the same kind, i.e., even if the various f_{Pi}'''s are different. In such cases, α_P'', the phase of F_P'', will differ from α_P' by an angle ϕ, not necessarily $\pi/2$. In fact,

$$\phi = \alpha_P' - \alpha_P'' \qquad \text{and} \qquad \alpha_P'' = \tan^{-1}(B_P''/A_P'')$$

where B_P'' and A_P'' are the imaginary and real parts of F_P'', i.e.,

$$B_P'' = \sum_{j=1}^{P} f_{Pj}'' \cos 2\pi\mathbf{H} \cdot \mathbf{r}_{Pj}$$

and

$$A_P'' = -\sum_{j=1}^{P} f_{Pj}'' \sin 2\pi\mathbf{H} \cdot \mathbf{r}_{Pj}$$

However, for a given incident λ, it is unlikely that there are more than one kind of anomalously scattering atoms. Therefore, hereafter we shall consider the case when all the atoms P are of the same kind, i.e., the various f_{Pj}'' are the same, and each equals the same value of f_P''. In such a case,

$$\tan \alpha_P'' = -\cot \alpha_P' \qquad \text{and} \qquad \phi = \pi/2$$

In another case of common occurrence, the anomalously scattering atoms may form a centrosymmetric configuration, while the rest of the structure is noncentrosymmetric. In such a case, α_P' is necessarily 0 or π and correspondingly α_P'' is $\pi/2$ or $3\pi/2$, so that the angle θ between F_P'' and F_N' becomes $(\pi/2 - \alpha_N')$. The expression for the intensity difference simplifies to

$$\Delta(\mathbf{H}, -\mathbf{H}) = 4|F_N'(\mathbf{H})|\,|F_P''(\mathbf{H})| \sin \alpha_N'(\mathbf{H})$$

Based on the formulas given above, several methods of determining the phase angles have been proposed.

The Imaginary-component Method. One method which is very useful is the one based on the violation of Friedel's law in the case of noncentric crystals.[68,69] The method involves collection of intensity data to a high degree of accuracy at a suitable incident wavelength. The intensities of both $\mathbf{H}$ and $-\mathbf{H}$ are experimentally measured, preferably with a Geiger counter or scintillation crystal spectrometer. The data are reduced to absolute scale, and values of $S(\mathbf{H}, -\mathbf{H})$ and $\Delta(\mathbf{H}, -\mathbf{H})$ are derived. Knowing the positions $\mathbf{r}_{Pi}$ (see *Location of the Atoms P*, below) and scattering powers

$$f_{Pj} = (f_{Pj}{}^0 + f_{Pj}') + if_{Pj}''$$

the following quantities are calculated:

$$F_P'' = i \sum_{j=1}^{P} f_{Pj}'' \exp +2\pi i \mathbf{H} \cdot \mathbf{r}_{Pj} \tag{147}$$

$$A_P'' = \text{real part of } F_P''$$

$$B_P'' = \text{imaginary part of } F_P''$$

$$\alpha_P'' = \tan^{-1} (B_P''/A_P'') \tag{148}$$

$$|F_P''|^2 = A_P''^2 + B_P''^2 \tag{149}$$

These calculated values are used in conjunction with the experimental values of $S(\mathbf{H}, -\mathbf{H})$ and $\Delta(\mathbf{H}, -\mathbf{H})$ to obtain $|F_N'|$. The angle θ is obtained from

$$\pm\theta = \cos^{-1} [\Delta(\mathbf{H}, -\mathbf{H})/4|F_N'|\,|F_P''|] \tag{150}$$

The phase angle $\alpha_N'(\mathbf{H})$ of $F_N'(\mathbf{H})$ may finally be calculated from

$$\alpha_N'(\mathbf{H}) = \alpha_P''(\mathbf{H}) \pm \theta \tag{151}$$

Equation (151) shows that the phase determination is ambiguous. The ambiguity may be resolved by the following techniques.

1. *The Quasi-heavy-atom Method.* Consider the usual case when the atoms P are chemically equivalent. Then $\alpha_P'' = \alpha_P' + \pi/2$ where α_P' is the phase of F_P', and

$$F_P' = \sum_{j=1}^{P} (f_{Pj}^0 + f_{Pj}') \exp +2\pi i \mathbf{H} \cdot \mathbf{r}_{Pj}$$

In such a case, the two values of $\alpha_N'(\mathbf{H})$ are

$$\alpha_1 = \alpha_P' + \pi/2 + \theta$$

$$\alpha_2 = \alpha_P' + \pi/2 - \theta$$

so that, if one solution is α, the other solution is $2\alpha_P' + \pi - \alpha$. It may be seen that one value is closer to α_P' than the other. The closer value (α_{clo}) may be taken to be the probable value of α_N' because the atoms P are usually heavy or quasi-heavy compared with the rest of the atoms Q. Structure determination may then be attempted from a Fourier synthesis calculated with coefficient $|F_N'(\mathbf{H})| \exp i\alpha_{clo}$. Examples of phase-angle determination by this technique are ephedrine hydrochloride[70] and L (+) lysine hydrochloride dihydrate.[71] In both cases, the anomalously scattering atoms were chlorine ($Z = 17$, $f'' = 0.69$, and $\lambda_K = 4.0$ Å), and the incident wavelength was Cu $K\alpha$ ($\lambda = 1.542$ Å). A more recent and beautiful work is that on vitamin B_{12}, as described by Dorothy Hodgkin in her Nobel lecture.[72]

2. *Another means of resolving the ambiguity* in α_N' consists in combining the anomalous dispersion method with the isomorphous replacement method (see below under Real-component Methods and Method of Isomorphous Replacement).

3. *β_{an} Synthesis and the Double-phased Fourier.* In cases where the ambiguity cannot be resolved, structure determination may be attempted from a Fourier synthesis in which the coefficient is phased with both possible values α_1 and α_2, i.e., the coefficient

$$|F_N'| (\exp i\alpha_1 + \exp i\alpha_2)$$

This double-phased synthesis is similar to the β_{an} synthesis,[73] which is a Fourier synthesis calculated with the coefficient $[\Delta(\mathbf{H}, -\mathbf{H})/F_P''^*]$, and can be proved to contain major positive peaks at atomic positions $\mathbf{r}_j$, ($j = 1, N$), against a background of minor, and mostly negative peaks. The β_{an} synthesis becomes particularly interesting in cases where the anomalously scattering atoms form a centrosymmetric configuration while the rest of the atoms are acentric. In such cases $\alpha_P' = 0$ or $180°$, and if one value of $\alpha_N'(\mathbf{H})$ is α, the second value becomes $(\pi - \alpha)$. The corresponding β_{an} synthesis contains a set of positive peaks for the structure and an equivalent set of negative peaks for the inverse structure. (The inversion occurs at the center of symmetry of the group of atoms P.) From the point of view of calculation, the β_{an} synthesis can be Fourier-summed with either the coefficient

$$\Delta(\mathbf{H}, -\mathbf{H}) \exp i\alpha_P''/|F_P''|$$

or else the coefficient $|F_N'(\mathbf{H})|$ (exp $i\alpha_1$ + exp $i\alpha_2$). Which coefficient is used is a matter of taste. The former saves some numerical work involved in computations of α_1 and α_2.

The advantage of β_{an} synthesis over the quasi-heavy-atom method is that the former may be calculated even if the data are on a relative scale. The advantage of either method over the conventional heavy-atom methods (see Fourier Methods in Sec. 8) is that any pseudo symmetry resulting from the positions of the heavy atoms is not really a disadvantage. Structure-determining methods based on effects of f'' yield the molecules in their absolute configuration, as a by-product of the analyses.

Real-component Methods. These methods are based on f' and its dependence on λ. Unlike those based on f'', they are applicable to both centric and acentric crystals. However, they involve collection of accurate intensity data with a minimum of at least two incident x-ray wavelengths λ_1 and λ_2. These wavelengths are so chosen that the values of $f_P'^{(1)}$ and $f_P'^{(2)}$ at λ_1 and λ_2 are significantly different. For the sake of generality, we shall consider the case of a set of P nonequivalent and anomalously scattering atoms. These atoms will be denoted by subscripts Pi and the remaining atoms by Qj where $j = 1, N - P$.

At λ_1,
$$f_{Pi}^{(1)} = f_{Pi}^0 + f_{Pi}'^{(1)} + if_{Pi}''^{(1)} \quad (152)$$
while at λ_2,
$$f_{Pi}^{(2)} = f_{Pi}^0 + f_{Pi}'^{(2)} + if_{Pi}''^{(2)} \quad (153)$$

We shall express $f_{Pi}^{(2)}$ in terms of $f_{Pi}^{(1)}$ as follows:

$$f_{Pi}^{(2)} = f_{Pi}^0 + f_{Pi}'^{(1)} + \Delta f_{Pi}' + if_{Pi}''^{(2)} \quad (154)$$
where
$$\Delta f_{Pi}' = f_{Pi}'^{(2)} - f_{Pi}'^{(1)}$$

For both λ_1 and λ_2, $f_{Qj} = f_{Qj}^0$.

Let $S^{(1)}$ be the sum of the intensities of a pair of inverse related reflections $\mathbf{H}$ and $-\mathbf{H}$ at λ_1, and $\Delta^{(1)}$ the difference. Let $S^{(2)}$ and $\Delta^{(2)}$ be the corresponding quantities at λ_2. From considerations similar to those above (see Formulas for Intensities),

$$\tfrac{1}{2}S^{(1)} = |F_N'^{(1)}|^2 + |F_P''^{(1)}|^2 \quad (155)$$
and
$$\tfrac{1}{2}S^{(2)} = |F_N'^{(1)}|^2 + |F_P'|^2 + |F_P''^{(2)}|^2 + 2|F_N'^{(1)}|\,|F_P'| \cos(\alpha_N'^{(1)} - \alpha_P') \quad (156)$$
where
$$F_P' = \sum_{j=1}^{P} \Delta f_{Pj}' \exp 2\pi i\mathbf{H}\cdot\mathbf{r}_{Pi} \quad (157)$$

α_P' is the phase of F_P', and $\alpha_N'^{(1)}$ is the phase of $F_N'^{(1)}$. Subtracting Eq. (155) from (156) we have

$$D = \tfrac{1}{2}(S^{(2)} - S^{(1)}) \quad (158)$$
$$D = |F_P'|^2 + |F_P''^{(2)}|^2 - |F_P''^{(1)}|^2 + 2|F_N'^{(1)}|\,|F_P'| \cos(\alpha_N'^{(1)} - \alpha_P') \quad (159)$$

Denoting $\alpha_N'^{(1)} - \alpha_P'$ by θ, we have

$$\pm\theta = \cos^{-1}\frac{(D - |F_P'|^2 - |F_P''^{(2)}|^2 + |F_P''^{(1)}|^2)}{2|F_N'^{(1)}|\,|F_P'|} \quad (160)$$
whence
$$\alpha_N'^{(1)} = \alpha_P' \pm \theta \quad (161)$$

The experiment gives, for each reflection $\mathbf{H}$, the quantities $S^{(1)}$, $S^{(2)}$, and therefore D. The various quantities pertaining to the atoms P can be calculated provided the positions $\mathbf{r}_{Pj}$ and scattering powers $f_{Pj}^{(1)}$ and $f_{Pj}^{(2)}$ are known. The amplitude $|F_N'^{(1)}|$ can be obtained from Eq. (155), whence the phase angle $\alpha_N^{(1)}$ may be derived, except for an ambiguity, from Eq. (160). This ambiguity is similar to the one discussed above (see Formulas for Intensities), except that here it is more serious. For instance, the ambiguity cannot be resolved by the quasi-heavy-atom method, because the two solutions are symmetrically disposed with respect to α_P'. The double-phased Fourier, however, can be synthesized with the coefficient

$$|F_N'|\ (\exp i\alpha_1 + \exp i\alpha_2)$$

where $\alpha_1 = \alpha_P' + \theta$ and $\alpha_2 = \alpha_P' - \theta$.

The synthesis contains peaks corresponding to the structure against background peaks which are mostly positive. If the configuration of the P atoms is centric, the double-phase Fourier will yield the structure duplicated by its positive inverse. Determination of the structure from such double-phased Fouriers may be possible only if some stereochemical information of the molecule is available.

The calculation of the double-phased synthesis is, however, simple because it is similar to the β synthesis relevant to this particular case. The latter is simply a synthesis calculated with the coefficient

$$D \exp i\alpha_P'/|F_P'|$$

An unambiguous determination of $\alpha_N'^{(1)}$ is possible provided the difference $\Delta^{(1)}$ (or $\Delta^{(2)}$) is also available. It is then possible to obtain an independent pair of solutions for α_N' by the imaginary-component method outlined above. These two solutions will not be symmetric about α_P'. In fact, one of the solutions derived from $\Delta^{(1)}$ will be seen to agree with one of the solutions derived from D, and can be taken to be the correct value of α_N'. It will be noted that this procedure of resolving the ambiguity is equivalent to combining the real-component method with the imaginary-component method. It is also equivalent to adding the two relevant β syntheses, after proper scaling. In other words, the procedure is equivalent to calculating a synthesis with the coefficient

$$\frac{K_1\Delta^{(1)} \exp i\alpha_P''}{|F_P''^{(1)}|} + \frac{K_2 D' \exp i\alpha_P'}{|F_P'|} \tag{162}$$

where K_1 and K_2 are constants, necessary to bring the two syntheses to the same scale.* It will be noted that the first term leads to a synthesis which gives the structure against a negative background, while the second term leads to the synthesis which gives the structure against an equivalent positive background. The composite synthesis, then, yields just the structure against a negligible background.

The discussion, so far, is for acentric crystals. The real-component method is applicable to centric crystals as well.

The same formulas are valid, with the added simplification that α_P' as well as $\alpha_N'^{(1)}$ can only be 0 or 180°, and there is no ambiguity in the sign determination. The real-component method has been used in only a very few cases.[74,75]

Method of Isomorphous Replacement. This method is equivalent, in principle, to the real-component method. However, the variation of scattering power is achieved by chemical substitution of a set of atoms in the unit cell, for instance, replacing a set of chlorine atoms ($Z = 17$) with a set of bromine atoms ($Z = 35$), and so on. The obvious advantage is that the change Δf achieved in f is much larger than that achieved by changing the incident λ. For this reason, this method has become one of great power and wide scope. In fact, it is presently the standard technique of studying giant molecules, such as proteins.[76,77] However, it is to be noted that methods based on change of λ assure strict isomorphism compared with those involving chemical substitution of the atoms. In the former method, changes of intensity, if and when measured accurately, can be safely attributed to changes of scattering power. In the latter methods, one has to be sure that such changes in intensity are not due, in part, to possible changes in atomic positions.

In the isomorphous method, intensity data are usually collected from a pair of "isomorphous" crystals, at one and the same wavelength. Let us consider such a pair of crystals, each containing a total number of N atoms, out of which a small number P

* The quantity $D' = D - |F_P'|^2 - |F_P''^{(2)}|^2 + |F_P''^{(1)}|^2$. The calculation of D' is possible only if the data are on an absolute scale. However, the quantity D may be used in place of D'. This may introduce some positive background peaks but requires only the relative scale K_1/K_2.

are located at $\mathbf{r}_{Pi}$ and the remaining $Q(= N - P)$ atoms are located at $\mathbf{r}_{Qj}$. (The subscript $Pi = 1, P$ and $Qj = 1, Q$.) The two crystals are thus identical except that in crystal (1), the scattering factor at $\mathbf{r}_{Pi}$ is $f_{Pi}^{(1)}$ while in crystal (2), it is $f_{Pi}^{(2)}$. Let $|F_N^{(1)}(\mathbf{H})|^2$ and $|F_N^{(2)}(\mathbf{H})|^2$ be the intensities of the same reflection $\mathbf{H}$ given by the two crystals. Let $\Delta(\mathbf{H})$ be the difference $|F_N^{(1)}(\mathbf{H})|^2 - |F_N^{(2)}(\mathbf{H})|^2$. Let $f_{Pi} = f_{Pi}^{(2)} - f_{Pi}^{(1)}$. (In this discussion, we neglect dispersion effects so that the various f_j's are f_j^0's of the previous discussion.) We have

$$F_N^{(2)}(\mathbf{H}) = F_N^{(1)}(\mathbf{H}) + F_P(\mathbf{H})$$

where

$$F_P(\mathbf{H}) = \sum_{j=1}^{P} f_{Pj} \exp +2\pi i \mathbf{H} \cdot \mathbf{r}_{Pj}$$

whence

$$\Delta(\mathbf{H}) = |F_N^{(2)}(\mathbf{H})|^2 - |F_N^{(1)}(\mathbf{H})|^2 = |F_P(\mathbf{H})|^2 + 2|F_N^{(1)}|\,|F_P| \cos (\alpha_N^{(1)} - \alpha_P) \quad (163)$$

The quantities $\Delta(\mathbf{H})$, $|F_N^{(1)}|^2$, and $|F_N^{(2)}|^2$ are obtained directly from experiment. The various quantities pertaining to P can be calculated provided the positions $\mathbf{r}_{Pi}$ and scattering powers of the replaceable atoms P are known, so that the phase angle $\alpha_N^{(1)}$ of $F_N^{(1)}$ can be obtained from

$$\alpha_N^{(1)} = \alpha_P \pm \theta$$

where θ is derived from

$$\pm\theta = \cos^{-1} \frac{\Delta(\mathbf{H}) - |F_P(\mathbf{H})|^2}{2|F_N^{(1)}|\,|F_P|} \quad (164)$$

and α_P is the phase of F_P.

It will be noted that, as usual, the phase determination is ambiguous. The nature of the ambiguity is similar to that discussed under the real-component methods. The double-phased Fourier is the β_{is} synthesis[73] calculated with the coefficient

$$\Delta(\mathbf{H}) \exp i\alpha_P/|F_P|$$

and yields the structure against a positive background.

The ambiguity in α_N may be resolved by combination with the anomalous dispersion method, provided the crystals contain anomalous scatterers and suitable incident x-ray wavelengths are available.

The ambiguity may also be resolved by the method of double isomorphous replacement. This method involves data collection from three isomorphous crystals. Crystals (1) and (2) are isomorphous, with a set of atoms P as the replaceable atoms. Crystals (1) and (3) should be isomorphous, but with a replaceable set of atoms R different from those of P. Then, it will be possible to obtain two pairs of solutions as follows:

$$\alpha_{1,2} = \alpha_P \pm \theta_P$$
$$\alpha_{1,3} = \alpha_R \pm \theta_R$$

One value from the second set $(\alpha_{1,3})$ will agree with one value from the first set $(\alpha_{1,2})$ and that value is to be taken as the correct value of $\alpha_N^{(1)}$.

For unambiguous solution, it is therefore necessary to have a minimum of three derivatives. However, in most cases, structure determination may be successfully achieved from two crystals, via the β_{is} synthesis.

Finally the method is applicable to both noncentric and centric crystals. (There is no ambiguity involved in the latter case.)

The above theory is for the isomorphous replacement technique and can be carried over easily to the isomorphous addition technique. In the latter technique, crystal (1) contains a set of atoms, Q in number, and crystal (2) contains a total number of $(P + Q)$ atoms. The positions of the Q atoms are the same in both crystals. The theory, in this case, may be derived from that of the replacement method by putting $f_{Pi}^{(1)} = 0$.

A good number of crystal structures have been solved by these methods, and we give some which are illustrative of the basic principles.

Centrosymmetric Case: the metal phthalocyanines and the metal-free phthalocyanine $C_{32}H_{16}N_8$.[78] The metal atom (Ni) is the replacement atom. Both crystals belong to space group $P2_1/a$ and have two molecules per unit cell.

Noncentrosymmetric Crystal. The structure of strychnine sulfate pentahydrate (space group $C2$) was solved from a study of the sulfate and the selenate.[79]

Some Special Self-convolutions. It is possible to calculate some special Patterson functions and determine the structure by image-seeking procedures, in the case of both anomalous dispersion and isomorphous replacement techniques.

The P_s Function. This function is available in the imaginary-component method[80] and is calculated by means of a Fourier synthesis in which the coefficients are the intensity differences between pairs of inverse related reflections, i.e.,

$$P_s(\mathbf{u}) = (1/V) \sum_{\mathbf{H}=-\infty}^{+\infty} \Delta(\mathbf{H},-\mathbf{H}) \exp +2\pi i\mathbf{H}\cdot\mathbf{r} \tag{165}$$

On summing over reflections **H** and $-$**H**, this expression reduces to

$$P_s(u,v,w) = (2/V) \sum_h \sum_k \sum_l \Delta(hkl,\bar{h}\bar{k}\bar{l}) \sin 2\pi(hu + kv + lw) \tag{166}$$

(In the summation h and $k = -\infty$ to $+\infty$, $l = 0$ to $+\infty$.)

The peaks contained by $P_s(\mathbf{u})$ can be worked out easily by expressing Δ in terms of the structure-factor components and applying the convolution integral theorem. The important result is that $P_s(\mathbf{u})$ contains only the peaks corresponding to the interatomic vectors between the anomalous scatterers P and the nonanomalous scatterers Q, i.e., only the peaks $\pm(\mathbf{r}_{Pi} - \mathbf{r}_{Qj})$; the vectors such as $(\mathbf{r}_{Qi} - \mathbf{r}_{Qj})$ get suppressed. Further, peaks such as $(\mathbf{r}_{Qj} - \mathbf{r}_{Pi})$ are positive (i.e., height $+f_{Qj}{}^0 f_{Pi}''$) while those at $(\mathbf{r}_{Pi} - \mathbf{r}_{Qj})$ are negative (i.e., height $-f_{Qj}{}^0 f_P''$). This attractive result means that the number of images in $P_s(\mathbf{u})$ is only P, the number of anomalous scatterers present in the unit cell.* This result is to be contrasted with that of the conventional Patterson function which contains a large number N of images. Inasmuch as $P \ll N$, the $P_s(\mathbf{u})$ is a convenient starting point for further image seeking. Note that in applying such image-seeking procedures to $P_s(\mathbf{u})$, it is a good idea to reset $P_s(\mathbf{u})$ to a zero value wherever $P_s(\mathbf{u})$ is negative.

It is to be noted that $P_s(\mathbf{u})$ is the imaginary part of the complex Patterson function that is obtained by synthesizing the anomalous dispersion data. In fact, in general,

$$P(\mathbf{u}) = (1/V) \sum_{\mathbf{H}=-\infty}^{+\infty} |F(\mathbf{H})|^2 \exp -2\pi i\mathbf{H}\cdot\mathbf{r} = (1/V)[P_c(\mathbf{u}) - iP_s(\mathbf{u})] \tag{167}$$

where

$$P_c(\mathbf{u}) = \sum_{\mathbf{H}=-\infty}^{+\infty} |F(\mathbf{H})|^2 \cos 2\pi(\mathbf{H}\cdot\mathbf{r}) \tag{168}$$

and

$$P_s(\mathbf{u}) = \sum_{\mathbf{H}=-\infty}^{+\infty} |F(\mathbf{H})|^2 \sin 2\pi(\mathbf{H}\cdot\mathbf{r}) \tag{169}$$

[Equation (169) reduces to (166) on summing over **H** and $-$**H**.]

The cosine synthesis $P_c(\mathbf{u})$ is similar to conventional Patterson functions except for small differences in peak heights. The heights at $\pm(\mathbf{r}_{Pi} - \mathbf{r}_{Pj})$ are $(f_{Pi}{}^0 + f_{Pi}') \times (f_{Pj}{}^0 + f_{Pj}') + f_{Pi}''f_{Pj}''$; those at $\pm(\mathbf{r}_{Pi} - \mathbf{r}_{Qj})$ are $(f_{Pi}{}^0 + f_{Pi}') \times f_{Qj}{}^0$; and those at $\pm(\mathbf{r}_{Qi} - \mathbf{r}_{Qj})$ are $f_{Qi}{}^0 f_{Qj}{}^0$. The total number of nonorigin peaks in $P_c(\mathbf{u})$ is $(N^2 - N)$, where $N = P + Q$, and all the peaks are positive. The total number of peaks in $P_s(\mathbf{u})$ is, however, only $2PQ$. Even out of these $2PQ$ peaks, only half are positive while the other half are negative.

* Further, the heights of the peaks which correspond to "inverse images P" are negative.

The $DP(\mathbf{u})$ Function. The $DP(\mathbf{u})$, or the difference Patterson,[81] is quite useful in the case of the isomorphous methods. It is calculated by Fourier-synthesizing with coefficient $D(\mathbf{H})$, the difference between the intensities of reflection $\mathbf{H}$, given by the two crystals, i.e.,

$$DP(\mathbf{u}) = (1/V) \sum_{\mathbf{H}=-\infty}^{+\infty} D(\mathbf{H}) \exp 2\pi i \mathbf{H} \cdot \mathbf{u} \tag{170}$$

where

$$D(\mathbf{H}) = |F_N^{(2)}(\mathbf{H})|^2 - |F_N^{(1)}(\mathbf{H})|^2 \tag{171}$$

The main advantage of the $DP(\mathbf{u})$ function is that it does not contain vectors such as QQ (i.e., $\mathbf{r}_{Qi} - \mathbf{r}_{Qj}$). There is an origin peak of strength*

$$\sum_{i=1}^{P} (f_{Pi}^{(2)})^2 - (f_{Pi}^{(1)})^2$$

peaks of strength $f_{Pi}^{(2)} f_{Pj}^{(2)} - f_{Pi}^{(1)} f_{Pj}^{(1)}$ corresponding to PP vectors at $(\mathbf{r}_{Pi} - \mathbf{r}_{Pj})$, and peaks of strength $f_{Pi} f_{Qj}$ corresponding to PQ vectors at $\pm$ $(\mathbf{r}_{Pi} - \mathbf{r}_{Qj})$ (where $Pi = 1, P$; and $Q_j = 1, Q$; also $f_{Pi} = f_{Pi}^{(2)} - f_{Pi}^{(1)}$). The total number of nonorigin peaks is thus $(P^2 - P) + 2PQ$, and all the peaks are positive. The $DP(\mathbf{u})$ contains only P images of the structure (i.e., the images as seen from the replaceable atoms), as compared with a total of N images contained by the Patterson function of the individual crystals. The $DP(\mathbf{u})$ is therefore a convenient starting point for carrying out subsequent image-seeking procedures. A difference Patterson is also available in the case of the real-component method. In this case, the function is to be synthesized with $D(\mathbf{H})$, where D is the difference in intensities of the reflection $\mathbf{H}$ measured at the two incident wavelengths λ_1 and λ_2.

In either technique, the two sets of intensity data $|F_N^{(1)}|^2$ and $|F_N^{(2)}|^2$ need not be on an absolute scale but should be on the same relative scale. It is also preferable to have the data sharpened by some suitable procedure. The relative scale and a certain degree of sharpening are achieved in a simple way if the normalized intensities $|E^{(1)}(H)|^2$ and $|E^{(2)}(H)|^2$ are used in place of $|F^{(1)}(H)|^2$ and $|F^{(2)}(H)|^2$.

Image Seeking. When structure determination is attempted by image-seeking procedures performed on the $DP(\mathbf{u})$ or $P_s(\mathbf{u})$, as the case may be, the following points should be borne in mind.

1. The first-order image-seeking function calculated with an interatomic vector $\mathbf{u}$ will, in principle, yield the structure duplicated by inverse about the midpoint of $\mathbf{u}$, only if $\mathbf{u}$ is a PP vector, i.e., $\mathbf{u} = \mathbf{r}_{Pi} - \mathbf{r}_{Pj}$. If $\mathbf{u}$ is a PQ vector (i.e., $\mathbf{u} = \mathbf{r}_{Pi} - \mathbf{r}_{Qj}$), one may obtain only the atoms P and their inverses about the midpoint of $\mathbf{u}$. [Note the duplication does not occur in the $P_s(\mathbf{u})$ because the heights of the peaks of the inverse images are negative.]

2. In performing iterative cycles of calculations of image functions, it is not useful to use the positions of the atoms Q as input for the simple reason that the $DP(\mathbf{u})$ does not contain the peaks which correspond to the QQ vectors. If such iterations involving atoms Q are desired, they are probably better carried out with the individual Patterson function of either crystal.

Location of the Atoms P. It is obvious from the above discussions that the atoms P must be located beforehand, particularly in techniques based on deriving the phase angles. In most cases, this location is not difficult, because the atoms P are either heavy atoms or at least quasi-heavy compared with the atoms Q. Therefore, the atoms P can be located by examining the Patterson function, Harker sections, and/or the implication function of order 0. However, there may arise cases where such a straightforward location is not possible. For instance, the atoms P may not be heavy, or else the number of light atoms Q may be very large. In such cases, it may be necessary to resort to other methods, such as those involving accumulation functions.

* The term strength is to be understood as the peak height at the center of the peak corresponding to the interatomic vector.

Without going into the details, we just quote the following functions which are used in methods based on accumulation functions:

$$1MA(\mathbf{u}) = \int_V \min\,[(p(\mathbf{r}),\ p(\mathbf{r} + \mathbf{u})]\ dv$$

$$1PA(\mathbf{u}) = \int_V p(\mathbf{r})p(\mathbf{r} + \mathbf{u})\ dv$$

where $p(\mathbf{r})$ can be the $DP(\mathbf{r})$ function or the $P_s(\mathbf{r})$ function as the case may be. Both $1MA(\mathbf{u})$ and $1PA(\mathbf{u})$ contain[33] very strong peaks at the interatomic vectors such as PP, and enable location of the positions of the atoms P. Between the two functions, $1MA(\mathbf{u})$ is probably better than $1PA(\mathbf{u})$ from the point of view of less spurious peaks, but its calculation is more involved. On the other hand, the calculation of $1PA(\mathbf{u})$ is achieved by means of a Fourier synthesis whose Fourier coefficients are D^2 or Δ^2 as the case may be. Some workers prefer to use the squares of the differences in amplitudes, rather than those in the intensities. Techniques such as those described above are extensively used in the analysis of protein crystals.[82,83]

8. REFINEMENT OF CRYSTAL STRUCTURES

Refinement of crystal structures is usually undertaken after the phase problem has been circumvented by some means or other and a plausible model of a trial structure has been obtained. The basic idea behind refinement is to determine that set of atomic parameters which is most consistent with the observed intensities, the latter being taken to be free from systematic errors, such as absorption and extinction, and subject only to random errors of measurement. No precise definition is, as yet, available for this consistency. However, one is guided by two important factors, namely, (1) the model is to be chemically meaningful; and (2) the agreement between F_c, the calculated value of the structure factor, and F_0, the observed value, must be good over a considerable range of the F's. Some measure of this agreement between F_0 and F_c is given by the residual

$$R = \sum_{\mathbf{H}} |\Delta F(\mathbf{H})| \Big/ \sum_{\mathbf{H}} |F_0(\mathbf{H})|$$

where

$$\Delta F(\mathbf{H}) = |F_0(\mathbf{H})| - |F_c(\mathbf{H})| \tag{172}$$

and where the summation is over all the reflections. Under the assumption that the atomic parameters are random and completely uncorrelated with those of the correct structure, the value of R is 0.828 for a centric crystal and 0.586 for an acentric crystal.[84] These values throw some light on the question whether it is worthwhile refining a particular trial structure or not. It is a matter of experience to attempt refinement of structures which give values of R less than 0.6 for centric and 0.4 for acentric crystals. These values are for equal-atom structures. For structures containing a few heavy atoms, the corresponding values of R should be considerably lower. In any case, the emphasis should be on the overall agreement between selected sets of individual reflections. In other words, reflections which have been observed to be strong must have large calculated values, and equally important, reflections which are observed to have values close to zero must on calculation have reasonably small values. These are some of the factors to be borne in mind, at least in the early stages of strucural refinement. Once a fairly satisfactory trial structure has been obtained, the refinement may be carried out by analytical methods, such as the method of least squares, and/or Fourier methods, such as "direct," "difference," or "differential" Fourier syntheses.

Analytical Methods of Refinement. Presently, the standard technique of refinement is the method of least squares.[85] In its application to the crystallographic problem, the theory of least squares may be outlined as follows: Let us consider the calculated F_c of a given structure factor $\mathbf{H}$, as a function of $\{X\}$, where $\{X\}$ denotes a set $X_1, X_2, \ldots, X_M$ of parameters relevant to the problem. This set, in a general case, is constituted by a total number of M parameters (i.e., $i = 1, M$).

The position of the jth atom is defined by the coordinates x_j, y_j, and z_j, and the thermal vibration of the jth atom is given by an ellipsoid defined by the six parameters β_{11_j}, β_{22_j}, β_{33_j}, β_{12_j}, β_{23_j}, and β_{31_j}. The total number of parameters describing the P atoms is then $9P$. Therefore, the quantity $\{X\}$ denotes the set (Xi), where the subscript i assumes all values from 1 to $9P + 1$. Taking $M = 9P + 1$, the value $i = 1$ corresponds to the scale factor S, the values $i = 2$ up to $i = 10$ describe the 9 parameters of atom 1, the values $i = 11$ up to $i = 19$ refer to the parameters of atom 2, and so on, until the values of $i = M - 8$ up to $i = M$ describe the parameters of the Pth atom. Thus, we see that

$$F_c = f\{X\} \tag{173}$$

and

$$F_0 = f\{X + e\} \tag{174}$$

where $\{X + e\}$ denotes the set $(x_i + e_i)$, e_i being the shift in the ith parameter x_i. The e_i's are the corrections to be applied to the parameters of F_c. If each one of the e_i's becomes zero, $F_0 = F_c$. Therefore, we can develop $|F_0|$ as a Taylor series around $|F_c|$, so that

$$|F_0| = |F_c| + \sum_{i=1}^{M} (\partial|F_c|/\partial x_i)e_i + \tfrac{1}{2}\left[\sum_{i=1}^{M} (\partial|F_c|/\partial x_i)e_i\right]^2 + \text{etc.} \tag{175}$$

If each one of the M shifts is small enough, the higher-order terms in the series (175) can be neglected, and denoting $|F_0| - |F_c|$ by $\Delta|F|$, one obtains

$$\Delta|F| = \sum_{i=1}^{M} (\partial|F_c|/\partial x_i)e_i \tag{176}$$

Multiplying both sides of Eq. (176) by $\partial|F_c|/\partial x_j$, the partial derivative of $|F_c|$ with respect to the jth parameter, we obtain

$$\Delta|F|^q \frac{\partial|F_c|^q}{\partial x_j} = \sum_{i=1}^{M} \frac{\partial|F_c|^q}{\partial x_i}\frac{\partial|F_c|^q}{\partial x_j} e_i \tag{177}$$

where the superscript q denotes that the various quantities refer to the reflection whose Miller indices are (h_q,k_q,l_q). Let us consider a set of independent reflections, Q in number, where $Q > M$, the total number of parameters. We have one such equation (177) for each reflection (h_q,k_q,l_q). Summing up both sides of all such Q equations, we obtain

$$K_j = \sum_{i=1}^{M} a_{ij}e_i \tag{178}$$

where

$$K_j \text{ is } \sum_{q=1}^{Q} (\partial|F_c|^q/\partial x_j)\,\Delta|F_c|^q \tag{179}$$

and

$$a_{ij} \text{ is } \sum_{q=1}^{Q} (\partial|F_c|^q/\partial x_i)(\partial|F_c|^q/\partial x_j) \tag{180}$$

Note that the term on the left-hand side of Eq. (178) is a linear sum (over reflections) of Q terms, where each term involves, in addition to $\Delta|F|^q$, the partial derivative

$$\partial|F_c|^q/\partial x_j$$

of the corresponding $|F_c|$ with respect to a specific parameter fixed by the subscript j. The right-hand side, on the other hand, is a linear sum of M terms, the ith term of which involves the shift e_i and the term a_{ij}, where a_{ij} itself is a linear sum (over reflections) of Q terms, the qth term being the product of the two derivatives of $|F_c|^q$, one with respect to the parameter x_i of the running subscript i and the second with respect to that of the fixed subscript j [as can be seen from Eq. (180)].

It is possible to set up one such equation (178) for each one of M parameters; the M resultant equations are compactly given by

$$\{K\} = \|a\|\{e\} \tag{181}$$

where $\{K\}$ is a column vector,

$$K = \begin{pmatrix} K_1 \\ K_2 \\ \cdot \\ \cdot \\ \cdot \\ K_j \\ K_M \end{pmatrix} \tag{182}$$

$\{e\}$ is another column vector, the ith element of which is the shift of the ith parameter X_i,

$$e = \begin{pmatrix} e_1 \\ e_2 \\ \cdot \\ \cdot \\ \cdot \\ e_j \\ e_M \end{pmatrix} \tag{183}$$

and $\|a\|$ is a square matrix of M columns and M rows, the element a_{ij} at the ith row and the jth column being given by Eq. (180). If the determinant $|a|$ does not vanish, the matrix $\|a\|$ is said to be nonsingular, and the inverse matrix $\|b\|$ can be found so that

$$\{e\} = \|b\|\{K\} \tag{184}$$

From Eq. (184) it is clear that the shift in the ith parameter is

$$e_i = \sum_{j=1}^{M} b_{ij}K_j \tag{185}$$

where b_{ij} is the ijth element of the inverse matrix b.

It is the essence of the theory of least squares that parameter shifts e_i obtained by this procedure tend to minimize the quantity $\sum_q (\Delta|F|^q)^2$. The underlying assumption of the procedure is then as follows: The differences between the calculated and measured values arise only because of random errors in $|F_0|$. If so, the corrected parameters obtained by the procedure correspond to that set which gives the best fit between the set of calculated values and the set of observed values.

A broad outline of an actual calculation of the shifts by the method of least squares is as follows:

The first step is to calculate the values of $F_c(\mathbf{H}_q)$ on the basis of the set of trial parameters $\{x_i\}$. The calculation is to be done for all the available reflections. This, and subsequent calculations, need an expression for F_c in terms of the parameters. In general, we have

$$F_c(\mathbf{H}) = S \sum_{j=1}^{p} f_j \sum_{s=1}^{n} t_{js}T_{js} \tag{186}$$

In Eq. (186), S is the overall scale-factor parameter. The quantities f_j, t_{js}, and T_{js} are, respectively, the scattering factor, the temperature factor, and the trigonometric factor of the atom j in equivalent point s, for the reflection $\mathbf{H}$. The first summation is over the asymmetric unit, which is assumed to contain a certain number p of atoms, and the second is over the n equivalent points of the space group. The scattering factors can be taken from standard tables, and relevant values of f_j for given $\mathbf{H}$ (i.e., $\sin\theta/\lambda$) can be obtained by interpolation. The temperature factor, in the case of anisotropic vibration, is

$$t_{js} = \exp - (\beta_{11js}h^2 + \beta_{22js}k^2 + \beta_{33js}l^2 + 2\beta_{12js}hk + 2\beta_{23js}kl + 2\beta_{31js}lh) \quad (187)$$

The expression (187) is for the general case in which each atom is assigned an individual anisotropic temperature factor. The starting parameters β_{11j}, etc., are obtained, usually, from an initial isotropic trial parameter β_j using the formulas

$$\beta_{11j} = \tfrac{1}{4}\beta_j a^{*2} \qquad \beta_{12j} = \tfrac{1}{4}\beta_j a^* b^* \cos \gamma^*$$

etc., where a^*, b^*, $\cos \gamma^*$, etc., refer to the reciprocal cell. If the vibration is assumed to be isotropic, Eq. (187) simplifies to

$$t_j = \exp (-\beta_j \sin^2 \theta/\lambda^2)$$

If the vibration is completely isotropic, with an overall temperature factor β, the corresponding term $t = \exp (-\beta \sin^2 \theta/\lambda^2)$ can be conveniently taken out and placed in front of the summation signs in Eq. (186). The expression for the trigonometric factor T_j is more complicated, and depends on the space group. For an acentric crystal, $T_j = A_j + \sqrt{-1}\, B_j$ where the real part $A_j = \cos 2\pi(hx_{js} + ky_{js} + lz_{js})$ and the imaginary part $B_j = \sin 2\pi(hx_{js} + ky_{js} + lz_{js})$. For centric crystals the origin can be chosen on a symmetry center so that B_j becomes zero. Once F_c has been computed, the calculation of $|F_c|^2$ and $\Delta|F|$ is straightforward.

The second step is to set up the matrix $\|a\|$ and invert it. This is by far the most tedious part of the calculation. First of all, the derivatives of a given F_c with respect to each one of the M parameters are to be obtained. For an acentric crystal, a typical derivative is of the form

$$\partial_i = \partial|F_c|/\partial x_i = \cos \alpha(\partial A/\partial x_i) + \sin \alpha(\partial B/\partial x_i)$$

where α is the phase angle of the reflection and A and B are the real and imaginary parts of F_c. Then the various derivative products $\partial_i\, \partial_j$ are to be computed, for values of $i, j = 1, M$ where $i > j$. The total number of such products is not M^2 but only $\tfrac{1}{2} M(M + 1)$, in view of the symmetric nature (i.e., $a_{ij} = a_{ji}$) of the matrix $\|a\|$. The calculations are repeated for each one of the Q reflections. The various sums of $\partial_i\, \partial_j$ over the range of Q reflections give the matrix elements a_{ij}, and therefore the matrix $\|a\|$. The vector $\{K\}$ can also be set up during the same calculations. The next step is to invert $\|a\|$ and finally obtain the shifts e_i.

Such an elaborate calculation is called a full-matrix refinement and is extremely tedious if not impossible on a desk calculator. The calculation, however, is eminently feasible with high-speed digital computers.

When calculations are performed manually, or on a small digital computer, it is the usual practice to neglect the off-diagonal elements a_{ij} of the matrix $\|a\|$, calculate only the diagonal elements, and obtain the parameter shifts from the diagonal formula

$$e_i = K_i/a_{ii} \quad (188)$$

The justification for neglecting the off-diagonal terms comes from the fact that each matrix element a_{ij} where $i \neq j$ can be expected to be quite close to zero in view of the summation of a large number of trigonometric terms involving sines and cosines. This is true so long as the arguments of the various trigonometric terms are not all constrained to the same specific value such as 0 or $\pi/2$, a constraint brought about by some types of rational dependencies in the atomic coordinates, such as $\mathbf{r}_i = \mathbf{r}_j$ and $\mathbf{r}_i = -\mathbf{r}_j$. For a centric crystal, both types of rational dependencies mean that atoms i and j overlap, and therefore the diagonal formulas (188) may not be usable for refinement of two-dimensional projection data unless the relevant projection is fairly well resolved. Thus the effect of off-diagonal terms is negligible to some extent only in three dimensions. For noncentric crystals, the dependence $\mathbf{r}_i = -\mathbf{r}_j$ may lead to nonnegligible off-diagonal terms, even if the refinement is three-dimensional, particularly in the case of crystals containing a centrosymmetric group of heavy atoms.[86] In such cases the various phase angles $\alpha(\mathbf{H})$ may be expected to be close to 0 or π, the deviations from these values arising because of the scattering from the noncentric group of light atoms.* If any two light atoms i and j have atomic parameters having a dependence such as $\mathbf{r}_i = -\mathbf{r}_j$, the corresponding off-diagonal matrix elements may be nonnegligible. These and similar conclusions may be easily arrived at by studying the circumstances under which matrix elements a_{ij} vanish. For instance, consider the matrix element which is representative of the interaction between the derivatives with respect to the x coordinate of two atoms i and j. Such a matrix element will be of the form

$$a_{ij} = 4\pi^2 \sum_s \sum_q f_i f_j h^2 \sin(\theta_{is} - \alpha) \sin(\theta_{js} - \alpha)$$
$$= 2\pi^2 \sum_s \sum_q f_i f_j h^2 [\cos(\theta_{is} - \theta_{js}) - \cos(\theta_{is} + \theta_{js} - 2\alpha)]$$

where $\theta_i = 2\pi(hx_i + ky_i + lz_i)$. If α is close to 0 or π, and $\mathbf{r}_i = -\mathbf{r}_j$ so that $\theta_i = -\theta_j$, then the second cosine term will always be close to unity, and there is no reason why a_{ij} should be small.

Similar arguments may be used to show that the diagonal formula is not applicable in the refinement of anisotropic thermal parameters. In view of this discussion it is advisable to use the diagonal formula only in three-dimensional refinements involving isotropic temperature factors, and even then with reservations.

A compromise between the full-matrix method and the diagonal method is probably the block-diagonal method, in which a set of square matrices replaces the full matrix. The scale factor S is usually refined with a 2×2 matrix, involving the interactions between the overall scale factor and an overall isotropic temperature factor, a procedure probably leading to better convergence of the scale factor. The positional parameters of each atom are refined with a 3×3 matrix while the six anisotropic thermal parameters of each atom are treated by a 6×6 matrix. This procedure is probably satisfactory from the point of view of thermal parameters but may not mean any substantial improvement over the diagonal formula from the point of view of positional parameters. The reason for the last statement is that the block-diagonal method neglects the large number of interatomic interactions and considers only the interactions between the three derivatives of one and the same atom with respect to the three coordinate axes.

The theory described so far has formed the mathematical basis of a good number of programs that have been written for digital computers, a good example being the set of programs written by Busing and Levy[87] for computers such as IBM 704, 709, and 7090. The theory is essentially for atoms in general positions, and relevant modifications are necessary if some of the atoms happen to be in special positions. Aside from this fact, certain other minor details should be borne in mind when the methods are used. For instance, any manipulation which makes the matrix $\|a\|$ singular is to be avoided. Singularity of the matrix $\|a\|$ implies that any two rows or columns have identical elements, or else all elements in a given row or column are identically zero. These situations may arise if any two atoms overlap exactly, or else an obvious constant is mistaken as a parameter and is varied. For instance, for acentric crystals in space groups such as $P2_1$ or $P4_1$ (assuming the screw axes are parallel to the c axis) the z coordinate of at least one atom should not be varied so that the origin is uniquely fixed. Singularity of the matrix can also arise when $Q < M$, as well as when redundant parameters are varied, such as the z coordinate in a refinement involving only the ($hk0$) data, or when the overall temperature factor is varied when the individual temperature factors are also being varied in a full-matrix refinement.

The main advantage of the analytical methods of refinement is the possibility of assigning weights $w(hkl)$ to individual observations. This gives a convenient tool for rejecting observations which are dubious. A number of weighting schemes have been proposed; the theory described above assumes unit weights for all the observations,

* This is true, because the usual practice in such cases is to choose the origin on the symmetry center of the heavy-atom configuration.

a scheme supposed to be not really quite satisfactory. There are instances where not only faster convergence but also more satisfactory bond lengths and angles could be obtained when a weighting scheme similar to the one suggested by Hughes[85] is adopted. The weight w is taken as constant if $|F|^2 < |F_{\text{opt}}|^2$ and is taken to be inversely proportional to $|F|^2$ if $|F|^2 > |F_{\text{opt}}|^2$. The value of $|F_{\text{opt}}|^2$ is such that about half the number of reflections have intensity values greater than $|F_{\text{opt}}|^2$, and half of them have values less than $|F_{\text{opt}}|^2$. When weighting schemes such as this one are incorporated, the least-squares calculations are to be carried out after replacing the quantity $\Delta|F|$ by $\sqrt{w}\,\Delta|F|$, and the quantity ∂_i by $\sqrt{w}\,\partial_i$. The procedure, then, tends to minimize $\Sigma(w^{1/2}\,\Delta|F|^q)^2$. A weighting scheme is meaningful if it tends to make $w = 1/\sigma^2$, where σ is the standard deviation of $|F|$.

A second advantage of the method of least squares is the possibility of varying thermal parameters in an attempt to derive meaningful conclusions. If the temperature factors are isotropic, a given β_j, on refinement, is physically meaningful only if the said $\beta_j > 0$, the reason being that β_j is proportional to the mean-square displacement of the atom j.* For the same reason, too large a value of β_j is also unacceptable; it usually means that the positional parameters and/or the scattering factor of the particular atom are incorrect. This fact can sometimes be used to identify and eliminate incorrect atoms in the trial structure during the earlier stages of structure determination, and probably even identify the chemical nature of the atom during the final stages of the refinement. For example, the usual procedure in the refinement of organic crystals is to treat most of the light atoms as carbon atoms, and in the end try to distinguish the oxygen and nitrogen atoms from the carbon atoms by considerations of the thermal parameters. One example of this is casimidine.[88] In fact, this technique, under fortunate circumstances, may be carried out to the extent of settling uncertainties in chemical composition of the crystal, as was the case of $KTeO(OH)_5H_2O$.[89]

Similar considerations apply to the six anisotropic thermal parameters β_{ijk} of the atom k. However, not all the six parameters need be positive. The condition to be obeyed, for the symmetric vibration tensor to be meaningful, is that the determinant β of order 3, the diagonal elements, and the minors associated with them should not be negative, where

$$\beta = \begin{vmatrix} \beta_{11} & \beta_{12} & \beta_{13} \\ \beta_{12} & \beta_{22} & \beta_{23} \\ \beta_{13} & \beta_{23} & \beta_{33} \end{vmatrix}$$

The quantities β_{ij} are related to the corresponding mean-square displacements by relations such as $U_{11} = \beta_{11}/(2\pi^2 a^{*2})$ and $U_{12} = \beta_{12}/(2\pi^2 a^* b^*)$.

A third advantage of the least-squares procedure is the possibility of introducing and refining more than one overall scale factor. This becomes useful in cases where the $|F_0|$ data are collected in sets or layers, as in photographic techniques. Each set can be assigned a separate scale factor, and subsequent iterative cycles of the least-squares refinement take care of any errors in the correlation of the data belonging to the different sets.

The theory described so far is exclusively for those cases where anomalous dispersion is not involved. The effects of the latter on the refinement are usually negligible. However, taking proper account of anomalous dispersion is not much of a problem either, and warrants proper inclusion in the computation of the derivatives. In any case, a given derivative is

$$\partial|F|/\partial x_i = \cos\alpha(\partial A/\partial x_i) + \sin\alpha(\partial B/\partial x_i)$$

where A and B are the real and the imaginary parts of the whole structure factor, that is, including contributions from f_P'' of the anomalously scattering atoms P. The same expression is valid for both noncentric and centric crystals, because even though

* In all this work based on the positivity of β_j, it is important not to forget that the quantities β_j are affected by systematic errors in the data, these errors being introduced by effects such as absorption.

the crystal is centric the structure-factor equations are still complex, in view of the B_P term arising from f_P''.

A second analytical method of refinement is the method of steepest descents.[90] This method is not very commonly used, probably because in its latest form[91] it is equivalent, in principle, to the method of least squares in the diagonal approximation.

Fourier Methods. Refinement of crystal structures may be achieved by means of certain Fourier syntheses as well. The main advantage of the Fourier method over the least-squares method is that in addition to ease of computation, the former may give information that is not present in the input. To be specific, let us consider a model in which some of the atoms are incorrectly located. The Fourier synthesis, computed with the observed amplitudes and calculated phases, yields not only the strong peaks at the positions of the input atoms (whether these atoms are placed correctly or incorrectly) but also a certain number of weak peaks, some of which may correspond to the correct atoms. This statement is particularly true in the case of noncentrosymmetric crystals. For this reason, the present practice is to follow a cycle of least squares with a calculation of the Fourier synthesis. A combined study of the two outputs may enable one to improve the trial structure considerably. After a few such iterations, it may be possible to discover the completely correct structure. Further refinement is usually carried out exclusively by the method of least squares. The last step is a calculation of the Fourier synthesis, based on the final set of parameters. The final values of the residual R are usually of the order of 10 per cent, though values as low as 5 per cent are not uncommon, an example being chlorotetraammine (sulfur dioxide) ruthenium (II) chloride.[92]

The synthesis which is calculated in each iterative cycle is usually either the "direct" Fourier or preferably the "difference" Fourier synthesis. The former is synthesized with the coefficient $|F_0| \exp i\alpha_c$, and the latter is synthesized with $\Delta|F| \exp i\alpha_c$ where $|F_0|$ is the observed amplitude, α_c is the phase angle calculated on the basis of the trial parameters, and $\Delta|F| = |F_0| - |F_c|$, F_c being the calculated structure factor.

The method of structure determination by iterative Fouriers is best discussed in terms of "heavy-atom" structures. The latter are structures which contain a small number of atoms of large scattering power f_H in addition to a large number of atoms of smaller scattering powers f_L. These structures are usually solved by first locating the positions of the heavy atoms from the Patterson function, and then locating the light atoms from iterative cycles of Fouriers. There is no precise criterion for the heaviness of the atoms H, but it is usually not necessary to have $\sum_H Z_H > \sum_L Z_L$. Instead it has been found that a sufficient condition is $\sum_H Z_H{}^2 = \sum_L Z_L{}^2$. The success or failure of an analysis depends not so much on the heaviness of the atoms involved, but rather on their positions. The most favorable case is a centrosymmetric crystal with the heavy atom situated at a symmetry center, as is the case in Pt-phthalocyanine.[93] The least favorable example is a noncentrosymmetric crystal in which the heavy atoms form a centrosymmetric array, as found in cholesteryl iodide[94] and casimidine dihydrochloride[88] among others. The main difficulty is that the Fourier, which is synthesized on the basis of the phases (i.e., signs) of the heavy atoms, is centrosymmetric whereas the structure is noncentric. In other words, one is confronted here with the problem of eliminating the unwanted peaks of the inverse structure and extracting the true structural peaks. This factor, together with other false peaks usually present in the Fourier, complicates the structure determination. In such cases, successful structure determinations are usually achieved by a very careful analysis of the peaks of the heavy-atom Fouriers, building mechanical models, and attempting to identify stereochemically meaningful fragments of the structure. Difficulties introduced by the pseudosymmetry of the heavy-atom positions may, however, be circumvented more easily by means of anomalous dispersion (see Method of Isomorphous Replacement in Sec. 7), because in that case the inverse peaks are negative.

Examples of structures solved by the method of heavy atoms are many. One of the earlier examples was Pt-phthalocyanine;[93] cholesteryl iodide[94] was an early problem which involved complications of pseudosymmetry. Other examples of such structures solved in the early days are calciferol[95] and strychnine.[96] Some examples of such structures solved in recent times are diglycine hydrobromide,[97] aureomycin,[98] casimidine,[88] and morellin.[99] No determination has, as yet, surpassed the beauty of the classic analysis of vitamin B_{12} by D. Hodgkin and her coworkers.[72]

In general, the solution of a heavy-atom structure is not supposed to be very difficult, when compared with that of an equal-atom structure. However, what is difficult is the attainment of a high degree of accuracy in the parameters of the light atoms. It is not only necessary to measure intensity data quite accurately but also to apply proper corrections for effects of absorption, etc. In addition, errors arising out of finite termination of the Fourier series become quite important in view of the presence of the heavy atoms. Generally, finite Fourier transforms have the property that the major peaks are accompanied by alternating positive and negative ripples. The effect of the ripples is usually to displace the peaks. In some cases, the effect may become so drastic as even to suppress the peaks of some of the light atoms. One method of correcting for series-termination errors is to compare the "direct" Fourier, involving $|F_0| \exp i\alpha_c$ as the coefficient, with the calculated Fourier, involving $|F_c| \exp i\alpha_c$ as its coefficient. The former corresponds to the observed structure while the latter corresponds to the calculated structure. Corrections to atomic parameters can be derived on the assumption that the effect of series termination is more or less the same on both the observed and the calculated structures. Thinking along these lines led to the discovery and exploitation of the properties of the difference Fourier.[100] The latter is calculated with the coefficient $\Delta|F| \exp i\alpha_c$ where $\Delta|F|$ is the difference between the observed and calculated structure amplitudes. This function $D(\mathbf{r})$ is defined, in general, as

$$D(\mathbf{r}) = (1/V) \sum_{\mathbf{H}} \Delta|F(\mathbf{H})| \exp i\alpha_c \exp -2\pi i\mathbf{H}\cdot\mathbf{r} \qquad (189)$$

and simplifies, in the case of centrosymmetric crystals, to

$$D(\mathbf{r}) = (2/V) \sum_{\mathbf{H}} s(\mathbf{H})\, \Delta|F(\mathbf{H})| \cos 2\pi\mathbf{H}\cdot\mathbf{r}$$

where $\Delta|F(\mathbf{H})| = |F_0(\mathbf{H})| - |F_c(\mathbf{H})|$, α_c is the phase angle, and $s(\mathbf{H})$ is the sign of the calculated F_c.

In forming $D(\mathbf{r})$, the calculated structure gets subtracted from the observed structure, so that any deviations between the two are exhibited quite prominently. In addition, the coordinates derived from the $D(\mathbf{r})$ are to a large extent free from termination errors. Secondly, the $D(\mathbf{r})$ synthesis can be used to refine the atomic parameters. Qualitatively, the procedure is to draw contours of constant D around the assumed positions and shift the atoms along and up the gradients $\partial D/\partial x_i$. The procedure is continued in a series of iterative cycles of calculations of $D(\mathbf{r})$ until the atoms lie in regions of zero gradients. Quantitative expressions have also been developed; these are similar to the expressions discussed under the method of differential synthesis. A refinement procedure such as this one may be shown to minimize the function

$$R' = \sum (1/f)(F_0 - F_c)^2$$

In fact, the procedure becomes equivalent to the least-squares method, in its diagonal approximation, and under the assumption that the weights w are inversely proportional to an average scattering factor f. However, such a weighting scheme is not really correct from the point of view of the theory of least squares.

A third important property of $D(\mathbf{r})$ is that sometimes the synthesis shows clear evidence of anisotropic thermal vibration. In such cases the assumed positions are usually flanked by smaller positive and negative peaks. The most important property of the difference Fourier is that in the last stages of structural refinement, $D(\mathbf{r})$ sometimes gives very useful clues regarding the positions of very light and supposedly inefficient scatterers of x-rays, such as hydrogen atoms.

All these factors, together with the ease of computation, have made the difference Fourier a very important tool in structure analysis. However, presently it is not the usual practice to rely solely upon $D(\mathbf{r})$, but instead the usual practice is to use it in conjunction with the least-squares method. This is especially true in laboratories that have access to high-speed digital computers. The $D(\mathbf{r})$ synthesis is used to locate additional atoms not present in the input, and the least-squares method is used to refine the structure; the peak heights in the former and the behavior of the positional and thermal parameters in the latter are carefully watched. Thus, incorrect atoms are taken out and new ones put in. The two calculations go hand in hand, and the correctness of the final structure is confirmed by a clean, flat difference Fourier containing very few small peaks, all of which can be reasonably attributed to experimental and rounding-off errors.

The Differential Synthesis. The precursor of the above methods is the three-dimensional differential synthesis.[101] The principle of the method is that at the true position (x_0,y_0,z_0) of a given atom, the electron-density function $\rho(x,y,z)$ is a maximum, so that, at x_0, y_0, z_0,

$$\partial\rho/\partial x = \partial\rho/\partial y = \partial\rho/\partial z = 0$$

If the assumed position (x,y,z) deviates from the true position by small amounts e_x, e_y, and e_z, then the derivative at the true position can be developed in terms of the derivatives at the assumed position and can be set equal to zero, thus obtaining

$$\partial\rho/\partial x + (\partial^2\rho/\partial x^2)e_x + (\partial^2\rho/\partial x\,\partial y)e_y + (\partial^2\rho/\partial x\,\partial z)e_z = 0 \tag{190}$$

where

$$\rho(x,y,z) = 1/V \sum_{-H}^{+H} \sum_{-K}^{+K} \sum_{-L}^{+L} |F(hkl)| \cos 2\pi(hx + ky + lz - \alpha) \tag{191}$$

$$\partial\rho/\partial x = -(2\pi h/V)\Sigma\Sigma\Sigma|F(hkl)| \sin 2\pi(hx + ky + lz - \alpha) \tag{192}$$

$$\partial^2\rho/\partial x^2 = -(4\pi^2 h^2/V)\Sigma\Sigma\Sigma|F(hkl)| \cos 2\pi(hx + ky + lz - \alpha) \tag{193}$$

$$\partial^2\rho/\partial x\,\partial y = -(4\pi^2 hk/V)\Sigma\Sigma\Sigma|F(hkl)| \cos 2\pi(hx + ky + lz - \alpha) \tag{194}$$

and so on. Similar equations may be derived for the derivatives of ρ with respect to the y and z axes. The shifts are to be obtained by solving the three linear equations such as (190). These equations are given below, where the notations d_x, d_{xx}, d_{xy}, etc., are respectively $\partial\rho/\partial x$, $\partial^2\rho/\partial x^2$, $\partial^2\rho/\partial x\,\partial y$, etc., and where $d_{xy} = d_{yx}$, and so on.

$$\begin{aligned} d_x + d_{xx}e_x + d_{xy}e_y + d_{xz}e_z &= 0 \\ d_y + d_{xy}e_x + d_{yy}e_y + d_{yz}e_z &= 0 \\ d_z + d_{xz}e_x + d_{yz}e_y + d_{zz}e_z &= 0 \end{aligned} \tag{195}$$

Refinement consists in calculating the quantities d_x, d_{xx}, d_{xy}, etc., and solving the three linear equations for the parameter shifts e_x, e_y, and e_z. Thus the main part of the calculation is the nine summations at each assumed atomic position. The work involved can be considerably reduced if it is assumed that close to the center of the atom the electron density is spherically symmetric. In such a case, it is not necessary to find all the nine quantities d_x, d_{xx}, etc.; it is sufficient if one quantity, say d_{xx}, is found, in addition to d_x, d_y, and d_z. The other quantities are related to d_{xx} as follows:

$$\begin{aligned} d_{yy} &= d_{zz} = 2d_g \\ d_{xy} &= 2d_g \cos\gamma \\ d_{yz} &= 2d_g \cos\alpha \\ d_{xz} &= 2d_g \cos\beta \qquad \text{where } d_g = \tfrac{1}{2}d_{xx} \end{aligned} \tag{196}$$

The above relations arise because of reasons given below. Under the assumption of spherical symmetry

$$\rho(x,y,z) = f(g)$$

where, in the triclinic case,

$$\begin{aligned} g = (x - x_0)^2 + (y - y_0)^2 + (z - z_0)^2 + 2(x - x_0)(y - y_0)\cos\gamma \\ + 2(y - y_0)(z - z_0)\cos\alpha + 2(z - z_0)(x - x_0)\cos\beta \end{aligned} \tag{197}$$

If d_g denotes df/dg, the various relations may be obtained from Eqs. (195). These relations, which are approximate, are based essentially on the fact that e_x, e_y, and e_z are small. Substituting Eq. (197) in (195) the linear equations simplify to

$$\begin{aligned} e_x + e_y \cos \gamma + e_z \cos \beta + dx/2d_g &= 0 \\ e_x \cos \gamma + e_y + e_z \cos \alpha + d_y/2d_g &= 0 \\ e_x \cos \beta + e_y \cos \alpha + e_z + d_z/2d_g &= 0 \end{aligned} \tag{198}$$

If the crystal system is orthogonal, the shifts are given more simply as

$$e_x = -d_x/2d_g \qquad e_y = -d_y/2d_g \qquad \text{and} \qquad e_z = -d_z/2d_g$$

In this method, it is possible to refine not only the atomic parameters but also the phase angles. It has since been shown that refinement of the phase angle is automatically achieved if the corrections applied to the parameters are taken as n times the values e_i.[102] For crystals that are completely acentric $n = 2$. For those which are completely centric $n = 1$. In other cases where some or all of the three projections are centric, the value is between 1 and 2. This rule, called the n-shift rule, is applicable not only to methods involving differential syntheses but to other Fourier methods as well, and usually leads to faster convergence.

Functions and Errors. On completion of the refinement of the parameters x_i, the usual task is to analyze the results and draw conclusions therefrom which are of interest from the viewpoint of chemistry, etc. Usually, this consists in calculating certain functions of the parameters and the standard errors associated with the various functions. Principal causes for the errors are not only the random errors involved in the experimental data but also the errors in the dimensions of the unit cell. The latter, however, can be made negligible by taking suitable precautions.

The functions, which are usually calculated, are the bond distances between pairs of atoms, the bond angle subtended at a given atom by two other atoms, and the principal axes of the ellipsoid of thermal vibrations, etc. Detailed formulas are available in Buerger's book,[103] but here we give some of the general formulas. Let $(X_1Y_1Z_1)$ and $(X_2Y_2Z_2)$ denote the coordinates of two atoms 1 and 2. These coordinates are obtained by expressing the fractional coordinates $(x_jy_jz_j)$ in angstroms. The distance between atoms 1 and 2 is given by

$$\begin{aligned} D_{12} = [(X_1 - X_2)^2 + (Y_1 - Y_2)^2 + (Z_1 - Z_2)^2 \\ - 2(X_1 - X_2)(Y_1 - Y_2) \cos \gamma - 2(Y_1 - Y_2)(Z_1 - Z_2) \cos \alpha \\ - 2(Z_1 - Z_2)(X_1 - X_2) \cos \beta]^{1/2} \end{aligned} \tag{199}$$

The angle subtended at 2 by 1 and 3 is given by

$$\theta = \cos^{-1} \frac{D_{12}^2 + D_{32}^2 - D_{13}^2}{2D_{12}D_{32}} \tag{200}$$

The standard errors are obtained easily in cases where the refinement has been carried out by the "full-matrix" least-squares method. The central principle of the least-squares method is the minimization of X^2, where

$$X^2 = (1/\sigma^2) \Sigma w\Delta^2 \tag{201}$$

where each w is the weight of the corresponding observation. These weights are to be inversely proportional to the corresponding variances, whence the constant of proportionality is σ^2. The quantity σ is the standard error of fit of the observations, and an external estimate of σ^2 is, essentially,

$$\sigma^2 = \Sigma w\Delta^2/X^2 \tag{202}$$

On the assumption that in the long run the mean value of X^2 is the same as the number of degrees of freedom, the error of fit is

$$\sigma = \left(\frac{\Sigma w\Delta^2}{Q - M}\right)^{1/2} \tag{203}$$

where $\Delta = |F_0| - |F_c|$, Q = number of independent observations, and M = total number of parameters. The standard errors in the individual parameters x_i are obtained from the well-known fact that the diagonal elements b_{ii} of the inverse matrix are proportional to the variances of the parameters x_i, and that the off-diagonal elements b_{ij} are proportional to the various covariances. The constant of proportionality is again σ^2, whence the standard error in the ith parameter is given by

$$\sigma(X_i) = \sigma \sqrt{b_{ii}} \tag{204}$$

The standard error of a given function $f = f(x_i, \ldots, x_m)$ of the parameters is correspondingly given by

$$\sigma(f) = \sigma \sqrt{S} \tag{205}$$

where $S = \sum_{j=1}^{M} \sum_{i=1}^{M} (2 - \delta_{ij})(\partial f/\partial x_i)(\partial f/\partial x_j)b_{ij}$, δ_{ij} being the Kronecker delta,* and b_{ij} being the ijth element of the (symmetric) inverse matrix. In cases where f is a function not only of the atomic parameters x_i but also of the unit-cell parameters a_i, the effect of the latter, if desired, may be taken into account in a similar fashion. In the general triclinic case, the total number of a_i's is six. The standard error is obtained from $\sigma_t = (\sigma_x^2 + \sigma_a^2)^{1/2}$, where σ_x is given by Eq. (204), σ_a is given by a similar expression, involving $\partial f/\partial a_i$, $\partial f/\partial a_j$, and c_{ij} in place of the corresponding quantities, the value of $M = 6$, and c_{ij}'s are the 21 elements of the symmetric 6×6 matrix of the variances and covariances of the cell parameter.

The above discussion is for a general case of an independent set of parameters. Suitable modifications are necessary for cases in which the parameters are constrained by factors such as special positions and so on. Manual calculations are usually very tedious, unless simplifying assumptions, such as neglecting the covariances, are made. For laboratories having access to high-speed computers, good programs such as the "function and error" program by Busing and Levy for the IBM 7090 computer[104] are available.

In manual calculations, it is probably easier to use the final-difference Fourier[105] to assess the accuracy of the structure. In such cases, the standard deviation in the electron-density function is given by

$$\sigma(\rho_0) = \sqrt{\langle D^2 \rangle} \tag{206}$$

and that in parameter X_i is

$$\sigma(X_i) = [\langle(\partial D/\partial X)^2\rangle]^{1/2}/C_i \tag{207}$$

where $D(x,y,z)$ stands for the value of difference Fourier synthesis at x, y, z, and $C_i = \partial^2\rho_c/\partial X^2$; the curvature at the center of the ith atom is obtained from a direct Fourier employing the same weighting scheme as the D synthesis. The average may be taken either over the unit cell or over those points at which D is supposed to be zero. The standard deviations, so obtained, should of course be multiplied by the n of the n-shift rule (see The Differential Synthesis above.)

The calculations of the standard errors are usually accompanied by an unbiased assessment of the significance of the results. It is not possible to lay down precise rules for this assessment, but some useful conclusions may be derived from the following example.[106] Let us suppose that two bond lengths A and B have been measured with standard deviations σ_A and σ_B. Let us suppose that dl is the difference between the two. The question to settle is whether dl is significant or not. Let P denote the probability that the two bonds will differ by dl by chance. The two bonds are otherwise supposed to be equal. The following tabulation may be useful.

$P > 5$ per cent	dl is not significant
1 per cent $< P <$ 5 per cent	dl is of possible significance
0.1 per cent $< P <$ 1 per cent	dl is significant

* $\delta_{ij} = 1$ if $i = j$, and $\delta_{ij} = 0$ if $i \neq j$.

A further level of $P < 0.1$ is sometimes used. dl is then said to be highly significant. The choice of the above levels is supposed to be suitable for crystallographic purposes. The following tabulation gives dl in terms of $\sigma = \sqrt{\sigma_A{}^2 + \sigma_B{}^2}$ for a Gaussian distribution, in which case $P = \frac{1}{2} - (1/\sqrt{\pi}) \int_0^x e^{-t^2}\, dt$, the parameter x being $dl/(\sqrt{2})\sigma$.

$$P = 5 \text{ per cent} \qquad dl = 1.645\sigma$$
$$P = 1 \text{ per cent} \qquad dl = 2.327\sigma$$
$$P = 0.1 \text{ per cent} \qquad dl = 3.090\sigma$$

Thus for practical purposes, a difference of three times the standard deviation can be taken to be significant.

For example, it was found in the study of a compound of tellurium[89] that there were six Te—O distances, five of which were distributed about a mean of 1.926 Å, with a maximum deviation of 0.026, while the sixth one was 1.83 Å. The estimated standard deviations in bond lengths were between 0.01 and 0.02 Å. In this case $dl = 0.1$ Å and $\sigma = 0.03$, so that dl is probably significant. By this statistical inference, it was possible to propose that the sixth oxygen was the oxide, while the other five were hydroxyls, and that the molecule is probably $KTeO(OH)_5H_2O$.

In conclusion, it may be stated that the major tasks of crystal-structure analyses are the collection of accurate intensity data, circumvention of the inherent phase problem, derivation of the structure, refinement of the various independent parameters of the structure, calculation of various functions of the parameters and their standard errors, and an assessment of the overall significance. Our aim, in this chapter, has been to outline the general principles involved. More detailed discussions can be found in the standard textbooks and the published papers.

REFERENCES CITED

1. J. L. Katz and B. Post, The Crystal Structure and Polymorphism of N-Methyl Acetamide, *Acta Cryst.*, **13**:624 (1960).
2. *International Tables for X-ray Crystallography*, vol. I, Symmetry Groups; vol. II, Mathematical Tables; vol. III, Physical and Chemical Tables, The Kynoch Press, Birmingham, England, 1952.
3. E. R. Howells, D. C. Phillips, and D. Rogers, The Probability Distribution of X-ray Intensities, *Acta Cryst.*, **3**:210 (1950).
4. E. Jahnke and F. Emde, *Functionen Tafeln mit Formeln und Kurven*, B. G. Teubner Verlagsgesellschaft, mbH, Leipzig, 1933.
5. J. Iball and K. J. Mackay, The Crystal and Molecular Structure of 9:10-Anthrahydroquinone Dibenzoate, *Acta Cryst.*, **15**:148 (1962).
6. A. J. C. Wilson, Determination of Absolute from Relative X-ray Intensity Data, *Nature*, **150**:152 (1942). See also A. J. C. Wilson, The Probability Distribution of X-ray Intensities, *Acta Cryst.*, **2**:318 (1949).
7. J. Karle and H. Hauptman, The Probability Distribution of the Magnitude of a Structure Factor, I, The Centrosymmetric Crystal, *Acta Cryst.*, **6**:131 (1953); II, The Non-centrosymmetric Crystal, *Acta Cryst.*, **6**:136 (1953).
8. G. N. Ramachandran and R. Srinivasan, A New Statistical Test for Distinguishing between Centrosymmetric and Non-centrosymmetric Structures, *Acta Cryst.*, **12**:410 (1959).
9. A. I. Kitaigorodskii, The Theory of Crystal Structure Analysis, translated from the Russian by David and Katherine Harker, Consultants Bureau, New York, 1961.
10. A. D. Booth, Two New Modifications of the Fourier Method of X-ray Structure Analysis, *Trans. Faraday Soc.*, **41**:434 (1945).
11. W. Cochran and H. B. Dyer, Some Practical Applications of Generalized Crystal Structure Projections, *Acta Cryst.*, **5**:634 (1952).
12. C. A. Beevers and H. Lipson, A Rapid Method for the Summation of a Two Dimensional Fourier Series, *Phil. Mag.*, **17**(7):855 (1934). See also *Nature*, **137**:825 (1936); *Proc. Phys. Soc.* (*London*), **48**:772 (1936); and W. Cochran, *Acta Cryst.*, **1**:54 (1948).
13. R. Pepinsky, An Electronic Computer for X-ray Crystal Structure Analysis, *J. Appl. Phys.*, **18**:601 (1947).

14. W. G. Sly and D. P. Shoemaker, MIFR1: A Two and Three Dimensional Crystallographic Fourier Summation Program for the IBM 704, in *Computing Methods and the Phase Problem in X-ray Crystal Analysis*, pp. 129–139, Pergamon Press, London, 1961.
15. A. Zalkin. Direct inquiries regarding Fordaper, a Fourier program for IBM 7090, to Dr. A. Zalkin, Chemistry Department, Lawrence Radiation Laboratory, University of California, Berkeley, Calif.
16. D. Hall and R. Shiono, An IBM 1620 Program: Three-dimensional Fourier Synthesis. Direct inquiries to Dr. R. Shiono, Crystallographic Laboratory, University of Pittsburgh, Pittsburgh 13, Pa.
17. A. L. Patterson, A Fourier Series Method for the Determination of the Components of Interatomic Distances in Crystals, *Phys. Rev.*, **46**:372 (1934). See also A. L. Patterson, A Direct Method for the Determination of Interatomic Distances in Crystals, *Z. Krist.* (*A*), **90**:517 (1935).
18. I. N. Sneddon, Functional Analysis, in S. Flügge (ed.), *Handbuch der Physik*, II, Mathematische Methoden II, Springer-Verlag OHG, Berlin, 1955. See also S. Bochner and K. Chandrasekharan, Fourier Transforms, *Ann. Math. Studies*, no. 19, Princeton, N.J., 1949.
19. M. J. Buerger, *Vector Space and Its Application in Crystal Structure Investigation*, chap. 10, John Wiley & Sons, Inc., New York, 1959.
20. M. J. Buerger, *Vector Space and Its Application in Crystal Structure Investigation*, chap. 9, table 1, pp. 202–211, John Wiley & Sons, Inc., New York, 1959.
21. R. A. Jacobson, J. A. Wunderlich, and W. N. Lipscomb, The Crystal and Molecular Structure of Cellobiose, *Acta Cryst.*, **14**:598 (1961).
22. R. A. Alden, G. H. Stout, J. Kraut, and D. F. High, The Molecular and Crystal Structure of the Plant Pigment Harunganin, *Acta Cryst.*, **17**:109 (1964).
23. A. L. Patterson, A Direct Method for the Determination of the Components of Interatomic Distances in Crystals, *Z. Krist.* (*A*), **90**:517 (1935).
24. D. Harker and J. S. Kasper, Phases of Fourier Coefficients Directly from Crystal Diffraction Data, *Acta Cryst.*, **1**:70 (1948).
25. S. Raman and W. N. Lipscomb, The Patterson Approach to Phase Problem, in G. N. Ramachandran (ed.), *Crystallography and Crystal Perfection*, p. 79, Academic Press Inc., New York.
26. J. Karle and H. Hauptman, Positivity, Point Atoms, Pattersons, *Acta Cryst.*, **17**:392 (1964).
27. S. Raman and J. L. Katz, An Analytical Method of Obtaining Sharp Patterson Functions, *Z. Krist.* (to be published).
28. G. N. Ramachandran and S. Raman, Syntheses for the Deconvolution of the Patterson Function, pt. I, General Principles, *Acta Cryst.*, **12**:957 (1959).
29. S. Raman, Syntheses for the Deconvolution of the Patterson Function, pt. II, Detailed Theory for Non-centrosymmetric Crystals, *Acta Cryst.*, **12**:964 (1959). See also pt. III, Theory for Centrosymmetric Crystals, *Acta Cryst.*, **14**:148 (1961).
30. R. Srinivasan, Syntheses for the Deconvolution of the Patterson Function, pt. IV, Refinement of the Theory and a General Comparison of the Various Syntheses, *Acta Cryst.*, **14**:607 (1961).
31. R. Srinivasan and C. A. Aravindakshan, Test of the Various Syntheses for Centrosymmetric Crystals, *Acta Cryst.*, **14**:612 (1961).
32. S. Raman and W. N. Lipscomb, Application of Fourier Transform Theory to Electron Density Extraction of Patterson Functions, *Z. Krist.*, **119**:30 (1963).
33. S. Raman and W. N. Lipscomb, Two Classes of Functions for the Location of Heavy Atoms and Solutions of Crystal Structures, *Z. Krist.*, **116**:314 (1961). See also Ref. 25.
34. S. Raman and J. L. Katz, Accumulation Functions in X-ray Determination of Crystal Structures, *Z. Krist.* (to be published).
35. F. B. Gerhard, Jr., The Crystal Structure of the Mineral Pachnolite, Ph.D. Thesis, Rensselaer Polytechnic Institute, Troy, New York.
36. M. J. Buerger, *Vector Space and Its Application in Crystal Structure Investigation*, chap. 7, John Wiley & Sons, Inc., New York, 1959.
37. P. G. Simpson, R. D. Dobrott, and W. N. Lipscomb, The Symmetry Minimum Function: High Order Image Seeking Functions in X-ray Crystallography, *Acta Cryst.*, **18**:169 (1965). See also A. D. Mighell and R. A. Jacobson, Analysis of Three Dimensional Patterson Maps Using Vector Verification, *Acta Cryst.*, **16**:443 (1963).
38. D. Harker and J. S. Kasper, Phases of Fourier Coefficients Directly from Crystal Structure Data, *J. Chem. Phys.*, **15**:882 (1947).
39. J. Gillis, The Application of the Harker-Kasper Method of Phase Determination, *Acta Cryst.*, **1**:174 (1948).

40. J. S. Kasper, C. M. Lucht, and D. Harker, The Crystal Structure of Decaborane, $B_{10}H_{14}$, *Acta Cryst.*, **3**:436 (1950).
41. E. W. Hughes, Limitations on the Determination of Phases by Means of Inequalities, *Acta Cryst.*, **2**:34 (1949).
42. J. Karle and H. Hauptman, The Phases and Magnitudes of the Structure Factor, *Acta Cryst.*, **3**:181 (1950). See also H. Hauptman and J. Karle, Relations among the Crystal Structure Factors, *Phys. Rev.*, **80**:244 (1950).
43. D. Sayre, The Squaring Method: A New Method for Phase Determination, *Acta Cryst.*, **5**:60 (1952).
44. W. Cochran and M. M. Woolfson, The Theory of Sign Relations between Structure Factors, *Acta Cryst.*, **8**:1 (1955).
45. M. M. Woolfson, An Equation between Structure Factors for Structures Containing Unequal or Overlapped Atoms, I, The Equation and Its Properties, *Acta Cryst.*, **11**:277 (1958); II, An Application to Structure Determination, *Acta Cryst.*, **11**:393 (1958).
46. Refer to the following papers: (*a*) Ref. 45. (*b*) W. Cochran, Paper 22, "Computing Methods and the Phase Problem in X-ray Crystal Analysis," edited by R. Pepinsky, J. M. Robertson, and J. C. Speakman, Pergamon Press, New York. (*c*) M. M. Woolfson, Paper 23 in reference to above. (*d*) W. Cochran, R. Srinivasan, and P. Tollin, in G. N. Ramachandran (ed.), *Crystallography and Crystal Perfection*, p. 67, Academic Press Inc., New York, 1963. (*e*) W. Cochran and A. S. Douglas, The Use of a High Speed Digital Computer for the Direct Determination of Crystal Structures, I, *Proc. Roy. Soc.* (*London*) (*A*), **227**:486 (1955); II, *Proc. Roy. Soc.* (*London*) (*A*), **243**:281 (1957).
47. I. L. Karle and J. Karle, 1963. See Ref. 51.
48. W. Cochran and B. R. Penfold, The Crystal Structure of L-Glutamine, *Acta Cryst.*, **5**:644 (1952).
49. W. H. Zachariasen, A New Analytical Method for Solving Complex Crystal Structures, *Acta Cryst.*, **5**:68 (1952).
50. G. H. Stout and L. H. Jensen, Rubrofusarin: A Structure Determination Using Direct Phase Calculation, *Acta Cryst.*, **15**:451 (1962). See also *Acta Cryst.*, **15**:1060 (1962).
51. I. L. Karle and J. Karle, An Application of a New Phase Determination Procedure to the Structure of Cyclo(hexaglycyl) Hemihydrate, *Acta Cryst.*, **16**:969 (1963).
52. I. L. Karle and J. Karle, The Crystal and Molecular Structure of the Alkaloid Jamine, $C_{21}H_{35}N_3$, *Acta Cryst.*, **17**:1356 (1964).
53. H. Hauptman and J. Karle, The Solution of the Phase Problem, I, The Centrosymmetric Crystal, *Am. Cryst. Assoc. Monograph* 3, Edward Brothers, Inc., Ann Arbor, Mich.
54. H. Hauptman, "On Direct Methods of Phase Determination," Paper 21 in Ref. 46(*b*).
55. H. Hauptman and J. Karle, Phase Determination from New Joint Probability Distributions, *Acta Cryst.*, **11**:149 (1958). See also J. Karle and H. Hauptman, *Acta Cryst.*, **11**:264 (1958).
56. W. Cochran and M. M. Woolfson, Have Hauptman and Karle Solved the Phase Problem? *Acta Cryst.*, **7**:450 (1954). See also V. Vand and R. Pepinsky, The Statistical Approach of Hauptman and Karle to the Phase Problem, *Acta Cryst.*, **7**:451 (1954).
57. W. Cochran, Structure Factor Relations and the Phase Problem, *Acta Cryst.*, **11**:579 (1958). See also A. Klug, Joint Probability Distribution of Structure Factors and the Phase Problem, *Acta Cryst.*, **11**:515 (1958).
58. C. L. Christ, J. R. Clark, and H. T. Evans, The Structure of Colemanite, CaB_3O_4-$(OH)_3 \cdot H_2O$, Determined by the Direct Method of Hauptman and Karle, *Acta Cryst.*, **7**:453 (1954).
59. I. L. Karle, H. Hauptman, J. Karle, and A. B. Wing, Crystal and Molecular Structure of p,p′-Dimethoxybenzophenone by the Direct Probability Method, *Acta Cryst.*, **11**:257 (1958).
60. H. Hauptman, I. L. Karle, and J. Karle, Crystal Structure of Spurrite, $Ca_5(SiO_4)_2CO_3$, I, Determination by the Probability Method, *Acta Cryst.*, **13**:451 (1960). See also J. V. Smith, I. L. Karle, and J. Karle, The Crystal Structure of Spurrite, II, Description of Structure, *Acta Cryst.*, **13**:454 (1960).
61. K. Lonsdale and H. J. Grenville-Wells, Sign Determination in Crystal Structure Analysis, *Acta Cryst.*, **7**:490 (1954).
62. See discussion between W. N. Lipscomb and H. Hauptman, Ref. 46(*b*), p. 314.
63. G. Kartha and A. deVries, Structure of Asparagine Monohydrate, *Nature*, **192**:862 (1961).
64. K. Banerjee, Determination of the Signs of the Fourier Terms in Complete Crystal Structure Analysis, *Proc. Roy. Soc.* (*London*) (*A*), **141**:188 (1933).
65. H. Ott, Zur Methodik der Structuranalyse, *Z. Krist.*, **66**:136 (1927). See also Melvin

Avrami, Direct Determination of Crystal Structure from X-ray Data, *Phys. Rev.*, **54**:300 (1938).

66. C. H. Dauben and D. H. Templeton, A Table of Dispersion Corrections for X-ray Scattering of Atoms, *Acta Cryst.*, **8**:841 (1955).
67. D. Cromer, Anomalous Dispersion Corrections Computed from Self-consistent Field Relativistic Dirac-Slater Wave Functions, *Acta Cryst.*, **18**:17 (1965).
68. J. M. Bijvoet, Phase Determination in Direct Fourier Syntheses of Crystal Structures, *Proc. Koninkl. Ned. Akad. Wetenschap.* (*B*), **52**:313 (1949).
69. G. N. Ramachandran and S. Raman, A New Method for the Structure Analysis of Non-centrosymmetric Crystals, *Current Sci.* (*India*), **25**:348 (1956). See also Y. Okaya and R. Pepinsky, New Formulation and Solution of the Phase Problem in X-ray Analysis of Non-centric Crystals Containing Anomalous Scatterers, *Phys. Rev.*, **103**:1645 (1956).
70. S. Raman, Anomalous Dispersion Method of Determining Structure and Absolute Configuration of Crystals, *Proc. Indian Acad. Sci.*, **47**:1 (1958). See also S. Raman, Theory of the Anomalous Dispersion Method, *Proc. Indian Acad. Sci.*, **50**:95 (1959).
71. S. Raman, Determination of the Structure and Absolute Configuration of L(+)-Lysine Hydrochloride Dihydrate by the Anomalous Dispersion Method, *Z. Krist.*, **111**:301 (1959).
72. D. C. Hodgkin, The X-ray Analysis of Complicated Molecules, *Science*, **150**:979 (1965).
73. See Refs. 28 and 29. See also G. N. Ramachandran and R. Ramachandra Ayyar, Fourier Syntheses for Feeding in Isomorphous Replacement and Anomalous Dispersion Data, in G. N. Ramachandran (ed.), *Crystallography and Crystal Perfection*, pp. 25–41, Academic Press Inc., New York.
74. S. Ramaseshan, K. Venkatesan, and N. V. Mani, The Use of Anomalous Scattering for the Determination of Crystal Structures—$KMnO_4$, *Proc. Indian Acad. Sci.*, **46**:95 (1957).
75. S. Ramaseshan and K. Venkatesan, The Use of Anomalous Scattering without Phase Change in Crystal Structure Analysis, *Current Sci.* (*India*), **26**:352 (1957).
76. D. Harker, The Determination of the Phases of the Structure Factors of Non-centrosymmetric Crystals by the Method of Double Isomorphous Replacement, *Acta Cryst.*, **9**:1 (1956).
77. M. F. Perutz, Isomorphous Replacement and Phase Determination in Non-centrosymmetric Space Groups, *Acta Cryst.*, **9**:901 (1956).
78. J. M. Robertson, An X-ray Study of the Structure of the Phthalocyanines, pt. I, The Metal Free, Nickel, Copper, and Platinum Compounds, *J. Chem. Soc.*, 1935, p. 615. See also pt. II, *J. Chem. Soc.*, 1936, p. 1195; pt. III, *J. Chem. Soc.*, 1937, p. 219.
79. C. Bokhoven, J. C. Schoone, and J. M. Bijvoet, On the Crystal Structure of Strychnine Sulfate and Selenate, pt. I, *Proc. Koninkl. Ned. Akad. Wetenschap.*, **50**:823 (1947); pt. II, *Proc. Koninkl. Ned. Akad. Wetenschap.*, **51**:990 (1948); pt. III, *Proc. Koninkl. Ned. Akad. Wetenschap.*, **52**:313 (1949).
80. Y. Okaya, Y. Saito, and R. Pepinsky, New Method in X-ray Crystal Structure Determination Involving the Use of Anomalous Dispersion, *Phys. Rev.*, **98**:1857 (1955).
81. M. J. Buerger, A New Fourier Series Technique for Crystal Structure Determination, *Proc. Natl. Acad. Sci. U.S.*, **28**:281 (1942). See also G. N. Ramachandran and G. Kartha, Applications of the Difference Patterson Technique in Structure Analysis, *Acta Cryst.*, **8**:195 (1956).
82. M. G. Rossman, The Position of Anomalous Scatterers in Protein Crystals, *Acta Cryst.*, **14**:383 (1961).
83. J. C. Kendrew, Myoglobin and the Structure of Proteins, *Science*, **139**:1259 (1963).
84. A. J. C. Wilson, Largest Likely Values for the Reliability Index, *Acta Cryst.*, **3**:397 (1950).
85. E. W. Hughes, The Crystal Structure of Melamine, *J. Am. Chem. Soc.*, **63**:1737 (1941).
86. R. Pepinsky, J. M. Robertson, and J. C. Speakman (eds.), *Computing Methods and the Phase Problem in X-ray Crystal Analysis*, Pergamon Press, New York, 1961. See Paper 6 by D. W. J. Cruickshank, D. E. Pilling, A. Bujosa, F. M. Lovell, and M. R. Truter, pp. 32–78. See Paper 17 by R. A. Sparks, pp. 170–187. See also R. Srinivasan, On the Method of Least Squares as Applied to the Refinement of Crystal Structures, *Acta Cryst.*, **14**:1163 (1961).
87. W. R. Busing and H. A. Levy, see Paper 13 in Ref. 86, pp. 146–153.
88. S. Raman, J. Reddy, and W. N. Lipscomb, Casimidine, a Fragment of Casimiroedine, *Acta Cryst.*, **16**:364 (1963).
89. S. Raman, Crystal Structure of $KTeO(OH)_5H_2O$, *Inorg. Chem.*, **3**:634 (1964).

90. A. D. Booth, A New Refinement Technique for X-ray Structure Analysis, *J. Chem. Phys.*, **15**:415 (1947).
91. M. M. Quarashi, Optimum Conditions for Convergence of Steepest Descents as Applied to Structure Determination, *Acta Cryst.*, **2**:404 (1949).
92. L. H. Vogt, Jr., J. L. Katz, and S. E. Wiberley, The Crystal and Molecular Structure of Ruthenium–Sulfur Dioxide Coordination Compounds, I, Chlorotetraammine(sulfur dioxide)ruthenium (II) Chloride, *Inorg. Chem.*, **4**:1157 (1965). See also A. Tulinsky, C. R. Worthington, and E. Pignataro, Basic Beryllium Acetate, pt. I, The Collection of Intensity Data, *Acta Cryst.*, **12**:623 (1959); pt. II, The Structure Analysis, *Acta Cryst.*, **12**:626 (1959); pt. III, Evidence for Chemical Bonding; Assessment of Accuracy, *Acta Cryst.*, **12**:634 (1959).
93. J. M. Robertson and I. Woodward, An X-ray Study of the Phthalocyanines, pt. IV, Direct Quantitative Analysis of the Platinum Compound, *J. Chem. Soc.*, 1940, p. 36.
94. C. H. Carlisle and D. Crowfoot, The Crystal Structure of Cholesteryl Iodide, *Proc. Roy. Soc.* (*London*) (*A*), **184**:64 (1945).
95. D. Crowfoot and J. D. Dunitz, Structure of Calciferol, *Nature*, **162**:608 (1948).
96. J. H. Robertson and C. A. Beevers, Crystal Structure of Strychnine Hydrobromide, *Nature*, **165**:690 (1950).
97. M. J. Buerger, E. Barney, and T. Hahn, The Crystal Structure of Diglycine Hydrobromide, *Z. Krist.*, **108**:130 (1956).
98. S. Hirokawa, Y. Okaya, F. M. Lovell, and R. Pepinsky, The Crystal Structure of Aureomycin Hydrochloride, *Z. Krist.*, **112**:439 (1959).
99. G. Kartha, G. N. Ramachandran, H. B. Bhat, P. M. Nair, V. K. V. Raghavan, and K. Venkataraman, The Constitution of Morellin, *Tetrahedron Letters*, **50**:459 (1963).
100. H. Lipson and W. Cochran, *Crystalline State*, vol. III, chap. 9, sec. 4, pp. 298–307, G. Bell & Sons, Ltd., London, 1953.
101. A. D. Booth, Fourier Technique, in *X-ray Organic Structure Analysis*, pp. 46–52, Cambridge University Press, New York, 1948.
102. D. W. J. Cruickshank, The Convergence of the Least Squares and Fourier Refinement Methods, *Acta Cryst.*, **3**:10 (1950). See also D. P. Shoemaker, J. Donohue, V. Schomaker, and R. B. Corey, *J. Am. Chem. Soc.*, **72**:2328 (1950).
103. M. J. Buerger, *Crystal Structure Analysis*, chap. 23, pp. 629–634, John Wiley & Sons, Inc., New York, 1960.
104. W. R. Busing and H. A. Levy, see Paper 12 in Ref. 86.
105. H. Lipson and W. Cochran, *Crystalline State*, vol. III, pp. 307–311, G. Bell & Sons, Ltd., London, 1953. See also G. A. Jeffrey and D. W. J. Cruickshank, *Quart. Rev. Chem. Soc.*, **8**:335 (1953).
106. D. W. J. Cruickshank, The Accuracy of Electron Density Maps in X-ray Analysis with Special Reference to Dibenzyl, *Acta Cryst.*, **2**:65 (1949). See also D. W. J. Cruickshank and A. P. Robertson, The Comparison of Theoretical and Experimental Determinations of Molecular Structures, with Applications to Naphthalene and Anthracene, *Acta Cryst.*, **6**:698 (1953).

Part 4

X-RAY EMISSION SPECTROSCOPY

Chapter 30

INTRODUCTION TO X-RAY EMISSION SPECTROSCOPY

Emmett F. Kaelble

Monsanto Company

The analytical method discussed in this part of the handbook involves the following: (1) excitation of characteristic x-ray lines of elements in a specimen, (2) measurement of the wavelengths of these lines to identify the elements present (qualitative analysis, Chap. 35), and (3) measurement of the intensity of the lines to determine the concentration of the elements present (quantitative analysis, Chap. 36).

This is the method commonly called "x-ray fluorescence spectroscopy." While there is no serious objection to this term when the source of excitation is a beam of primary x-rays (by far the most common situation at present), "x-ray emission spectroscopy" is a more suitable general term in that it includes the other methods of generating x-ray spectra as well.

Moseley laid the groundwork for x-ray emission spectroscopy as a method of chemical analysis in 1913.[1] In this paper he showed that the lines of copper were stronger than those of zinc in the spectrum from a brass target. The following quotation is truly remarkable: "The prevalence of lines due to impurities suggests that this may prove a powerful method of chemical analysis. Its advantage over ordinary spectroscopic methods lies in the simplicity of the spectra and the impossibility of one substance masking the radiation from another. It may even lead to the discovery of missing elements, as it will be possible to predict the position of their characteristic lines."

The technique began with electron excitation, and this method of excitation has now again achieved great importance in electron-probe microanalysis (Chap. 39). Following the extensive study of Glocker and Schreiber,[2] however, primary x-ray excitation gradually took over as the major method of producing x-ray spectra for purposes of chemical analysis. The main limitation of electron excitation is its inconvenience. It is much more efficient than x-ray excitation (though it also produces a higher background level), and it is less subject to absorption and enhancement effects. In special applications (e.g., the measurement of film thickness, Chap. 44), radioactive isotopes have proved to be valuable sources for exciting x-ray spectra. The use of secondary x-rays as a source of excitation has also been suggested[3] for cases where intensity can be sacrificed for a clean spectrum.

In terms of the Bragg equation ($n\lambda = 2d \sin \theta$), x-ray emission spectroscopy can be thought of as the reverse of x-ray diffraction. The experimental parameter measured in both cases is the angle θ (or 2θ). In diffraction, a monochromatic x-ray beam of known wavelength (λ) is used, and the interplanar spacings (d) corresponding to measured reflections are determined. In emission, a crystal monochromator of known d is used so that the wavelengths of emitted lines can be determined. Both methods involve measuring intensities for quantitative analysis. The information obtained from diffraction is in terms of crystalline substances, while that from emission is in terms of chemical elements. There is no requirement in emission that the specimen be crystalline; solids, liquids, and powders are equally applicable (see Chap. 33).

For years, x-ray emission spectroscopy was limited to elements of atomic number 11 and greater. Recently, however, the technique has been extended to lighter elements (see Chap. 38). It enjoys its greatest sensitivity for elements in the approximate atomic-number range of 24 to 40 (see Chap. 32). It is generally less sensitive than optical emission spectroscopy (ultraviolet, visible), but the gap between the two

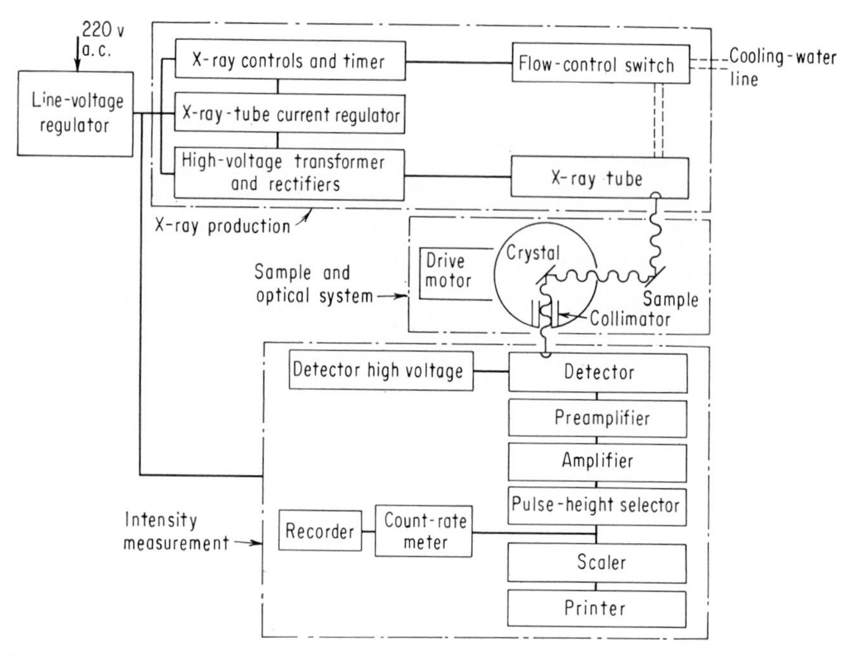

FIG. 1. Block diagram of a modern x-ray spectrograph. (*H. A. Liebhafsky* et al., *X-ray Absorption and Emission in Analytical Chemistry*, p. 243, *John Wiley & Sons, Inc., New York*, 1960. *Reprinted by permission.*)

methods is rapidly being narrowed, and trace analysis has become an important area of x-ray emission spectroscopy (Chap. 37). A detailed comparison of x-ray and optical emission spectroscopy is given in Chap. 36, Sec. 22. The principal advantages of x-ray emission spectroscopy over chemical methods of analysis are its speed and its nondestructive nature.

The equipment used for x-ray emission spectroscopy is very similar to that used for diffraction. An instrument intended for one technique can readily be adapted to the other. Modern diffractometers predated modern emission spectrographs and, for a time, most spectrographs were modified diffractometers. However, we are now past that era. The rapid progress made by x-ray emission spectroscopy is shown by the fact that in new installations it is becoming more common to hear of "diffraction attachments" for spectrographs than the reverse!

The components of an x-ray spectrograph can be grouped into three broad areas: (1) x-ray production, (2) sample and optical system, and (3) intensity measurement. These three areas are treated separately in this book (Chaps. 2, 31, and 3, respectively).

A block diagram of a modern x-ray spectrograph is shown in Fig. 1, and a representative commercial instrument is pictured in Fig. 2. Much attention is now being directed toward automating spectrographs and moving them out of the laboratory and onto production lines (see Chap. 40).

FIG. 2. At right is Norelco Universal vacuum x-ray spectrograph with associated equipment. Center unit is electronic circuit panel with recorder, and at left is x-ray generator (with diffraction equipment). (*Courtesy of Philips Electronic Instruments, Mount Vernon, N.Y.*)

REFERENCES CITED

1. H. G. J. Moseley, *Phil. Mag.*, (6)**26**:1024 (1913).
2. R. Glocker and H. Schreiber, *Ann. Physik*, **85**:1089 (1928).
3. L. S. Birks, *X-ray Spectrochemical Analysis*, p. 16, Interscience Publishers, Inc., New York, 1959.

GENERAL REFERENCE

Liebhafsky, H. A., et al.: *X-ray Absorption and Emission in Analytical Chemistry*, John Wiley & Sons, Inc., New York, 1960.

Chapter 31

OPTICS

Isidore Adler

Goddard Space Flight Center

1. NONDISPERSIVE SYSTEMS

Description. Nondispersive x-ray spectroscopy is a form of spectral analysis in which x-ray wavelengths are separated for measurement by means other than crystal dispersion. Among the various techniques used are filtering by foils, voltage discrimination, detector discrimination, and finally electronic discrimination. The first three methods are limited in application and the simplest to apply and are described only briefly. The method of electronic discrimination is the most important and will be dealt with in greater detail.

Filters. By selecting foils of various materials it is possible to absorb certain wavelengths more strongly than others and so obtain a rough selection of wavelengths. The most effective filters are those having an absorption edge between two wavelengths. The shorter wavelength will be most strongly absorbed. For example, this procedure is followed in "monochromatizing" radiation for diffraction where a separation between $K\alpha$ and $K\beta$ lines is desired. The method as a whole has serious disadvantages for x-ray emission, however. It provides only crude discrimination, introduces substantial loss of intensity of the desired radiation, and requires the availability of a large variety of absorbing materials. Balanced or Ross filters may be used, but a high degree of skill in achieving balance between two filters is required.

Voltage Discrimination. Under some circumstances it is possible to separate desired from undesired radiation by operating the exciting x-ray tube at a potential less than that required to excite the harder radiation. In this fashion only the desired longer-wavelength radiation is excited. This method is limited in scope but has been used successfully in specific applications such as thickness gauging on continuous-strip tin-plating assembly lines.[1] By adjusting the voltage on the x-ray tube to the proper value only the iron in the substrate is excited to fluorescence. The most serious disadvantage of this procedure is the loss of intensity caused by the reduced excitation voltages.

Detector Discrimination. Counter tubes may be filled with suitable gas fillings and sealed with windows that make the counter more efficient for a particular wavelength region, thereby excluding appreciable response from other wavelength regions. This method of discrimination has the same disadvantages cited above. The discrimination is very broad and the technique limited in application.

Electronic Discrimination. This is the most useful of the nondispersive systems and will be described in detail. The basis for the method is that certain types of x-ray detectors, specifically proportional and scintillation counters, are energy-sensitive, emitting pulses whose mean amplitude is proportional to the x-ray energy being measured. The specific pulse energies or amplitudes corresponding to specific x-ray wavelengths are separated and measured by means of appropriate discriminating circuits. One such arrangement is shown in Fig. 1, the basic components consisting of a high-energy x-ray tube, an energy-sensitive detector, a linear preamplifier and amplifier, a pulse-height analyzer, and finally counting and recording circuits.

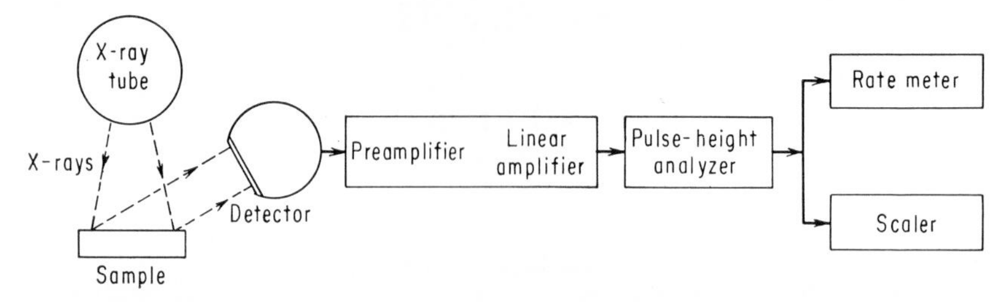

Fig. 1. The basic components of a pulse-analysis system for x-ray spectroscopy. Secondary x-rays from the sample are detected by an energy-sensitive detector (proportional counter, scintillation counter). The signals are amplified by the detector and amplifier and then discriminated electronically by means of a pulse-amplitude analyzer before being integrated.

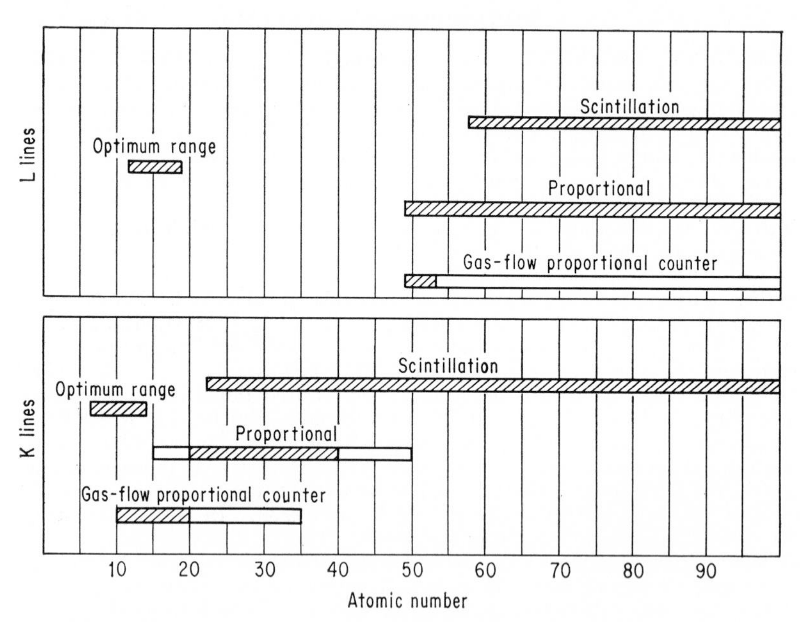

Fig. 2. The optimum elemental range for some of the commercially available energy-sensitive detectors.

A proper understanding of this type of nondispersive x-ray spectroscopy requires a knowledge of the role of the detector as well as the associated electronics. Each of these is described briefly below.

Proportional Counter. The proportional counter is similar in many respects to the Geiger counter. It features an outer metallic or metallized shell, a central anode, and suitable gas filling. Two types of proportional counters are widely used in x-ray spectroscopy, the sealed counter and the thin-windowed gas-flow counter.

The proper choice of counter depends on the spectral region of interest. For elements whose spectral lines are sufficiently hard to be measured in air, sealed proportional counters are a better choice. The thin-windowed gas-flow proportional counter is most useful for the longer wavelengths, generally measured in a helium atmosphere or vacuum. Figure 2 shows the optimum elemental range for some of the commercially available energy-sensitive detectors. Detailed discussion on requirements and characteristics of counters made may be found in Chap. 3 of this handbook as well as in a number of other publications.[2,3,4] The essential difference in behavior between the Geiger and proportional counter follows from the applied operating voltage. In the Geiger region the applied voltage is so high that each ionizing event builds up the maximum charge permitted by the positive-ion sheath that forms around the wire. The resulting pulses emitted by the Geiger counter are all of uniform size and completely independent of the energy of the ionizing radiation. The ionization in the

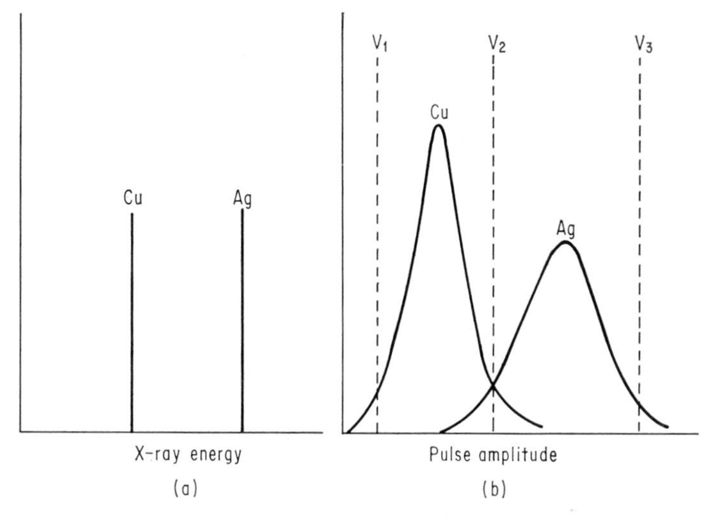

FIG. 3. (*a*) The monoenergetic character of the Cu *Kα* and the Ag *Kα* lines is represented above. The energy of the Ag *Kα* is almost three times as great as that of the Cu *Kα* line. (*b*) The Gaussian distribution of voltage pulse amplitudes corresponding to the monoenergetic Cu *Kα* and the Ag *Kα* lines of *a* is shown in *b*. The pulse amplitudes overlap, but most of the Ag *Kα* pulses are higher in amplitude than the Cu *Kα* pulses. (*L. S. Birks, X-ray Spectrochemical Analysis, p.* 45, *Interscience Publishers, Inc., New York,* 1959.)

proportional counter, because of lower applied voltages, is confined closely to the region in which the x-ray quantum is absorbed. The number of ionizations increases with the energy of the x-ray quantum, and the output pulse is thus proportional to the energy of the absorbed quantum. An example of this process is given by Birks[5] for Cu *Kα* and Ag *Kα* radiation which have energies of 8.02 and 22.1 kv, respectively. In a xenon-filled proportional counter where the ionization potential of the xenon is approximately 12 volts, the absorbed Cu *Kα* causes 665 initial ionizations as compared with 1,830 initial ionizations caused by the Ag *Kα* quantum. As a consequence the output pulse of the Ag *Kα* line will be approximately 2.8 times as great in voltage amplitude as that from the Cu *Kα*. The number of initial ionizations given as 665 for the Cu *Kα* and 1,830 for the Ag *Kα* are only average values. The actual output of pulse amplitudes shows a Gaussian distribution because of the normal statistical nature of ion-pair production. Figure 3*a* shows the monoenergetic character of the x-ray energies for the Cu *Kα* and Ag *Kα* lines. The corresponding output from the proportional counter is shown in Fig. 3*b*. The pulse amplitudes are spread and show a Gaussian distribution of pulses with a standard deviation equal to $\sqrt{N_i}$ where N_i

is the calculated initial number of ionizations. Examination of the pulse-amplitude curves shows that most of the pulses produced by the Ag $K\alpha$ quanta have greater amplitudes than those produced by the Cu $K\alpha$ radiation. The peak of the Ag $K\alpha$ pulses occurs at approximately three times the amplitude of the Cu $K\alpha$ pulses. The proportionality between quantum energy and *mean* pulse amplitude is shown in Fig. 4 for a proportional counter filled with a mixture of argon and ethylene. Hendee and Fine[6] have shown that the percentage half width, defined as "the amplitude difference between those pulses comprising the pulse-height distribution that occurs at half the maximum rate," is proportional to energy in the same fashion that atomic number is related to energy in Moseley's law. They have also demonstrated that the ability of a proportional counter to resolve characteristic x-radiations of adjacent elements is approximately constant for all elements.

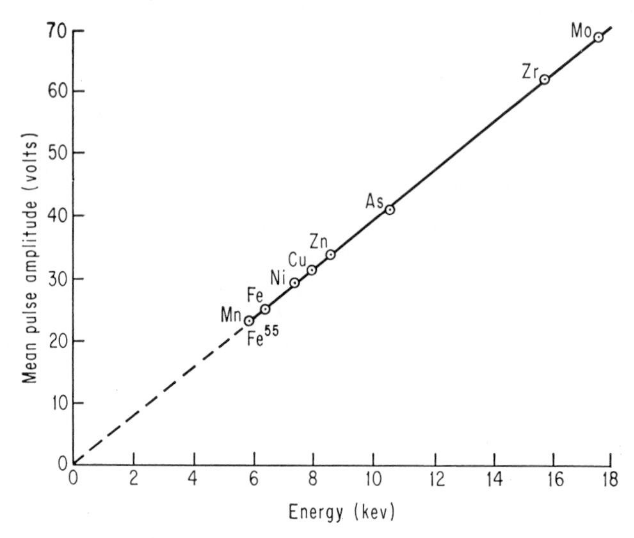

FIG. 4. The direct proportionality between quantum energy expressed in kev pulse amplitude is shown. Measurements were made with a side-window proportional counter filled with 90 per cent argon and 10 per cent ethylene to 15 cm Hg; proportional counter grain 3.5×10^4. (*Courtesy of Friedman, Birks, and Brooks, U.S. Naval Research Laboratory, Washington, D.C., private communication.*)

Scintillation Counter. The scintillation counter is currently the most widely used x-ray detector, primarily because of its very high detection efficiency for most of the useful analytical region from 3 Å down. Like the proportional counter the scintillation counter is also energy-sensitive, although the detection mechanism is different. The counter consists of thallium-activated sodium iodide phosphor which converts some fraction of the x-ray energy into visible light. The light is transformed in turn into electrical pulses by means of a photomultiplier tube. The scintillation counter has a much higher efficiency for detection than any of the existing gas detectors and in the region of x-ray wavelengths from 0.5 to 3 Å is nearly 100 per cent efficient. The pulse distribution given by the scintillation counter is, however, approximately twice as broad as given by the proportional counter for the same energies. A consequence of the broader distribution is a greater overlap of neighboring wavelengths and poorer resulting energy resolution.

Electronics. The output pulses from the proportional or scintillation counter are small and must be amplified before measurement. The final pulse amplitudes which are fed to the analyzer circuits represent the combined effect of the d-c voltage applied to the detector and the amplification supplied by the linear amplifier. The optimum settings of both should yield the maximum signal-to-noise ratio. Figure 5 demonstrates the effect of increasing applied d-c voltage on the growth of mean pulse amplitudes for the proportional and scintillation counter. Power supplies for pulse-height analysis must have a long-term stability of better than 1 part in 1,000 because of the sensitivity of pulse amplitude to voltage. The preamplifier and amplifier must be completely linear so that the relative sizes of all output pulses from the detector are maintained. It is also essential that the preamplifier and amplifier be relatively free of inherent electronic noise or that the noise be of sufficiently low amplitude to cause no interference with the x-ray pulse amplitudes. The variation in output pulse distribution with amplifier gain setting is shown in Fig. 6. As the gain of the amplifier is increased the peaks shift to higher voltages but decrease in height and become broader. It can be shown, however, that the integrated number of counts or energy under the curves is the same for different amplifications. After amplification the pulses are fed to an electronic energy sorter or pulse-height analyzer which passes only those pulses lying between two preselected levels. This circuitry lies between the amplifier and final counting circuits, as shown in Fig. 1. The voltage window is set by an adjustable base-level control and a window-width control. These controls are found on all single-channel analyzers, and most of the commercial x-ray spectrographic equipment today has some form of single-channel analyzer. Pulses smaller in size than the base-level setting or greater than the sum of the base

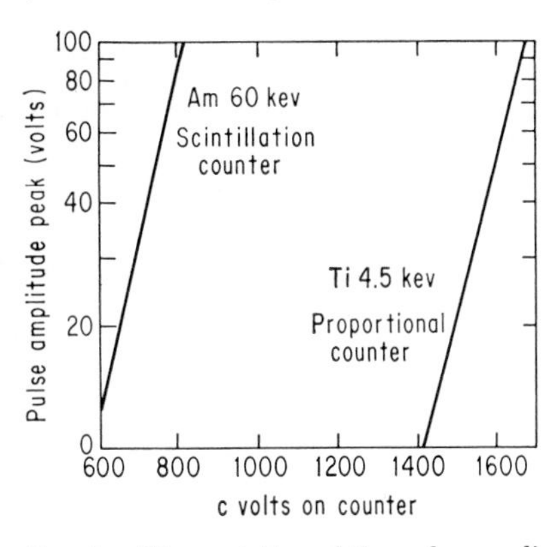

FIG. 5. The variation of the pulse-amplitude peak with applied detector voltage is shown for a scintillation counter and proportional counter. The exciting radiation was taken from americium embedded in a plastic wafer. The energy of the exciting radiation was of the order of 60 kev. (*After M. C. Lambert, AEC Research and Development Rept.* HW-58967.)

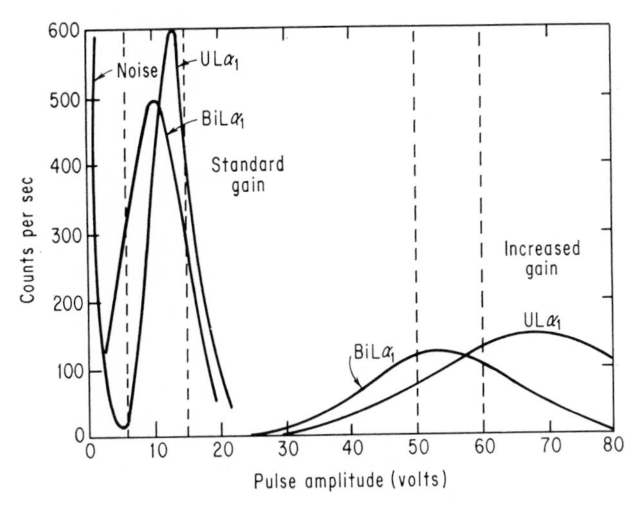

FIG. 6. The effect of window width and window position on the amount of energy passed at two different gains using a scintillation counter. At the low gain almost all the energy due to the U and Bi $L\alpha$ lines is passed. At the high amplification a much smaller proportion of these radiations is passed. (*After M. C. Lambert, AEC Research and Development Rept.* HW-58967.)

level plus window width are rejected. For example, a discriminator with the base level set at 5 volts and a window width of 10 volts will reject all pulses smaller than 5 volts and greater than 15 volts. Referring to Fig. 3*b*, the pulses due to the copper radiation are seen to lie almost entirely between V_1 and V_2 while those due to the Ag lie almost entirely between V_2 and V_3. If the pulse-height analyzer is set to detect those amplitudes which lie between V_1 and V_2, only the Cu radiation will be detected and most of the Ag radiation rejected. On the other hand, if the pulse-height-analyzer window is set to accept only the pulses between V_2 and V_3 then the Ag radiation will be detected and most of the Cu radiation rejected.

The effect of window width and window position can be seen with reference to Fig. 6. The dashed lines include the portions of the pulse-distribution curves passed by a 10-volt window set correspondingly at two different base levels, 5 and 50 volts. One observes that at a 5-volt base level all the noise pulses are rejected and the 10-volt window serves to pass all but a very small portion of the pulses due to the U and Bi *Lα* lines. At the higher amplification the same 10-volt window passes only a small

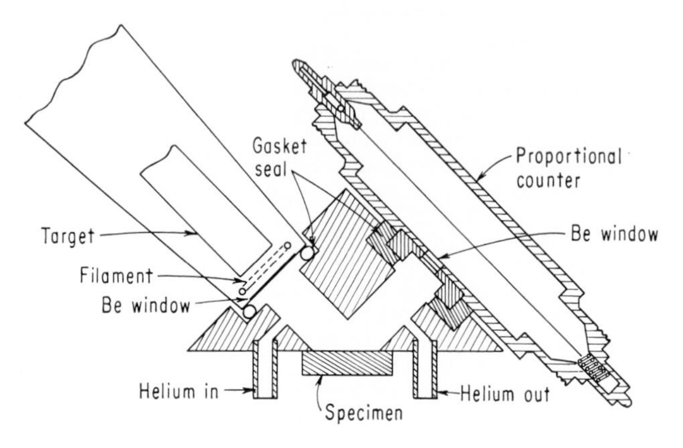

FIG. 7. An example of the close coupling between the sample, the excitation source, and the detector possible with nondispersive optics. The x-ray spectrum is sorted by means of pulse-amplitude analysis. (*L. S. Birks, X-ray Spectrochemical Analysis, p.* 38, *Interscience Publishers, Inc., New York,* 1959.)

proportion of these radiations. It follows from this that it is desirable to use lower amplification so that one can detect the radiation at high counting efficiencies with smaller window widths. It is generally recommended that the amplification be adjusted to bring the peak of the pulse distributions to about 10 volts. Details of operation of pulse-height systems may be found in a number of publications.[7,8] These papers describe methods for obtaining optimum performance and techniques (see also Chap. 3 of this handbook).

Advantages and Limitations. The principal advantages of nondispersive x-ray geometries are simpler instrumentation and greater intensities. The crystals used in crystal geometries are relatively inefficient and cause a thousandfold loss of intensity. Similarly the collimators cause further intensity loss, and by eliminating these, more compact geometries are possible. Figure 7 is an example of a nondispersive arrangement showing the close coupling of x-ray tube, sample, and detector possible. This arrangement has proved successful in the determination of the very light elements such as magnesium and sodium.

The most serious disadvantage of nondispersive optics is the poor energy resolution relative to crystal monochromators. It has already been shown that monochromatic x-rays produce a spread of pulse amplitudes for each energy and that the energy resolution of neighboring elements is very poor; in fact, the resolution of elements two or three atomic numbers apart is partial under the best conditions. Figure 8 shows the pulse distribution for Ca, Ti, Cr, and Fe obtained with a proportional counter. For elements two atomic numbers apart, the separation is such that one can be resolved only at the expense of sacrificing a large part of the total response of the other, thereby reducing counting efficiency to a very low value. The situation is even worse for the scintillation counter.

One consequence of the poor resolution is the difficulty in determining minor concentrations of elements. Birks[5] points out that resolution of energies by pulse-height analysis is sufficiently incomplete so that elemental concentrations below 1 per cent cannot be determined with great accuracy. The problem of resolution is further complicated by the escape-peak phenomenon. This effect is particularly troublesome in applications involving the flow counter. The escape peak may seriously interfere with and even mask an x-ray line being measured. Escape-peak formation is a consequence of the absorbed quantum causing x-ray emission from the counter gas.

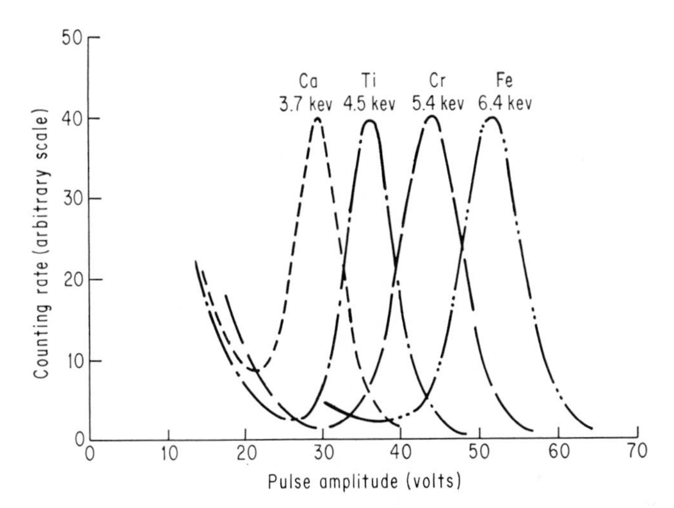

FIG. 8. The pulse-amplitude distribution for Ca, Ti, Cr, and Fe obtained with a proportional counter. For elements two atomic numbers away one cannot be completely resolved without sacrificing a large part of the total intensity of the other element, thereby reducing counting efficiency to a very low value. (*Courtesy of Friedman, Birks, and Brooks, private communication.*)

When these x-rays escape from the active volume of the counter because of the transparency of the gas to its own radiation an escape peak results which represents the difference in energy between the exciting x-rays and the x-ray energy emitted by the active gas of the detector. An example may be cited involving the separation of Cu and Cr by pulse-height analysis with an argon-filled detector. The energy of the Cu $K\alpha$ line is 8.98 kev. Because the energy of the A $K\alpha$ line is 3.2 kev an escape peak of 5.8 kev ($E_{\text{Cu}\,K\alpha} - E_{\text{A}\,K\alpha}$) will be generated by the Cu $K\alpha$ line that is almost coincident with the 6-kev line of the Cr $K\alpha$ and will not be resolved from it.

Despite the limitations described above, nondispersive analysis has a number of applications and is a very useful approach. Hall[9] has described the application of this technique to the analysis of biological tissue for trace elements.

Dolby and Cosslett[10] use nondispersive techniques in electron-probe analysis and describe a matrix-theory method for canceling interferences from adjacent elements.

An application of particular interest is the one described recently by Mellish[11] on the use of radioactive sources in nondispersive x-ray spectroscopy. The higher sensitivities of the nondispersive optics have made it possible to use exciting sources whose output is smaller than that of conventional x-ray tubes by a factor of 10^{-12}. Figure 9 shows the experimental arrangement, and Table 1 lists some of the useful sources.

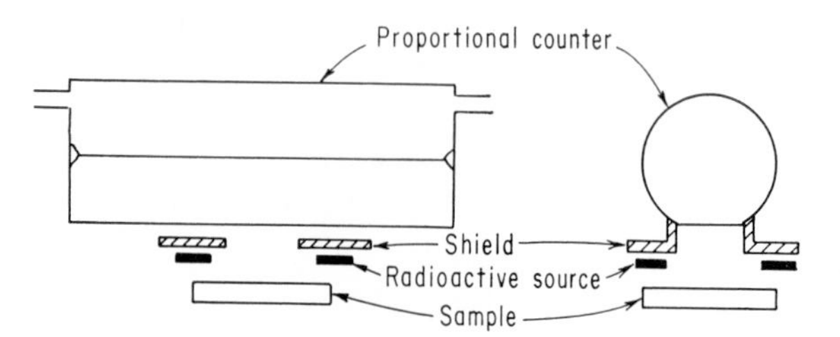

FIG. 9. Instrumental arrangement for nondispersive analysis using a radioactive source. [*After C. E. Mellish, Research (London), vol.* 12, 1959.]

Table 1. Radioactive Sources for X-ray Fluorescence Analysis

Possible sources	*Half-life*
Am 241	470 years
Cs 131	9.7 days
Fe 55	2.9 years
Tritium	12.3 years
W 181	140 days

2. FLAT-CRYSTAL SYSTEMS

Geometry. The arrangement of the various components of the nonfocusing flat-crystal x-ray spectrograph is shown in Fig. 10*a* and 10*b* in the equatorial plane and axial plane, respectively. The adjustment of the various components for obtaining maximum intensities and peak-to-background signals has been described in considerable detail by Spielberg, Parrish, and Lowitsch.[12] The orientation of the equatorial plane varies in commercial equipment. The Philips and Applied Research Laboratories goniometers rotate in the vertical plane while the General Electric and Siemens goniometer rotate in the horizontal plane.

The components of the flat-crystal system consist of the x-ray tube, specimen, and the crystal spectrometer. The spectrometer is made up in turn of analyzing crystal, collimators, and detector. The x-ray tube is the source of primary radiation which is used to excite the secondary or characteristic x-rays from the sample which may be a solid, liquid, or mixture of powders. The essential requirement for the sample is a uniform surface if precise analyses are attempted. Since the characteristic x-rays are emitted in all directions, collimators are used to limit the x-rays striking the analyzing crystal to a parallel beam. The crystal diffracts the parallel beam of x-rays in accordance with Bragg's law

$$n\lambda = 2d \sin \theta$$

where n is the order of diffraction, λ is the wavelength in angstroms, d is the lattice constant, e.g., the interplanar spacing of the diffracting crystal in angstroms, and θ is the angle between the incident x-radiation and the crystal surface. For each crystal only a single wavelength satisfying Bragg's law will be diffracted if only first-order reflections are considered. In practice, harmonics of λ will also be diffracted except in the case of special crystals for which certain higher orders are absent. The diffracted radiation leaves the crystal at an angle θ with respect to the crystal face and at 2θ with respect to the incident beam. The modern commercial goniometer is so arranged that the detector automatically moves at twice the angular speed of the crystal and is always in position to detect the diffracted radiation. A spectrum can be traced out as the crystal rotates from 0 to 90° while the detector swings through an arc of 0 to 180°.

Collimation. The function of the collimator is to allow only a parallel bundle of x-rays to impinge on the analyzing crystal. Unless this is done the same crystal in any particular position will reflect x-rays of different wavelengths which simultaneously strike the crystal at different incident angles in the fashion shown in Fig. 11. Because of the large acceptance angle of the detector, many of the varied wavelengths will be accepted, resulting in broad lines or even multiple reflections.

The collimator plays an important role in determining line resolution, which is a function of both the divergence allowed by the collimator and the rocking angle of the

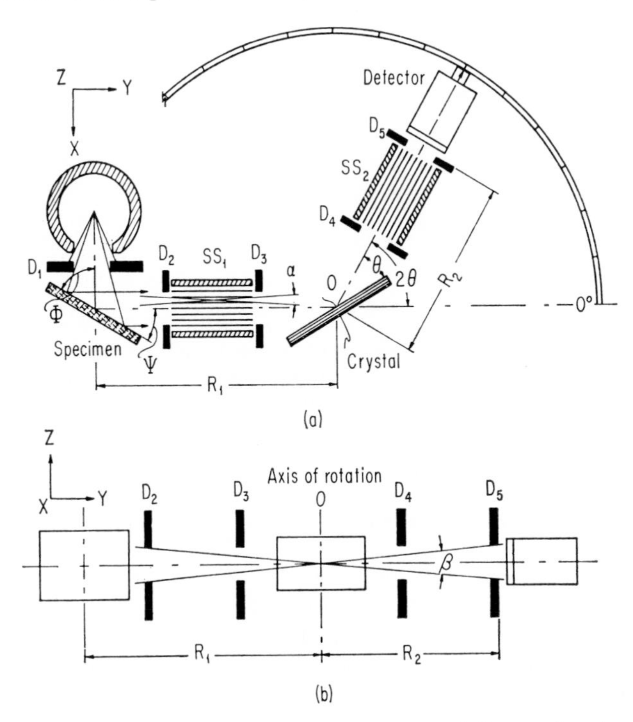

FIG. 10. (*a*) Arrangement of the various components of the nonfocusing flat-crystal x-ray spectrograph in the equatorial plane. (*b*) Arrangement of the nonfocusing flat-crystal spectrograph in the axial plane. (*After N. Spielberg, W. Parrish, and K. Lowitzsch, Spectrochim. Acta, vol.* 8, 1959.)

crystal. The intensity passing through a collimator has a triangular distribution with angle as shown in Fig. 12*a*. The breadth at half maximum is B_c, being determined by the collimator length l and the spacing between the blades s according to the equation

$$B_c = \arctan (s/l)$$

The intensities diffracted by a crystal of a parallel x-ray beam is represented by a Gaussian curve with a half maximum B_m (see Fig. 12*b*). With a single collimator the total line breadth is obtained by assuming that the collimator line breadth is actually Gaussian and combining the two distributions. The final line breadth (Fig. 12*c*) is given by the expression

$$B^2 = B_c^2 + B_m^2$$

The figures quoted by Birks[13] are as follows: With an LiF crystal B_m is about 0.2° and B_c about 0.07° for a 4-in. collimator with 0.005-in. spacing between the foils.

The total line breadth is 0.21° for a single collimator. For a more perfect crystal such as quartz B_m may be as low as 0.05°, and since B_c remains unchanged, the total B will be 0.085° for a single collimator. For two identical collimators using LiF the total B will be 0.13° and for quartz two collimators will give a line breadth of approximately 0.042°.

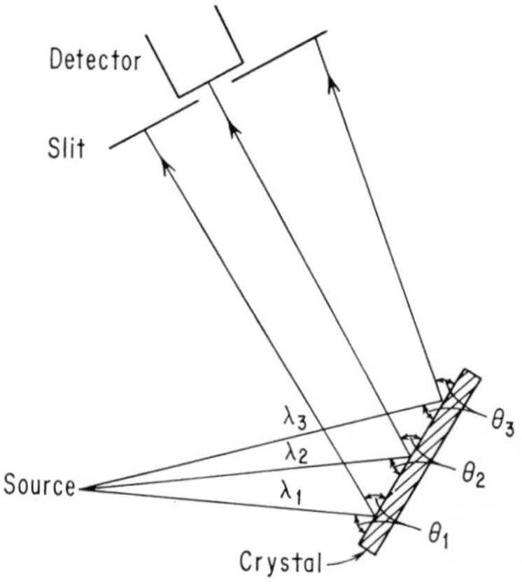

FIG. 11. Diffraction of the x-ray beam by a large crystal. Slits or collimators are required to guarantee that only a single wavelength (in this instance λ_2) is received by the detector.

Collimator Geometry. Friedman, Birks, and Brooks[14] used a box of thin-walled nickel tubes in their original instrument. This arrangement was convenient to construct but produced a sharp loss of intensity because divergence is limited in both the equatorial and axial planes. Spielberg, Parrish, and Lowitzsch[15] have shown that limiting the axial divergence causes a large reduction of intensity without significant improvement of line shape.

Soller[16] has described a collimator consisting of a number of parallel, equally spaced thin lead strips where the angular reflection is determined by the length and separation of the strips. The Soller-type collimator is the principal type used in commercial x-ray fluorescence equipment today. Collimators may be used either singly before or after the analyzing crystal, or in various dual combinations on each side of the crystal. The effect of various combinations of collimators on line breadth and intensity is shown in Table 2 taken from the paper of Spielberg et al. mentioned above. The improvement in resolution achieved by the use of two collimators is described by

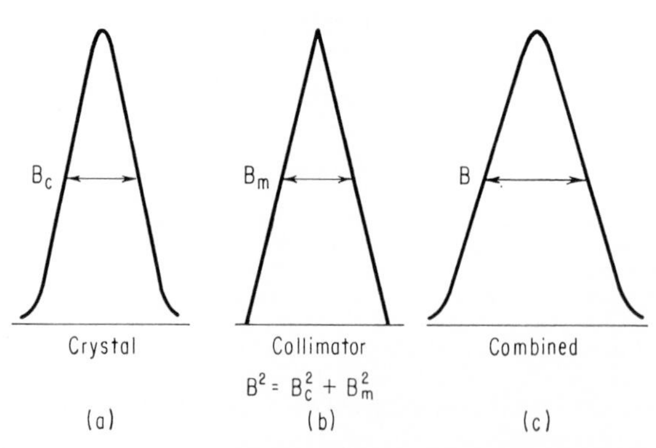

FIG. 12. The effect of collimator divergence and crystal rocking angle on line breadth. The x-ray intensity passing through the collimator has a triangular distribution with angle as shown in (*a*). The breadth at half maximum B_c is determined by the collimator length l and the spacing between the blades s. The intensity diffracted by a crystal of a parallel beam is represented by a Gaussian curve (*b*) with a half maximum B_m. The final breadth of the line (*c*) is approximated by the expression $B^2 = B_c^2 + B_m^2$. (*Courtesy of L. S. Birks, Naval Research Laboratory.*)

Campbell, Leon, and Thatcher[17] and shown in Fig. 13. The resolution of the Mn $K\beta$ line from the Fe $K\alpha$ line is clearly demonstrated. As a precaution, the use of dual collimators requires much greater care in the alignment of the goniometer. There is

Table 2. Effect of Equatorial Divergence of Collimators on Line Breadth and Intensity*

Collimator 1	Collimator 2	Half breadth	Intensity	Peak to background
0.005	.....	0.24	53	8
0.010	.....	0.42	91	5
0.020	.....	0.74	100	3
0.005	0.005	0.15	27	100
0.005	0.01	0.20	37	45
0.005	0.02	0.24	40	35
0.010	0.010	0.28	57	35

* Cu $K\alpha$, quartz crystal $(10\bar{1}1)$, 0.0007-in. nickel foil to absorb Cu $K\beta$ and scattered W L from x-ray tube. All collimators 4 in., nickel-foil thickness 0.002 in.

a greater likelihood of tracking error, particularly if the goniometer is used over the entire 90° range.

In summary, the use of two collimators causes a reduction of intensity but greatly improves resolution and suppresses line tails. In dealing with portions of the x-ray

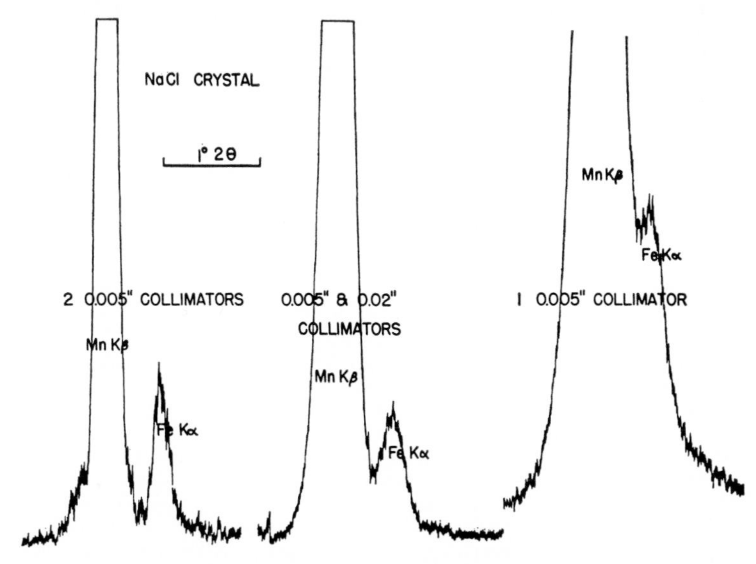

FIG. 13. Improvement in the resolution of the Mn $K\beta$ line from the Fe $K\alpha$ line by the use of increased collimation. (*Courtesy of Campbell, Leon, and Thatcher, U.S. Bureau of Mines, private communication.*)

spectrum where lines are widely separated, particularly in the soft-wavelength region above 3 to 4 Å, coarse collimation is usually adequate and results in greater intensity.

3. CURVED-CRYSTAL SYSTEMS

Curved-crystal systems, commonly referred to as focusing systems, are used to obtain an increased luminosity of the x-ray spectrograph. Cylindrically curved crystals are used in either transmission or reflection and x-rays from a point or line source are imaged as a line. The curved crystal behaves in an analogous fashion to the concave diffraction grating used in optical emission spectroscopy.

Reflection Geometry. The configuration of the x-ray optical elements in reflecting-type focusing instruments is of either the Johannson or Johann type. In every case the arrangement is such that Bragg's expression for diffraction $n\lambda = 2d \sin \theta$ is satisfied. This relationship has already been discussed in the section of Flat-crystal Geometries. The Johannson arrangement in theory provides true focusing, a point source imaging as a line. The crystal is bent to a radius R and ground to $R/2$. The bending radius of the crystal is the diameter of the focal circle known as the Roland circle (see Fig. 14*a*). It can be shown that, when Bragg's focusing conditions are met for any wavelength, $L_1 = L_2$, where $L = n\lambda R/2d$, d is once again the lattice parameter or spacing between the diffracting planes in angstroms, λ is the wavelength in angstroms, n is the order of diffraction, and R is the radius of bending of the crystal. Since Johannson-type optics requires both bending and grinding of the crystal the number of suitable crystal materials is limited because of the technical difficulties encountered in the grinding of crystal surfaces.

Figure 14*b* is a representation of the Johann focusing spectrometer. The crystal is bent to a radius R but is unground. The radius of bending is the diameter of

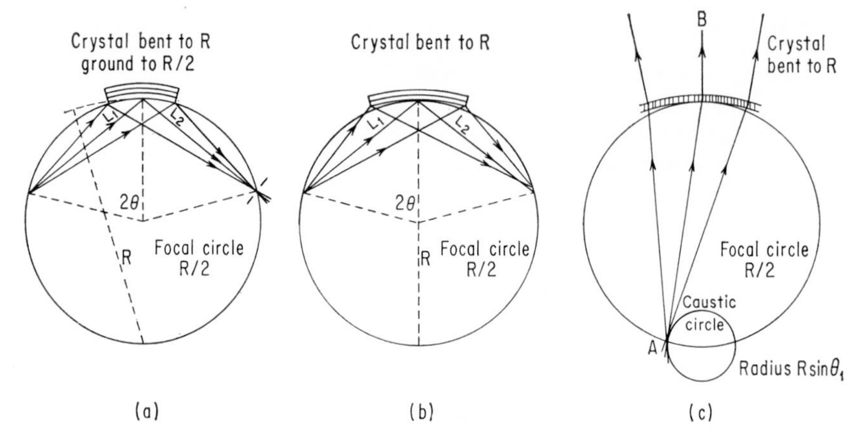

FIG. 14. Various types of focusing geometry. (*a*) Johannson arrangement utilizing a curved and ground crystal. (*b*) Johann arrangement; the crystal is bent but unground. (*c*) Cauchois transmission optics.

the focal circle. This method of focusing is usually used with crystals that are not readily ground such as mica. In this arrangement a point source is also imaged as a line, but unlike the Johannson spectrometer it gives a line with some extension and the focusing is not so sharp. This focusing defect is asymmetric and decreases with increasing angle. It is most serious at glancing angles but becomes insignificant at angles greater than 45° θ.

Transmission Geometries. The principle of the transmission-type (Cauchois) focusing spectrometer is shown in Fig. 14*c*. A cylindrically curved crystal is used to focus x-rays transmitted through the crystal. The crystal planes perpendicular to the crystal surface are used to diffract the x-rays. The radius of curvature of the crystal is equal to the diameter of the focal circle. No grinding of the crystal is required. This spectrometer may be used in two ways, either to focus a converging beam of x-rays from a large sample to a line on the Rowland circle (B to A) or to look at a point source of x-rays on the Rowland circle and diffract a divergent beam (A to B). The principal advantage of the transmission arrangement is that one can readily measure x-rays which diffract at very low Bragg angles.

A number of mechanical arrangements for curved-crystal spectrometers are available and have been described by Sandstrom,[18] Birks and Brooks,[19] and Kemp and Andermann.[20] In the design described by Birks and Brooks the axis of the focusing circle is fixed with respect to the specimen slit. The crystal and detector are mounted on separate arms and are turned by concentric shafts. The detector arm turns at twice the angular rate of the crystal arm so that the detector is always in position to intercept the diffracted radiation. In order to keep the detector pointed toward the crystal it is fixed on a circular plate that is free to rotate in its mount at the end of the detector arm. A pulley half the diameter of the circular plate is fixed to the crystal-arm shaft and connected to a circular plate by a wire (Fig. 15). As the crystal and detector arms turn, the pulley arrangement rotates the circular plate in the opposite direction at half the rate of the detector-arm motion. As the crystal arm turns from 0 to 45°, the detector arm rotates from 0 to 90° but the circular plate is turned backward by 45°, as shown in the figure. This type of goniometer is very compact and uses a very simple drive mechanism. The major disadvantage found in this type of spectrometer is that the field of view changes with angle.

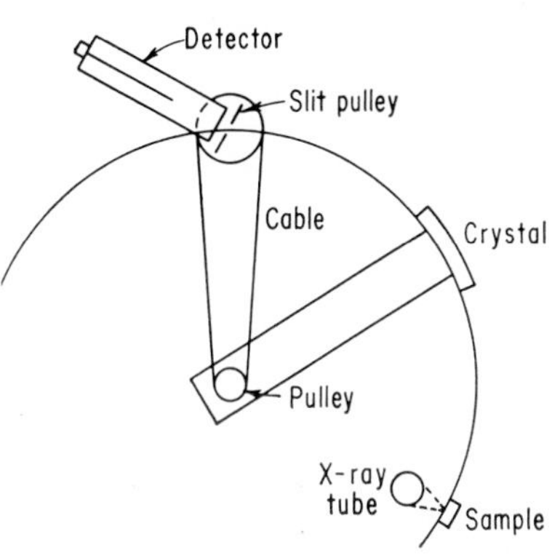

FIG. 15. An arrangement of a reflection-type curved-crystal optics. The detector arm turns at twice the angular rate of the crystal arm so that the detector is always in position to intercept the diffracted radiation. The detector is kept pointed at the center of the crystal by means of a pulley system. (*After Birks and Brooks, Anal. Chem., vol.* 27, 1955.)

A fixed-field-of-view spectrometer developed by the Applied Research Laboratories is shown in Fig. 16. The crystal is restrained so that it moves in a straight line away from the specimen. As it moves through increasing 2θ angles the crystal and detector lie in a series of focal circles pivoting about the specimen. The detector

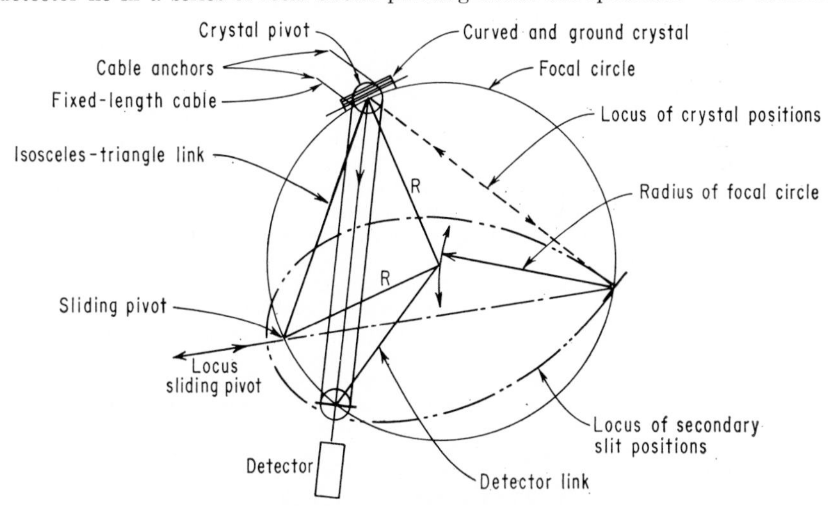

FIG. 16. The fixed-field-of-view spectrometer used in Applied Research Laboratories equipment. The crystal is restrained so that it moves in a straight line away from the specimen. (*Courtesy of Applied Research Laboratories, Inc.*)

must move along a complex curve called the four-leaf rose. This type of spectrometer is found in the spectrographs and electron microprobe manufactured by Applied Research Laboratories, Inc.

Preparation of Plastically Curved Crystals. The preparation of plastically curved crystals has been covered in detail by Birks.[21] He points out that it is essential in preparing a curved crystal to reorient the crystalline planes along the arc of the circle by realigning the mosaic blocks. Care must be taken not to produce large angular misorientations at any point in the crystal. For example, in alkali halides the individual mosaic blocks are about 500 Å in size and misoriented with respect to each other by 10 sec of arc or greater on the average. If there are no misorientations between mosaic blocks, curving the crystal to a radius of 10 cm will introduce only 0.1 sec of arc difference of orientation between adjacent mosaic blocks of 500 Å size, and thus curving the crystal should not cause any noticeable increase in mosaic spread. If proper precautions are taken no increase in diffracted-line breadth should result.

Plastically curved crystals are generally prepared according to the method of Johannson. Crystals may be first bent and then ground or the reverse order followed. If the radius of the Rowland circle is R the crystal is first curved to $2R$ and then ground to R. If the reverse process is followed the crystal is ground to $2R$ and then curved to R.

The procedure recommended by Birks follows. It is relatively simple and yields a high percentage of good crystals provided the starting material is good.

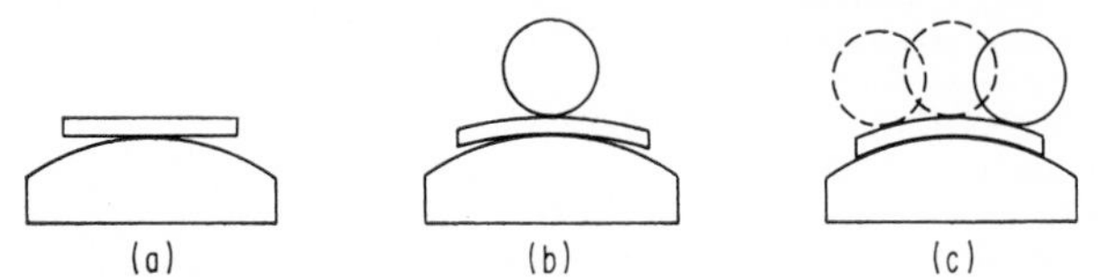

FIG. 17. Progressive steps in the plastic curving of a crystal. (*L. S. Birks, X-ray Spectrochemical Analysis, p.* 129, *Interscience Publishers, Inc., New York,* 1959.)

The initial step in preparing a curved crystal is to cleave a suitable thickness from a larger block of either rock salt or lithium fluoride. For greater curvatures thicker plates are necessary, about ⅛ in. for a 10-cm circle and about 1/16 in. for a 20-cm circle. Cleaving crystal plates requires skill and practice, and not all large single crystals cleave with equal ease. As an alternative it is possible to obtain commercial crystals thin enough to bend. If the surface of the cleavage section is not smooth, it may be smoothed by careful abrading on 400 Aloxite paper or similar abrasive and then etched to remove the worked material. A 50-50 alcohol-water mixture is suitable for sodium chloride. For lithium fluoride a solution of dilute hydrochloric acid containing dilute acetic acid plus a few tenths per cent ferric chloride is suitable. Care must be taken in abrading the crystal not to cut the crystal at an appreciable angle to the cleavage planes.

The cleaved plate is heated slowly on a flat surface to the same temperature as the curved die, approximately 300° C. When it has reached this temperature it is placed along the convex side of the die as shown in Fig. 17*a*. A ball made by winding asbestos cord around a tennis ball to a thickness of about ½ in. makes a suitable press for curving the hot crystal. It should be pressed down slowly in the center at first as shown in Fig. 17*b* and gradually worked out toward the ends as in Fig. 17*c* until the entire length of the crystal is uniformly curved to the die. Once the crystal has been curved to the die it is allowed to cool slowly with it. A weighted concave die of the proper curvature may be placed on the crystal during the cooling period. After cooling, the crystal is cemented to a metal form cut to fit the convex surface. There are a number of suitable cements. The most permanent and suitable of these are the cold-setting epoxy resins. The metal support and crystal are mounted in a vise and the grinding curvature is obtained by running strips of coarse grinding paper between the crystal face and a metal form of the proper grinding radius. A succession of progressively finer papers is used down to 400 or 600 corundum paper. Finally the crystal may be etched as described above to remove the worked material. The crystal curvature may be checked by the following method described by Birks: The crystal is used to focus light from a distant source (the sun, for example) on an opaque white screen held slightly below the direct line of sight. If the curvature is uniform, a sharp line image will be formed when the crystal-to-screen distance is equal to half the bending radius. Many curved crystals may now be obtained commercially from a number of sources such as Applied Research Laboratories, Harshaw, Iso-Met Corporation, and Philips Electronic Instruments. It is even possible to obtain excellent nonplastic crystals such as quartz both curved and ground for use in Johannson-type spectrometers.

For Johannson optics requiring only bent unground crystals, thin crystal plates may be curved elastically and maintained in correct curvature by suitable crystal holders. The simplest arrangement is to cement the crystal plates to plates milled to the proper curvature. A number of crystal holders of other types are described in the *Encyclopedia of Physics,* vol. XXX on X-rays.[18]

4. EDGE-CRYSTAL GEOMETRY

This crystal method of dispersion has been described by Sandstrom[18] and Birks and Brooks.[22] The planes parallel to the thin edge of a crystal are used for diffraction in the manner shown in Fig. 18. The breadth of each diffraction line is the width of the crystal edge projected onto a circle. Crystals as thin as 0.005 in. have been prepared, and Birks and Brooks have been able to resolve the Cr $K\beta$ from the Mn $K\alpha$ line.

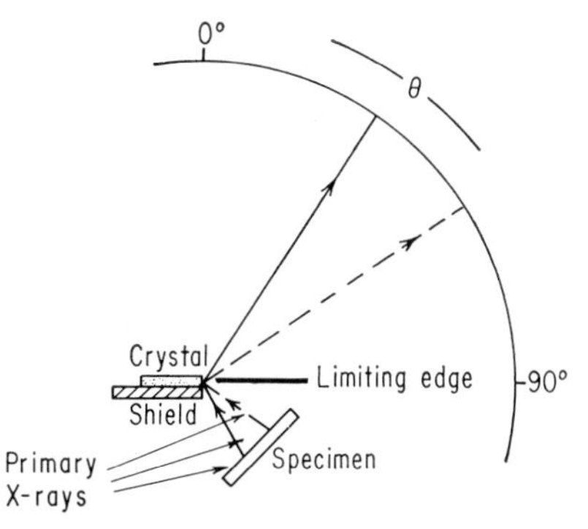

FIG. 18. The edge-crystal spectrograph. Planes parallel to the thin edge of a crystal are used for diffraction.

The edge-crystal spectrograph has a number of advantages. It has no moving parts and is extremely simple in construction. The complete spectrum is recorded at once on photographic film placed along the arc of a circle, and the total time for recording compares favorably with more elaborate x-ray spectrographs. There are, however, a number of disadvantages. Since different wavelengths arise from different portions of the specimen a homogeneous sample is required for precise analytical work. In addition, photographic calibration is required to reduce the line densities to intensities.

Small edge-crystal spectrographs are available commercially and can be used with modern diffraction equipment to provide elemental analysis. The x-rays emerging from the diffraction port can be used as a source of primary x-radiation.

5. COMPARISON OF VARIOUS SYSTEMS

Sensitivity. Among the various systems described above, nondispersive optics is the most sensitive in terms of absolute quantities measurable. This statement is true for those limited situations, however, where the traces are actually major constituents of minute samples. The case for minor constituents in large samples has been discussed under the section on nondispersive optics. Hall[9] has described a special nondispersive x-ray fluorescence unit for the analysis of biological-tissue sections. By using a specially designed x-ray tube and proportional counter he has reported a sensitivity figure of about 5×10^7 counts/sec/g zinc/tube ma and estimates that absolute amounts as low as 10^{-10} g of some elements may be detected.

A direct comparison of the relative sensitivities of flat-crystal vs. curved-crystal optics is difficult because of the large number of parameters involved. Sensitivities depend in large measure on a number of factors such as alignment, crystal quality, and type of excitation used. Generally in dealing with large samples comparable sensitivities may be obtained by either flat or focusing optics. In the long-wavelength region focusing optics are advantageous because no collimation is required.

Focusing optics is decidedly more efficient for small sample sizes. Whereas in flat-crystal optics the aperture width is limited by the sample size, the aperture of curved-crystal optics is limited only by the available crystal size. The curved-crystal spectrometer is a much more efficient collector of x-ray energy, and thus much smaller sample sizes can be used.

Resolution. The resolution of the x-ray spectrograph depends on two factors, the resolving power of the analyzing crystal and the geometrical resolving power of the x-ray spectrograph. Comparable resolutions can be obtained by either flat- or curved-crystal spectrometers if other factors such as specimen size and distance of the specimen to crystal and crystal to detector are kept constant. If considerable care is exercised in the preparation of curved crystals one can obtain some improvement in signal to noise by placing a slit in front of the detector at the focal point and passing only the radiation in the line image. Once again, such comparisons are difficult to make because of the number of factors involved, and the differences that are observed are relatively small.

Element resolution by nondispersive optics is very much poorer. Under ideal conditions one can just begin to separate elements two atomic numbers apart with proportional counters. The resolution of elements by means of scintillation counters is poorer still.

6. CHOICE OF CRYSTALS

Diffracting crystals used in x-ray spectroscopy must meet a number of requirements. The more important characteristics of the analyzing crystal are interplanar spacing, coefficient of reflection for first-order reflection, coefficients of reflection for higher-order reflections, degree of crystal perfection, and fluorescence of the crystal.

It can be seen from the Bragg equation, $n\lambda = 2d \sin \theta$, that the longest wavelength that can be reflected equals $2d$, twice the lattice constant of the reflecting planes. It has been observed in practice that the intensity of reflection falls off rapidly at large angles and is weak above 120° (2θ). It is not desirable to use a crystal to reflect wavelengths much larger than d. At low angles, because of the geometry of plane crystal spectrographs, the crystal must be long to intercept all the radiation emerging from the collimator. As the angle becomes small the crystal will intercept only a portion of the radiation emerging from the collimator. A practical lower 2θ limit may be taken as 10°. Below these angles a loss of intensity is experienced because of the failure to utilize all the emergent x-rays.

The chemical composition of the crystal is important and should be of such a nature that its own fluorescence should not cause interference with the elements being measured. These analyses are usually performed in air, and most crystals in use today emit fluorescent x-radiation that is entirely air-absorbed. For elements below atomic number 20 the crystal fluorescence may contribute a large share of the background, and depending on the element analyzed, this fluorescence may be only partially rejected by the pulse-height analyzer. For example, one must expect phosphorus K radiation from ADP crystals, chlorine K radiation from NaCl, and silicon K radiation from quartz crystals.

The reflecting surface must be reasonably perfect and free of distortions caused by cleaving or grinding. The crystal should not have a pronounced mosaic structure, which may vary in angular orientation in different portions of the crystal. The effect of this would be to spread the angular width of the line, reduce peak intensities, and even produce multiplicity of peaks.

Finally the analyzing crystal should have a suitable lattice spacing d for diffraction. For any given wavelength λ the 2θ value will be greater the smaller the d spacing for the crystal. For the reasons described above the value d of the selected crystal should be small enough so that the smallest selected λ should diffract at a 2θ value greater than 10°. It can also be shown from the relationship for dispersion $d\theta/d\lambda = n\lambda/2d \cos \theta$ that the smaller the d spacing the greater the separation of wavelengths. As a general rule one should select a crystal giving the greatest intensities with adequate resolution for the particular job.

Available Crystals. The x-ray spectroscopist has available to him a large variety of high-quality analyzing crystals which may be obtained commercially from a number of sources. In addition to the suppliers of x-ray equipment, companies such as Iso-Met and Harshaw will supply particular crystals on demand. A list of some of the crystals is shown in Table 3. Many of these crystals can be obtained either flat

Table 3. Analyzing Crystals for X-ray Spectroscopy

Crystal	Reflecting planes	$2d$, Å	Reflectivity
SiO_2 (quartz)	$50\bar{5}2$	1.624	Low
Topaz	303	2.712	High
SiO_2 (quartz)	$20\bar{2}3$	2.750	Low
LiF	200	4.026	High
NaCl	200	5.641	High
Si	111	6.271	High
Fluorite	111	6.32	High
Ge	111	6.54	High
SiO_2 (quartz)	$10\bar{1}1$	6.686	High
SiO_2 (quartz)	$10\bar{1}0$	8.510	Medium
EDdT*	020	8.803	Medium
ADP†	101	10.64	Medium
Gypsum	020	15.12	Medium
Mica	002	19.92	Medium
KAP‡	$10\bar{1}0$	26.4	Medium

* Ethylenediamine-*d*-tartrate.
† Ammonium dihydrogen phosphate.
‡ Potassium acid phthalate.

or curved from the manufacturers. The classification of the crystals in the column marked Reflectivity is an approximate one which depends on the particular crystal and the wavelength region and can be used only as a rough guide.

Comparison of Crystals. The useful wavelength limits of a crystal depend on the geometry of the spectrograph at low angles and the decrease of intensity with high angles of reflection. Figure 19 shows the range of wavelengths covered for 2θ angles between 10 and 160° for a number of crystals. The hatched areas show the most useful regions for some of the more commonly used crystals. These are not to be taken as strict limits, however. For example, an ADP crystal may be used in the same region as EDdT although its reflectivity and dispersion are somewhat lower than those of the EDdT crystal. For many analyses the ADP crystal may yield adequate intensities and resolution.

Dispersion and Resolution. As discussed above, the dispersion of neighboring wavelengths is given by the expression $d\theta/d\lambda = n\lambda/2d \cos \theta$ obtained by differentiating Bragg's law. As d, the lattice parameter, decreases, the separation of wavelengths increases. Increasing wavelength separation, however, does not result in increased resolution if the collimation is inadequate or if the crystal is sufficiently imperfect to yield broad lines with broad tails. With proper collimation and reasonably perfect crystals, dispersion and resolution may be taken as essentially identical. Table 4 shows the angular separation of two close spectral lines Fe $K\alpha_1$ ($\lambda = 1.936$) and Cr $K\beta_1$ ($\lambda = 2.085$) for several different crystals.

Extinction of Higher-order Reflections. The problem of interferences due to higher-order reflections is a frequent and serious problem in x-ray spectroscopy. One method of successfully dealing with this problem is to use crystals whose second-order reflections are missing or weak.[24] Silicon or germanium crystals, cut parallel to the 111 plane, show extinction in the second order. Such crystals have been used in studies of the niobium-tantalum and zirconium-hafnium systems where second-order interference is severe.[24] Silicon and germanium crystals of good quality may be obtained commercially. The performance of these crystals has been studied, and the following figures have been reported: Germanium was found to give approximately 50 per cent intensity for the Ni $K\alpha$ relative to LiF. Silicon reflected at about 75

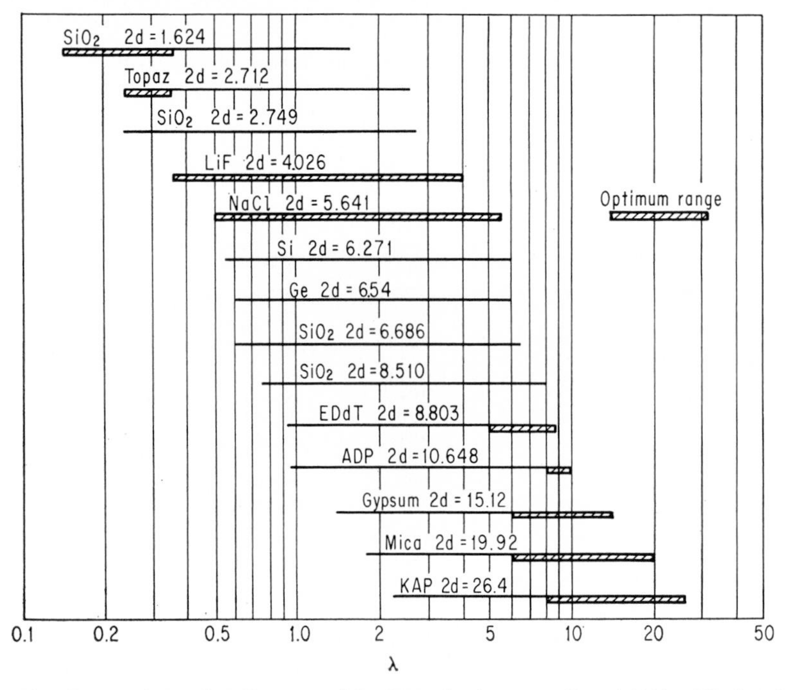

FIG. 19. Range of wavelengths covered for 2θ angles between 10 and 160°. The hatched areas represent the most useful wavelength regions for some of the more common crystals.

Table 4. Separation of Fe $K\alpha$ and Co $K\beta$ for Various Crystals

Crystal	$2d$	$\Delta 2\theta$
Topaz	2.712	1.56
LiF	4.026	1.14
NaCl	5.641	0.56
EDdT	8.803	0.34
ADP	10.648	0.28

per cent of the intensity of LiF for the same wavelength. The half breadth of the line was 0.2θ for silicon compared with $0.3°\ 2\theta$ for germanium and LiF.

By contrast to the above some crystals have intense higher-order reflections. An example of this is the mica crystal. The odd orders are very strong and the even orders weak. The effect of this is to crowd the spectrum in the light-element region when mica is used in reflection.

Relative Sensitivities for Various Wavelengths. The reflectivities of crystals will vary with wavelength and with individual crystals. Different crystals of the same type may vary in reflectivity by as much as a factor of 2. Campbell, Leon, and Thatcher[25] have listed some characteristic properties of analyzing crystals shown in Table 5. Table 6[25] shows the effect of crystal surface with wavelength. It can be observed that the performance of crystals may be substantially improved by surface treatment. For example, etched surfaces are more efficient at shorter wavelengths whereas polished surfaces are more highly reflecting for longer wavelengths.

Table 5. Comparison of Various Crystals for Reflectivites and Half Breadth

Crystal	*hkl*	*d* spacing	*I*/*I**	*W*(½)†	*I*/I_2‡
NaCl	200	2.821	100	0.25	4.6
LiF	200	2.013	155	0.20	8.4
SiO_2	101	3.343	64	0.19	6.4
SiO_2	112	1.818	24	0.19	12.5
SiO_2	211	1.541	8.8	0.20	6.9
Topaz	...	1.398	27	0.19	15§
Topaz	303	1.352	26	0.19	15§

* Pb $L\beta_1\beta_2$ lines intensity from the various crystals compared with that from sodium chloride.

† Width of Pb $L\beta_1\beta_2$ lines at half line height in degrees 2θ.

‡ Ratio of intensities of first-order to second-order Pb $L\beta_1\beta_2$.

§ Ratio of intensities of first-order to second-order Th $L\beta_2$.

Table 6. Relative Reflectivity of Etched to Polished Surfaces for Quartz (101) as a Function of Wavelength

$K\alpha$ spectral line	Wavelength, Å	*I* etched/*I* polished
Sn	0.490	2.3
Zr	0.784	1.7
Br	1.038	1.5
Zn	1.432	1.2
Fe	1.932	0.95
Cr	2.285	0.71
Ti	2.743	0.52
Ca	3.352	0.51
K	3.734	0.49
Cl	4.718	0.40

The treatment of crystals for improved reflectivity has been described by Birks and Seal[26] and White.[27] Truly perfect crystals would give very low diffracted intensities because of primary extinction and are of little value as analyzing crystals. The degree of imperfection of natural and synthetic crystals varies. The ideally imperfect crystal should contain small mosaic blocks of the order of 10^{-5} cm in size, misoriented by not more than a few minutes of arc with respect to each other. Such crystals give much greater diffracted intensities. The alkali halide crystals such as LiF or NaCl are examples of ideally imperfect crystals. Quartz tends to be more perfect but can be made more mosaic by a gentle abrading of the surface. As shown in Table 6, the diffracted intensities for harder radiation can be approximately doubled by the abrasion. Birks states that "for a given crystal the deliberate introduction of elastic or plastic strain usually increases the diffracted intensity without excessive broadening of the diffracted line." White, for example, showed a 20-fold increase in elastically strained quartz. Birks and Seal have increased the peak intensity of lines diffracted by LiF by a factor of from 4 to 10. In general, crystals such as ADP and EDdT used for the lighter elements give better intensities when smoothly polished because rough-surfaced crystals tend to absorb the diffracted longer wavelengths.

Finally Table 7 lists the most suitable crystals for specific ranges of elements.

Table 7. Most Suitable Crystals for Specific Range of Elements

Elements	*Crystals*
K series:	
Te(52) to K(19)	LiF(1), NaCl(2)
Cl(17) to S(16)	NaCl(1), EDdT(2)
P(15) to Al(13)	EDdT(1), ADP(2)
Mg(12)	ADP(1), gypsum(1), KAP(2)
Na(11)	KAP(1), gypsum(1), mica(2)
L series:	
U(92) to In(49)	LiF(1), NaCl(2)
RU(44)	NaCl(1), EDdT(2)
Rb(37)	EDdT(1), ADP(2)
As(33)	ADP(1)

EDdT = ethylenediamine-*d*-tartrate.
KAP = potassium acid phthalate.
ADP = ammonium dihydrogen phosphate.

REFERENCES CITED

1. H. F. Beeghly, *J. Electrochem. Soc.*, **97**:152 (1950).
2. W. Parrish and T. R. Kohler, *Rev. Sci. Instr.*, **27**:795 (1956).
3. C. F. Hendee, S. Fine, and W. B. Brown, *Rev. Sci. Instr.*, **27**:531 (1956).
4. H. Friedman, L. S. Birks, and E. J. Brooks, *Am. Soc. Testing Mater. Spec. Tech. Publ.* 157, p. 3, 1954.
5. L. S. Birks, *X-ray Spectrochemical Analysis*, pp. 45–47, Interscience Publishers, Inc., New York, 1959.
6. C. F. Hendee and S. Fine, *Phys. Rev.*, **95**:281–282 (1954).
7. D. C. Miller, *Norelco Reptr.*, **IV**:2 (1957).
8. M. C. Lambert, *U.S. At. Energy Comm. Rept.* NW-58967, 1959.
9. T. Hall, A Non-dispersive X-ray Fluorescence Unit for the Analysis of Biological Tissue Sections, in *Advances in X-ray Analysis*, vol. 1, p. 297, W. M. Mueller (ed.), Plenum Press, Inc., New York, 1960.
10. R. M. Dolby and V. E. Cosslett, A Spectrometer System for Long Wavelength X-ray Emission Microanalysis, in *X-ray Microscopy and X-ray Microanalysis*, p. 351, A. Engström, V. E. Cosslett, and H. Pattee (eds.), Elsevier Publishing Company, Amsterdam, 1960.
11. C. E. Mellish, *Research (London)*, **XII**(6):212 (1959).
12. N. Spielberg, W. Parrish, and K. Lowitzsch, *Spectrochim. Acta*, **8**:564–583 (1959).
13. L. S. Birks, *X-ray Spectrochemical Analysis*, pp. 22–23, Interscience Publishers, Inc., New York, 1959.
14. H. Friedman, L. S. Birks, and E. J. Brooks, *Am. Soc. Testing Mater. Spec. Tech. Publ.* 157, p. 3, 1954.
15. N. Spielberg, W. Parrish, and K. Lowitzsch, *Spectrochem. Acta*, **8**:564–583 (1959).
16. W. Soller, *Phys. Rev.*, **24**: (1924).
17. W. J. Campbell, M. Leon, and J. Thatcher, Flat Crystal X-ray Optics, in *Advances in X-ray Analysis*, vol. 1, p. 193, W. M. Mueller (ed.), Plenum Press, Inc., New York, 1960.
18. A. E. Sandstrom, *Encyclopedia of Physics*, vol. XXX (*X-rays*), pp. 108–124, Springer-Verlag OHG, Berlin, 1957.
19. L. S. Birks and E. J. Brooks, *Anal. Chem.*, **27**:437 (1955).
20. J. W. Kemp and G. Andermann, Fifth Annual Conference on Industrial Applications of X-ray Analysis, Denver Research Institute, University of Denver, Denver, Colo., August, 1956.
21. L. S. Birks, *X-ray Spectrochemical Analysis*, Appendix 2, Interscience Publishers, Inc., New York, 1959.
22. L. S. Birks and E. J. Brooks, *Anal. Chem.*, **27**:1147 (1955).
23. T. Hall, *Proc. Sixth Annual Conference on Industrial Applications of X-ray Analysis*, Denver, Colo., 1957.
24. P. Lublin, A Novel Approach to Discrimination in X-ray Spectrographic Analysis, in *Advances in X-ray Analysis*, vol. 2, p. 229, W. M. Mueller (ed.), Plenum Press, Inc., New York, 1960.
25. W. J. Campbell, M. Leon, and J. Thatcher, Flat Crystal X-ray Optics, in *Advances in X-ray Analysis*, vol. 1, p. 193, W. M. Mueller (ed.), Plenum Press, Inc., New York, 1960.
26. L. S. Birks and R. T. Seal, *J. Appl. Phys.*, **28**:541 (1957).
27. J. E. White, *J. Appl. Phys.*, **21**:885 (1950).

Chapter 32

FACTORS WHICH DETERMINE SENSITIVITY

Merlyn L. Salmon

FLUO-X-SPEC Laboratory

1. INTRODUCTION

"Sensitivity" as it is generally considered in x-ray emission spectroscopy can be defined as the rate of change of net (peak − background) x-ray line intensity with mass or concentration of the element. For most situations the sensitivity is expressed as some equivalent of counts per second/per cent when the sample is infinitely thick. In cases of extraction and concentration of the element as a representative fraction of the original sample, the units of sensitivity may be counts per second/microgram.

It is desirable to have a high sensitivity for the element(s) to be determined, and the purpose of this discussion is to consider experimental factors that are reported in Chaps. 1, 2, 3, 31, and 33 to 39 of this Handbook and in other references.

Sensitivity in x-ray spectroscopy is based on experimental calibration results with known standards and consideration of the effects of pertinent variables in the procedure. It is necessary to be aware of the effects of such systemic factors as sample composition and sample preparation and such instrumental factors as choice of the x-ray tube and power applied, selection of the analyzing crystal, choice of the collimator, choice and operation of the detector, effects of background, use of helium or a vacuum, and other characteristics and manipulations of the spectrographic instrument.

Evaluation of the experimental results will also show precision, accuracy, and limit of detection. The limit of detection is defined by Birks[1] in terms of statistics. The line intensity must be above the background by at least three standard deviations of the background intensity. Use of this relationship with a sensitivity determined at a low concentration indicates the minimum amount of the element which can be detected in that type of sample with the experimental procedure used.

Henke[2] gives a similar expression for minimum limit of detection based on weight per cent, statistical variation of the background, and net peak intensity. Campbell, Spano, and Green[3] base their definition on a 10-min counting time for each measurement.

These definitions are based on statistical considerations of intensities measured by fixed-count or fixed-time procedures. Chart records of scans can be used, and it is possible to differentiate peaks from background with practice and experience. However, the limit of detection is not so readily defined.

2. SYSTEMIC FACTORS OF THE SAMPLE

Sample Composition. Many factors of sample composition affect the sensitivity such as absorption/enhancement of the radiation emitted from the element to be determined by another element or elements in the sample. These effects can be studied by reference to the values of mass-absorption coefficients and absorption edges tabulated in Tables 1 and 5 of Chap. 1. The net result of absorption/enhancement is dependent on the relative wavelengths of emitted radiation and absorption edges as shown in Fig. 5 of Chap. 1 and tabulated in Table 17 of Chap. 36.

Farquhar and English[4] show a nine-fold effect on the sensitivity for thorium in a matrix of lithium fluoride compared to a matrix of tungstic oxide. Bernstein[5] indicates relative sensitivities for KCl in various host materials. Comprehensive evaluations of the effects of different host materials on sensitivity are presented by Dwiggins[6] for organic substances and by Mitchell and Hopper[7] for inorganic substances.

Sample Preparation. Some elements can be determined by x-ray spectroscopy in the total bulk of the host material, and others require separation to yield a concentrate of the element as an aliquot of the original host material.

Campbell, Brown, and Thatcher[8] show a classification of these samples as 1 and 2 respectively and list 43 references concerning different sample species in both classes.

Chapter 33 of this Handbook has a comprehensive coverage of many considerations in sample preparation and significant effects on sensitivity.

Sensitivity can be seriously reduced if there is too much dilution of the original sample with an obvious extreme to a possible concentration below the detection limit. There are advantages for dilution in instances where the concentration is sufficiently high and the sensitivity can be improved by addition of material with low absorption characteristics. This can also be done to reduce self-absorption by the element to be determined where the slope of the calibration curve may approach zero for a range of concentration near 100 per cent of the element.

Rose, Adler, and Flanagan[9] show the effects of four different dilution mixtures on the sensitivity for silicon. Hooper[10] also reports some dilution effects of borax fusions for magnesium, aluminum, silicon, calcium, and manganese. Welday, Baird, McIntyre, and Madlem[11] made a thorough study of types and ratios of diluents in fusions applicable to rock analysis. Goldman and Anderson[12] varied the type and ratios of briquetting agents to note the effects on sensitivity for strontium in bone ash and limestone.

Concentration procedures make it possible to determine compositions that would otherwise be below detectable limits for the element in the original bulk sample. Reported sensitivity values are generally obtained by calculation of the results for the concentrate by material balance back to the composition of the original sample. These techniques may involve ion-exchange resins (Chap. 34, Sec. 15, and Chap. 37, Sec. 2); ashing (Chap. 37, Sec. 2); organometallic complexes (Chap. 36, Sec. 17, and Chap. 37, Sec. 2); inorganic oxides (Chap. 36, Sec. 17); or other mechanical and chemical means for concentrating the desired element to improve sensitivity.

Carpenter, Nishi, and Fehler[13] report results for vanadium, chromium, manganese. iron, cobalt, nickel, and copper impurities in beryllium. Blank and Heller[14] separated zirconium from uranium to determine trace concentrations with good sensitivity. Use of ion-exchange resins by Miles, Doremus, and Valent[15] to concentrate traces of chromium, vanadium, niobium, tantalum, arsenic, cobalt, molybdenum, rhenium, antimony, tin, strontium, and thallium in titanium alloys yielded good sensitivities. Papers impregnated with ion-exchange resins were evaluated by Campbell, Spano, and Green[3] and Hubbard and Green[16] for 28 cations and anions, and an excellent tabulation of sensitivities is given.

There are many modes of sample mounting, and the effects on sensitivity should be considered with regard to sample area and sample bulk or thickness. When samples with less than the normal area or critical thickness are examined (Chap. 36, Tables 2 and 3), the sensitivity must be evaluated for the particular setup.

Some of the results for clinical analyses by Natelson et al.[17] and Mathies and Lund[18] represent typical determinations for small samples. Use of thin films is discussed by Finnegan[19] and Salmon[20] where the samples are less than infinitely thick.

3. CHARACTERISTICS OF THE INSTRUMENT

The basic x-ray emission spectrograph includes means for production of primary x-rays, exposure of the sample to the primary x-ray beam, collimation and diffraction of the fluorescent x-rays from the sample, and detection of the fluorescent x-ray intensities. Design and applications of the components of the basic instrument can strongly influence resultant sensitivities.

Spectrograph. The block diagram of Fig. 1, Chap. 30, indicates the normal components of an instrument.

X-ray Production. The stability of the high-voltage transformer and rectifiers is extremely critical. Relative merits of the various types of power supplies for the x-ray tubes are discussed in Sec. 3 of Chap. 2.

X-ray Tube. The general design features of x-ray tubes are outlined in Chap. 2, Sec. 2.

The important effects of the x-ray tube on sensitivity are involved with (1) choice of target material—line spectra and continuum characteristics, (2) total power that can be applied—kv/ma ratings, and (3) design features such as window thickness, internal geometry of the cathode and anode, and external dimensions and shape that determine the closeness of coupling the primary beam and the sample surface.

The absorption/enhancement effects previously mentioned in regard to sample composition can also be considered in a similar way for the effects of the primary x-ray beam on sensitivity for the element to be determined. If the primary x-ray beam from the tube has characteristic line radiation or a high continuum just on the short wavelength side of the absorption edge of the element to be determined, the fluorescent x-ray intensity for the element will be higher than for another element where the continuum and line intensity are not so high at the absorption edge. These effects are summarized in the comparison of tungsten and molybdenum tubes in Fig. 4 of Chap. 35.

The importance of choice of target material is also demonstrated in the improved excitation of elements with atomic numbers 22 and lower by chromium in comparison to tungsten radiation. Comparable sensitivities are 0.8 cps/0.01 per cent Al for a chromium tube and 0.24 cps/0.01 per cent Al for a tungsten tube.[21] Net peak intensities for magnesium, aluminum, silicon, phosphorus, and sulfur improve about four-fold by using chromium instead of tungsten.[22]

Other tube target materials are compared as they affect the sensitivity for molybdenum, uranium, tungsten, iron, calcium, sulfur, and aluminum.[23]

The characteristic lines of the target element will interfere with determination of low concentrations of that element and sometimes other elements in the sample. A simple approach for improvement of the sensitivity by the use of filters in the primary x-ray beam is discussed in Sec. 3 of Chap. 35.

The power of the x-ray tube can be varied in the level of accelerating potential (kv) for electrons between the cathode and the anode and in the electron emission efficiency from heating the cathode filament (ma). The first important consideration is that the kv input to the x-ray tube exceeds the excitation potential of the element (Table 1 of Chap. 1). A nominal value of at least twice the excitation potential is used for the kv to get good sensitivity. The filament current (ma) can then be adjusted within the power rating of the tube to get the maximum power in the primary x-ray beam from the tube.

Some effects of 100 kv vs. 50 kv are shown in Figs. 10 and 11 of Chap. 35.

Alexander[24] indicates x-ray fluorescence intensity as a function of x-ray tube voltage for barium, silver, strontium, arsenic, osmium, manganese, and calcium.

The relative values of tube kv and excitation potential can sometimes be used to advantage to improve sensitivity for an element with a longer wavelength by using kv low enough to avoid excitation of the element with a shorter wavelength, as discussed in Sec. 1 of Chap. 31.

The importance of window thickness is demonstrated by Dryer[25] in a comparison of chromium and tungsten tubes.

Construction details and design parameters for the types of x-ray tubes and other-components most successfully used for soft x-ray emission spectroscopy in the 10- to 150-Å region are discussed in Chap. 38.

Sample Chamber. The housing of the spectrograph includes a shielded chamber for exposure of the sample surface to the primary x-ray beam. Important factors with respect to sensitivity are the close coupling of the primary x-ray beam and the sample surface to get the maximum effective excitation of elements in the sample and a geometric arrangement to get a proper view of the sample surface by the collimation system with no viewing of other surfaces of the sample chamber.

Collimators. The function of the collimators is discussed in Chap. 31, Sec. 2, and demonstrated in Fig. 13 of Chap. 31 and Figs. 5, 6, and 7 of Chap. 35. Optimum sensitivity for elements in simple mixtures may be obtained with very broad and open collimation with poor resolution but, as the mixtures get more complex, the resolution must be improved and the sensitivity will be reduced. In general, the collimation must produce a good balance of net line intensities with acceptable resolution and the sensitivities will be affected accordingly.

A good demonstration of the mathematical considerations vs. experimental data is given by Henke[2] for the determination of fluorine.

Analyzing Crystal. Various diffraction crystals can be chosen, and widely varying sensitivities for an element can be obtained with different crystals. The choice of crystals is detailed in Sec. 6 of Chap. 31; Fig. 19 of Chap. 31 summarizes the optimum ranges for many of the common analyzing crystals.

Five different crystals are compared by Wagner and Bryan[26] with a tabulation of sensitivities for sulfur, phosphorus, silicon, and aluminum.

In addition to the selection of crystals by chemical composition and crystalline orientation, physical conditions and manipulations may produce improved sensitivities as outlined in Chap. 31, Sec. 6.

Gratings are used in place of crystals for some soft x-rays; general considerations are discussed in Sec. 3 of Chap. 38. Gratings and crystals are also compared by Nicholson and Wittry.[27]

Detector. A comprehensive consideration of detectors used for x-ray emission spectroscopy is covered in Chap. 3. Details of requirements, comparison, selection, use, etc., are listed in Secs. 3 to 6 of Chap. 3. Guides for selection are shown in Fig. 12 of Chap. 3 and Fig. 2 of Chap. 31.

High sensitivities from detector operation are dependent upon efficient measurements of net peak intensities above background and signal stability. A suggested procedure for operation of a scintillation counter for the wavelength range of 0.15 to 2.85 Å is discussed in Sec. 3 of Chap. 35 and some factors affecting sensitivity are shown in Figs. 8 and 9 of Chap. 35.

Detectors for special application to soft x-ray detection are discussed in Sec. 4 of Chap. 38.

Data Registers. Most instrumentation will include scaler and rate-meter circuits with associated printers and/or recorders for indication and recording of the experimental data.

The scaler is generally used for fixed-count or fixed-time determinations at a particular wavelength, and the rate meter is used when scanning a range of wavelengths. Although there is a difference in purpose in these two methods, sensitivity may be the most important factor in selection of the preferred technique.

Experimental parameters for fixed-time and fixed-count techniques are discussed in the sections on statistics (Chap. 3, Sec. 10, and Chap. 36, Sec. 21). A comparison of fixed-time to fixed-count results is given in the latter section.

Experimental parameters and a standard operating procedure for a scanning technique are given in Sec. 3 of Chap. 35. Important characteristics of the rate meter are illustrated in Figs. 32 and 34 of Chap. 3.

Electronic Discrimination. A properly used discriminator establishes a rejection threshold for noise pulses and improves the sensitivity based on net peak intensity above background. A pulse-height analyzer can improve the sensitivity in cases where higher-order diffractions of shorter wavelengths overlap a first-order diffraction at a particular angle. Effects and conditions of electronic discrimination are discussed in Sec. 7 of Chap. 3 and Sec. 1 of Chap. 31. A method of synchronization of electronic discrimination with goniometer movement for scanning is discussed in Sec. 3 and shown in Fig. 13 of Chap. 35.

Kiley[28] indicates the effects of pulse-height analysis on sensitivities for silicon in iron, aluminum in nickel, and sulfur in oil.

Helium or Vacuum. The use of controlled atmospheres of helium or vacuum in the optical path of the spectrograph improves the sensitivity for many elements and is necessary for the determination of some. There is about a four-fold improvement at 3 Å as shown in Fig. 12 of Chap. 35. Alexander[24] reports a 2.8-fold increase for manganese-K and a 74-fold increase for calcium-K radiation when helium is used to displace the air in the instrument chamber.

Advantages of a vacuum compared to helium are reported by Hoskins[29] to show a 24 per cent improvement of sensitivity for magnesium. Requirements for determinations of sodium, aluminum, silicon, potassium, and calcium are outlined by Williams.[30]

More discussion of the vacuum system for soft x-rays is included in Sec. 5 of Chap. 38.

Filters. Sensitivities can be improved by the use of filters in several ways for different purposes. As previously mentioned, a filter on the window of the x-ray tube can absorb the characteristic line spectra of the target material and allow determination of that element in the sample. Sensitivity is also improved for other elements in the sample that have characteristic wavelengths near line spectra from the target element. The general approach is outlined in Sec. 3 of Chap. 35.

A filter in the primary x-ray beam from the tube will also reduce some of the high background due to continuum to improve resolution of net peak intensities above background.

Filters can also be used in the fluorescent x-ray beam from the sample. Specific absorption edges are important in the use of filters with this approach to assist in resolution of weak peaks from the long-wavelength tail of a peak for another element present in high concentrations, i.e., filter of europium to resolve cobalt K-alpha from iron K-beta.[31]

The use of Ross filters is discussed by Dunne[32] for the determination of aluminum and silicon by nondispersive analysis.

4. EXPERIMENTAL DETERMINATION OF SENSITIVITY

An easy method for calculation of sensitivities is based on the typical form of a calibration curve for a binary system plotted on Cartesian coordinates with net peak intensity as a function of concentration. This plot normally shows a linear relationship at low concentrations, and the sensitivity corresponds to the slope of the calibration curve. As the curve departs from linearity, it is necessary to determine the slope of the tangent at the point of interest to evaluate sensitivity. Calculations for this case are discussed by Lambert[33] for a range of uranium concentrations in aluminum rods. His values in Table V of the reference show the changes in sensitivity for a range from 165 cps/per cent uranium for 2 per cent uranium to 31 cps/per cent uranium for 20 per cent uranium.

The same approach can be used when the concentration of one element varies in a multicomponent host material with the relative concentrations of the host elements remaining essentially constant. A typical curve for this case is shown in Fig. 22 of Chap. 35. These results can be calculated to show a sensitivity of 16,000 cps/per cent uranium.

When the concentration of one of the host elements varies by known amounts, a family of curves may be produced such as shown in Fig. 4 of Chap. 36. Sensitivities for zinc can be calculated for each curve with barium concentration as the parameter for identification of the values. These values are 1,500, 1,200, and 1,000 cps/per cent Zn for the curves with 0.0, 0.3, and 0.6 per cent barium, respectively.

Random variations of many elements in the host material may make it impractical to consider host-element concentrations as parameters. Minerals are commonly in this class and may be classified for simple calibration curves on the basis of some instrumentally measured systemic property. A very common procedure is the use of scattered radiation (background) as a parameter. This is shown by Salmon.[34]

5. TYPICAL SENSITIVITIES

Sensitivities should always be qualified with regard to the sample species, element, and range of concentration, as well as all of the pertinent experimental conditions. Values in the literature have some usefulness as "figures of merit," but it is difficult to make absolute comparisons of results by different investigators because qualifying conditions are commonly not reported in sufficient detail. An excellent form that could serve as a suggested model is shown in Table 1 of Chap. 33. These results reported by Campbell, Leon, and Thatcher show sensitivities for several elements in water solutions.

The fundamental review (X-ray Absorption and Emission) in *Analytical Chemistry* is a good source for references to current sensitivities with different procedures. In 1966, Campbell, Brown, and Thatcher[8] showed 343 references for articles about 54 different elements in several types of samples.

The importance of checking current reports is demonstrated by noting the very rapid improvement recently in light-element sensitivities reported by Henke[2,35,36] for 1964–1966. These intensities are given for 53.3 per cent oxygen in silicon dioxide:

1964.............	150 cps
1965.............	8,600 cps
1966.............	13,290 cps

Similar trends are noted in the same articles for other elements. An increase from 2,500 cps in 1965 to 3,840 cps in 1966 for 56.4 per cent nitrogen in boron nitride is reported. Intensities for 100 per cent carbon in graphite increased from 13,000 cps to 21,680 cps in the same years.

Reported sensitivities may indicate the best value for the individual element obtained by choices of optimum experimental conditions for each element. Data of this type of study are tabulated for water solutions in Table 1 of Chap. 33. The choice of x-ray tube current, analyzing crystal, helium or air, and type of detector is indicated for each value. Sensitivities for the same element based on L and K lines are shown in some cases. A fixed-time procedure was used for intensity measurements of peak and background.

In chart-scanning procedures for several elements in the same sample, the experimental conditions are chosen to get the best average results for the group of elements. This general approach is discussed in Chap. 35. Sensitivities for K and L lines for several elements with atomic numbers 22 to 92 are shown in Figs. 1 and 2. These results were obtained with a set of fixed operating conditions as tabulated in Table 1. Synthetic standards with 0.25, 0.50, 0.75, and 1.00 per cent of the element mixed in −325 mesh silica as a host material were used.

Table 1. Operating Conditions for Figs. 1 and 2

Philips 100-kv spectrograph, constant-potential, inverted optics.
Samples examined as loose powders in EC16 CaPlugs with 14-mil Mylar windows.
FA-100 tungsten target x-ray tube.
Scintillation detector operated at 900 volts direct current.
Lithium fluoride analyzing crystal.
4-in. × 0.005-in. spacing parallel-blade collimator between sample and crystal, and 1½-in. × 0.023-in. spacing parallel-blade collimator between crystal and detector.
Air at atmospheric pressure in optical path.
Goniometer scanning speed 16° per min.
Rate-meter time constant 0.24 sec.
Sample spinner used.
Discriminator but no pulse-height analysis used.

Higher sensitivities would be obtained by use of 100 kv for elements of atomic number greater than 38 (Chap. 35, Fig. 10) and by use of helium or vacuum for elements of atomic number less than 30 (Chap. 35, Fig. 12).

Hudgens and Pish[37] describe an x-ray spectroscopic study of halogen-gas mixtures. They report intensities of 1,800 cpm for both gases in a 50-50 mixture of bromine and iodine. Typical sensitivity values are not available because of the limited work in this area. Because of the nature of these systems, comprehensive description of pressure-temperature-volume relationships is required to properly denote sensitivities.

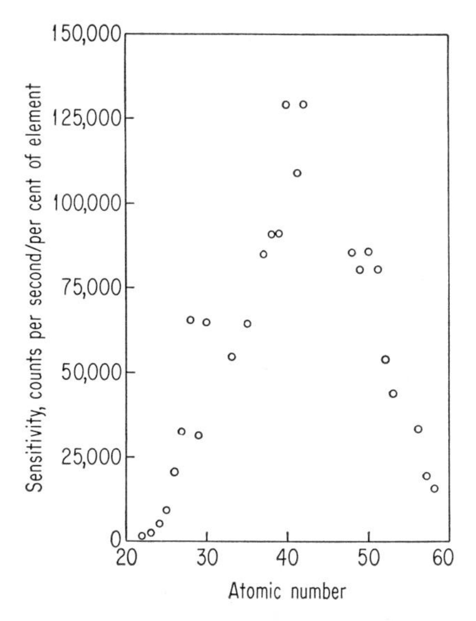

FIG. 1. Sensitivities for *K*-alpha wavelengths of elements in synthetic standards with operating conditions given in Table 1.

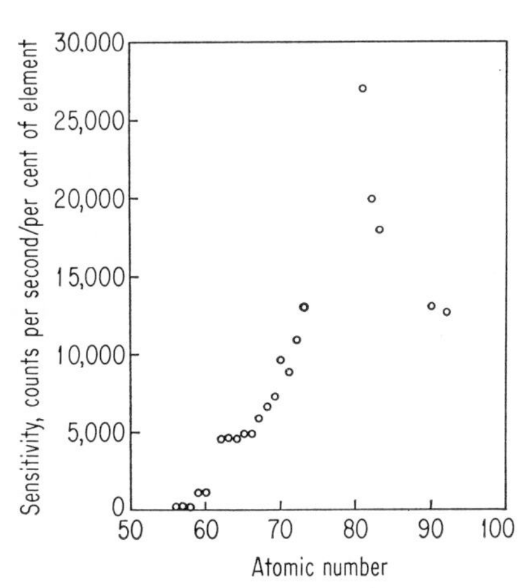

FIG. 2. Sensitivities for *L*-alpha wavelengths of elements in synthetic standards with operating conditions given in Table 1.

The sensitivity values for other types of samples also require considerable description of the physical character of the specimen. Kaelble and McEwan[38] report a value for silica-coated paper of 200 cps for paper containing 0.25 lb silica per 1,000 sq ft of paper surface.

Limits of detection are also important in the evaluation of experimental procedures and results. By using the limit of detection and the sensitivity, it is possible to determine the minimum concentration of the element that can be detected. It is interesting to note in Table 1 of Chap. 33 that the highest values for sensitivity do not always produce the lowest values for minimum detectable concentration.

REFERENCES CITED

1. L. Birks, *X-ray Spectrochemical Analysis*, p. 54, Interscience Publishers, Inc., New York, 1959.
2. B. Henke, *Advan. X-ray Anal.*, **7**:460(1964).
3. W. Campbell, E. Spano, and T. Green, *Norelco Reptr.*, **XIII**:77 (1966).
4. M. Farquhar and M. English, *Advan. X-ray Anal.*, **7**:584 (1964).
5. F. Bernstein, *Advan. X-ray Anal.*, **8**:231 (1965).
6. C. W. Dwiggins, *Anal. Chem.*, **36**:1577 (1964).
7. B. Mitchell and F. Hopper, *Appl. Spectry.*, **20**:172 (1966).
8. W. Campbell, J. Brown, and J. Thatcher, *Anal. Chem.*, **38**:416R (1966).
9. H. Rose, I. Adler, and F. Flanagan, *Appl. Spectry.*, **17**:83 (1963).

10. P. Hooper, *Anal. Chem.*, **36**:1271 (1964).
11. E. Welday, A. Baird, D. McIntyre, and K. Madlem, *Am. Mineralogist*, **49**:889 (1964).
12. M. Goldman and R. Anderson, *Anal. Chem.*, **37**:718 (1965).
13. L. Carpenter, J. Nishi, and R. Fehler, *Appl. Spectry.*, **20**:359 (1966).
14. G. Blank and H. Heller, *Norelco Reptr.*, **IX**:23 (1962).
15. M. Miles, E. Doremus, and D. Valent, *Norelco Reptr.*, **XIII**:32 (1966).
16. G. Hubbard and T. Green, *Anal. Chem.*, **38**:428 (1966).
17. S. Natelson, A. Vassilevsky, K. de Paritosh, and W. Whitford, *J. Microchem.*, **8**:295 (1964).
18. J. Mathies and P. Lund, *Norelco Reptr.*, **VII**:134 (1960).
19. J. Finnegan, *Advan. X-ray Anal.*, **5**:500 (1962).
20. M. Salmon, *Advan. X-ray Anal.*, **5**:398 (1962).
21. *Theory and Practice of X-ray Fluorescence,* Philips Electronic Instruments, Mount Vernon, New York.
22. *Ibid.* p. 18.
23. *Ibid*, p. 13.
24. G. Alexander, *Appl. Spectry.*, **18**:1 (1964).
25. H. Dryer, *Advan. X-ray Anal.*, **7**:615 (1964).
26. J. Wagner and F. Bryan, *Appl. Spectry.*, **18**:157 (1964).
27. J. Nicholson and D. Wittry, *Advan. X-ray Anal.*, **7**:508 (1964).
28. W. Kiley, *Norelco Reptr.*, **VII**:143 (1960).
29. J. Hoskins, *Norelco Reptr.*, **VII**:111 (1960).
30. J. Williams, *Norelco Reptr.*, **XI**:120 (1964).
31. M. Salmon, *Advan. X-ray Anal.*, **6**:301 (1963).
32. J. Dunne, *Norelco Reptr.*, **XIII**:21 (1966).
33. M. Lambert, *Norelco Reptr.*, **VI**:37 (1959).
34. M. Salmon, *Advan. X-ray Anal.*, **3**:139 (1960).
35. B. Henke, *Advan. X-ray Anal.*, **8**:272 (1965).
36. B. Henke, *Advan. X-ray Anal.*, **9**:430 (1966).
37. C. Hudgens and G. Pish, *Anal. Chem.*, **37**:414 (1965).
38. E. Kaelble and G. McEwan, *Norelco Reptr.*, **VII**:98 (1960).

GENERAL REFERENCES

Clark, G. L. (ed.), *Encyclopedia of X-rays and Gamma Rays*, Reinhold Publishing Corp., New York, 1963.

Liebhafsky, H., H. Pfeiffer, E. Winslow, and P. Zemany, *X-ray Absorption and Emission in Analytical Chemistry*, John Wiley & Sons, Inc., New York, 1960.

Chapter 33

SPECIMEN-PREPARATION TECHNIQUES

John F. Croke and William R. Kiley

Philips Electronic Instruments

1. INTRODUCTION

X-ray emission spectroscopy is a nondestructive, reliable, precise, accurate, and simple method of chemical analysis. It is the most versatile of all instrumental analytical methods with respect to the variety of sample forms to which it is readily applicable. The gamut of sample size extends from the micron sample area of the electron-probe microanalyzer to the meters of metal sheet examined by the coating-weight gauge. The range of elements presently includes the entirety of the periodic table down to and including the element boron, atomic number 5. Today samples are analyzed routinely and elements are determined quantitatively which, as little as 5 years ago, would have been considered beyond the scope and capability of the x-ray method.

The key to the successful application of this method to the solution of the routine as well as the unusual analytical problem is to be found in the area of sample preparation. In order to cover this important topic in a manner that is meaningful both to the beginner and to the experienced worker, a simple mathematical procedure for evaluating sample preparation as well as other variables will be discussed, followed by some general rules to guide experimentation in sample preparation. Finally, sample-preparation techniques for the handling of static and dynamic samples will be discussed in detail.

2. THE DETERMINATION OF THE VARIATION DUE TO SAMPLE PREPARATION

In x-ray spectrochemical analysis the accuracy of the answer that is obtained is defined by the agreement with known composition, as determined by an absolute method of analysis such as chemical analysis. A calibration curve or a calibration curve and a correction factor can be used to adjust the x-ray results to known chemical values, so that the accuracy of the method is approximately as good as the attainable precision. The precision of the method is defined as the ability to repeat x-ray intensity measurements, all variables being included. The precision can be expanded to include repeatability over long or short periods of instrument operating time.

In order to evaluate properly the effects of sample preparation on the overall precision associated with the x-ray intensity measurement, a method of separating the sample-preparation variable from the other variables present at the time of the x-ray measurement is described.

The variation due to sample preparation cannot be measured directly but can only be determined by defining the total variation of measured data and subtracting out the effect of all other variations from the total. Thus the variation due to the sample preparation is arrived at by the process of elimination.

The following are contributing factors to the total variation of the measured data:

1. The counting error in the x-ray measurement.
2. Variation associated with the instrument operation. This includes the setting of angles, crystals, electronics, detectors, kv and ma, and other operating parameters.
3. Instrument variation. This would include long- and short-term drift of the x-ray generator, power supplies, and other instrument parameters.
4. Specimen heterogeneity.

The counting error in the x-ray measurement is dependent only on the number of pulses accumulated for the intensity measurement and this value can be readily calculated. The variation associated with the instrument operation is minimized only by the careful and experienced worker. The instrumental variation has a limiting factor that is usually associated with the stability of the generator. An important practical limitation in quantitative spectrochemical analysis occurs when the instrumental variation becomes the limiting factor in the precision of a single x-ray measurement, rather than the number of intensity pulses accumulated. It is important to know that a point is reached where the accumulation of more intensity pulses will not improve the precision of a single x-ray measurement. In general, specimen heterogeneity accounts for the major variation of the measured data. Methods for determining this variation will be discussed.

Since the variation due to sample preparation cannot be measured directly, a mathematical treatment is required. As often stated in the literature,[1,2,3] the total variation of the measured data can be expressed by Eq. (1):

$$\sigma_T = \left(\frac{\Sigma_d{}^2}{N-1}\right)^{1/2} \tag{1}$$

where σ_T = total variation, expressed as the standard deviation
N = number of readings
d = deviation of each reading from the average

The total variation can also be determined from the square root of the sum of the squares of each variation present at the time of the intensity measurement. Thus the total variation is also expressed by Eq. (2):

$$\sigma_T = (\sigma^2_{\text{s.p.}} + \sigma^2_{\text{x-ray}} + \sigma^2_{\text{instr}} + \sigma^2_{\text{oper}})^{1/2} \tag{2}$$

where σ_T = total variation, expressed as the standard deviation
$\sigma_{\text{s.p.}}$ = sample-preparation variation
$\sigma_{\text{x-ray}}$ = standard counting error
σ_{instr} = instrument variation
σ_{oper} = errors of instrument operation

The Counting Error. From Eq. (2) it is obvious that each of the individual variations due to x-ray counting error, instrument variation, and errors of instrument operation must be determined in order to calculate the sample-preparation variation.

Since the generation of x-ray quanta is a random rather than a constant-rate phenomenon, the variation expected in a single x-ray measurement will be statistical and can be calculated from Eq. (3):

$$\sigma_{\text{x-ray}} = N^{1/2} \tag{3}$$

where $\sigma_{\text{x-ray}}$ = standard counting error expressed as the standard deviation
N = number of intensity pulses accumulated

The relative counting error, which expresses the standard counting error as a per cent of the measured quantity, is determined by Eq. (4):

$$\text{Per cent } \sigma_{\text{x-ray}} = 100(N)^{1/2}/N = 100/N^{1/2} \tag{4}$$

Thus the larger the total number of intensity pulses accumulated, the smaller will be the relative counting error. In all cases, the relative counting error defines the best possible precision that can be attained for a particular determination.

For example, if one wishes to determine the nickel content of a stainless steel to 1 per cent of the amount present, the minimum number of counts to be accumulated at the nickel-line position would be

$$\begin{aligned} 1 \text{ per cent} &= 100/N^{1/2} \\ N^{1/2} &= 100 \\ N &= 10{,}000 \text{ pulses} \end{aligned}$$

To accumulate fewer pulses would be equivalent to introducing an error that is greater than the accuracy requirement. As a general rule, if an element is to be determined to 1 per cent of the amount present, then sufficient intensity pulses should be accumulated to reduce the relative counting error to ± 0.1 per cent. For the case described, this would require the accumulation of 1,000,000 nickel intensity pulses. This is done to keep the contribution of $\sigma^2_{\text{x-ray}}$ on the right-hand side of Eq. (2) as small as possible.

Instrument Variation and Errors of Instrument Operation. The instrument variation is defined as the ability of the instrument to reproduce x-ray intensity measurements on a given sample within a period of time. In order to exclude the sample-preparation variation, replicate measurements are taken on a single sample devoid of x-ray orientation effects. To exclude errors associated with instrument operation, the replicate measurements can be taken with a given set of operating parameters that remain fixed. Thus Eq. (2) can be reduced to Eq. (5):

$$\sigma_T = (\sigma^2_{\text{x-ray}} + \sigma^2_{\text{instr}})^{1/2} \tag{5}$$

With σ_T known from Eq. (1) and $\sigma_{\text{x-ray}}$ from Eq. (3), σ_{instr} is determined. An example of the determination of σ_{instr} is shown below where replicate measurements were made on a cement sample for Ca $K\alpha$ radiation.

No.	Total counts	d	d^2
1	7,130,816	8,612	74,166,544
2	7,128,076	5,872	34,480,384
3	7,119,973	2,231	4,977,361
4	7,122,878	674	454,276
5	7,112,338	9,866	95,337,956
6	7,119,146	3,058	9,351,364
Avg.	7,122,204		Σ218,767,885

From Eq. (1) the total variation of the measured data can be calculated:

$$\sigma_T = \left(\frac{218{,}767{,}885}{5}\right)^{1/2} = 6{,}615$$

$$\sigma_T \text{ per cent} = \frac{6{,}615 \times 100}{7{,}122{,}204} = 0.091 \text{ per cent}$$

Since $\sigma_T^2 = \sigma^2_{\text{x-ray}} + \sigma^2_{\text{instr}}$,

$$\sigma_{\text{instr}} = (\sigma_T^2 - \sigma^2_{\text{x-ray}})^{1/2} = (43{,}753{,}577 - 7{,}122{,}204)^{1/2} = 6{,}052 \text{ or } 0.085 \text{ per cent}$$

Using the above technique, the instrument variation can be determined for both short and long time durations.

Errors of instrument operation are those variations associated with a change in the intensity measurement caused by the improper settings of angles, crystals, electronics, detectors, kv and ma, and other operating parameters. In the majority of cases careful attention to those details will exclude their occurrence. The errors of instrument operation can be determined by taking replicate intensity measurements on a singular sample whereby all operating parameters are reestablished for each intensity measurement taken. Thus Eq. (2) can be reduced to Eq. (6):

$$\sigma_T = (\sigma^2_{\text{x-ray}} + \sigma^2_{\text{instr}} + \sigma^2_{\text{oper}})^{1/2} \tag{6}$$

where σ_T is known from Eq. (1), $\sigma_{\text{x-ray}}$ is known from Eq. (3), and σ_{instr} is known from Eq. (5), thus permitting the determination of σ_{oper}.

Variations Due to Sample Preparation. The variation due to sample preparation is that variation in the x-ray intensity measurement associated with replicate introduction of prepared specimens of the same sample to the x-ray instrument. The variation due to sample preparation is determined from Eq. (2) once the other errors are determined.

The following example will serve to illustrate the method for determining the variation due to sample preparation. Assume that the weight per cent of calcium oxide in finished cement is to be determined at the 66 per cent level with a relative standard deviation of ±0.3 per cent of the amount present. Assume also that five replicate specimens of the same sample were prepared by grinding five aliquots of the cement in a grinder for 3 min and compacting a single wafer or pellet from each ground aliquot. A single intensity measurement on each sample at the calcium $K\alpha$ line position generated the following data:

Specimen No.	*Total count*
1	6,578,577
2	6,600,331
3	6,595,967
4	6,604,534
5	6,598,973
Avg.	6,595,676

The relative counting standard deviation, as calculated from Eq. (4), is

$$\text{Per cent } \sigma_{\text{x-ray}} = 100/N^{1/2} = 100/(6{,}595{,}700)^{1/2} = \pm 0.04 \text{ per cent}$$

The total standard deviation in these x-ray measurements is calculated from Eq. (1) to be ±10,000 counts or ±0.15 per cent.

If σ_{instr} is 0.1 per cent and σ_{oper} is neglected, the standard deviation due to sample preparation can be calculated from Eq. (2) as follows:

$$\sigma_{\text{s.p.}} = (\sigma_T{}^2 - \sigma^2_{\text{x-ray}} - \sigma^2_{\text{instr}} - \sigma^2_{\text{oper}})^{1/2}$$
$$S_{\text{s.p.}} = (0.15^2 - 0.04^2 - 0.1^2)^{1/2} = \pm 0.1 \text{ per cent}$$

It is obvious that the variation due to sample preparation contributes significantly to the total variation. When the total variation in the x-ray intensity measurements was referred to the calibration curve, it defined a variation of ±0.1 per cent CaO or ±0.15 per cent relative.

Sample-preparation techniques are adequate, therefore, when they reduce the variation due to sample preparation to a value where the overall precision required of the method is attainable.

All the above variations are concerned with the ability to provide precision in x-ray intensity measurements. Since x-ray intensity measurements are not absolute, they must be referred to a calibration curve constructed with appropriate standards. In this way, the precision of the x-ray intensity measurement can be related to the accuracy required.

A realistic value for the accuracy required for the determination of the element of interest must be made prior to any experimentation in sample preparation. This accuracy is derived from the requirements for control of a process or product. Accuracy requirements that are more stringent than necessary are expensive in time required for x-ray measurement and for specimen preparation.

Sample-preparation techniques are tantamount to time and money and for this reason the simplest type of sample handling should be attempted first. The variation associated with each attempt at sample preparation should be evaluated by Eq. (2), which relates the variation due to sample preparation, the total variation, the instrument variation, the counting error, and the errors of instrument operation.

3. SAMPLE-PREPARATION TECHNIQUES FOR STATIC SAMPLES

The sample presented to the instrument for analysis must be truly representative of

1. The bulk sample from which it was derived
2. The sample used for wet-chemical or some other absolute method of quantitative analysis

Since the analysis of samples by x-ray techniques is a surface phenomenon, care must be taken in surface preparation and in establishing a condition whereby the surface of the sample is representative of the bulk material.

There are two general categories of sampling techniques, static and dynamic sampling. A static sample can be defined as a batch sample the quantitative analysis of which is extrapolated to arrive at the analysis of the whole. This can be achieved on batch samples in either a manual or a programmed automatic x-ray instrument. A dynamic sample is a continuously moving sample whose moment-by-moment x-ray intensity data contribute to the analysis of the whole.

There are two dramatic differences in these techniques. First the static sample is representative of the sample as it existed 10 min, 30 min, or even 6 hr ago whereas a dynamic sample is a continuously changing sample, which by definition is representative of the most recent sample change. In static-sampling techniques, the analysis depends upon a single specimen and its preparation. In dynamic sampling, the analysis depends upon the averaging of a large number of momentary samples. Dynamic sampling entails the examination of larger quantities of samples during analysis, and in this way, it can be considered as being more representative of the whole.

Static-sampling techniques are suitable for systems with a relatively long response time or when the highest accuracy is required. Dynamic-sampling techniques are suitable for systems having a short response time or when trend information is desired. The two sampling techniques will be discussed separately.

Solid Samples. Solid samples are derived from metal, glasses, ceramics, plastics, rubber, minerals, and a vast array of other sources. Solid samples are convenient to handle, are readily prepared, and can be permanently stored. When a solid sample is selected for x-ray analysis, it must be truly representative of the bulk sample from which it was derived, as well as being representative of the sample selected for wet-chemical analysis. Therefore, the sample for x-ray analysis should be selected as proximate as possible to the portion used for wet-chemical analysis. A limited number of standards are available and may be purchased from National Bureau of Standards,[8] Bureau of Analyzed Standards; Spex Industries, Inc., 3880 Park Ave., Metuchen, N.J.; and from various professional societies. For cases where no standards are available, one must refer to wet-chemical analysis for standardization or convert the solid sample to a powder or solution where synthetic standards are more readily prepared.

In the preparation of solid samples care must be taken to surface the standards and unknowns in exactly the same manner. Preparation of solid samples consists of cutting out a piece of material that is dimensionally compatible with the sample cups of the spectrograph and grinding and polishing one surface to flatness. The texture introduced into the surface of the solid should be oriented in one direction and this orientation should be preserved from specimen to specimen when the samples are introduced into an instrument where sample rotation is not available. The higher the weight per cent and the lower the atomic number of the element to be determined, the more significant are the errors introduced by surface texture. Good optical-emission techniques in sample preparation[4] apply to the preparation of metal samples.

In general, surface finishing with a 120- or 180-grit dry-belt grinder is satisfactory. However, it has been found that surface preparation is critical when determinations in the order of ±0.5 per cent of the amount present are required or when it is necessary to minimize the effects of certain metallurgical differences. Borst[5] has reported the determination of nickel in the 30 to 50 per cent range to ±0.5 per cent of the amount present in nickel-iron alloys by a surface preparation that involves a double grinding on two new 240-grit sanding disks. The required surface reproducibility is attainable with the use of a second new sanding disk.

Additional care must be exercised when dealing with matrices containing soft elements such as lead. These soft elements will tend to smear over the surface of the sample during the surfacing operation, rendering the surface nonrepresentative of the remainder of the sample. Machining techniques have been devised which minimize the amount of soft-element smearing. "Fly cutting" is a common machining technique used in the preparation of specimens containing soft elements. In this technique, the cutting tool is passed over the surface of the sample in a series of interrupted strokes. This is contrasted to the usual lathe-surfacing technique whereby the cutting tool is continuously in contact with the surface of the sample as the sample is rotated. The fly-cutting technique generates less heat since the cutting tool is in less continuous contact with the specimen being surfaced. The use of sharp cutting tools is indispensable. Kilday and Michaelis[6] report that surface preparation was found to be a critical factor when a change occurs in the particle size of an undissolved constituent or in the metallurgical structure size. They obtained best results for lead in leaded steels using a final finish of ¼-micron diamond-dust abrasive. Similar results were obtained for the determination of silicon in hypereutectic silicon in aluminum alloys and for the analysis of white-cast-iron samples using metallographically polished surfaces.

All specimens should be degreased after surfacing, cutting, or grinding. This is particularly important in the determination of the light elements, where the radiation to be measured for analysis originates principally from the surface of the sample. The presence of grease or any other foreign matter will absorb this radiation before it can be detected and can introduce another error into the determination.

Handling Small Samples. The sample holders for the commercially available spectrographs are regimented with regard to the length, width, and height of sample that they will routinely accept. Small or odd-shaped samples present a handling and loading problem to the operator. In many instances, serious consideration should be given to the handling of such samples by solution techniques, and the reader is referred to the section of this chapter dealing with solutions.

Solid samples that are smaller than the opening of the sample holder can be accommodated by constructing a mask whose inner diameter corresponds to the smallest sample area to be handled and whose outer diameter corresponds to the inner diameter of the sample cup. If the sample for analysis is smaller than the area irradiated by the primary x-ray beam, then care must be exercised to locate the sample in the same area of the x-ray beam for each specimen loading.

The reproducibility of positioning of small specimens is critical because of the intensity gradient of primary radiation across the irradiated sample area. Random location of a small sample in the x-ray beam will introduce a large variation in the x-ray intensity measurement for analysis. Location of the circular mask opening in the center of the cup will eliminate this variable.

The mask should be constructed from a material that

1. Will not introduce interfering x-ray lines
2. Will adequately absorb the shortest characteristic x-ray radiation emitted from that area of sample beneath the mask
3. Will provide the necessary support for the routine introduction of specimens

The absorption of the shortest characteristic radiation from areas of sample beneath the mask is controlled by the atomic numbers of the material from which the mask is constructed and its thickness. The higher-atomic-numbered elements also produce more x-ray lines and the possibility of spectral interference with the line to be measured for analysis. The thickness of the mask should be minimal, in that the mask increases the sample to x-ray tube distance, resulting in a significant loss in x-ray intensity.

The mask thickness required from the absorption standpoint can be calculated from the usual absorption equation, using an arbitrary value such as 0.001 for I/I_0, the ratio of transmitted to incident intensity.

Odd-shaped samples can be conveniently converted to standard-sized samples. Commercially available button arc furnaces can be used to melt odd-shaped samples. This melt, when allowed to cool, can be solidified in the form of a conveniently shaped button which can be surfaced and used for x-ray data. This method lends itself to handling metal chips or rods which are electrically conductive. It is not readily adaptable when small amounts of sample are available for analysis. Wire samples can be melted and solidified in a button furnace as previously described. Care must be taken to consider the possible loss of those elements with a high vapor pressure when using a button furnace. Another alternative is to wrap the wire around a spool and present the wrapped spool for x-ray analysis. Again, serious consideration should be given to the solution technique. The decision to handle small and odd-shaped samples as solids or solutions should be based upon

1. The amount of time that is available to prepare the sample.
2. The atomic number of the elements to be determined. The light-element determinations can be detrimentally affected by solution techniques because of the necessity to dilute.
3. The concentration range of the elements of interest. High concentrations lend themselves to solution techniques, while low concentration ranges are more difficult.
4. The effect of the matrix on the determination of interest. Matrix effects are minimized by solution techniques where the solvent becomes the matrix.

Bulk-type attachments for x-ray spectrographs are available for the handling of large-sized samples. These bulk attachments find great usefulness in the x-ray spectrochemical analysis of finished machined pieces, where removing a small section for analysis damages the part. Commercially available bulk spectrographs can be readily modified to accept very large samples. If this modification is attempted, care should be exercised to

1. Maintain the specimen to x-ray tube distance as short as possible, and strictly reproducible from one sample to another
2. Keep the surface being analyzed flat, and representative of the entire sample
3. Establish proper shielding from stray radiation

Internal-standard techniques[7] to correct for matrix absorption and enhancement are not readily available, unless the internal-standard element can be conveniently added to the melt. Ratio measurements of intensity can be used, in which the intensity of the characteristic radiation is ratioed to the intensity of an x-ray tube line or background. These ratio data are most effective in reducing absorption and enhancement effects when the wavelength of interest and the reference wavelength lie on the same side of the absorption edge of the matrix element.

Powdered Samples. X-ray spectrochemical techniques are readily adaptable to the analysis of powdered samples. Sample preparation for the instrument is both rapid and simple, and samples can be kept permanently for future reference.

The powdered samples that are presented to the analytical laboratory originate from many sources and are usually in the form of converted bulk solids, particularly for ceramics, minerals, ores, etc. Metal chips, precipitates, ashed organic materials, and solutions evaporated to dryness may also be considered as sources of samples.

Preparation of Calibration Standards. There is a much greater flexibility in the preparation of powdered samples than is available in the solid samples previously discussed. A variety of calibration standards[8] are available from the National Bureau of Standards and from the manufacturers, the processors, and the vendors of materials. Professional societies have generated intraindustry standards which are also available for instrument calibration.

Standards for calibration can be made up by mixing known quantities of chemically pure powders in a manner that simulates the concentration range of the element in a matrix in which it is to be determined. Chemically pure powders should be mixed to homogeneity and the particle-size distribution of both calibration standards and samples for analyses should be as similar as possible.[9]

Reagent chemicals can be added to pure matrix powders to establish a concentration range of the element of interest. Such chemicals can be added as powders but the ultimate in homogeneity is realized by adding the reagent chemical as a solution, drying, and grinding.[7,10] The concentration range may also be adjusted by diluting the pure matrix powder. This procedure may produce a change in the intensity level of the x-ray background. A background subtraction from the peak intensity will usually correct for this change in the background intensity level. When the highest degree of sample homogeneity is demanded to satisfy the accuracy requirements of the determination, constituents of the powdered standards may be coprecipitated from solution. This procedure is required when there is a difference in the grinding characteristics of the samples to be analyzed and the standards that are available for instrument calibration.[11,12]

Some of the more elaborate techniques just discussed involve taking the powdered material into solution. If dilution is not a prohibitive factor, solution techniques may be more desirable; and the attention of the reader is directed to the section of this chapter covering solution techniques.

The commonest method used to develop a series of calibration standards is careful wet-chemical analysis on aliquot samples representative of the raw material or finished product to be controlled and the x-ray samples to be used for instrument calibration. These samples are selected to represent a concentration range of the element of interest.

Grinders for Powder Specimens. The grinding and pelletizing of powdered samples is routine in the preparation of powdered materials for x-ray analysis. Particle-size determination also provides useful information for arriving at optimum preparation procedures.

The goal to be achieved in the grinding of powdered samples is homogeneity in particle-size distribution rather than the ultimate in particle-size reduction. It is the homogeneity of particle-size distribution that produces reproducible x-ray intensity measurements from one replicate specimen preparation to another. Many grinders are commercially available that are proficient at this task. Such grinders fall into two general categories, namely, disk mills and ball mills.

The disk mill uses a series of concentric rings and a metal disk, all contained within a grinding vessel. The reduction of particle size is realized by the abrasive action of the disk against the concentric rings, and the rings against the walls of the grinding vessel, as the entire vessel is rotated about its vertical axis. Such mills* are capable of grinding up to 50 g of sample but work most efficiently on smaller-sized samples. A sufficient quantity of ground material can be handled for replicate specimen preparations as required, or for storage for future use as calibration standards. Hardened-steel vessels are usually supplied with such grinders, but tungsten carbide vessels are available to minimize contamination of powdered samples by wearing of the vessel itself. The above mills come in various sizes. The Shatterbox is available in two configurations, one with a grinding container with 100 ml capacity and the second with a rack for holding seven containers of 15 ml capacity each. The Bleuler rotary mill can effectively handle samples up to 100 g. The Laboratory Disc Mill is available with capacities of 100 ml, 250 ml, and a suspended production model having six containers each with a capacity of 100 ml.

Particle-size reduction is also accomplished in a paint-mixer-type ball mill by the impact of the steel balls with the walls of the grinding vessel, and with each other, as the vessel is oscillated in a figure-eight motion. Such mills† are capable of handling

* Shatterbox, Spex Industries, 3880 Park Ave., Metuchen, N.J.; Bleuler Mill, Applied Research Laboratories, Inc., 20200 West Outer Drive, Dearborn, Mich.; Laboratory Disc Mill, Angstrom, Inc., 2454 W. 38th St., Chicago, Ill.

† Mixer/Mill, Spex Industries; Pica grinder, Pitchford Scientific, 1901 Painters Run Rd., Pittsburgh, Pa.

limited quantities of sample, and the reduction in particle-size distribution is very dependent on the quantity of sample introduced per loading. The limitations to the reduction in particle size lie in the fact that the smaller particles buffer the grinding action on the larger particles, giving rise to a dependence of particle-size reduction on the initial weight of material introduced to the grinding vessel. To bypass this limitation, a ball mill* is commercially available that provides for the removal of those particles which are smaller than a specified screen size. The small particles are removed through a mesh screen by the action of a dried air stream, alternately introduced at opposite sides of the grinding vessel. Those particles so removed from the grinding vessel are gathered in a collecting bottle. A grinding operation of this type tends to segregate components of the matrix according to their ability to be ground. The soft components are removed first, and the more difficult to grind fractions follow. It is therefore imperative that all the samples introduced into the grinding vessel pass through the screen and that the ground material within the collecting bottle be mixed to restore homogeneity.

Pellet Presses and Accessories. Powders can be pressed into wafers by compacting the material within a die under suitable pressure. Pellet preparation of powders has the following advantages:

1. A reproducible density is established and maintained in replicate pellet preparations.
2. Pellets are self-supporting within the sample cups and do not require a film or membrane for support. Eliminating the need for a supporting membrane such as mylar enhances light-element sensitivity, particularly for the elements below phosphorus in atomic number. A 0.00025-in. mylar membrane will absorb 60 per cent of the aluminum radiation available from the sample for analysis.

A wide variety of hand-operated and motor-driven pellet presses are commercially available. Motor-driven presses are recommended when large numbers of samples are to be handled. Such presses have the additional advantage of a presettable maximum pressure that is reproduced by the press from one pellet preparation to another.

A selection of dies and plungers is also commercially available. The implements fall into two categories, those which form a pellet without benefit of a retaining ring and those which accommodate a retaining ring or receptacle in which the pellet is formed after compacting.

The use of retaining rings or receptacles for pellet formation lends greater permanency to the pellet and permits the pellet to be handled routinely without damage. The receptacles† are sufficiently inexpensive to be disposable, and since all the powder is contained within the receptacle, the cleaning of the die is minimal. Retaining rings can be constructed by cutting ¼-in. sections of aluminum or copper pipe, the outer diameter of which is dimensionally compatible with the spectrograph sample holder. Soft materials such as copper or aluminum are recommended, in that the ring or cap is deliberately crushed and distorted under compacting pressure. This distortion will permanently affix the pellet within the receptacle. Such receptacles are used but once and therefore must be disposable. A section of ¼-mil mylar, placed between the pressing plate and the powder to be compacted, will prevent the buildup of compacted powder on the pressing plate. Placing a paper section between the plunger and the powder to be compacted will allow the analyst to write on the sample for identification.

Retaining rings can be used so that they are not distorted in the pelletizing process. The plunger is so constructed that its outer diameter is somewhat smaller than the inner diameter of the ring. When pressure is applied by the plunger on the powder, the pellet is formed within the ring without distorting the ring. Such rings are reusable and are constructed from harder and more resilient materials such as low-alloy or stainless steel.

Pellets formed without benefit of a receptacle are generally compacted at higher pressure. A layer of soft material such as cornstarch, borax, or ethyl cellulose can be

* Selective Particle Size Grinder, Pitchford Scientific.

† Spec. Caps, Spex Industries; Handy-Kaps, Angstrom, Inc., 2454 W. 38th St., Chicago, Ill.

compacted on the side of the pellet not exposed to the x-ray beam to add greater strength to the pellet and to permit the pellet to be written on for identification.

Binders and Grinding Aids. The use of binders is helpful both to the formation of pellets upon compaction and to the grinding operation per se. Binders and grinding aids are generally soft organic materials such as wax, starch, ethyl cellulose, lucite, and detergents. These materials act as grinding aids, in that they bring about improved particle-size reduction and make cleaning the grinding vessel easier. The surfactant sodium alkyl lauryl sulfonate has found wide use as a grinding aid, particularly when the determination of sulfur is not of interest. Microcrystalline cellulose, marketed under the trade name of Avicel by the American Viscose Company of Marcus Hook, Pa., is an excellent binder material. The average particle size is about 50 microns, and the material contains no x-ray detectable elements beyond the parts per million concentration range.

Binders are added to the sample prior to the grinding operation, so that both mixing and grinding occur in one step. A binder is added in a weighed portion so that it makes up 5 to 20 per cent of the total weight of sample to be ground. The amount of binder added should be kept to a minimum, in that it tends to dilute the sample, but should be sufficient to form a reasonably permanent pellet. The weighing of binder and sample ensures optimum reproducibility from sample to sample.

Binders contain moisture which tends to be removed in vacuum- or helium-purged spectrographs.

Techniques for Powders. The optimum preparation of a powdered sample is dictated by the accuracy requirements of the work being done. This requirement should be carefully considered, in that it will determine the simplicity or the complexity of the sample-preparation routine.

The simplest method of sample preparation should be attempted first and the repeatability of the x-ray intensity data determined and evaluated in terms of weight per cent of the element to be determined. It is this variation that must be compatible with the accuracy requirements of the determination that have previously been determined.

If the sample preparation is singled out to be the major factor in the total intensity variation, then the sample-preparation error must be reduced by suitable means. Grinding and pelletizing of the sample are recommended. Particle-size effects substantially disappear if the powders are ground to minus 400 mesh or smaller. It is important that the calibration standards and the samples for analysis have the same particle-size distribution.

A number of techniques which have proved useful in handling powders are described below. Descriptions of actual examples may be found in Chap. 36.

Dilution Techniques. The chemical combination of the element of interest within the matrix will affect the intensity of the available characteristic radiation to be measured for analysis. This effect is caused by absorption or enhancement of the characteristic radiation by the combining elements. This phenomenon of absorption and enhancement will vary with both the atomic number of the combining elements and their weight per cent in the matrix. Any unpredictable variation in these factors will generate a corresponding intensity change independent of a change in the weight per cent of the element to be measured.

Heterogeneity[13] in powdered samples can be minimized by matrix dilution. In general, light-element diluents such as cornstarch, spectrographic graphite, and lithium carbonate are used.[14,15] In this way, the absorption properties of the matrix are predictably stabilized by the diluent. The use of light-element diluents will seriously affect the sensitivity of light-element analysis from both dilution and absorption. In this area, dilution techniques are not recommended.

External Standards. The use of external standards is helpful in some cases to compensate for matrix absorption and enhancement and in all cases to calibrate the x-ray instrumentation for long-term variations. An external standard is an x-ray intensity, measured from either a tube line, an element line of a material external to the sample, or scattered background that is used as a monitor for the element intensity that is being measured for analysis. The element intensity of the sample is ratioed to the intensity of the external standard, and this ratio is related to the weight per cent of the element in the standards. If the external standard line is affected by the matrix in the same manner as the element line, then the ratio will compensate for matrix variations. In all cases, however, this ratio is a calibration of the operation of the instrument at that particular moment in time and thus the use of ratios will minimize the effect of long- and short-term instrument variations.

A standard specimen can also be used to provide a reference intensity for elemental analysis. Moment-by-moment instrument calibration can be realized by ratioing the intensity of the element to that of the standard specimen and plotting intensity ratios rather than absolute intensity values against the weight per cent of the element. The use of these ratio data will compensate for long- and short-term instrument variations.

Internal Standards. The general principles of the internal-standard method have been described by Adler and Axelrod,[16] and in Chap. 36, Sec. 11, of this book. The internal-standard method[17] is based on a comparison of the intensity of a line emitted by the element to be determined with the intensity of a line from a neighboring standard element artificially introduced into the specimen in an accurately known concentration by weight. To carry out the analysis, it is assumed that this intensity ratio is proportional to the ratio of the concentrations by weight. Since the concentration of the reference standard remains constant through careful weighing, the change in intensity ratio is directly related to a change in the weight per cent of the element to be determined. In general, an internal-standard element is selected to fulfill the following conditions:

1. The enhancement and the absorption of the internal-standard element by the matrix should be as similar as possible to that of the element being determined.
2. The internal-standard element should not drastically alter the absorption characteristics of the matrix for other elements to be determined.
3. The x-ray intensity of the internal-standard element and the element to be determined should be approximately the same at the middle of the concentration range of interest.

Elements of one or two atomic numbers higher or lower than the element to be determined should be considered first. A Table of Emission and Critical Absorption Energies[18] or table of mass-absorption-coefficient values should be consulted to approximate the matrix absorption or enhancement of the element to be determined and the internal-standard element (see tables in Chap. 1).

The internal-standard technique reduces the dependence of the determination on the composition of the sample. Matrix-absorption and -enhancement effects are reduced, in that they affect the element and the standard to the same extent.

The disadvantages of this method are the extra time required to weigh out, add, and mix the internal-standard material to each sample and the need to measure and ratio two intensities.

Fusion Techniques. The fusion of a powdered sample is realized by mixing an aliquot of the powdered sample to be analyzed with a fluxing agent such as potassium pyrosulfate, sodium carbonate, or lithium tetraborate and heating the mixture within a platinum or graphite crucible to a preset temperature in order that the powdered sample may be taken into solution by the fluxing agent. The flux is allowed to cool and the resulting cast button is used as a specimen or is ground, pelletized, and presented to the x-ray spectrograph for analysis. The heterogeneity of the sample is destroyed in the fusion process, and the sample, after fusion, is free of enhancement and absorption effects related to heterogeneity.

A popular fusion technique has been described by Claisse.[19] Modifications of this technique have been used in the analysis of ceramics,[20] rare earths,[21] and nonmetallics.[22] Internal-standard[16] and matrix-dilution techniques have been applied and incorporated in the fusion technique. Fusion techniques, involving the use of potassium pyrosulfate in the determination of copper in mattes and slags, is reported by Cullen.[23] Fusion techniques were required to eliminate absorption and enhancement effects and heterogeneity in copper-slag samples when matrix dilution with powdered carbon and the addition of internal standards proved ineffective.

Fusion techniques for routine analysis have several disadvantages. The procedure is time-consuming and requires considerable care. The samples are diluted in the fusion in which the weight ratio flux to sample can be as high as 9:1. Andermann,[24] however, has described a minimum flux technique for the analysis of cements and raw mix, in which the weight ratio flux to sample is 1:1. The intensity of light element is attenuated not only by dilution but also by absorption in the flux. The fused pellets are usually stressed and sometimes require grinding and pelletizing before presentation to the x-ray spectrograph.

Fusion techniques do offer advantages inherent in no other specimen-preparation technique involving powdered samples. The composition of the sample after fusion is homogeneous. Standards are easily prepared, in that all constituents involved are taken into solid solution, with the flux as the matrix. Matrix effects are reduced by the leveling effect of the flux. Internal-standard techniques are easily applicable if necessary.

Solution Techniques. Solution techniques have the widest flexibility of application for samples involved in x-ray spectrochemical analysis. The commonest reasons for the use of solution techniques are the necessity to analyze samples in a variety of shapes and forms and the unavailability of standards for calibration in those shapes and forms.

The solution technique is an ideal vehicle for the presentation of those samples which are inconvenient or impractical to present to the x-ray instrument. In this way, samples such as bar, foil, drillings, filings, powder, and fabricated parts can be readily handled. A single-solution technique and a set of standards can deal with all samples.

Once the samples to be analyzed are in solution, little or no additional preparation is required. The standards and samples are perfectly homogeneous for chemically stable solutions and the analytical results are representative of the bulk specimen and not merely the surface. Surface treatments and particle-size effects are thus eliminated. Standard addition[25] and dilution techniques which preclude the need for chemically analyzed standards are applicable, and matrix effects are reduced or eliminated by the leveling effect of the solvent.

Many excellent general review papers on solution techniques have been published by Campbell and his coworkers,[25,26,27] Gunn,[28] Lambert,[29,30] and Bertin and Longobucco.[31] Campbell and Thatcher[32] have intercompared the solution technique for the determination of calcium in wolframite concentrates, grinding to small particle size and briquetting, and sodium carbonate fusion followed by grinding and briquetting. Alexander[33] and Dwiggins[34] have reviewed applications of solution techniques to biological fluids and petroleum products, respectively. Pierron and Munch[35] have compared solution and powder techniques for analysis of mixed oxides of titanium, vanadium, cobalt, nickel, copper, and molybdenum. Friedlander and Goldblatt[36] have compared the precision of solid powder and liquid techniques for the analysis of high-temperature alloys.

Sensitivity. Solution techniques involve dilution of samples, which can prove to be a limitation to the sensitivity of the method. Much can be done to improve the sensitivity of the method through additional sample handling, and this will subsequently be discussed in detail in the section on microanalysis.

The sensitivity of the x-ray method for specified *K*- and *L*-series lines for 25 elements with a concentration of 1 mg/ml is detailed in Table 1. Line and background intensities are given for the *K*-series lines of 15 elements and the *L*-series lines for 10 elements. Minimum detectable limits are also stated, with the minimum detectable limit being defined as that concentration of an element which is required to generate a net line intensity equal to three times the standard deviation of the background intensity for a 2-min counting time.

Figure 1[25] details the x-ray intensities that are available from solutions containing 1 mg/ml for specified *K*- and *L*-series lines, using a tungsten-target x-ray tube. The highest yield of elemental radiation occurs when the exciting primary radiation lies on the short-wavelength side of the absorption edge of the element being excited. A variety of x-ray tubes (tungsten, chromium, molybdenum, and platinum anodes) is available to achieve this relationship. The choice of x-ray tube is generally based on providing the best sensitivity for the range of elements to be analyzed.

Sources of Liquid Samples and Standards. The solution technique offers a wide latitude of available methods for the preparation of calibration standards for x-ray spectrochemical analysis. Synthetic standards may be prepared by dissolution of matrix and the elements to be determined in an appropriate solvent. The silicon, phosphorus, sulfur, chlorine, bromine, and iodine content of organic media[37,38] can be adjusted by introducing these elements in the form of their organic compounds. Metallic elements may be introduced as organometallic compounds or as salts of organic acids.[39,40]

A simple way to arrive at a series of solution standards with the required concentration range for analyses is to take a base liquid of known composition and treat it with known amounts of the element to be determined. In this way, a series of solution standards can be prepared having a higher concentration range of the element than the matrix or base material. Conversely, known amounts of the pure solvent or matrix solution can be added to a given solution to prepare standards having a lower concentration range of the element of interest than the base liquid.

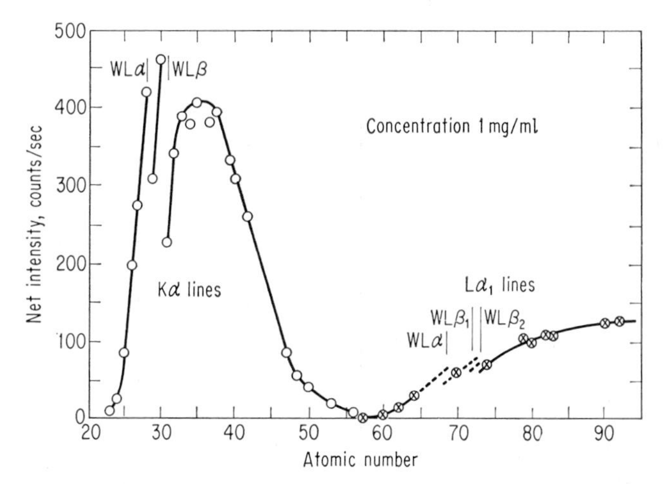

Fig. 1. X-ray intensities as a function of atomic number. (*Reproduced with permission from W. J. Campbell, M. Leon, and J. W. Thatcher, U.S. Bur. Mines Rept.* 5497, 1959.)

Standard samples, in the form of solids or chips, may be obtained from sources such as The National Bureau of Standards,[41] The American Society for Testing and Materials,[42] or private laboratories. These samples can be dissolved and used as calibration standards.

Finally, selected samples of the material for spectrochemical analysis may be analyzed by independent methods and retained as standards.

Favorable Features. Many of the favorable features of solution techniques, such as feasibility of internal-standard techniques, matrix-addition and -dilution techniques, and the reducing of the matrix effect by the leveling effect of the solvent, have already been discussed. Of equal importance is the relative ease in preparing calibration standards accurately without benefit of wet-chemical analysis and in a manner which simulates the matrix of the samples to be routinely analyzed. Solution techniques eliminate the heterogeneity effects in powders and solids. Presentation to the instrumentation for analyses is simple, particularly in inverted-optics spectrometers where the sample is supported over the x-ray tube and the underside of the sample is irradiated. Solution samples are more representative of the solid or powdered sample from which they were derived in that a more representative part of the entire sample, rather than the sample surface, is involved in the analysis.

Unfavorable Features, and Precautionary Measures That Can Be Applied. There are basic disadvantages to the use of solution techniques which must be recognized and

Table 1. Sensitivity of X-ray Secondary-emission (Fluorescence) Spectrometry for Elements in Water Solution. Minimum Detectable Concentrations and Intensities for a Concentration of 1 mg/ml under Optimum Conditions for Each Element*

At. No.	Element and line	X-ray tube current,† ma	Crystal	Path	Detector‡	Intensity for 1 mg/ml, counts/sec		Min detectable concentration,§ μg/ml
						Line (net)	Background	
16	S $K\alpha$	25	EDDT	He	Flow	3	2	140
17	Cl $K\alpha$	25	EDDT	He	Flow	7	2	62
19	K $K\alpha$	25	LiF	He	Flow	320	14	3.2
20	Ca $K\alpha$	25	LiF	He	Flow	311	7	2.3
23	V $K\alpha$	25	LiF	He	Flow	772	19	1.5
24	Cr $K\alpha$	25	LiF	He	Flow	1,030	370	5.1
26	Fe $K\alpha$	25	LiF	Air	Scint.	2,000	170	1.8
29	Cu $K\alpha$	10	LiF	Air	Scint.	2,100	350	2.4
33	As $K\alpha$	10	LiF	Air	Scint.	3,140	460	1.8
38	Sr $K\alpha$	10	LiF	Air	Scint.	6,400	1,300	1.5
42	Mo $K\alpha$	10	LiF	Air	Scint.	8,000	3,300	2.0
48	Cd $K\alpha$	10	LiF	Air	Scint.	3,200	4,000	5.4
53	I $K\alpha$	10	LiF	Air	Scint.	1,200	2,800	12
56	Ba $K\alpha$	10	LiF	Air	Scint.	1,070	3,200	14
57	La $K\alpha$	10	LiF	Air	Scint.	635	2,540	20
42	Mo $L\beta_1$	25	EDDT	He	Flow	18	11	49
48	Cd $L\beta_1$	25	LiF	He	Flow	75	8	10
53	I $L\alpha$	25	LiF	He	Flow	232	13	4.2
56	Ba $L\alpha$	25	LiF	He	Flow	275	23	4.8
57	La $L\alpha$	25	LiF	He	Flow	275	29	5.3
62	Sm $L\alpha$	25	LiF	He	Flow	440	45	4.1
70	Yb $L\alpha$	25	LiF	Air	Scint.	675	285	6.8
79	Au $L\alpha$	10	LiF	Air	Scint.	690	2,400	19
82	Pb $L\alpha$	10	LiF	Air	Scint.	1,060	460	5.5
90	Th $L\alpha$	10	LiF	Air	Scint.	1,200	850	6.5

* Data from Campbell, Leon, and Thatcher.[25,26] The instrument was a Philips inverted three-position spectrometer; a 4- × 0.020-in. collimator and pulse-height discrimination were used for all measurements.

† Philips type FA-60 x-ray tube having a tungsten target and operating at 50-kv peak.

‡ Flow signifies a gas-flow proportional counter having a 0.00025-in. mylar window; Scint. signifies a scintillation counter having a NaI:Tl scintillator crystal.

§ Defined as that concentration which gives a net line intensity equal to three times the square root of the background intensity for a 2-min counting time.

evaluated prior to use in routine analysis. If the sample to be analyzed is not already in solution, an additional step is required to dissolve the sample. The time and effort involved depend primarily on the sample and the ease with which it can be taken into solution. The solvents used are selected not only on their ability to dissolve the sample but also on the absorption effects that the cations and anions have on the intensity of the element to be determined. Nitric acid is the best of the mineral acids from this standpoint.

Samples may be difficult to take into and keep in solution. If the dissolution process is too time-consuming, other methods of sample preparation should be considered.

The intensity of the background radiation from solution samples is high because of the scattering properties of the light elements which make up the matrix. The background levels can be reduced and the signal-to-background ratios enhanced by the use of fine collimation for the determination of the intermediate and heavy elements in solutions and the use of open collimation and pulse selection (pulse-height analyzer) for the determination of the light elements.

Solutions present a sample handling problem. Volatile liquids can evaporate during irradiation, resulting in increased absorption of the radiation to be measured for analysis and in concentration changes in the sample. The evaporated vapors replace the air or the helium in the x-ray path, producing an intensity loss by absorption. This loss can be drastic in the case of the long wavelengths associated with the determination of the light elements. The use of cool operating x-ray tubes and the introduction of a stream of helium in the vicinity of the sample cup can minimize this problem.

The handling of corrosive liquids can also be troublesome as care must be exercised not to damage the metal parts of the instrumentation and the x-ray tube. Sample cups, constructed of polyethylene, are available for corrosive liquids in which no part of the sample cup is exposed to the solution. Metal sample cups have been successfully coated with Teflon in order to accommodate corrosive samples. Volatile corrosive samples are handled in sample cups equipped with a cover and are never used in a vacuum path. The cover of the sample cup can be as simple as the use of a mylar section attached to the top of the cup with a rubber band. Disposable-plastics sample receptacles dimensionally compatible with the sample cups routinely supplied with commercial instrumentation are also available. These are available from Spex Industries, and Caplugs are available from Protective Closures Co., Inc., Buffalo, N.Y.

The beryllium window of the x-ray tube is vulnerable to damage from corrosive solutions in the event of spillage or the rupture of the mylar support membrane. Additional protection can be afforded to the x-ray tube window by strapping a piece of mylar over the window or by the use of a second removable beryllium window.[25]

Bubble formation can occur during irradiation of solution samples. This phenomenon can distort the sample to x-ray tube distance, resulting in an intensity change in the elemental radiation to be measured for analysis. This condition can be minimized by the use of cool operating x-ray tubes.

Certain solutions, particularly silver salts and mercury, will undergo precipitation in the x-ray beam. The most convenient method for handling these samples is to keep the time of analysis as short as possible and avoid the taking of duplicate intensity measurements on the same sample. If this proves to be unsatisfactory, other methods of sample preparation must be investigated.

As with powdered samples, the use of internal-standard techniques involves one more step in routine sample preparation. In some instances, the standard element can conveniently be built into the sample cup rather than added to each specimen for analysis. Such a cup might contain a metallic rod[43] mounted on the cover of the sample cup and terminating near the mylar window. The standard element can be bonded to the end of the rod and the rod immersed in the solution to be analyzed. The distance between rod and the mylar window of the sample cell can be made adjustable. Intensity measurements on the element to be determined and the standard element can be made, ratioed, and plotted against the elemental concentration.

Low concentrations of elements are difficult to determine with solution techniques because of the dilution of the sample which is usually involved. Concentration procedures are applicable to solutions which will enhance sensitivity by presenting more of the atoms of the element to be determined to the x-ray beam per given volume of matrix. A detailed discussion of concentration techniques is presented below in the section on microanalysis.

The determination of light elements using solution techniques brings about a reduction in sensitivity not only by the necessary dilution of the sample but also by the high absorption of the light-element radiation in the matrix and in the membrane which supports the solution over the x-ray tubes. One-quarter-mil mylar, when used as a support membrane, will absorb 60 per cent of aluminum radiation generated within the solution. Mylar is a carbon-hydrogen-oxygen polymer, and the oxygen is primarily responsible for light-element absorption. The use of polymers that do not contain oxygen will reduce light-element absorption, and support membranes such as polyethylene and polypropylene are recommended.

The availability of high-intensity thin-window chromium-target x-ray tubes and thin-window proportional x-ray detectors has improved the sensitivity of light-element analysis in solutions. Without benefit of concentration techniques, Croke, Pfoser, and Solazzi[44] have reported limits of detectability in the parts per million range for magnesium, silicon, and aluminum as detailed in Table 2. The limit of detectability was defined as that concentration of the element which generates a peak intensity equal to three times the standard deviation of the background. Hale and King[45] have reported the determination of 0.1 ppm nickel in petroleum oil, without benefit of concentration techniques.

Table 2. Analysis of Lubricating Oils

Element	% element ± standard deviation, ppm	Limit of detectability, ppm	Time of analysis, sec
Mg	10.3 ± 3.6	15	100
Al	10.1 ± 1.7	6	100
Si	10.2 ± 5.4	12	100
Ag	19.7 ± 6.6	18	20
Sn	10.2 ± 0.7	0.5	10
Pb	10.8 ± 3.8	10	10
Fe	10.3 ± 0.62	1	10
Ni	10.1 ± 1.3	2	10
Cu	10.3 ± 1.2	2	10

Finally, solution techniques are destructive when applied to the analysis of powder or solid samples.

Microtechniques. One of the major limiting factors in the use of solution techniques is a loss of sensitivity due to the dilution of the sample. Concentration methods have been devised for solution samples which enhance sensitivity by removal of the matrix. By removal of the matrix, more of the atoms of the element to be determined are presented to the x-ray beam for irradiation and excitation.

Small volumes of solutions can be carefully and accurately pipetted into a receptacle and evaporated to dryness.[46,47,48] It is suggested that the variation in sample preparation be evaluated and determined to be compatible with the overall accuracy that is required of the determination. The reader is referred to the introduction of this chapter, where this method is covered in detail. Natelson[49,50,51,52,53] has developed a highly refined filter-paper technique for the analysis of biological fluids and clinical samples that is readily applicable to other solution samples. In this technique, filter papers are treated with hydrochloric acid to remove trace impurities and a wax ring is impregnated into the paper using molten wax and an appropriate-sized cork borer. Samples are micropipetted into the rings,[53] where they are contained for x-ray analysis. The pipetted solution can be caused to remain in the center of the ring (paper) by situating the paper on an apparatus combining a ring oven and aspirator. The periphery of the paper is heated by the ring oven and the center of the paper is cooled by a stream of air. The pipetted solution will remain in the center of the paper for optimum presentation to the x-ray instrumentation for analysis.

The pipetting of solutions onto filter papers,[54,55,56,57,58] millipore filters,[59] and chromatographic papers[56] followed by evaporation to dryness has also been described.

Concentration of the element to be determined may be realized by precipitation,[60,61] by liquid-liquid extraction,[62,63] by ion-exchange resins, [27,64,65,66,67] or with ion-exchange membranes[27,68] or papers. Removal of the solvent by distillation or evaporation and using the residue as an x-ray specimen are also readily available concentration techniques. Campbell and Carl[69] reported a technique in which the solutions were evaporated to near saturation and then absorbed in cellulose. The cellulose was then dried, briquetted, and used as an x-ray specimen.

Small volumes of solutions may be evaporated on thin mylar film. Such films give very low background compared with other support membranes such as filter paper.[70,71] Wetting agents have been used to attain uniform sample distributions. Hydrocarbon liquids may be burned and the residue collected and analyzed for nonvolatile components.

There is, in theory, no limit to the sensitivity of the x-ray method, provided that the element to be measured can be sufficiently concentrated by suitable physical and chemical treatments.

4. SAMPLE-PREPARATION TECHNIQUES FOR DYNAMIC SAMPLES

With the development of rapid and automated x-ray analytical instruments, preparation of the sample can take much more time than the actual analysis. Thus the time spent in preparation of the sample must be consistent with the desired quality control. For samples used in on-stream equipment, the elapsed time must be consistent with the response time of the process. For static samples the sample-preparation method is chosen according to the end result desired. In general, choice of sample-preparation techniques is more flexible for static samples then for dynamic systems. Although a dynamic sampling system is less flexible, the amount of sample analyzed in a comparable time is increased by a factor of 100 or more, thus permitting a more representative analysis of the material, all other factors being equal. Bernstein[72] reported that in a static raw-mix sample, the silicon and the calcium intensities emanated from 25 and 75 mg of sample, respectively. This compared with 197 and 578 g of material for the silicon and calcium intensities measured from a dynamic sample flowing at the rate of 8 in.^{3}/min. Although the integrated intensity is representative of much larger quantities of material, errors due to particle-size distribution and matrix and mineralogical changes can result in less accurate determinations than those obtained on a static sample.

Sampling systems for on-stream applications can be reduced to the following modes:

1. Slurry
2. Powder
3. Briquetted powder
4. Dewatered slurry
5. Liquid

Slurry. Sampling systems for slurry and powder materials are described by P. E. Cook,[73] who emphasizes the very basic point that the analysis by the instrument can be no more reliable than the sample presented to it. Figure 2 is a typical sampling system suggested by Cook for the handling of slurries. The design of a system for good sampling is one which will frequently cut or sample across the entire stream and pump the sample to the analyzer in such a way that it retains its individual characteristics. The pump and sump engineering should permit the handling of small volumes of pulp in a continuous stream to exclude settling and air entrapment. At the end of the line is a head tank with agitator to keep the solids in suspension. The sample is then fed by gravity through an x-ray cell. There are essentially two types of x-ray sample-handling systems. In the first system, a single cell is used and the head tank is flushed after each sample has been analyzed.[74] In the second system, individual cells and head tanks are maintained for each sample stream,[75] and the x-ray analyzers are sequentially moved to analyze each stream.[76] One problem which a slurry presents is that the measured x-ray intensity is a function not only of the elemental concentration but also of the pulp density. Pulp-density corrections are made by monitoring background radiation, monitoring radiation emanating from a metal ring which is measured after its characteristic radiation passes through the sample being analyzed, or by an isotope gauge. Typical results of an on-stream analyzer operating on slurry are given by M. L. Fuller and P. E. McNarry.[77]

Powder. Figure 3 shows a typical sample-handling system described by Cook for coarse, granular, dry materials. A similar system is described by Furbee[74] in which

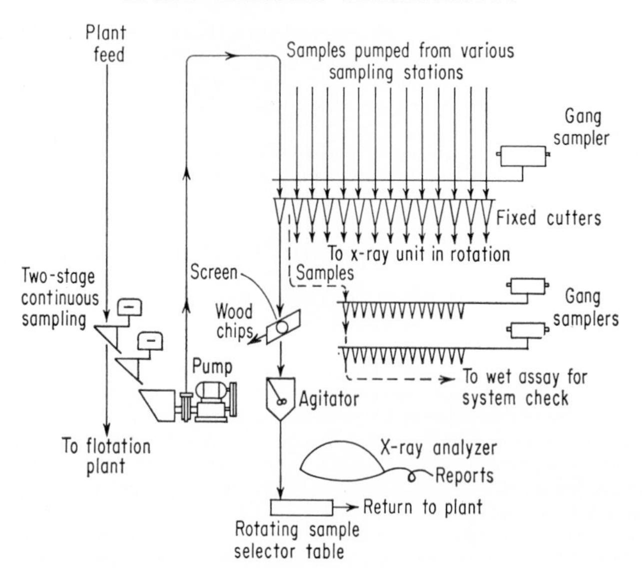

FIG. 2. Sample-handling system for handling slurries. (*Reproduced with permission from P. E. Cook, Non-metallic Minerals Processing, March*, 1962, *p*. 19.)

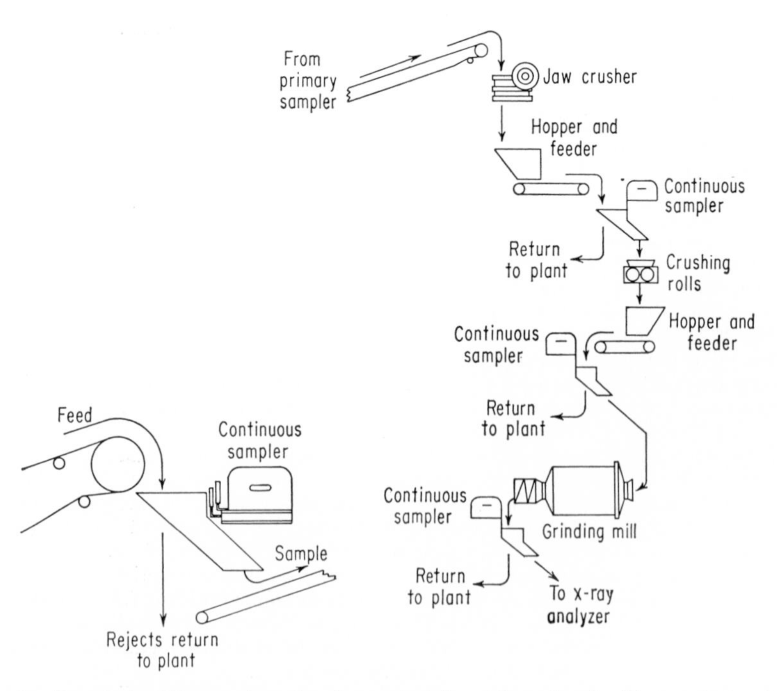

FIG. 3. Sample-handling system for dry materials. (*Reproduced with permission from P. E. Cook, Non-metallic Minerals Processing, March*, 1962, *p*. 19.)

the output sample from an automatic grinding system is minus 300 mesh for a minus-80-mesh input. The resulting powder sample is fed at the rate of 8 in³./min onto a wheel, compacted, and analyzed in a helium atmosphere. Furbee and Bernstein[78] state that representative analysis of a wide variety of raw-mix samples of different origin can be within the limits stated below. These are compared with typical results from a static sample as reported by O. E. Brown.[79]

Constituent	Concentration, %	Dynamic accuracy, % abs	Static accuracy, % abs standard deviation
CaO	45	±0.3	±0.10
SiO_2	15	±0.3	±0.13
Al_2O_3	3	±0.3	±0.14
Fe_2O_3	2	±0.05	±0.08

Briquetted Powder. Another sampling configuration for the handling of fine powders was described by Smallbone[80] in which the system uses an air centrifugal grinder to grind minus-80-mesh material to a fineness of −2 microns. The resulting material was automatically briquetted and automatically fed to an x-ray spectrometer.

Dewatered Slurry. Systems have been devised for dewatering pulp samples. D. C. Miller[81] described a system in which a vacuum filter drum rotated into a tank of material and discharged the dewatered material into a hopper for mixing and extruding a sample for x-ray analysis. The described system was later modified to analyze the material on the top surface of the vacuum filter drum. Laurila et al.[82] devised a dewatering system for the determination of titanium and ilmenite in which the material is thickened and applied to a rotating drum covered with a foam plastic which absorbs the water. The material is later washed from the drum and the water is pressed away from the foam plastic by means of a roller. Sundkvist et al.[83] devised a sampling system for the determination of Pb and Zn in tailings. A wet-sample splitter delivers a sample containing 6 to 12 g of material to the instrument. A funnel performs the task of vacuum filtering and drying and delivers the dry sample in the form of a brittle cake to a mixing device. The cake is dried by displacing the water with acetone and then passing hot air through it. The cake is broken up and the resulting powder is mixed and delivered to a sample cup. After analysis the powder is removed from the cup by vacuum. The above operation is controlled automatically.

In another dewatering process, Furbee and Bernstein[78] mention the use of a continuous dryer between the main-stream samples and x-ray analyzer to permit the determination of aluminum and silicon in raw-mix slurry. The material was dewatered because of the high absorption of aluminum and silicon radiation by water in a slurry sample.

Liquid. Campbell[84] has reported a sampling apparatus for the continuous monitoring of solutions. The sample chamber is constructed of Plexiglas and a 1-mil mylar window. A variable-speed pump transports the liquid from the reaction vessel to the sample cell. The solution flow through the cell is from bottom to top, thus reducing the formation of bubbles. The apparatus was used to study various rate processes such as displacement reactions and solubility rates. Concentration changes in the reaction vessel were continuously measured where the response of the x-ray system was in the order of several seconds.

Summary. The two major factors affecting the accurate analysis of ores and minerals in a static sample apply also to dynamic sampling procedures. These effects are diminished to a degree by the dilution factor provided by the water matrix, but corrections for these effects are still necessary for accurate determinations. These two factors are well known and have consumed the attention of many workers.[85,86] Simply stated they are:

1. Matrix effects—the effects on the intensity of the element of interest caused by the variation of other elements present in the sample
2. Heterogeneity—the effects on the intensity of the element of interest caused by particle size, surface irregularities, and mineralogical history of the sample

For a static sample, many techniques are cited here and in the literature for the elimination and control of matrix effects and heterogeneity effects. These range from grinding procedures to fusion techniques. The only appropriate control for dynamic sampling is the consistency of grinding of the material such that a uniform particle-size distribution is maintained. This cannot be overemphasized, as the effect of particle size is shown in Table 3 for a typical ore sample.

Table 3

Mesh size	Wt. % in size fraction	Zn, %	Pb, %	Fe, %
+48	4.19	0.79	0.05	1.10
−48 to +65	9.09	0.66	0.05	1.18
−65 to +100	12.51	0.61	0.07	1.76
−100 to +150	12.06	0.33	0.08	2.52
−150 to +200	11.52	0.23	0.07	2.90
−200 to +270	6.19	0.19	0.06	3.10
−270	44.44	0.28	0.37	2.95
Avg. value		0.37	0.20	2.52

The average chemical value of the ore varies dramatically from the chemical assay of each weight fraction of particle size. Although there are many ores that are uniform, variations such as those above can occur within the confines of a given process. Thus in any dynamic sampling system strict attention must be paid to the uniformity of material presented to the x-ray analyzer.

If we assume that the x-ray analyzer is looking at a uniform sample, then an attempt can be made to correct for effects due to matrix changes or interelement effects. This correction can be reduced to a problem of data handling provided that the proper radiation intensities are measured. The exact radiation intensities that must be measured will be determined by a definition or determination of the matrix or interelement problem. Systems using computers have been investigated by Birks[87] and Gillieson,[88] and results were within a few per cent of the chemical value. Thus it would appear that computers are a necessary tool for data interpretation when analyzing complex ores or materials in which matrix and interelement effects are serious.

REFERENCES CITED

1. L. S. Birks, *X-ray Spectrochemical Analysis*, pp. 51–59, Interscience Publishers, Inc., New York, 1959.
2. H. A. Liebhafsky, H. G. Pfeiffer, E. H. Winslow, and P. D. Zemany, *X-ray Absorption and Emission in Analytical Chemistry*, chap. 10, John Wiley & Sons, Inc., New York, 1960.
3. T. P. Schreiber, A. C. Ottolini, and J. A. Johnson, *Appl. Spectry.*, **17**:17 (1963).
4. R. E. Michaelis and B. A. Kilday in W. M. Mueller (ed.), *Advances in X-ray Analysis*, vol. 5, p. 405, Plenum Press, New York, 1962.
5. P. W. Borst, *Norelco Reptr.*, **10**:2 (1963).
6. B. A. Kilday and R. E. Michaelis, *Appl. Spectry.*, **16**:4 (1962).
7. J. H. Cope, *Norelco Reptr.*, **3**: 41 (1956).
8. R. E. Michaelis, *ASTM Spec. Tech. Publ.* 58-D, 122 (1960).
9. S. C. Sun, *Anal. Chem.*, **31**:1322 (1959).
10. C. V. Dyroff and P. Skiba, *Anal. Chem.*, **26**: 1774 (1954).
11. W. J. Campbell and H. F. Carl, *Anal. Chem.*, **28**:960 (1956).

12. D. M. Mortimore, P. A. Romans, and J. L. Tews, *Appl. Spectry.*, **8**(1):24 (1954).
13. F. Claisse and C. Samson in W. M. Mueller (ed.), *Advances in X-ray Analysis*, vol. 5, p. 335, Plenum Press, New York, 1962.
14. E. L. Gunn, *Anal. Chem.*, **29**:184 (1957).
15. C. M. Davis and G. R. Clark in W. M. Mueller (ed.), *Advances in X-ray Analysis*, vol. 1, p. 351, Plenum Press, New York, 1958.
16. I. Adler and J. M. Axelrod, *Spectrochim. Acta*, **7**:91 (1955).
17. M. A. Blokhin, *Methods of X-ray Spectroscopic Research*, p. 322, Pergamon Press, New York, 1965.
18. S. Fine and C. F. Hendee, Table of X-ray "K" and "L" Emission and Critical Absorption Energies for All the Elements, *Nucleonics*, **3**:86 (1955).
19. F. Claisse, *Norelco Reptr.*, **4**:3 (1957).
20. R. J. Longobucco, X-ray Spectrometric Determination of Major and Minor Constituents in Ceramic Material, *12th Pittsburgh Conf. Anal. Chem. Appl. Spectry.*, 1961.
21. D. R. Maneval and H. R. Lovell, *Anal. Chem.*, **32**:1289 (1960).
22. Applied Research Laboratories, Inc., X-ray Analysis of Metallic Elements in Nonmetallic Material, *ARL Spectrographer's News Letter*, **7**(3):1 (1954).
23. T. J. Cullen, *Anal. Chem.*, **32**:516 (1960).
24. G. Andermann, Suggested Method for Spectrochemical Analysis of Cement Raw Mix by the Lithium Tetraborate Fusion Technique Using an X-ray Spectrometer, *ASTM Suggested Method* E-2 SM10-20.
25. W. J. Campbell, M. Leon, and J. W. Thatcher, *U.S. Bur. Mines Rept.* 5497, 1959.
26. W. J. Campbell, *ASTM Spec. Tech. Publ.* STP-349, p. 48, 1964.
27. W. J. Campbell and J. W. Thatcher, *Develop. Appl. Spectry.*, **1**:31 (1962).
28. E. L. Gunn, ASTM STP-349, p. 70, 1964.
29. M. C. Lambert in W. M. Mueller (ed.), *Advances in X-ray Analysis*, vol. 2, p. 193, Plenum Press, New York, 1959.
30. M. C. Lambert, *Norelco Reptr.*, **6**:37 (1959).
31. E. P. Bertin and R. J. Longobucco, *Norelco Reptr.*, **9**:31 (1962).
32. W. J. Campbell and J. W. Thatcher, *U.S. Bur. Mines Rept.* 5416, 1958.
33. G. V. Alexander, *Appl. Spectry.*, **18**:1 (1964).
34. C. W. Dwiggins, Jr., *U.S. Bur. Mines Rept.* 6039, 1962.
35. E. D. Pierron and R. H. Munch, in J. R. Ferraro and J. S. Ziomek (eds.), *Developments in Applied Spectroscopy*, vol. 2, p. 360, Plenum Press, New York, 1963.
36. S. Friedlander and A. Goldblatt, *Appl. Spectry.*, **13**:91 (1959).
37. C. W. Dwiggins and H. N. Dunning, *Anal. Chem.*, **31**:1040 (1959).
38. C. W. Dwiggins and H. N. Dunning, *Anal. Chem.*, **32**:1137 (1960).
39. C. C. Kang, E. W. Keel, and E. Solomon, *Anal. Chem.*, **32**:221 (1960).
40. T. P. Schreiber, A. C. Ottolini, and J. L. Johnson, *Appl. Spectry.*, **17**:17 (1963).
41. *Natl. Bur. Std.* (*U.S.*) *Circ.* 552, 3d ed., 1959.
42. R. E. Michaelis, *ASTM Spec. Tech. Publ.* 58-E, 1963.
43. R. A. Jones, *Anal. Chem.*, **31**:1341 (1959).
44. J. F. Croke, W. Pfoser, and M. Solazzi, *Norelco Reptr.*, **11**:129 (1964).
45. C. C. Hale and W. H. King, Jr., *Anal. Chem.*, **33**:74 (January, 1961).
46. L. S. Birks, E. J. Brooks, et al., *Anal. Chem.*, **22**:1258 (1950).
47. E. N. Davis and B. C. Hoeck, *Anal. Chem.*, **27**:1880 (1955).
48. J. C. Mathies and P. K. Lund, *Norelco Reptr.*, **7**:130 (1960).
49. S. Natelson and B. Sheid, *Clin. Chem.*, **6**:299 (1960).
50. S. Natelson and B. Sheid, *Anal. Chem.*, **33**:396 (1961).
51. S. Natelson and B. Sheid, *Clin. Chem.*, **7**:115 (1961).
52. S. Natelson and B. Sheid, *Clin. Chem.*, **8**:17 (1962).
53. S. Natelson, M. R. Richelson, et al., *Clin. Chem.*, **5**:519 (1959).
54. E. J. Felten, I. Fankuchen, and J. Steigman, *Anal. Chem.*, **31**:1771 (1959).
55. P. K. Lund and J. C. Mathies, *Norelco Reptr.*, **7**:127 (1960).
56. W. M. MacNevin and E. A. Hakkila, *Anal. Chem.*, **29**:1019 (1957).
57. J. C. Mathies and P. K. Lund, *Norelco Reptr.*, **7**:134 (1960).
58. H. G. Pfeiffer and P. D. Zemany, *Nature*, **174**:397 (1954).
59. J. S. Rudolph and R. J. Nadalin, *Anal. Chem.*, **36**:1815 (1964).
60. J. E. Fagel, Jr., E. W. Balis, and L. B. Bronk, *Anal. Chem.*, **30**:1918 (1958).
61. W. L. Kehl and R. G. Russell, *Anal. Chem.*, **28**:1350 (1956).
62. G. R. Blank and H. A. Heller, in W. D. Ashby (ed.), *Developments in Applied Spectroscopy*, vol. 1, p. 3, Plenum Press, New York, 1962.
63. R. A. Wolfe and R. A. Fowler, *J. Opt. Soc. Am.*, **35**:86 (1945).
64. R. L. Collin, *Anal. Chem.*, **33**:605 (1961).
65. J. N. Van Niekerk and J. F. De Wet, *Nature*, **186**:380 (1960).

66. J. N. Van Niekerk, J. F. De Wet, and F. T. Wybenga, *Anal. Chem.*, **33**:213 (1961).
67. J. N. Van Niekerk, F. W. E. Strelow, and F. T. Wybenga, *Appl. Spectry.*, **15**:121 (1961).
68. W. T. Grubb and P. D. Zemany, *Nature*, **176**:221 (1955).
69. W. J. Campbell, *Anal. Chem.*, **28**:960 (1956).
70. M. B. Cavanagh, *U.S. Naval Res. Lab. Rept.* 4528, 1955.
71. E. L. Gunn, *Anal. Chem.*, **33**:921 (1961).
72. F. Bernstein in W. M. Mueller and M. Fay (eds.), *Advances in X-ray Analysis*, vol. 6, p. 436, Plenum Press, New York, 1963.
73. P. E. Cook, *Non-metallic Minerals Processing*, March, 1962, p. 19.
74. A. D. Furbee in W. M. Mueller (ed.), *Advances in X-ray Analysis*, vol. 5, p. 464, Plenum Press, New York, 1962.
75. W. R. Kiley and R. W. Deichert in W. M. Mueller (ed.), *Advances in X-ray Analysis*, vol. 6, p. 436, Plenum Press, New York, 1963.
76. F. L. Holderreed and W. Lucy, *Mining Congr. J.*, **46**:82 (June, 1960).
77. M. L. Fuller and P. E. McNarry, *Eng. Mining J.*, April, 1962.
78. A. D. Furbee and F. Bernstein, ISA 18th Ann. Conf., 1963, no. 31-1-63.
79. O. E. Brown, "Use of X-ray Emission Spectroscopy in Chemical Analysis of Cement, Raw Materials and Raw Mix," ASTM Annual Meeting, June, 1963.
80. A. H. Smallbone, "New X-ray Fluorescence Analytical Techniques and Material Handling Methods," Pittsburgh Conference on Analytical Chemistry and Applied Spectroscopy, 1965.
81. D. C. Miller, "Instrumentation of Continuous Analysis of Tailings from a Flotation Separation Process," 7th Annual Conference Industrial Application of X-ray Analysis, Denver Research Institute, 1958.
82. E. A. Laurila, L. Saari, and O. Castreu, AIME Reprint 60B19, 1960.
83. G. F. Sundkvist, F. O. Lundgren, and L. J. Lidstrom, *Anal. Chem.*, **36**:2091 (1964).
84. W. J. Campbell, *Appl. Spectry.*, **14**:26 (1960).
85. F. Claisse and C. Samson in W. M. Mueller (ed.), *Advances in X-ray Analysis*, vol. 5, p. 335, Plenum Press, New York, 1962.
86. E. L. Gunn in W. M. Mueller (ed.), *Advances in X-ray Analysis*, vol. 4, p. 382, Plenum Press, New York, 1961.
87. L. S. Birks, "Fundamental Parameters versus Empirical Coefficients in Quantitative X-ray Fluorescence Analysis," Eastern Analytical Symposium, 1965.
88. A. H. Gillieson, "Mathematical Methods for the Correction of Inter-element Effects," Eastern Analytical Symposium, 1965.

GENERAL REFERENCES

Birks, L. S.: *X-ray Spectrochemical Analysis*, Interscience Publishers, Inc., New York, 1959.
Blokhin, M. A.: *Methods of X-ray Spectroscopic Research*, Pergamon Press, New York, 1965.
Clark, G. L.: *Encyclopaedia of X-rays and Gamma Rays*, Reinhold Publishing Corporation, New York, 1963.
Liebhafsky, H. A., H. G. Pfeiffer, E. H. Winslow, and P. D. Zemany: *X-ray Absorption and Emission in Analytical Chemistry*, John Wiley & Sons, Inc., New York, 1960.
Symposium on X-ray and Electron Probe Analysis, *ASTM Special Technical Publication* 349, American Society for Testing and Materials, Philadelphia, 1964.

Chapter 34

EFFECTS OF CHEMICAL STATE OF SPECIMENS

William T. Cave

Monsanto Company

1. INTRODUCTION

Following the early work of Hjalmar[1] and Lindh,[2] Parratt,[3] in 1936, demonstrated that the wavelengths of the $K\alpha_1K\alpha_2$ doublet for sulfur are different for the sulfate and the sulfide. Two years later, Johnson[4] observed similar displacements for the sodium $K\alpha$ line in various compounds. It is now known that band shape and intensity can also alter significantly.

Although such shifts are small, generally less than an electron volt, they are greater than experimental error for modern x-ray fluorescence spectrometers and must therefore be recognized and anticipated, particularly for quantitative analyses. Although these effects may present hazards for the analyst, as Zemany[5] points out, they are related to chemical state and thus can also be used to obtain a better understanding of structure if they can be rationalized.

2. THEORY

It is known that the formation of chemical bonds of whatever type produces electron redistributions which are defined, with reference to the neutral atom, by altered energy levels. This is particularly true of the valence electrons. When such electrons are involved in the fluorescence transition, it follows that the wavelengths of their lines will be different for the neutral atom as compared with the combined atom. Shuvaev[6] has given mathematical treatment to this concept, and his results are consistent in direction with experimental data for both wavelength shift and intensity change. However, such predictions are not in precise agreement with experimental data, and this is due to the simplified assumption that bond character alone is significant.

3. EXPERIMENTAL CORRELATIONS

Oxidation State. As the data of Faessler[7] on sulfur prove so elegantly, there is no doubt that oxidation state is the major determinant, although other effects are discernible. A. E. Sandström[8] has summarized data for elements 19 through 29 and 40 through 46, and these confirm the importance of valence in fixing not only the $K\alpha$ and $K\beta$ lines but also the L lines for elements of higher atomic number.

Other Factors. Even when valence is nominally unchanged, however, there are other factors which can affect electron-density distribution. White[9] has shown for aluminum that coordination number can be correlated to wavelength shifts of the $K\alpha$ line. Inductive effects, the electronegativities of ligands, different cations, and different lattice structures are shown to be operative in Faessler's[7] measurements on organic and inorganic sulfur compounds. Bond type is another possible contributor to wavelength shifts, and from his work on alkali polysulfides Faessler[10] questions the assumption of a covalent bond for $A^{II}B^{VI}$ compounds. Certainly at the moment no quantum-mechanical treatment has been made to fit the general case, and the possibilities of complex interactions must be considered empirically for each specific problem.

Typical Studies. In this manner, using precision spectrographs, Korsunskii[11] has examined the $L\beta_2$ and $L\gamma_1$ lines of niobium and concluded that in the formation of stoichiometric nitrides, carbides, and diborides there is a decrease in the filling of the $4d$ states. Zhurakovskii[12] measured the $K\beta$ lines for titanium and its compounds with the light elements C, N, and O and concluded that the separation of the $K\beta''$ and $K\beta_5$ lines was linearly related to the electronegative difference between the elements. Alloys of aluminum with transition metals have been examined by Nemnorov.[13] From shifts in the $K\beta_x$ line and changes in its contours he concludes that the metallic type of bond is supplemented by an interaction similar to the ionic-covalent bonding between aluminum and oxygen in Al_2O_3.

4. INSTRUMENTATION

Most of this type of data has been obtained from specially built tube spectrographs designed for high sensitivity and resolution. However, commercially available spectrometers have now reached levels of performance that, at controlled temperatures, provide evidence of wavelength shifts due to changes in the chemical state of the sample. Table 1 indicates what is obtained on standard equipment. These data show that, when precautions are taken to standardize experimental conditions, measurable shifts are apparent and a basis for analysis exists.

Table 1

Compound	Line	Δ, 2θ	Δ, ev	Author	Compound	Line	Δ, 2θ	Δ, ev	Author
Aluminum:					$Na_2S_2O_3$	$K\alpha$	−0.04	0.24	‡
Al (foil)	$K\alpha$	0	0	†	S	$K\beta$	0	0	*
Al_2O_3	$K\alpha$	−0.08	0.34	†	FeS_2	$K\beta$	−0.005	0.03	*
Si	$K\beta$	0	0	‡	ZnS	$K\beta$	−0.01	0.11	*
SiO_2	$K\beta$	0.25	−3.2	‡	$SrSO_4$	$K\beta$	−0.13	1.4	*
Phosphorus:					$CaSO_4 \cdot 2H_2O$	$K\beta$	−0.11	1.2	*
P (red)	$K\alpha$	0	0	†	Chlorine:				
$(C_2H_5)_3PO_3$	$K\alpha$	−0.035	0.43	†	$KClO_4$	$K\alpha$	0	0	*
$NaPO_3$	$K\alpha$	−0.092	0.68	†	$KClO_3$	$K\alpha$	0.03	−0.44	*
$Na_4P_2O_7$	$K\alpha$	−0.087	0.66	†	NaCl	$K\alpha$	0.10	−1.4	*
$CaHPO_4 \cdot 10H_2O$	$K\alpha$	−0.093	0.68	†	$KClO_4$	$K\beta$	0	0	*
Sulfur:					$BaCl_2$	$K\beta$	0.18	−3.5	*
S	$K\alpha$	0	0	†	$SnCl_2$	$K\beta$	0.18	−3.5	*
BaS	$K\alpha$	−0.01	0.07	†	NaCl	$K\beta$	0.19	−3.7	*
CuS	$K\alpha$	−0.07	0.46	†	Iron:				
Na_2S	$K\alpha$	0.06	−0.39	†	Fe	$K\beta$	0	0	*
$CaSO_4 \cdot 2H_2O$	$K\alpha$	−0.19	1.2	†	FeS_2	$K\beta$	0.005	−0.16	*
$CuSO_4$	$K\alpha$	−0.19	1.2	†	Fe_2O_3	$K\beta$	−0.02	0.76	*
Na_2SO_4	$K\alpha$	−0.15	1.0	‡	$FeCl_2$	$K\beta$	−0.02[3]	0.92	*
Na_2SO_3	$K\alpha$	−0.11	0.70	‡	$FeCl_3$	$K\beta$	−0.02[3]	0.92	*

* Measurements and calculations made from data of E. W. White et al.[9] (GE-XRD-5).
† J. L. Ogilvie, Monsanto Company, unpublished data. (Philips, Norelco Vacuum spectrograph.)
‡ F. N. Hodgson, Monsanto Research Corporation, private communication (GE-XRD-5).

REFERENCES CITED

1. E. Hjalmar, *Z. Physik*, **7**:341 (1921).
2. A. E. Lindh and O. Lundquist, *Arkiv Mat. Astron. Fysik*, **18**:3 (1924).

3. L. G. Parratt, *Phys. Rev.*, **49**:14 (1936).
4. N. G. Johnson, *Phys. Rev.*, **53**:434 (1938).
5. P. D. Zemany, *Anal. Chem.*, **32**:595 (1960).
6. A. T. Shuvaev, *Izv. Akad. Nauk SSSR Ser. Fiz.*, **25**:986 (1961).
7. A. Faessler and M. Goehring, *Naturwiss.*, **39**:169 (1952).
8. A. E. Sandström, *Encyclopedia of Physics*, p. 158, S. Flügge (ed.), Springer-Verlag, Berlin, 1957.
9. E. W. White, H. A. McKinstry, and T. F. Bates, Crystal Chemical Studies by X-ray Fluorescence, in *Advances in X-ray Analysis*, vol. 2, p. 239, W. M. Mueller (ed.), Plenum Press, Inc., New York, 1960.
10. A. Faessler and P. Mecke, *Z. Electrochem.*, **64**:587 (1960).
11. M. I. Korsunskii, *Bull. Acad. Sci. USSR, Phys. Ser.*, **24**:457 (1960).
12. E. A. Zhurakovskii, *Dokl. Akad. Nauk SSSR*, **129**:1269 (1959).
13. S. A. Nemnorov, *Izv. Akad. Nauk SSSR Ser. Fiz.*, **27**:1007 (1961).

GENERAL REFERENCE

Liebhafsky, H. A., H. G. Pfeiffer, E. H. Winslow, and P. D. Zemany: *X-ray Absorption and Emission in Analytical Chemistry*, John Wiley & Sons, Inc., New York, 1960.

Chapter 35

QUALITATIVE AND SEMIQUANTITATIVE TECHNIQUES

Merlyn L. Salmon

FLUO-X-SPEC Laboratory

1. INTRODUCTION

Qualitative and semiquantitative analytical techniques of x-ray spectroscopy yield satisfactory solutions to many problems and offer simplicity, reliability, and versatility in the treatment of routine and nonroutine samples. As sufficient experience is gained with various types of samples, the procedures can be modified and improved with systematic control of experimental conditions and treatment of systemic properties within a framework of universal reference parameters for all types of samples.

Chart-scanning procedures are the most practical for positive qualitative identification of elements in the sample, and with proper standardization of experimental conditions sufficient data are also exhibited on the chart to enable semiquantitative evaluation of the concentrations of these elements.

There is no doubt of the meaning of "qualitative" in the vernacular of x-ray spectroscopists, but there are varieties of opinions in the differentiation of "semiquantitative" and "quantitative" as descriptions of results or techniques. "Quantitative" generally indicates absolute concentration within a known range of accuracy determined by reference to the most specific calibration information unique to the particular sample type. "Semiquantitative" generally does not preclude less accuracy but indicates a lesser degree of reliability due to the generalized treatment of data by reference to universal calibration information pertinent to many sample types.

In some instances, with respect to calibration information available, semiquantitative treatment of a series of ideal samples will yield results with accuracy comparable with quantitative values, but as the character of the unknown samples departs from the norm for the reference standards there may be a bias of results in comparison with actual concentrations. Successful programs for semiquantitative analyses evolve from systematic appraisal of the reasons for the bias and evaluation of systemic properties that can be used as parameters to minimize the bias by normalization of the data in universal calibration systems.

The development of semiquantitative x-ray spectrographic techniques includes consideration of sample preparation, instrumental examination, and data evaluation. Simplicity, reliability, and versatility are principal objectives in the formulation of these phases of the techniques.

The ultimate aims for qualitative and semiquantitative techniques for wide varieties of sample types are as follows: to do a minimum of sample preparation to get an acceptable sample or sample aliquot; to spend little time in instrumental examination to get a comprehensive chart recording of intensities for the range of wavelengths of the x-ray spectra that are characteristic of elements in the sample; and to establish simple but reliable systems for treatment of the experimental data to normalize the effects of variety in sample character.

The discussion that follows is concerned only with analyses for elements with atomic numbers higher than 21 (titanium and above in the periodic table), although some of the information is also pertinent to analytical techniques for elements with lower atomic numbers.

2. SAMPLE PREPARATION

General. Procedures and effects of sample preparation and handling are discussed in Chaps. 33 and 36.

Simplicity of procedure is important in developing a standard method, and it is advisable that control of the method be incorporated in the spectrographic technique.

FIG. 1. Individually sealed plastic cups for x-ray spectrographic samples.

Solutions may be analyzed as liquids, slurries, or dried residues from evaporation or ashing. Homogeneous solids may be examined directly or as finely divided powders, and heterogeneous solids are prepared as finely divided, well-mixed powders to represent the average composition of the specimen bulk. In many cases, such as pulverized mineral or ore samples, it is possible to use the samples as previously prepared for routine sampling or other analytical processes. Preconcentration or classification of fractions of the sample or additions of other materials to the original bulk of sample involve complications beyond the "simplicity" desired for a standard method, and the general objective of these more complicated procedures is a trend to quantitative assays.

The ultimate criterion for sample preparation is to prepare representative aliquots so that a standard area of sample with a proper thickness can be exposed in a reproducible manner to the x-ray beam from the tube in the spectrograph.

A system of individually sealed sample cups with Mylar windows offers several advantages for sample handling: The sealed cups minimize the chance for contamination of the instrument and laboratory area; they can be filed for future reference and convenient reexamination; they reduce the consumption of instrument time for loading and unloading samples; and they can be chosen from a variety of sizes to standardize the sample area exposed in the spectrograph.

A series of plastic cups ranging from ⅜ to 1 in. in diameter of the area exposed through the Mylar window is shown in Fig. 1. The adapter rings to hold the cups in a reproducible position in the standard sample carrier can be made from nylon, Teflon, or Micarta. The plastic cups can be obtained from CaPlugs Division of Protective Closures Company and from Spex Industries. The retaining rings to hold the Mylar film cover on the cup can be obtained from Drapery Hardware Manufacturing, Kirsch Company, and Spex Industries.

FIG. 2. Sequential loading of individual samples in numbered plastic cups.

The convenience and simplicity of the system are evident in Fig. 2 showing the sequential and individual loading of a series of ore samples prepared as finely divided powders. These samples are being loaded for examination in a spectrograph with a horizontal plane of sample presentation and the x-ray tube below the sample surface. Incorporation of experimental control of sample preparation into the spectrographic procedures for loosely packed powders has been discussed for this type of spectrograph.[1]

In other types of instruments it may be more difficult to expose a uniform and reproducible layer of loosely packed powder, and packed planchets, briquettes, or other modes for maintaining a layer of powder may be required. The spectrographic evaluation for single aliquot specimens of these types of packed samples offers only the measurement of instrumental precision, and unless replicate compacts are prepared from the same sample there is no experimental indication of sample homogeneity. The homogeneity of loosely packed powder samples in sealed cups is easily checked by agitation of the same cup between runs and sequential examination of essentially different aliquots in each run.

Natural Samples. Spectrographic evaluation of loosely packed powder aliquots of the same specimen subjected to different grinding processes is shown in Fig. 3. Supplemental grinding for an hour in a high-speed ball mill produced no substantial change of peak intensities from those indicated in groups *B* and *C* of Fig. 3.

The deviations of peak intensities for the coarse samples in group *A* of Fig. 3 can be attributed to lack of homogeneity of the powder sample, and comparison of the maximum value with the average for groups *B* and *C* indicates not more than 10 per cent difference. This difference reflects a deviation comparable with that expected for a concentration determination.

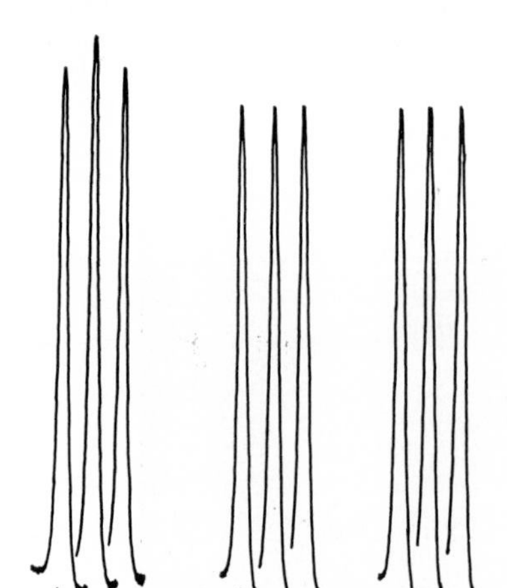

FIG. 3. Reproducibility of copper $K\alpha$ x-ray intensity in aliquots of same sample with different grinding treatments. (*A*) Coarse grinding in rotary disk pulverizer with some particles as coarse as 35 mesh. (*B*) Fine grinding in rotary disk pulverizer to nominal particle size of 100 mesh and finer. (*C*) High-speed ball-mill grinding to nominal particle size of 200 mesh and finer with large fraction that will pass 325 mesh. Samples run as loose powders in individually sealed plastic cups with Mylar window. Full-scale intensity 1,600 counts/sec. Scanning rate 8° per minute. Time constant 0.64 sec.

Fine pulverizer grinding (100 mesh and finer) with no screening has been found satisfactory for mineral and ore samples or other dry powders for use as loosely packed powders in the sample cups inverted in the spectrograph so that a uniform layer is formed on the Mylar window of the cup. Visual examination of the layer indicates the degree of uniformity necessary prior to placing the inverted cup in the spectrograph.

Preparation of solids as finely divided powders and loading the powders or solutions into individually sealed plastic cups is a simple and reliable mode for treatment of routine and nonroutine samples. The spectrographic control of sample preparation is preferred over other criteria such as mesh size or fixed-time grinding processes.

Synthetic Standards. Synthesis of reliable reference standards is another important area of sample preparation since the availability of reliable reference standards of natural materials analyzed by other procedures is quite often limited in number and/or variety. The limitation of natural standards with reliable assays becomes especially critical in programs to establish universal reference parameters for normalization of matrix effects because the overall variation in matrices found in unknown samples may not be completely represented by the natural materials with known values.

The mere presence of a known weight fraction of a particular element in a mixture of materials is an insufficient criterion for use of the mixture as a reference standard unless blending of all components is adequate for near approximation of the conditions in finely divided powders of natural mineral and ore samples. Most of the difficulties in the use of synthetic standards seem to result from the coating of one component on particles of another component, with consequent enhancement of intensity for elements in the coating material and reduced intensity of elements in the coated particles due to absorption by the coating.

No universal system has been found that is adequate for preparation of synthetic standards for all varieties of materials that may be subjected to examination, but one or more of the following procedures may be suitable for preparation of reference standards for powder samples:

1. Known weights of dry materials with the same nominal density can be blended by vigorous mixing if all components are finely divided (325 or 400 mesh) as weighed. If there is a gradient in mesh size or coarse particles of materials as weighed, the mixing

action must be accompanied by sufficient grinding to reduce all components to the same finely divided state.

2. When materials have a great difference in density (i.e., uranium oxide and graphite) the blending of dry powder compounds is generally not satisfactory. A measured volume of a standard solution of the heavier material can be evaporated on a measured weight of the lighter material, and the resulting dry mixture can be well mixed and ground to a finely divided state.

3. Synthetic-glass mixtures of high-temperature melts or lower-temperature melts that can be prepared with appropriate fluxing agents can be ground to powders to treat materials that are difficult to blend otherwise.

3. INSTRUMENTAL EXAMINATION

General. Installation of the instrument in an area with close to normal and constant room temperature, free of excessive vibration, and with a stable source of power is important for semiquantitative techniques. The day-to-day operation of the instrument with easily reproducible operating conditions improves reliability of the techniques and minimizes the needs for intermediate recalibration except for periodic reference to known samples.

Long-range stability of the instrumentation is improved by installation of high-volume ventilation systems in the cabinets and racks containing electronic components so that the temperature is nearly constant and only 3 to 5° above room temperature. The cost of the systems is amortized in the reduction of tube-replacement costs.

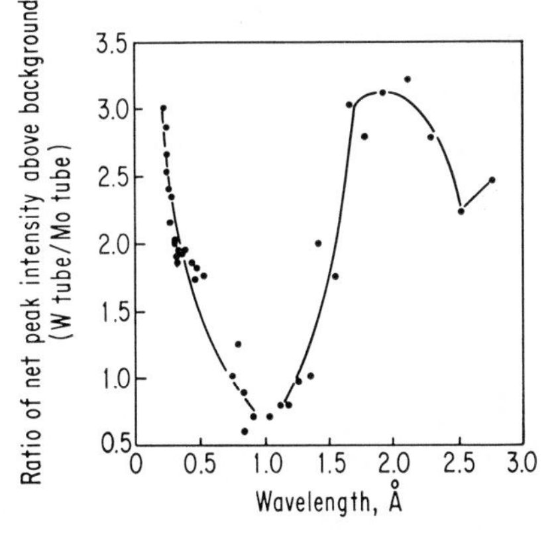

Fig. 4. Comparable excitation efficiency of tungsten- and molybdenum-target x-ray tubes.

The primary objective of the instrumental examination is to produce a comprehensive chart of the x-ray spectra characteristic of elements in the sample. The chart may include several regions of overlays indicating spectra obtained with variation in operation of the instrument to optimize desired effects for particular wavelengths.

Choice of detector, collimation, analyzing crystal, x-ray tube, and goniometer scanning rate must be established for a standard method.[1] The following supplementary processes can be applied to improve the quality of the chart: adjustment of x-ray tube power up to 100 kv, use of helium or a vacuum, continuous synchronized electronic discrimination,[2] and use of filters over the window of the x-ray tube or in the beam of fluorescent x-rays from the sample.[3]

X-ray Tube. The ideal choice of x-ray tube is one that emits characteristic lines and high-intensity white radiation for the most effective excitation of x-ray spectra for elements in the sample (see Chap. 32).

A comparison of tungsten and molybdenum tubes is shown in Fig. 4. The tungsten tube shows higher efficiency of excitation except for the wavelength range from 0.75 to 1.25 Å. The tungsten tube is used in the overall scanning procedure for the wavelength range from 0.15 to 2.85 Å, and the molybdenum tube is used only for single-element determinations near the wavelength of 1 Å.

Analyzing Crystal. A good balance of resolution and diffracted peak intensity makes lithium fluoride the most commonly used crystal for the total scan up to 2.85 Å. Rock salt produces less resolution but reasonably high diffracted peak intensities, and topaz yields much better resolution but low diffracted peak intensities (about 25 per cent of the value for LiF). Other analyzing crystals are discussed in Chap. 31.

Collimation. There are two zones for collimation of the fluorescent x-ray beam from the sample, between the sample and the analyzing crystal and between the analyzing crystal and the detector. Most commercial instrumentation provides a variety of collimators with different spacings, and it is also possible to construct units with different characteristics.

The quality of the chart is highly dependent upon the proper collimation, and the ideal case produces high values of net peak intensity above background with acceptable resolution of adjacent wavelengths. Sufficient collimation for absolute resolution of all adjacent wavelengths reduces intensity too much, and maximum intensity is obtained with sacrifice of necessary resolution.

The latter condition is shown in Fig. 5 by the comparison of results for a 4-in. parallel-blade collimator with 0.020-in. spacing with results for a collimator with 0.005-in. spacing in the beam between the sample and the crystal. There is approximately a 4:1 gain of net peak intensity above background with the coarser collimator,

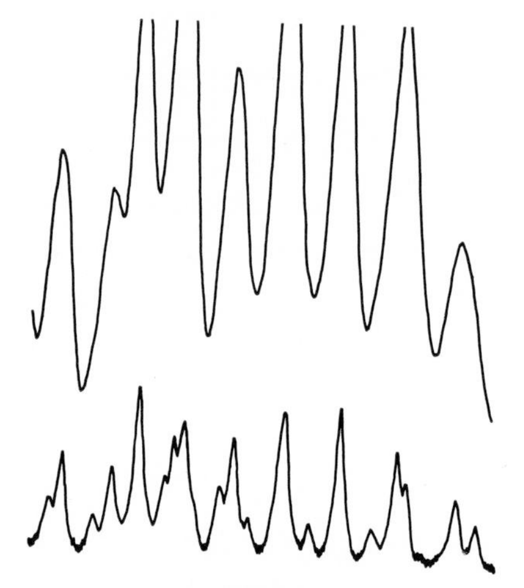

FIG. 5. Comparable resolution of parallel-blade collimators in the beam between the sample and the analyzing crystal. Upper: 4-in.-long by 0.020-in. blade spacing. Lower: 4-in.-long by 0.005-in. blade spacing.

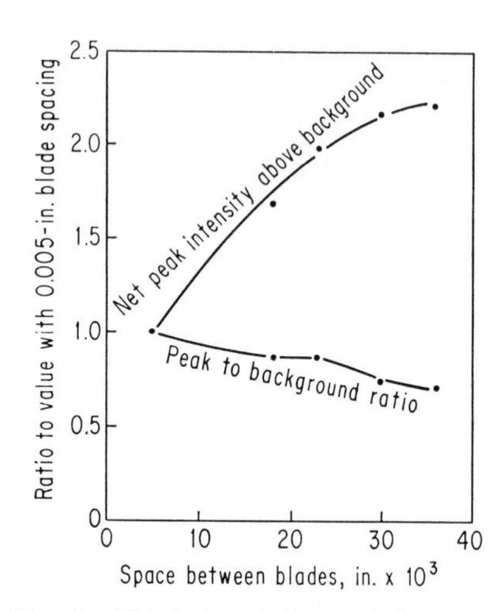

FIG. 6. Effects of variation of blade spacing of collimator in beam between analyzing crystal and detector.

but the resolution is unsatisfactory for these spectra. Trials of collimators up to 6 in. in length and with spacings in the range less than 0.005 up to 0.020 in. in the beam between the sample and the crystal show that the 4-in.-long collimator with 0.005-in. spacing produces the best overall balance of net peak intensity and resolution for the general scanning procedure.

Effects for several spacings of collimator blades in the beam between the analyzing crystal and the detector are summarized in Fig. 6, and results for comparison of a 1½-in.-long collimator with 0.023-in. and 0.005-in. spacings are shown in Fig. 7. In this case the peak intensity is doubled with little loss of resolution and only a 20 per cent decrease in peak-to-background ratio when the 0.023-in. spacing is substituted for the 0.005-in. spacing.

The general scanning procedure is done with a 4- by 0.005-in. collimator between the sample and the crystal and a 1½- by 0.023-in. collimator between the crystal and the detector.

Detector Operation. The scintillation counter shows the best overall detection efficiency for the wavelength range from 0.15 to 2.85 Å.

Barium $L\alpha$ radiation has the longest wavelength for an analytical line in this range, and the voltage applied to the scintillation counter is adjusted to the optimum for this wavelength. Figure 8 indicates the effects of voltage on net peak intensity and photomultiplier noise. The detector is operated at 900 volts direct current to optimize high signal and low noise for the general scanning procedure.

Linear response to high counting rates is important, and the overall performance of the scintillation counter, amplifier, scaler, and rate-meter circuits is shown in Fig. 9. Direct measurement of counting rates in excess of 100,000 counts/sec is not performed in the scanning technique, and indicated intensities up to this value can be used with no correction for departure of the scintillation counter, amplifier, scaler, and rate-meter circuits from linearity in overall response. See Chap. 3 for a complete discussion of detectors.

X-ray Tube Power. The overall scanning procedure is conducted with x-ray tube voltage of 50 kv for the wavelength range of 0.30 to 2.85 Å. However, the net

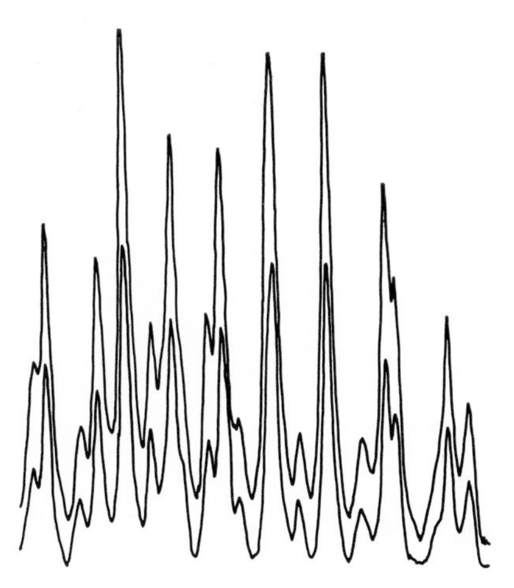

FIG. 7. Comparable resolution of parallel-blade collimators in the beam between the analyzing crystal and detector. Upper: 1½-in.-long by 0.023-in. blade spacing. Lower: 1½-in.-long by 0.005-in. blade spacing.

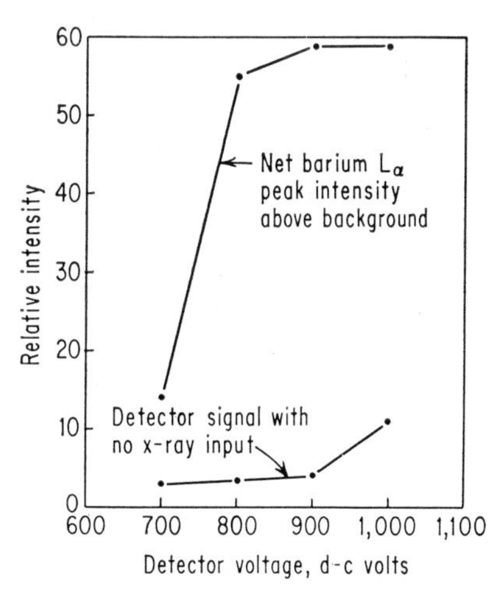

FIG. 8. Effects of d-c voltage applied to scintillation counter for measurement of barium $L\alpha$ radiation.

peak intensities above background can be increased when 100 kv is used for the range of 0.3 to 0.9 Å, as shown in Fig. 10.

The use of 100 kv also makes it possible to use additional spectra in the range of 0.15 to 0.3 Å that are not available with 50 kv. Relative intensities for K spectra of the lanthanides obtained with 100 kv and L spectra for these elements obtained with 50 kv with air and with helium in the optical path of the spectrograph are indicated in Fig. 11.

Helium. Net peak intensities above background for wavelengths greater than 1 Å can be increased with the use of helium or a vacuum in the optical path of the instrument. A general trend of the increase is shown in Fig. 12.

Electronic Discrimination. The use of a pulse-height analyzer at a fixed goniometer position is common in x-ray spectrographic techniques to improve the signal-to-noise ratio and/or minimize interferences due to multiple-order diffractions of radiation with shorter wavelengths. To take advantage of these improvements in the chart for the complete scan, a simple technique was developed for continuous adjustment of the baseline voltage of the pulse-height analyzer in synchronism with

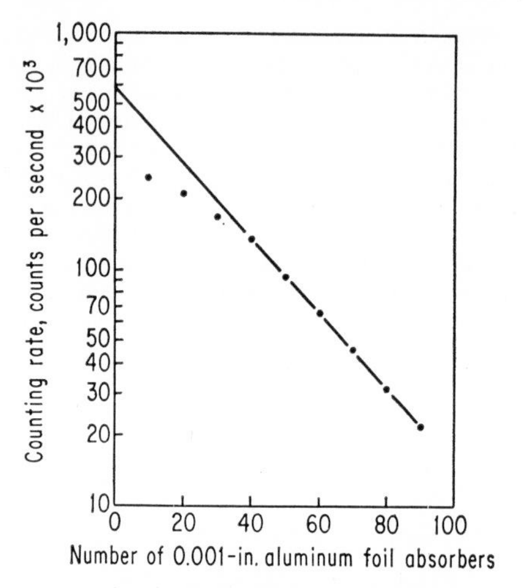

FIG. 9. Overall linearity in response of scaler, rate-meter, amplifier, and detector circuits.

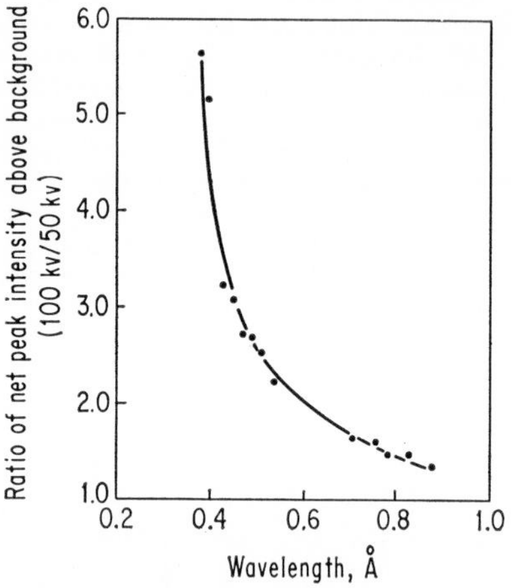

Ratio of net peak intensity above background (100 kv/50 kv)

6.0 5.0 4.0 3.0 2.0 1.0

0.2 0.4 0.6 0.8 1.0

Wavelength, Å

FIG. 10. Effects of 100-kv x-ray tube power.

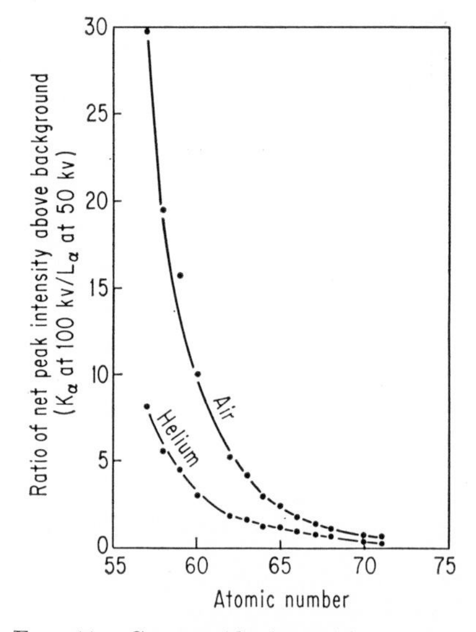

FIG. 11. Comparable intensities of lanthanide K spectra with 100 kv x-ray tube power and L spectra with 50 kv.

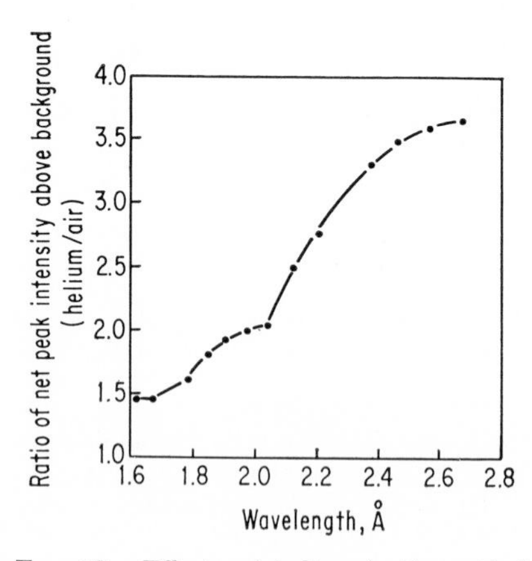

FIG. 12. Effects of helium in the optical path.

goniometer movement.[2] An automatic electromechanical baseline adjustment unit was developed for this purpose by Technical Equipment Corporation.

Results for the procedure are shown in Fig. 13 for improvement of resolution of first-order diffractions of spectra for hafnium, nickel, and iron from second-order diffractions of zirconium, lead, and strontium lines.

Filters. Filters may be used in the supplemental techniques to filter the output of the x-ray tube or adjacent wavelengths in the fluorescent x-ray beam from the sample.[3]

Improved resolution of selenium and germanium lines is shown in Fig. 14 when the output of the tungsten target of the x-ray tube is filtered to reduce the intensity of the tungsten lines emitted by the target.

Goniometer Scanning Rates. To increase the speed of overall scanning techniques, the instrument at FLUO-X-SPEC Laboratory was modified to extend the rate up to 32° per minute.[4] The modifications include the following: an auxiliary time-constant circuit to provide time constants of 0.02, 0.04, 0.14, 0.24, 0.44, and 0.64 sec in addition to the 1-, 2-, 4-, 8-, and 16-sec time constants available in the standard instrument; a supplementary shaft installation to compound the drive ratios of the standard goniometer gears; replacement of the 2-rpm goniometer drive motor

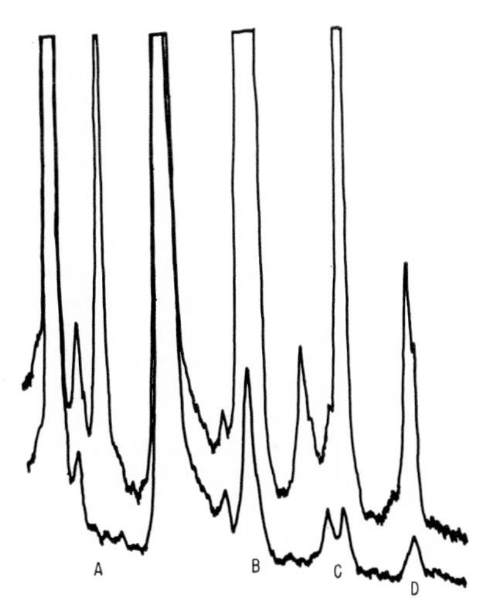

FIG. 13. Effects of synchronized electronic discrimination. Upper: without discrimination, all orders of diffracted radiation. Lower: with discrimination, first-order diffractions.

Position	Multiple-order diffractions	First-order diffractions
A	Zr $K\beta$	Hf $L\beta_1$
B	Zr $K\alpha$	Hf $L\alpha$
C	Pb $L\gamma$	Ni $K\alpha$, W L_l
D	Sr $K\alpha$	Fe $K\beta$

with an 8-rpm unit; and installation of a ¼-sec Brown recorder, Model 153x16-VH-II-III-118, to replace the unit with slower response. The auxiliary time-constant circuit was built and installed by Technical Equipment Corporation, and the goniometer drive was modified by Hyatt Instrument Company.

Comparable results for scanning rates of 2 and 32° per minute are shown in Figs. 15 and 16.

When the recorder response is satisfactory, the time constant is the important variable affecting peak shape, peak intensity, precision of indicated intensities, and resolution of adjacent lines. Traverse of the same peak with a series of time constants is shown for scans at 32° per minute in Fig. 17 (cf. Figs. 21 and 22 of Chap. 9). Per cent of full-scale deflection as a function of time constants at different scanning rates is correlated in Fig. 18.

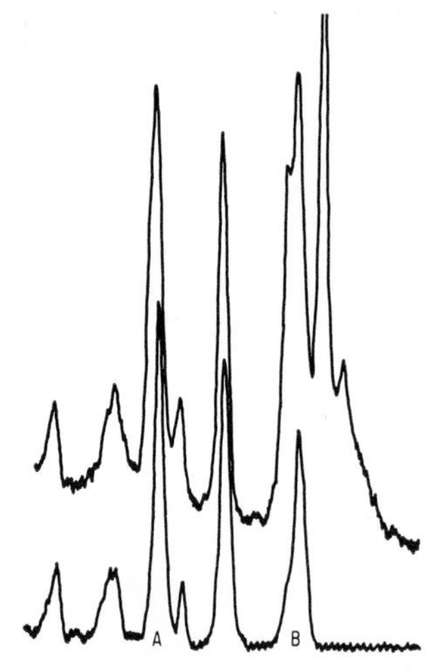

FIG. 14. Effects of synchronized electronic discrimination and filtering of the beam from the x-ray tube with 2 mils of aluminum, 1 mil of brass, and ½ mil of iron foil. Upper: with no filter or discrimination, full-scale intensity 3,200 counts/sec. Lower: with discrimination and filter, full-scale intensity 800 counts/sec. A: Se $K\alpha$ and W $L\gamma_1$. B: Ge $K\alpha$ between W $L\beta_1$ and W $L\beta_2$.

Precision of indicated intensities for approximately 5,000 counts/sec (80 chart units indicated at scale factor of 6,400 counts/sec full scale) is tabulated in distribution curves for 100 values at each scanning rate in Fig. 19. As a matter of general comparison it is apparent that 99 per cent confidence levels for all results agree well with the value of 4.2 per cent that would be predicted for a fixed-count measurement of 5,000 counts.

At FLUO-X-SPEC Laboratory, general-purpose scanning procedures for trace, minor, and major concentrations are conducted at a scanning rate of 8° per minute; only procedures for minor or major concentrations are conducted at rates of 16 or 32° per minute. Standard procedures are summarized in the following paragraphs.

Standard Operating Procedure. The standard method of instrumental examination of samples by scanning for elements with atomic numbers 22 and higher consists of several phases. Portions of phases or selected phases are used if information is desired for only a limited number of elements.

The following instrumentation is used: a modified 100-kv spectrograph manufactured by Philips Electronic Instruments, Inc., equipped with an FA100 tungsten-target x-ray tube; a lithium fluoride analyzing crystal; a 4- by 0.005-in. parallel-blade collimator between the sample and the crystal; a 1½- by 0.023-in. parallel-blade collimator between the crystal and the detector; and a scintillation counter. Standard operating conditions are adjusted by reference to calibration checks and a known standard or standards.

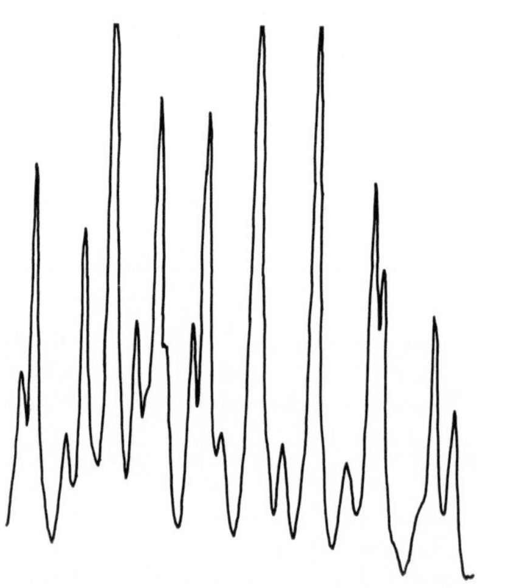

FIG. 15. Standard scan of Spex #1031 rare-earth standard at scanning rate of 2° per minute and time constant of 1 sec.

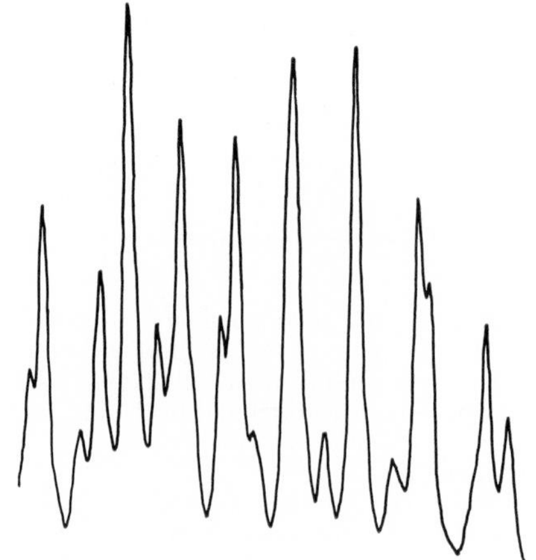

FIG. 16. Accelerated scan of Spex #1031 rare-earth standard at scanning rate of 32° per minute and time constant of 0.14 sec.

A general résumé of the conditions and results of the phases of the standard operation is as follows:

1. X-ray tube power 50 kv, 33 ma; air path in instrument; a modified Model 510 pulse-height analyzer manufactured by Baird-Atomics and an automatic electromechanical baseline-voltage-adjustment unit manufactured by Technical Equipment Corporation used as accessories for synchronized electronic discrimination during complete scan; scan begins at 90° 2θ with goniometer movement at 8° per minute to lower angle limit of 3° 2θ; time constant 0.44 sec; scale factor is set at 800 counts/sec full scale at 90° and automatically switched to 1,600 at 60, 3,200 at 31, and 6,400 counts/sec full scale at 17° 2θ. The chart obtained with synchronized electronic discrimination indicates complete qualitative information and intensity data for semiquantitative determinations of trace and minor concentrations except for interferences due to lines from tube target.

2. Chart is rerolled to starting position and capillary pen changed to ink of different color; pulse-height analyzer and baseline-adjustment unit removed from circuit; other

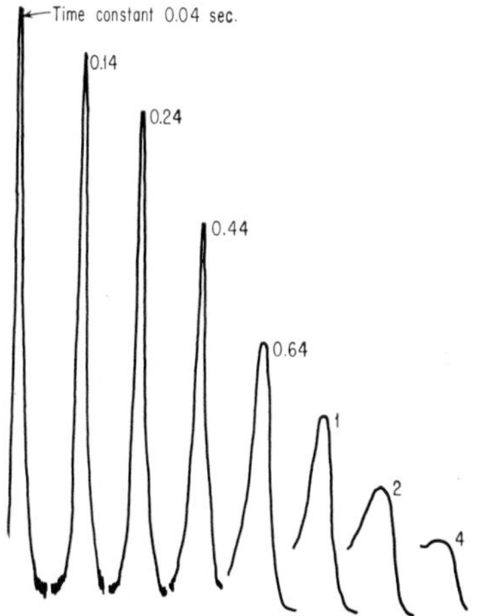

FIG. 17. Effects of time constant at scanning rate of 32° per minute.

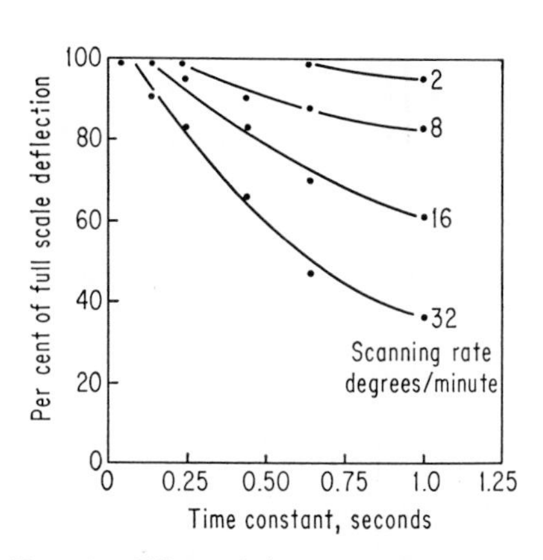

FIG. 18. Effects of time constants at scanning rates of 2, 8, 16, and 32° per minute.

conditions are same as phase 1. The chart overlay shows the gross intensity at all wavelengths with no discrimination of multiple-order diffractions. The goniometer, scale factor, and chart positions are adjusted for reruns of regions where peaks show off-scale values in the basic scan. Intensity information is available for trace, minor, and major concentration determinations to supplement the data from phase 1.

3. A third scan begins at 40 and ends at 28° 2θ; scale factor 400 counts/sec full scale; filter of 2 mils of aluminum foil, 1 mil of brass shim stock, and 0.5 mil of iron foil placed over the window of the x-ray tube; chart rerolled and recorder-pen assembly changed to different color of ink; other conditions same as phase 1. The tungsten lines emitted by the target of the x-ray tube are suppressed so that analytical lines for tungsten, germanium, mercury, gold, selenium, platinum, thallium, gallium, rhenium, and tantalum in the sample can be observed without interferences from the lines emitted from the tube target.

4. This phase uses conditions of phase 1 or 2 depending upon interferences of multiple-order diffractions. In regions of overlapping first-order diffractions of spectra at adjacent wavelengths, a filter with the required absorption edge can be placed in the fluorescent x-ray beam from the sample to preferentially absorb the radiation with the shorter wavelength and improve resolution.

5. Adjust tube power to 100 kv, 16.5 ma; set goniometer to 26° 2θ; adjust chart to proper position and change recorder pen; other conditions of phase 1 or 2. Improved intensity at some wavelengths and additional lines available at other wavelengths to improve determinations of trace concentrations of elements with atomic numbers 38 to 74.

6. X-ray tube power to 50 kv, 33 ma; goniometer adjusted to 90°; helium atmosphere into optical path of spectrograph; other conditions same as phase 1 or 2. Increased intensity is observed for wavelengths higher than 1 Å, and improved determinations of trace concentrations of manganese, chromium, vanadium, titanium, and some of the lanthanides are possible.

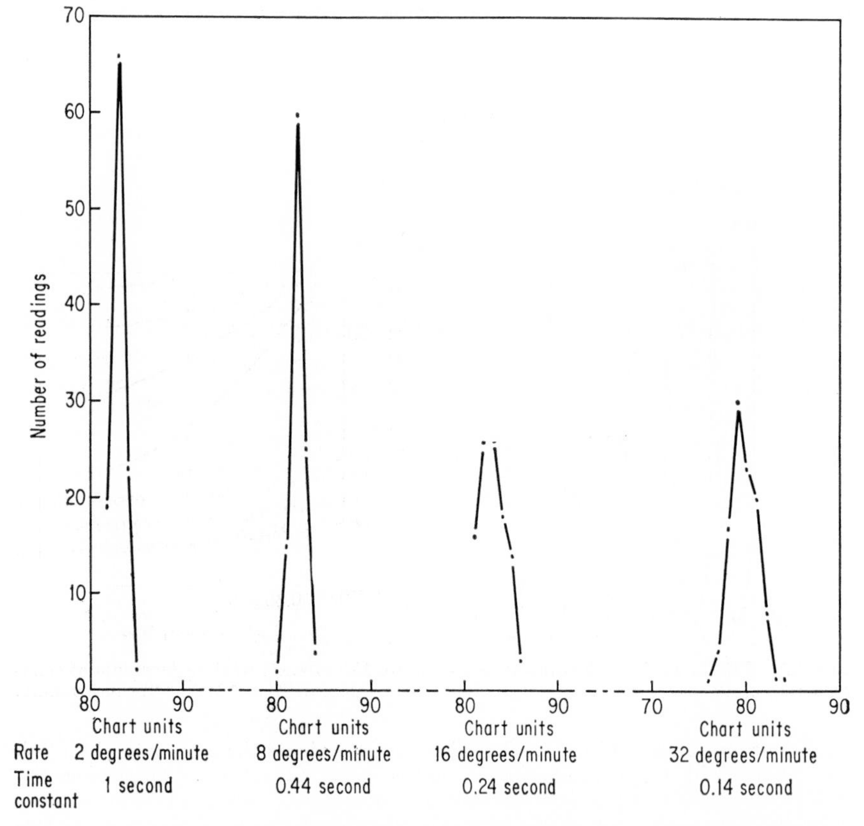

FIG. 19. Precision of replicate runs at different scanning rates and optimum time constants.

Completion of these six phases or those required generally is sufficient for instrumental examination to yield satisfactory data, but the versatility of the method still provides additional means for improved resolution by change of the analyzing crystal or collimator, improved detection limits with slower scanning rates and longer time constants, and other supplementary processes to optimize specific conditions.

With satisfactory completion of the instrumental examination of the sample, a chart record is available that clearly indicates the 2θ angles and intensities of x-rays emitted by elements in the sample.

4. DATA EVALUATION

General. The first objective of the interpretation of the chart is to determine the elements present. Several tables of values of wavelengths, 2θ angles, etc., for the various analyzing crystals are now available, and it is possible to tabulate all information from the chart for interpretation by reference to the appropriate tables. This process is sometimes time-consuming, and in the interest of better efficiency for chart reading, a direct-reading template was developed[1] by reference to the tables prepared by Powers.[5] The template is shown mounted on a rotary-drum illuminator manufactured by Technical Equipment Corporation in Fig. 20. A chart in process of being read is shown on the illuminator in Fig. 21.

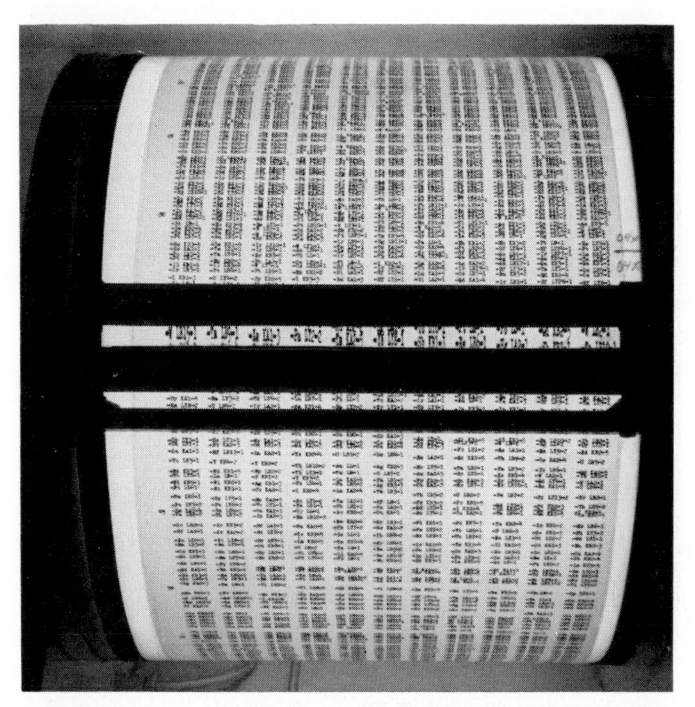

Fig. 20. Chart-reader template mounted on rotary-drum illuminator.

The chart is used as a work sheet to label the peaks to show the element or elements that can be associated with each peak. All possibilities for a particular peak are shown by direct reference to the template, and cross checks for indications of an element at other 2θ angles are made easily. Completion of the qualitative interpretation of the chart provides a tabulation of the elements present in the sample and indicates the elements contributing x-ray intensities at the peaks shown at the different 2θ angles.

The semiquantitative evaluation of the concentration of an element is primarily dependent upon the net intensity of a line characteristic of the element. The net intensity can be measured directly if no other elements exhibit x-ray intensities at the 2θ angle of the element to be determined. If the x-ray intensity at a particular 2θ angle includes contributions from more than one element, the desired net intensity for the particular element can be calculated from reference to other unobscured lines for that element. It is generally most convenient to establish calibration systems by reference to one particular line for each element.

In the ideal case where the unknown samples can be preclassified on the basis of similar overall characteristics to known reference standards, subsequent reference can be made to a specific calibration curve established with these reference standards by a simple correlation of net peak intensity and concentration. Such a case is summarized in the calibration curve of Fig. 22 and in experimental results in Table 1 for some uranium-bearing sandstone ores all mined from the same area. This mine shows very little variation in overall mineralization from sample to sample except for changes in uranium concentration, and x-ray values determined by this simple calibration system checked very well with chemical assays for several hundred samples.

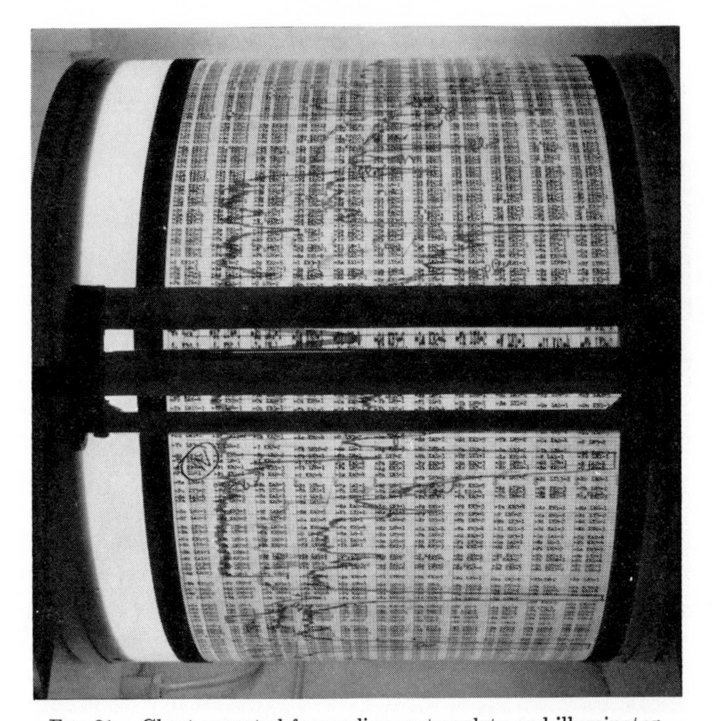

Fig. 21. Chart mounted for reading on template and illuminator.

The general plot of intensity vs. concentration for many types of uranium-bearing materials such as lignites, lignite ashes, sandstones, and other common ores that have significantly different overall mineralization is shown in Fig. 23. Although the chemical values do not represent the accuracy required for use as primary standards, the accuracy is believed to be within ± 5 per cent of the uranium content, and it is obvious that no single linear curve will suffice to correlate all values of intensity and concentration properly.

There are several curves that could be defined in Fig. 23 to represent typical materials of different classes within the total group of 200 samples, but success of this approach is dependent upon the choice of calibration curve that is assumed to be proper for the unknown sample. As degrees of mineralization vary considerably and the information to use for proper preclassification of the unknown sample becomes limited, the choice of the calibration curve becomes more difficult and unreliable.

To assist in the establishment and choice of proper calibration information for wide

Table 1. Replicate Analyses of Uranium Standards

	S124	S125	S126	S127	128	S129
	Chemical assay, % uranium					
	0.049	0.108	0.179	0.248	0.458	0.665
	X-ray values, % uranium					
1	0.052	0.10	0.18	0.24	0.48	0.66
2	0.055	0.11	0.17	0.23	0.46	0.67
3	0.050	0.11	0.18	0.25	0.48	0.67
4	0.050	0.11	0.18	0.24	0.47	0.67
5	0.048	0.11	0.18	0.25	0.47	0.65
6	0.052	0.12	0.18	0.24	0.46	0.67
7	0.045	0.11	0.18	0.25	0.46	0.67
8	0.050	0.11	0.18	0.25	0.46	0.66
9	0.045	0.10	0.18	0.25	0.46	0.66
10	0.048	0.11	0.18	0.24	0.45	0.67

Operating conditions: 16° per minute scanning rate, time constant 0.24 sec, samples completely removed from sample carrier and agitated in individually sealed plastic cups between each run in sequence.

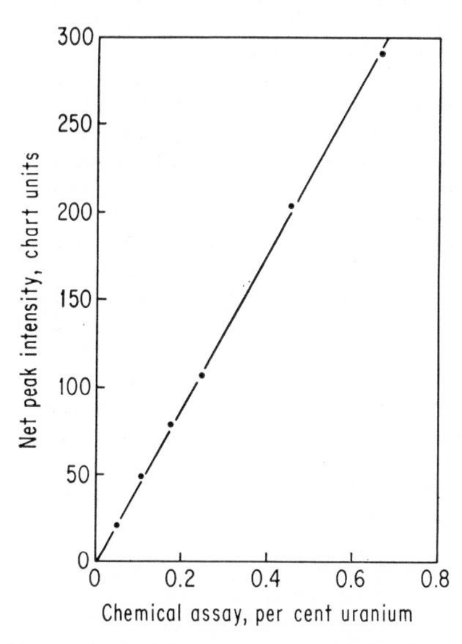

FIG. 22. Calibration curve for suite of uranium-ore samples from same mine. Net peak intensities equivalent to 32 counts/sec per chart unit. Scanning rate 16° per minute. Time constant 0.24 sec.

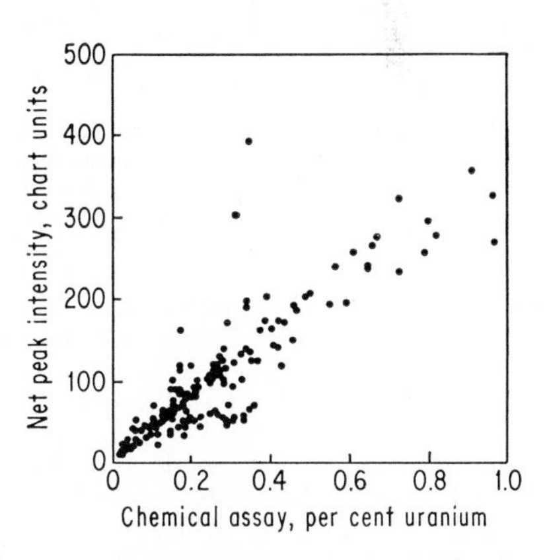

FIG. 23. Composite of results for lignite, lignite ash, sandstone, and other uranium ores. Net peak intensities equivalent to 32 counts/sec per chart unit. Scanning rate 16° per minute. Time constant 0.24 sec.

varieties of sample types several procedures can be used: (1) conversion of all the different sample types to a standard form to enable direct reference to a simple curve, (2) addition of a reference material to the matrix for use in normalization of matrix effects, and (3) instrumental measurement of systemic properties in addition to net peak intensities for use as reference parameters. Procedures for 1 and 2 and some procedures for 3, such as absorptiometric analyses with thin layers of the sample, generally involve sample preparation too complex for practical applications in qualitative and semiquantitative techniques. These and other techniques are used, however, in quantitative analysis and are described in Chap. 36.

Several procedures have been outlined for evaluation of instrumental parameters for normalization of matrix effects for variations of sample character, and the simplest is based on measurements of intensity of background radiation scattered by the sample as a systemic parameter. Kemp and Anderman[6] and Kalman and Heller[7] base their procedures on measurement of intensity of scattered radiation at a particular wavelength for use as a reference parameter in a ratioing calculation to normalize matrix effects. Salmon and Blackledge[8] use background at the wavelength of the line to be measured for establishment of families of curves relating net peak intensity and concentration with background intensity as the reference parameter.

The chart record obtained in the experimental evaluation of the sample provides sufficient data for application of scattered background-intensity parameters. Background can be read directly at 2θ angles where no peaks occur or by interpolation of background levels between properly resolved 2θ angles exhibiting no peaks.

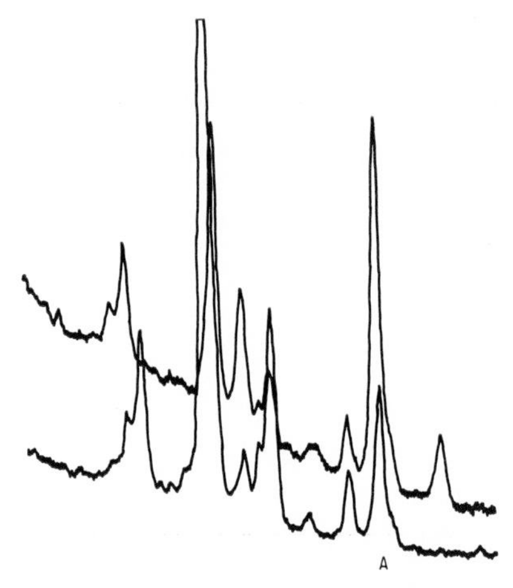

Fig. 24. Comparable charts for uranium samples. Upper: sandstone containing 0.304 per cent uranium. Lower: lignite ash containing 0.312 per cent uranium. Uranium $L\alpha$ peak at A.

A simple multielement system[9] was devised to yield results based on the background parameters with a minimum of effort and nominal accuracy within ± 50 per cent of the amount of the element present. The inverse relationship between overall mass absorption coefficient of the matrix and scattered background radiation intensity at a particular wavelength was demonstrated to show the validity of using scattered background radiation intensity at that wavelength as a reference parameter for normalization of absorption effects.

The comparison of charts for two different types of uranium-bearing materials in Fig. 24 shows the general basis of the technique. Concentration of uranium per unit of peak intensity for the lignite ash is more than twice the corresponding value for the sandstone ore. This is compensated, however, by the lower background displayed by the lignite ash.

Background Reference Parameter at Peak Wavelength. Experimental results obtained for sensitivity ratios and background values for the uranium-ore samples (the same suite shown in Fig. 23) are plotted in Fig. 25 with additional values for processed samples containing more than 60 per cent uranium. Tables were prepared from Fig. 25 by tabulation of background values and the corresponding sensitivity ratios. The x-ray values for concentration of uranium in the ore samples as calculated from these tables are shown in Fig. 26 in comparison with the chemical assays. X-ray values for only 10 to 12 samples of the 200 deviate more than 10 per cent from the chemical assay.

The inflection at point B of Fig. 25 and the change in slope of AB to less effective normalization of sample character demonstrate a limitation of the system for samples containing high concentrations of the element to be determined. Dilution of the sample bulk to reduce the concentration of the element is required for direct examination of the samples with high concentrations.

Background Reference Parameter at Absorption Edge. Continuing investigations of the background parameters[1] indicated the significance of the intensity of scattered background radiation at the absorption edge of the element to be determined (the L_I edge when L spectrum lines are measured). Sensitivity ratios and background values at the absorption edge (L_I) for the ore and process samples are plotted in Fig. 27. The log-log plot in this case shows a single linear relationship that extends from sensitivity ratios of 5 to 200 ppm per unit of net peak intensity with corresponding background values of 120 and 8 chart units at the absorption edge. This range represents the extremes of low concentrations in lignites to the 99.99+ oxide concentrates. Calculated concentration values from the x-ray data for the ore samples are plotted vs. chemical concentrations in Fig. 28.

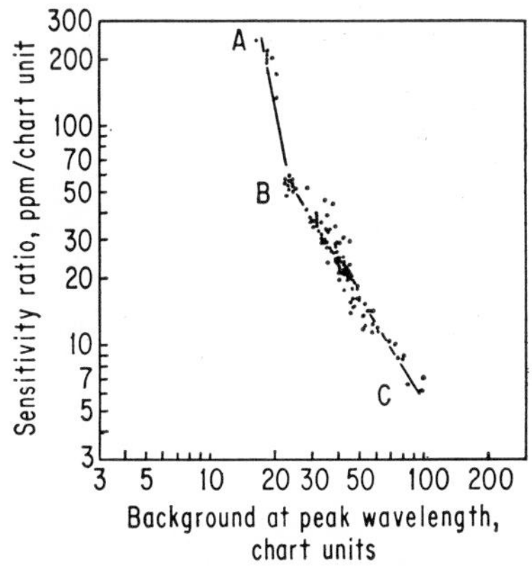

FIG. 25. Background at wavelength of uranium $L\alpha$ peak and sensitivity ratios for uranium ores and process concentrates. *AB*: process concentrates. *BC*: ores. Chart unit equivalent to 32 counts/sec. Scanning rate 16° per minute. Time constant 0.24 sec.

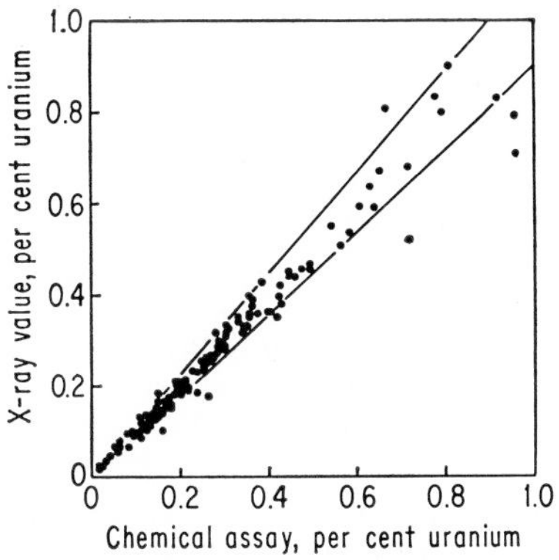

FIG. 26. X-ray values determined by parameters of Fig. 25 vs. chemical assays for uranium ores. Scanning rate 16° per minute. Time constant 0.24 sec. Solid lines represent 10 per cent accuracy limits.

The major difficulties with application of the background parameters at the absorption edge result from excessive enhancement effects by high concentrations of elements with radiation at shorter wavelengths than the absorption edge of the element to be determined or from the presence of high concentrations of elements with absorption edges between the wavelengths of the absorption edge and the peak of the element to be determined. The background parameters at the peak position seem to yield better results for these situations that are typical of many minerals and ores.

There is some overlap of light-element matrices and aqueous solutions in extension of the calibration systems demonstrated in Figs. 25 and 27, but organic solutions and other liquids with specific gravities that vary from unity generally require special consideration.

Calibration systems with background parameters are convenient and reliable to apply if proper precautions are taken to optimize experimental conditions to obtain charts with high net peak intensities above background and with moderate background intensities to provide a significant range of measurement for correlation to corresponding sensitivity ratios. The chart is ideal for the application because the complete picture of peak and background profiles is presented to enable positive identification of elements present in the sample, to allow proper allocation of intensities at

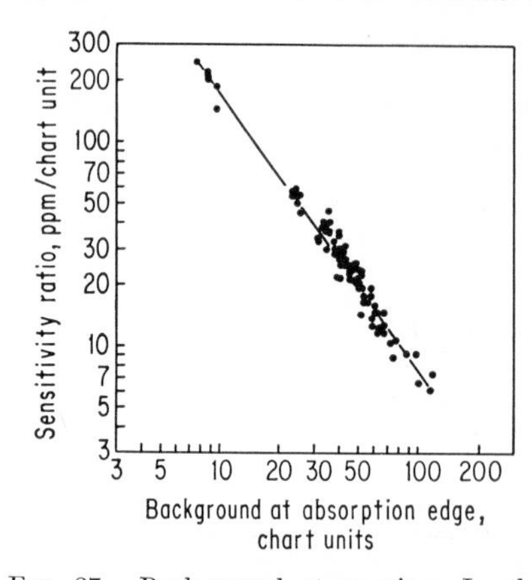

FIG. 27. Background at uranium L_I absorption edge and sensitivity ratios for uranium ores and process concentrates. Chart unit equivalent to 32 counts/sec. Scanning rate 16° per minute. Time constant 0.24 sec.

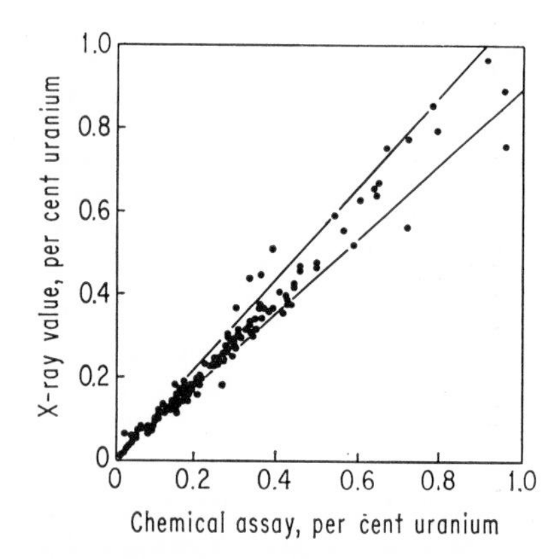

FIG. 28. X-ray values determined by parameters of Fig. 27 vs. chemical assays for uranium ores. Scanning rate 16° per minute. Time constant 0.24 sec. Solid lines represent 10 per cent accuracy limits.

all 2θ angles, and to show presence of elements that cause special precautions to be taken in application of background parameters at the absorption edge or peak wavelength for normalization of matrix effects.

REFERENCES CITED

1. M. Salmon, The Effects of Operating Variables in the Application of Multielement Calibration Systems for Fluorescent X-ray Spectrographic Analyses of Mineral Samples, in W. M. Mueller (ed.), *Advances in X-ray Analysis*, vol. 4, p. 433, Plenum Press, New York, 1961.
2. M. Salmon, Improved Trace Analysis with the Use of Synchronized Electronic Discrimination in an X-ray Scanning Procedure, in W. M. Mueller, et al. (eds.), *Advances in X-ray Analysis*, vol. 7, p. 604, Plenum Press, New York, 1964.
3. M. Salmon, Practical Applications of Filters in X-ray Spectrography, in W. M. Mueller and M. Fay (eds.), *Advances in X-ray Analysis*, vol. 6, p. 301, Plenum Press, New York.
4. M. Salmon, "Fast Scanning Method for Fluorescent X-ray Spectrography," Twelfth Annual Symposium on Spectroscopy, Chicago, Ill., 1961.
5. M. Powers, *X-ray Fluorescent Spectrometer Conversion Tables*, Philips Electronics, Mount Vernon, N.Y., 1957.
6. G. Anderman and J. Kemp, Scattered X-rays as Internal Standards in X-ray Emission Spectroscopy, *Anal. Chem.*, **30**:1306 (1958).
7. Z. Kalman and L. Heller, Theoretical Study of X-ray Fluorescent Determination of Traces of Heavy Elements in a Light Matrix, *Anal. Chem.*, **34**:946 (1962).
8. M. Salmon and J. Blackledge, "Rapid and Improved Mineral Analyses with Fluorescent X-ray Spectrography," Pittsburgh Conference on Analytical Chemistry and Applied Spectroscopy, Pittsburgh, Pa., 1956.
9. M. Salmon, A Highly Simplified Multielement Calibration System for Semiquantitative X-ray Spectrographic Analysis, in W. M. Mueller (ed.), *Advances in X-ray Analysis*, vol. 3, p. 139, Plenum Press, New York, 1960.

Chapter 36

QUANTITATIVE TECHNIQUES

E. L. Gunn

Humble Oil & Refining Company

1. INTRODUCTION

The basic premise of quantitative x-ray fluorescence analysis is that the intensity of characteristic fluorescent x-rays emitted by an element under arbitrary conditions of excitation is proportional to the quantity of that element which emits them. The absolute amount of characteristic radiant energy emitted by the element per unit of time could be calculated approximately from fundamental physical relations, but at the present state of development this approach is much too involved and tedious for general use. In practice the intensity of radiation emitted by an element in an unknown is not of itself an absolute parameter for measuring concentration; rather, its value in terms of relative internal consistency or in comparison with that of a reference substance—a common practice in several types of instrumental analysis—is used as a measure of concentration. Thus completely theoretical treatments still are unreliable and recourse must be taken to methods which, to a certain extent, are empirical for providing highest accuracy.

The proportionality between concentration and intensity upon which all x-ray emission analyses depend often is not directly linear. Furthermore, if a linear relationship were established for a given system this by no means assures that the analysis of a specimen of that general type but of uncertain composition will be accurate by reference. The reasons for this are based fundamentally on the effects of x-ray–matter interactions which take place between elemental components themselves within the material, or possibly with minute separate physical entities or particles existing therein. Interaction effects will, of course, be encountered in varying degrees in any practical scheme of analysis by x-rays. Ideally, one never totally escapes from these effects but successfully surmounts them only by compensation or by reducing them to an insignificant level. Interaction effects, therefore, probably produce the most perplexing problems with which the analyst must contend to obtain accurate results. Both theory and application recognize these effects, as discussions in previous chapters of this book have pointed out. The examples which are to be presented in forthcoming sections of the present chapter further amplify this recognition by presenting a variety of specific means which have been employed to cope with them.

As has been pointed out, quantitative x-ray fluorescence analysis depends upon relative comparisons of intensity for standardization and interpretation. Standardization may involve reference intensity measurements which are internal with reference to the sample, external, or a combination of both. The methods and procedures to be presented illustrate something of the variety of techniques which have been devised for quantitative interpretation. Examples which illustrate these techniques were selected from among a number of others, some of which might have served as well for illustration as the ones selected. The main objective, however, is to use illustrations which represent a range of differences in technique, interpretation, and the fundamental concepts upon which they are based, rather than to catalogue methods.

Copious use of methods described in the literature has been made for selections which illustrate different techniques. The outline of methods, key concepts, and illustrative data necessarily have been condensed—particularly through tabulation—not only to conserve space but to provide a functional format which emphasizes working essentials. If additional details are desired, they may be obtained by reference to the literature cited or to other sources bearing on the same subject.

2. USE OF THIN FILM AS SAMPLE SUPPORT

Fundamental Basis. The analysis of a minute amount of sample supported by thin film probably is the simplest system one encounters in x-ray analysis because, within a limit, it is essentially free of the interaction effects produced by absorption and enhancement in specimens of normal depth.[1] Furthermore, it provides a means of obtaining the ultimate in sensitivity using conventional apparatus. It appears appropriate that the use of thin film be the first considered among the various quantitative techniques. The simplicity and high sensitivity afforded by thin-film analysis can be understood by the application of certain basic principles of absorption and emission.

Assume that a thin, uniform film deposit is irradiated by an x-ray beam and that a characteristic fluorescent line of an element is thereby excited. The intensity I of the fluorescent line from a minute unit of volume in the deposit having a depth dx is given by the following expression:

$$dI = C \csc \phi_1 I_0 e^{-(\mu_1 \csc \phi_1 + \mu_2 \csc \phi_2)\rho x}\, dx \tag{1}$$

where C = proportionality constant
I_0 = incident intensity
ϕ_1 = angle between incident beam and sample surface
ϕ_2 = angle between emergent beam and sample surface
μ_1 = effective absorption coefficient of incident beam
μ_2 = effective absorption coefficient of emergent beam
ρ = sample density
x = sample thickness

If the sample deposit is kept very thin, the absorption of x-rays by it will be very small or practically zero. This signifies that the exponential term of the foregoing equation approximates a value of unity, or

$$dI = C \csc \phi_1 I_0\, dx \tag{2}$$

Incrementally, one may write

$$\Delta I = C \csc \phi_1 I_0\, \Delta x \tag{3}$$

For a constant-deposit area,

$$\Delta N \sim \Delta x \tag{4}$$

where N is the number of atoms of the element in the deposit which emit fluorescence. Hence

$$\Delta I = C' \csc \phi_1 I_0\, \Delta N \tag{5}$$

Thus, in the region of limited thickness, the physical significance of this expression is that a direct linear proportionality between mass per unit area and intensity will be observed. As long as sample absorption is negligible, this proportionality will be maintained. Illustrations of thin-film applications will now be given.

Film Measurement of Surface Oxidation. Pfeiffer and Zemany demonstrated the use of filter paper as a film support for microgram amounts of zinc and other metals.[2]

Rhodin[3] has employed thin film as a support in measuring the surface effects of passivity and oxidation on steels. In this application ultra-thin deposits on the film were made both by evaporation (10^{-5} mm Hg) and by chemical action on the metal surface. An outline of the method of analysis for surface oxidation products on steels is given in Table 1.

Table 1. Film Measurement of Surface Oxidation

Sample treatment	From the metal oxide film by floating the metal film, reinforced with Formvar, onto a solution of 5% HNO_3, 0.5% $K_2Cr_2O_7$ at 60° C for 30 to 100 min. Scoop the reinforced film onto ¼-mil Mylar film; metal and Formvar are dissolved away. Isolate oxide film from metal by anhydrous 1% bromine-methanol in inert-gas atmosphere. Metal and oxide films are weighed with microbalance
Instrument	North American Philips. X-ray tube selected for low background
Standardization	Use both microcolorimetric chemical analysis and microbalance on film standards
Excitation	Tungsten target, 50 kv, 35 ma
Optics	LiF crystal, 6-in. collimator with 0.005-in. leaves
Analytical lines	$K\alpha$ lines, first order, for Fe, Ni, Cr; $L\alpha$ lines for Nb and Mo
Detection	Geiger counter, argon-filled
Register	Use fixed time scaling to give probable error of 1.0%
Analytical range	1–100 γ

The agreement of x-ray with microchemical analysis on the same films was found to be excellent.

The effects of film thickness on x-ray intensity are given in Tables 2 and 3. The symbol γ is for micrograms.

Table 2. Effect of Film Thickness of Pure Metals on Specific Radiation Intensity*

Metal	Surface concentration, γ/sq cm†	Approx film thickness, Å‡	Total intensity, counts/sec	Specific intensity, (counts/sec)/(γ)(sq cm)
Iron	7.7	97	128	16.6
Nickel	6.3	70	170	26.9
Chromium	12.0	169	102	8.5
Iron	12.1	153	200	16.5
Nickel	11.1	125	298	26.8
Chromium	20.5	289	174	8.5
Iron	19.0	240	314	16.5
Nickel	17.8	200	455	26.7
Chromium	31.1	437	264	8.5
Iron	26.2	332	430	16.4

* From Rhodin, *Anal. Chem.*, **27**:1857 (1955). Courtesy of *Analytical Chemistry.*
† Obtained by dividing weight of film by its area.
‡ Estimated from surface concentration by using bulk density.

Film Depth and Linearity. The amount of sample deposit which can be placed on thin films without incurring absorption loss is significant because an excessive depth of sample causing such loss will, as has been pointed out, affect the linear relation between intensity and concentration. Gunn[4] has made a study of depth and absorption on several inorganic salts deposited from solution onto Mylar film. Although

Table 3. Effect of Film Thickness of Type 304 Stainless Steel on Specific Radiation Intensity*

Component metal	Surface concentration γ/sq cm†	Approx film thickness, Å‡	Total intensity, counts/sec	Specific intensity, (counts/sec)/(γ)(sq cm)
Pure metal:				
Chromium	31.0	437	264.0	8.5
Iron	26.2	332	430.0	16.4
Nickel	17.8	200	455.0	26.7
Type 304	....	104		
Chromium	1.5	....	12.8	8.5
Iron	7.1	....	115.7	16.3
Nickel	0.7	....	18.7	26.8
Type 304	....	410		
Chromium	6.4	....	55.3	8.5
Iron	23.0	....	372.6	16.2
Nickel	2.6	....	68.6	26.6
Type 304	....	808		
Chromium	12.1	....	104.1	8.6
Iron	53.8	....	866.2	16.1
Nickel	6.2	....	161.2	26.5
Type 304	....	1300		
Chromium	18.5	....	160.9	8.7
Iron	75.7	....	1,211.2	16.0
Nickel	8.5	....	216.8	26.4

* From Rhodin, *Anal. Chem.*, **27**:1857 (1955). Courtesy of *Analytical Chemistry.*
† Obtained by dividing weight of film by its area.
‡ Estimated from surface concentration by using bulk density.

uniform deposition onto the film is difficult, the results give a reasonable estimate of the upper limit of the amount of deposit for linearity to maintain. Figures 1 and 2 illustrate the influence of absorption for both the x-ray emission and transmittance of a selected wavelength through thin deposits of iron. The experimental points are somewhat scattered at higher concentration values because of the nonuniformity of the deposits, but departure from linearity is shown at about 150 γ in both figures. The transmittance properties shown in Fig. 2 are for wavelengths on either side of that for the *K*-absorption edge of iron (1.743 Å). Although the scatter of experimental points makes the fit of the curves only an uncertain approximation, it appears that the absorption of 1.54 Å is greater than that for 1.94 Å, which should be expected because of the higher absorption coefficient of iron for 1.5-4Å x-rays.

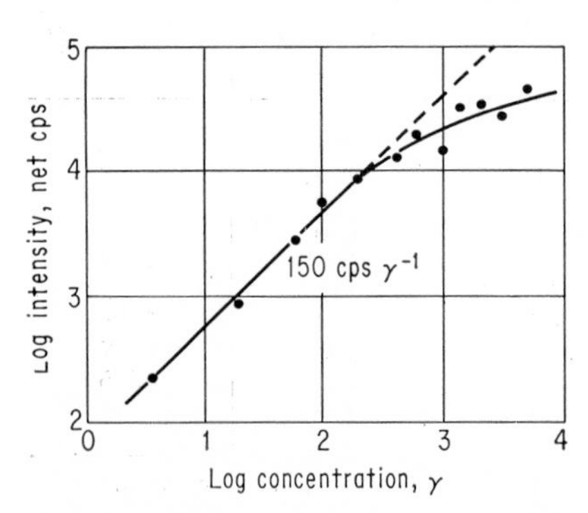

Fig. 1. Relation of fluorescent intensity of Fe *Kα* to concentration of iron (ferric oxalate). [*Gunn, Anal. Chem.*, **33**:921 (1961). *Courtesy of Analytical Chemistry.*]

Such measurements made on aqueous deposits indicate the manner in which the intensity of each is affected by deposit depth. The linear sensitivity, upper concentration limit of linearity, and concentration for maximum change in sensitivity shown in Table 4 were obtained by these measurements.

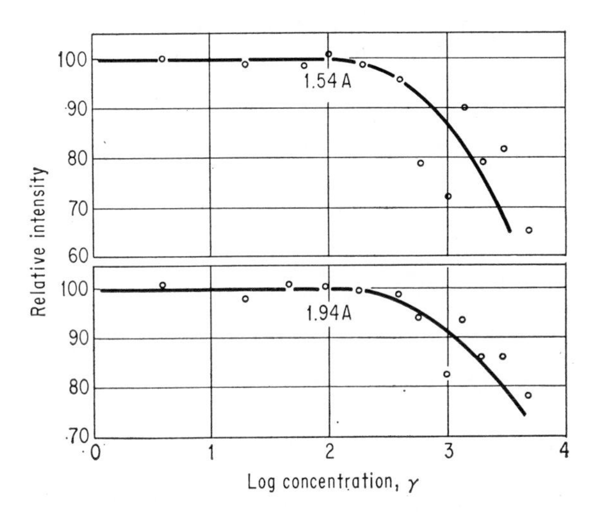

FIG. 2. X-ray transmittance of ferric oxalate. [*Gunn, Anal. Chem.*, **33**:921 (1961). *Courtesy of Analytical Chemistry.*]

Table 4. The Effect of Deposit Depth on Intensity

	Sensitivity, cps γ^{-1}	Linearity limit, γ	Max sensitivity change, cps γ^{-2}
Ca(20)	0.7	400	
Ti(22)	5.9	100	200
Fe(26)	60	100	250
Cu(29)	63	100	300
Sr(38)	4.9	1,000	2,500
Mo(42)	1.4	>20,000	

The sensitivity of the detector, absorption by the nonmetallic components in the deposit, optical geometry, fluorescent yield, and distribution of energies in the primary excitation spectrum are factors which account for the marked differences between elements shown by these data. The upper limit of sensitivity and point of maximum change tend to increase with the atomic number of the element.

3. THE USE OF SCATTERED RADIATION AS CALIBRATION REFERENCE

Andermann and Kemp[5] have shown that the use of a scattering-ratio technique is a valuable tool in compensating for various instrumental and sample variables. Both theoretical and experimental considerations were made of the use of scattered radiation as a calibration reference. Use of this concept has been made in determining trace metals in oil, employing both single-channel and multichannel instruments.

Single-channel Instrument. The use of scattered radiation as the calibration reference in fluorescence analysis is very satisfactory where the element measured occurs in low concentrations in a low-atomic-number matrix. In the Humble Research Laboratories, Baytown, Tex., a single-channel instrument is used regularly as a means of measuring the nickel content of oils, especially deasphalted oils which are used as components of feed stocks to catalytic cracking. The conditions for the analysis are given in Table 5 for the direct measurement of nickel in oil.

Table 5. Analysis of Catalytic Feed-stock Oil for Nickel: Single-channel Instrument

Sample treatment	None
Instrument	Philips Electronics single-channel inverted geometry, sample cell with ¼-mil Mylar bottom
Standardization	Use oils of the type being analyzed on which chemical values for nickel are available for x-ray fluorescence standardization
Excitation	Tungsten target, 55 kv, 40 ma
Optics	LiF crystal, port collimator 0.02-in. leaf spacing, arm collimator 0.02 in.
Analytical lines	Ni $K\alpha$ 1.660 Å, scattered radiation at 1.680 Å
Detection	Scintillation counter, pulse-height discrimination
Register	Fixed count (102,400) taken at each position; four replicates taken in sequence for the pair of positions
Interpretation	Take the average ratio of the intensity of the nickel peak to that of the scatter position for four replicates as the parameter of nickel concentration. A high and a low standard are measured concurrently with the unknown
Analytical range	0.2 to 10 ppm nickel, linear response

The time required for measuring an oil sample with four replicates is approximately 14 min.

A typical set of measurements is exemplified as follows:

A reference standard containing 0.20 ppm nickel gave an intensity ratio of 0.8657.

A reference standard containing 3.10 ppm nickel gave an intensity ratio of 0.9482.

The unknown gave an intensity ratio of 0.9154, for which a value of 1.95 ppm nickel is interpolated.

A test of the accuracy of the measurement has been made by comparing x-ray fluorescence with chemical colorimetric values obtained on the same samples. On a set of 35 typical samples ranging in nickel content from 0.2 to 3 ppm nickel the average deviation between methods was 0.10 ppm and the maximum 0.27 ppm, with a single determination being made on each sample by each method.

The precision of the method on a day-to-day basis is shown by the data of Table 6.

Table 6. Precision of Nickel Measurement on a Typical Oil on Different Days*

Day	*Ni, ppm*
1	2.89
2	3.09
3	2.85
4	2.87
5	3.06
6	3.06
7	2.97
8	3.02
9	3.12
10	3.11
11	2.89
12	3.01
13	2.92
14	2.89
Avg.	2.99

σ = 0.10, coefficient of variation = 3.3%

* Unpublished data by V. Harleston, Humble Research and Development Laboratories.

A change in sample composition can influence the character of the spectrum in the region in which measurements are made. If scattered radiation is used as a reference the intensity ratio will be affected, and this in turn will produce an inaccu racy in the result unless compensation is made in the interpretation for the effect of the composition change. This type of interference is well illustrated in the present method by the effect which the presence of sulfur in the oil produces on the spectrum. This is shown graphically in Fig. 3. The nickel $K\alpha$ peak is measured at 48.70° and the scatter background at 49.3° 2θ, the latter being the position of the W $L\gamma$ peak of the primary

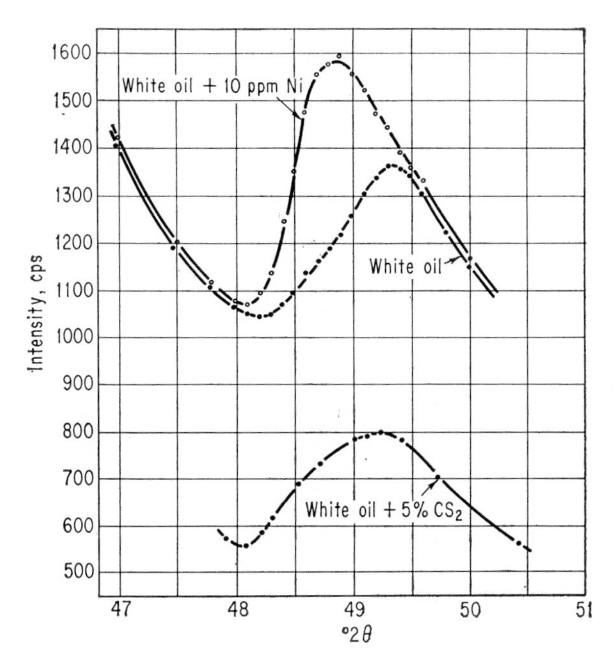

Fig. 3. X-ray fluorescent spectrum of nickel in oil. Each point 102,400 counts. Tungsten target, 55 kv, 40 ma.

beam. Not only is the intensity considerably lowered by the presence of sulfur but the character of the profile is modified as well; specifically, the peak is broadened by the presence of sulfur. The effect where nonsulfur standards are used for the nickel calibration is to increase the apparent nickel value where sulfur is present in the unknown; e.g., in the white oil it was observed that, in the presence of 3 per cent added

Table 7. Analysis of Catalytic Feed-stock Oil for Nickel: Multichannel Instrument

Sample treatment......	None
Instrument...........	Applied Research Laboratories XOQ, multichannel, fixed optics, inverted geometry, sample cell with ¼-mil Mylar bottom
Standardization.......	Use oils which have been analyzed chemically for nickel or synthetic blends of known nickel content for reference
Excitation............	Tungsten target, 50 kv, 35 ma
Optics................	LiF curved crystals, bent to 8 in. radius, ground to 4 in. radius. Primary slit 20 mils, secondary 10 mils
Analytical lines........	Ni $K\alpha$, background at position 0.01 Å removed from Ni $K\alpha$ position
Detection.............	Multitron (Applied Research Laboratories)
Register..............	Count integration for 30 min
Interpretation.........	Electrometer or strip-chart deflection is proportional to nickel concentration
Analytical range.......	About 0.1 ppm and greater

sulfur, a measured value of nickel 0.4 ppm greater than the actual amount present was obtained. Empirical corrections to compensate for the effects of sulfur are applied to provide an accurate value.

Multichannel Instrument. Hale and King[6] also have used scattered radiation as a reference for measuring nickel in oil at the 0.1 ppm level with an x-ray fluorescence multichannel instrument. Characteristic nickel and scattered radiation are measured

Table 8. Results of Analyses of Actual Plant Samples*

Plant sample description	Sulfur, %	Nickel, ppm	
		X-ray	Chem. lab.
Refinery 1			
High-sulfur visbreaker gas oil	1.72	0.14	0.14
Low-sulfur visbreaker gas oil	1.45	0.09	0.06
Pitch distillate	1.66	0.30	0.43
660° F + virgin gas oil	0.98	0.01	<0.02
Vacuum gas oil	1.31	0.13	0.12
Heavy virgin gas oil	1.17	−0.01	<0.02
Refinery 2			
Mixed crude gas oil	2.27	0.05	<0.02
Vacuum gas oil	2.77	−0.02	<0.02
Vacuum gas oil	2.65	0.10	0.04
Gas oil	1.23	−0.01	<0.02
Vacuum gas oil	2.28	−0.01	<0.02
Heavy gas oil	2.99	0.12	0.12
Refinery 3			
Light gas oil	0.78	0.10	0.04
Vacuum gas oil	0.94	0.01	0.05
Combined gas oil	0.88	0.18	0.24
Heavy blend	1.67	0.23	0.12
Refinery 4			
Mixed crude heavy gas oil	1.32	1.83	1.95
Mixed crude light gas oil	1.24	0.00	0.05
Mixed crude medium gas oil	1.22	0.55	0.57
Mixed crude medium gas oil	0.26	0.28	0.20
Mixed crude blended gas oil	0.43	0.04	0.09
Refinery 5			
Mixed crude gas oil no. 1	0.26	0.01	<0.05
Mixed crude gas oil no. 2	0.46	0.39	0.39

* From Hale and King, *Anal. Chem.*, **33**:74 (1961). Courtesy of *Analytical Chemistry*.

simultaneously, the latter being measured at a position only 0.01 Å from the nickel peak. The conditions used are summarized in Table 7.

Under the foregoing conditions of measurement, matrix changes produced by carbon-hydrogen ratio difference or by sulfur content have relatively minor effects on the result for nickel. The data shown in Table 8 illustrate this, as well as excellent agreement of the x-ray with chemical analysis.

When applied to somewhat lower concentrations of nickel, i.e., 0.01 to 0.6 ppm, the x-ray results still were in excellent agreement with chemical. The standard deviation of the x-ray values on 21 samples in this range was 0.035 ppm.

4. METHOD OF STANDARD ADDITION

The method of standard addition is well known in spectroscopy and has been applied successfully in optical emission analysis for a number of years. Jones[7] has applied this concept very effectively to the determination of sulfur in gasoline. It not only serves as a means of standardization but compensates for the adverse influences of matrix change as well. The conditions of analysis are outlined in Table 9.

Table 9. Determination of Sulfur in Gasolines

Sample treatment	Use two 50.0-ml portions of the sample. To one portion add 5.00 ml of sulfur-free isooctane, to the other 5.00 ml of a sulfur standard containing 0.13 g of sulfur per 5 ml (sulfur-free isooctane and di-tert-butyl disulfide are recommended for the latter)
Instrument	Single channel, inverted geometry, cell bottom ¼-mil Mylar
Standardization	Achieved through sample treatment
Excitation	Tungsten target, 55 kv, 40 ma
Optics	NaCl crystal, port collimator 0.125-in. spacing, arm collimator 0.02 in.
Analytical lines	Sulfur $K\alpha$ 5.373 Å, background 5.353 Å
Detection	Flow proportional. Use helium flow in optical path to minimize absorption loss
Register	Select fixed counts for peak and background to provide pre-selected precision desired
Analytical range	Greater than 0.002% sulfur. Modification in standardization is applied for samples containing more than 0.15% sulfur
Interpretation	Calculate from following relations:

$$E = \frac{I_A C}{I_B - I_A} \tag{6}$$

where E = weight in grams of sulfur in solution A
I_A = net counts per second for solution A
A = solution without added sulfur
I_B = net counts per second for solution B
B = solution with added sulfur
C = weight in grams of sulfur added to B

Then

$$\text{Sulfur, wt. }\% = 2E/D \tag{7}$$

where D = specific gravity of original sample

Jones discussed the selection of optimum conditions of counting to provide desired precision levels in terms of the statistics of counting.[7] The reported agreement of x-ray with lamp sulfur values on the same samples is excellent. The precision and accuracy of the method are illustrated by the data in Table 10.

The choice of an ethylenediamine ditartrate (EDDT) crystal rather than of sodium chloride may actually provide greater sensitivity for sulfur. Although the sodium chloride crystal may be a more efficient analyzer in general, Cl $K\alpha$ emission from it may produce a high background which tends to offset its advantage over EDDT for measuring sulfur.

Table 10. Precision and Accuracy*

Base stock	% sulfur		
	Present†	Found‡	Standard deviation from mean
Isooctane	0.0088	0.0098	0.0007
	0.0418	0.0425	0.0010
	0.0788	0.0794	0.0011
	0.1235	0.1244	0.0008
Gasoline *A*	0.0101	0.0098	0.0020
	0.0403	0.0393	0.0004
	0.0828	0.0839	0.0017
	0.1196	0.1219	0.0016
Toluene	0.0083	0.0068	0.0004
	0.0390	0.0386	0.0012
	0.0780	0.0777	0.0006
	0.1204	0.1213	0.0008

* From Jones, *Anal. Chem.*, **33**:71 (1961). Courtesy of *Analytical Chemistry.*
† Includes added sulfur plus that from base stock.
‡ Average of four determinations.

5. MUTUAL-STANDARDS CONCEPT

The mutual-standards concept depends on the relative internal consistency between intensity measurements and composition for minor components in a system in which a dominant component, to a large measure, controls the effects of matrix variation Additional corrections made for matrix interactions, therefore, are minor or may be neglected entirely.

Chodos and Nichiporuk[8] have employed the mutual-standards concept to the analysis of meteoritic sulfide nodules for eight elements. The composition of this system is rather typified in that, on a sulfur-free basis, the iron concentration ranged from 88 to 100 per cent. The principle of the method is based on the assumption that the total of all the elements determined is 100 per cent—a key point in this type of approach. Therefore, the concentration relationships are presented by

$$(\mathrm{Fe})_c = 100/[1 + (\mathrm{As/Fe})_c + (\mathrm{Co/Fe})_c + (\mathrm{Cr/Fe})_c + (\mathrm{Cu/Fe}_c) + (\mathrm{Ni/Fe})_c + (\mathrm{V/Fe})_c + (\mathrm{Zn/Fe})_c] \quad (8)$$

where each ratio represents the concentration of that element to iron.

Analytical working curves based on known compositions and the respective measured intensities are established in which the intensity ratio of the element peak to the iron peak is plotted against the element-to-iron concentration ratio. Both the standards and the unknown are dissolved in nitric acid, evaporated, and ignited at 600° C preliminary to the x-ray measurements. Having determined the seven concentration ratios from the x-ray measurements, they are inserted into Eq. (8), which is solved for iron, then for the respective concentration values of the other seven elements.

The data of Table 11 illustrate the precision and accuracy of the mutual-standards method.

Under the conditions of analysis used, the intensity ratios for a given sample remained constant over a 6-month period. The mutual-standards concept is simple, straightforward, rapid, and precise for special materials in which a dominant element coexists with other known elements of lower concentration.

Table 11. Analysis of Synthetic Samples*

Element	% added	% found
Fe	89.62	89.65
	96.37	96.85
	98.10	98.05
	98.59	98.58
As	0.020	0.019
	0.100	0.093
Co	0.024	0.018
	0.053	0.052
	0.20	0.22, 0.23
	0.40	0.40
	1.00	1.07, 1.09, 1.11
	1.80	2.07
Cr	0.020	0.026
	0.040	0.039
	0.20	0.21
	0.22	0.21
	0.95	0.98
	1.00	0.99, 0.99
	1.82	1.94
	9.15	9.09
Cu	0.020	0.015, 0.025, 0.016
	0.12	0.14
	0.20	0.17, 0.22
	0.60	0.54
	0.90	0.76
	1.00	0.79
Ni	0.080	0.083
	0.20	0.15, 0.20, 0.21
	0.22	0.24
	0.40	0.37
	1.00	1.03
	1.80	1.65, 1.73
	1.82	1.98
	3.00	2.78
V	0.010	0.0094, 0.0102
	0.020	0.019
	0.069	0.065
Zn	0.019	0.021
	0.100	0.083

* From Chodos and Nichiporuk, in *Advances in X-ray Analysis*, vol. 2, p. 247, W. M. Mueller (ed.), Plenum Press, Inc., New York, 1960, by courtesy of editor.

6. RATIO-COMPARATOR METHOD

An instrument which provides accurate comparison of the fluorescent radiation from a given component in an unknown to that in a reference standard has been used by Stoner[9] for the determination of zirconium, zinc, thorium, cerium, neodymium, praseodymium, and lanthanum in magnesium alloys. This instrument, Philips Electronics' Autrometer (cf. Chap. 40, Sec. 2), is automatically programmed so that, after the sample and reference standard are inserted, successive measurements are made at the respective positions of the analytical lines for both specimens, and the line ratio of sample to reference for each element is then calculated to four places and printed out. If interaction effects are negligible and the reference count is a power of 10, the read-out is direct. As many as 24 angle settings may be compared with this instrument. The instrument is especially adaptable to a system like magnesium containing alloying elements which do not vary enough in concentration to change markedly the absorption characteristics of the sample. In the present application, however, it was found that interaction effects do occur, and to obtain highest accuracy, corrections for these effects must be made. The procedural steps of analysis are given in Table 12.

Table 12. Autrometer Analysis of Magnesium Alloy

Sample treatment	Prepare alloy sample by turning on end mill, providing a fine finish, to fit specimen holder
Instrument	Philips Electronics Autrometer
Standardization	Use samples analyzed chemically and spectrographically for reference. The concentration of the measured elements in the standard should be intermediate to that of the unknowns
Excitation	Tungsten target, 60 kv, variable milliamperes current setting to provide half-scale rate-meter reading for each element
Optics	LiF crystal, fine collimation between sample and crystal
Analytical lines	Zr $K\beta_1$ .... 0.701 Å Th $L\alpha_1$ .... 0.956 Å Zn $K\alpha_1$ .... 1.435 Å Pr $L\beta_1$ .... 2.259 Å Nd $L\beta_1$ .... 2.166 Å Ce $L\alpha_1$ .... 2.561 Å La $L\alpha_1$ .... 2.691 Å
Detection	Flow proportional counter
Register	Preselect statistical counting to provide 0.5, 1.6, or 5.0 % accuracy
Analytical range	~0.1–6 %
Interpretation	Ratios from Autrometer are never a direct measure of element concentration. Develop and apply an empirical correction for each read-out ratio as follows: (1) The ratio between the direct read-out value and the chemical value on each of several specimens is established. (2) A "net-density" value is calculated for each specimen by multiplying the per cent of each element (Autrometer) by the density of that element (obtained from density tables). (3) The Autrometer-chemical ratio is plotted against "net density" to obtain a correction curve. (4) On an unknown the "net-density" value is applied to the curve to obtain the correction factor. The direct Autrometer value is divided by the correction factor to provide the corrected answer. *Example.* Suppose that a direct zirconium value of 0.280 % is to be corrected where other elements are present to mitigate the direct result.

Element	%	Density	"Net density"
Ce	1.51	6.9	10.4
Pr	0.19	6.5	1.2
Nd	0.59	6.9	4.1
La	0.73	6.15	4.5
			Σ 20.2

From the curve, a "net-density" value of 20.2 provides a correction factor of 0.768.

$$\frac{0.280\ \%}{0.768} = 0.36\ \%, \text{ the corrected answer}$$

A complete analysis for the alloying elements can be performed in less than an hour. A comparison of x-ray with chemical values for three components is given in Table 13.

Table 13. Comparison of X-ray and Chemical Values*

Chemical	*X-ray*
% zinc	
2.01	1.97
1.98	1.95
1.98	1.81
1.38	1.41
5.47	5.26
6.69	5.96
2.01	1.99
1.99	1.84
6.05	6.04
6.22	6.19
% thorium	
3.07	3.06
3.39	3.08
3.07	3.08
2.81	2.71
3.08	3.07
3.14	3.10
1.69	1.64
% zirconium	
0.36	0.37
0.73	0.74
0.77	0.74
0.73	0.76
0.54	0.55
0.63	0.58
0.65	0.62

* From Stoner, *Anal. Chem.*, **34**:123 (1962). Courtesy of *Analytical Chemistry.*

7. CORRECTION FOR INTERACTION BY FAMILY OF CURVES

Davis and Van Nordstrand[10] have encountered elemental interaction effects in determining additive elements—barium, calcium, and zinc—in lubricating oils, even at concentrations less than 1 per cent of the blended composition. The effect of 0.6 per cent barium on 0.1 per cent zinc in an oil was to lower the zinc intensity by nearly 30 per cent, for example. A family of curves was found to be a satisfactory solution for this problem. The experimental procedure is given in Table 14.

The x-ray method of analysis requires 3 to 12 min per element, depending on the level of precision selected. The accuracy was found to be at least equal to that of chemical methods. Comparisons between x-ray and chemical results are given in Table 15.

Davis and Van Nordstrand[10] made absorption calculations on additive-containing oils both to confirm the validity of their results and to predict interference. Their calculations of theoretical intensity furnish an instructive example of how such an approach may be utilized. The considerations are different from those used for a metallic alloy. The mass absorption (μ/ρ) constants of elements in the blended oil for Zn $K\alpha$ radiation were employed. The total absorption is the sum of the products of weight fraction W and absorption coefficient of the respective elements (absorption by hydrogen ignored):

$$\mu/\rho = 49.3W_{Zn} + 307W_{Ba} + 75W_S + 59W_P + 4.43W_C \tag{9}$$

Since

$$W_C = 1 - (W_{Zn} + W_{Ba} + W_S + W_P + W_H) \tag{10}$$

$$\mu/\rho = 44.9W_{Zn} + 303W_{Ba} + 70.6W_S + 55W_P + 4.43(1 - W_H) \tag{11}$$

Table 14. Analysis of Lubricating Oils for Barium, Calcium, and Zinc

Sample treatment......	None
Instrument...........	North American Philips. Special sample cell is used with facilities for cooling by water circulation and a level indicator for adding oil to an exact level each time
Standardization.......	Use standards for calibration which are prepared from metal sulfonates or naphthenates of known concentration blended with a neutral oil of medium viscosity
Excitation............	Molybdenum target, 50 kv, 40 ma, for barium and calcium; 50 kv, 30 ma for zinc
Optics................	NaCl crystal, He in optical path. Seven-inch nickel-tubing collimator is used between sample and crystal; no other collimator
Analytical lines........	Zn $K\alpha$ 1.435 Å, Ba $L\alpha$ 2.562 Å, Ca $K\alpha$ 3.353 Å. No background correction
Detection.............	Geiger counter
Register..............	Preselect fixed number of counts to provide the level of precision desired
Analytical range.......	Barium 0–1.0%, calcium 0–0.6%, zinc 0–0.12%
Interpretation.........	To correct zinc determinations made in the presence of barium, prepare a family of curves by increasing the concentration of barium in sets of standards in steps of 0.1%. Interpolation between curves is made to obtain the correct value for zinc on an unknown. Typical curves are shown in Fig. 4

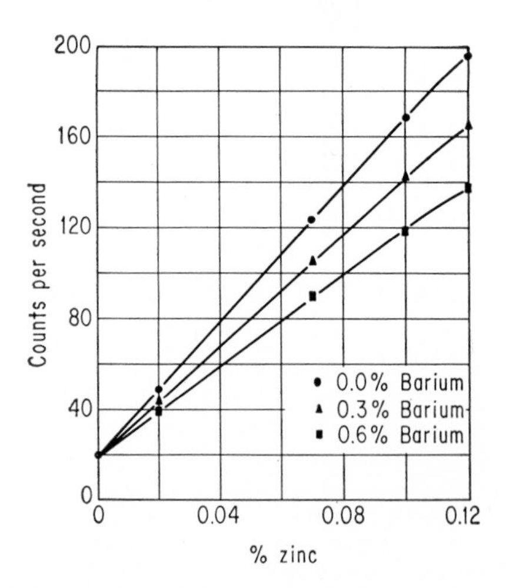

FIG. 4. Calibration curve for zinc using a molybdenum tube at 50 kv and 30 ma with helium. [*Davis and Van Nordstrand, Anal. Chem.*, **26**:973 (1954). *Courtesy of Analytical Chemistry.*]

The intensity of the zinc radiation with no absorption in the sample is

$$I_{0(\mathrm{Zn})} = K_{\mathrm{Zn}} m \rho W_{\mathrm{Zn}} \tag{12}$$

where K_{Zn} = constant which includes voltage and target of x-ray tube, absorption and emission characteristics of zinc, geometrical factors, and detection efficiency

m = tube current, ma

ρ = density

Table 15. X-ray and Chemical Analyses for Barium, Calcium, and Zinc*

Sample	% barium		% zinc		% calcium	
	X-ray	Chemical	X-ray	Chemical	X-ray	Chemical
1	0.51	0.51	0.068	0.068		
2	0.22	0.22	0.101	0.100		
3	0.11	0.12	0.089	0.090		
4	0.08	0.10	0.086	0.086		
5	0.24	0.23	0.103	0.100		
6	....	....	.....	.....	0.021	0.020
7	....	....	.....	.....	0.099	0.097
8	....	....	.....	.....	0.196	0.195
9	....	....	.....	.....	0.586	0.582

* From Davis and Van Nordstrand, *Anal. Chem.*, **26**:973 (1954). Courtesy of *Analytical Chemistry.*

Allowing for absorption coming from a depth of sample x,

$$I_{\mathrm{Zn}(x)} = I_{0(\mathrm{Zn})} \exp\left[-(\mu/\rho)\rho x\right] \tag{13}$$

For different depths,

$$I_{\mathrm{Zn}} = \int_0^\infty I_{\mathrm{Zn}(x)}\, dx \tag{14}$$

Substituting,

$$I_{\mathrm{Zn}} = K_{\mathrm{Zn}} m \rho W_{\mathrm{Zn}} \int_0^\infty \exp\left[-(\mu/\rho)\rho x\right] dx \tag{15}$$

$$= \frac{K_{\mathrm{An}} m W_{\mathrm{Zn}}}{\mu/\rho} \tag{16}$$

$$= \frac{K_{\mathrm{Zn}} m W_{\mathrm{Zn}}}{44.9W_{\mathrm{Zn}} + 303W_{\mathrm{Ba}} + 70.6W_{\mathrm{S}} + 55W_{\mathrm{P}} + 4.43(1 - W_{\mathrm{H}})} \tag{17}$$

The value of 0.1 per cent zinc and zero barium was used to calculate a K_{Zn} value of 19.5×10^3 for specific experimental conditions. A comparison of observed and calculated intensities is given in Table 16, in which excellent agreement between experiment and theory is reflected.

Table 16. Zinc Radiation from Oils in Counts per Second above Background*
(Comparison of calculated and experimental values)

% Ba	Counts/sec							
	0.02% Zn		0.07% Zn		0.10% Zn		0.12% Zn	
	Observed	Calculated	Observed	Calculated	Observed	Calculated	Observed	Calculated
0.00	29	30	103	103	147†	147†	175	176
0.30	24	24	85	84	120	119.7	143	143
0.60	19	20.3	70	70	99	100.9	118	119

* From Davis and Van Nordstrand, *Anal. Chem.*, **26**:973 (1954). Courtesy of *Analytical Chemistry.*

† This value used for calculating the K_{Zn} value for use in Eq. (11). Other components of this oil were phosphorus 0.1%, sulfur 0.05%, hydrogen 13%, and carbon approximately 85%. The density of the oil was 0.865.

8. EFFECTS OF ABSORPTION AND ENHANCEMENT OF LINE PAIRS

The problem of absorption and enhancement in x-ray analysis, especially as it applies to selective effects on elemental line pairs, was thoroughly treated in 1932 in Von Hevesey's monograph on chemical analysis by x-rays.[11] More recently, Adler and Axelrod[12] have further considered this problem using modern improved instrumentation as applied to adjacent pairs in the periodic table. In this latter investigation using multichannel measurements, the conditions under which absorption-enhancement effects on line pairs occur were considered in light of selected systems, ranging in content from light to heavy elements in the periodic series. These conditions are outlined in Table 17 and include illustrations of the effects which they produce. Adler and Axelrod concluded that neighboring elements in the periodic series make good internal standards for one another by compensating for absorption and enhancement, except when there is a strong line between the edges involved or when there is an edge between the compared lines. In the selection of a substance for use as an internal standard these conclusions should serve as a guiding principle to be applied to any specific problem or system of interest to the analyst.

Table 17. Effects of Absorption and Enhancement on Line-pair Intensity Ratio

Case	Emission		Absorption		Observed effects
	Pair	Wavelength, Å	Matrix*	Wavelength, Å	
I. Absorption Effects					
1. Element with absorption edge on long-wavelength side of two emission lines measured	Nb $K\alpha$/Mo $K\alpha$ Cr $K\alpha$/Mn $K\alpha$	0.746, 0.709 2.290, 2.102	PnO-Li_2CO_3 SnO_2-Li_2CO_3	0.782 (Pb) 2.777 (Sn)	Line intensities markedly reduced by increase of Pb, Sn in matrix; intensity ratio of emission pair almost constant
2. Element with absorption edge between two emission lines measured	Cr $K\alpha$/Pr $L\beta_1$	2.285, 2.254	V†	2.265 (V)	Ratio shifted 63% in favor of Cr emission by presence of V
II. Excitation Effects					
1. Emission line of third element occurs between absorption edges of element pair measured	Th L_{III}, Tl L_{II}	0.761, 0.843	ZrO_2-Li_2CO_3	0.786 (Zr $K\alpha$)	Tl $L\beta$/Th $L\alpha$ line ratio increased by presence of Zr but maximum enhancement was only 10%
2. Emission line of third element occurs between absorption edges of element pair measured but very close to the longer-wavelength edge	As K, Ge K	1.045, 1.117	Se-Li_2CO_3	1.105 (Se $K\alpha$)	Ge $K\alpha$/As $K\alpha$ line ratio increased by presence of Se to a maximum of 30%, chiefly through Ge $K\alpha$ enhancement

* Matrix components varied from 0 to 100%; contained fixed amount of emitting elements.
† Based on results of Von Hevesey for V/Pr atomic ratio of 4; cf. p. 123 of Ref. 11.

Interelement effects in various complex systems are discussed by Mitchell in Clark's *Encyclopedia of Spectroscopy.*[13]

A final word of caution should be given as applied to the addition of internal standards: it is possible by imperfect mixing to introduce greater errors than those one intends to eliminate through the use of the internal standard (see Sec. 21).

9. THEORETICAL CALCULATION OF INTENSITY

The theoretical work of Sherman[14] on the correlation of fluorescent intensity and elemental composition has been monumental in elucidating this complex relationship.

Noakes[15] has shown how the fluorescent intensity emitted by an element in a binary iron-nickel alloy can be calculated by using fundamental expressions in which the intensity is related to the absorption constants of the elements and the thickness of the sample. The experimental data employed for illustration were those of Koh and Caugherty;[16] the relative intensity of nickel for selected concentrations is used for comparison. Noakes points out that the fundamental integral expression relating these parameters cannot be evaluated. Hence simplifying assumptions are made to accomplish the calculations. An imaginary depth below the surface is assumed to be the origin or virtual source of the fluorescence. The absorption-coefficient values of nickel for different composition ratios of the alloy are used in an exponential equation to evaluate the depth t of the virtual source. The incident value I_0 is obtained by multiplying the relative intensity of pure nickel by the weight fraction of nickel in the sample.

Example. The alloy considered is 50 per cent nickel. The linear absorption coefficient of Ni $K\alpha$ in this alloy is 1,877 and that of pure nickel 514. The intensity of Ni $K\alpha$ emitted by the alloy was found experimentally to be 34 relative to 100 for pure nickel.

$$I = I_0 \exp(-\mu t) \tag{18}$$

Then

$$\ln {}^{34}\!/_{50} = -(1{,}877 - 514)t$$

$$t = 2.83 \times 10^{-4} \text{ cm}$$

By calculations based on nine composition ratios, Noakes found the average value of t to be 2.75×10^{-4} cm. The average value of t can be employed to calculate nickel intensity I for a given composition. For 30 per cent nickel,

$$I = 30 \exp[-(2{,}424)(2.75 \times 10^{-4})]$$

This value is normalized by multiplying it by 100/86.8 to give 17.8. (The same calculation for 100 per cent nickel gave 86.8.)

A comparison of intensities for different iron-nickel compositions was found to be as follows:

% Ni	I_{obs}	I_{calc}	Δ
10	6	5.1	−0.9
20	13	11.0	−2.0
30	20	17.8	−2.2
40	28	25.6	−2.4
50	34	34.4	+0.4
60	43	44.6	+1.6
70	53	55.9	+2.9
80	66	68.8	+2.8
90	82	83.4	+1.4
100	100	100	0

Thus reasonable agreement between experimental observation and Noakes's[15] calculation from theory is shown. Noakes also made further applications to ternary alloys in which enhancement—"negative absorption"—occurs by applying absorption-enhancement coefficients with promising results.

Mitchell[17] has proposed a practical means for predicting the intensity of an element in any matrix. Essentially, the method consists in introducing the element or its compound in known concentration into a matrix composed of another substance and measuring its fluorescent intensity. A few key matrix materials are selected and a plot is made relating the atomic number of the matrix to the intensity emitted by the element under investigation. The observed intensity obviously is the resultant of and accounts for matrix interaction, i.e., absorption-enhancement effects. The variation in intensity is, in general, inverse to the mass absorption coefficient. Exceptions are found near the absorption edge of the measured element, however. The matrix elements, having emission lines just on the short-wavelength side of the absorption edge of the measured element, enhance its intensity, thus partially compensating for the matrix absorption loss This is shown for the element tin, in Fig. 5. for various matrices. The highest intensity for Sn $K\alpha$ is shown not in the matrix of lowest absorption, Z-47, Ag, but in Z-54, Xe, several atomic numbers higher. Extrapolations located the peak at Z-54. A reminder that the K-absorption edge of tin is at 0.425 Å and the $K\alpha$ emission line of xenon at 0.416 Å exp'ains the enhancement of the characteristic tin emission in theoretical mixture with xenon. Mitchell applied this concept to several other matrix mixtures. The validity of using this approach to predict the fluorescent intensities of elements in matrices of varying atomic number is shown in Table 18. The agreement between predicted and observed intensities is remarkably good.

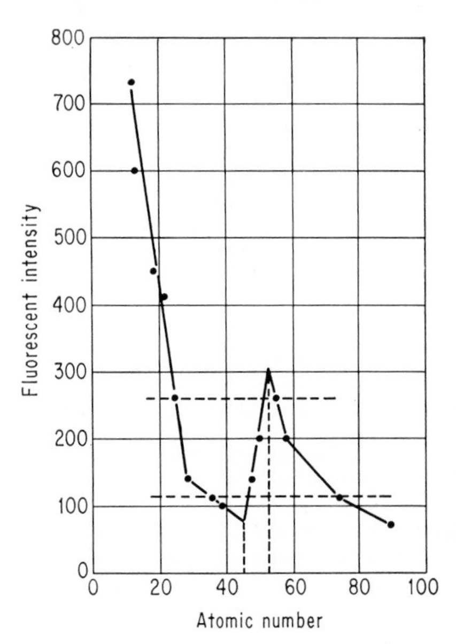

FIG. 5. Fluorescent intensity–atomic number pattern for 10 per cent SnO_2. [*Mitchell, Anal. Chem.*, **33**:917 (1961). *Courtesy of Analytical Chemistry.*]

Table 18. Accuracy of Estimated Fluorescent Intensities*

Element	Matrix		Estimated intensity	Measured intensity
	Substance	Atomic No.		
10% SnO_2	Ni_2O_3	28	185	191
	V_2O_5	23	400	407
	Sm_2O_3	62	170	169
10% MoO_3	CeO_3	58	95	94
	Sm_2O_3	50	135	139
10% Fe_2O_3	V_2O_5	23	185	183
	CuO	29	608	610

* From Mitchell, *Anal. Chem.*, **33**:917 (1961). Courtesy of *Analytical Chemistry*.

10. EMPIRICAL ABSORPTION-ENHANCEMENT INDICES

A calibration method for determining four components—chromium, iron, nickel, and molybdenum—in a quaternary metal alloy was developed by Beattie and Brissey,[18] also in terms of theoretical considerations of absorption-enhancement effects. A set of simultaneous equations contains empirical corrections for these effects, the unknowns in them representing composition. Coefficients of the equations are based on the internal consistency existing between intensity measurements of each pure metal element and the intensity measurements of the binary alloys of the four metals. For the latter, known composition values must be available.

Equations for the expressions from which the absorption-enhancement indices are calculated are

$$A_{ab} = (W_a/W_b)\,(R_a - 1)$$

and

$$A_{ba} = (W_b/W_a)\,(R_b - 1) \tag{19}$$

where A_{ab}, A_{ba} is the absorption parameter for the absorption enhancement of a to b, b to a, and thus for other pairs.

W_a, W_b, etc., is the fractional weight of the element in an alloy. W_a/W_b, W_b/W_a, W_a/W_c, etc., is the weight ratio of the elements in a binary alloy and R_a, R_b, etc., is the ratio of the intensity of the pure metal element to that of the element in a binary compound. Then

$$-(R_a - 1)W_a + A_{ab}W_b + A_{ac}W_c + \cdots = 0 \tag{20}$$

$$A_{ba}W_a - (R_b - 1)W_b + A_{bc}W_c + \cdots = 0 \tag{21}$$

$$A_{ca}W_a + A_{cb}W_b - (R_c - 1)W_c + \cdots = 0 \tag{22}$$

$$W_a + W_b + W_c + \cdots = 1 \tag{23}$$

and so on for additional components. (Note that the sum of the weight fractions of the metal elements in the alloy must equal unity.)

Absorption Parameters. The method of evaluating the absorption parameters and of calculating the results from the foregoing equations can best be illustrated by using data given by Beattie and Brissey.[18] The net line intensities were read from all samples for a given element without any change being made in the instrument. The composition of the binary alloys which were used is given in Table 19.

Table 19. Chemical Analyses of the Binary Alloys*

Analysis for	Binary partner			
	Cr	Fe	Ni	Mo
Cr...........	.....	48.24	48.07	74.28
Fe...........	50.83	.....	51.53	65.33
Ni...........	48.19	46.65	.....	53.70
Mo..........	23.53	34.44	46.27	

* From Beattie and Brissey, *Anal. Chem.,* **26**:980 (1954). Courtesy of *Analytical Chemistry.*

Table 20. Intensity Ratio for Binary Alloys*

Radiating element	Binary partner			
	Cr	Fe	Ni	Mo
Cr...........	1.000	1.760	1.815	1.841
Fe...........	3.360	1.000	1.613	1.835
Ni...........	2.860	3.670	1.000	1.954
Mo..........	3.770	2.787	2.461	1.000

* From Beattie and Brissey, *Anal. Chem.,* **26**:980 (1954). Courtesy of *Analytical Chemistry.*

The intensity ratios for the same alloys were found by measurement to be as shown in Table 20.

The data in these two tables were substituted into Eqs. (19) to determine the absorption parameters; these are given in Table 21.

Table 21. Absorption Parameters*

Radiating element	Absorbing element			
	Cr	Fe	Ni	Mo
Cr.	1.000	0.721	0.813	2.660
Fe.	2.482	1.000	0.676	1.582
Ni.	1.863	2.420	1.000	1.108
Mo.	0.877	0.9435	1.260	1.000

* From Beattie and Brissey, *Anal. Chem.*, **26**:980 (1954). Courtesy of *Analytical Chemistry.*

With the absorption parameters evaluated, these were then inserted into Eq. (20), etc.

$$-(R_{Cr} - 1)Cr + 0.721\ Fe + 0.813\ Ni + 2.660\ Mo = 0 \quad (24)$$
$$2.482\ Cr - (R_{Fe} - 1)Fe + 0.676\ Ni + 1.582\ Mo = 0 \quad (25)$$
$$1.863\ Cr + 2.420\ Fe - (R_{Ni} - 1)Ni + 1.108\ Mo = 0 \quad (26)$$
$$0.877\ Cr + 0.9435\ Fe + 1.260\ Ni(R_{Mo} - 1)Mo = 0 \quad (27)$$

Sample Calculation. If alloy 4 from Table 22, which gives the intensity ratios of the ternary and quaternary alloys, is chosen, iron is seen to have the lowest intensity ratio; therefore, it is taken as the most abundant element. Equation (25) is omitted' the equations are divided through by Fe, the constant terms are transposed, and the intensity ratios from Table 22 are substituted.

Table 22. Intensity Ratios for Ternary and Quaternary Alloys*

$R_a = I_{aa}\dagger / I_{as}$

Alloy No.	Cr	Fe	Ni	Mo
1	3.610	1.918	14.34	
2	3.535	6.620	2.152	
3	2.477	3.665	5.373	
4	5.04	2.346	6.640	15.34
5	4.01	1.942	14.72	41.35
I_{aa}‡	597	2,795	3,270§	1,076

* From Beattie and Brissey, *Anal. Chem.*, **36**:980 (1954). Courtesy of *Analytical Chemistry.*

† Intensity in counts per second on pure element corrected for background.

‡ Intensity from a 0.75- by 0.75-in. sample area. Bent mica crystal was 0.0016 in. thick.

§ Nickel intensities were determined with a W-target x-ray tube operating at 24.1 ma and 48.5 kvp. All other elements were determined under 49.6 ma and 48.5 kvp.

$$-4.04\ Cr/Fe + 0.813\ Ni/Fe + 2.660\ Mo/Fe = -0.721 \quad (28)$$
$$1.863\ Cr/Fe - 5.640\ Ni/Fe + 1.108\ Mo/Fe = -2.420 \quad (29)$$
$$0.877\ Cr/Fe + 1.260\ Ni/Fe - 14.34\ Mo/Fe = -0.9435 \quad (30)$$

If the denominator determinant of the coefficient times the adjustment factor is denoted by k, then the numerator determinants are

$$k\ \mathrm{Cr/Fe} = \begin{vmatrix} -0.721 & 0.813 & 2.660 \\ -2.420 & -5.640 & 1.108 \\ -0.9435 & 1.260 & -14.34 \end{vmatrix} = 108.61 \tag{31}$$

$$k\ \mathrm{Ni/Fe} = \begin{vmatrix} -4.04 & -0.721 & 2.660 \\ 1.863 & -2.420 & 1.108 \\ 0.877 & -0.9435 & -14.34 \end{vmatrix} = -163.42 \tag{32}$$

$$k\ \mathrm{Mo/Fe} = \begin{vmatrix} -4.04 & 0.813 & -\ 0.721 \\ 1.863 & -5.640 & -\ 2.420 \\ 0.877 & 1.260 & -\ 0.9435 \end{vmatrix} = -39.37 \tag{33}$$

Multiplying Eq. (25) by k/Fe and transposing, the resulting constant term (with R_{Fe} substituted in from Table 22) yields

$$2.482k\ \mathrm{Cr/Fe} + 0.676k\ \mathrm{Ni/Fe} + 1.582k\ \mathrm{Mo/Fe} = 1.346k \tag{34}$$

The above three numerator determinants are substituted into this equation, and the result is solved for k, giving

$$k = -328.62$$

Equation (23) can now be used to evaluate the four unknowns as follows (disregarding the negative signs):

$$k\ \mathrm{Cr/Fe} = 108.61 \tag{35}$$
$$k\ \mathrm{Ni/Fe} = 163.42 \tag{36}$$
$$k\ \mathrm{Mo/Fe} = 39.37 \tag{37}$$
$$k = k\ \mathrm{Fe/Fe} = 328.62 \tag{38}$$
$$k/\mathrm{Fe(Cr + Ni + Mo + Fe)} = 640.02 = k/\mathrm{Fe} \tag{39}$$

giving

$$\mathrm{Cr} = 108.61/640.02 = 16.97 \text{ per cent}$$
$$\mathrm{Fe} = 328.62/640.02 = 51.35 \text{ per cent}$$
$$\mathrm{Ni} = 163.42/640.02 = 25.53 \text{ per cent}$$
$$\mathrm{Mo} = 39.37/640.02 = 6.15 \text{ per cent}$$

for the analysis. The foregoing data and example of sample calculation were taken from Beattie and Brissey.[18]

By application of the absorption-enhancement equations to the analysis of five typical alloys these investigators found that the relative deviation from chemical analysis averaged 3.4 per cent for the four metal elements, the maximum deviation being 8.6 per cent.

11. CHOICE OF ADDED INTERNAL STANDARD

The use of an internal standard added to the substance to be analyzed provides a well-recognized means of compensating for matrix or interaction effects. The element used as an internal standard should be close in atomic number to the element measured and homogeneously dispersed in the sample containing it. In this way the absorption properties and fluorescent yields of the standard and unknown will be similar. The amount of added internal standard also is significant. Ideally, the fractions of unknown and internal-standard element should be about the same and the intensity ratio of the lines should be unity near the mid-concentration range of the element being measured. Practically, because of a number of considerations, this ideal may be difficult to achieve. Usually, depending on the absorption characteristics involved, the concentration of the added internal standard should not exceed 10 per cent of the total blended composition.[19] More than this fractional amount may modify the matrix to such an extent as to produce errors in the results. The effects of absorption and enhancement on line pairs (cf. Sec. 8) are of paramount importance in the selection of an internal standard. See Sec. 21 for a discussion of errors which may be introduced by the addition of internal standards to powder specimens.

12. COMPENSATIVE REFERENCE STANDARDIZATION

A novel use of an internal standard in which the reference substance is measured within the sample, yet is not a part of its composition, has been described by Jones.[20] Manganese in soluble organic form in gasoline is measured using an iron rod positioned in the liquid sample at a fixed distance from the cell window as the reference. This reference compensates for differences in base stock or additives in the samples analyzed. The conditions of analysis are given in Table 23.

Table 23. Determination of Manganese in Gasoline

Sample treatment......	None
Instrument...........	Single channel, inverted geometry, cell bottom ¼-mil Mylar
Standardization.......	Prepare known standards by blending manganese naphthenate with gasoline to contain 0–1.0 g of manganese per gallon. Prepare working curve based on x-ray measurement by plotting manganese-iron intensity ratio vs. concentration
Excitation............	Tungsten target, 55 kv, 45 ma
Optics................	LiF crystal, collimator 0.02 in. Cell cap with center post, iron rod ¼ in. diameter attached. Place four 0.35-mil layers of nickel foil over collimator when measuring iron to attenuate beam
Analytical lines........	Mn $K\alpha$ 2.103 Å, Fe $K\alpha$ 1.937 Å
Detection.............	Scintillation, pulse-height analyzer
Register..............	Fixed count, 32,000 to 256,000 counts taken depending on concentration; make no background correction
Analytical range.......	Examples show 0.1–1.0 g/gal

This technique of compensative standardization applied especially to liquids. The position of the iron rod in reference to the cell bottom must be established by trial to determine the depth for exact compensation, i.e., neither over nor under. The precision and accuracy of the method are given in Table 24.

Table 24. Precision and Accuracy*

Base stock	Manganese concentration, g/gal		
	Added	Found†	Standard deviation from mean
Isooctane...........	0.989	0.992	0.007
	0.494	0.494	0.007
	0.247	0.247	0.003
	0.124	0.124	0.002
Gasoline *A*..........	1.026	1.031	0.005
	0.513	0.513	0.006
	0.256	0.256	0.003
	0.128	0.131	0.002
Gasoline *B*..........	1.047	1.049	0.008
	0.524	0.528	0.006
	0.262	0.263	0.003
	0.131	0.136	0.003

* From R. A. Jones, *Anal. Chem.*, **31**:1341 (1959). Courtesy of *Analytical Chemistry*.
† Average of six determinations.

13. CHEMICAL SOLUTION OF SAMPLES

Chemical solution affords a very effective means of minimizing matrix interaction effects and of eliminating small-order inhomogeneities and surface effects. A method for determining uranium in fuel elements composed of stainless steel and uranium dioxide which involves a chemical-solution technique has been described by Silverman et al.[21] It was found that large amounts of iron, chromium, or nickel in the solution do not affect the determination of uranium. The procedural steps are given in Table 25.

Table 25. Chemical-solution Technique

Sample treatment......	Dissolve 1 g of UO_2 stainless steel in 20 ml of aqua regia. Add several drops of hydrofluoric acid and 15 ml perchloric acid, then evaporate to dense fumes. Cool, add 2 ml strontium nitrate (2 mg/ml in final solution). Cool, dilute to 100 ml in volumetric flask
Instrument...........	North American Philips, inverted geometry. Additional voltage stabilizer used for electronic panel
Standardization.......	Use perchloric acid solutions of synthetic mixtures containing UO_2 and stainless steel to prepare working curve. Strontium used as internal standard
Excitation............	Tungsten target, 50 kv, 30 ma
Optics................	LiF crystal, plate collimators
Analytical lines........	Sr $K\alpha$ 0.877 Å; U $L\alpha$ 0.912 Å
Detection.............	Scintillation counter. A special lead shield on counter must be used to prevent pickup of scattered radiation
Register..............	Take 204,800 counts for each line
Analytical range.......	15–25% UO_2 in fuel element

Table 26. Accuracy of Results*

Sample %	No. of reading pairs	Coefficient of variation	Standard deviation expressed as % UO_2	UO_2 in solution, mg/ml
15.0	9	0.426	0.064	1.5 ± 0.006
	9	0.298	0.045	1.5 ± 0.004
17.0	9	0.495	0.084	1.7 ± 0.008
20.0	9	0.458	0.091	2.0 ± 0.009
	9	0.446	0.089	2.0 ± 0.009
22.0	9	0.436	0.096	2.2 ± 0.009
	9	0.295	0.065	2.2 ± 0.006
24.0	9	0.461	0.110	2.4 ± 0.011
24.0	9	0.473	0.113	2.4 ± 0.011
25.0	9	0.474	0.118	2.5 ± 0.012

* Silverman et al., *Anal. Chem.*, **29**:1762 (1957). Courtesy of *Analytical Chemistry.*

Examples of precision and accuracy are reflected by the data of Table 26.
A comparison of x-ray with chemical results on the same samples is given in Table 27.

14. FUSION METHODS

Fusion of a solid sample prior to x-ray analysis has several advantages. One important requirement in the properties of the flux material is that its absorption of the characteristic x-rays from the sample be low so as to avoid drastic fluorescent-intensity loss. The use of a low atomic flux is usually dictated by this requirement. Even then, intensity loss of low-atomic-number elements may be problematic. Two

Table 27. Comparison of X-ray and Chemical Methods*

Lab. No.	UO_2, %	
	X-ray	Wet chemical
1	17.6	17.3
2	15.8	15.9
3	15.4	15.5
4	16.2	16.3
5	16.5	16.2
6	15.2	15.2
7	15.0	15.1
8	15.8	16.0
9	16.0	15.8

* Silverman et al., *Anal. Chem.*, **29**:1762 (1957). Courtesy of *Analytical Chemistry.*

techniques will be described—one in which a high flux ratio is used, the other a low ratio.

Borax-fusion Matrix. A method of sample preparation through dilution of the sample in borax by a hundredfold, followed by fusion of the mixture, has been applied in the analysis of minerals and ores by Claisse.[22] The dilution reduces matrix effects to a negligible level and fusion eliminates the particle-size effects which are so prominent in the analysis of ores. Claisse concludes that, because of the particle effect, accurate analyses cannot be made on any substance in the powder form. Other workers have found that the magnitude of the particle-size effect depends considerably upon the average particle-size distribution and the specific identity of the components in the system under study;[23] i.e., some systems in powder form can be dependably and

Table 28. Borax-fusion Method

Sample preparation....	Prepare a fused glass disk of borax containing the sample. Accurately weigh about 0.1 g of sample, add 10 g of fused borax, using a platinum crucible. Mix contents, fuse over hot flame of a gas burner. An electric hot plate with aluminum cover top is previously heated to about 450° C. A 1¼-in.-diameter ring made of Chromel A wire is placed on the hot plate and the melt immediately poured. After 1 to 2 min remove the disk from the hot plate, cool on a Transite plate. Temperature of hot plate, time of disk removal, and cooling are critical in avoiding sticking to plate, irregular disk surface, or cracking from annealing stresses
Instrument...........	North American Philips instrument
Standardization.......	Prepare fused disks containing known quantities of the elements to be determined. Use of barium sulfate in matrix recommended for standards and unknown where sulfides and graphite are present in the unknown or in case a further reduction in matrix effect is desired; about 10% used
Excitation............	Not given
Optics................	LiF crystal
Analytical lines........	For Fe, Mn, Zn, Cu, Cr in minerals use the $K\alpha$ lines; for lead, use the $L\beta$ line
Detection.............	Geiger counter
Register..............	102,400 counts taken; background correction is made only if background and line are comparable in magnitude
Analytical range.......	Composition of typical ores varied from 40–65% iron, 0.2–23% manganese. Other examples of broad variations given in Table 29

accurately analyzed in that state.[24] Moreover, Heidl and Fassel[25] found that in the analysis of scandium ores, dry grinding with silicon carbide provided better precision than borax fusion. In the fused preparations, the net intensity of vanadium was reduced by threefold and of scandium ninefold, in comparison with dry grinding.

An outline of the borax-fusion technique is given in Table 28.

The accuracy of the x-ray borax-fusion technique on sulfide ores of known composition is indicated by a mean deviation of 0.1 to 0.2 per cent from the known value. Comparisons are shown in Table 29.

Table 29. Comparison of Assay Results for Sulfide Ores*

% Fe			% Zn			% Pb			% Cu		
Given	Found	Deviation	Given	Found	Deviation	Given	Found	Deviation	Given	Found	Deviation
11.8	11.6	0.2	(x)	(x)	. . .	0.89	0.80	0.1	0.26	0.22	0.04
11.8	12.0	0.2	11.7	11.7	0.0	49.1	49.0	0.1	0.07	0.27	0.20
17.6	17.6	0.0	13.0	13.3	0.3	35.6	35.8	0.2	0.07	0.08	0.01
24.8	24.8	0.0	14.0	13.9	0.1	17.4	18.2	0.8	0.08	0.24	0.16
27.7	27.7	0.0	5.5	5.7	0.2	26.1	26.0	0.1	0.12	0.24	0.12
29.8	29.8	0.0	8.8	8.7	0.1	5.74	5.74	0.0	0.45	0.45	0.00
34.2	34.7	0.5	2.6	2.6	0.0	1.05	1.05	0.0	0.16	0.00	0.16
36.5	36.5	0.0	3.3	3.9	0.6	1.30	1.60	0.3			
36.9	36.8	0.1	6.9	6.9	0.0	3.44	3.55	0.1			
40.2	40.2	0.0	4.7	4.7	0.1	1.40	1.35	0.05	1.40	1.40	0.00
38.6	38.9	0.3	4.5	4.3	0.1	0.78	0.90	0.1	0.91	0.95	0.04
Mean deviation. . .		0.1	Mean deviation. .		0.15	Mean deviation. .		0.2	Mean deviation. . .		0.1

* From Claisse, *Norelco Reptr.*, **3**:3 (1957). Courtesy of *Norelco Reporter.*

The influence of matrix was dramatically shown by Claisse through diluting a fixed amount of iron in powder and in fused matrices. In low-atomic-number matrices, e.g., alumina, silica, or borax, the measurements agreed exactly or closely with theory; in the oxides of the higher-atomic-number elements, tantalum, chromium, and tin, the measurements were about one-third theory, as shown in Table 30.

Table 30. Matrix Effect on the Analysis of a Sample Containing 20 Per Cent Fe_2O_3*

20 % Fe_2O_3 in	% Fe_2O_3 found		
	Nondiluted powders	Sample fused in borax	Sample fused in borax and $K_2S_2O_7$
Al_2O_3.	20.0	20.0	20.0
SiO_2.	19.0	19.7	20.1
Ta_2O_5.	7.4	19.2	19.8
Cr_2O_3.	5.1	19.4	19.7
SnO_2.	5.6	18.3	19.2

* From Claisse, *Norelco Reptr.*, **3**:3 (1957). Courtesy of *Norelco Reporter.*

Minimum-flux Method. Andermann[26] has applied a technique called the minimum-flux method to the analysis of cement raw mix. The purpose of this method is to surmount the errors encountered in the direct inspection of this material. The sources of error encountered in the x-ray analysis of a cement mix prepared in powder form were attributed to four causes: mineralogical differences, variations from one particle to another, phase or composition variations within a particle, and interelement effects. To circumvent all these except the last, the sample is fused. The flux material, lithium borate, is kept at a minimum ratio to the sample to avoid excessive dilution loss of intensity, especially from the low-atomic-number elements in the mix; hence the name "minimum-flux method." The technique employed in the minimum-flux method is given in Table 31.

Table 31. Minimum-flux Technique for Cement Raw Mix

Sample preparation.... Weigh 1 g of sample and 1 g of $Li_2B_4O_7$ with a maximum error of 0.005 g, mix, and pour into a graphite crucible. Ignite in muffle at 2500° F for 1½ min. Pour onto copper metal block, cool. Resulting solid fused bead ground to a fine powder with Spex mixer mill in tungsten carbide vial. Prepare briquette of powder, using cellulose powder in bottom of mold to give more strength to briquette. Krylon spray gives additional strength

Instrument........... Applied Research Laboratories vacuum polychromator. Nonscanning optics

Standardization....... Either cement raw mix or synthetic blends containing MgO, Al_2O_3, Fe_2O_3, SiO_2, and $CaCO_3$ can be used. Concentration of each elemental component is correlated with instrumental read-out for that element

Excitation............ Tungsten target, 50 kv, 35 ma

Optimum selection of crystals, slit widths, and detectors for elements studied:

Element	Line	Wavelength, Å	Crystal	Slit width, in. Primary	Slit width, in. Secondary	Detector
Fe	$K\alpha$	1.937	LiF	0.020	0.040	Multitron
Ca	$K\alpha$	3.360	LiF	0.065	0.040	Multitron
Si	$K\alpha$	7.126	EDT	0.060	0.090	Minitron
Al	$K\alpha$	8.338	EDT	0.090	0.050	Minitron
Mg	$K\alpha$	9.889	ADP	0.090	0.050	Minitron
External standard (ES) nondispersive						Multitron

Register.............. External standard, a small piece of brass, controls exposure time for accumulation of counts. Make two 2½-min runs on each briquette. Read-out for each element is displayed at end of run

Analytical range....... The analytical range for each measured component:

SiO_2, 8–28%
CaO, 34–54%
Fe_2O_3, 0.5–8%
Al_2O_3, 1–5%
MgO, 0.4–2.5%

Interpretation......... Divide original concentration by $(2.00 - L)$ where L is loss upon ignition expressed as a decimal fraction. Calculation is reversed for unknown. For further compensation of errors due to ignition, dilution losses and interelement effects apply an empirical correction equation

Example. Determination of SiO_2:

$$I_T = I_M \exp(Kg) \tag{40}$$

where I_T is true intensity ratio, I_M the measured ratio, K a correction factor, and

$$g = C_{MgO} + C_{Al_2O_3} + C_{Fe_2O_3} - (C_{flux} - 60) \tag{41}$$

where the nominal flux is 60% and the other terms are concentration values in % of the flux components

The simultaneous intensity measurements of the several elements afforded by the instrument obviously make this a rapid method. The precision of x-ray analysis on a sample from a selected source was determined for the powder and the fused specimen. The data of Table 32 show that fusion improves the precisions for SiO_2 and Al_2O_3.

Table 32. Precision Data on Samples from Company A*

	Fe_2O_3		CaO		SiO_2		Al_2O_3		MgO	
	UF	F	UF	F	UF	F	UF	F	UF	F
Instrumental precision	0.01	0.01	0.09	0.10	0.10	0.12	0.05	0.06	0.09	0.11
Total precision	0.04	0.05	0.12	0.12	0.23	0.16	0.09	0.06	0.10	0.11
Concentration range	0.5–7		35–47		13–24		1–5		0.4–0.8	

Legend: UF, unfused. F, fused.
* From Andermann, *Anal. Chem.*, **33**:1689 (1961). Courtesy of *Analytical Chemistry*.

The improvement in precision resulting from applying the type of correction given under Minimum-flux Method is considerable. The data of Table 33 refer to corrected and uncorrected curves in which concentration is plotted against an intensity parameter, the latter being for both corrected and uncorrected ratios.

Table 33. Accuracy Summary on Cement Raw Mix*

	MgO		Al_2O_3		SiO_2		CaO		Fe_2O_3	
	UF	F	UF	F	UF	F	UF	F	UF	F
Single curve:										
Uncorrected	0.12	0.09	0.50	0.19	2.61	0.56	1.63	0.46	0.16	0.10
Corrected	....	....	....	....	....	0.22	....	0.19	....	0.08
Separate curves:										
Uncorrected	0.07	0.09	0.23	0.14	1.35	0.40	1.33	0.36	0.12	0.07
Corrected	....	....	....	....	....	0.12	....	0.19	....	0.06

Legend: UF, unfused. F, fused.
* From Andermann, *Anal. Chem.*, **33**:1689 (1961). Courtesy of *Analytical Chemistry*.

15. ION-EXCHANGE RESIN AS SAMPLE SUPPORT

In connection with clinical studies of human bone mineral, an x-ray method was developed by Collins[27] for the determination of strontium. The technique involves the separation of strontium in calcium acetate solution by means of an ion-exchange resin, with the resin in turn serving as a support in the x-ray analysis. The use of an ion-exchange resin has the advantage of extracting minor or trace amounts of an element from a substrate which interferes in the determination, while at the same time providing a support of low absorptive properties for the characteristic x-rays of the element itself. The steps of the analytical procedure are given in Table 34.

Sixteen standards containing from 20 to 1,000 μg of strontium were analyzed. A regression analysis showed a standard deviation of the concentration-intensity ratio coordinate points from a straight line to be 5.2 per cent of the amount of strontium present. The data are given in Table 35.

Table 34. Determination of Strontium in 0.1M Calcium Acetate Solution

Sample treatment	Pretreat Dowex resin 50-W-X8 with HCl, then wash it to neutrality with distilled water. Pour 1.5 ± 0.1 g of washed resin suspended in water into a 10-mm-diameter glass tube. The resin column has an exchange capacity of 0.0038 equivalent. After water level drops to level of resin, add 10 ml of calcium acetate sample and 1 ml of rubidium chloride containing 280 μg of Rb per ml, the latter to serve as an internal standard. After water level drops to level of resin, add 5 ml of distilled water and allow to drain. Wash resin out of tube into sintered glass funnel. Dry, rinse with acetone. Remove resin and add to it 1 ± 0.1 g of boric acid to serve as a binder. Powder the mixture with Wig-L-Bug mechanical mixer. Press into a ¾-in.-diameter pellet in a mold using 45,000 psi
Instrument	General Electric XRD-3
Standardization	Prepare standards as described under Sample Treatment to contain known amounts of Sr. Use I_{Sr}/I_{Rb} as a measure of Sr
Excitation	Tungsten target, 45 kv, 50 ma
Optics	LiF crystal
Analytical lines	Sr *Kα* 0.875 Å, Rb *Kα* 0.926 Å
Detection	Krypton proportional counter
Register	Take 16,384 counts. Measure each line intensity four times and average the results. No background correction is made
Analytical range	20–100 μg Sr

Table 35. Analysis of Standard Strontium Solution*

Sr added, μg	I_{Sr}/I_{Rb}	Sr found, μg
20	0.692	20
30	0.718	42
50	0.727	48
70	0.745	63
89	0.767	80
99	0.785	95
149	0.855	151
199	0.922	205
298	1.038	298
397	1.160	395
497	1.302	509
596	1.412	598
695	1.520	683
795	1.661	796
894	1.808	913
993	1.887	977

* Collins, *Anal. Chem.*, **33**:605 (1961). Courtesy of *Analytical Chemistry.*

The precision of replicate analysis on the same sample is given in Table 36.

Collins[27] made an assessment of sources of error in the resin-support method. A significant contribution to error is the very high background which is produced by the low-atomic-number matrix, viz., resin and boric acid. It was found that 300 μg of strontium was required to produce a peak height above background equal to the background. Another source of error is the inhomogeneous character of the sample. The coefficient of variation due to mixing statistics alone was estimated to be 3 per cent of the amount of strontium present.

Liebhafsky et al. have completely recovered and determined 1 μg of cobalt per liter using an ion-exchange membrane.[1]

Table 36. Replicate Analysis of a 0.1M Calcium Acetate Solution Containing Approximately 95 μg Strontium per 10 ml*

I_{Sr}/I_{Rb}	*Sr found, μg*
0.7843	94.3
0.7868	96.3
0 7837	93.8
0.7724	84.8
0.7852	95.1
0.7911	99.7
0.7775	88.9
0.7746	86.5
0.7775	88.9

Mean I_{Sr}/I_{Rb} = 0.7814 or 92.0 μg strontium.
* Collins, *Anal. Chem.*, **33**:605 (1961). Courtesy of *Analytical Chemistry.*

16. POWDER-DILUTION TECHNIQUE

In Sec. 1, it was pointed out that in practical applications matrix interaction effects were coped with by a compensative technique or calculation, or by minimizing these effects to an insignificant level by sample attenuation. Another well-known technique for minimizing matrix effects is that of matrix dilution in which the sample is dispersed in high ratio in a low-atomic-number carrier material. Solid as well as liquid diluents may be used. In specific applications the analyst may be fortunate in having a type of sample in which the determination of minor or trace elements in the material of low atomic number may be made directly without further dilution. The sample can be inspected "as is," or at most, it may only require further powdering to provide uniformity, or possibly the introduction of an internal standard. More commonly, however, the sample must be finely powdered and dispersed in a selected low-atomic-number carrier material. Applications of both the "ready-made" and the dilution carrier-type matrix will now be considered.

Cracking Catalyst. Cracking catalyst used in petroleum technology is composed of silicon-aluminum oxides, thus inherently constituting a matrix of relatively low absorption properties for the fluorescent x-rays of the contaminant metals which occur in it. Dyroff and Skiba[24] have employed x-ray spectrography for the determination of iron, nickel, and vanadium. Their procedure is presented in Table 37.

About 15 min is required for a complete analysis. The precision of the method was given as follows for a 2σ confidence level: iron 3 per cent (relative), nickel 0.002 per cent, and vanadium 0.002 per cent.

The possibility of interference from absorption-enhancement effects was investigated. Samples containing one constituent were compared with those containing more than one. Statistical tests of significance were applied to the data, and it was concluded that, over the analytical ranges established, the interferences were insignificant. It was found, however, that iron contamination picked up through mechanical attrition of the equipment by the moving fluid catalyst was not so uniformly dispersed in the catalyst as were nickel and vanadium. The latter two elements are indigenous to the oil which is catalytically cracked by the catalyst.

Both the accuracy and precision of the method can be shown by data in which chemical and x-ray values are compared. These are given in Table 38.

Low-atomic-number Carrier. The powder-dilution technique requires the selection of materials which have low absorption properties for the x-rays to be measured. Gunn[28] has applied a matrix-dilution technique using lithium carbonate–starch as a carrier for elements covering a broad range in atomic number, viz., 20 to 42. A 1:1 weight ratio of lithium carbonate and starch provides a diluent carrier which has high purity, low absorption, good mixing properties, and is suitable for preparing briquetted specimens for x-ray inspection. Borax and cellulose powder are also good diluents. In applying a dilution technique of this type to elements differing con-

Table 37. Procedure for Cracking-catalyst Analysis

Sample preparation	Mechanically grind the sample to a fine powder
Instrument	North American Philips, provided with helium flow attachment
Standardization	Prepare a set of synthetic samples by impregnating fresh catalyst with solutions of the metals. Ni and Fe solutions prepared by dissolving the pure metals in HNO_3; vanadium by dissolving ammonium metavanadate in distilled water. Add solutions to weighed amount of catalyst, grind in jar mill for 2 hr. Dry overnight in oven at 110° C. Regrind for 1 hr, ignite in muffle furnace for 1 hr at 500° C. These standards are measured by x-ray fluorescence; concentration is plotted against net intensity to provide each working curve
Excitation	Tungsten target, 50 kv, 50 ma, for V; 35 kv, 20 ma, for Fe and Ni
Optics	Sample collimator used with all 1/32-in. tubes removed from 3/8-in.-square aperture holder. Detector collimator, 1/32-in. nickel tubes. LiF crystal, He gas in optical path to minimize V *Kα* intensity loss
Analytical lines	Ni *Kα* 1.660 Å, Fe *Kα* 1.936 Å, background 1.83 Å; V *Kα* 2.503 Å, background 2.424 Å
Detection	Geiger counter, measurements in linear region of detection
Register	Take fixed counts: Ni *Kα* ... 128,000 Background ... 6,400 Fe *Kα* ... 512,000 V *Kα* ... 256,000 Background ... 12,800
Analytical range	Fe 0.1–1.0%, Ni 0.002–0.1%, V 0.002–0.1%

siderably in atomic number, some degree of compromise between minimizing matrix effects and reducing the intensity of low-atomic-number elements through dilution necessarily has to be made. A universal or ideal dilution method completely applicable to all composition types is not known. Obviously, the technique becomes more precise and the degree of compromise less significant for samples in which the atomic-number range of the elements is narrow. The method is given in Table 39.

The accuracy of the method is reflected by comparing x-ray results with chemical and with synthetic values, given in Tables 40 and 41, respectively.

The results for blend *A* shown in Table 41 are for metals ranging from calcium (atomic number 20) to molybdenum (atomic number 40). Preliminary considerations indicated that chromium would be affected by the proximity of other interfering lines; the high value obtained for this element appeared to bear this out. An explanation for the low value for molybdenum is not readily apparent. Excluding chromium, the average deviation of analysis from synthesis is 0.6 per cent in this sample of broad range in elements.

The influence of elements in the sample other than those used to establish the calibrations is of interest. Interaction effects of elements of lower or of somewhat higher atomic number than the group of elements selected for study should be more detectable than of those measured in this intermediate range (Table 42).

The deviations as a whole are somewhat greater than observed for calibration blends. The presence of a large amount of highly absorptive lead—46 per cent—in the same composition produces a negative relative error ranging from as much as 20 per cent for iron to 61 per cent for molybdenum.

The presence of sodium chloride produces a relative positive error of 12 and 16 per cent for iron and molybdenum, respectively. The absorptivity of sodium chloride for their radiations is low, which produces high results in their measurements. A negative error of 20 per cent is observed for calcium, however. The very high absorption coefficient of chlorine for calcium radiation (*Kα* 3.35 Å), as interpolated approximately, offers an explanation for the low calcium value.

For the blend containing several atomic-number components (sodium chloride, silica, alumina) the absolute errors for iron and molybdenum are of the order of those

Table 38. X-ray Spectrographic Results for Analysis of Catalysts*

Per Cent Found

Sample No.	1937†			92348†			33966†		
Description	API, fresh natural catalyst			API, artificially contaminated synthetic catalyst					
Constituent	Iron‡	Nickel	Vanadium	Iron	Nickel	Vanadium	Iron	Nickel	Vanadium
	0.895	0.0050	0.0080	0.4550	0.1009	0.1012	0.2500	0.0835	0.0670
	0.920	0.0050	0.0113	0.4725	0.1012	0.1005	0.2550	0.0890	0.0670
	0.885	0.0060	0.0110	0.4725	0.1018	0.1015	0.2525	0.0825	0.0700
	0.900	0.0045	0.0098	0.4600	0.1027	0.1008	0.2498	0.0825	0.0710
	0.920	0.0055	0.0085	0.4555	0.1008	0.1006	0.2550	0.0835	0.0745
	0.895	0.0050	0.0110	0.4550	0.1015	0.1006	0.2500	0.0825	0.0725
	0.895	0.0045	0.0095	0.4600	0.1018	0.1015	0.2525	0.0830	0.0700
	0.900	0.0060	0.0115	0.4550	0.1020	0.1005	0.2450	0.0880	0.0725
	0.915	0.0055	0.0100	0.4555	0.1000	0.1010	0.2550	0.0835	0.0690
	0.885	0.0050	0.0100	0.4600	0.1010	0.1010	0.2500	0.0835	0.0700
Avg.	0.901	0.0052	0.0101	0.4601	0.1014	0.1009	0.2514	0.0842	0.0704
Precision, 2σ	0.026	0.0010	0.0023	0.014	0.0015	0.0008	0.0063	0.0047	0.0048
Chemical§	0.947	0.0026	0.0081	0.416	0.119	0.101	0.251	0.086	0.070

Sample No.	21715			21261		
Description	Regular production catalyst					
Constituent	Iron	Nickel	Vanadium	Iron	Nickel	Vanadium
	0.2444	0.0120	0.0112	0.0925	0.0113	0.0575
	0.2444	0.0180	0.0105	0.0950	0.0120	0.0600
	0.2422	0.0110	0.0124	0.1025	0.0115	0.0565
	0.2422	0.0130	0.0115	0.0950	0.0145	0.0560
	0.2460	0.0120	0.0123	0.0925	0.0130	0.0580
	0.2450	0.0125	0.0115	0.0925	0.0115	0.0570
	0.2444	0.0130	0.0120	0.0950	0.0120	0.0560
	0.2450	0.0110	0.0115	0.0960	0.0115	0.0575
	0.2430	0.0115	0.0112	0.0920	0.0110	0.0580
	0.2460	0.0120	0.0120	0.0950	0.0115	0.0565
Avg.	0.2433	0.0126	0.0116	0.0948	0.0120	0.0573
Precision, 2σ	0.0028	0.0044	0.0011	0.0061	0.0022	0.0024
Chemical	0.239	0.0109	0.0072			

* From Dyroff and Skiba, *Anal. Chem.*, **26**:1774 (1954). Courtesy of *Analytical Chemistry*.

† These samples and chemical analyses were received through courtesy of Committee on Analytical Research of American Petroleum Institute.

‡ Obtained by extrapolation of calibration curve.

§ Average of replicate determinations in several laboratories.

Table 39. Analysis of Powdered Solids by Matrix Dilution

Sample treatment............. Powder the sample to pass 200-mesh sieve, add it to 19 times its weight of Li_2CO_3-starch by careful analytical weighing. Thoroughly mix by mortar and pestle. Prepare 1-in.-diameter briquette with mold pressure of 80,000 psi

Instrument.................. North American Philips with provisions for He flow in optical path

Standardization.............. Use high-purity oxides of metals ground to pass 200 mesh, preignite at 500° C for 2 hr. Portions of the oxides are weighed out to contain designated concentration of each metal. Briquetted specimens are prepared exactly as described above. Concentration is plotted vs. net intensity to provide linear working curve

Excitation and analytical lines.. Tungsten target (excitation values and choice of lines are only suggested, since selections may depend on specific system examined)

Element	*K* peak	λ, Å	X-ray tube	
			kv	ma
Ca	α	3.360	35	20
Background	...	3.280		
V	α	2.503	25	15
Background	...	2.424		
	β	2.285	35	20
Background	...	2.340		
Cr	α	2.290	20	10
Background	...	2.210		
	β	2.085	25	15
Background	...	2.014		
Mn	α	2.102	20	10
Background	...	2.014		
	β	1.910	25	15
Background	...	2.014		
Fe	β	1.757	25	15
Background	...	1.830		
Co	α	1.789	20	10
Background	...	1.866		
	β	1.621	25	15
Background	...	1.866		
Ni	α	1.658	14	10
Background	...	1.866		
	β	1.500	25	15
Background	...	1.410		
Cu	α	1.542	20	10
Background	...	1.625		
	β	1.392	25	15
Background	...	1.361		
Zn	α	1.435	20	10
Background	...	1.361		
	β	1.296	20	10
Background	...	1.361		
As	α	1.175	20	10
Background	...	1.127		
Mo	α	0.709	30	15
Background	...	0.578		

Optics.............. LiF crystal, 0.02-in. spacing collimator before detector

Detection........... Geiger tube, correction for counting coincidence must be made

Register............ Fixed counts, 102,400 for peak, 12,800 for background

Analytical range..... 1.0–100% of each metal oxide

Table 40. Molybdenum in Molybdenum-alumina Catalyst*

	% MoO_3
Chemical†	7.9
X-ray fluorescence	7.88

* From Gunn, *Anal. Chem.*, **29**:184 (1957). Courtesy of *Analytical Chemistry.*
† Gravimetric, lead molybdate precipitation.

Table 41. Analysis of Synthetic Blends, Per Cent*

Element	Added	Found	Diff.
Blend *A*, 10% of Each Metal Oxide			
Ca	4.0	4.6	+0.6
Fe	7.0	7.0	0.0
Mo	6.7	4.5	−2.2
Cu	8.0	9.0	+1.0
Zn	8.0	7.7	−0.3
V	5.6	5.7	+0.1
Mn	6.3	7.0	+0.7
Cr	6.8	10.5	+3.7
Co	7.1	6.9	−0.2
Ni	7.9	8.0	+0.1
Blend *B*, 20% ZnO, As_2O_3, Cr_2O_3; 15% NaCl, $CaSO_4$; 15% Fe_2O_3			
Zn	16.1	14.3	−1.8
As	15.1	17.3	+2.2
Cr	13.7	13.5	−0.2

* From Gunn, *Anal. Chem.*, **29**:184 (1957). Courtesy of *Analytical Chemistry.*

Table 42. Influence of Elemental Composition*

Composition of sample	Added	Found	Diff.	% relative error
50% PbO, 50% Fe_2O_3	Fe 35.0	28.0	−7.0	−20
50% PbO, 50% MoO_3	Mo 33.3	13.0	−20.3	−61
50% PbO, 50% CaO	Ca 35.8	28.0	−7.8	−22
50% NaCl, 50% Fe_2O_3	Fe 35.0	39.3	+4.3	+12
50% NaCl, 50% MoO_3	Mo 33.3	38.5	+5.2	+16
50% NaCl, 50% CaO	Ca 35.8	29.8	−6.0	−17
30% NaCl, 26% SiO_2, 4% Al_2O_3, 10% Fe_2O_3, 10% MoO_3, 10% CaO	Fe 7.0	8.5	+1.5	+21
	Mo 6.7	7.5	+0.8	+12
	Ca 14.3	9.0	−5.3	−37

* From Gunn, *Anal. Chem.*, **29**:184 (1957). Courtesy of *Analytical Chemistry.*

observed in calibration; i.e., the composition effect is minor. Again the value for calcium is low, probably because of chlorine absorption.

These measurements clearly indicate that the unknown should contain elements that are relatively close to the calibration standards in atomic number. For samples containing extremes in atomic number, i.e., where elements of low and high absorptivity coexist, reference standards should be prepared containing the same elements in approximately the same concentrations as in the unknown to assure a reasonable degree of accuracy.

17. PRECIPITATION FROM SOLUTION

There are certain advantages inherent in dissolving a solid sample and producing a precipitate which contains the elements to be determined. Two types of precipitation will be exemplified, one in which the major sample components are precipitated as metallic oxides, the other in which organometallic complexes of trace components in the sample are precipitated and segregated from the bulk of the sample.

Inorganic Oxides. A method for the determination of niobium and tantalum in rare-earth monazite ores in which solution of the sample and reprecipitation are effectuated has been reported by Mortimore et al.[29] The purpose of sample dissolution and precipitation is twofold: to minimize particle effects and to incorporate an internal standard intimately with the sample. The procedure is given in Table 43.

Table 43. Determination of Niobium and Tantalum

Sample treatment	One hundred mg of sample are fused with excess Na_2O. Dissolve fused mass in 300 ml of water, add 25 ml of concentrated HCl. Add a few drops of HF to dissolve meta acid precipitate of elements, then 2 g of boric acid to complex excess fluoride. Add 10 ml internal-standard solution. Precipitate Zr, Nb, Hf, and Ta with concentrated NH_4OH; heat to boiling. Separate by filtration, ignite precipitate
Instrument	North American Philips
Standardization	*Internal standard.* Dissolve 10 g of Zr-Hf mixture (1:1) in HF. Add 50 ml concentrated H_2SO_4, heat to fuming. Dilute with water to 1 liter
	Nb and Ta standards. Fuse 1 g of each separate oxide of Nb and Ta in Na_2O. Dissolve fused mass in 600 ml of water and 50 ml concentrated HCl. Add a few drops HF, complex excess with 2 g of boric acid. Dilute with water to 1 liter. Select aliquots to prepare desired standards. Add 10 ml of internal standard. Precipitate with concentrated NH_4OH, heat to boiling. Separate by filtration, ignite. Grind oxides to 200 mesh. Mix 100 mg of sample, 100 mg of internal standards, and 1 g of cornstarch in agate mortar. Press into 1-in.-diameter pellet with mold pressure of 40,000 psi. From x-ray measurement of the standard pellets the intensity ratios to be plotted against concentration are obtained
Excitation	Tungsten target, 50 kv, 30 ma
Optics	LiF crystal, Soller collimation
Analytical lines	Nb $K\alpha$ 0.746 Å, Zr $K\alpha$ 0.786 Å, Ta $L\alpha$ 1.522 Å, Hf $L\alpha$ 1.570 Å (latter two second order)
Detection	Geiger counter
Register	Number of counts preselected to provide the desired probable error
Analytical range	~0.2–70% of element

The time requirement for a single determination is 40 min. The standard deviation at the 2 per cent level for niobium or tantalum was found to be 5 per cent.

The influence of other elements in the matrix which absorb selectively may be compensated in two ways: one, a family of curves for each element may be plotted in which each curve represents a different amount of an element; two, an internal standard may be employed, provided it has the proper absorption relationship to the other elements. By way of illustration, the influence of iron on the niobium-tantalum ratio is depicted by a family of curves in Fig. 6.

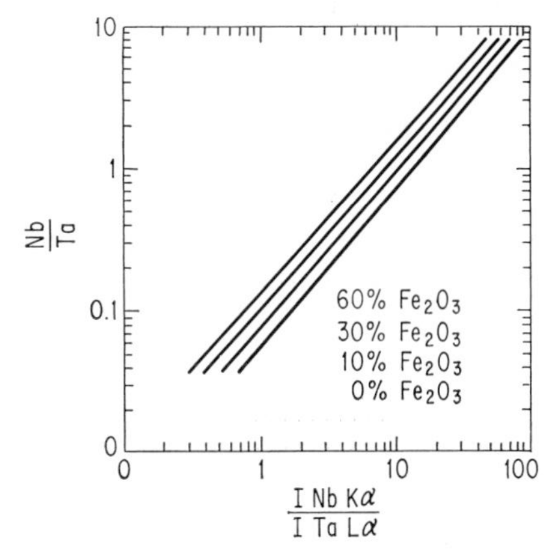

FIG. 6. Effect of iron on niobium-tantalum ratio. [*Mortimore et al., Appl. Spectry.*, **8**:24 (1954). *Reprinted by courtesy of Applied Spectroscopy.*]

The foregoing conditions of Table 43 would be improved through the use of a pulse-height selector. Furthermore, the use of a silicon crystal, which provides second-order extinction of the [111] reflection, would be an additional aid in resolving second-order Nb *Kα* from first-order Ta *Lα*.

Organometallic Complexes. Two advantages are achieved by precipitation of sought elements as organometallic complexes: the elements may be abstracted from the original sample and concentrated; a more favorable matrix from the standpoint of uniformity and detectability is obtained. Fagel et al.[30] used a complexation technique on alkali-metal carbonates containing traces of iron, manganese, copper, nickel, and chromium. These elements were concentrated about fivefold by complexation with 8-quinolinol. The method of analysis is given in Table 44.

The agreement between chemical and x-ray results was within a factor of 2 to 3 for recorded spectra interpretation. Count measurement is recommended where better accuracy is required. Any organic reagent, or combination of reagents, can be used to concentrate the minor constituents of a sample as is done in the present application.

Table 44. Trace Metals in Alkali Carbonates by 8-Quinolinol Precipitation Technique

Sample treatment......	Dissolve sample, add aluminum ion to the solution to serve as carrier and provide bulk. Precipitate with 8-quinolinol by conventional method. Collect metal 8-quinolinolates, dry, mortar grind, press into 1-in. briquette with mold pressure of 6,000 psi.
Instrument...........	General Electric XRD-3 generator, North American Philips goniometer
Standardization.......	Prepare standards from known solutions in exactly the same manner as for unknowns
Excitation............	Tungsten target
Optics................	LiF crystal
Analytical lines........	*Kα* line of Fe, Mn, Ni, Cu, Cr
Detection............	General Electric No. 1 SPG argon proportional tube
Register..............	Measure x-ray intensities directly from strip-chart recorded spectra. Accuracy is improved by counting. Correct for background
Analytical range.......	10–100 ppm

18. ROASTING IN SAMPLE PREPARATION

Wood and Bingham[31] have applied x-ray spectrography to the determination of copper in low-grade porphyry ores. A systematic study of factors involved in sample preparation was made in which 10 factors were investigated, including those involved in sample roasting. A total of 8 analyses of variance was carried out to show that only the following factors among the 10 were significant: particle size, sample size, temperature of roast, time of roast, use of an oxidizer, and the presence of air in roasting. The analytical procedure was subsequently designed to take into account each of these factors in sample preparation. The functions attributed to roasting were those of breaking down the close contact between iron and copper atoms in an ore and producing a more homogeneous sample than could otherwise be obtained by grinding alone. The procedure for the analysis is given in Table 45.

Table 45. Determination of Copper in Porphyry Ore

Sample treatment......	Grind 1.300 g of sample (<100 mesh), 0.4000 g of PbO_2, and 0.300 g of finely powdered SiC in a mortar for 30 to 60 sec. Muffle heat in a porcelain crucible at 800° C for 30 min. Cool, break, mix sintered products in a mortar. Place loosely in sample holder, level surface with spatula
Instrument...........	General Electric XRD-5S
Standardization.......	Use mill tailing material (<0.1% Cu), 0.0200 g Fe_2O_3 added to each sample portion to simulate unknown, and varying known amounts of c.p. CuO to prepare the standards. Sample treatment procedure is followed as above
Excitation............	Tungsten target, 50 kvp, 40 ma
Optics................	LiF crystal, 0.010-in. Soller slit 3½ in. long
Analytical lines........	Cu $K\alpha$ 1.541 Å, Pb $L\gamma_1$ 0.840 Å (second order)
Detection.............	Krypton-filled proportional counter
Register..............	Measure each line of pair for a fixed time of 100 sec. Their intensity ratio is used to determine concentration
Analytical range.......	0.5–1.2% Cu

A comparison of methods of sample treatment was made in which the results by each method were expressed as the deviation from the chemical wet assay on the same samples. Scattered radiation (0.528 Å) was used as a reference before the introduction of the internal standard. The data of Table 46 summarizing the results indicate a significant improvement in accuracy through use of the internal standard and a further significant improvement from the roasting treatment of the sample.

Table 46. Estimated Deviation from Wet Assay*

	% copper		
	No treatment	Internal standard	Roasting
Avg. diff.............................	0.028	0.0135	0.0078
Estimated standard deviation..........	0.034	0.0195	0.0103

* From Wood and Bingham, *Anal. Chem.*, **33**:1344 (1961). Courtesy of *Analytical Chemistry*.

Table 47 compares the x-ray results (on synthetic standards) with those of two laboratories using the same sodium thiosulfate titration method. The agreement between x-ray and chemical methods is almost equivalent to that between the two laboratories using the same titration method.

19. SAMPLE ROTATION

Sample surface irregularities and minute area segregations in a sample both adversely affect the precision of measurement of intensity emitted by an element, e.g., in a

Table 47. Comparison of Results by X-ray and Titration Methods*

Sample	% copper		
	Lab. 1	Lab. 2	X-ray
1	0.855	0.860	0.855
2	0.805	0.800	0.800
3	0.860	0.860	0.855
4	0.845	0.840	0.850
5	0.810	0.810	0.830
6	0.860	0.865	0.845
7	0.840	0.850	0.835
8	0.915	0.930	0.915
9	0.825	0.820	0.820
10	0.810	0.805	0.820
11	0.880	0.870	0.875
12	0.860	0.865	0.865
13	0.830	0.830	0.835
14	0.860	0.840	0.865
15	0.725	0.720	0.750
16	0.655	0.630	0.625
17	0.880	0.890	0.885
18	0.795	0.785	0.775
19	0.805	0.800	0.810
20	0.720	0.725	0.715
Avg.	0.822	0.820	0.821
Estimated standard deviation	.....	.....	0.010

* From Wood and Bingham, *Anal. Chem.*, **33**:1344 (1961). Courtesy of *Analytical Chemistry.*

metallurgical sample. The influence of these surface effects in a solid specimen can be averaged out by rotating the specimen during x-ray analysis so that the area presented to the excitation beam is changed in a regular manner during the analysis. Currently manufactured x-ray instruments have facilities for sample rotation; special attachments for rotation may be procured for older-type instruments. Cullen[32] has applied the sample-rotation technique to the analysis of briquetted copper-alloy drillings for tellurium and zirconium. Tellurium is concentrated in the grain boundaries by

Table 48. Analyzing Copper-alloy Drillings

Sample treatment	Briquette 10 g of sample drillings at 15,000 psi mold pressure to produce a 1¼-in.-diameter specimen
Instrument	General Electric XRD-5; Spex Industries sample turntable with 25 rpm rotation
Standardization	Use samples of chemically analyzed alloys. Intensity ratio vs. concentration gives linear curves
Excitation	Tungsten target, 50 kv, 40 ma
Optics	LiF, 0.01-in. Soller slit
Analytical lines	Te $K\alpha$ 0.451 Å, Zr $K\alpha$ 0.786 Å; use W $L\gamma$, 1.099 Å scattered radiation from primary beam as reference
Detection	Scintillation counter
Register	Take 50,000 counts for each intensity measurement
Analytical range	Tellurium 0.01–1.0%, zirconium not given

machining the metal, thus producing an alloy which gives rise to small chips. Turnings from sample drilling are briquetted to obtain the specimen for analysis. The procedure for the analysis is given in Table 48.

The effects of sample rotation are shown in Tables 49 and 50 for tellurium and zirconium, respectively. The results are obviously improved by sample rotation.

Table 49. Deviations*
(Briquetted drillings, 0.60 per cent tellurium)

Static		Rotating	
Te $K\alpha$, counts/sec	Te $K\alpha$/W $L\gamma_1$	Te $K\alpha$, counts/sec	Te $K\alpha$/W $L\gamma_1$
320	4.36	321	4.36
312	4.35	318	4.35
309	4.28	310	4.35
330	4.39	320	4.37
322	4.38	332	4.37
300	4.29	331	4.36
315	4.30	328	4.36
332	4.38	335	4.34
360	4.43	335	4.39
311	4.35	319	4.37
Avg. 321.1	4.351	324.9	4.362
Coefficient of variation 4.95	1.17	2.74	0.48

* From Cullen, *Anal. Chem.*, **33**:1342 (1961). Courtesy of *Analytical Chemistry*.

Table 50. X-ray and Chemical Determinations of Zirconium*

% Zr			Diff., % Zr	
Stationary sample	Rotating sample	Chemical†	Stationary	Rotating
0.090	0.085	0.085	0.005	0.000
0.085	0.081	0.081	0.004	0.000
0.099	0.095	0.099	0.000	0.004
0.106	0.104	0.103	0.003	0.001
0.131	0.137	0.138	0.007	0.001
0.099	0.103	0.103	0.004	0.000
0.106	0.106	0.107	0.001	0.001
0.082	0.087	0.087	0.005	0.000
0.175	0.170	0.170	0.005	0.000
0.182	0.186	0.184	0.002	0.002
0.106	0.095	0.099	0.007	0.004
			Avg. 0.004	0.001

* From Cullen, *Anal. Chem.*, **33**:1342 (1961). Courtesy of *Analytical Chemistry*.
† Photometric alizarin red S determinations, average of two determinations on two separate portions of sample reported.

The effect of difference in sample form of the same sample is given in Table 51. From the intensity ratios no difference in sample form is reflected.

Excellent agreement between chemical and x-ray determinations of tellurium over a broad range in concentration is shown by the data of Table 52.

Table 51. Effect of Different Sample Forms*

Sample form	Te $K\alpha$/W $L\gamma_1$ (0.60% Te)
Briquetted sawings	4.364
Briquetted filings	4.362
Solid piece of alloy	4.360

* From Cullen, *Anal. Chem.*, **33**:1342 (1961). Courtesy of *Analytical Chemistry.*

Table 52. X-ray and Chemical Tellurium Determinations*

% Te, chemical	Te $K\alpha$/W $L\gamma_1$	% Te, x-ray	Diff.
0.001	2.091	0.00	0.00
0.05	2.273	0.05	0.00
0.10	2.448	0.11	0.01
0.40	3.465	0.39	0.01
0.60	4.362	0.60	0.00
1.00	5.857	0.99	0.01

* From Cullen, *Anal. Chem.*, **33**:1342 (1961). Courtesy of *Analytical Chemistry.*

20. BACKGROUND-CORRECTION PROBLEM

The success of x-ray fluorescence measurement of an element in minor or trace concentrations depends upon spectrally resolving the characteristic line intensity of the element from that of the background upon which it is superimposed. A specific description of this spectral situation has been illustrated in Sec. 3, in which the line "signal" is very weak compared with the background. The more commonly used method of correcting a peak measurement for background consists in measuring a spectral position free of interference on one or both sides of the peak. The precision desired for the net line measurement is selected in terms of the statistics of counting (cf. Sec. 21).

Lytle and Heady[33] encountered the problem of resolving the lines of rare earths in low or trace concentrations from background in determining these elements in rare-earth oxides. The usual method of background correction was found to be inadequate. The absolute background of each analytical line measured in a specific matrix was evaluated by the use of an extremely high purity form of that matrix. In each case careful inspection and preparation were required to assure the matrix material of highest purity. For the trace concentrations measured, it was concluded that matrix interaction effects were negligible.

The method of analysis is given in Table 53.

Table 53. Impurities in Rare-earth Oxides

Sample treatment	None
Instrument	General Electric XRD-5, provisions for helium flow
Standardization	Prepare standards by precipitation as the oxalate from acid solution to simulate the composition type analyzed. Vary the concentrations of impurity elements in steps from 0.005 to 1.0%. Ignite for 1 hr at 1000° C. Grind under alcohol with mechanical mortar for 20 min. Reignite at 1000° C; keep in tightly capped bottle
Excitation	Tungsten target, 50 kv, 40 ma
Optics	LiF crystal, 0.005-in. Soller slit
Analytical lines	See Table 54
Detection	Argon proportional tube
Register	Duplicate measurement of 4,000 counts for each line
Analytical range	0.005–1.0% of La, Ce, Pr, Nd, Sm, Y in matrices shown in Table 54

Table 54. Analytical Angles for Each Matrix, Net Intensity, and Peak-background Ratios* at 1 Per Cent Concentration Level†

	Element					
	La	Ce	Pr	Nd	Sm	Y
	Analytical angle					
	$L\alpha_1$, 82.85	$L\alpha_1$, 78.96	$L\beta_1$, 68.23	$L\beta_1$, 65.06	$L\beta_1$, 59.48	$K\alpha_1$, 23.75
	CeO_2 matrix					
Air:						
Net intensity, cps.....	6.74	....	15.43	20.80	20.29	
Ratio...............	3.29	....	1.46	1.22	3.20	
Helium:						
Net intensity, cps.....	24.00	....	39.90	42.96	37.34	
Ratio...............	5.10	....	1.80	1.23	3.81	
	Pr_6O_{11} matrix					
Helium:						
Net intensity, cps.....	4.55	6.94	.....	20.33	20.55	55.85
Ratio...............	3.03	1.81	.....	4.52	3.14	5.82
	Element					
	La	Ce	Pr	Nd	Sm	Eu
	Analytical angle					
	$L\alpha_1$,	$L\alpha_1$,	$L\beta_1$,	$L\beta_1$,	$L\beta_1$,	$L\beta_{1\text{-}2}$, 144.85
	Nd_2O_3 matrix					
Helium:						
Net intensity, cps.....	5.03	8.00	14.00	.....	30.10	4.65
Ratio...............	0.59	2.32	2.33	.....	0.96	1.21

Table 54 gives the 2θ positions for measuring the rare-earth elements in various matrices. The net peak intensity and peak-to-background ratio also are given for a 1 per cent concentration level for each contaminating element, which readily show how a small change in their relationship can produce a very serious error in the analytical result.

The background determination for a high-purity matrix of cerium oxide containing lanthanum is given in Table 55. A plot of concentration vs. net peak is linear for the data given. The lanthanum concentration in the "blank" as well as the standards containing added lanthanum were corrected to the Johnson-Matthey reference.

Table 54. Analytical Angles for Each Matrix, Net Intensity, and Peak-background Ratios* at 1 Per Cent Concentration Level† (*Continued*)

	Element					
	Ce	Pr	Nd	Eu	Gd	Y
	Analytical angle					
	$L\alpha_1$, 78.96	$L\beta_1$, 68.23	$L\alpha_1$, 72.08	$L\beta_{1-2}$, 144.85	$L\alpha_1$, 61.05	$K\alpha$, 23.75
	Sm_2O_3 matrix					
Helium:						
Net intensity, cps	6.86	14.46	18.51	6.45	63.96	32.24
Ratio	2.25	1.50	6.11	1.29	3.85	5.89
	Element					
	Eu	Gd	Tb	Dy	Er	Yb
	Analytical angle					
	$L\alpha_1$, 63.51	$L\alpha_1$, 61.05	$L\alpha_1$, 58.76	$L\beta_1$, 50.24	$L\beta_1$, 46.41	$L\alpha_{1-2}$, 112.25
	Y_2O_3 matrix					
Helium:						
Net intensity, cps	55.49	73.17	62.74	48.27	81.77	12.35
Ratio	6.80	8.88	7.20	2.19	3.33	1.08

$$* \text{ Peak/background} = \frac{\text{gross cps} - \text{background cps}}{\text{background cps}}$$

† From Lytle and Heady, *Anal. Chem.*, **31**:809 (1959). Courtesy of *Analytical Chemistry*.

A summary evaluating the accuracy of each element for several concentration levels in each matrix is given in Table 56.

21. SOURCES OF ERROR IN X-RAY FLUORESCENCE ANALYSIS

Variance Statistics. There are a number of physical or nonoperator variables in x-ray fluorescence analysis which tend to reduce the precision with which a measurement is made—some instrumental, others residing in the nature or properties of the sample. We may write

$$\sigma^2_{\text{total}} = \sigma^2_a + \sigma^2_b + \sigma^2_c + \cdots + \sigma^2_n \tag{42}$$

where σ^2_a, σ^2_b, σ^2_c, . . . , σ^2_n are separate sources of variance which contribute to the total variance σ^2_{total}. Variance, being additive, is a convenient statistic where one wishes to break down the sources or to isolate a given source contributing to error.[34]

Instrumental Precision. X-ray counting exhibits random fluctuations which may be assumed to vary about a mean value in a statistically predictable manner. According to the Poisson distribution,

$$\sigma = \sqrt{N} \quad \text{or} \quad CV = 100/\sqrt{N} \tag{43}$$

where σ is the standard deviation, N is the number of counts taken, and CV is the coefficient of variation (equivalent to σ expressed on a relative basis in per cent). The statistical confidence level of counting can be expressed in terms of σ or CV: 1σ (or CV) $\sim$ 67, 2σ (or $2CV$) $\sim$ 95, 3σ (or $3CV$) $\sim$ 99.7 per cent confidence, respectively. Counting precisions for selected numbers of counts at three confidence levels are given in Table 57. At 10,000 counts, for example, more than 99 out of 100 measurements taken may be expected to fall within 3 per cent relative to the mean of the measurements. Only the counting error, of course, not those from other sources, is included in these data.

Examples can be taken to illustrate the interrelationship among statistical confidence, number of counts, and precision.

Example 1. Suppose a measurement is to be made in which a relative precision of 0.8 per cent with a statistical confidence of 99.7 per cent is specified. How many counts are required to meet this precision specification?

Solution: The requirement is that $3CV = 0.8$. From Eq. (43), $CV = 100/\sqrt{N}$. Therefore, $300/\sqrt{N} = 0.8$.

$N = 140{,}625$ counts required.

Table 55. Background Determination of High-purity Sample. Lanthanum Oxide in Cerium Oxide*

Standard No.	La_2O_3 added, %	Intensity† La $L\alpha_1$, cps	Less matrix background, 11.79 cps
Ce-1	1.0	70.67	58.88
Ce-2	0.5	41.02	29.23
Ce-3	0.2	23.05	11.26
Ce-4	0.1	17.05	5.26
Ce-5	0.05	14.11	2.32
Ce-6	0.01	12.02	0.23
Ce-7	0.005	12.00	0.21
Ce-8 (blank)‡	0.0	11.79	
Ce-JM§	.....	11.14	

* From Lytle and Heady, *Anal. Chem.*, **31**:809 (1959). Courtesy of *Analytical Chemistry*.
† Values taken in helium atmosphere with 0.010-in. Soller slit.
‡ Lanthanum 0.01% by reference to Johnson-Matthey sample.
§ Johnson-Matthey Catalog 304, 99.99% pure CeO_2 relative to rare earths present; analysis by supplier indicated no lanthanum.

Table 56. Accuracy of Analysis Summary*,†

Concentration range	Element, avg %‡ error							
	La	Ce	Pr	Nd	Sm	Eu	Gd	Y
0.3-0.8	15	2	4	4	1	6	2	0
0.06-0.2	21	9	7	4	5	6	0	7
0.01-0.05	29	5	14	19	15	15	32	0

* From Lytle and Heady, *Anal. Chem.*, **31**:809 (1959). Courtesy of *Analytical Chemistry*.
† All figures as % oxide.
‡ Based on comparison of average of five determinations to known value.

Table 57. Statistical Precision of Counting

Counts	Relative precision, %		
	67% confidence (CV)	95% confidence ($2CV$)	99.7% confidence ($3CV$)
100	10	20	30
500	4.5	8.9	13.4
1,000	3.2	6.3	9.5
5,000	1.4	2.8	4.3
10,000	1.0	2.0	3.0
50,000	0.45	0.89	1.3
100,000	0.32	0.63	0.95
500,000	0.14	0.28	0.43
1,000,000	0.1	0.2	0.3

Example 2. Suppose one makes a determination in which the net line intensity is only three-fourths that of the background upon which it is superimposed. Peak and background positions are to be counted for the same fixed time. How should the fixed counting time be chosen to assure a relative counting precision for the net line of 1 per cent with 95 per cent confidence?

Solution: For this case,

$$CV = \frac{100 \sqrt{N_{l+b} + N_b}}{N_{l+b} - N_b} \tag{44}$$

where N_b = number of counts at background
N_{l+b} = number of counts at peak (line + background)
Twice the coefficient of variation must equal 1 per cent, or

$$\frac{200 \sqrt{N_{l+b} + N_b}}{N_{l+b} - N_b} = 1$$

But $N_{l+b} = 1.75N_b$. Therefore, $200 \sqrt{2.75 N_b}/0.75N_b = 1$. $N_b = 195{,}364$.

The fixed counting time should thus be chosen so that at least 195,364 counts are collected at background. In this length of time, since $N_{l+b} = 1.75N_b$, 341,887 counts would be collected at the peak position.

For a discussion of the mathematically optimum division of peak and background counting times to obtain a predetermined precision, the reader is referred to a paper by Mack and Spielberg.[35]

Fixed Time vs. Fixed Count. Birks and Brown[36] have compared the statistics for fixed-time and fixed-count measurements of line minus background in fluorescence analysis. Their calculations show that fixed-time operation is much faster than fixed-count because the background count is not required to be so large as that for the peak. Furthermore, they show that the coefficient of variation for fixed time is never greater than 1.1 times that for fixed-count operation. Hence fixed-time operation is recommended for all routine analysis.

A virtue of fixed-time measurement which is obvious is that an intensity value is obtained directly, without calculation being required as with fixed-count measurement.

Instrumental Adjustments. The ASTM Task Group on X-ray Fluorescence Spectroscopy has reported the cooperative effort of 16 laboratories on studies of the influence of several variables on precision.[37] Powder samples were measured for barium, molybdenum, zinc, and titanium, thus representing a broad range in the wavelengths measured.

Evaluation of the error of manually resetting the x-ray tube current and voltage is summarized from the pooled values of seven laboratories in Table 58.

Table 58. Precision of Resetting X-ray Tube Current and Voltage, Average Measured Values of Coefficient of Variation*

Ba $K\alpha$	Mo $K\alpha$	Zn $K\alpha$	Ba $L\beta_1$	Ti $K\alpha$
1.5	1.5	1.3	1.0	1.2

Total avg. $CV = 1.3$.
For 10^4 counts taken in each measurement, $CV_{statistical} = 1.0$. Therefore, $(1.3)^2 = CV^2_{reset}\,(1.0)^2$. $CV_{reset} = 0.83\%$.
* From *Appl. Spectry.*, **31**:3 (1959). Reprinted by courtesy of *Applied Spectroscopy.*

The error of repositioning the spectrometer was reported by two laboratories, each taking a different number of counts. A summary of the results is given in Table 59.

Table 59. Precision of Repositioning Spectrometer, Average Measured Values of Coefficient of Variation*

Counts taken	Ba $K\alpha$	Mo $K\alpha$	Zn $K\alpha$	Ba $L\beta_1$	Ti $K\alpha$
16,000	1.2	1.0	1.1	0.58	0.93
$CV_{count} = 0.79$		Total avg. $CV = 0.96$			
1,000,000					
$CV_{count} = 0.1$		Total avg. $CV = 0.15$			

For the laboratory taking 16,000 counts, $(0.96)^2 = (0.79)^2 + CV^2_{reposition}$. $CV_{reposition} = 0.55$.
For the laboratory taking 1,000,000 counts, $(0.15)^2 = (0.1)^2 + CV^2_{reposition}$. $CV_{reposition} = 0.11$.
* From *Appl. Spectry.*, **13**:3 (1959). Reprinted by courtesy of *Applied Spectroscopy.*

Since reposition error is independent of count level, the Task Force concluded that the first laboratory result had incorporated in it sources of variance over and above that of repositioning.

Sample Preparation. *ASTM Powder Mixing.* The foregoing ASTM Task Force[37] also made a study of sample properties which affect precision. One of these was the precision of powder mixing. Table 60 summarizes this study.

Table 60. Precision of Mixing Powders, Measured Values of Coefficient of Variation*

Composition	Ba $K\alpha$	Mo $K\alpha$	Zn $K\alpha$	Ba $L\beta_1$	Ti $K\alpha$
1	1.2	1.1	1.8	9.4	9.6
2	0.8	4.5	1.8	3.9	6.0
3	2.9	10.2	18.8	5.6	5.6
4	6.6	8.7	4.4	11.0	20.0
Avg.	2.9	6.1	6.7	7.5	10.2

Total avg. 6.7.
* From *Appl. Spectry.*, **13**:3 (1959). Reprinted by courtesy of *Applied Spectroscopy.*

The conclusion of the Task Force was that the mixing operation for powders may introduce more errors in the results than all other sources of error combined. This finding indicates that considerable caution must be exercised in adding internal standards to powder specimens (cf. Secs. 8 and 11).

Platinum Catalyst Treatment. Studies have been made of several variables which may affect the accuracy of determining platinum in reforming catalyst.[38] To evaluate the influence and significance of these variables in the treatment of the specimen on the result, recourse was taken to a statistical analysis of variance for each set of data pertaining to the variable under study. The influences of specimen preparation, heat-treatment, contaminants, and variation in time are summarized in order in Tables 61 to 64. The conclusion, based on a preselected confidence level of 95 per cent, is given in each table.

Table 61. Variation of Measurement between Specimen Preparations* (0.632 Per Cent Pt)

Specimen	Intensity measurement, counts/sec					
	1	2	3	4	5	6
A	450.3	448.2	449.4	450.5	446.6	461.4
B	448.6	438.8	466.4	440.0	440.8	443.1
C	443.4	442.7	440.8	443.7	447.3	450.0
D	444.1	449.4	450.0	441.5	442.0	443.2

Avg. 446.76.

Source	Sum of squares	Degrees of freedom	Variance
Within specimens..........	810.7	20	40.54
			$F_{0.95}(3,20) = 3.10$
Between specimen means...	157.2	3	52.4
Total..................	967.9	23	$F = 1.29$

Conclusion: The difference between means on different specimen preparation is not statistically significant.

* From Gunn, *Anal. Chem.*, **28**:1433 (1956). Courtesy of *Analytical Chemistry.*

Table 62. Influence of Heat-treatment on Measurements of Platinum* (0.632 Per Cent)

Heat-treatment	Counts/sec			t test
	N	Avg.	Standard deviation	
1000° F	6	446.2	4.8	Conclusion:† $t = 1.82$. Not significantly different
1800° F, 1 hr	6	441.6	4.0	

* From Gunn, *Anal. Chem.*, **28**:1433 (1956). Courtesy of *Analytical Chemistry.*

† At confidence level of 95%, $t = 2.23$ for 10 degrees of freedom represented by compared set of values.

Table 63. Influence of Contaminants on Measurement of Platinum*

Sample	Counts/sec†			t	Conclusion‡
	N	Avg.	Standard deviation		
Reference§ (0.632% Pt)........	6	446.2	4.8		
Reference + 10% graphite.....	6	435.3	3.4	4.54	Significantly different
Reference + 1% Fe_2O_3........	6	420.4	3.7	10.45	Significantly different
Reference (0.632% Pt).........	6	443.0	1.7		
Reference + 10% H_2O.........	6	439.7	3.0	2.39	Significantly different

* From Gunn, *Anal. Chem.*, **28**:1433 (1956). Courtesy of *Analytical Chemistry*.
† 1 count/sec ~0.00165% Pt by calibration.
‡ At confidence level of 95%, t = 2.23 for 10 degrees of freedom represented by compared sets of values.
§ Basis of analysis, 1000° F preignition.

Table 64. Variation of Measurement on a Specimen with Time* (0.632 Per Cent Pt)

Date of measurement	Intensity measurement, counts/sec								
	1	2	3	4	5	6	7	8	Avg.
4/13/1955	449.9	453.7	458.7	454.2	452.1	452.2	445.9	447.9	451.8
5/4/1955	450.6	450.3	452.1	449.3	453.3	451.3	.....	.....	451.2
5/19/1955	444.1	449.4	445.0	441.5	442.0	443.2	.....	.....	444.2

Source	Analysis of variance		
	Sum of squares	Degrees of freedom	Variance
Among day means..................	227.6	2	113.8 $F_{0.95}(2,17) = 3.59$
Within days......................	161.6	17	9.51 $F = 11.96$
Total.........................	389.2	19	

Conclusion: The difference between means for a specimen measured at different times is highly significant.
* From Gunn, *Anal. Chem.*, **28**:1433 (1956). Courtesy of *Analytical Chemistry*.

The differences observed in Table 64 probably are more attributable to instrumentation than to specimen changes, although it could be both. The foregoing examples which these tables furnish fully illustrate the general manner by which variables associated with x-ray fluorescence analysis may be isolated and statistically evaluated as to the significance of their influence on the method.

22. COMPARISON OF X-RAY AND OPTICAL-EMISSION SPECTROSCOPY

A comparison of the relative merits and limitations of x-ray and optical-emission elemental analysis obviously can be made with more meaning where a preknowledge of the composition and type of materials to be analyzed is available. Where many samples of the same type in composition and physical structure are to be analyzed over an indefinitely long period of time and a "tailor-made" instrument and procedure are dictated, the selection of an instrument usually is not extremely difficult. In many industrial laboratories, where the range and type of materials to be analyzed are broad and considerable analytical versatility is needed, it is found that the instruments are complementary rather than competitive. For example, for the analysis of substances containing boron or beryllium, optical emission would be required since the characteristic x-rays of these elements are not available using conventional instruments. On the other hand, complex compositions of rare earths may emit such complex optical-emission spectra that x-ray fluorescence becomes the obvious choice for coping with the resolution problem.

Table 65. Comparison of X-ray and Optical Emission* for Quantitative Analysis

Feature	X-ray	Optical
Ultimate sensitivity	$\sim 10^{-6}$ g	$\sim 10^{-8}$ g
Range of elements measured	Atomic No. 11 and greater with conventional equipment	All, with possible exception of H, O, N, halogens, inert gases (by atomic spectra)
Small samples (1–10 mg)	Sometimes problematic	Easily handled
Spectral coincidence	Usually minor	Often major
Analytical speed	Good	Good
Spectral versatility	Optics and detectors easily adapted to desired spectral position	Movable channels enable positioning to desired spectral position but changes are not rapid and spatial problems may arise
Interaction effects in excitation	Absorption enhancement can be predicted for specific case	Complex; cannot be predicted for specific case
Sample defacement or consumption	Very minor to none	Minor to total
Need for auxiliary qualitative instrument	Helpful but not required	Spectrograph highly desirable
Ease of operation and interpretation	Comparable with other physical analytical instruments	Comparable with other physical analytical instruments
Precision compared with competitive methods	Superlative in many cases	Good to excellent
Accuracy compared with competitive methods	Good to excellent	Good to excellent
Maintenance-service factor	Good	Good
Approximate floor area covered by units	30 sq ft	60 sq ft
Cost	\$20,000†	\$35,000–\$65,000 depending on number of elements desired
Internal standard	Sometimes desirable	Imperative

* Commercially available direct-reading instrument with provision for vacuum optics assumed.

† Fixed optics or automatically programmed x-ray instruments of certain types will cost more.

The comparison of features of Table 65 gives what is believed to be a consensus of opinion of those familiar with both instrumental principles and practice on each item of comparison. These comparisons are by no means presumed to cover all contingencies which may arise in a given laboratory. Careful study of present and future analytical needs, followed by consultation with those having a good working knowledge and experience of both, is recommended to those who are faced with the problem of choosing between instruments.

REFERENCES CITED

1. H. A. Leibhafsky, H. G. Pfeiffer, E. H. Winslow, and P. D. Zemany, *X-ray Absorption and Emission in Analytical Chemistry*, John Wiley & Sons, Inc., New York, 1960.
2. H. G. Pfeiffer and P. D. Zemany, *Nature*, **174**:397 (1957).
3. T. N. Rhodin, Jr., *Anal. Chem.*, **27**:1857 (1955).
4. E. L. Gunn, *Anal. Chem.*, **33**:921 (1961).
5. G. Andermann and J. W. Kemp, *Anal. Chem.*, **30**:1306 (1958).
6. C. C. Hale and W. H. King, Jr., *Anal. Chem.*, **33**:74 (1961).
7. R. A. Jones, *Anal. Chem.*, **33**:71 (1961).
8. A. A. Chodos and W. Nichiporuk, in *Advances in X-ray Analysis*, vol. 4, p. 247, W. M. Mueller (ed.), Plenum Press, Inc., New York, 1958.
9. G. A. Stoner, *Anal. Chem.*, **34**:123 (1962).
10. E. N. Davis and R. A. Van Nordstrand, *Anal. Chem.*, **26**:973 (1954).
11. G. Von Hevesey, *Chemical Analysis by X-rays and Its Applications*, McGraw-Hill Book Company, New York, 1932.
12. I. Adler and J. M. Axelrod, *Spectrochim. Acta*, **7**:91 (1955).
13. G. L. Clark, *The Encyclopedia of Spectroscopy*, p. 736, Reinhold Publishing Corporation, New York, 1960.
14. J. Sherman, *Spectrochim. Acta*, **7**, 283 (1955).
15. G. E. Noakes, *An Absolute Method of X-ray Fluorescence Analysis Applied to Stainless Steels*, pp. 57–62, ASTM STP157, Philadelphia, Pa., 1953.
16. P. K. Koh and B. Caugherty, *J. Appl. Phys.*, **23**:427 (1952).
17. B. J. Mitchell, *Anal. Chem.*, **33**:917 (1961).
18. H. J. Beattie and R. M. Brissey, *Anal. Chem.*, **26**:980 (1954).
19. L. S. Birks, *X-ray Spectrochemical Analysis*, Interscience Publishers, Inc., New York, 1959.
20. R. A. Jones, *Anal. Chem.*, **31**:1341 (1959).
21. L. Silverman, W. Houk, and L. Moudy, *Anal. Chem.*, **29**:1762 (1957).
22. F. Claisse, *Norelco Reptr.*, **4**:3 (1957).
23. E. L. Gunn, in *Advances in X-ray Analysis*, vol. 4, p. 247, W. M. Mueller (ed.), Plenum Press, Inc., New York, 1958.
24. G. V. Dyroff and P. Skiba, *Anal. Chem.*, **26**:1774 (1954).
25. R. H. Heidl and V. A. Fassel, *Anal. Chem.*, **33**:913 (1961).
26. G. Andermann, *Anal. Chem.*, **33**:1698 (1961).
27. R. L. Collins, *Anal. Chem.*, **33**:605 (1961).
28. E. L. Gunn, *Anal. Chem.*, **29**:184 (1957).
29. D. M. Mortimore, P. A. Romans, and J. L. Tews, *Appl. Spectry.*, **8**:24 (1954).
30. J. E. Fagel, Jr., E. W. Balis, and L. B. Bronk, *Appl. Spectry.*, **29**:1287 (1957).
31. R. E. Wood and E. R. Bingham, *Anal. Chem.*, **33**:1344 (1961).
32. T. J. Cullen, *Anal. Chem.*, **33**:1342 (1961).
33. F. W. Lytle and H. H. Heady, *Anal. Chem.*, **31**:809 (1959).
34. W. J. Dixon and F. J. Massey, Jr., *Introduction to Statistical Analysis*, McGraw-Hill Book Company, New York, 1951.
35. M. Mack and N. Spielberg, *Spectrochim. Acta*, **12**:169 (1958).
36. L. S. Birks and D. M. Brown, *Anal. Chem.*, **34**:240 (1962).
37. ASTM Task Group on X-ray Fluorescence Spectroscopy, *Appl. Spectry.*, **13**:3 (1959).
38. E. L. Gunn, *Anal. Chem.*, **28**:1433 (1956).

Chapter 37

TRACE AND MICROANALYSIS

T. C. Loomis and S. M. Vincent

Bell Telephone Laboratories

1. INTRODUCTION

During the rapid increase in popularity of x-ray emission spectroscopy in the middle 1950s, it was considered to be a field exclusively devoted to the determination of the major elements in macrosamples. Apologies were often made for the inability of the x-ray spectrometer to measure low concentrations or analyze small specimens. With the development of new instrumentation and techniques, however, it is now possible to perform both trace analysis and microanalysis by means of x-rays.

Trace and microanalysis will be considered separately in this chapter, although it is recognized that the two fields have much in common. Trace analysis is the determination of elements present at low concentrations. Microanalysis deals with the measurement of composition of small samples or small portions of larger specimens. The latter category includes such things as surface films or contaminants, inclusions, or selected areas of the surface of heterogeneous samples.

Frequently it is possible to determine elements by direct secondary x-ray emission when they are present at concentration levels generally considered as traces. Even in the early pioneering work of von Hevesy[1] sensitivities of less than 1 part in 10,000 (0.01 per cent) were reported. With modern equipment it is possible to extend this sensitivity at least an order of magnitude in favorable cases. However, since direct methods are the subject of previous chapters in this part of the book, the present discussion will be limited to trace analyses which involve special apparatus or techniques.

Microanalysis by means of x-ray emission may be carried out using conventional x-ray spectrometers or with the aid of specialized devices such as nondispersive spectrometers (see Chap. 31, Sec. 1), electron microprobes (see Chap. 39), or x-ray milliprobes. When conventional equipment is employed, some form of physical or chemical transformation of the sample is usually necessary. The x-ray milliprobe, on the other hand, frequently requires little or no preparation of samples.

2. TRACE ANALYSIS

Trace analysis may be carried out with conventional x-ray fluorescence equipment or modifications of it, usually on separated or concentrated portions of a sample.

Often the determination of trace amounts of sample involves low counting rates which are not far above background. An example of this is in the technique in which filter paper is used as a sample carrier. Precision attainable under realizable operating conditions with a relatively high background has been studied by Zemany, Pfeiffer, and Liebhafsky.[2] A sample of about 0.02 ml of solution of zinc nitrate containing about 10 μg of zinc/ml was evaporated on a 1.25-cm square of Whatman No. 1 filter paper and supported in a sample holder by a 0.6-cm-wide strip of 0.4-mil Mylar. Ninety values of total counts (N_T) for the Zn $K\alpha$ line at $2\theta = 41.77°$ (LiF crystal) were obtained for this spot, each N_T alternating with a background count (N_B) at $2\theta = 39.80°$ using only 40-sec counts. The background correction factor was determined by finding the time for 16,384 counts for a blank treated as in the formation of the zinc spot but with zinc omitted. These were 1,159.72 sec at 41.77° and 1,366.99 sec at 39.80°. Thus the correction factor obtained was 1,366.99/1,159.72, or 1.179. Then for the 90 individual determinations of zinc, N_B was estimated by multiplying the count made at 39.80° by 1.179. The true counting rate for zinc was determined on spots containing 4 or 8 μg of Zn and was found to be 16.0 counts/sec/μg. Results show that even with the short counting time of 40 sec the precision of the analysis can be satisfactorily predicted from statistical considerations and the theory of errors. Similar grounds for confidence in the method were obtained with 216 results for a spot containing 4×10^{-5} g of strontium.

Filter-paper Techniques. There are several ways in which samples may be put on filter paper for x-ray analysis. The paper may be impregnated by immersing it in a solution for qualitative analysis or the determination of relative amounts of unknowns. Precipitates may be transferred to paper by filtering techniques. Solutions may be transferred to confined spot areas by micropipet. The solution may be prevented from spreading farther than desired by impregnating the paper with a circle of molten paraffin applied with the end of a cork borer of suitable size. Other special techniques of applying and drying samples have been described, especially in connection with biological samples. In addition to confined spots, methods for examining strips of paper on which samples have been separated by chromatography or by electrophoresis have been used.

A possible source of error when using filter paper as a sample matrix was pointed out by Felten, Fankuchen, and Steigman.[3] Observed intensity ratios of binary unknowns may vary with changes of filter-paper thickness and also with the total amount of sample being measured owing to variations in matrix absorption effects. For example, filter paper was impregnated with sample by immersion in a solution containing two transition metals. The observed intensity ratio of the two metals varied as increasing numbers of layers of portions of this paper were stacked in a sample holder. The equipment used contained a tungsten-target x-ray tube operated at 40 kvp and 20 ma, a rock salt or LiF analyzing crystal, and a krypton-filled Geiger tube as detector. Intensities were determined by measuring the time required to accumulate 25,000 counts and recalculating to counts per second for each element after making a correction for the background. Backgrounds measured on untreated paper varied from 25 to 30 counts/sec, while the intensities being measured were of the order of 100 to 500 counts/sec. Unknowns were compared with knowns from standard solutions. For the most accurate results matrix effects of absorption are minimized as the sample thickness approaches zero. The ratios of intensities of the fluorescent radiations from the two components for decreasing numbers of stacked impregnated filter papers were determined. Extrapolation to zero thickness gave a limiting ratio which was directly proportional to the molar concentrations of the elements involved. Simple intensity ratios at a single thickness have some utility when compared with standards but showed errors up to 9 per cent. An internal-standard method worked well, with a single thickness of paper giving errors of 5 per cent or less.

X-ray fluorescence has been used by Wenger and coworkers as a quantitative supplement to paper electrophoresis for 10- to 100-μg amounts of Pb, Bi, Hg, and Sr with an accuracy of ± 10 per cent.[4] Again background corrections are necessary, and allowance must be made for spreading that occurs during the migration of the spots.

Quantitative trace analysis of zinc, gallium, and indium was carried out on paper chromatograms 10 mm wide by Jackwerth and Kloppenburg.[5] Molybdenum radiation at 40 kvp and 40 ma was used with a LiF analyzing crystal and a scintillation detector tube. For the "impulse-R_f diagram" method the area under the curve of intensity of the spot was shown to be proportional to the amount of the element present. (Special equipment was devised to draw the strip behind an 8- by 10-mm aperture at 2 mm/min.) The limiting concentrations were 0.33 μg for Zn, 0.30 μg for Ga, and 8.9 μg for In. In the "impulse-rate" method the intensity of fluorescence for each element was determined on a stationary chromatogram. The spots were made visible with 8-hydroxyquinoline. The limiting concentrations were 0.34 μg for Zn, 0.10 μg for Ga, and 10.4 μg for In. The impulse-rate method is simpler and quicker, but with large spots the impulse-R_f diagram method is more accurate.

Mylar Film as Sample Support (See also Chap. 36, Sec. 2). Another useful sample support for evaporated deposits which has the advantage of giving a low background intensity of scattered radiation is 0.25-mil Mylar film. It is more difficult to prepare a uniform deposit on Mylar than in and on a filter-paper disk, but the reduction in background to about 10 per cent of that from paper makes it attractive.

In work of Pfeiffer and Zemany[6] on trace metals in various acids, the metals, after separation, were deposited in "spots" on 0.25-mil Mylar film for study with a flat-crystal x-ray spectrograph. In this way 0.03 μg of iron/g of hydrofluoric acid and 0.005 μg of manganese/g of nitric acid were measured. The concentration limit was considered to be 0.001 μg of metal/g of acid. Sensitivity was of the order of 20 counts/sec/μg of metal, and less than 1 μg could be measured conveniently.

Pretreating the Mylar with a drop of solution containing a wetting agent, drying this, and then adding a drop of the sample to be evaporated helps localize the sample spot to the area covered by the wetting agent.[7] As with deposits on paper, use of an internal standard helps compensate for variation in film deposit. In a limited thickness region there is a direct linear proportionality between concentration and intensity of fluorescent radiation. The maximum thickness for this linearity varies from one element to another. Of six elements studied by Gunn[7] by evaporating successive 0.04- to 0.05-ml portions of standard solutions on pretreated Mylar diaphragms in spots of about 2 cm^2, linearity was found to exist up to 100 μg of deposit for Fe, Cu, and Ti; up to 400 μg for Ca; up to 2,000 μg for Sr; and for Mo the relationship was still linear at 20,000 μg.

Ion-exchange Resins as Sample Carriers (See also Chap. 36, Sec. 15). Synthetic ion-exchange resins in membrane, granular, or liquid form have been used effectively to separate, concentrate, and collect small quantities of ionic material from solutions too dilute for direct analytical determinations. When equilibrium has been achieved, the sample and resin are separated from the aqueous solution and irradiated directly in an x-ray spectrograph. The intensity of the fluorescent radiation of the elements collected by the resin is then measured. Absorption and enhancement effects due to coabsorbed elements, if present, can be overcome by the use of suitable internal standards.

Using an ion-exchange membrane as a sample carrier, Grubb and Zemany[8] were able to concentrate and collect cobalt present in a solution at a dilution of 1 μg/liter. In the same way, by stirring with a small piece of membrane in the solution, they collected and determined traces of Zn, Mn, and Fe in maple syrup. The times for equilibrium were 16 to 48 hr. Zemany and others[9] also recovered 5 to 150 μg of potassium from aqueous KCl solutions using a suitable membrane. This is of special interest because of the scarcity of relatively simple methods for determining potassium in the microgram range. In another application, they extracted potassium from mica surfaces where it is present as an exchangeable ion. The precision attainable was about ±15 per cent.

A similar concentration procedure was used by van Niekerk and de Wet,[10] except that the elements to be determined were collected on a granular or liquid ion-exchange resin which was irradiated directly in an x-ray spectrograph. Here rapid equilibrium of the order of a few minutes is attained provided the solid resins are soaked beforehand. The solid resins are transferred to a liquid-sample holder for analysis. If the variation of the particle size of the resin is small, no significant error is introduced by distributional variations in the resin bed. When present, absorption and enhancement effects can be overcome by the use of suitable internal standards. With a solid anionic resin, AG-1X, uranium can be detected down to 0.1 ppm in the barren sulfate effluent from ion-exchange columns used in uranium-industry processing plants. A liquid resin, Amberlite LA-2, also gave good extraction of the effluent, but because it must be used diluted with solvent its sensitivity limit is about 0.2 ppm.

Another application by van Niekerk and coworkers[11] of ion-exchange resins is the separation and determination of thorium present in low concentration in ores. Here a 0.5-g sample is dissolved in acid, extracted for 10 min with 2 g of AG 50 W-X 12 cation-exchange resin in the H^+ form. The resin is filtered on a sintered-glass crucible and, in the absence of iron, transferred with 5 ml of water to a sample holder. The net Th $L\alpha$ peak is then measured. In the presence of iron 5 ml of a 0.05 per cent KBr solution is used to transfer the resin and to serve as an internal standard. The ratio of Th $L\alpha$ to Br $K\alpha$ is then measured and the thorium is determined from a calibration curve. Results on three ores (0.2 to 0.6 per cent Th) agreed with those by chemical analysis within 3 per cent.

Excellent precision and accuracy for ultra trace analysis was shown by Luke[12] to be possible on metals first separated by conventional chemical methods, then taken up from water or dilute acid by a tiny disk of strong acid-type cation-exchange resin which was then subjected to x-ray spectrochemical analysis using a fully focusing curved-crystal x-ray milliprobe. This method can be used for the trace analysis of more than 30 cationic metals. As little as 0.01 μg of those elements for which the milliprobe has the greatest sensitivity can be determined. Also 12 or more elements can be determined similarly after takeup by a strong base anion-exchange resin.

Borax-fusion Techniques (See also Chap. 36, Sec. 14). A useful combination of techniques to determine trace amounts of material quantitatively starts with a standard chemical separation of a group of elements from the sample matrix and is followed by a borax fusion and subsequent x-ray spectrochemical analysis. For example, using conventional methods Luke[13] separated from the matrix the refractory metals Mo, W, Nb, and Ta, present in ferrous alloys and high-alloy steels in amounts from less than 0.1 to about 4 per cent, and converted the precipitate to mixed oxides which were then fused with borax. The fused disk was then analyzed by an x-ray spectrochemical procedure by comparing analytical line intensities with those from a series of standard disks containing combinations of the elements sought. This procedure eliminates the time-consuming separation of the individual refractory elements required in most other methods and yet gives comparable accuracy.

A check on the practical level of sensitivity for borax disks of elements with characteristic K or L radiation at wavelengths between those of Mo $K\alpha$ and Ca $K\alpha$ analyzed in conventional General Electric x-ray fluorescence equipment was made by Luke.[14] In the procedure used, the oxide or salt of a metal in amounts up to 20 mg was fused with 2 g of borax and the molten disk flattened with a heated Al block to $\frac{1}{16}$-in. thickness. The resultant disk is large enough to fill a $\frac{5}{8}$-in.-diameter aluminum sample mask in the specimen holder. Although these disks are not infinitely thick for radiation harder than zinc $K\alpha$, the loss in sensitivity is negligible. A large advantage for softer radiation is gained by increasing the area of a 2-g bead by flattening it. The background is relatively large and varies with the thickness of the disks; so thickness should be controlled rather closely. The counts obtained for radiation from the sample may be compared with those from calibration standards to obtain the weight of the metal in the sample. The sensitivity limits vary from about 1 μg for nickel to 10 μg for scandium and calcium when using the optimum tube target and counter for the element sought. Thus, based on the use of a 1-g sample of original alloy, this means that chemical separation combined with this technique will give a sensitivity of from 1 to 10 ppm, depending on the metal being determined. To reduce scattered background and in certain mixtures of metals to minimize absorption errors as the ratios of the metals vary, it was found advisable to add an x-ray-absorbing material such as bismuth to the standard and sample disks.

Organic Ashing. Trace metals in petroleum products have been concentrated by a new rapid-ashing procedure using benzene or xylene sulfonic acid.[15,16] An internal standard is added to the sample prior to the ashing. The ash may be supported by a glass-fiber filter disk or preferably on 0.25-mil Mylar and analyzed directly without further treatment or separation. This technique is especially valuable for metals present below 2 ppm but may be used for amounts up to several hundred ppm. Reagents used must be of low metal content to keep blank corrections to a minimum. A high-purity platinum-target x-ray tube was found to decrease the copper and iron interferences present when using a tungsten-target tube. Iron, nickel, vanadium, and copper were satisfactorily determined with results comparable with those obtained by the slower method of sulfuric acid ashing and optical spectrographic analysis.

Organometallic Precipitation (See also Chap. 36, Sec. 17). Organometallic precipitation of trace portions of samples is another approach to sample preparation prior to x-ray analysis. The precipitates as packed powders or briquettes made with a press are used directly in the sample holder. Standards can be made under identical conditions, thus maintaining the same relative particle size in precipitates and the same density in pressed briquettes. The precipitates may be formed using any organic reagent or combination of reagents necessary to separate the desired elements from the sample matrix. The organic composition of the reagent is usually immaterial in the final measurements.

For an investigation of the corrosion of stainless steels and monel metals by molten carbonates, samples of alkali-metal carbonates containing 0.01 to 0.001 per cent each of iron, manganese, nickel, copper, and chromium had to be analyzed.[17] The samples were dissolved and the heavy metals were precipitated with 8-hydroxyquinoline. In this case aluminum was added to the solution prior to precipitation to add bulk and to act as a carrier. The dried precipitates were ground, briquetted at 6,000 psi pressure, and compared in the x-ray spectrograph with standards prepared similarly. Useful semiquantitative results were readily obtained.

Lytel and coworkers[18] investigated x-ray fluorescence analysis for the determination of at least 15 trace elements in dry, ground forage (grass, clover, alfalfa) samples. Preconcentration with ion-exchange membranes was unsuccessful because the major elements collected by a cation-exchange membrane were alkali and alkaline earth metals which overloaded the membrane before trace elements of interest could be absorbed. Several elements could be absorbed as anionic complexes on an anion-exchange resin, but the best conditions varied with the elements, and recovery of known samples did not give reproducible results; so this method was reluctantly discarded. Instead, an organometallic precipitation following a careful wet-ashing procedure was found to be the best quantitative method for collecting at least 15 elements present in the plant material. The ashing step is the most critical one in this method. It was followed by a mixed precipitation using a combination of several reagents chosen to yield quantitative precipitation of as many elements as possible of biological interest while rejecting the alkali and alkaline earth metals. Here, too, aluminum was added as a carrier and as a good matrix for fluorescent x-ray analysis. It was found necessary to ignite the fluffy precipitate at 450° C, and to grind it before packing the mixed oxides into sample holders for analysis. In many cases the lower limit of detection was 0.01 ppm of the original sample.

Precipitation of a desired element with a suitable reagent in the presence of a known amount of cellulose powder has also been used by Smith as a sample-preparation technique, for example, for the determination of lead in gasoline.[19] The precipitate, intimately mixed with the powder, is filtered, dried, and compressed in a form suitable for x-ray analysis. Smith also proposed that light elements for which x-ray analytical sensitivity is relatively poor might be conveniently analyzed indirectly. For example, silicon might be determined by means of a precipitation of silicomolybdate oxine which has a Si:Mo ratio of 1:12 followed by an x-ray analysis for molybdenum. Conditions for this were not worked out, but the general idea may be useful.

Strontium in tap water has been determined by Stone using x-ray fluorescence analysis as a preliminary step to the determination of the strontium-90 content.[20] Calcium and strontium are coprecipitated as oxalates and converted to nitrates. A known amount of rubidium is added both as an internal standard and to compensate for the absorption effect of the varying concentration of calcium present in tap waters. The ratio of the intensities of the strontium $K\alpha$ and rubidium $K\alpha$ lines is measured. A linear relationship exists between the intensity ratio of the strontium and rubidium

$K\alpha$ radiations and the weight ratio of strontium to rubidium in the prepared sample. The samples finally used for the analysis are films evaporated on Mylar where as little as 0.5 μg of strontium can be measured.

3. MICROANALYSIS

Solution Analysis. Direct examination of solutions is useful for both trace and microanalyses. In some petroleum products trace quantities of metals may be determined directly since the matrix of hydrocarbons does not absorb the secondary x-rays excessively. Barium, calcium, and zinc in lubricating oils may be determined quickly with no sample preparation required by using a family of calibration curves to account for the interelement effect with varying barium concentrations.[21] A few ppm of nickel in oils have been determined on as little as 3 ml of sample with cobalt added as an internal standard.[22] Also 0.1 to 1 g of Mn/gallon of gasoline has been determined using a special liquid-sample holder containing an iron rod which serves as an internal standard and helps compensate for difference in the base stock of gasoline samples.[23]

Birks and Brooks[24] analyzed uranium solutions containing as little as 0.05 g/liter. Direct analysis of the solution gave a high scattered background near the uranium $L\alpha$ line because of the water. Better results were obtained by evaporating 1 ml of solution a drop at a time in a shallow spherical dish 1 cm across and 2 mm deep pressed into a strip of 0.001-in. aluminum foil. The strip was heated to about 100°C across the terminals of a low-voltage transformer. The dried specimen gave a much more favorable peak-to-background count ratio. Most impurities of common occurrence have no effect on the uranium calibration curve. If more than 10 per cent of lead by weight is present a family of calibration curves can be prepared to compensate for the absorption of uranium radiation by lead.

For microanalysis, dissolving the sample in a suitable solvent serves several purposes. It homogenizes the sample being studied, makes it possible to present the flat surface of a liquid-sample holder to the x-ray beam, and often dilutes the sample to a point where interelement effects are negligible. When tungsten or molybdenum from ores and ore residues was determined in solution the precision attained was better than that with powder or direct sample analysis.[25] Tungsten was determined in alkaline solution with bromine used as an internal standard. When the tungsten content of the sample is known the molybdenum content is determined by measuring the Mo $K\alpha$ to W $L\gamma$ ratio and comparing this ratio with ratios obtained from standards.

Microanalyses of stainless steel and of nickel-chromium alloys have been carried out on aqueous acid solutions. At the dilutions used no interelement effect was noted. With a scintillation counter and pulse-height discriminator the lower detection limit for Fe, Ni, and Cr is 5 to 10 μg/ml of sample. The method is especially useful when only a few milligrams of sample may be available, as in the analysis of a weld.[26] Other solution methods have been reported, including one in which the Ni, Cr, and Mo are determined directly in the solution while niobium in the sample is separated by conversion to Nb_2O_5 and determined separately after briquetting with cellulose powder.[27] A general x-ray spectrographic solution method for analysis of iron, chromium, and for manganese-bearing materials using an added internal standard has been described in which only a single calibration system per element is required for all materials and acid matrices. This work was carried out using an industrial quantometer. Samples in a 1 per cent solution may be determined in a range from 0.1 to 99.9 per cent of the original sample.[28]

Biological Analysis. Biological samples often require analysis of submicrogram quantities of the elements present. Numerous useful techniques have been devised to fill this need. The previously mentioned organometallic precipitation sample preparation of Lytel et al.[18] is an outstanding example. A series of papers by Natelson and coworkers describes several specific methods for specific types of samples and elements in chemical problems of clinical analysis. Many of the techniques end with the portion of the sample to be analyzed deposited on filter paper. For example, a direct determination of phosphorus, sulfur, chlorine, calcium, and potassium in blood serum can be made on a dried spot of a 0.2-ml sample. A general description of the methods used and a review of many of the specific problems handled have been published.[29,30]

A paper by Natelson and Sheid[31] describes a convenient, accurate x-ray technique for determining strontium in samples of human serum and bone. Ashing serum before the final sample preparation gives a much lower background than using serum itself directly on filter paper. A special ring oven is described for evaporating a strontium solution into filter paper to obtain a relatively uniform spot for analysis by x-ray spectrometry. Only 1 ml of serum is needed for the analysis where the range was 0.17 to 0.27 μg of strontium/ml.

Protein-bound iodine in blood serum was determined by the same investigators by an x-ray procedure requiring only 2 ml of serum.[32] The iodine is extracted from the acidified serum with 3:1 alcohol ether. Evaporation of this extract results in loss of the inorganic iodine. The residue is then extracted with ammoniacal methanol which is evaporated in a confined area on filter paper, and this product is exposed to the primary x-ray beam. The fluorescent iodine $L\alpha$ radiation is measured using a flow-proportional counter. A mean value found by this method was 4.7 μg/100 ml serum with a range of ± 0.6.

Several studies were made on elements that permitted direct estimation without processing of the serum. An automatic analysis scheme for chlorine and sulfur in ultramicro samples was reported.[33] Serum samples of only 20 μl are dried in confined spots on a long strip of filter paper. For analysis this is passed continuously through the x-ray beam and the element is assayed by the peak of the curve drawn on the recorder. A suitable attachment for the spectrometer is described. Results are comparable with those obtained by conventional methods with respect to accuracy and precision. It was shown that the ratio of sulfur to protein in human serum varied widely between healthy and diseased subjects. In an extension of this method[34] to evaluate the significance of sulfur content in abnormal serum, paper electrophoresis was performed on sera from 16 healthy adults. The patterns were drawn through the x-ray spectrometer at constant speed to determine the sulfur content of the various protein fractions. The patterns were then stained and the protein distribution determined. The total sulfur was determined on a separate sample, and from these data the percentage of sulfur in each of the protein fractions was calculated. Sera containing abnormal protein fractions were compared with the normal samples using the same techniques. The protein distribution was different, and since various fractions contain different amounts of sulfur the total sulfur was also different in the abnormal samples.

The phosphorus content of serum and total blood iron, using oxalated blood, as a measure of hemoglobin content were determined from dried spots of sample on filter paper by comparison with standard spots.[35] For example, for total phosphorus determinations 0.1-ml samples of serum were measured onto confined 19-mm-diameter spots on a 1½-in.-wide strip of Whatman No. 40 paper at 2-in. intervals. Unknowns and standards were measured on the same strip, which was threaded into the automatic conveyor and passed through the x-ray beam at the rate of 1 cm/min. A quartz analyzing crystal and a flow-proportional counter with a helium path were used for the analysis. The peak heights of the unknowns were compared with a standard curve plotted from the peaks obtained for the standards. To decrease the time lag between samples for determining iron an automatic sample changer was devised with 1/16-in. aluminum slide frames having holes 15 mm in diameter to center the confined spots in the x-ray beam. The spots of 0.05-ml samples of whole oxalated blood were measured onto confined spots 16 mm in diameter which were mounted in the frames. Concentration was determined from peaks drawn on the recorder as an automatic sequential sample changer placed samples in the x-ray field and withdrew them at 30-sec intervals. A lithium fluoride analyzing crystal, air path, and scintillation counter were used for this determination. The procedure was excellent for a busy routine clinical laboratory with respect to simplicity, speed, and accuracy.

Other elements of biological importance were assayed in human-serum and sea-water samples.[36] The elements were chromium, manganese, iron, cobalt, copper, and zinc. The serum is ashed before analysis. To eliminate excessive amounts of matrix from serum and sea-water residues, the chlorides of the trace elements are extracted with glacial acetic acid, leaving most of the rather insoluble NaCl behind. The high background of scattered tungsten radiation with the filter-paper sample matrix was effectively reduced for analysis of copper and zinc by using a 0.005-in. titanium filter in the primary x-ray beam.

Bromine normally present in human serum was assayed[37] after the sample was ashed, dissolved in HCl, and the solution was dehydrated with acetic anhydride and glacial acetic acid. The precipitated NaCl was centrifuged off and washed with glacial acetic acid. The combined acid solution was evaporated to dryness, and the residue was dissolved in methanol and transferred to filter paper for x-ray analysis.

Zinc, copper, and iron were determined by Alexander[38] by an x-ray fluorescence method on thermally ashed samples of biological tissues. About 100 mg of ashed material was mixed with 10 per cent of an internal standard (Na_2CO_3-$NiCO_3$, 9:1) and the mixture pressed into a 0.5-in.-square planchet for x-ray analysis. The intensity ratios of elements sought were determined using nickel as the internal standard. The procedure is relatively unaffected by changes in matrix and has a high enough sensitivity for zinc, copper, and iron to be of value. An example was given of the determination of zinc in plasma at the 1-ppm level.

A simple sensitive indirect procedure of the determination of nitrogen at the microgram and submicrogram level in biological materials has been described by Mathies, Lund, and Eide.[39] It employs a Conway diffusion procedure using a filter-paper disk impregnated with Nessler's reagent to trap ammonia. When the diffusion is complete the excess reagent is washed out, and the amount of nitrogen in the brown insoluble Nessler's chromogen retained in the filter paper is assayed indirectly by x-ray measurement of the mercury in the compound. Standard curves were prepared for samples containing from 0.2 to 5 μg of nitrogen.

4. X-RAY MILLIPROBE

The increasing emphasis on miniaturization of components, particularly in the electronics industry, is resulting in a corresponding increase in the already high demand for the analysis of small samples. There is also an increasing concern about the homogeneity of materials and a need to identify small inclusions, contaminants, and individual components of complex assemblies. X-ray milliprobes have been developed to assist the x-ray spectroscopist to meet this demand (cf. Chap. 39).

Basically an x-ray milliprobe can be defined as an x-ray fluorescence spectrometer utilizing a restricted beam of x-rays to measure the elements present in a small area of specimen. The aperture which restricts the x-ray beam may be between the x-ray tube and the sample (primary aperture) or between the sample and the analyzing crystal (secondary aperture). Flat-crystal, curved-crystal, or nondispersive x-ray optics may be employed. The instruments used range from rather simple conversions of conventional x-ray spectrographs to complete spectrometers designed exclusively for probe use.

Flat-crystal X-ray Milliprobe. The most widely used x-ray milliprobe is the "Heinrich miniature probe" (Fig. 1) supplied by the General Electric Company as an accessory for its XRD-5S spectrometer. It is patterned after a prototype constructed by K. F. J. Heinrich.[40] This device replaces the standard sample drawer and collimation system of the commercial flat-crystal spectrometer. The area of the specimen to be analyzed is selected by collimation of the secondary (fluorescent) x-ray beam. The sample is held by a clip arrangement in a stage that can be positioned by two micrometers, either of which may be motor-driven if desired. By passing a beam of light through the collimator in the direction opposite to that of the x-ray beam, the area to be sampled by the beam may be observed under a low-power microscope before inserting the device in the sample chamber. A somewhat similar probe attachment for the G.E. instrument was developed by Bertin and Longobucco.[41]

The best type of collimator to be used has been the subject of some controversy. The pinhole apertures initially supplied with the commercial device are unsatisfactory

FIG. 1. Heinrich miniature probe. (*Courtesy of General Electric Company, X-ray Department.*)

because the pinhole cannot be located close enough to the sample. Heinrich suggests the use of the shafts of hypodermic needles as collimators, since these are easily obtained and mounted and can be located close to the specimen surface. The authors prefer brass tapered pinhole apertures of the type shown in Fig. 2 which may also be

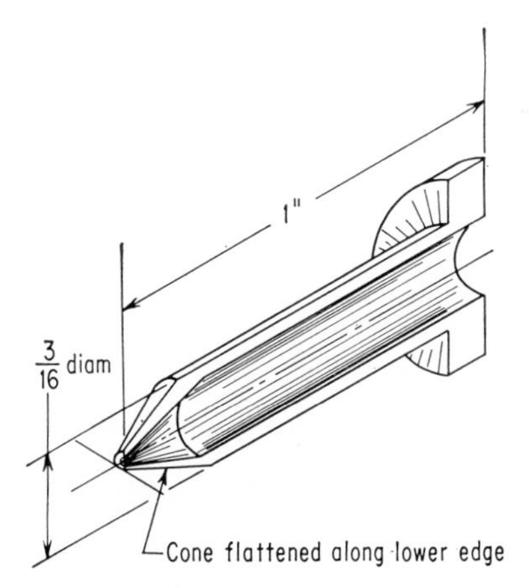

FIG. 2. Tapered secondary aperture.

located sufficiently close to the sample to prevent much spreading of the spot observed by the collimator. It is also possible to substitute tapered apertures between the x-ray source and the specimen. These primary apertures yield good intensity but make visual observation of the specimen spot somewhat more difficult. A comparison of intensities using various apertures is shown in Table 1, which also compares fully focusing, semifocusing, and flat-crystal optics.

Normally, the remainder of the spectrometer is not changed while using this probe, except that the Soller slit is replaced by an adjustable two-blade collimator. To increase the sensitivity of the probe, however, it is possible to use a curved crystal in place of the usual flat crystal. For a limited wavelength range which depends on the bending radius of the crystal, the instrument will function as a semifocusing spectrometer and yield higher intensities. Table 1 shows the improvement obtained for nickel using a lithium fluoride crystal bent to a radius of 14 in. and ground to a 7-in. radius over a flat lithium fluoride crystal with the G.E. x-ray milliprobe.

Table 1

Optics	Location	Aperture size, microns	Shape	Intensity, cps	
				Specimen	Matrix
Full-focus	Primary	340	Tapered	187	4
Semifocus	Primary	340	Tapered	89	3
	Secondary	125	Tapered	79	1
	Secondary	380	Tapered	99	5
	Secondary	790	Tapered	112	21
Flat	Primary	340	Tapered	10	1
	Secondary	125	Tapered	10	0.5
	Secondary	380	Tapered	10	1
	Secondary	790	Tapered	13	3
	Secondary	240	Needle	5	0.5
	Secondary	720	Needle	6	1

Specimen: Cross section of 40-micron-diameter nickel wire embedded in Wood's metal.
X-ray source: AEG 50S tungsten-target tube, 50 kvp, 50 ma.

Sloan[42] has described a probe adaptation of a Norelco x-ray spectrograph using secondary collimators made from Leroy lettering pens. The device was used in a study of the uniformity of vacuum-deposited Nichrome resistance films. A probe attachment for the Norelco spectrograph utilizing a specially designed pinhole collimator was also described by Miller.[43] A milliprobe accessory is available for the Siemens x-ray spectrograph. This includes a rotatable specimen holder which permits scanning along any specimen diameter up to a length of 15 mm. Apertures 0.1, 0.2, 0.5, and 1.0 mm in diameter are provided for insertion between the sample and the x-ray tube. The radiation emerging from the sample chamber is limited by an exit pinhole, and a simple two-slit collimator replaces the Soller slit in front of the detector. Also included is a holder for a microscope which enables an operator to select specific areas of a specimen for study. A detailed description of this probe has been published by Togel.[44]

Some applications of flat-crystal milliprobes may be found in the references relating to their design and construction. Others which should be mentioned are the investigation of wear tracks on gold-plated contacts by Zimmerman[45,46,47] and the measurement of the composition and thickness of thin layers by Weyl.[48]

Curved-crystal X-ray Milliprobe. Probably the first modern spectrometer designed especially for the analysis of small samples was that described by Birks and Brooks.[49,50] In this instrument a capillary-type specimen, consisting of powder cemented to a fine glass fiber, was mounted on the focusing circle of a curved-crystal spectrometer. Because of the configuration of the sample no aperture was required, the sample itself serving as a line source of secondary x-rays. Good line-to-background ratios were obtained for iron and manganese in an aluminum alloy, even though less than 10 μg of each element was present in the 1-mg samples. This instrument, while not a true milliprobe because of the lack of an x-ray beam aperture, served to point out the advantage of curved-crystal optics in such devices.

Adler and Axelrod[51,52,53] constructed a curved-crystal x-ray milliprobe specifically for mineralogical analysis. It was based on the optics proposed by Birks and Brooks shown in Fig. 3. The instrument used a Machlett OEG 50 tungsten-target x-ray tube for excitation of the sample through a conical lead pinhole aperture. The sample was mounted on a microscope stage capable of two-dimensional motion and was placed as close as possible to the aperture to reduce the divergence of the exciting x-ray beam. The authors state that the beam size was less than 250 microns. The lithium fluoride analyzing crystal was bent to a radius of 40 cm and the front surface ground to the radius of the focusing circle, 20 cm. A Geiger-Müller tube with standard electronics was used as the detector. The instrument was used successfully for many point-to-point analyses of heterogeneous mineralogical specimens and demonstrated the general utility of x-ray milliprobes. A milliprobe for mineralogical and metallurgical applications was built by Thatcher and Campbell.[54] Four interchangeable primary apertures (0.1, 0.25, 0.50, and 1.00 mm) were employed and detection was accomplished with a proportional counter. In other respects the design was similar to that of Adler and Axelrod. The data reported indicate that the spatial and wavelength resolution were excellent and that good x-ray intensities were obtained

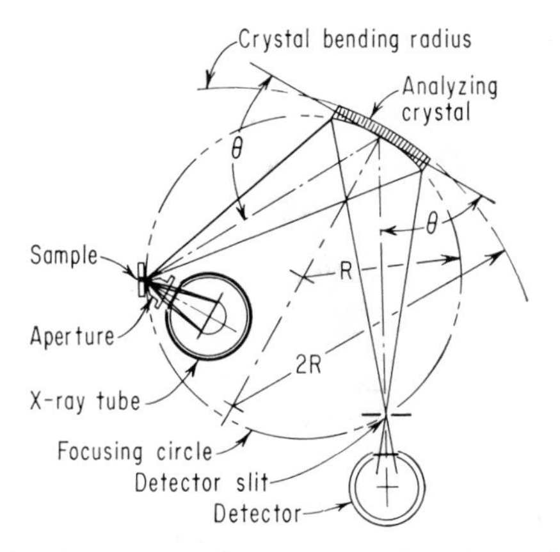

FIG. 3. Curved-crystal spectrograph for microanalysis.

with the larger apertures. The authors suggest that for smaller spot sizes, operating the unit as a nondispersive system, using selective filtration, pulse-height discrimination, or a combination of the two, might prove more satisfactory.

The x-ray milliprobe in the authors' laboratory (Fig. 4) is a converted General Electric flat-crystal spectrometer. A General Electric EA-75 tungsten-target x-ray tube with a 3.75-kw power supply serves as the excitation source. The primary radiation striking the specimen is limited in area by a gold aperture. The fluorescent radiation from the sample emerges from the sample chamber through a rectangular opening in a tantalum plate. This arrangement prevents excessive spillage of radiation past the analyzing crystal while permitting maximum coverage of the crystal with radiation. The focused radiation from the crystal then passes through an adjustable detector slit consisting of two tantalum blades and then into a conventional x-ray counter tube.

The entire sample chamber rotates on a vertical axis concentric with the x-ray aperture. A positioning rod pivoted at the analyzing crystal passes through a linear ball bearing in the base of the sample chamber to keep the fluorescing spot on the specimen and the tantalum exit port aligned with the center of the crystal. A plastic-bellows helium tunnel may be attached to the plate holding the tantalum exit port when measuring long-wavelength x-rays. The specimen holder accommodates samples up to 1¼ in. square by ¼ in. thick. The micrometer stage motion permits any

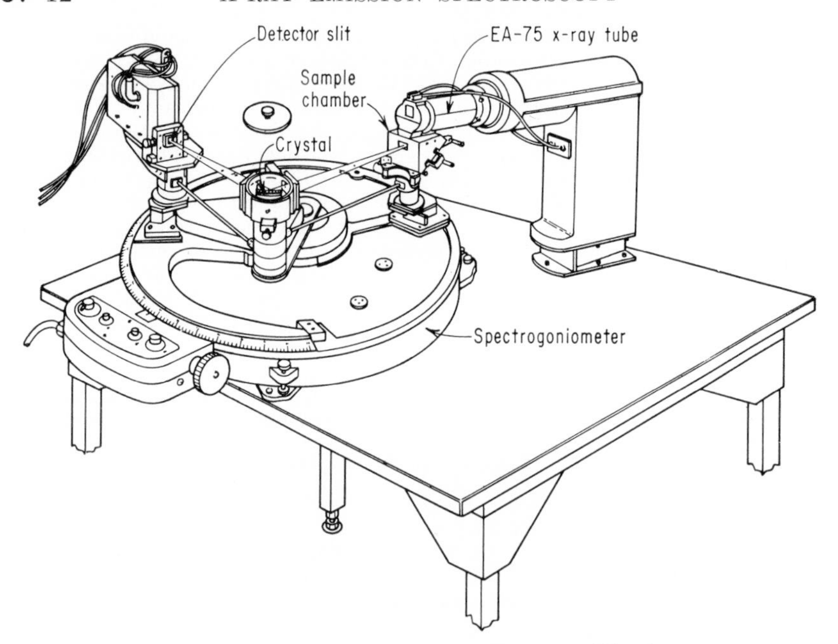

FIG. 4. Bell Telephone Laboratories x-ray milliprobe.

spot on the specimen within an area 1.35 cm^2 to be positioned under the aperture with a reproducibility of about 0.001 cm. The stage mechanism is removed for changing samples and may be placed in a specially designed microscope mount for locating the area to be studied. A cross-sectional view of the type of primary aperture found most satisfactory is shown in Fig. 5. To obtain maximum x-ray intensity the thick-

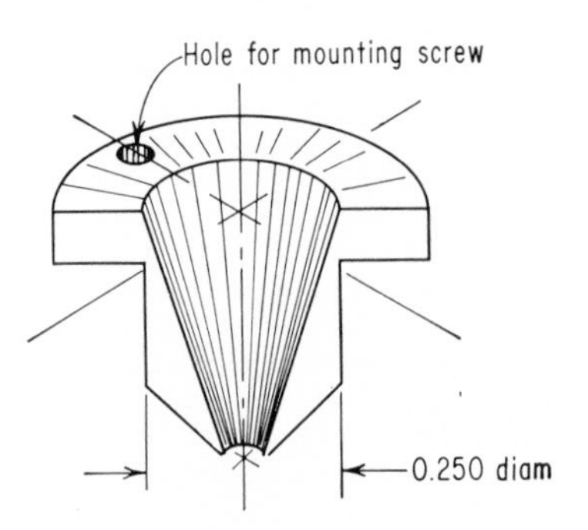

FIG. 5. Primary aperture.

ness of the actual pinhole was kept as small as possible relative to its diameter. To minimize the divergence of the primary beam, the distance between the pinhole and the specimen surface was also kept as small as possible without having the aperture block some fluorescent radiation from the specimen from reaching the crystal. The apertures now in use have openings 0.0075, 0.0135, 0.030, and 0.063 in. in diameter. The excited spots on the specimen are ellipses having a minor axis slightly larger than the diameter of the opening and a major axis about 25 per cent larger.

The analyzing crystals employed are bent to a radius of 14 in. and should be ground to a radius of 7 in. for maximum intensity, particularly at the smaller 2θ angles. The base for the crystal mount consists of a flat plate attached at one end to the original mounting surface for the flat-crystal holder. The other end supports a vertical shaft which in turn carries the curved-crystal adjusting mechanism and serves as a pivot for the collars of the rods that position the sample chamber and detector. The adjustment mechanism provides for rocking the crystal about its own axis as well as moving it "in and out" along a radius of the focusing circle.

The detector slit consisting of two tantalum blades in a movable frame is mounted on a ball-bearing support shaft directly over the intersection of the focusing circle with the center line of the original flat-crystal detector. The width of the slit may be varied from 0 to 0.1 in. by the adjusting screw. The positioning screw moves the slit frame horizontally in a plane perpendicular to the positioning rod that aligns the detector with the center of the analyzing crystal. The detector system is composed of a standard G.E. proportional or scintillation counter with conventional electronics except that 50- and 20-cps full-scale ranges were added to the rate meter.

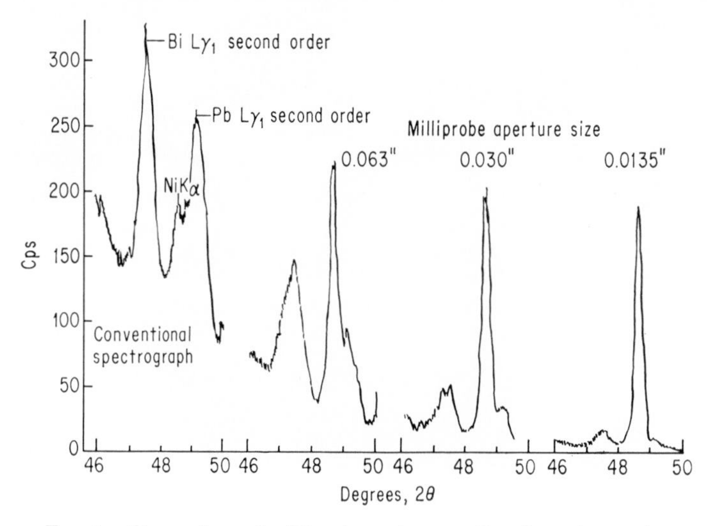

FIG. 6. Comparison of milliprobe and conventional spectrograph.

The goniometer is limited mechanically to 2θ angles between 20 and 95°. Using a lithium fluoride crystal the wavelength range covered is 0.700 to 2.970 Å. Substitution of an EDT crystal raises the upper limit to 6.490 Å. The wavelength resolution is affected by the size of the aperture, the crystal, the detector slit width, and the 2θ angle. Under normal operating conditions, the width at half maximum may be from 0.2° 2θ to 2° 2θ. The larger figure applies only to the largest aperture used at small 2θ angles.

The advantage of a milliprobe over a conventional spectrograph for the identification of very small inclusions is shown in Fig. 6. The specimen was prepared by embedding a 40-micron-diameter nickel wire in Wood's metal and grinding to obtain a cross section of the wire. Final polishing was done with No. 600 soft Buehler Microcut polishing paper. It should be noted in the figure that the second-order lines from the matrix material almost obscure the nickel $K\alpha$ peak when using the conventional G.E. spectrometer. Both instruments were operated at 50 kvp and 50 ma using a tungsten-target tube, a lithium fluoride crystal, a xenon-filled proportional counter, and an air path. The standard spectrograph had a 0.010-in.-spacing Soller slit.

An indication of the mass sensitivity of this x-ray milliprobe was obtained from the examination of a series of standard iron-nickel alloy films evaporated on glass slides. These measurements showed that about 5×10^{-10} g of nickel could be detected at the 99 per cent statistical confidence level under these favorable conditions using 100-sec x-ray counting times. This amount corresponds to a spot of nickel 0.77 mm^2 in area and 1 Å (1×10^{-7} mm) thick.

Philips Electronic Instruments has recently announced the availability of a "macroprobe" attachment (Fig. 7) for their vacuum x-ray spectrometer. This device employs continuously bent-crystal optics and incorporates an optical microscope for viewing the specimen during analysis. Samples as large as 2 in. in diameter can be accommodated and *x-y* scanning over the sample surface within a range of ½ in. in all directions from the center is provided for. Areas of from 50 to 500 microns in diameter can be examined with the probe.

Fig. 7. Philips macroprobe. (*Courtesy of Philips Electronic Instruments.*)

Probes Using Fine-focus X-ray Tubes. Long and Coslett[55] and Zeitz and Baez[56,57] have constructed x-ray milliprobes utilizing the Coslett-Nixon fine-focus x-ray tubes. In this type of instrument an electron gun and magnetic lens cause a focused electron beam to strike a thin window target. The x-rays emerging from the other side of the target pass through an aperture and bombard the specimen, which is normally a sufficiently thin section that it can be observed in transmission. Thick specimens could be examined in reflection, but only at a greater distance from the primary x-ray source, resulting in a loss in intensity or resolution. The fluorescent x-rays are detected by means of a suitably situated proportional counter. In the instrument of Long and Coslett no analyzing crystal was used, but limited wavelength discrimination was obtained through pulse-height analysis. The authors estimate the minimum detectable mass of calcium would be 7×10^{-11} g if the area of specimen irradiated were defined by a 50-micron aperture 0.8 mm from the specimen. By using a smaller aperture located still closer and operating at higher tube current and voltage, it is estimated that sensitivities of 10^{-12} to 10^{-13} g could be obtained.[58] Instruments of this type seem to be of somewhat limited application and appear to offer little advantage, if any, over the electron probe in their present state of development.

Nondispersive X-ray Spectrograph. A nondispersive x-ray probe has been designed and built by Hall[6,60] especially for the determination of certain mineral elements in individual biological-tissue sections. The instrument consists of a special high-power x-ray tube with a large "doughnut-shaped" anode, a built-in interchangeable secondary radiator, and a proportional counter and pulse-height discriminator system.

The use of interchangeable secondary radiators permits irradiation of the specimen with a spectrum consisting almost exclusively of the characteristic lines of the radiator element. The radiator is chosen so that these lines are just shorter in wavelength than the absorption edge of the element of interest. In this way, efficient excitation of the desired lines is obtained without excitation of any heavier elements present in the specimen. The pulse-height discriminator is set to reject x-rays from the lighter elements present in the sample. In general, this can be accomplished for all elements except the next lighter element in the periodic table.

The pulses from the proportional counter are fed to two single-channel pulse-height analyzers simultaneously. One of these is peaked for the fluorescent radiation of the element of interest and the other for the radiation from the secondary radiator. The counting rates in these two channels may be designated as R_e and R_t, respectively, and the ratio R_e/R_t as r. For quantitative calibration, the counting-rate ratios are obtained for four objects: the specimen r_s, a spot of a "pure organic" substance such as sucrose r_t, a pure sample of the element of interest r_e,* and a known mixture of the "pure organic" substance with a salt of the element of interest r_m. It can be shown that in nearly all practical cases the ratio of the concentration of the element in the specimen C_s to the concentration of the known mixture C_m can be computed from the simple expression

$$\frac{C_s}{C_m} = \frac{r_s - r_t}{r_m - r_t}$$

Appropriate corrections must be made for counter-tube background and for radiation from the next lighter element in the periodic table, if it is present.

The tissue sections, which are usually about 10 microns thick and 0.01 to 1 cm^2 in area, are prepared using special techniques to avoid contamination or leaching out the element of interest. The fact that the samples are very thin makes absorption and enhancement effects negligible. The rather poor resolution of the detector system is sufficient because the specimens contain only a few heavy elements dispersed in a light matrix.

The instrument has been used successfully for the analysis of a number of biological specimens. The determination of zinc in a section of dog prostate, for example, involved the use of a silver-plated anode and bromine K secondary radiation from a potassium bromide radiator. The total mass of zinc in the section was estimated at 10^{-8} g. A measurement of the zinc in human prostate fluid was carried out on the spot produced by evaporating the fluid on a thin nylon film.[61] The instrument has been used thus far only on biological specimens, but it should have applications in other fields as well.

REFERENCES CITED

1. G. von Hevesy, *Chemical Analysis by X-rays and Its Applications*, Cornell University Press, Ithaca, N.Y., 1932.
2. P. D. Zemany, H. G. Pfeiffer, and H. A. Liebhafsky, *Anal. Chem.*, **31**:1776 (1959).
3. E. J. Felten, I. Fankuchen, and J. Steigman, *Anal. Chem.*, **31**:1771 (1959).
4. P. E. Wenger, I. Kapetanidis, and W. von Janstein, *Pharm. Acta Helv.*, **37**:489 (1962); *Anal. Abstr.*, **10**:525 (1963).
5. E. Jackwerth and H. G. Kloppenburg, *Z. Anal. Chem.*, **179**:186 (1961).
6. T. Hall in J. H. Yoe and H J. Koch, Jr. (eds.), *Trace Analysis*, p. 458, John Wiley & Sons, Inc., New York, 1957.
7. E. L. Gunn, *Anal. Chem.*, **33**:921 (1961).
8. W. T. Grubb and P. D. Zemany, *Anal. Chem.*, **176**:221 (1955).
9. P. D. Zemany, W. W. Welbon, and G. L. Gaines, Jr., *Anal. Chem.* **30**:299 (1958).
10. J. N. van Niekerk and J. F. de Wet, *Nature*, **186**:380 (1960).

* This measurement is not necessary except in special cases.

11. J. N. van Niekerk, F. W. E. Strelow, and F. T. Wybenga, *Appl. Spectry.*, **15**:121 (1961).
12. C. L. Luke, *Anal. Chem.*, **36**:318 (1964).
13. C. L. Luke, *Anal. Chem.*, **35**:56 (1963).
14. C. L. Luke, *Anal. Chem.*, **35**:1551 (1963).
15. J. E. Shott, Jr., T. J. Garland, and R. O. Clark, *Anal. Chem.*, **33**:506 (1961).
16. W. A. Rowe and K. P. Yates, *Anal. Chem.*, **35**:368 (1963).
17. J. E. Fagel, Jr., E. W. Balis, and L. B. Bronk, *Anal. Chem.*, **29**:1287 (1957).
18. F. W. Lytel, W. B. Dye, and H. J. Sein, Determination of Trace Elements in Plant Material by Fluorescent X-ray Analysis, in W. M. Mueller (ed.), *Advances in X-ray Analyses*, vol. 5, p. 433, Plenum Press, New York, 1962.
19. G. S. Smith, *Chem. Ind.* (*London*), no. 22, 907 (1963).
20. R. G. Stone, *Analyst*, **88**:56 (1963).
21. E. N. Davis and R. A. Van Nordstrand, *Anal. Chem.*, **26**:973 (1954).
22. C. W. Dwiggins, Jr., and H. N. Dunning, *Anal. Chem.*, **31**:1040 (1959).
23. R. A. Jones, *Anal. Chem.*, **31**: 1341 (1959).
24. L. S. Birks and E. J. Brooks, *Anal. Chem.*, **23**:707 (1951).
25. J. E. Fagel, H. A. Liebhafsky, and P. D. Zemany, *Anal. Chem.*, **30**:1918 (1958).
26. W. W. Houk and L. Silverman, *Anal. Chem.*, **31**:1069 (1959).
27. R. W. Jones and R. W. Ashley, *Anal. Chem.*, **31**:1629 (1959).
28. B. J. Mitchell and H. J. O'Hear, *Anal. Chem.*, **34**:1620 (1962).
29. S. Natelson and S. L. Bender, *Microchem. J.*, **3**:19 (1959).
30. S. Natelson, *Microchem. J. Symp.*, 1961, pp. 133–165.
31. S. Natelson and B. Sheid, *Anal. Chem.*, **33**:396 (1961).
32. S. Natelson and B. Sheid, *Clin. Chem.*, **8**:17 (1962).
33. S. Natelson and B. Sheid, *Clin. Chem.*, **6**:299 (1960).
34. *Clin. Chem.*, **6**:314 (1960).
35. *Clin. Chem.*, **7**:115 (1961).
36. S. Natelson, D. R. Leighton, and C. Calas, *Microchem. J.*, **4**:539 (1962).
37. S. Natelson, B. Sheid, and D. R. Leighton, *Clin. Chem.*, **8**:630 (1962).
38. G. V. Alexander, *Anal. Chem.*, **34**:951 (1962).
39. J. C. Mathies, P. K. Lund, and W. Eide, *Norelco Reptr.*, **9**:92 (1962).
40. K. F. J. Heinrich, in W. M. Mueller (ed.), *Advances in X-ray Analysis*, vol. 5, p. 516, Plenum Press, New York, 1962.
41. E. P. Bertin and R. J. Longobucco, in W. M. Mueller (ed.), *Advances in X-ray Analysis*, vol. 5, p. 447, Plenum Press, New York, 1962.
42. R. D. Sloan, in W. M. Mueller (ed.), *Advances in X-ray Analysis*, vol. 5, p. 512, Plenum Press, New York, 1962.
43. D. C. Miller, in W. M. Mueller (ed.), *Advances in X-ray Analysis*, vol. 4, p. 513, Plenum Press, New York, 1961.
44. K. Togel, *Siemens-Z.*, **36**:497 (1962).
45. R. H. Zimmerman, in W. M. Mueller (ed.), *Advances in X-ray Analysis*, vol. 4, p. 335, Plenum Press, New York, 1962.
46. R. H. Zimmerman, *Iron Age*, **186**:84 (1960).
47. R. H. Zimmerman, *Metal Finishing*, **59**:67 (1961).
48. R. Weyl, *Z. Angew. Phys.*, **13**:283 (1961).
49. L. S. Birks and E. J. Brooks, *Anal. Chem.*, **27**:437 (1955).
50. L. S. Birks, E. J. Brooks, and G. W. Gourlay, *Rev. Sci. Instr.*, **29**:425 (1958).
51. I. Adler and J. M. Axelrod, *Am. Mineral.*, **41**:524 (1956).
52. I. Adler and J. M. Axelrod, *Econ. Geol.*, 1957, p. 694.
53. I. Adler, J. M. Axelrod, and J. J. R. Branco, in W. M. Mueller (ed.), *Advances in X-ray Analysis*, vol. 2, Plenum Press, New York, 1960.
54. J. W. Thatcher and W. J. Campbell, *U.S. Bur. Mines Rept. Invest.* 5500, 1959.
55. J. V. P. Long and V. E. Coslett, in V. E. Coslett, A. Engstrom, and H. H. Pattee, Jr. (eds.), *X-ray Microscopy and Microradiography*, p. 435, Academic Press Inc., New York, 1957.
56. L. Zeitz and A. V. Baez, in V. E. Coslett, A. Engstrom, and H. H. Pattee, Jr. (eds.), *X-ray Microscopy and Microradiography*, p. 417, Academic Press Inc., New York, 1957.
57. L. Zeitz, *Rev. Sci. Instr.*, **32**:1423 (1961).
58. V. E. Coslett and W. C. Nixon, *X-ray Microscopy*, p. 206, Cambridge University Press, New York, 1960.
59. T. Hall, in W. M. Mueller (ed.), *Advances in X-ray Analysis*, vol. 1, p. 297, Plenum Press, New York, 1958.
60. T. Hall, *Science*, **134**:449 (1961).
61. A. R. Mackenzie, T. Hall, and W. F. Whitmore, *Nature*, **193**:72 (1962).

Chapter 38

SOFT X-RAY EMISSION SPECTROSCOPY IN THE 10 TO 150 Å REGION

J. E. Holliday

United States Steel Corporation

1. INTRODUCTION*

The 10 to 150 Å region of the x-ray spectrum contains a number of important emission lines and bands. All the K-emission spectra of the second-period elements except Li occur in this region. The $L_{II,III}$-emission bands of the first-series transition metals and the $M_{II,III}$- and $M_{IV,V}$-emission bands of the second series, plus the intense $M_V N_{III}$ lines of the elements Y through Sn, occur in this region. Because of the large absorption coefficients of solids and gases to soft x-rays, any windows that are used must be extremely thin (1,000 to 2,000 Å) and all measurements must be done in vacuum. Because of the long wavelengths it has been necessary to use gratings at grazing incidence for the dispersive element. Recently, good inorganic crystals[1A] have become available that can be used out to about 27 Å, and some organic crystals[1,2] have been found that give reasonably good spectra out to about 80 Å. The present discussion will be confined to spectra obtained with gratings. Until recently the 10 to 150 Å region has been rather dormant, but the large interest in measurements of soft x-rays in outer space plus the desire to use x-rays for quantitative analysis of the light elements has created a renewed interest. In addition, improved instrumental methods and correction procedures make it possible to obtain spectra of the emission bands that provide valuable information on the electronic structure of solids.

Sections 2 through 7 are devoted to instrumentation and Secs. 8 through 10 to spectra. If the reader is interested only in spectra he can begin with Sec. 8 without any loss of continuity. However, if there is a lack of familiarity with gratings, it would be advisable to read Sec. 3 first.

2. SPECTROMETER

The grazing-incidence grating spectrometer showing one method of scanning is indicated schematically in Fig. 1.[3] Slits S_1 and S_2 and the curved grating are on the Rowland circle, which is one-half the radius of curvature of the grating. The x-rays from the target are directed by slit S_1 at glancing angle θ to the grating. The x-rays are diffracted through angle ϕ and are then focused on the Rowland circle. Since the diffracting angle ϕ is equal to $\alpha/2$, ϕ can be measured directly from the spectrometer. The analyzer slit S_2 is scanned across the Rowland circle by the spectrometer

* See Sec. 11, "Examples of Recent Developments," on page 38-39.

arm A. The arm is rotated at pivot point A by a system of gears external to the vacuum system. The gears are designed so that it is possible to read α to 0.001°. It is essential that the window of the proportional counter and slit S_2 remain collinear with the pole of the grating. This is accomplished by the guide arm B, which is pivoted below the grating (pivot point B, Fig. 1). A detailed drawing of the way arm B is pivoted below the grating is shown in Fig. 2.

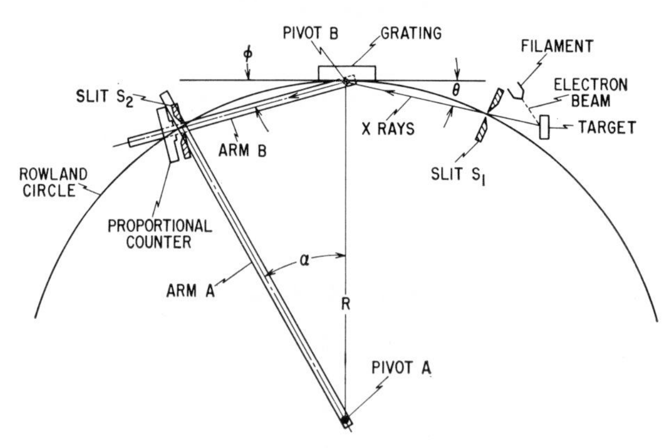

FIG. 1. Schematic of grazing-incidence soft x-ray spectrometer showing placement of gratings and slits on Rowland circle, and illustrating the principle of scanning slit S_2 with arm A. [*Reprinted by permission from J. E. Holliday, Rev. Sci. Instr.,* **31**:891 (1960).]

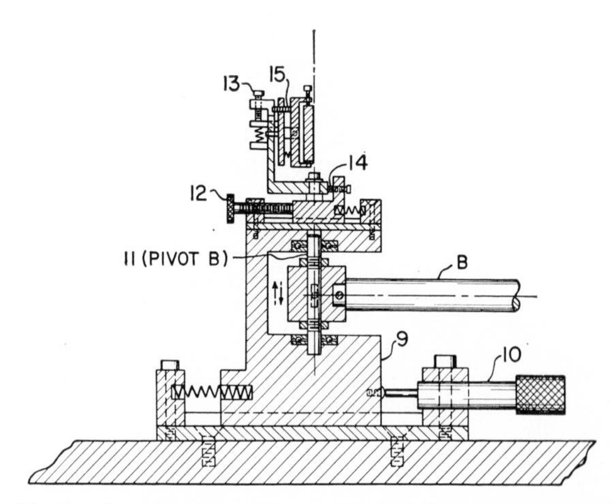

FIG. 2. Assembly drawing of grating holder and pivot B showing necessary adjustments required to align grating. [*Reprinted by permission from J. E. Holliday, Rev. Sci. Instr.,* **31**:891 (1960).]

Another method of scanning[4] is to move the detector and slit along a track which has a radius equal to the Rowland circle. Arm A is eliminated and arm B (Fig. 1) is threaded and has two angular rotations at pivot B. The rotation of arm B external to the vacuum system moves the analyzer slit and detector along the Rowland circle. There are advantages to each type of scanning mechanism. The first method of scanning the analyzer slit along the Rowland circle by the spectrometer arm A has the advantage that the center of the Rowland circle is known quite accurately and the alignment problem is greatly simplified. In addition, the diffracting angle can be obtained directly from the spectrometer, which is not true for the track method of scanning. The track method has the advantage that for a given radius of curvature a smaller vacuum housing will be required because arm A and pivot point A have been eliminated. Since the slit S_2 and the detector are positively driven in the track method, it is more suitable for gratings of large radius of curvature.

In order to align the spectrometer a number of adjustments must be built into it. These will be described for the spectrometer in Fig. 1 in the order in which they would be made in aligning the spectrometer. To align the spectrometer a vertical cathetometer and rotating microscope are required. In the rotating microscope the microscope is attached to one end of an adjustable arm and the other end is rotated about pivot point A (center of Rowland circle). The distance between the crosshairs of the microscope and pivot point A is set equal to the radius of curvature of the Rowland circle. In Fig. 3 the angular and linear motions for the grating are shown, and in Fig. 2 is shown the grating holder used to accomplish these motions in the present apparatus. The first step in aligning the spectrometer is indicated by motion a (Fig. 3) and brings the plane of the grating in parallel with shaft 11 and slits S_1 and S_2. This setting is accomplished by adjusting the vertical crosshairs of the cathetometer in line with shaft 11 and then tilting the grating with screw 15 (Fig. 2) until the grating surface is parallel to the vertical crosshair. Motion b (Fig. 3) is to set the grooves of the

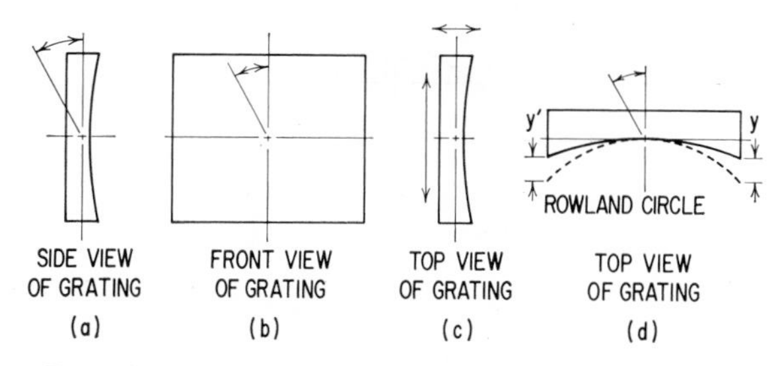

FIG. 3. The principal angular and linear motion required to align grating.

grating parallel to the slits S_1 and S_2. This adjustment is made by moving screw 13 (Fig. 2) until the grooves are parallel with the vertical crosshair. It is now necessary to bring pivot point B, the grating, and slits S_1 and S_2 onto the Rowland circle. To make these adjustments, it will be necessary to use the rotating microscope. Using micrometer-adjusting screw 10 (Fig. 2), the center line of shaft 11 (pivot point B) is set under the crosshairs of the rotating microscope. The center of the rulings on the grating and the surface at this point are made coincident with the center line of shaft 11 by bringing this point in line with the crosshairs. For this adjustment, two horizontal motions are required which are indicated in Fig. 3c and are accomplished by hand and adjusting screw 12. The rotation about the vertical axis indicated in Fig. 3d is necessary in order to make the plane of the grating tangent to the Rowland circle. This adjustment is accomplished by moving screw 14 (Fig. 2) until distances y and y' are equal. The distances y and y' can be measured by estimating the distance from the crosshairs to the end of the grating with the eye. The traveling microscope is next brought over the analyzer slit S_2, which is adjusted on the Rowland circle by bringing it in line with the crosshairs. It is very easy to set slit S_1 to the desired glancing angle on the Rowland circle with the rotating microscope. The crosshairs are set over the pivot point B and the arm is locked at pivot point A. The spectrometer is rotated to the right through an angle 2θ, where θ is the desired glancing angle. The slit S_1 is then set directly under the crosshairs. This method is very accurate and fast. Other methods of alignment mentioned in the literature were found to have insufficient accuracy to give reliable results at the shorter wavelengths, where small errors in the position of slit S_2 became of great importance. Because of his inability to adjust his photographic plates accurately, Chalklin[5] could not rely on first-order measurements below 50 Å.

3. GRATING

In the past, the gratings[6] used for the diffraction of soft x-rays have been lightly ruled with flat reflecting surfaces* between grooves. Calculations from simple optical theory show that the optimum efficiency in the first order is obtained when the groove width and flat area are equal. In general, gratings ruled for the soft x-ray region were made on this principle. However, gratings which were ruled in this fashion were found to have widely different characteristics. Some would give good intensity and P/B (peak-to-background ratio) while others would give no intensity beyond the zero order. This situation was particularly true for low glancing angles, between 1 and 3°. One reason for this difficulty was believed to be the piling up at the edge of the groove, giving a very poor reflecting surface. It was found that the blazed replica grating[7] could overcome the pile-up difficulty and also provide certain additional advantages which will be mentioned later. A typical shape of the replica grating is shown in Fig. 4. The blazed replica grating is able to eliminate the piling

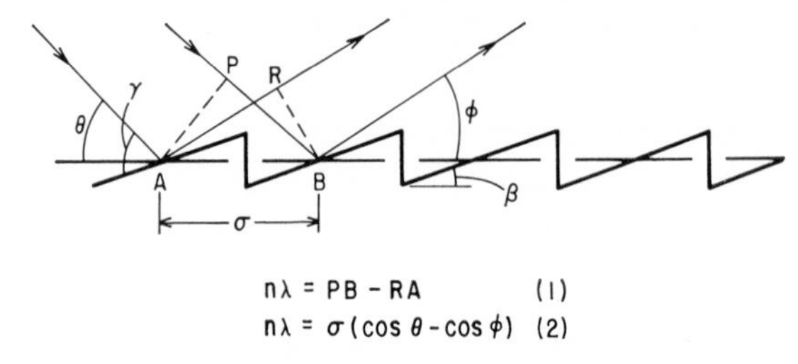

FIG. 4. Diffraction of x-rays from a flat (dashed line) and blazed grating. σ is the grating spacing for both flat and blazed gratings and β is the blaze angle. (*Reprinted by permission from J. E. Holliday, The Electron Microprobe, John Wiley and Sons, Inc.*[46])

up at the top of the groove because the bottom of the groove in the original ruling, which is very sharp, becomes the top of the groove in the first-generation replica.

Another advantage of the blazed grating is that the total reflected beam can be reflected into orders other than the zero. To fully appreciate the significance of this fact, it must be understood that the diffraction angle ϕ, at which the order times the wavelength appears, is independent of the angle γ (Fig. 4) that the incident x-rays make with the reflecting face of the grating, but the order in which the maximum reflected intensity occurs is dependent on γ. The fact that the ϕ is independent of γ can be seen from the following simple argument. In Fig. 4 is shown the diffraction from a flat grating (zero blaze) and a blazed grating. The x-rays at the glancing angle θ (angle between incident ray and the plane of the grating) are diffracted at an angle ϕ. The condition for maximum interference is an integral number of whole wavelengths, and from Fig. 4 this is

$$n\lambda = PB - RA \tag{1}$$

If the diffraction angle were dependent on γ, then the condition for maximum interference would be violated. The standard grating equation for any type of grating from Fig. 4 is

$$n\lambda = \sigma(\cos\theta - \cos\phi) \tag{2}$$

* The conventional gratings used in soft x-ray spectroscopy will be referred to as flat gratings. However, the word flat refers only to the reflecting surface which is parallel to the plane of the grating, which is not the case in the blazed grating. The conventional grating (the blazed grating also) is not really flat but has a concave surface, as indicated in Fig. 3*c* and *d*.

where σ is the grating constant. Thus the zero order occurs at an angle equal to the glancing angle for both plane and blazed gratings. However, the intensity reflected in the zero order will not be the same for the two types of gratings. For any type of grating, the reflecting face acting alone reflects a maximum of energy into the direction for which the angle from this face equals the angle of incidence. The $n\lambda$ which lies in this general direction will be stronger. In this way, a selective effect can be obtained. It will readily be seen that the flat grating will reflect the maximum intensity into the zero order. On the other hand, the blazed grating will reflect the maximum intensity into orders other than the zero. This fact is supported by the reflected intensity from the 15,000 lines/in. 1° blazed grating showing no intensity in the zero order. The maximum reflected intensity for a blazed grating will occur in the general vicinity of $\theta \pm 2\beta$. The sign of β is defined by the direction at which the incident x-rays strike the blaze. It is minus for the direction indicated in Fig. 5*a* and positive for Fig. 5*b*. The wavelength for which total reflection sets in is a function of the angle that the

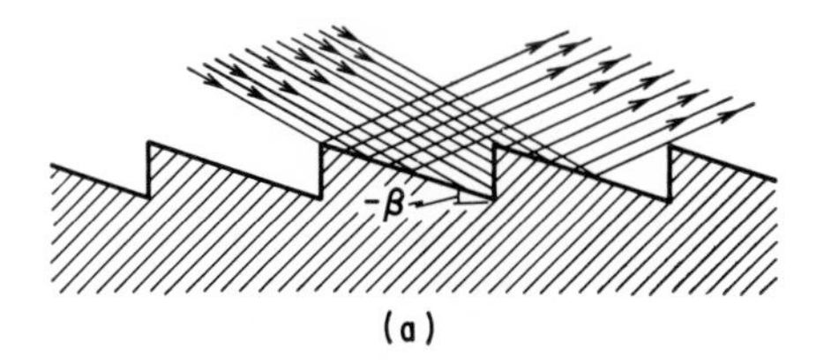

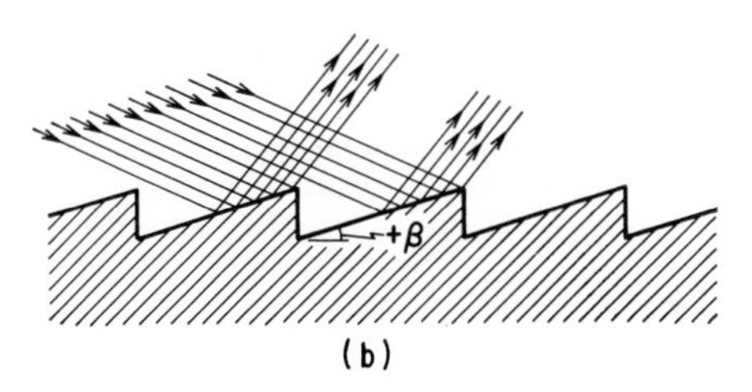

FIG. 5. (*a*) and (*b*) compare the two different directions at which the x-rays strike the blaze. For the direction indicated in (*a*), the blaze angle is $-\beta$ and for (*b*), it is $+\beta$.

incident x-rays make with the reflecting surface, which for the blazed grating is $\gamma = \theta \pm \beta$. This wavelength is called the "critical wavelength" and is not sharp,[6] as indicated in Fig. 6 ($\lambda_c \sim 13$ Å) for Mo white radiation using a 15,000 lines/in. 1° blazed grating with an aluminum surface and $\gamma = 3°$ ($\theta = 2°$).

The direction at which the x-rays strike the blaze (sign of β) is of considerable importance. It is evident from Fig. 5*a* that if $\beta > \theta$ and β is minus negligible intensity will be reflected, since the only surface that the x-rays would then see would be the point at the top of the groove. In Table 1 is shown the effect which changing the sign of β with respect to the incident beam has on the diffracted x-ray intensity for 15,000, 30,000, and 55,000 lines/in. 1° blazed gratings with a θ of 2°. The ratios of intensities for the C K band and the Zr $M_{\mathrm{V}}N_{\mathrm{III}}$ line for the two directions are approximately 11, 5, and 2 for the 15,000, 30,000, and 55,000 lines/in. gratings, respectively. The reduction in intensity as a result of changing the sign of β from plus to minus is due to the absorption of the incident and diffracted x-rays in the step of the blaze, as can be observed in comparing Fig. 5*a* and *b*. The reduction of the ratio with increasing number of lines per inch appears to be due to the step's becoming rounded and less pronounced. Experimental evidence for the selective effect is observed in the ratio of the intensities of the Fe $L_{\mathrm{II,III}}$-emission band for the two directions ($+\beta$ and $-\beta$)

of the blaze. This shows the selective effect, because for the incident x-rays striking the blaze in the $-\beta$ direction the maximum intensity is reflected into the unusable positive orders while for the $+\beta$ direction the maximum intensity will be reflected into negative orders. It will be observed from Fig. 5a that the amount of absorption in

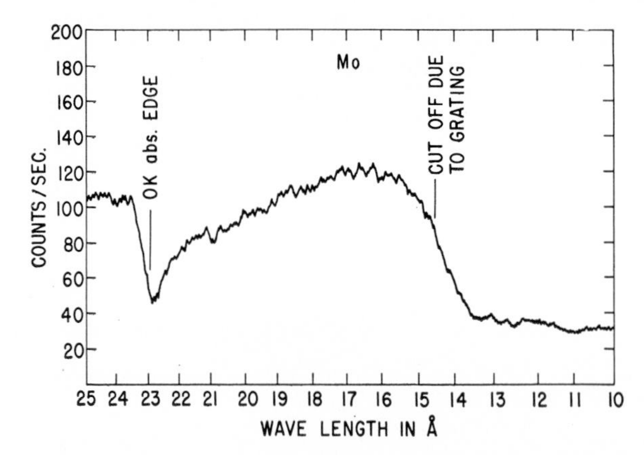

FIG. 6. White radiation from an Mo target showing cutoff of grating due to "critical wavelength" and the oxygen-absorption edge resulting from the oxygen in the counter window and the Al_2O_3 on the grating surface. The grating was aluminized with 15,000 lines/in. and $\beta = 1°$. The radiation below ~13 Å is due to scattered radiation from slits and grating. The target potential was 3.5 kv, beam current 1 ma, and slits 40 microns wide. *Reprinted by permission from J. Appl. Phys.*, **33**:3259 (1962).]

Table 1. Uncorrected Intensity in Counts/Second and P/B for the 15,000, 30,000, and 55,000 Lines/in. 1° Blazed Grating, Concave Radius 1 m, the Slits Set at 20 Microns, V_T = 3,500, and I_T = 1 ma

Grating and blaze orientation with respect to incident x-rays	Fe $L_{II,III}$ band, 17.67 Å		C K, 44.85 Å		Zr $M_V N_{III}$, 81.6 Å	
	Peak intensity, counts/sec	P/B	Peak intensity, counts/sec	P/B	Peak intensity, counts/sec	P/B
15,000 lines/in.						
$\beta = 1°$	4,000	45	8,300	180	800	40
$\beta = -1°$	120	7	610	30	70	5
30,000 lines/in.						
$\beta = 1°$	2,500	50	5,500	100	720	39
$\beta = -1°$	200	8	1,240	28	148	24
55,000 lines/in.						
$\beta = 1°$	1,250	38	1,150	55	300	45
$\beta = -1°$	635	20	635	30	145	40

the step will be a function of θ and ϕ. Calculations show that, for a θ of 2° and a ϕ of 3.3°, the ϕ of the Fe $L_{II,III}$-emission band using a 15,000 lines/in. grating, the diffracted intensity will be greater by about 3 times for $+\beta$ than for $-\beta$. Because the Fe $L_{II,III}$ band is near the "critical wavelength," there will be some decrease in intensity for the direction indicated by $+\beta$ owing to γ (angle to the reflecting surface) being increased from 1 to 3°. However, from Table 1 it will be observed that the intensity of the Fe $L_{\mathrm{II,III}}$ band has been increased by a factor of 30 for changing β from minus to plus using the 15,000 lines/in. grating. This large increase in intensity, over the calculated value given above and increasing γ, shows the selective effect of the blaze grating. Thus the blazed grating is most efficient when the incident x-rays strike the blaze in the direction indicated by $+\beta$ (Fig. 5*b*). Another advantage of the blazed grating over the flat grating is that there is no groove (Fig. 5*b*) to absorb a portion of the incident x-rays. Increasing the number of lines per inch will reduce the wavelength region in which the maximum reflected intensity occurs. Some evidence for this appears to be indicated in Table 1, where the intensity for the Fe $L_{\mathrm{II,III}}$ band is greater than that for the C K band (using the 15,000 lines/in. grating the C K band has twice the intensity of the Fe $L_{\mathrm{II,III}}$ band) and the P/B is reduced by a factor of 3 when using the 55,000 lines/in. grating. The selective effect, however, is not so pronounced for the 55,000 lines/in. grating. The ratios of the first-order intensity to that for the second-order are approximately 11, 8, and 1 per cent for the $+\beta$ direction and 25, 12, and 0 per cent for $-\beta$ directions using the 15,000, 30,000, and 55,000

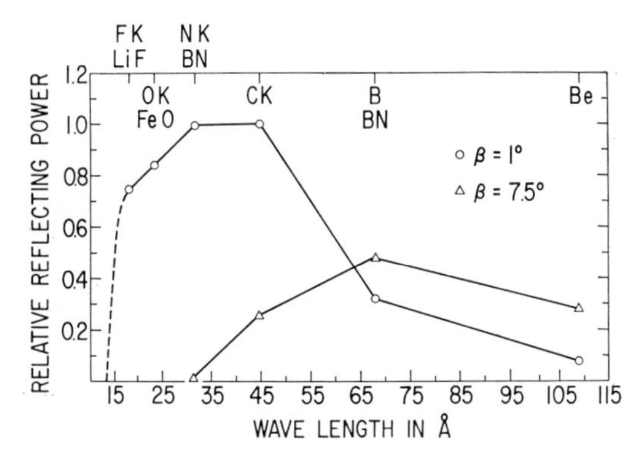

FIG. 7. Relative reflecting power referred to C K at 44.85 Å for two aluminized gratings having 15,000 lines/in., concave radius of 1 m, and a $\beta = 1°$ (○) and 7.5° (△). For both gratings $\theta = 2°$, giving a γ of 3° (○) and 9.5° (△).

lines/in. grating, respectively. The reduction in intensity as a result of increasing the number of lines per inch on the grating is due to the increased dispersion and the rounding of the step which reduce the amount of reflecting surface. It must be kept in mind that the above explanation for the changes in intensity indicated in Table 1 is a simplified explanation for a complex process.

The relative reflecting power as a function of wavelength for two gratings with 15,000 lines/in., having a $\beta = 1$ and 7.5° and $\theta = 2°$, is shown in Fig. 7. Since a known source of continuous radiation was not available, the peak intensities of the radiation of the second-period elements were used to measure the relative efficiency of the gratings as a function of wavelength. The K radiation from elements in compounds was corrected to that which would be obtained for 100 per cent of the element. For the K spectra obtained from compounds, the source is indicated in Fig. 7. All the intensity measurements were corrected for absorption in the counter window. Campbell,[8] who was using a nondispersive system, has shown that for $5 \leq Z \leq 9$ the K x-ray yield varies as $Z^{3/2}$. He was not able to verify the $Z^{3/2}$ dependence for Be K because of instrumental problems at 110 Å. His measurement of Be K was 40 per cent below the predicted value. However, for the curves in Fig. 7 it was assumed that the K yield of Be obeyed the $Z^{3/2}$ dependence. Since the intensity of the C K band was the most reliable value, all the intensities were normalized with respect to C K using the $Z^{3/2}$ dependence.

One can definitely see the selective effect of the 1° blazed grating in Fig. 7. The maximum reflected intensity will occur in the vicinity of 31 Å, which is close to that indicated in Fig. 7. The drop in relative reflecting power of the 1° blazed grating for O K and F K is due to a combination of the selective effect and the "critical wavelength" for a $\gamma = 3°$. The dashed portion of the curve is obtained by an extrapolation to λ_c, which is approximately 13 Å (Fig. 6). For the 7.5° blazed grating γ has increased to 9.5°, which will increase the "critical wavelength." This can be seen in Fig. 7, where it will be observed that for $\beta = 7.5°$ it was not possible to detect the O K and F K band and just barely possible to detect the N K band. It will also be noted that the 7.5° blazed grating has a higher reflecting power than the 1° blazed grating for wavelengths greater than about 64 Å. This appears to be due to the selective effect since the 7.5° blazed grating will reflect a maximum intensity into a larger $n\lambda$ than the 1° blazed grating.

The effect of different reflecting materials[8a] on diffracted x-ray intensity is shown in Table 2 for a platinum- and aluminum-coated 55,000 lines/in. 1° blazed grating at a γ of 3°. It will be noted that the platinum surface has the effect of reducing the "critical wavelength" or reducing the angle made to the reflecting surface. The intensity of the Cu L_{III} band using a Pt-coated 55,000 lines/in. grating was greater than for an Al-coated 15,000 lines/in. 1° blazed grating. The intensity of the C K

Table 2. Comparison of Intensities in Counts/Second for a Pt- and Al-coated, 55,000 Lines/in. 1° Blazed Grating*

Coating	Cu L_{III} band, 13.55 Å		Fe L_{III} band, 17.67 Å		C K, 44.85 Å	
	Intensity, counts/sec	P/B	Intensity, counts/sec	P/B	Intensity, counts/sec	P/B
Pt.	1,500	38	2,800	35	1,050	53
Al.	400	20	1,250	38	1,150	55

* Reprinted by permission from J. E. Holliday, *The Electron Microprobe*, John Wiley and Sons, Inc.[46]

band, which is away from the "critical wavelength," is slightly less than for the aluminum-coated grating.

Crisp[9] has stated that an aluminized grating cannot be used for grazing-incidence spectroscopy. He bases his conclusion on results he obtained from two aluminum gratings which gave him much poorer P/B and intensity than did his glass grating. From the glass grating using a graphite target, Crisp reported[10] obtaining a peak intensity for C K of 4,000 counts/sec and a P/B of 80 for a potential of 4 kv and a current of 1 ma. As indicated in Table 9, it is possible to obtain with an aluminum grating a peak intensity for C K of 24,000 counts/sec and a P/B of 180, for a l-ma beam current and 3.5 kv. However, comparison of a given line or band intensity and P/B obtained on different instruments is very unreliable because of the number of factors affecting the P/B and intensity. Besides the grating, the following parameters have been found to affect the P/B and intensity: slit widths, electron-beam focusing, type of detector, condition of target surface, angle with which the x-rays strike the target, and x-ray takeoff angle. Experience with aluminized gratings has indicated that intensity and P/B depend to a great extent on the condition of the aluminum surface. One aluminum-coated grating which had a dull appearance gave good intensity but poor P/B. Out of five aluminized gratings tested this was the only one that gave poor results. It has also been found that under certain conditions the intensity of spectra near the "critical wavelength" will become less with time. This is due to small amounts of contaminating materials (less than about 10 Å) depositing on the surface of the Al gratings. The effect of different materials on the intensity of spectra near the "critical wavelength" is illustrated in Table 2. However, contaminating materials will also affect a glass grating in a similar way. Crisp[9] also reported changes of shape of the emission band and increased background with time when using aluminum gratings. In the present work with emission lines and bands using aluminized gratings, no change of shape or background with time was observed. These bands were recorded by a point-by-point process, requiring approximately 7 hr to record. For the Nb M_{V} emission band at 61.5 Å six different curves were taken and there was no change in shape or background.

4. DETECTORS

The first type of detector to be used in soft x-ray grating spectroscopy was photographic film, and this is still being widely used today. The technique for using film has been adequately given by Tomboulian[11] and Sagawa[12] and will not be discussed here.

The electronic counters in use today fall into two categories: gas counters and photoelectric detectors. The first photodetector was introduced by Piore *et al.*[13] This instrument was a photomultiplier detector of the Allen type with an open end and dynodes made of CuBe. The soft x-rays impinge on the first-stage generating photoelectrons. The detector then functions like any standard electron multiplier. A number of other investigators[14–17] have successfully used the CuBe photomultiplier since the work of Piore and others. One disadvantage to the photomultiplier detector has been the change of the photoemission and secondary-emission ratio of the dynode surface due to the contaminating vapors in the vacuum and when exposed to air. However, Williams[18] reports that he has been able to obtain CuBe surfaces whereon the electron-emission characteristics are not appreciably affected by exposure to air. McIlraith[19] has successfully employed a scintillation counter using $CoWO_4$:Pb phosphor for the detection of soft x-rays.

The gas counter has the advantage of reproducibility in intensity. Its insensitivity to ions and low-energy electrons results in low background. It is relatively easy to repel the high-energy electrons with the proper biasing on the analyzer slit. The gas counter has been found to have higher efficiency below 100 Å, but for longer wavelengths the photomultiplier detector is more efficient. In 1954, Rogers and Chalklin[20] reported using a Geiger counter in the 20 to 200 Å region. Since 1954, several other investigators[21,22] have reported using a Geiger counter in this wavelength region. In 1959, Holliday[3] reported the use of a flow-proportional counter in a grating spectrometer in the wavelength region of 20 to 200 Å. At about the same time, Dolby[23] reported a method for using a flow-proportional counter in a nondispersive system. When the proportional counter is used as the analyzing element, the resolution is very poor and it is barely possible to resolve nitrogen and carbon. This results from the large variation in pulse height (as much as 50 per cent for O K) for a monoenergetic soft x-ray beam. This effect is due to statistical fluctuation in the number of ion pairs generated by quanta of a given energy. However, there is a reduction in the average pulse height for increasing wavelength. The average difference in pulse height for a given wavelength separation becomes less with increasing wavelength, resulting in reduced resolution. For the purpose of detecting the light elements, investigators using this method believe that improved efficiency resulting from the greater number of x-rays reaching the counter per incident electron outweighs the disadvantage of poor resolving power.

Since commercial Mylar and similar plastics with a thickness of 0.025 in. will transmit only about 10 per cent of carbon radiation at 44.8 Å, the windows on the counter must be extremely thin in order to transmit sufficient intensity at 150 Å. Experiments have shown that windows of from 1,000 to 2,000 Å in thickness are sufficiently thin to give adequate intensity and thick enough to give an average life of 30 days. The films can be made of any suitable plastic material such as formvar, zapon, or cellulose nitrate. The choice seems to be largely up to the individual investigator since various people have reported good success with different types of plastic. The author has had good success with cellulose nitrate, but recent results indicate that formvar has greater strength. In Table 3 is shown the absorption in a

Table 3. Per Cent Absorption in 0.026 mg/cm² Cellulose Nitrate Window

λ, Å	15	24	45	52	64	82
% absorption	5	8	12	16	22	34

0.026 mg/cm² cellulose nitrate window at various wavelengths. Since the window contains oxygen, nitrogen, and carbon there will be absorption edges at 23.3, 31, and 43.8 Å with a high percentage of absorption at the bottom of the edges. The oxygen-absorption edge due to the cellulose nitrate window and Al_2O_3 on the grating surface, using white radiation from an Mo target, is indicated in Fig. 6. The oxygen-absorption edge has a finite width because of the instrumental error and K-level width. The wavelength at the short-wavelength limit of the edge is 22.8 Å and 23.3 at the long-wavelength limit. The published wavelength of the oxygen-absorption edge is 23.3 Å. There is 85 per cent absorption at the bottom of the oxygen-absorption edge and 8 per cent at the top, showing that any comparison of intensities of spectra occurring near the bottom of the absorption edges of oxygen, carbon, and nitrogen would be in considerable error if not corrected for the counter window.

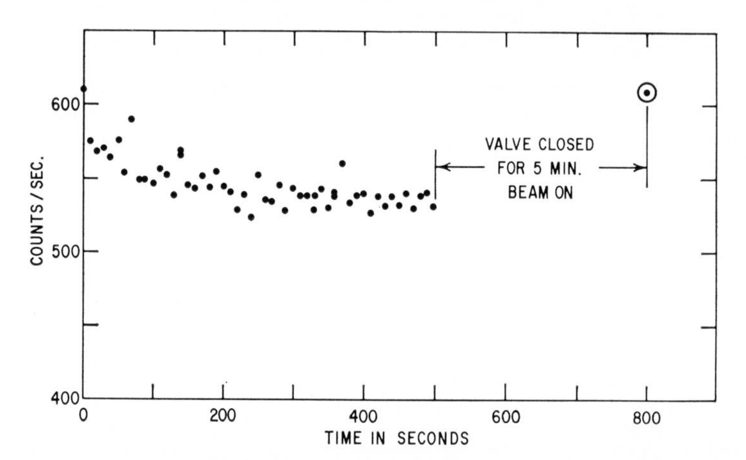

FIG. 8. Reduction in intensity of Nb $M_V N_{III}$ line with time due to charging of cellulose nitrate counter window with ±1.4 per cent deviation.

Conductive coatings on counter windows were found to be important at least in rapid intensity determination. In Fig. 8 is shown intensity in counts per second measured as a function of time. It will be noted that the first few seconds the beam is on the statistics are poor and the x-ray intensity drops rapidly. After about 5 min the intensity has reached a constant value and the statistics are nearly normal. In order to determine if the drop in intensity was due to the counter window, the valve between the x-ray chamber and spectrometer was closed, with the beam left on, for 5 min. As will be noted in Fig. 8, after 5 min the intensity had returned to its original value. To determine that the grating was not the source of trouble, the counter was moved off the peak with the x-ray beam still striking the grating. After 5 min the counter was returned to the peak and again the original intensity of 610 counts/sec was measured by the counter. There was no reduction in intensity with time for x-ray intensities below about 100 counts/sec.

The counter window is placed between two plates with slits in them. A cross-section drawing of the assembled counter with slits and location of window is indicated in Fig. 9. The counter wire is a loop as indicated. The wire loop has the advantage of ease of replacement and very small diameter wire can be used. There was no change of efficiency between this counter and a side-window counter. The slit in plate 2 was a mesh which was made on a spark-cutting machine with 90 per cent open area. The slit size that gave a long window life at 8 cm pressure was 0.03 inches wide and ¾ in. long. In order to make the window leaktight, the two plates must be flat and free of scratches. The counter has a pumping system separate from the spectrometer, and gas was pumped continuously through it. A manostat is placed in the system to keep the pressure constant in the counter. In order to prevent the window from breaking, it is necessary for the counter to have a vacuum connection to the spectrometer so that no pressure differential is established between them when the spectrometer is pumped down or brought up to atmospheric pressure.

To operate a gas counter in the proportional region for soft x-rays the gas amplification A will have to be sufficient to give pulse heights of approximately 0.25 mv for

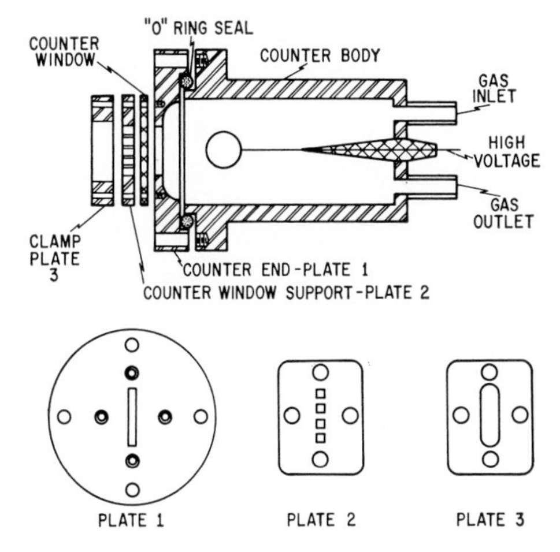

FIG. 9. Cross-section drawing of flow-proportional counter showing details of plates required to support thin counter window.

the signal to be above the noise. The pulse height on the central wire in volts is given by[24]

$$V = e(AN/C) \tag{3}$$

where N is the number of electrons formed in the initial ionizing event which will be small for soft x-rays, C is all the distributed capacity the counter sees, and e is the charge on the electron. The gas amplification depends on the voltage, the pressure of the gas, the kind of gas, and inversely on the wire radius. Since the pressure will be low and consequently the voltage will also be low, the wire radius will have to be small and the gas must have a high rate of increase of ionization cross section with energy in order to have an adequate gas gain. A gas pressure of 8 cm Hg was found to give the best operating performance when considering both window life and pulse height. Argon and methane will give the largest gas amplification in the hard x-ray region, and tests with various gases indicate that this was still the case out to about 100 Å. The gas combination used was 90 per cent argon and 10 per cent methane, which is standard P-10 gas. Higher percentages of methane are being used due to the increased gas amplification and longer x-ray penetration in the gas. However, higher percentages of methane were found to affect the life of the cellulose nitrate window adversely. For P-10 gas at a pressure of 8 cm and a wire diameter of 1 mil, the operating voltage for the proportional counter in Fig. 9 was 950 volts. To keep the capacitance to a minimum a cascade circuit[25] can be used next to the counter in the vacuum. This circuit has the advantage that only one tube and a grid resistor are in the vacuum, which reduces the heating problem to a minimum. After the cascade circuit are a preamplifier and linear amplifier. The signal can then go to either a rate meter or a scaler.

5. VACUUM SYSTEM AND TARGET PREPARATION

In the 10 to 150 Å region the vacuum requirements are not so stringent as they are at 200 or 300 Å. This is because at the shorter wavelengths the first few monolayers

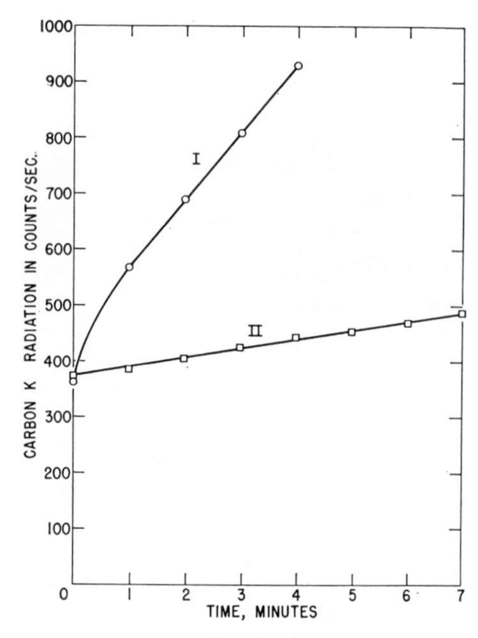

Fig. 10. Comparison of carbon contamination on a Mo target for oil- and Hg-diffusion pumps. Curve I for oil-diffusion pumps and neoprene O rings and curve II for Hg-diffusion pump and gold O rings. The C K intensity at zero time is residue carbon on the surface of Mo. Target was not cleaned in vacuum.

do not contribute significantly to the x-ray intensity. However, even in the shorter-wavelength region a significant percentage of the electrons comes from near enough to the surface to require a vacuum in the 10^{-8} to 10^{-9} region. For example, at a potential of 2 kv and for the carbon K radiation from a graphite target the majority of soft x-rays come from approximately the first 200 Å. Unless indicated otherwise, the vacuum in the x-ray chamber was in the 10^{-8} mm Hg region before the spectra reported in this chapter were recorded.

It is well known that carbon contamination is a serious problem, and it is a deciding factor in determining the type of diffusion pump and seals to be used. Figure 10 shows the difference in the rate of carbon contamination between an oil-diffusion pump with neoprene O rings and a mercury-diffusion pump with gold O rings. The target was Mo which was polished metallographically before being placed in the x-ray chamber. The spectrometer was set for C K, and the change in intensity was measured as a function time. The thickness of the carbon was estimated by measuring the intensity in counts per second from a carbon film of known thickness on a Mo target. The rate of carbon contamination was 35 Å/min for the oil-diffusion pump (curve I, Fig. 10) with liquid-nitrogen cold trap and neoprene O rings and 3.7 Å/min for the Hg-diffusion pump and gold O rings (curve II, Fig. 10). This shows that oil-diffusion pumps and neoprene O rings should not be used in the x-ray chamber. It is also advisable not to use an oil-diffusion pump in the spectrometer chamber. It has

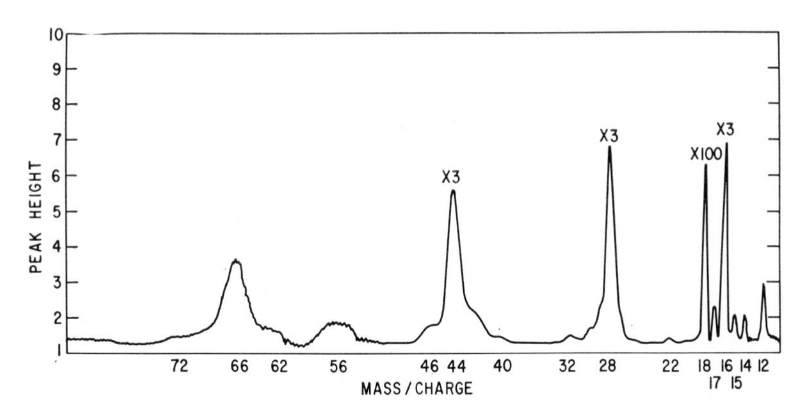

FIG. 11. Typical mass spectrum of gases in x-ray chamber before liquid-nitrogen cold trap is filled. The heavier mass numbers, 56 to 72, originate from hydrocarbons, vacuum 5×10^{-5} mm Hg.

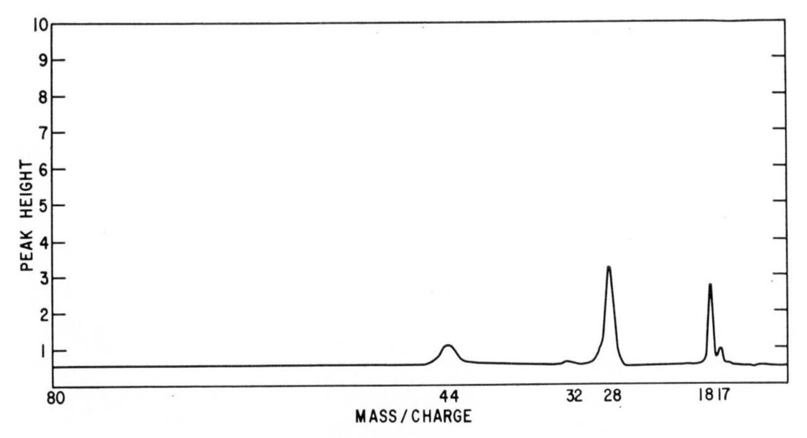

FIG. 12. Typical mass spectrum of residual gases in x-ray chamber after liquid-nitrogen trap is filled, vacuum 1×10^{-7} mm Hg.

been found that liquid-nitrogen cold traps are not adequate to stop back-streaming oil from diffusion pumps but are quite effective in the x-ray chamber in reducing the carbon contamination. The gettering action of the cold trap for contaminating vapors is shown from the mass spectrum of the x-ray chamber before and after the trap is filled in Figs. 11 and 12. Before the trap is filled, there are hydrocarbon vapors indicated by masses 56 through 72. After the trap has been filled, these mass peaks disappear.

Even with the absence of hydrocarbon vapors, which is indicated in Fig. 12, there was still evidence of carbon being deposited on the target during electron bombardment. This contamination is associated with the gases coming from the target. The Mo target was baked for 15 hr at 350° C. The rate of contamination after baking the target is shown in Fig. 13. It will be noted that for the first 20 min there was no increase in the amount of carbon. During this time, there was no increase in pressure and the vacuum remained constant at 3.8 × 10^{-7} mm Hg. However, when the pressure rose, so did the amount of carbon on the target. The rate of carbon

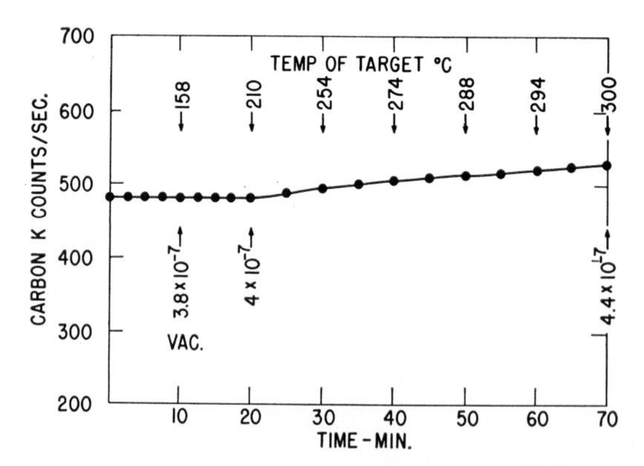

Fig. 13. Rate of carbon contamination after baking Mo target for 15 hr at 350° C. Pressure remained constant at 3.8 × 10^{-7} mm Hg for first 20 min.

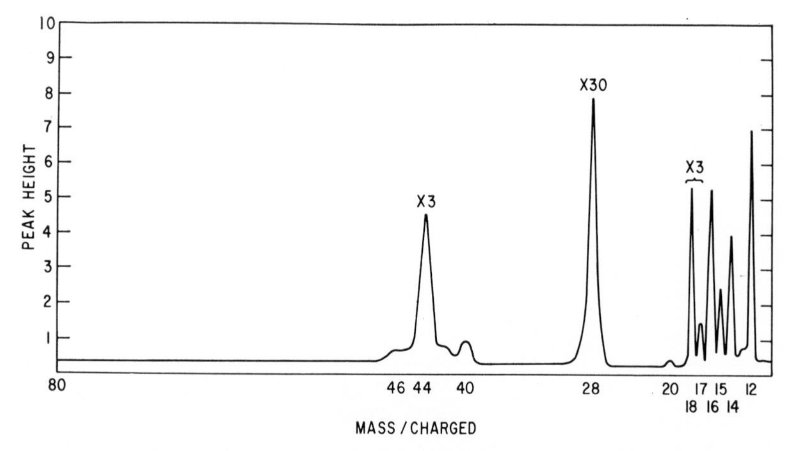

Fig. 14. Mass spectrum of gases evolved from Mo target when heated to 600° C. Pressure rose to 1 × 10^{-5} mm Hg.

contamination was 0.25 Å/min, which is considerably less than the 3.7 Å/min before baking. This result shows a definite relation between the gas coming from the target and the rate of carbon contamination. The gas that is evolved from the Mo target, which is heated at 600° C, is shown by the mass spectrum in Fig. 14. The mass spectrum before heating is shown in Fig. 12. It will be noted that there is a large increase in masses 12 and 28. The large increase in mass 12 indicates that mass 28 is largely CO rather than nitrogen, and the intensity of CO has increased about 100 times over that before heating. At elevated temperatures and in the presence of a suitable catalyst (the electron beam and metal surface) carbon monoxide disproportionates to carbon and carbon dioxide.

$$2CO \leftrightarrows C + CO_2 \tag{4}$$

Further evidence for the fact that carbon contamination comes from the carbon within the material is given by tests made on two different stainless-steel materials, one containing 0.001 carbon and the other 0.07 carbon. It was found that after about 5 hr of electron bombardment there was no evidence of a contamination from the 0.001 carbon but there was for the 0.07 carbon stainless steel. The test was made for the same power input and vacuum conditions.

In order to clean the carbon, and any other contaminants, off the target surface ion bombardment is very effective, and any damage to the surface can be removed by

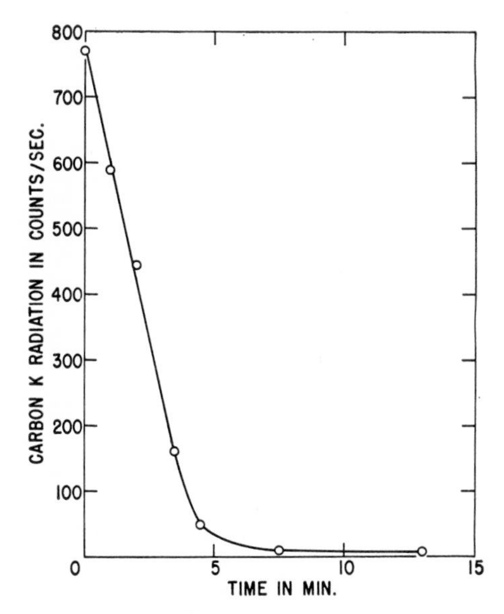

FIG. 15. Removal of carbon from surface of Mo by ion bombardment with argon at pressure of approximately 1 micron, target potential of −400 volts, and ion current density of 1 ma/cm^2.

annealing. In addition it is possible by ion cleaning to obtain bulk materials with clean surfaces, and thus avoid the necessity of using evaporated films which generally have unknown structures. To perform ion cleaning, spectroscopically pure argon, which is further cleaned by passing it over chips of Ti heated to 850° C, is used in the x-ray chamber at a pressure of approximately 1 micron, a target potential of 400 volts, and an ion current density of 1 ma/cm^2. Figure 15 shows the effectiveness of ion-bombardment cleaning in removing carbon from a Mo surface. The intensity of the radiation from the carbon film before removal was 770 counts/sec, which is approximately 180 Å of carbon. This amount of contamination is visible to the eye. The ordinate is the intensity of the carbon peak less background. The rate of removal is approximately 0.5 Å/sec. Repeated tests have shown that the rate of contamination is considerably reduced directly after cleaning. This is especially true for targets that have not been degassed over long periods of time. This result is explained by the fact that sputtered metal collects on the walls of the x-ray chamber and acts as a getter for the CO and other contaminating gases being evolved from the target.

The effect of heat alone on carbon contamination is indicated in Fig. 16. The Mo target was heated to 500° C by an electron beam striking the side opposite to where the carbon measurements were to be made. The fact that the temperature has reached 500° C and the amount of carbon is still increasing shows that operating the target at elevated temperatures does not eliminate carbon contamination. The intensity of carbon K band was measured every 10 min. The maximum rate of contamination under these conditions is 0.35 Å/min. The relation between rate of carbon contamination and gas pressure is evident. This result gives further evidence that the carbon is formed by the reaction of CO on a heated metal surface rather than merely by cracking of oil vapors by the electron beam, since there is no electron-beam action in this case. However, the electron beam does act as a catalyst in the process [Eq. (4)] since the carbon contamination is considerably greater where the beam strikes the target.

The above results show that carbon contamination can be controlled if the following points are observed: (1) use no oil-diffusion pumps and nonmetal seals, at least in the x-ray chamber; (2) place a liquid-nitrogen trap near the target; (3) thoroughly degas the target and filament of the electron gun and all heated parts; and (4) use ion

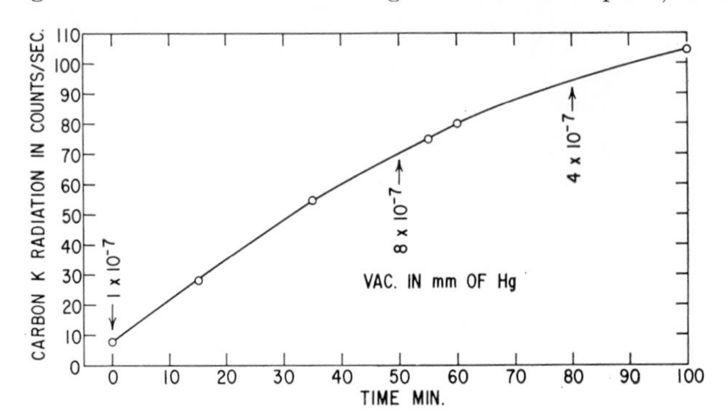

FIG. 16. Rate of carbon contamination due to heating Mo target to 500° C.

bombardment of the target both for cleaning and to provide a gettering material around the target to absorb contaminating gases such as CO.

6. ELECTRON GUN

A number of electron guns described in the literature[26] would be satisfactory for generating soft x-rays. For high power requirements Henke[27] has designed a very good electron gun. To obtain the maximum x-ray efficiency for the lowest electron density a line filament (rectangular electron spot) is preferred over a point. Experience has shown that, in general, a tungsten filament gives less contamination and a more stable current than an indirectly heated cathode in a demountable system. Using a tungsten filament and proper regulation[28] it has been possible to maintain a 1.5 ma beam current to within ± 1 per cent for 8 hr. Although a tungsten filament will not give so much current as an activated cathode, it has been found that large beam currents are not required with electronic detectors. For most emission spectra in the soft x-ray region, beam currents of 1 or 2 ma with a target potential of 3 to 4 kv are sufficient. When film is used, much higher beam currents are required.

Since x-rays result from transitions within the atom, the efficiency of production will not depend on the direction of the incident beam. However, several other considerations do determine the angle at which the beam strikes the target and the x-ray takeoff angle. For the maximum number of x-rays to reach the grating per incident electron and maximum P/B, the incident beam should strike the target at an angle such that the least amount of white radiation reaches the grating and the rectangular electron spot has a minimum width. Since the maximum number of soft x-rays will leave the target at an angle in which they will traverse the least amount of material, the maximum number of soft x-rays will leave the target at 90° to the surface. With these considerations in mind, the arrangement of gun, target, and grating is that shown in Fig. 17. Angle θ is the glancing angle and is determined by the shortest wavelength that is desired to be measured. Angle ψ should be as small as possible and still not have the x-rays striking the electron-gun structure. The 21.8 cm is for the present apparatus and is determined by the geometry of the spectrometer, x-ray chamber, and the valve between the two. The distance Y is determined by θ and the radius of curvature of the Rowland circle. All the blazed gratings described in this chapter were ruled on a blank 2.5 by 3.0 cm with a ruled area of 2.0 by 2.0 cm and a concave radius of 1 m.

As indicated above, the rectangular electron spot should have minimum width to obtain good P/B. This is especially true for wavelengths near the zero order. If the electron spot is wider than about 1 mm for the geometry in Fig. 17, the x-rays will strike the unruled area of the grating, which will give rise to high intensity in the zero order and a central image. The tails of the central image extend over a large angle of ϕ, which increases the background and reduces the P/B ratio for lines and bands that occur near the zero order.

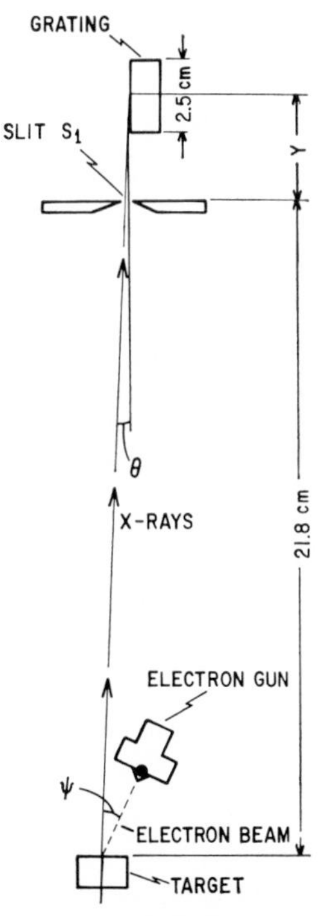

FIG. 17. Arrangement of target, electron gun, entrance slit, and grating in soft x-ray spectrometer.

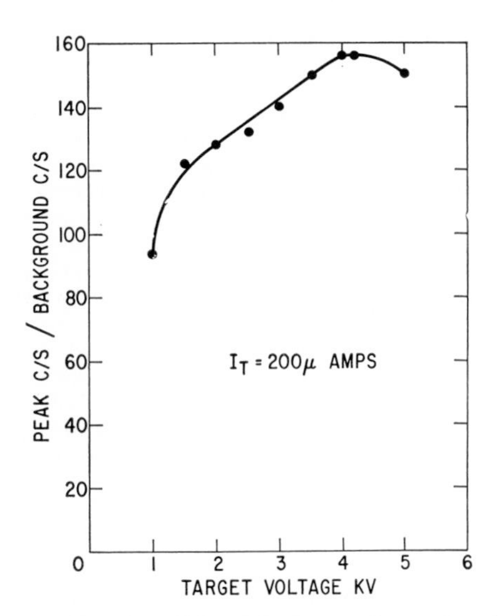

FIG. 18. Peak of C K band/background as a function of voltage for graphite target.

Farnsworth,[29] in his surface studies, found it necessary to use a bent gun to prevent tungsten evaporated from the filament of the electron gun from reaching the target. As a result, some believe it necessary to use a bent gun in soft x-ray measurements. Since the $N_V N_{VIII}$ line of tungsten appears at 58.5 Å, it was possible to study tungsten contamination as was done for carbon. After a bombardment of several hours, no trace of this line could be found, indicating that tungsten contamination was not a problem, at least in the 10 to 150 Å region.

The target potentials in soft x-ray spectroscopy that investigators have used have varied from several hundred volts to 5 kv. Gyorgy and Harvey[30] measured the Cu $M_{II,III}$-emission band at 172 Å with a potential of 500 volts, while Skinner[31] used 5 kv to measure Fe L_{III} emission band at 17.67 Å. The argument for the lower potentials is that a potential considerably in excess of the ionization potential of the inner level, of the transition being investigated, would distort the spectrum. Measurements made on emission bands with an inner level of around 200 volts have indicated no change in varying the potential from 2 to 4 kv.* In Fig. 18 is shown a curve of P/B as a function of voltage for the carbon K band at 44.8 Å from a solid graphite target. It will be noted that the maximum P/B occurs at approximately 4 kv. Since the results showed that there was no distortion of the spectrum in going to higher voltages and the maximum P/B occurs near 4 kv, potentials between 3.5 and 5 kv for measuring spectra in the 10 to 150 Å region were used.

7. DETERMINATION OF INSTRUMENT ERROR

The slits and grating cause a smearing out of the x-ray spectrum. It is generally considered that the errors, other than the grating, introduced by the spectrometer will be Gaussian. There has been some controversy as to what type of error curve the grating will contribute. Some investigators have proposed a trapezium shape,[32] others a Gaussian.[31] The type of error curve which the grating contributes can be determined by measuring the Zr $M_V N_{III}$ line at 81.6 Å with the 15,000 and 55,000 lines/in. gratings. It is found that the line appears to be more nearly Gaussian when using the 15,000 lines/in. grating than when the 55,000 lines/in. grating is used. This indicates that the Gaussian-error curve is a good approximation for the error introduced by the grating. More complete evidence that the grating contributes a Gaussian error to the spectra will be given later.

The half width (width at half maximum intensity) of the Gaussian-error curve due to the instrument can be determined from the two curves of the Zr $M_V N_{III}$-emission line measured with the 15,000 and 55,000 lines/in. gratings. Two different gratings were chosen instead of two different orders of the same grating, because the intensity from the first order of the 55,000 lines/in. grating was considerably greater than the nearly equivalent fourth-order line of the 15,000 lines/in. grating.

Let $G(E)$ be the Gaussian error due to grating and slits, and $L(E)$ be the true curve of the emission line. It has been found that the true shape of an emission line can be closely approximated by a Lorentzian curve which is given by the following equation:

$$I = \frac{A}{1 + (2B/W_{1/2})^2} \tag{5}$$

where B is the incremental-energy abscissa and is zero at the maximum intensity A, and is equal to $W_{1/2}/2$ at half maximum intensity. The curve of the emission line obtained from the instrument can be closely approximated by the following convolution integral:[33]

$$I(E') = \int_{-\infty}^{+\infty} L(E)G(E' - E)\,dE \tag{6}$$

Mack, Stephan, and Edlen[34] have shown that the resolving power is a linear function of the product of the grating constant and the slit widths, and if it is assumed that the Gaussian half width has an inverse linear relation with the resolving power and the slit widths remain constant the following relation can be written:

$$G'_{1/2} = nG''_{1/2} \tag{7}$$

where $G'_{1/2}$ is the Gaussian-error half width of the 15,000 lines/in. grating and slits, $G''_{1/2}$ is the Gaussian-error half width for the 55,000 lines/in. grating and slits, and n is the ratio between the grating constants. Subtracting $G''_{1/2}$ from both sides of Eq. (7), and dividing by $n - 1$,

$$G''_{1/2} = \frac{G'_{1/2} - G''_{1/2}}{n - 1} \tag{8}$$

* See Sec. 11, "Examples of Recent Developments," on page 38–39.

the half width of the Gaussian-error curve can be found from Eq. (8) if $(G'_{1/2} - G''_{1/2})$ can be determined. The value of $(G'_{1/2} - G''_{1/2})$ is found from the following convolution integral:

$$I'(E') = \int_{-\infty}^{+\infty} I''(E)g(E' - E)\,dE \tag{9}$$

where $I''(E)$ is the $M_{V}N_{III}$ line of Zr obtained from the spectrometer using the 55,000 lines/in. grating and the Gaussian-error curve $g(E)$ has a half width of $(G'_{1/2} - G''_{1/2})$. Integral equation (9) can be solved for $g(E)$ by a folding process on the analog computer or by graphical integration if a computer is not available. Various half widths of $g(E)$ are assumed until a curve $I'(E)$ (Fig. 19) is obtained that best fits the $M_{V}N_{III}$ line of Zr obtained with the 15,000 lines/in. grating (open circles, Fig. 19). The close fit of the two curves in Fig. 19 shows that the Gaussian-error curve is a reasonable

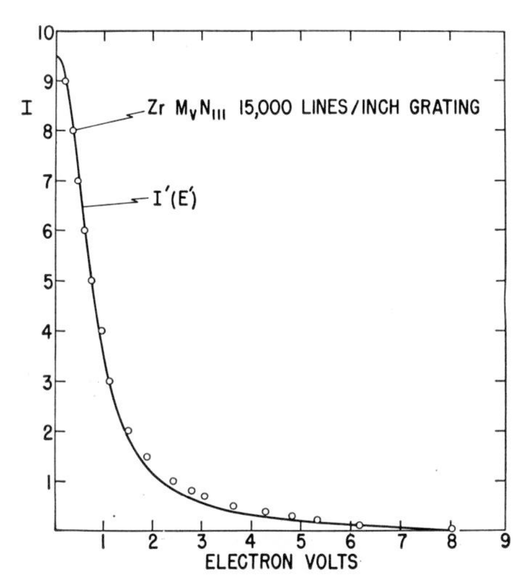

Fig. 19. Comparison of Zr $M_{V}N_{III}$ line (open circles) obtained by using grating having 15,000 lines/in. with $I'(E')$ (solid curve).

approximation for the error introduced by the grating. The $(G'_{1/2} - G''_{1/2})$ from Eq. (9) is 0.8 ev, giving a $G''_{1/2}$ from Eq. (8) of ~0.31 ev at 81.6 Å (peak λ of the Zr line) or ~0.16 Å. This $G''_{1/2}$ was obtained using slit widths of 20 microns.

8. EMISSION LINES

As indicated earlier, a number of important emission lines and bands occur in the wavelength region between 10 and 150 Å. The typical transitions that occur in the 10 to 100 Å region for the second-series transition metals are indicated in the conventional energy-level diagram for Y in Fig. 20. The energy levels are in close agreement with those given by Sandström.[35] The level widths are only approximate. The M-series transitions indicated in Fig. 20 which are in the soft x-ray region were first investigated by Siegbahn and Magnusson,[36] Kiessig,[37] and Chalklin and Chalklin.[38] In most cases only the wavelengths were measured, and consequently there is very little information on line shape, width, and P/B ratios for these lines and bands. The $M_{II}N_{I}$, $M_{III}N_{I}$, $M_{II}M_{IV}$, $M_{III}M_{V}$, $M_{III}M_{IV}$ are all weak lines with a P/B of about 2 or less. Transitions to the M_{III} level are approximately twice as intense as transitions to the M_{II} level. This intensity ratio is in close agreement with theory. According to the statistical weight of a level represented by $(2j + 1)$, transitions to

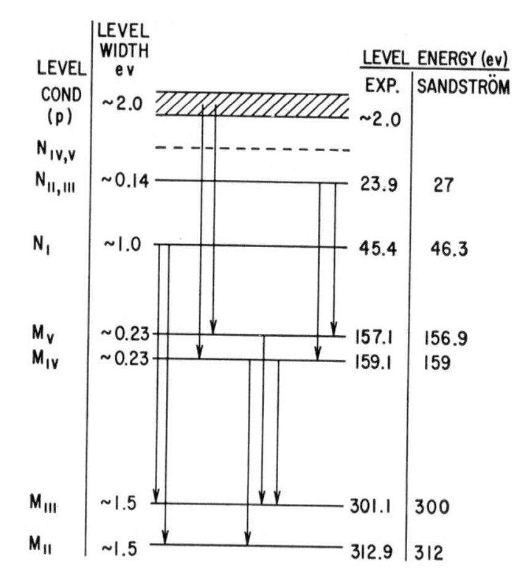

FIG. 20. Conventional energy-level diagram for solid yttrium.

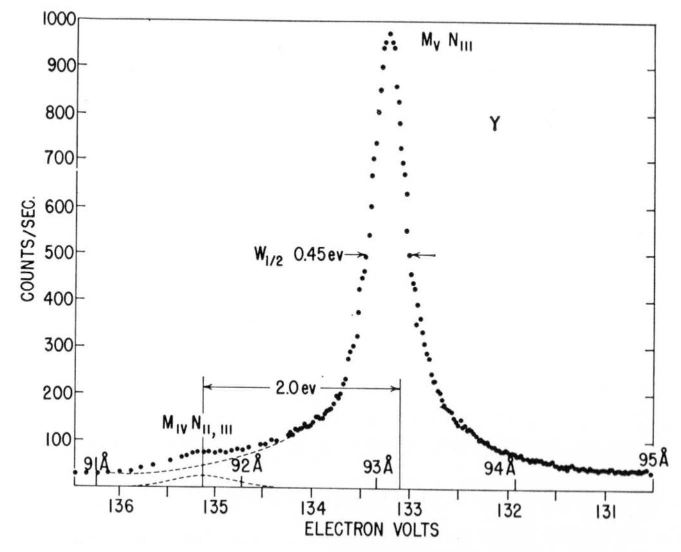

FIG. 21. $M_{IV}N_{II,III}$- and M_VN_{III}-emission lines of bulk yttrium using Al grating having 55,000 lines/in. and 20-micron slits. Target potential 5 kv, beam current 1.4 ma, and ±1.4 per cent deviation.

the M_{III} level should have two times the intensity of transitions to the M_{II} level. These emission lines have relatively large half widths because of the large level widths of the M_{II}, M_{III}, and N_I levels. The M_{IV} and M_V levels are much narrower than the other M levels. As will be shown later, a narrow inner-level width is essential in determining band shape. The M_VN_{III} and $M_{IV}N_{II,III}$ lines of Y are indicated in Fig. 21 for a potential of 5 kv and a beam current of 1.4 ma. The M_VN_{III} line occurs at 93.2 Å with a peak intensity of 975 counts/sec and a P/B of 30. The width at half maximum intensity is 0.45 ev. The true line half width $W(E)_{1/2}$ is determined from Eq. (6). The instrumental Gaussian-error half width at 93.2 Å was 0.23 ev. Several trial Lorentzian curves with different half widths were substituted in Eq. (6) and the solution of the integral obtained from an analog computer. A Lorentzian half width of 0.36 ev gave an $I(E)$ half width of 0.45 ev. Thus the half width of the $M_{V}N_{III}$ line of Y after correcting for instrumental error is 0.36 ev. It is important to point out that the actual line half width is greater than the difference between the

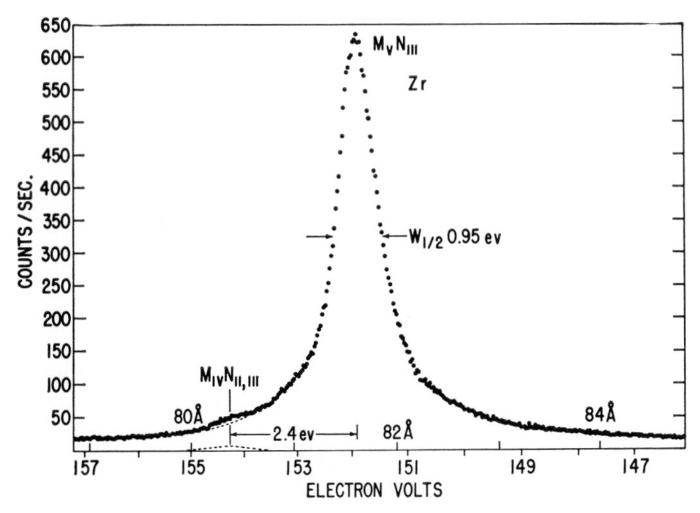

FIG. 22. $M_{IV}N_{II,III}$- and $M_{V}N_{III}$-emission lines of bulk Zr using Al grating having 55,000 lines/in. and 20-micron slits. Target potential 5 kv, beam current 1.4 ma, and ±1 per cent deviation.

Table 4. Wavelength and Corrected $W_{1/2}$ for $M_{V}N_{III}$ Line of Y to Mo Using 55,000 Lines/in. Grating and 20-micron Slits

Element	Peak λ, Å	$W_{1/2}$, ev
Y	93.2	0.36
Zr	81.6	0.85
Nb	71.95	1.2
Mo	64.2	1.85

experimental line half width and the Gaussian-error half widths. The experimental curves of the $M_{V}N_{III}$ and the $M_{IV}N_{III}$ lines for Zr, Nb, and Mo[39,40] are shown in Figs. 22 to 24. The $M_{IV}N_{II}$ peak is observed for Mo giving a separation of the $N_{II}N_{III}$ levels for Mo of 1.5 ev. The curves were obtained using a 55,000 lines/in. grating. The target current and potential for each metal are indicated in the figures. The wavelength at which the emission lines occur and the corrected half width for the $M_{V}N_{III}$ line of Y, Zr, Nb, and Mo are indicated in Table 4. The widths are considerably narrower than what Kiessig[37] reported for these lines. For example, Kiessig reported a half width of 3.44 ev for the Nb $M_{V}N_{III}$ line. One reason for the difference is that Kiessig used a 15,000 lines/in. grating and did not correct for the instrumental error. The half width of the $M_{V}N_{III}$ line increases at a greater rate in going from Y

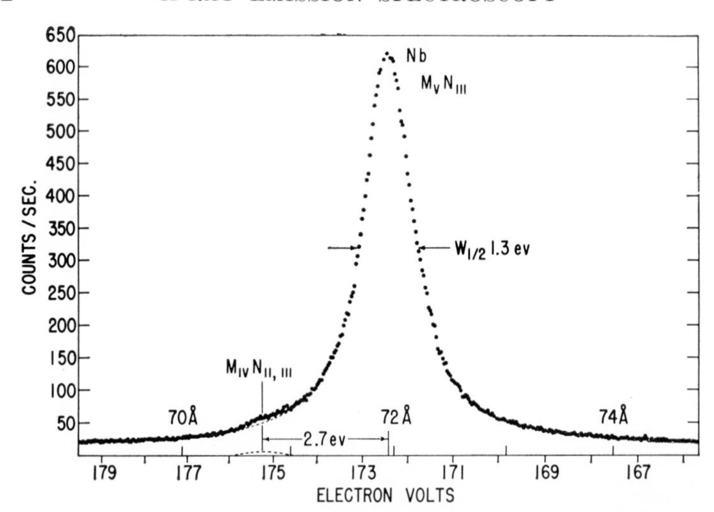

FIG. 23. $M_{IV}N_{II,III}$- and M_VN_{III}-emission lines of bulk Nb using Al grating having 55,000 lines/in. and 20-micron slits. Target potential 4 kv, beam current 1.4 ma, and ±1 per cent deviation.

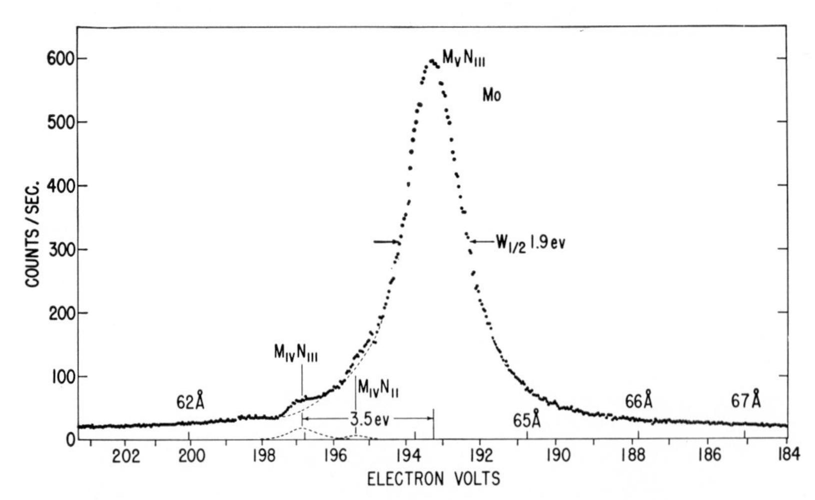

FIG. 24. $M_{IV}N_{II,III}$-, $M_{IV}N_{II}$-, and M_VN_{III}-emission lines of bulk Mo using Al grating with 55,000 lines/in. and 20-micron slits. Target potential 4 kv, beam current 1 ma, and ±1 per cent deviation.

to Mo than is predicted by the Z^4 dependence. Cooper[41] has shown that this increase in width is due to a rapid widening of the N_{III} level rather than the M_V level and has attributed it to a Koster-Kronig transition of the type $N_{II,III} \rightarrow N_{IV,V}N_{IV,V}$. Further evidence that the increase in width is due to the N_{III} level will be given when limits placed on the width of the M_V level by band shape are discussed.

It will be observed that the M_VN_{III}-emission line in Figs. 21 to 24 has a definite Lorentzian shape even without correction. The lines were recorded by a point-by-point process. Although a rate meter and recorder are faster than a point-by-point

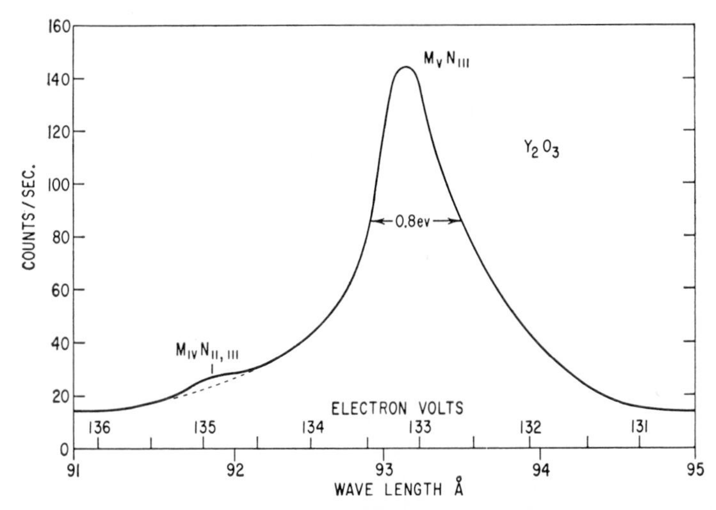

FIG. 25. $M_{IV}N_{II,III}$- and M_VN_{III}-emission lines of yttrium oxide using Al grating with 55,000 lines/in. and 20-micron slits. Target potential 3.5 kv, beam current 1 ma, and ±2.5 per cent deviation.

Table 5. Wavelength, Intensity in Counts/Second, and P/B for M_VN_{III} Line Using 15,000 Lines/in., 1° Blazed Al Grating, 40-micron Slits, V_T = 3,500, and I_T = 1 ma

Element	Peak λ, Å	Peak intensity, counts/sec	P/B
Y.........	93.2	1,250* 700	35
Zr.........	81.6	4,100* 2,700	40
Nb........	71.95	5,500* 4,000	50
Mo........	64.2	5,850* 4,500	75
Ru........	52.4	7,150* 6,000	80
Pd........	43.8	4,000* 3,500	45
Ag........	39.8	2,600* 2,300	23
Cd........	36.5	2,230* 2,000	20
Sn.........	31.4	3,280* 3,000	15

* Corrected for counter window.

process, they are not as accurate. Attempts were made to adjust the time constant and speed of the spectrometer to obtain maximum accuracy. However, it was still not possible to equal the accuracy of the point-by-point method. If a recorder and rate meter must be used, the time constant and speed of the spectrometer must be adjusted so that statistical variations can be observed in the recorder trace. Smooth lines are to be avoided. False shapes to lines and bands appear in the literature as a result of poor recording techniques. Williams[18] has discussed a method using a multichannel pulse analyzer and rapid scanning of the peak that equal the accuracy of the point-by-point method.

It was mentioned earlier that the M_VN_{III} lines from Y to Sn can be of considerable value in calibrating the spectrometer. They are also of interest for solid-state studies since their widths and shape change with chemical combination. This is shown in Fig. 25, where the M_VN_{III} line of Y_2O_3 shows considerable asymmetry and $W_{1/2}$ has increased from 0.45 ev for Y to 0.8 ev for Y_2O_3. In Table 5 are listed the peak wavelengths, P/B, and the peak intensity with and without correcting for the counter window of the M_VN_{III} lines. The M_VN_{III} lines of Tc, Ru, and In were not measured. The lines were measured with the 15,000 lines/in. 1° blazed grating with a beam current of 1 ma and potential of 3.5 kv. The wavelengths are approximate and were determined by using the oxygen and carbon K bands, which can be measured to a number of orders, as standards. The wavelengths of the M_VN_{III} lines are in close agreement with those obtained by Siegbahn and Magnusson.[36] The M_VN_{III} line has a high-energy satellite. This satellite has been observed from Y to Sn and has about one-fiftieth the intensity of the M_VN_{III} line. It was originally called, by Siegbahn and Magnusson,[36] the $M_{IV,V}Y_I$ line, where Y was an unknown energy level and is listed this way in all wavelength tables of lines and bands. However, it has been shown by Holliday[42] that this peak is a satellite of the M_VN_{III} line.

9. ENERGY BANDS

Since this is a handbook of results rather than theory, no attempt will be made here to relate shape or band width to solid-state theory. However, the shape and widths of the band and the necessary correction will be given so investigators making measurements on these bands will have spectra to compare their measurements with. The types of transitions that originate in energy bands in the second-series transition metals are like those indicated for the energy-level diagram of Y in Fig. 20. The M_{II}- and M_{III}-emission bands are $[(4d + 5s) \rightarrow 3p]$ transitions and give the shape of $4d$ and $5s$ bands. No transition of this type has been observed for Y or Zr. However, Shaw and Jossem[43] and Liefield[44] have observed the $[(4d + 5s) \rightarrow 2p]$ transition for Zr. The M_{II}- and M_{III}-emission bands have not been observed previously for Nb and Mo and were first reported by Holliday.[45] These transitions are weak with a P/B of 1.2, which may explain why they have been difficult to find. The M_{III}-emission band is about twice as intense as the M_{II} band. As indicated earlier, the M_{II} and M_{III} levels are broad and thus prevent any detailed shape of the $4d$ band from being observed.

The other transitions for the second-series transition metals involving band electrons are from the conduction band to the $3d$ level. By dipole-selection rules, this transition would be from a p-type electron in the band and be of the type (cond $p - 3d$). These transitions were first discussed by Siegbahn and Magnusson[36] and were called $M_{IV,V}Y_{II}$. The level Y_{II} was called an unknown energy level. This notation was used by Siegbahn because according to the periodic chart there are no $5p$ electrons in the second-series transition metals. However, according to the idea of wave-function admixture and hybridization there can be, for example, p-band electrons when there are no corresponding electrons of this type in the free atom. Thus, according to modern ideas of solid-state theory, there is no need to use the Y_{II} notation.

The $M_{IV}M_V$-emission bands of Nb[46,47] obtained directly from the instrument are indicated in Fig. 26. It will be noted that even without any corrections there are a sharp emission edge and a double peak. Band calculations have predicted a double peak for the energy bands of the transition metals, but a double peak has not been observed before in x-ray emission-band spectra of transition metals. Parratt[48] has shown that before the emission bands can be compared with the density-of-states curve a number of corrections must be made. Even after making all the corrections that are possible, one does not obtain a density-of-states curve but a density-of-states times transition-probability curve. This is because the theory has not been developed far enough to make the correction for transition probability. The corrections that will be described here for the M_V-emission bands are instrumental error, background, M_{IV}-emission-band overlap, width of inner level, and tailing effect. The corrections for the background and the M_{IV} band are indicated by the dashed lines in Fig. 26. It will be noted that the background rises slightly in going from the high-energy to the low-energy side of the band. This was also true for Y, Zr, and Mo. The rise is due to the tail of the intense $M_V N_{III}$ line. The present method of correcting for the inner level and instrumental error is similar to that given by Tomboulian in the *Handbuch der Physik*[11] and Shaw and Jossem.[43] A more elaborate method has been given by Porteus and Parratt,[49] but because of inaccuracies in determination of inner-level width and experimental measurements it does not appear that elaborate

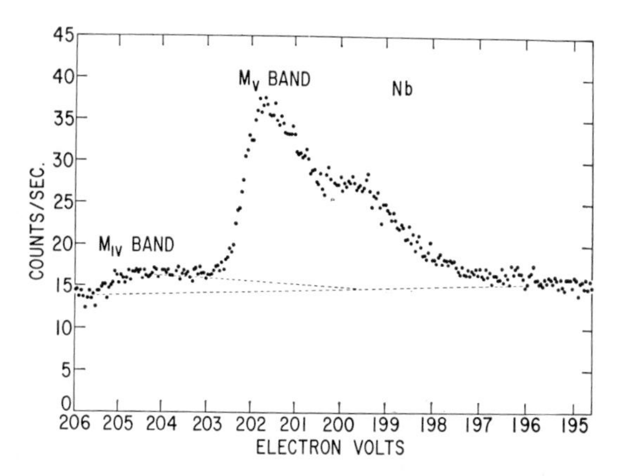

FIG. 26. M_{IV}- and M_V-emission bands of bulk Nb using Al grating with 55,000 lines/in. and 20-micron slits. Target potential 4 kv, beam current 1.4 ma, and ±2.4 per cent deviation. Dashed lines indicate background and M_{IV} band. (*Reprinted by permission from J. E. Holliday, The Electron Microprobe, John Wiley and Sons, Inc.*[46])

methods are justified in the present work. The inner-level width and the instrumental error are corrected by a relation having the form of Eq. (6). The experimental emission-band curve $P(E')$ is given by

$$P(E') = \int_{-\infty}^{+\infty} T(E)S(E' - E)\,dE \tag{10}$$

where $T(E)$ is the trial density-of-states times transition-probability curve, the smearing function $S(E)$ is made of two parts, the instrumental Gaussian error and the inner level, which is assumed to have a Lorentzian shape. As indicated earlier, the close approximation of the $M_V N_{III}$ line to a Lorentzian curve shows that this is a good approximation for the shape of the $3d$ level. For the Nb M_V-emission band, the Gaussian-error half width was 0.52 ev, and the inner-level width was approximately 0.28 ev, giving a smearing function by Eq. (6) of 0.64 ev half width, which is indicated in Fig. 27. After the smearing function is obtained a trial density-of states times transition-probability curve $T(E)$ is assumed. The smearing function is passed through the $T(E)$ curve in equal incremental steps of energy Δe, as indicated in Fig. 27. The products formed by the overlapping ordinate form a new curve whose area is the ordinate i of the $P(E')$ curve (Fig. 27) at an abscissa value E' given by the peak of the smearing function $S(E)$. The smaller the incremental shift Δe the greater the accuracy. This process could be done by graphical integration, but the computer can do it much faster and with greater accuracy. For the present work the reference was taken as the peak of the trial density-of-states curve $T(E)$ and given a value of zero electron volts.

In Fig. 28 the calculated $P(E')$ (the dotted open circle) is compared with the experimental M_V-emission band of Nb, which has been corrected for background and M_{IV}-emission band. The partially corrected M_V band is an average of three separate band measurements. The $T(E)$ curve in Fig. 28 must be altered so that a $P(E')$ curve is obtained that will fit the partially corrected M_V band. The $T(E)$ curve giving the best fit is indicated in Fig. 29. The $T(E)$ curve in Fig. 29 represents the product of the density of p-type states in the band, viz., $N_p(E)$, and transition probability. The width of the emission edge is 0.32 ev. Before corrections the width

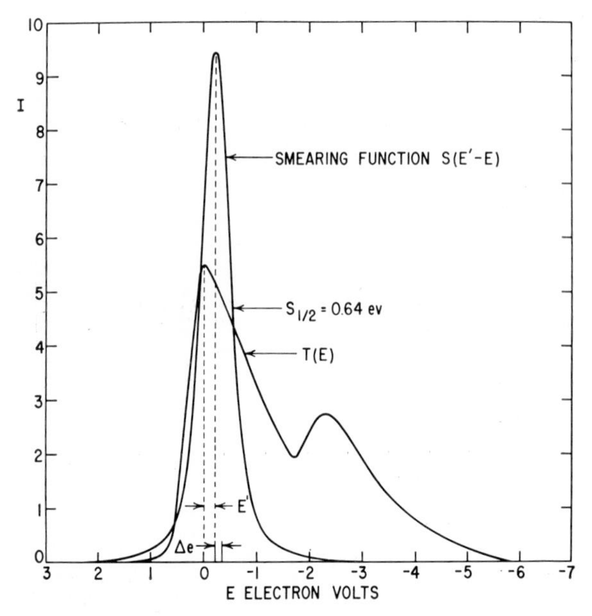

Fig. 27. Illustrating smearing function $S(E' - E)$ being passed through $T(E)$ curve in incremental steps ΔE.

was 0.8 ev, giving an edge correction of 0.48 ev. The width after correction is generally ascribed to temperature, which according to Skinner[31] is equal to $6KT$. Since the temperature of the target was 350° C, the edge should have a width of 0.324 ev. Considering experimental error, the emission edge of the Nb M_V band has zero width after temperature corrections. The $T(E)$ curves [$N_p(E)$ times transition probability] and partially corrected M_V band for Y, Zr, and Mo[47] are indicated in Figs. 30 to 32. As would be expected, the emission edge becomes sharper and the double peak (for the bands indicating a double peak in the experimental curve) is more pronounced after the corrections have been made. The exact shape of the bottom of the emission band of Y is somewhat uncertain since it had to be corrected for the $M_{II}M_{IV}$ line, which overlapped the low-energy portion of the curve. Each partially corrected M_V band in Figs. 30 to 32 is an average of several measurements of the emission band.

There is a degree of uncertainty in determining the inner-level width. This is partly due to the lack of reliable measurements of the emission-line half width and the lack of proper correction for instrumental error. Even with the lack of reliable values for the inner-level width, the shape of the emission band will set certain definite

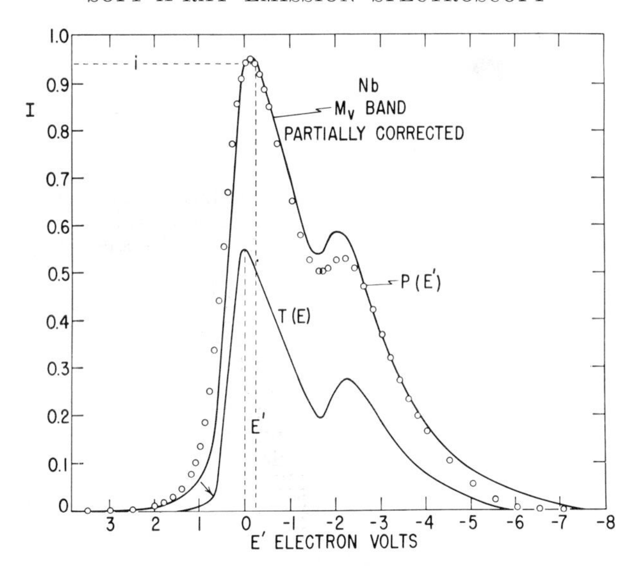

FIG. 28. Comparison of calculated $P(E')$ curve with experimental Nb M_V-emission-band curve, which is an average of three M_V band spectra and corrected for background and M_{IV} band.

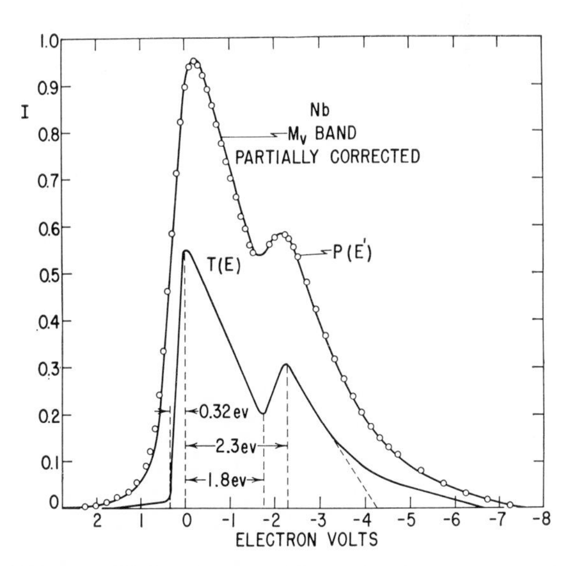

FIG. 29. The $T(E)$ curve [$N_p(E)$ times transition probability] giving best fit with partially corrected M_V-emission band. (*Reprinted by permission from J. E. Holliday, The Electron Microprobe, John Wiley and Sons, Inc.*[46])

limits on the width of the inner level. For example, it was found that if the Lorentzian half width of the inner level had been greater than about 0.4 ev for Nb the double peak would not have been observed in the experimental measurements. In other words, the inner level has the same effect as the instrumental error in reducing the resolution. Another portion of the $T(E)$ curve that sets an upper limit to the value of the inner-level width is the bend at the bottom of the emission edge indicated by the arrow (Fig. 28). It will be noted that the corrected emission band of Nb (in Fig. 29) has been made sharper in this region in order to obtain a fit. If the inner-level width were assumed to be greater than 0.28 ev, it would not be possible to obtain a fit with the experimental curve without making the ordinate of the $T(E)$ curve double-valued in this region. The inner-level width cannot be assumed to be sufficiently wide so the width of the corrected emission edge is equal to $6KT$. This is well illustrated for the M_V-emission band of Mo, where it will be noted that after correction the emission edge width is 1.5 ev. Since Mo was operated at the same temperature as Nb, the edge width after temperature correction would still be approximately 1.2 ev. If the inner-level width were made sufficiently wide in order to correct for the additional 1.2 ev, the double peak would not be observed. A similar situation exists for the Zr emission edge (Fig. 31), where the edge width after temperature correction is 0.78 ev. From measurements of the half width of the $L_{III}M_V$, M_VN_{III}, $M_{III}M_V$ lines and L_{III}-level width plus the restriction placed on the width of the inner level by the M_V-emission band, the M_V-level width of Zr was found to be approximately 0.25 ev. The limit of the M_V level set by the shape of the M_V-emission bands from Y to Mo shows that M_V level is not being widened by the Auger process and obeys

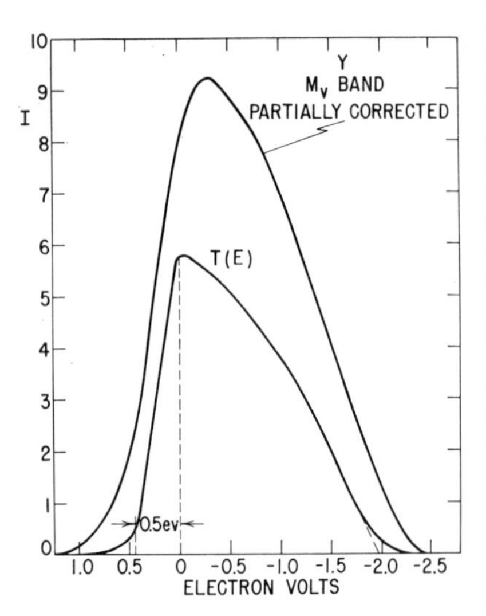

Fig. 30. $N_p(E)$ times transition-probability curve $T(E)$ for bulk Y and the experimental M_V-emission band corrected for background, M_{IV}-emission band, and $M_{II}M_{IV}$ line.

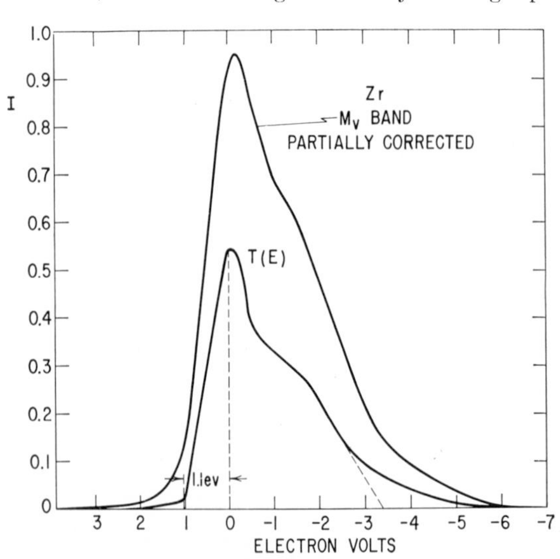

Fig. 31. $N_p(E)$ times transition-probability curve $T(E)$ for bulk Zr, and experimental M_V-emission band corrected for background and M_{IV}-emission band.

the Z^4 dependence. The approximate widths of the M_V level from Y to Mo plus the emission edge in electron volts are indicated in Table 6. The values of the M_V-level width indicated in Table 6 show that the rapid increase in the half width of the $M_V N_{III}$ line (Table 4) is a result of the rapid widening of the N_{III} level rather than the M_V level. As indicated earlier, this widening is due to the Auger process.

Some investigators[50] have corrected the emission-edge width for instrumental broadening by estimating that the Gaussian-error curve contributes about one-third of its half width $G_{1/2}$ to the edge width b. The edge width for uncorrected spectra is

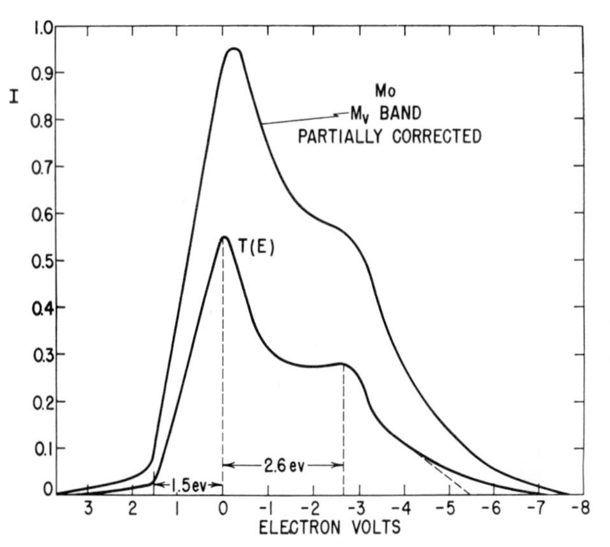

FIG. 32. $N_p(E)$ times transition-probability curve $T(E)$ for bulk Mo and experimental M_V-emission band corrected for background and M_{IV}-emission band.

Table 6. Data on Corrected M_V-emission Band from Y to Mo

Element	Emission edge M_V band, ev	Width of band by extrapolation, ev	M_V = level width, ev
Y.........	157.1	2.0	0.23
Zr.........	179.85	3.4	0.25
Nb........	202.3	4.2	0.28
Mo........	229.0	5.4	0.31

defined as the energy interval over which the intensity falls from 95 to 5 per cent. However, calculations on the analog computer have shown that this is applicable only under special conditions, namely, when $G_{1/2} \sim b$ and the bandwidth w is about 20 times $G_{1/2}$. When $G_{1/2} \sim b$ but w is only about twice $G_{1/2}$, the error curve will contribute only about $\frac{1}{6}G_{1/2}$ to the edge width. For $G_{1/2} \gg b$ and w equals two or three times $G_{1/2}$, the Gaussian-error curve will contribute a width greater than $G_{1/2}$ to the breadth of the emission edge. Thus the only accurate way of correcting the emission edge is by a folding process described above. The variation in the amount of correction to the edge width, for different initial edge widths, can be observed in comparing the corrected and uncorrected emission edges in Figs. 29 to 32. It will be noted that Y and Nb have relatively greater edge correction than do Zr and Mo.

The energy width of the band is difficult to determine since there is no definite low-energy limit observed even after correction. The curves fall away gradually toward lower energies. According to theory, the density-of-states curve at the bottom of the band varies as $E^{1/2}$. Theory also shows the bottom of the band will be modified by the inner level, which is $E^{3/2}$ and $E^{1/2}$ for the K and $L_{II,III}$ levels, respectively. There is no detailed theory to predict what the exponential value will be for the $M_{IV,V}$ levels. The modification of the low-energy portion of the band from that indicated above arises from a tailing effect. An explanation for the low-energy tailing effect, as given by Skinner,[31] is that it is caused by Auger transition within the band. From the appearance of the shape near the bottom of the band in Figs. 29 to 32, the $T(E)$ curve shows a strong tailing, except possibly for Y where the exact shape of the bottom of the band is uncertain. In order to establish a lower limit to the band, a linear extrapolation of the curve was employed. In Figs. 29 to 32 it will be noted that there is also some tailing on the high-energy side of the emission edge for the corrected emission bands. Shaw and Jossem[44] and Liefield[45] obtained considerable high-energy

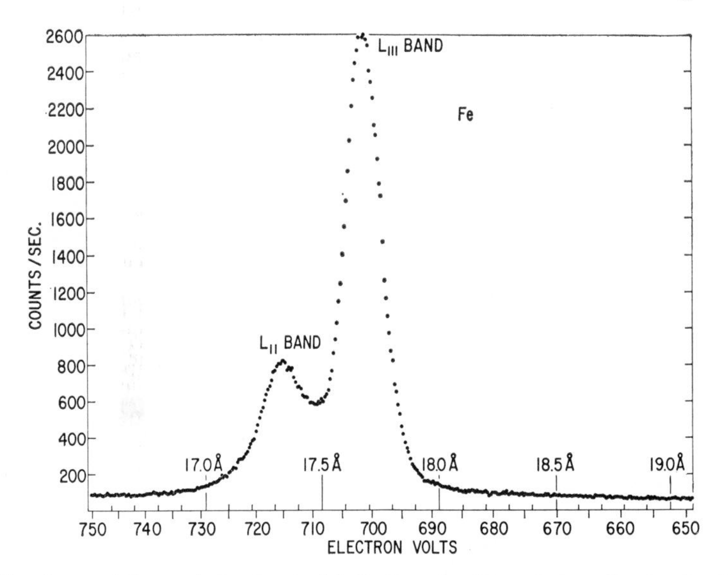

FIG. 33. L_{II}- and L_{III}-emission band of bulk Fe using Pt-coated grating having 55,000 lines/in. and 1° blaze. Target potential 4 kv, beam current 1 ma, slits 20 microns wide, and ±0.8 per cent deviation.

tailing after correcting the $L\gamma_1$ band of Zr. Skinner[31] attributed the high-energy tailing to band satellites, but other explanations for this tailing appear to be in order. The width of the band from the top of the emission edge to the point where the linear extrapolation intersects the axis is given in Table 6 for Y, Zr, Mo, and Nb. Shaw and Jossem[43] and Liefield[44] obtained a value of approximately 3 ev after correcting the $L\gamma_1$ emission band, $[(4d + 5s) \rightarrow 2p]$ transition, of Zr.

The L_{II}- and L_{III}-emission bands, $[(3d + 4s) \rightarrow 2p]$ transition, of the first-series transition metals occur in the wavelength region of 15 to 30 Å. Skinner's[31] spectra of these bands did not indicate an emission edge, as was shown above for some of the second-series transition metals. This fact was attributed to wide L_{II} and L_{III} levels.[46] However, preliminary measurements with a 90,000 lines/in. grating indicate that some of the early first-series transition metals do have an emission edge. The $L_{II,III}$-emission band of Fe using a Pt-coated 55,000 lines/in. grating is indicated in Fig. 33. The peak intensity ratio of the L_{III}/L_{II} band is approximately 4. This ratio is closer to the predicted value of 2 (calculated from the statistical weight of a level $[2J + 1]$) than the ratio of 10 obtained by Skinner, Bollen, and Johnston.[51] The intensity and

P/B for the $L_{II,III}$-emission bands and the Ll line for the first-series transition metals using the 15,000 lines/in. 1° blazed grating are shown in Table 7. The peak intensities have been corrected for counter window (Table 3) and grating (Fig. 7). Hydrogenic theory predicts that a $(d \rightarrow p)$ transition will be about ten times more probable than an $(s \rightarrow p)$ transition, but it is of interest to note that the $(3d \rightarrow 2p)$ transition of Ti has about the same intensity as the $(3s \rightarrow 2p)$ transition. This is further evidence[45] that hydrogenic transition probabilities are not in general applicable to solid-state transitions. In Table 8 are listed a number of emission bands and lines for Y, Nb, and Mo[45] which have not been observed before.

Table 7. Intensity* in Counts/Second and P/B for the L_{III} Band and Ll Line of the First-series Transition Metals Using the 15,000 Lines/in. 1° Blazed Grating, 20-micron Slits, V_T = 3,500, and I_T = 1 ma

Element	L_{III} band $[(3d \rightarrow 4s) \rightarrow 2p]$			Ll line $(3s \rightarrow 2p)$		
	λ, Å	Intensity	P/B	λ, Å	Intensity	P/B
Ti	27.4	1,150	25	31.4	1,350	32
V	24.3	3,000	24	27.7	2,340	20
Cr	21.9	2,460	22	25.1	1,500	20
Mn	19.4	3,550	36	22.2	1,700	13
Fe	17.7	6,700	45	20.1	1,650	10
Co	16.1	8,158	46	18.5	1,350	7
Ni	15.2	9,500	41	17.1	1,270	6.5

* Corrected for counter window (Table. 3) and grating (Fig. 7).

Table 8. Wavelengths in Angstroms of Previously Unreported Transitions in Y, Nb, and Mo

	Y experi-mental, λ	Y calcu-lated, λ[35]	Nb experi-mental, λ	Nb calcu-lated, λ[37]	Mo experi-mental, λ	Mo calcu-lated, λ[37]
$M_I N_{II,III}$ line	.....	.....	28.4	28.3	26.4	26.3
M_{II} band	.....	.....	32.6	32.8	30.3	30.3
M_{III} band	.....	.....	34.0	34.2	31.5	31.65
$M_{II} N_I$ line	46.48	46.66	38.4	38.3	35.3	35.9
M_{IV} band	78.28	77.98				
M_V band	79.34	79.02				
$M\ \xi$ satellite	86.64					

10. SECOND-PERIOD ELEMENTS

Because of the interest in the second-period elements and the lack of any recent measurements* of their K-emission spectra except for Be[52] and Li,[53-56] it is believed that a section should be devoted to these. Without including Ne, the K-emission spectra of the second-period elements cover a wavelength region from about 18 to 250 Å. By dipole-selection rules the K-emission spectra of the second-period elements are of the type $(2p \rightarrow 1s)$. For the second-period elements the $2p$ level is a band, and consequently all the K-emission spectra will be bands. In the case of the metals Be and Li there is a considerable amount of wave-function admixture; so the K spectrum of these elements will be a combination of $2s$ and $2p$ bands. The $2s$ and $2p$ bands of the nonmetals are separated and thus have more significance in regard to x-ray

* See Sec. 11, "Examples of Recent Developments," on page 38-39.

measurements. Siegbahn and Magnusson,[57] Chalklin and Chalklin,[38] Prins,[58] Tyren,[59] Skinner,[31] and O'Bryan and Skinner[60] were some of the early investigators who measured the *K*-emission spectra of the light elements. Siegbahn and Magnusson, who were mainly interested in wavelength determinations, measured the O *K* band out to the fourteenth order and the N *K* band from boron nitride to the seventh order. Tyren and Skinner measured the shape of the *K*-emission spectra for a number of fluorine and oxygen compounds. Because they did not have modern experimental techniques their power input was considerable (100 to 200 watts) and the P/B low. This led to the belief that the use of *K*-emission spectra for quantitative analysis was impractical. However, it will be shown below that high intensity and P/B can be obtained for the *K*-emission spectra of the second-period elements with relatively low input power. The detailed structure of *K*-emission bands will be discussed and compared with spectra of earlier investigations.

Table 9 indicates the intensity and P/B ratios for the *K*-emission spectra of all the second-period elements except Ne. The target current and the potential are indicated

Table 9. Intensity and P/B of *K*-emission Spectra of Second-period Elements Using 15,000 Lines/in., 1° Blaze, Al Grating, and 40-micron Slits

Radiation	Source	Peak intensity, counts/sec	P/B	I_T, ma	Voltage	Blaze, °
F *K*.	LiF	17,800* 16,100	130	1	3,500	1
O *K*.	FeO	17,400* 16,000	40	1	3,500	1
N *K*.	BN	17,000* 15,300	125	1	3,500	1
C *K*.	Graphite	27,200* 24,000	180	1	3,500	1
B *K*.	BN	2,730* 2,050	55	1	3,500	1
Be *K*.	Be	4,150* 1,500	42	1	4,000	7.5
Li *K*†.	Li	2,000	35	4	4,000	0

* Corrected for counter window. † Crisp's measurement using glass grating.[10]

Reprinted by permission from J. E. Holliday, *The Electron Microprobe*, John Wiley and Sons, Inc.[46]

in the table. The emission bands were obtained with a 15,000 lines/in. 1° blazed grating, except in the case of Be and Li. The Be *K* spectrum was measured with the Al 15,000 lines/in. 7.5° blazed grating. The Li *K* spectrum is the work of Crisp,[10] who used a 15,000 lines/in. glass grating. As indicated earlier (Fig. 7), the 7.5° blazed grating gave a higher intensity for spectra having wavelengths greater than about 64 Å than did the 1° blazed grating. However, the P/B of the Be *K* band did not differ appreciably for the two gratings. The sources from which the spectra were obtained are indicated in Table 9. As indicated earlier, the efficiency of the production of the second-period elements for $5 \leq Z \leq 9$ varies as $Z^{3/2}$.[8] It will be observed, however, from Table 9 that the intensity of the *K* spectra of the second-period elements increases with Z but does not vary as $Z^{3/2}$. This is due to the change in reflecting power of the grating with wavelength (Fig. 7). However, the use of peak intensities as a measure of the efficiency of x-ray production is of limited value because the area under the curve for a given band or line (Fig. 25) will change considerably with chemical combination. For example, the half width of the C *K* band from NbC is one-third the half width of the C *K* band from graphite. In addition, the determination of x-ray yields is considerably more complex for emission bands from compounds than for emission bands from pure elements. This is especially true for compounds containing elements of widely varying atomic numbers. Some of the factors which cause a variation in x-ray intensity for an element in chemical combination from that of the pure element can be demonstrated by consideration of the O K band from FeO; these are: (1) the higher absorption of the O K radiation by the iron over that due to the oxygen alone, (2) the O K radiation produced by fluorescence radiation of the Fe $L_{II,III}$-emission band at 17.67 Å, and (3) increased number of back-scattered electrons from Fe. The P/B of the O K band will also be determined by the element with which it is in chemical combination. The higher the Z the lower the P/B. Because Fe has a much higher Z (the amount of white radiation is a function of Z) than Li and B, the P/B of O K from FeO is far less than those of the F K and N K bands (Table 9). Considering the large intensity and P/B for the small power input, the efficiency of production of the F K, O K, N K, and C K bands is considerably greater than had been estimated from previous measurements. The large drop in intensity for the B K band from that of C K is due to the selective effect of the 1° blazed grating (Fig. 7). The large reduction of intensity of the Be K band over that of the higher-Z elements of the second period is partly due to changes in grating efficiency. Although the 7.5° blazed grating is more efficient than the 1° at 110 Å, the 7.5° blazed grating is not so efficient at 110 Å as the 1° is at 44 Å.

With the P/B and intensity of C K indicated in Table 9 the minimum amount of carbon that could be measured by soft x-rays should be about 0.1 atomic per cent. The carbon-contamination problem prevented a reliable comparison of small percentages of carbon in solids, measured by x-rays, with that determined by chemical analyses. Since nitrogen can be thoroughly removed from the surface by ion cleaning, and there is no nitriding of the surface by electron bombardment, the N K spectrum was measured in Nb containing small percentages of nitrogen. For the lowest percentage measured, the intensity of N K was 30 counts/sec above background and the P/B was $\sim$1.1. By chemical analysis it was found that this Nb target contained $\sim$0.1 atomic per cent nitrogen. In order to ensure that there was no change in the surface of the target after cleaning, the N K band was measured rapidly with a rate meter and recorder. Because of the poor statistics, it was just possible to observe the peak above the background. By using longer counting times to obtain better statistics, it would be possible to measure lower percentages of nitrogen. From a comparison of intensities and P/B of the F K, O K, and C K bands with the N K band it should be possible to measure the same percentage of fluorine, oxygen, and carbon. For the rest of the second-period elements (Table 9) it does not appear possible to measure boron, beryllium, and lithium to the same low percentage as was possible for nitrogen, with the present instrumentation.

Dowell and Berwaldt[61] were the first to report fluorescent spectral bands of oxygen, nitrogen, and carbon. They used film as a detector, and laminated lead stearate crystal was the dispersing element. The O K, N K, and C K bands were excited by x-rays from a windowless gaseous x-ray tube operated at 3,000 volts and 200 ma. Henke[62] has found that with an intense x-ray source and close coupling between source, sample, crystal, and detector, and by using flow-proportional counting, it is possible to extend fluorescence analysis to the light elements fluorine through boron. Effective sample size is typically a few milligrams. As little as 0.11 per cent carbon has been detected. To accomplish this, the C K band was excited by the $L_{II,III}$ band of Cu at 13.55 Å. The Cu target was bombarded with 330-ma beam current and a potential of 6 kv. The proportional counter had a double-layer parlodion window with a total thickness of 4,000 Å. The dispersing element was a 100-layer lead stearate crystal with a $2d$ spacing of 100 Å.

In order to obtain higher resolution to investigate the detailed structure of the emission bands of the second-period elements, it was necessary to use the 55,000 lines/in. grating and reduce the slit width to 20 microns. The emission bands of the second-period elements from F to Li are indicated in Figs. 34 to 41. In Table 10 are listed the emission-edge wavelength, the peak wavelength, and the bandwidth. The peak and emission-edge wavelengths and bandwidths are compared with results of other investigations for these elements, where this information is available. In comparing the present peak wavelengths with previous measurements, it will be noted that they are within about 0.1 Å of each other. The determination of the emission-edge wavelength for nonmetal emission bands is rather arbitrary because of the diffuse edge. The arbitrariness of determining the high-energy end point of the emission band of nonmetals plus the tailing effect at the low-energy end of the band makes the determination of the bandwidth of nonmetals less certain than for metals.

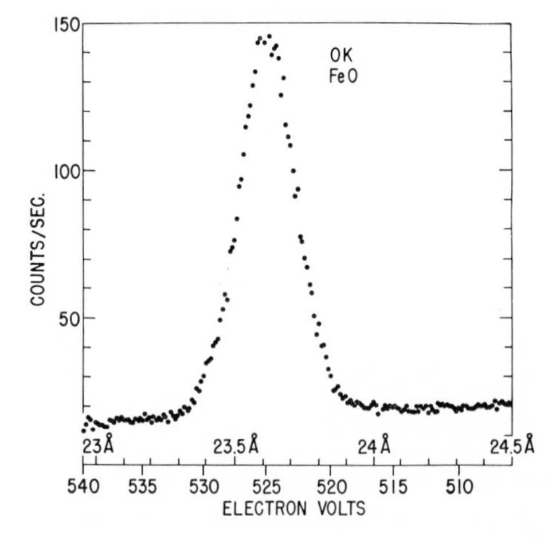

FIG. 34. O K band from FeO using Al-coated grating having 55,000 lines/in., 1° blaze, and slits 20 microns wide. Target potential 3.5 kv, beam current 1 ma, and ±3 per cent deviation.

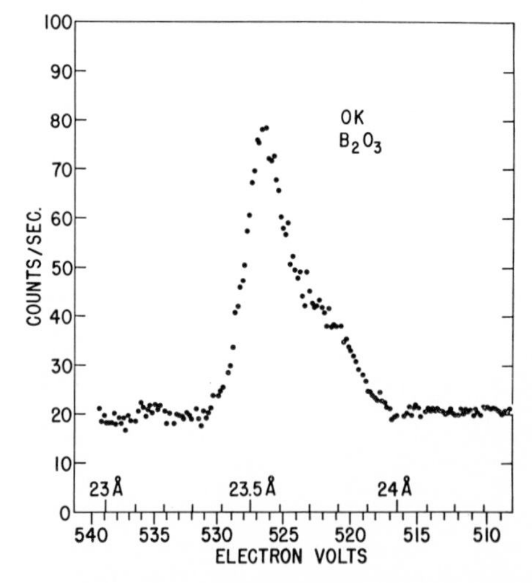

FIG. 35. O K band from B_2O_3, target potential 3.5 kv, beam current 1 ma, and ±2.5 per cent deviation.

However, it will be observed that the emission bands of the negative ions of the insulators generally have less tailing than some of the metals and semiconductors. For example, compare the N K band in Fig. 37 with the C K and Be K bands in Figs. 38 and 40. Despite these uncertainties, for completeness, approximate bandwidths are listed in Table 10. No corrections have been applied to these bands for instrumental error or inner-level width.

It will be observed in Figs. 34 to 41 that some of the bands have considerable amounts of detail and others do not. The O *K* band at 23.62 Å of iron oxide in Fig. 34 shows a complete lack of detail and has a symmetrical peak. The absence of detail is not due to a lack of resolution because O'Bryan and Skinner[60] measured this

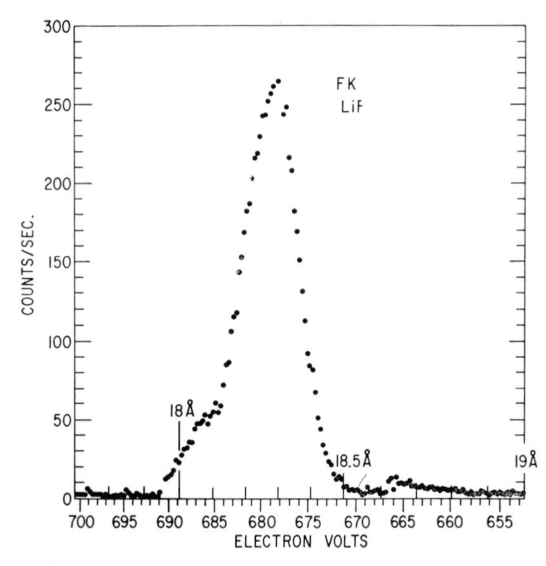

FIG. 36. F *K* band from single crystal of LiF. Target potential 5 kv, beam current 1 ma, and ±2.5 per cent deviation.

Table 10. Wavelength and Bandwidth Data for Second-period Elements Using 55,000 Lines/in., 1° Blazed Grating, and Slits Set at 20 Microns

Radiation	Source	Present measurement: Emission edge λ, Å	Emission edge ev	Peak λ, Å	Peak ev	Approx bandwidth λ, Å	Approx bandwidth ev	Previous measurement: Emission edge, Å	Peak λ, Å	Bandwidth, ev
F *K*..........	LiF	17.94	691.1	18.28	678.2	0.6	22	......	18.3	18[60]
O *K*..........	Fe_3O_4	23.3	532.10	23.62	524.89	0.7	15	......	......	19[60]
O *K*..........	B_2O_3	23.3	532.10	23.53	526.90	0.7	15	23.5	23.5	19[60]
N *K*..........	BN	31.20	397.4	31.56	392.84	1.2	13	31.18	31.42	14[59]
C *K*..........	Graphite	43.5	285.2	44.85	276.3	4.31	25	43.69	44.8	18[5] 30[31]
B *K*..........	BN	66.5	186.5	68.7	180.4	13.6	13	......	......	13[60]
Be *K*..........	Be	110.85	112.2	113.75	109.10	12.25	14.8	110.9	113.7	14.7[31]
Li *K*..........	Li	......	......	......	......	......	....	226.65	228.5	4.2[31]

band with three times the present resolution and obtained a symmetrical peak with no detail. Not all O *K* bands are symmetrical, as is indicated for that from boron oxide in Fig. 35. This band is strongly asymmetrical with a hump on the low-energy side. O'Bryan and Skinner[60] were not able to show any further separation between the

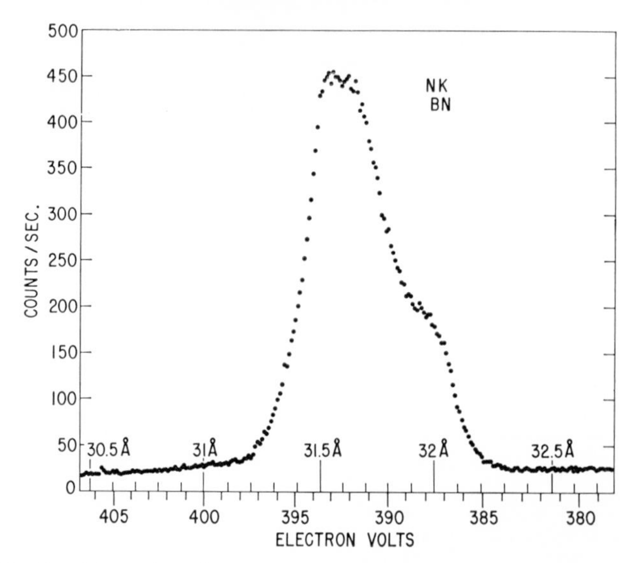

FIG. 37. N K band from bulk BN, target potential 5 kv, beam current 1 ma, and ±1.4 per cent deviation.

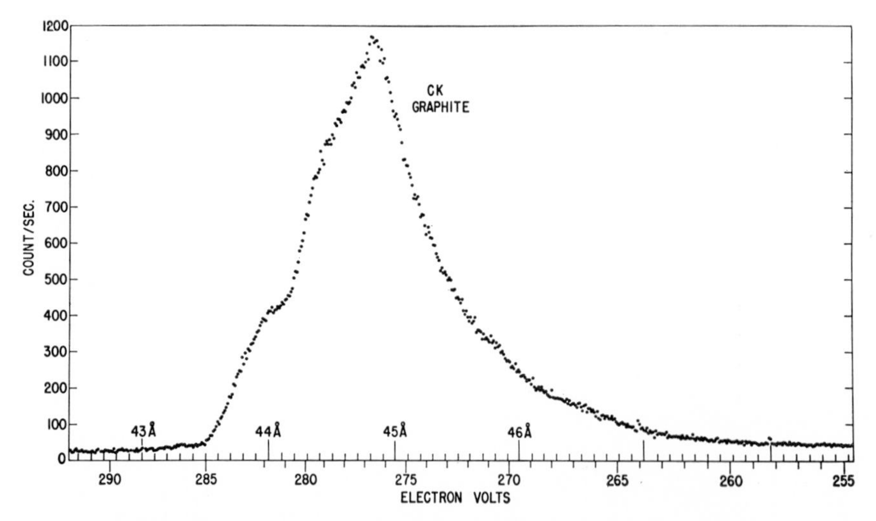

FIG. 38. C K band from bulk graphite, target potential 4 kv, beam current 1 ma, and ±1.5 per cent deviation.

hump and the main peak. They considered this part of the band rather than a satellite. The low-energy hump has an intensity of 40 per cent of the main peak, which is in agreement with their measurement. It will be noted that there is an apparent reduction in the peak wavelength from that of iron oxide by 0.09 Å. Not all the O K bands have the low-intensity hump on the low-energy side of the main peak. That of SrO has a low-intensity peak on the high-energy side.

The F K band at 18.28 Å from LiF is indicated in Fig. 36. The hump at approximately 18.1 Å on the high-energy side of the main peak was shown by O'Bryan and

Skinner,[60] with more resolving power, to be a second peak. As indicated above, this was not the case for B_2O_3. O'Bryan and Skinner proposed that the low-intensity peak was not part of the band but was a band satellite and was a transition from the $2p$ band to the K level of a neutral fluorine atom. The peak at 18.28 Å is a transition from the $2p$ band to the K level of a singly ionized fluorine atom. The intensity of the higher-energy peak shown here is about 20 per cent of the high-intensity peak, while O'Bryan and Skinner obtained about 40 per cent. A number of other fluorine K bands show this double peak.

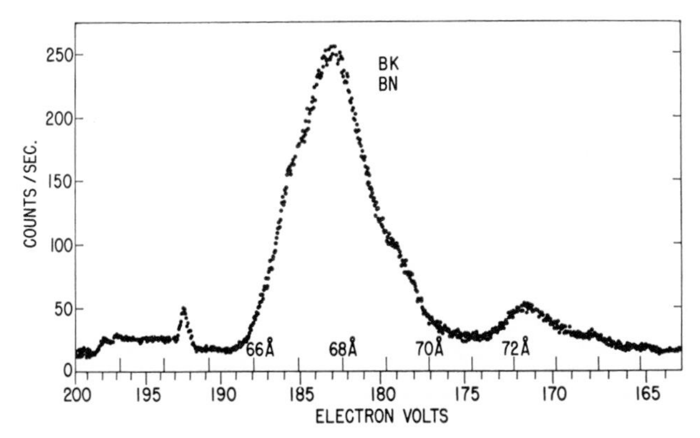

FIG. 39. B K band from BN, target potential 5 kv, beam current 1 ma, and ±2 per cent deviation.

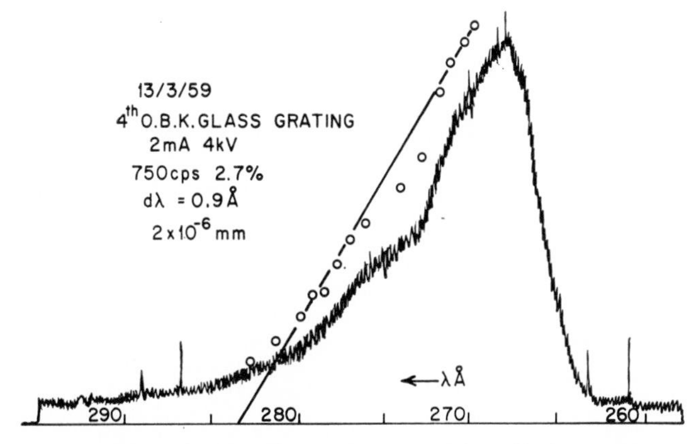

FIG. 40. Fourth-order B K band from amorphous boron. Detector was an open CuBe photomultiplier. [*Reprinted by permission from R. S. Crisp and S. E. Williams, Phil. Mag.*, **6**:365 (1961).]

In Fig. 37 is indicated the N K band at 31.56 Å for boron nitride. There is a double peak at the top of the emission band with a hump on the low-energy side. Tyren's[59] measurements of N K from boron nitride showed the same structure with no further resolution of the peaks. It would appear that all the structure is part of the band and not due to satellites. The low-energy hump has an intensity of about 20 per cent of the main peak, while Tyren obtained 70 per cent. Considering the uncertainty in determining the end points of the band, the bandwidths are in relatively close agreement, as indicated in Table 10.

The C K band for a graphite target is indicated in Fig. 38. A number of different wavelengths have been reported for the peak of the C K band. However, our value of 44.85 Å agrees very closely with Chalklin's[5] value of 44.8 Å. The present measurements do not indicate a double peak at the top of the band as was reported by Chalklin. The hump at approximately 44 Å has one-third the intensity of the peak while Chalklin obtained a value of two-thirds. As in the case of the N K band all the structure is part of the band and not due to satellites. From Table 10 it will be noted that there is considerable variation in reported bandwidths for C K. As indicated earlier, this is due to the difficulty of determining the end points of the band. However, the 18 ev reported by Chalklin appears from Fig. 38 to be too small.

It was stated at the beginning of this section that the $2s$ and $2p$ band had more significance for the K spectra of nonmetals than for the K spectra of metals. Transitions to the K level for the negative ion will be from the $2p$ band. O'Bryan and Skinner[60] indicated that a part of the K spectrum for the metal ion represented the $2s$ band. In Fig. 39 is indicated the boron K spectrum from boron nitride. This has a large peak at 68.7 Å and two smaller peaks on each side of the main peak. The large peak was considered by O'Bryan and Skinner to be the $2s$ band, and the low-intensity peak at approximately 64 Å on the high-energy side was considered to be the $2p$ band. Their conclusion was based partly on the fact that their spectrum of

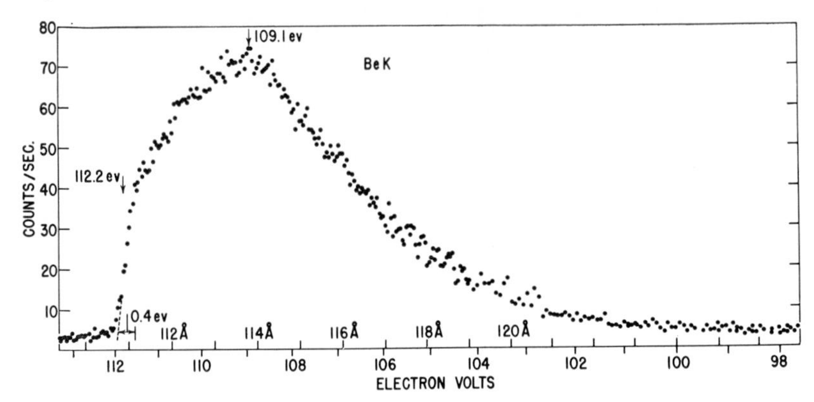

Fig. 41. Be K band from bulk beryllium, target potential 4 kv, beam current 1.4 ma, and ±2.5 per cent deviation.

the large peak had no detail (the $2s$ band was supposed to be diffuse and lack detail) and a correspondence between the N K band from BN in Fig. 35, which is the $2p$ band, and the high-energy peak at 64 Å in Fig. 39. However, it will be noted that in the present measurements there is no correspondence between the peak at 64 Å and that in Fig. 37 as to shape or bandwidth. In addition, the main peak in Fig. 39 has definite structure with a hump at 68 Å and a bump at 70 Å. All the structures indicated for the peaks in Fig. 39 were found on the four different measurements of the B K spectrum from BN. From Table 10 the N K band of BN has the same bandwidth as the main peak of B K band from BN at 68.7 Å. There is also considerably more similarity between the shape of these two peaks than between the N K band in Fig. 37 and the peak at 64 Å. By dipole-selection rules transitions of the type ($2p \rightarrow 1s$) will be much more intense than the quadrupole transition ($2s \rightarrow 1s$). From the above facts there is more evidence that the B K peak at 68.7 Å is the $2p$ band ($2p \rightarrow 1s$) transition than that it is the $2s$ band ($2s \rightarrow 1s$) transition. The change in structure of the band as a result of chemical combination is well illustrated from a comparison of the B K band from pure boron with that of the B K band from BN. The measurement of Crisp and Williams[52] of the B K band from pure boron in Fig. 40 shows no distinct peaks on either side of the large peak. Their measurements, as observed in Fig. 40, do indicate, however, a distinct bump at about the same distance from the peak as the bump at 70 Å in Fig. 39. There was no hump on the emission-edge side of pure boron to correspond to the hump at 68 Å for B *K* from BN. Also the peak wavelength of the B *K* band from BN has shifted toward a longer wavelength.

The only metals in the second period are Be and Li, and the *K*-emission spectra for these metals are indicated in Figs. 41 and 42. The Li *K* spectrum is the work of Crisp and Williams.[56] Because of the wavelength of the Li *K* band it was not possible to obtain a good spectrum of Li with the flow-proportional counter. The spectrum for Li in Fig. 42 is for the fourth order and was detected with an open-end CuBe photomultiplier. The metal emission edges are quite sharp in contrast to the nonmetals. Skinner[31] reported the mean emission-edge wavelengths of the Be *K* and Li *K* spectra at 110.9 and 226.5 Å, respectively. The present measurements indicated the emission edge of Be at 110.8 Å. It will be observed that the emission edges of the Li *K* and Be *K* spectra do not extend to the peak as is common for other metals such as the Nb M_V band in Fig. 29. For the Be *K* band the edge extends to about 40 per cent of the maximum intensity where a discontinuity of slope is observed. A similar effect occurs

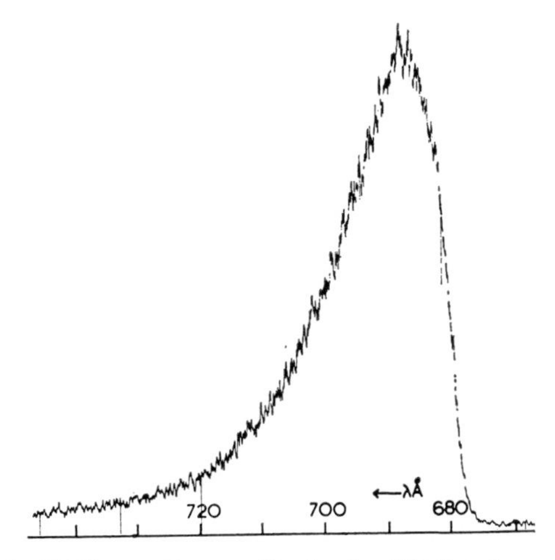

FIG. 42. Third-order Li *K* using 1-m grating having 576 lines/mm and 40-micron slits. Detector was an open CuBe photomultiplier. Target potential 4 kv, beam current 1 ma, and chamber pressure 1×10^{-6} mm Hg. [*Reprinted by permission from R. S. Crisp and S. E. Williams, Phil. Mag.,* **5**:525 (1960).]

for the Li *K* band at about 75 per cent peak intensity. This phenomenon is contrary to the prediction of the simple band model. Several theoretical explanations have been given which will not be discussed here but will be found in the literature.[53,54,56,63] The reported bandwidths for the Li *K* and Be *K* bands in Table 10 are 4.2 and 14.8 ev, respectively. The present value of 14.8 for the Be *K* band is in agreement with that of Skinner.[31] From Table 10 it will be noted that the present value of 113.75 Å for the peak wavelength is very close to the reported value of 113.70 Å. The shape of the Be *K* band in Fig. 41 is in agreement with the measurement of Skinner except for some structures on the low-energy side of the band, which he attributed to Si and SiO_2 in the glass grating.

11. EXAMPLES OF RECENT DEVELOPMENTS

Between the time this article was sent to the publisher and the publication of the handbook there have been a large number of articles published on soft X-ray spectroscopy. The largest number of these deal with the organic crystal analyzers and light element spectra obtained from this type of crystal. Also, during the interim period spectra have been published, using a grating analyzer and electronic detector that have been discussed in this article. For example, Zimkina et al.[64] in Russia and Wiec[65] in Germany have recently published M emission spectra of Zr, Nb, and Mo. Recent experimental results using high resolving power spectrometers have shown that varying the excitation voltage between 1 and 5 kv does have some effect on the shape of the emission band from certain types of solids. The largest change appears to be for solids with strong ionic bonding.

Some of the material on instrumentation was presented at the Mid-America Spectroscopy Symposium.[66]

REFERENCES CITED

1*A*. Y. Cauchois, C. Bonnelle, and J. Orcel, *Bull. Franc. Mineral Crist,* **85**(2): 188–189 (1962).
1. D. W. Beard and T. C. Furnas, *Tech. Documentary Rept.* ASP-TDR-62-519, 1962.
2. W. L. Baun and D. W. Fisher, *Tech. Documentary Rept.* ASP-TDR-63-310, 1963.
3. J. E. Holliday, *Rev. Sci. Instr.*, **31**:891 (1960).
4. P. Fisher, R. S. Crisp, and S. E. Williams, *Op. Acta (Paris)*, **5**:31 (1958).
5. F. C. Chalklin, *Proc. Roy. Soc. (London)*, **A194**:42 (1948).
6. G. Sprague, D. H. Tomboulian, and D. E. Bedo, *J. Opt. Soc. Am.*, **45**:756–767 (1955).
7. J. E. Holliday, *J. Opt. Soc. Am.*, **52**:1312 (WB17) (1962).
8. A. J. Campbell, *Proc. Roy. Soc. (London)*, **A274**:319 (1963).
8*a*. D. O. Landon, *Appl. Opt.*, **2**:450 (1963).
9. R. S. Crisp, *Opt. Acta,* **8**:137 (1961).
10. R. S. Crisp, private communication.
11. D. H. Tomboulian, *Handbuch der Physik,* vol. 30, pp. 246–304, S. Flügge (ed.), Springer-Verlag OHG, Berlin, 1957.
12. T. Sagawa, *Sci. Rept. Tohoku Univ.*, **44**:115–125 (1960).
13. R. E. Piore, G. G. Harvey, E. M. Gyorgy, and R. H. Kingston, *Rev. Sci. Instr.*, **23**:8 (1952).
14. J. A. Catterall, J. A. Wilson, and J. Trotter, *J. Sci. Instr.*, **35**:393–395 (1958).
15. L. Jacob, R. Nobel, and H. Yee, *J. Sci. Instr.*, **37**:460–463 (1960).
16. D. E. Bedo and D. H. Tomboulian, *Rev. Sci. Instr.*, **32**:184–188 (1961).
17. A. P. Lukirskii, M. A. Rumsh, and L. A. Smirnov, *Opt. Spectr.*, **9**:265 (1960).
18. S. E. Williams, *J. Quant. Spectr. Radiative Transfer*, **2**:621 (1962).
19. A. H. McIlraith, *J. Sci. Instr.*, **39**:504 (1962).
20. J. L. Rogers and F. C. Chalklin, *Proc. Phys. Soc. (London)*, **B67**:348 (1954).
21. A. P. Sukuskii, *Radioetekhn. i. Elektron,* no. 3, pp. 328–333 (1957).
22. D. L. Ederer and D. H. Tomboulian, *J. Opt. Soc. Am.*, **52**:1312 (WB18) (1962).
23. R. M. Dolby, *Proc. Phys. Soc. (London)*, **73**:81 (1959).
24. S. A. Korff, *Electron and Nuclear Counters*, p. 10, D. Van Nostrand Company, Inc., Princeton, N.J., 1955.
25. R. Wilson, *Phil. Mag.*, **41**:66 (1950).
26. W. Ehrenberg and W. E. Spear, *Proc. Phys. Soc. (London)*, **B64**:67 (1951).
27. B. L. Henke, "Microanalysis with Ultrasoft X-radiations," in *Advances in X-ray Analysis*, vol. 5, W. M. Mueller (ed.), Plenum Press, Inc., New York, 1962.
28. R. S. Crisp, *J. Sci. Instr.*, **35**:470 (1958).
29. H. E. Farnsworth, *Rev. Sci. Instr.*, **21**:102 (1950).
30. E. M. Gyorgy and G. G. Harvey, *Phys. Rev.*, **87**:861 (1925).
31. H. W. B. Skinner, *Phil. Trans. Roy. Soc. (London)*, **A239**:95 (1940).
32. P. Fisher, *J. Opt. Soc. Am.*, **44**:665 (1954).
33. John G. Truxal, *Automatic Feedback Control System Synthesis*, p. 56, McGraw-Hill Book Company, New York, 1955.
34. J. E. Mack, J. R. Stephan, and B. Edlen, *J. Opt. Soc. Am.*, **22**:245 (1932).
35. A. E. Sandström, *Handbuch der Physik*, vol. 30, pp. 224–225, S. Flügge (ed.), Springer-Verlag OHG, Berlin, 1957.
36. M. Siegbahn and T. Magnusson, *Z. Physik*, **88**:559 (1934).
37. H. Kiessig, *Z. Physik*, **95**:555 (1935).
38. F. C. Chalklin and L. P. Chalklin, *Phil. Mag.*, **16**:363 (1933).
39. J. E. Holliday, *Bull. Am. Phys. Soc.*, **6**:284 (1961).
40. J. E. Holliday, *Bull. Am. Phys. Soc.*, **7**:416 (1962).
41. J. N. Cooper, *Phys. Rev.*, **65**:155 (1944).
42. J. E. Holliday, *Phil. Mag.*, **6**:801 (1961).

43. C. H. Shaw and E. L. Jossem, *U.S. Atomic Energy Commission* no. AT (11-1)-191, pp. 50–55, 1959.
44. R. J. Liefield, *Dissert. Abstr.*, **20**:4147–4148 (Ann Arbor, Mich., 1960).
45. J. E. Holliday, *J. Appl. Phys.*, **33**:3259 (1962).
46. J. E. Holliday, "Change in Shape of the k Emission Spectra of the Light Elements with Chemical Combination," *The Electron Microprobe*, T. O. McKinley, H. F. J. Heinrich, and D. B. Wittry (eds.), pp. 3–22 John Wiley and Sons, Inc., New York, 1966.
47. J. E. Holliday, *Bull. Am. Phys. Soc.*, **8**:248 (1963).
48. L. G. Parratt, *Rev. Mod. Phys.*, **3**:616 (1959).
49. J. O. Porteus and L. G. Parratt, *Tech. Rept.* 7, AFOSR TN59-754, 1959.
50. J. A. Catterall and J. Trotter, *Phil. Mag.*, **3**:1424 (1958).
51. H. W. B. Skinner, T. Bollen, and J. E. Johnston, *Phil. Mag.*, **45**:1070 (1954).
52. R. S. Crisp and S. E. Williams, *Phil. Mag.*, **6**:365 (1961).
53. D. E. Bedo and D. H. Tomboulian, *Phys. Rev.*, **109**:35 (1958).
54. J. A. Catterall and J. Trotter, *Phil. Mag.*, **4**:1164 (1959).
55. R. S. Crisp and S. E. Williams, *Phil. Mag.*, **5**:1205 (1960).
56. R. S. Crisp and S. E. Williams, *Phil. Mag.*, **5**:525 (1960).
57. M. Siegbahn and T. Magnusson, *Z. Physik*, **87**:291 (1934).
58. J. A. Prins, *Z. Physik*, **69**:618 (1931).
59. F. Tyren, *Nova Acta Rec. Soc. Sci. Upsaliensis*, **12**:7 (1940).
60. H. M. O'Bryan and H. W. Skinner, *Proc. Roy. Soc. (London)*, **176**:229 (1940).
61. L. G. Dowell and O. E. Berwaldt, *Rev. Sci. Instr.*, **33**:340 (1962).
62. B. L. Henke, "X-ray Fluorescence Analysis for Sodium Fluorine, Oxygen, Nitrogen, Carbon, and Boron," in *Advances in X-ray Analysis*, vol. 7, Plenum Press, Inc., New York, 1964.
63. J. A. Catterall and J. Trotter, *Phil. Mag.*, **3**:1424 (1958).
64. J. M. Zimkina, O. A. Ershow, and A. P. Lukirskii, *Bull. Acad. Sci. U.S.S.R. Phys. Ser.* **28**(5):744–748 (May, 1964, Publ. 1965).
65. Gerhard Wiec, Dissertation zur Erlangung der Doktorwürde, der Ludwig-Maximilians-Universität, München, December, 1964.
66. J. E. Holliday, *Developments in Applied Spectroscopy*, vol. 5, pp. 77–105, L. R. Pearson and E. L. Grove, editors, Plenum Press, New York, 1966.

Chapter 39

ELECTRON-PROBE MICROANALYSIS

L. S. Birks

U.S. Naval Research Laboratory

1. INTRODUCTION

Foregoing chapters in Part 4 have shown how characteristic x-ray spectra excited by fluorescence may be used to analyze average composition down to parts per million, local regions of a few tenths of a millimeter on inhomogeneous specimens, and trace quantities of a few micrograms. In countless problems in metallurgy corrosion, biology, etc., however, the above applications are far too gross for satisfactory understanding of the processes and reactions involved. In the newer, more sophisticated alloys, for instance, it is usually precipitates of the order of a micron in size that determine the properties of the material and whose analysis or variation in analysis is desired.

Electron-probe microanalysis extends x-ray spectrochemical analysis to local regions of the order of a micron in size and to quantities less than a micromicrogram. It accomplishes this by using a fine-focused beam of electrons rather than primary x-rays to excite the characteristic spectra. One advantage of using electrons is that the flux contained in a focused 1-micron beam of electrons is sufficient to excite strong x-ray spectra whereas a masked beam of primary x-rays would be far too weak. A second advantage is that the penetration of the electrons as well as the diameter of the beam is of the order of a micron, so that the total volume of specimen excited is of the order of a cubic micron. With the use of an auxiliary microscope to position the electron beam on the exact specimen area desired, one has an extremely powerful tool for localized analysis. Figure 1 shows the components of an electron probe schematically. *A* is the electron optics column for forming the focused electron beam. The source of electrons is an electron gun similar to those used in electron microscopes. Two (or more) electromagnetic lenses focus the electrons to a beam diameter of about a micron on the specimen. The whole electron optics column is evacuated and the specimen is contained in the vacuum chamber. *B* represents the x-ray spectrometers (curved analyzer crystals are required) for measuring the wavelength and intensity of the characteristic x-rays. *C* is the auxiliary microscope used for positioning the desired area of the specimen under the electron beam.

Certain similarities and differences between electron-probe analysis and fluorescent x-ray spectroscopy should be noted:

1. The elements that may generally be measured by the techniques are similar, namely, those elements of atomic number 11 (Na) or greater. There is great interest in extending the range to lower atomic numbers, however, and already there has been limited laboratory success in measuring carbon with electron excitation.[1]

2. The minimum concentration detectable with the electron probe is not so low as for x-ray fluorescence because of the stronger continuous background interference generated by electron excitation. Calculations indicate that 30 ppm is likely to be about the limit for present electron probes[2] while 1 ppm or less may often be achieved with contemporary x-ray fluorescence equipment.

3. The minimum quantity of an element that may be detected is different from the minimum concentration, and it is here that the electron probe excels. With the electron probe, about 10^{-14} g is detectable if it is contained in a micron-sized area; with x-ray fluorescence, the minimum quantity detectable is about 10^{-8} g if it is contained in an area of a few tenths of a millimeter.[3]

4. The viewpoint or purpose of analysis is often completely different for the two techniques. X-ray fluorescence (except for the milliprobe discussed in Chap. 37) is

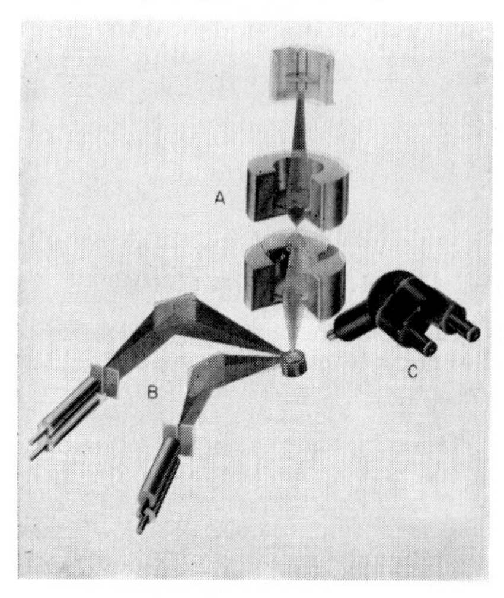

FIG. 1. Schematic of electron-probe microanalyzer. (*A*) Electron optics for focusing the electron beam to a fine spot on the specimen. (*B*) X-ray spectrometers for measuring wavelength and intensity of characteristic x-rays. (*C*) Auxiliary microscope for selecting the exact area to be analyzed.

in direct competition with wet chemical analysis or emission spectroscopy. The purpose is average chemical analysis of a bulk specimen, and the same criteria of speed and accuracy apply. Electron-probe analysis, on the other hand, is in competition with metallography or mineralogy for the identification of minute phases, is in competition with physical chemistry for the study of diffusion or corrosion rates, is in competition with staining and microscopy for the localization of important heavy elements in biological sections. Thus the electron probe should not be considered merely as an extension of x-ray fluorescence, although many of the same principles apply.

2. EQUIPMENT AND OPERATION

Commercial electron probes are available from a number of sources both in the United States and abroad. There is, of course, variation in instrument design, but most of the electron probes contain many of the same features as follows:

1. Operating energy for the electrons is usually adjustable from about 5 to 50 kev with most practical measurements being made in the 10- to 25-kev range. The higher the electron energy, the greater the penetration into the specimen and the larger the volume in which characteristic x-rays are generated. Much current opinion favors use of L-series spectra for elements from $Z = 35$ to 75 and M-series spectra above $Z = 75$ so that effective excitation potential may be kept below 20 kev and the

effective x-ray source size may remain of the order of 1 micron. Some workers are even working with M-series spectra for lower atomic numbers, but there is some question whether this is desirable in view of the shift in wavelength and shape of M lines with chemical bonding.

2. The electron-beam diameter may be controlled by the operator with the minimum diameter being of the order of 0.1 to 1.0 micron. There is little advantage in reducing the diameter below 1 micron for x-ray measurements when the operating voltage is greater than 15 kev because the penetration of electrons into the specimen remains of the order of a micron, and therefore the effective x-ray source size is a micron or larger. There is an advantage in using a diameter as small as 0.1 micron if the specimen thickness is of that same order of magnitude or if back-scattered electrons rather than characteristic x-rays are to be measured because the source size is then of the order of the beam diameter.

3. Characteristic x-rays from the point source are measured with curved-crystal spectrometers or by energy dispersion. The detectors, crystals, and electronics are much the same as for x-ray fluorescence and have been discussed in earlier sections on x-ray fluorescence. Because of the curved-crystal requirement, the variety of suitable crystals is not so great as for the flat-crystal spectrometers of x-ray fluorescence. Table 1 lists some of the more common crystals for electron-probe analysis.

Table 1. Crystals for Use with Electron-probe Microanalyzers

Material	*hkl* planes	2*d*, Å	Method of curving
LiF	200	4.02	Plastic or elastic
Quartz	1011	6.70	Elastic
EDDT*	020	8.76	Plastic
Gypsum	020	15.2	Elastic
Mica	002	19.8	Elastic
KAP†	1010	26.4	Uncertain

* Ethylene diamine-*d*-tartrate.
† Potassium acid phthalate.

4. Most electron probes have provision for simultaneous measurement of three or more elements but some have provision for only two elements. Simultaneous measurement is far more important than in x-ray fluorescence because the specimen must be moved past the electron beam in order to determine the distribution of composition. If only a single element is measured at a time, the scanning process must be repeated for the several elements of interest. Wavelength scanning for qualitative analysis is of less importance because usually the elements present are known in advance for electron-probe specimens.

5. Most electron probes have provision for electrostatic or electromagnetic deflection of the electron beam to sweep out a square raster on the specimen surface. When the changing x-ray intensity is used to modulate the brightness on a cathode-ray tube sweeping in synchronism with the electron probe, a television-type display in terms of the selected element results, as shown in Fig. 2.[4] This allows a useful pictorial representation and aids in selection of the exact area for quantitative analysis.

6. The electron current collected by the specimen (beam current minus back-scattered electrons) is measured by isolating the specimen from ground potential with a resistance of several megohms. An electronic ammeter capable of reading in the range 10^{-9} to 10^{-6} amp measures the current through the resistor. When the current signal is used to modulate the brightness of the cathode-ray tube of item 5 above, a scanning electron micrograph results. Physical discontinuities are rendered more easily visible by measuring the back-scattered electron intensity with a scintillation crystal at an oblique angle to the surface. Either collected or back-scattered current varies slowly with composition because of the relation between back-scattered fraction R and atomic number Z, as shown in Fig. 3.[5] For binary alloys of known

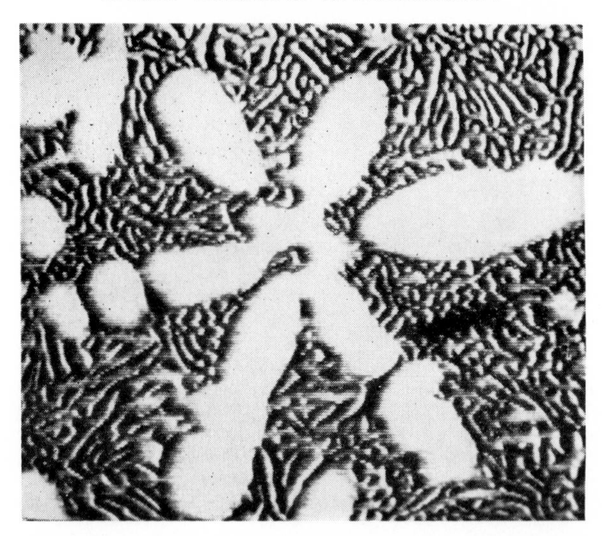

FIG. 2. X-ray display of a Mg–37 per cent Th alloy. The white areas are rich in Mg.[4]

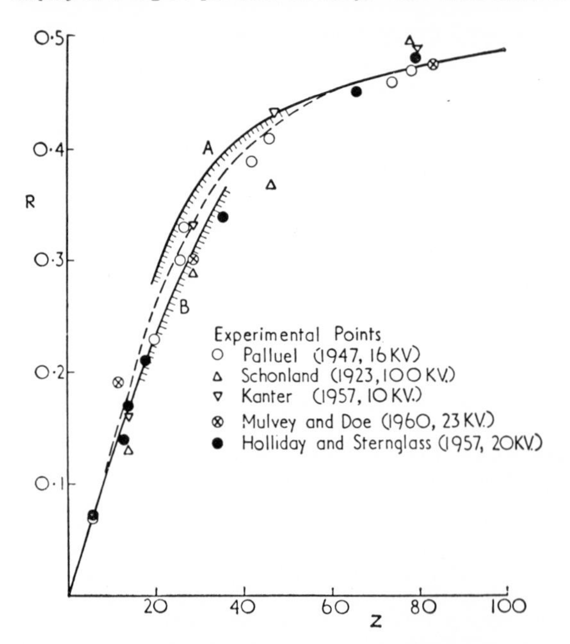

FIG. 3. R is the fraction of electrons back-scattered and Z is the atomic number.[5] Curve A, diffusion; curve B, elastic collisions.

atomic number Z_1 and Z_2, the variation in specimen current may actually be used for quantitative analysis from the relation

$$Z' = Z^2{}_1 A_1 / Z^2{}_2 A_2 \tag{1}$$

where Z' is the mean atomic number obtained from measured R; A_1 and A_2 are the atomic fractions of elements Z_1 and Z_2.

3. TYPES OF SPECIMENS AND SPECIMEN PREPARATION

Solids. The most easily prepared and measured specimens are conducting solids such as metals or minerals which may be polished to a flat smooth surface and which do not decompose under the action of the electron beam in vacuum. Polishing is done after the fashion of metallography, namely, grinding and abrading. The most suitable abrasive is diamond dust because it cuts hard portions of the specimen nearly as well as soft portions and leaves the surface flat. Final polishing is also with diamond abrasive of $\frac{1}{4}$- to $\frac{1}{2}$-micron size on automatic wheel polishers. No etching should be used on the specimen before electron-probe examination because etching selectively removes some constituents from the surface. If etching is required for prior microscope examination, a light etch should be used, and the surface should be photographed and marked with a microhardness indenter to indicate the areas of interest. Then the final stages of polishing should be repeated in order to remove the etched surface layer but leave remnants of the microindenter marks. Figure 4[6] shows the appearance

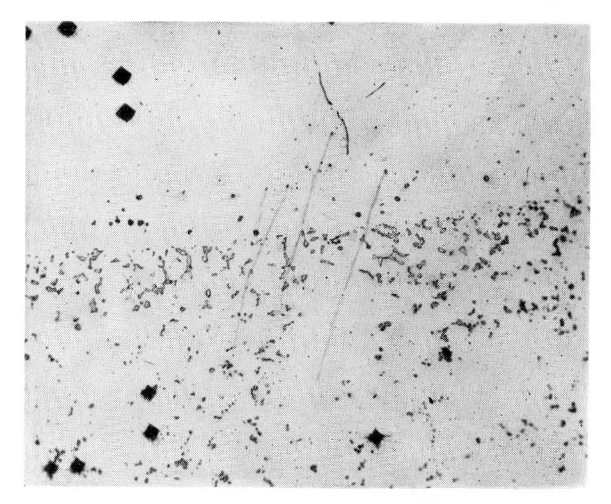

FIG. 4. Polished surface of a specimen showing square black identification marks made with a microhardness indenter.[6]

of a surface suitably marked. It is seen that precipitates are often visible even on an unetched surface of slight discontinuities at their borders.

For nonconducting specimens where the resistivity is of the order of 10^9 ohm-cm or greater, charging under the electron beam often causes erratic beam deflection and usually leads to lower relative x-ray intensity, thus interfering with quantitative analysis. Such specimens should be coated with an evaporated layer of a few hundred angstroms of aluminum or other low-atomic-number metal. This layer does not interfere with excitation or emission of x-rays, but the standard specimens should be coated at the same time to ensure best quantitative comparison. Even with an evaporated layer coating, some insulators with resistivities of the order of 10^{12} ohm-cm may never yield the full proper relative x-ray intensity.

Liquids. Liquids are not suitable for measurement in ordinary electron probes, and even some low-melting metals such as gallium may be difficult to measure because of melting under the action of the electron beam. There have been special electron probes built[7] wherein the electron beam is brought out into air through a small orifice at the end of the electron optics column. With such an instrument, it is possible to examine liquids although boiling and vaporization lead to less dependable x-ray intensity.

Particulate Matter and Extractions. Some specimens such as airborne dust, pigments, and extraction products cannot be prepared in the manner of solids. With these materials it is necessary to mount them on a conducting substrate such as carbon or pure aluminum. A particularly useful specimen of this type is the extraction replica used to advantage in electron microscopy.[8] Here, a polished metal specimen is etched carefully to free the precipitates and inclusions from the matrix metal but leave them in their original position on the surface. Then carbon is evaporated over them and stripped off and mounted on a supporting grid or substrate. The specimen may be examined in a microscope in the usual way and the particular individual precipitates of interest selected in the electron probe. Even better than evaporated carbon is a block of high-purity aluminum, chemically polished in nitric-phosphoric acid[9] and pressed against the extraction surface to embed the freed precipitates in the aluminum. This makes an excellent conducting support and has high reflectivity for microscope examination.

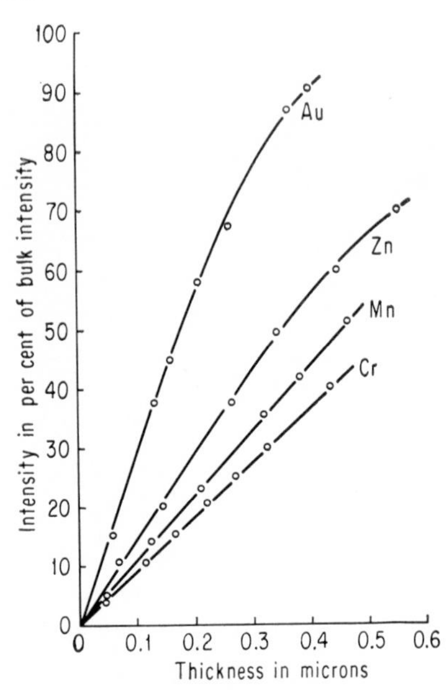

FIG. 5. Relative x-ray intensity vs. film thickness for evaporated Cr, Mn, Zn, and Au.[11]

Biological Specimens. Tissue sections and other biological specimens are prepared[10] by freeze-drying or fixing to remove water, embedding in methacrylate, sectioning to a few microns, mounting on a conducting substrate, removal of embedding material, and coating with an evaporated metal layer. Small local concentrations of metal atoms are easily distinguished in membrane sections and cells. The variation of normally occurring calcium or phosphorus may be followed in a quantitative fashion. Staining with osmium may be used to enhance various physical or structural features because osmium K x-rays are easily measured in the electron probe. The direct measurement of carbon or oxygen in biological specimens is not likely in the immediate future, although it may come someday. Hydrogen, of course, is unlikely ever to be measured in electron-probe instruments.

Thin Films. Evaporated metals and corrosion layers are often too thin to stop all the incident electrons in an electron probe. This leads to reduced x-ray intensity from the elements contained as compared with bulk specimens. This very feature may be turned to advantage and the relative intensity used as a measure of the film thickness in angstroms or in mg/cm^2 (cf. Chap. 44). Figure 5 shows the result of measurements on evaporated layers of chromium, manganese, zinc, and gold.[11] Extrapolation would indicate that a layer as thin as 10 angstroms should be distinguishable. In alloy films, by measuring the mg/cm^2 for each constituent, an approximate quantitative analysis is possible.

4. QUANTITATIVE ANALYSIS (cf. Chap. 36)

Much early work with the electron probe consisted of mere qualitative identification of elements in precipitates or other regions of interest. As the electron probe has been applied to more difficult problems, there has naturally been increased demand for

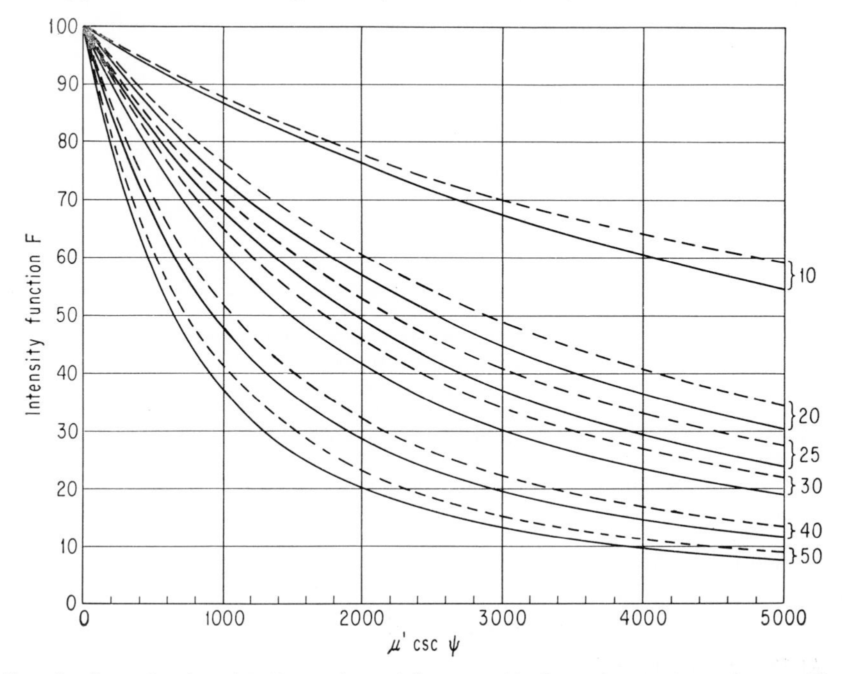

FIG. 6. Intensity function F vs. μ' csc ψ for several values of operating voltage. The voltage is in kev. Solid curves are for electrons striking the specimen at normal incidence, and dashed curves are for electrons incident at 30° away from the normal.

quantitative analysis. If intermediate standards similar to the unknown in composition are available, composition of the unknown is found from a simple ratio just as in x-ray fluorescence.

$$W_U/W_S = I_U/I_S \tag{2}$$

W_U and W_S are the weight fractions of the desired element in the unknown and standard; I_U and I_S are the measured x-ray intensities (background subtracted) from the unknown and standard. However, intermediate standards for electron-probe analysis are much more difficult to find than for x-ray fluorescence because they must be homogeneous on a micron-size scale. About the only materials that really satisfy the homogeneity requirement are single crystals and certain stoichiometric phases in metals and minerals. Therefore, the procedure generally used in electron-probe analysis is to employ 100 per cent standards (not necessarily high purity) of the elements themselves. The intensity from the desired element in the unknown is divided by the intensity from the 100 per cent standard to obtain relative x-ray intensity. This term is then used with equations and curves that have been established to take account of electron energy, matrix absorption, and enhancement.

Figure 6 shows the intensity parameter F, which is related to the electron energy, the total mass absorption coefficient μ' of the specimen for the desired characteristic radiation, and csc ψ, where ψ is the takeoff angle between the specimen surface and the emergent x-radiation. For a given element A which is not excited by characteristic radiation from other elements in the matrix, the equation relating x-ray intensity and composition is

$$I_A/I_{100A} = F_A W_A / F_{100A} \tag{3}$$

where I_A/I_{100A} is the measured relative x-ray intensity, F_A and F_{100A} are the values of the intensity parameter for the unknown and the 100 per cent standard, W_A is the weight fraction of element A in the unknown. If element A is also excited by the characteristic radiation from other elements in the matrix, then Eq. (3) must contain an enhancement coefficient term K_F and becomes

$$I_A/I_{100A} = F_A W_A (1 + K_F)/F_{100A} \tag{4}$$

There is an additional small correction for atomic number that occurs when the specimen components are far apart in atomic number but it contributes only a few per cent of the amount present and is often overshadowed by uncertainties in parameters such as the tabulated mass absorption coefficients. A complete discussion of the equations above and tables of the coefficients required are contained in the book *Electron Probe Microanalysis*.[2]

The following examples show the steps in quantitative analysis and use the tables and curves of Ref. 2.

Binary Systems. Much phase-diagram work is being done using the electron probe to measure diffusion couples. For these or any other binary systems, the simplest approach is to plot calibration curves for the two elements. Iron-chromium will be considered as the example because both absorption and enhancement must be considered. Let the electron energy be 25 kev and $\psi = 30°$.

Calculation for Fe *Kα*

1. Find the mass absorption coefficients for Fe $K\alpha$ from tables.

$$\mu_{\text{FeFe}} = 76 \qquad \mu_{\text{CrFe}} = 460$$

2. Find the total absorption coefficients μ'_{Fe} at compositions of 10, 30, 50, 70, 90 per cent Fe using the equation

$$\mu'_{\text{Fe}} = \mu_{\text{FeFe}} W_{\text{Fe}} + \mu_{\text{CrFe}} W_{\text{Cr}}$$

At 10 per cent Fe, for instance,

$$\mu'_{\text{Fe}} = 76 \times 0.1 + 460 \times 0.9 = 421.6$$

3. Prepare a table of μ' and μ' csc ψ values and look up the F value from Fig. 6.

Table 2. Relative Intensity of Iron in Iron-Chromium Alloys

% Fe	μ'	μ' csc	F_{Fe}	$F_{\text{Fe}}/F_{100\ \text{Fe}}$	$I_{\text{Fe}}/I_{100\ \text{Fe}}$, %
10	421.6	843.2	71.6	0.762	7.6
30	344.8	689.6	75.8	0.808	24.2
50	268.0	536.0	80.6	0.859	43.0
70	190.2	380.4	89.6	0.912	63.9
90	114.4	228.8	90.9	0.968	87.1
100	76.0	152.0	93.9	1.0	100.0

Calculation for Cr *Kα*

1. Find the mass absorption coefficients for Cr $K\alpha$ from tables.[2]

$$\mu_{\text{FeCr}} = 125 \qquad \mu_{\text{CrCr}} = 107$$

2. Find the total absorption coefficient μ'_{Cr} as before.
3. Prepare a similar table as for Fe $K\alpha$ but fill in the values only as far as $F_{Cr}/F_{100\ Cr}$ in column 5.

Table 3. Relative Intensity of Chromium in Iron-Chromium Alloys

Step 3					Step 7	
% Cr	μ'	μ' csc	F_{Cr}	$F_{Cr}/F_{100\ Cr}$	K_F	$I_{Cr}/I_{100\ Cr}$, %
10	123.1	246.2	90.4	0.988	0.32	13.1
30	119.5	239.0	90.6	0.990	0.15	34.2
50	116.0	232.0	90.8	0.992	0.075	53.4
70	112.3	224.6	91.1	0.995	0.035	72.1
90	108.7	217.4	91.4	0.998	0.009	90.5
100	107.0	214.0	91.5	1.0	0	100.0

4. Find the contribution due to excitation of Cr $K\alpha$ by Fe $K\alpha$ radiation. The term K_F is evaluated from the equation[12]

$$K_F = 0.6E_{CrFe}W_{Fe}(\mu_{CrFe}/\mu'_{Fe})(V - V_{0\ Fe})^2/(V - V_{0\ Cr})^2 \tag{5}$$

Here E_{CrFe} is the excitation efficiency for excitation of Cr $K\alpha$ by Fe $K\alpha$. From tables[2] it is 0.165. V is the electron energy (25 kev); $V_{0\ Fe}$ and $V_{0\ Cr}$ are the excitation potentials for Fe and Cr radiation.

$$V_{0\ Fe} = 7.1 \text{ kev} \qquad V_{0\ Cr} = 6.0 \text{ kev}$$

5. As an illustration consider the composition 30 per cent Cr–70 per cent Fe and substitute in the equation for K_F.

$$K_F = 0.6 \times 0.165 \times 0.7(460/190.2) \times 321/362 = 0.15$$

6. Substituting in Eq. (4), the value is

$$I_{Cr}/I_{100\ Cr} = 0.99 \times 0.3(1 + 0.15) = 34.2 \text{ per cent}$$

7. Calculate K_F for the other chromium-iron concentration and finish filling out Table 3 as shown.

After Tables 2 and 3 have been prepared it is helpful to plot the calibration curves as shown in Fig. 7. Any measured value of relative intensity for Fe $K\alpha$ or Cr $K\alpha$ is quickly translated into weight per cent from the figure.

One precaution in interpretation of data should be noted. Often the weight percentages for a binary specimen will not add up to 100 per cent, and they may deviate on occasion by as much as 10 per cent. If the observer cannot find any reason for erroneous values of measured relative intensity such as a difference in takeoff angle or position for the 100 per cent standards and unknown, then his best choice is to normalize the observed weight percentages by scaling the sum to 100 per cent. It should be kept in mind, however, that this is an artificial process and the accuracy of the answer may be no better than the deviation of the original sum from 100 per cent.

Multielement Specimens. In the previous discussion of binary specimens, the simplest procedure was to plot calibration curves by calculating relative intensities for various concentrations. When the specimen contains three or more elements, the number of calibration curves required becomes unwieldy and there is no unique relation between weight per cent and relative intensity for a given element. The procedure then becomes one of starting with measured relative x-ray intensity and calculating weight per cent by an iterative process. Figure 8 is a copy of the work sheet used at Naval Research Laboratory for multielement specimens. The example contained is for the ternary system Ta-Co-V. The work sheet is designed for specimens where all the elements may be measured, so that the sum of weight percentages should equal 100 per cent. If not all the elements can be measured, then estimated values for those other elements must be included in columns 6 and 9 in scaling to 100 per cent. This is not unreasonable because if the specimen is an oxide, for instance, one may estimate the oxygen from the first estimate of weight per cent of the metal elements.

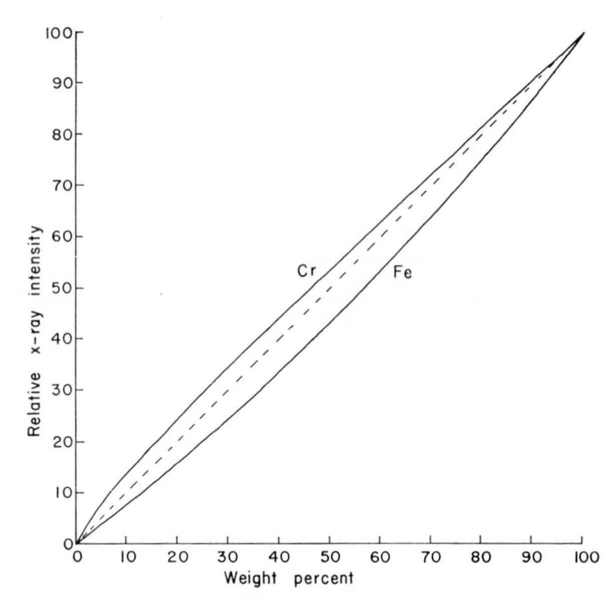

FIG. 7. Calculated calibration curves for iron and chromium at 25 kev and 30° takeoff angle.

Directions for use of the work sheet are as follows:

Column

1 List elements to be calculated
2 Peak intensity in cps
3 Background intensity in cps
4 Measured relative x-ray intensity (RXI) compared with 100% standard (these need not be scaled in finding F_A)
5 $W_C = RXI(F_{100A}/F_A)[1/(1 + K_F)]$
6 Scale W_C values so that $W_C = 100\%$ to get X_1
7 Find calculated relative intensity

$$Y_1 = I_C = (F_A/F_{100A})X_1(1 + K_F)$$

8 Find second estimate of weight per cent from the equation

$$W'_C = W_C \times RXI/I_C$$

9 Scale W'_C values so that $W'_C = 100\%$ to get X_2
10 Find second estimate of calculated relative intensity

$$I'_C = (F'_A/F_{100A})X_2(1 + K_F)$$

11 Plot X_1, Y_1, and X_2, Y_2 points on graph paper to obtain calibration curve; using RXI find corresponding Wg
12 Scale Wg values so that $Wg = 100\%$. These are the final estimates of weight per cent

13 From the weight fraction find the atomic per cent

14 To get the approximate number of atoms of each element, divide the smallest atomic per cent into the others as a lowest common denominator; this is only an approximate division so as to keep the numbers as small as possible

15 It may be desirable to list a compound that is only in approximate agreement with column 14 in order to have small whole numbers

NRL Electron Probe Work Sheet EP 194 Date 10/17/62

Specimen Ta-Co-V

kev 26 μA 2×10^{-8} cscψ 9.54 Crystal LiF

Element	Peak	Bdg.	Meas. RX1	W_c	X_1 Scale W_c	Y_1 I_c	W_c'	X_2 Scale W_c'	Y_2 I_c'	W_g	Scale W_g	Atom %	Small intg.	Possible comp.
Ta			31.2	29.6	41.4	33.5	38.6	41.9	34.0	39.1	40.8	17.7	1	
Co			22.4	25.7	35.9	24.3	33.1	35.9	24.3	35.9	37.5	50.3	3	$TaCo_3V_2$
V			12.4	16.2	22.7	13.7	20.5	22.4	13.4	20.8	21.7	32.0	2	

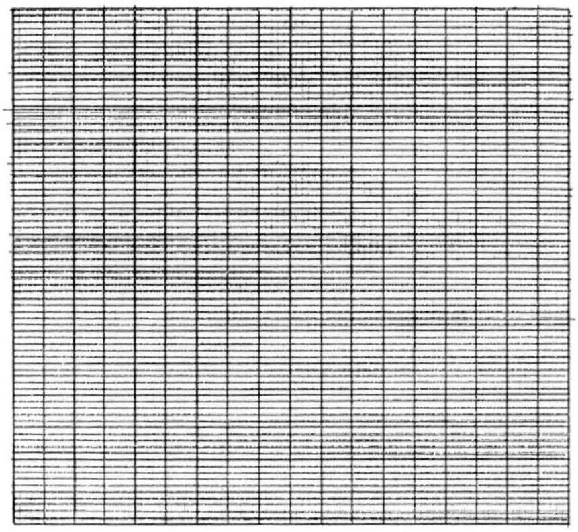

Fig. 8. Work sheet for iterative intensity calculations in multicomponent systems.

5. CONCLUSION

The majority of early electron-probe applications were in metallurgy, where it was an adjunct to other methods of interpretation such as microscopy. The probe was very useful in these applications because it allowed the elements present in precipitates and inclusions to be identified with much greater surety. Once identified, some reasons could often be found for the reactions that caused them and their effect on material properties. Similar applications in mineralogy, biology, etc., followed with equal success.

The long-range future use of electron-probe analysis appears to be much more powerful than a mere aid in solving existing problems, however. With the electron probe as the measuring tool, extensive experiments may be designed to study the reactions in solids under controlled conditions in controlled systems of elements. This will lead first to better understanding of practical diffusion, corrosion, effects of impurities on reactions, etc. Second, it will provide the required data for testing new theories in solid-state physics and chemistry so that eventually we shall be able to design new materials on the basis of knowledge rather than crude cut-and-try experiments.

REFERENCES CITED

1. T. Mulvey, *Iron Steel Inst. (London) Spec. Rept.* 68, 255 (1960).
2. L. S. Birks, *Electron Probe Microanalysis*, Interscience Publishers, Inc., New York, 1963.
3. L. S. Birks, *X-ray Spectrochemical Analysis*, Interscience Publishers, Inc., New York, 1959.
4. P. Duncumb, private communication, May 29, 1962.
5. G. D. Archard, *J. Appl. Phys.*, **32**:1505 (1961).
6. L. S. Birks, unpublished research.
7. B. W. Schumacher, *Ontario Res. Found. Rept.* 5904, September, 1959.
8. H. M. Tomlinson, *Phil. Mag.*, **3**:867 (1958).
9. Aluminum Co. of America, R-5 bright dip solution for polishing aluminum.
10. E. J. Brooks, A. J. Tousimis, and L. S. Birks, *J. Ultrastruct. Res.*, **7**:56 (1962).
11. W. E. Sweeney, R. E. Seebold, and L. S. Birks, *J. Appl. Phys.*, **31**:1061 (1960).
12. L. S. Birks, *J. Appl. Phys.*, **32**:387 (1961).

GENERAL REFERENCES

Castaing, R.: Thesis, University of Paris, 1951.
Wittry, D. B.: Thesis, California Institute of Technology, 1957.

Chapter 40

HIGH-SPEED AUTOMATIC SPECTROMETERS AND CONTINUOUS ANALYZERS

J. W. Kemp

Formerly of Applied Research Laboratories, Inc.

1. INTRODUCTION

Production-control instruments in the sense used here are instruments specifically designed for the routine repetitive analysis of the same types of samples for the same elements on a day-after-day basis. Designers of such instruments attempt to maintain the precision inherent in the x-ray fluorescence technique, while at the same time reducing time or man-hours per analysis. Another design goal is reduced dependence on the capabilities of the operator in obtaining acceptable analyses.

Production-control instruments are generally set up in a central laboratory with the sample being prepared and presented to the instrument by an operator. Process-control instruments, on the other hand, are on-line and require intercession of an operator only occasionally for calibration or adjustment.

A large number of production-control laboratories carry out satisfactory routine analytical operations using the more usual laboratory-type instruments not specifically designed for this purpose. This type of instrument has also been modified for experiments in process-control techniques but generally is not used in actual on-line applications.

2. PRODUCTION-CONTROL INSTRUMENTS

Sequential Analyzers. Sequential analyzers provide improved efficiency for routine operations by relieving the operator of the chore of wavelength setting for each element in each sample. These instruments are, basically, automated single-crystal monochromators. Once an analysis cycle has been started, the instrument automatically moves from x-ray line to x-ray line, stopping at each one for a predetermined integration time and recording the result of such integration before moving to the next line. Since crystal and detector efficiencies vary with wavelengths it is desirable to change crystals and detectors as one proceeds through a program. These operations may also be taken out of the hands of the operator as may collimator changing as required in flat-crystal instruments.

Four typical sequential instruments are the Hilger Fluoroprint[1] (Fig. 1), the Norelco Autrometer,[2,3] the Philips PW1210, and the Solartron XZ1030. All these instruments are programmed flat-crystal goniometers. With the exception of the Autrometer, they are also all vacuum instruments. All use counting techniques for integration, as well as two detectors, a scintillator, and a flow proportional counter. As part of the overall programming, the detectors are programmed in and out of use as required. The integration period of all these instruments is based on fixed-count operation, with the fixed count to be used for each line being programmed. The controlling fixed count is obtained from a monitor channel in the Hilger instrument and from a standard sample in the other three.

FIG. 1. Hilger Y155 Fluoroprint. (*Courtesy of Engis Equipment Company.*)

The Autrometer has a two-position sample holder, one for a standard and one for the sample. At each wavelength setting of the goniometer, the instrument counts to a fixed count on the standard sample and then automatically switches to the unknown sample, counting for the length of time required to reach fixed count on the standard sample. The resulting recorded output is the ratio of the unknown to the standard sample. The PW1210 operates in a similar fashion but has a four-sample holder

Table 1. Sequential Instruments

Instrument	Max elements per sequence	Program control	Programmed variables				
			kv	ma	Collimators	Crystals	PHA* setting
Fluoroprint.........	20	Patch panel	...	...	2	2	Yes
Autrometer.........	24	Manual	...	Yes	...	3	
PW1210...........	15	Patch panel	Yes	Yes	2	3	Yes
XZ1030...........	24	Punched card	...	...	...	...	Yes

* Pulse-height analyzer.

permitting operation to absolute-count basis for four samples at each wavelength setting.

The XZ1030 uses two identical x-ray channels and therefore integrates the output of the sample and standard channel simultaneously, again giving a ratio as an output.

The features in which these four instruments differ are shown in Table 1. The number of elements it is possible to set up in a single sequence varies among the instruments, as does the method of changing the program or element sequence. The instrumental variables that are programmed from instrument to instrument also vary as noted. The Fluoroprint and XZ1030 are 50-kv instruments, and the Autrometer and PW1210 are 100-kv instruments. The crystals available for each instrument are shown in Table 2.

Table 2. Available Crystals

	Gypsum	Ammonium dihydrogen phosphate	Ethylene diamine *d*-tartrate	Quartz	Lithium fluoride	Topaz
Fluoroprint	...	x	x	...	x	x
Autrometer			Various			
PW1210	x	x	x	x	x	x
XZ1030*	...	x	...	...	x	

* Others available on special order.

Simultaneous Analyzers. These instruments provide high speed and efficiency by simultaneously integrating the output of several monochromators, each one set to detect the radiation from one element in the sample. They are based on x-ray polychromators, which are instruments generally consisting of a centrally located x-ray tube to provide the primary excitation, surrounded by a number of x-ray crystal monochromators, all receiving radiation from the sample but each set to a different wavelength. This arrangement allows the best choice of crystal, detector, collimator, or slit widths to be chosen for each element to be detected.

The earliest instruments of this sort were the Applied Research Laboratories XRQ[4] and XIQ. Both of these used several fixed-crystal monochromators. The XRQ used flat crystals and the XIQ used flat crystals to begin with and later curved and ground focusing crystals. A one-of-a-kind instrument of this type was constructed by Adler and Axelrod,[5] using several flat-crystal scanning goniometers. The Applied Research Laboratories instruments used simultaneous capacitor integration of detector outputs and high-speed sequential read-out upon termination of integration. The Adler and Axelrod instrument was provided with individual scaler read-outs for each goniometer.

Two simultaneous analyzers are currently available, the Applied Research Laboratories VXQ (Fig. 2) and VPXQ. Both these instruments use curved and ground focusing crystal monochromators, with various combinations of fixed and scanning monochromators being available. Both instruments are vacuum instruments but may be used with helium or air atmospheres. The read-out system is that used in the Applied Research Laboratories line of optical-emission quantometers. During the integration period each detector charges a capacitor, and at the end of integration the charge on each capacitor is read out sequentially using an electrometer-recorder combination. Each instrument, in addition to its crystal monochromators, has a nondispersive channel viewing an auxiliary sample that, in effect, monitors the primary x-ray beam intensity. The integrated output of this channel controls the integration period so that the result obtained is the ratio of integrated intensities of the individual element lines to the monitored radiation. It is also possible to use any of the monochromator outputs as the integration control signal. This permits ratioing to internal standards or background.

Standardization is carried out by running standard samples on a schedule that is determined by drift characteristics of a particular installation. The results of such standardization runs are used to determine any corrective adjustments of zero and scale spread controls. Since the read-out system does not operate on a pulse or count basis, these adjustments can be made with precision potentiometers.

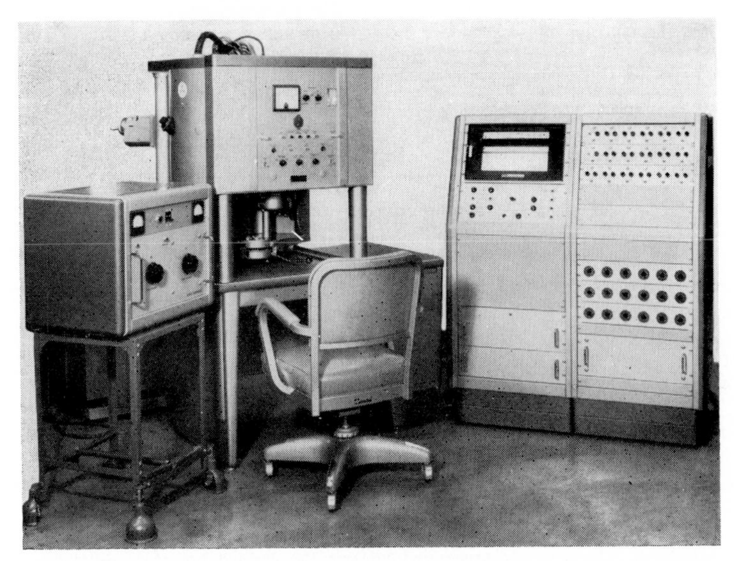

FIG. 2. Applied Research Laboratories, Inc., Vacuum X-ray Quantometer.

Both instruments are 50-kv instruments. Other important characteristics are given in Table 3. Table 4 lists the crystals available and Table 5 the detectors available for these instruments.

Table 3

	Max No. monochromators	Max No. scanners	Tube target sample distance, in.	Max sample size, in.
VXQ.........	9	3	2.125	3 diam × 1
VPXQ.......	22	5	3.000	4 diam × 1¾

Table 4. Available Crystals

Curved and ground	*Curved only*
Ammonium dihydrogen phosphate	Mica
Ethylenediamine *d*-tartrate	
Sodium chloride	
Germanium	
Quartz (various planes)	
Lithium fluoride	

Table 5. Available Detectors

Type	Window	Principal gas
Flow Geiger counter	Al or Be	Ne
Flow proportional counter	Be	A
Sealed, high count rate, gas detector	Be	Ne or A or Kr

Capabilities. Generally, the analytical results obtainable with production-control instruments are of the same quality as those obtainable with similar laboratory instruments.[6] Some of the sequential analyzers can be used as simple scanning instruments and, as such, will do the same job as the usual laboratory goniometer. The simultaneous analyzers can all be equipped with scanning monochromators and thus can also be used in the same fashion as the simpler laboratory types. Because of the dual nature of these instruments, they often are used for developmental and investigational purposes, as well as for routine control analysis.

Both types of production-control instruments make it unnecessary for the operator to peak his instrument on each line to be measured in each sample, as would be necessary with the simpler laboratory-type instruments. The sequential analyzers do this by preprogramming the required lines and automatically setting them for the operator. Any loss in analytical precision attributable to this method of operation would be due to nonreproducibility of peak settings. In the Autrometer, this is partially compensated for by the method of standardization. In the simultaneous analyzers, the individual monochromators are prepeaked, and any loss of precision with this system of analysis would be due to mechanical drift of the monochromators off the peaks.

The sequential analyzers save time since the line-setting operation is generally done faster by the automatic instrument than can be done by an operator. The total instrument time per sample is the sum of the individual counting times for each element and a few seconds for each peak-setting operation. Where no low-atomic-numbered elements are involved, total instrument time can be as low as 2 min for several elements in a sample. The simultaneous analyzers often show important time savings since all integrations are carried out simultaneously. This characteristic is more important where a number of elements per sample are being analyzed for. The total instrument time is the sum of the integration required for that element requiring the longest integration time, and a few seconds per element for the sequential read-out operation. This could be as short as 30 to 45 sec where only high-atomic-numbered elements are involved, and as long as 4 to 5 min where elements such as magnesium in low concentrations are being determined.

Since the sample-preparation techniques (see Chap. 33) and the results obtainable with production-control instruments are little different from the techniques used and the results obtained with laboratory instruments, there is not an extensive literature on the use of production-control instruments. The analysis of low-alloy steels,[7]

Table 6. Matrices

Matrices
Cement materials
Copper-mining materials
Ferroalloys
High-alloy steel
Low-alloy steel
Nickel-mining materials
Rocket fuel
Steel slags and sinters
Zirconium alloys

Table 7. Analyses

Mg	V	Se	Ba
Al	Cr	Y	Ce
Si	Mn	Zr	Hf
P	Fe	Nb	Ta
S	Co	Mo	W
Cl	Ni	Ag	Re
K	Cu	Sn	Pb
Ca	Zn	Sb	Bi
Ti	As	Te	Th

magnesium alloys,[8] and highly alloyed specialty materials[3] has been reported recently. Nonmetallic applications reported include a variety of metallic oxides,[9] materials of interest to the cement industry,[10-12] and petroleum products.[13] A summary of the production problems to which the simultaneous analyzers have been applied is given in Table 6. Table 7 lists the elements that have been determined with this type of installation.

3. PROCESS-CONTROL INSTRUMENTS

Since the basic principles used in continuous analyzers for process control are no different from those used in the more usual x-ray fluorescence instruments, it is possible to modify either laboratory[14] or production-control instruments for continuous process control. For example, a slurry chamber is available for attachment to the Applied Research Laboratories VXQ production-control instrument discussed above. Provided an appropriate location can be found for the installation of this laboratory-type instrument, the attachment permits on-line analysis of solution of slurry streams.

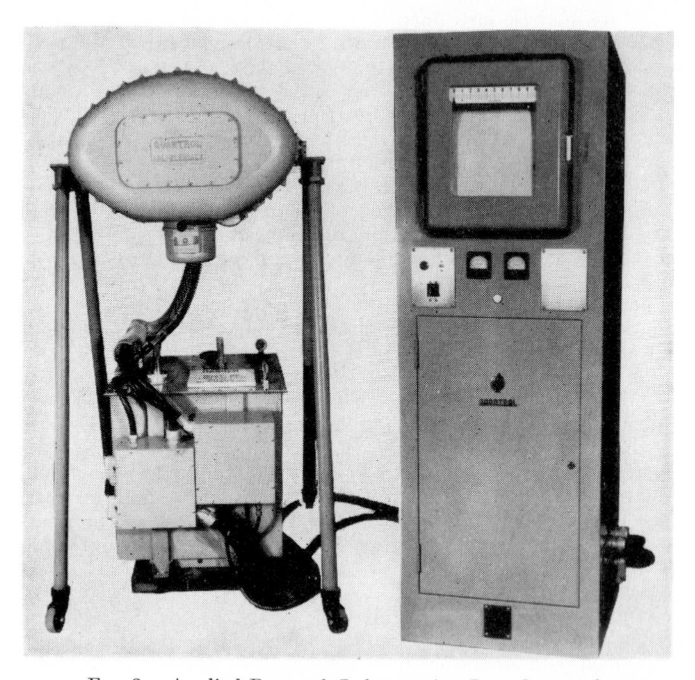

FIG. 3. Applied Research Laboratories, Inc., Quantrol.

At least three instruments are currently available designed specifically for on-stream analysis. These are the Applied Research Laboratories Quantrol[15] (Fig. 3), the General Electric XEG,[16] and a recently announced instrument by Philips Electronic Instruments[17] (Fig. 4). The ARL instrument has two dispersive and one nondispersive channel; the other two have six dispersive channels available.

The ARL instrument operates at 50 kv, the Philips instrument at 60 or 100 kv, and the G.E. instrument at 75 kv. The ARL instrument uses curved and ground crystals and the G.E. instrument a combination of flat and curved crystals.

With the instruments designed especially for on-line process control, the manufacturers aim for designs that will operate reliably under plant conditions, these being somewhat different from the conditions encountered in the use of the laboratory- and the production-control-type instruments. The ARL Quantrol, for example, was designed to operate under severe dust, humidity, and temperature conditions, and the G.E. XEG has been used both under in-plant conditions and in separate air-conditioned cubicles.

In many industrial processes, a truly continuous analysis is not required. A report every 10 min, 20 min, ½ hr, or 1 hr may be satisfactory. In situations of this sort, it may only be necessary to automate the sample collection and handling for a production-control instrument in order to solve a process-control problem. This same characteristic may permit a single process-control instrument to be used to establish control over several related processes, or over several different points in the same process. The latter is accomplished by programming the sample-collection portion of the installation among several process streams. This approach to process control, of course, leads to important economies in investment in x-ray fluorescence instruments for any process that can be controlled in this fashion.

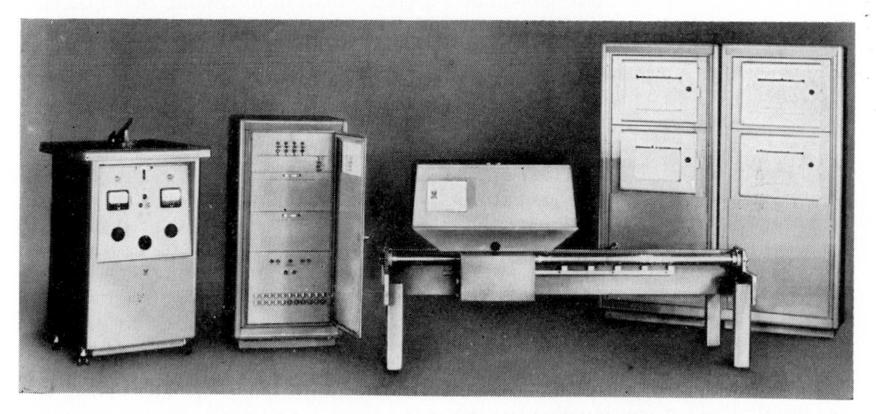

FIG. 4. Norelco On-Stream Analyzer. (*Courtesy of Philips Electronic Instruments.*)

Capabilities of Continuous Analyzers. Compared with laboratory and production-control instruments the continuous analyzers encounter unusual difficulties in sampling, sample handling, and sample preparation, and in the analysis of low-atomic-numbered elements. If, in order to get an accurate analysis, it is necessary to provide additional grinding of the sample, drying, briquetting, dilution, addition of standards, fluxing, or any other special treatment, this must be automated in order to make a truly continuous analyzer out of the complete system. The requirement for these extra steps may sometimes be eliminated by the use of scattered radiation as an internal standard,[18] but the success or failure of this technique can only be determined by experiment. The problem of continuous analysis of many materials is not a problem in x-ray fluorescence analysis, but a problem in materials-handling engineering.

If the sample is anything but dry, a sample window will be required and the results obtained in the analysis of the low-atomic-numbered elements will leave much to be desired. Because of the window requirement, instruments set up for these analyses are generally helium-flushed rather than vacuum.

Considering the inherent stability that is possible to build into x-ray components at the present state of the art, standardization presents another problem for continuous-analyzer installations. If the installation is to be truly automatic, it is necessary to devise automatic means of standardization. It is relatively simple to insert standards into the instrument and obtain readings by simple automatic devices, but it is somewhat more of a problem to have the results of such standard runs automatically make circuit adjustments to compensate for component drift. Since it is contemplated that many on-line installations will be only a part of a completely computer-controlled process, it is sometimes simpler to have a computer make corrections on subsequent data upon receipt of standardizing information.

In view of the problems mentioned above, little progress has been made in the actual application of x-ray fluorescence continuous analyzers to production processes. In the field of solids, experimental installations have been operated for the analysis of the raw-mix materials used in cement manufacture. This material has also been handled experimentally as a slurry. A variety of materials of importance in the flotation process of copper-ore concentration have been successfully analyzed in the slurry form with a continuous analyzer.[19] An installation for the experimental analysis of materials of interest in a zinc-concentration mill has been reported.[16]

Finally, a use for continuous analyzers that should be included here is in the measurement of coating thickness (cf. Chap. 44). There are a number of techniques which are based on x-ray absorption phenomena used for thickness and coating measurement. However, for certain problems the measurement of the fluorescence emission of the coating material will give a better analysis of coating thickness than the absorption technique. One such case is the measurement of the tin plated on steel.[20] Several x-ray fluorescence continuous analyzers have been installed for the measurement of tin plate.

4. SUMMARY

A large number of production-control laboratories use x-ray fluorescence instrumentation in their routine operations. This instrumentation may be ordinary laboratory fluorescence equipment, modified laboratory equipment, or instruments specifically designed for production control, such as have been discussed in this chapter. These installations are generally highly satisfactory to the user, and their operation is of such a routine nature that there are seldom detailed reports in the literature concerning their operation.

A quite different situation exists in process-control instrumentation. This equipment can only be said to be in the experimental stages. Often the problem is not one for the x-ray specialist, but for the materials-handling expert. In any event, very few installations of continuous x-ray fluorescence analyzers are operating as routine process controllers.

REFERENCES CITED

1. J. R. Stansfield, *Hilger J.*, **VI**(2):2 (1960).
2. F. A. Behr, *Norelco Reptr.*, **III**:80 (1956).
3. J. S. Buhler, *Norelco Reptr.*, **VI**:3 (1959).
4. *Spectrographer's News Letter*, **VI**(3): 1 (1953).
5. I. Adler and J. M. Axelrod, *JOSA*, **43**:769 (1953).
6. D. C. Miller, Results Obtained with the Modified Norelco Autrometer, in *Advances in X-ray Analysis*, vol. 1, p. 283, W. M. Mueller (ed.), Plenum Press, Inc., New York, 1960.
7. R. E. Michaelis, R. Alvarez, and B. A. Kilday, *J. Res. Natl. Bur. Std.*, **65C**:71 (1961).
8. G. A. Stoner, *Anal. Chem.*, **34**:123 (1962).
9. B. J. Mitchell, *Anal. Chem.*, **32**:1652 (1960).
10. G. Andermann, J. L. Jones, and E. Davidson, The Evaluation of the PXQ for the Analysis of Cements and Related Materials, in *Advances in X-ray Analysis*, vol. 2, p. 215, W. M. Mueller (ed.), Plenum Press, Inc., New York, 1960.
11. G. Andermann, *Anal. Chem.*, **33**:1689 (1961).
12. G. Andermann and J. D. Allen, *Anal. Chem.*, **33**:1695 (1961).
13. C. C. Hale and W. H. King, Jr., *Anal. Chem.*, **33**:74 (1961).
14. W. J. Campbell, *Appl. Spectry.*, **14**: 26 (1960).
15. *Spectrographer's News Letter*, **X**(1): 1 (1957).
16. W. F. Loranger, *Nonmetallic Minerals Process.*, **2**:(7): 15 (1961).
17. *Chem. Eng. News.*, July 2, 1962, p. 41.
18. G. Andermann and J. W. Kemp, U.S. Patent no. 2897367 (1959).
19. F. L. Holderreed and W. Lucy, *Mining Congr. J.*, July, 1960.
20. P. S. Goodwin and C. L. Winchester, *Plating*, January, 1959.

Part 5

X-RAY ABSORPTION METHODS

Chapter 41

ABSORPTIOMETRY WITH POLYCHROMATIC X-RAYS

Maurice C. Lambert

Pacific Northwest Laboratories
Battelle Memorial Institute

1. INTRODUCTION

Absorptiometry with polychromatic x-rays is a field which includes a greater variety of techniques and applications than any other use of x-rays. This chapter will not discuss the many applications in industrial x-ray radiography as this is a large and varied subject in itself. It will emphasize the use of polychromatic x-rays in chemical analyses and will include brief descriptions of some of the less common problems to which x-ray absorptiometry has been successfully applied. It is intended that the discussion of the various factors involved in the absorption of x-rays, of instrumentation, and of the analytical applications described will give a practical feel for both the usefulness and the limitations inherent in absorptiometry with polychromatic x-rays.

2. PRINCIPLES

The absorption of polychromatic x-rays can be compared with colorimetry or photometry with white light. All the wavelengths emitted by the x-ray source, the continuous spectrum as well as the characteristic lines, are allowed to pass through, or at least into, the sample. The attenuation, or degree of absorption of the polychromatic beam, or of different energy portions of the beam, provides information about the sample as regards its composition, homogeneity, and thickness or density.

Unlike colorimetry, in which certain groups of atoms in the sample may selectively absorb only narrow bands of light, x-rays of all wavelengths are absorbed to some extent by every atom. This points up the chief limitation to this method: it is not specific for any element or group of elements. The absorption of x-rays, however, is an exponential function of the atomic number and is generally much greater for heavy atoms than for lighter ones. Consequently, x-ray photometry is well suited to the determination of a single substance having a mass number that is high relative to those of the other elements present.

In contrast to ultraviolet, visible, and infrared rays which are absorbed by the outer electrons that determine the chemical properties of an element, x-rays have high energy, and their absorption usually involves only the electrons near the nucleus. For all practical purposes, then, absorption of x-rays is independent of the chemical or physical state of an element and of whether the element is free, ionized, or combined with others. Thus, x-ray absorption is dependent only upon the number and kinds of atoms through which the x-rays pass.

Historically, absorptiometry with polychromatic x-rays developed before other more specific absorption methods because of the very high intensities available from such sources. This is the chief advantage to the use of a polychromatic beam. As an example of the intensity of the beam from a typical x-ray photometer, the energy in a ½-in.-diameter cross section of the beam at a sample position 6 in. from the source was measured at approximately 20,000 r/hr for x-rays generated at 75 peak kilovolts (kvp) and 5 ma. The use of monochromatic x-rays simplifies calculations and interpretations of results because only one wavelength is involved. However, in order to obtain a reasonably monochromatic beam by diffraction and collimation, a 10^5- to 10^6-fold loss of intensity is suffered. A polychromatic x-ray beam is also about 10^5 times as intense as a beam from a practical-size source of the best radioactive isotope. Consequently, where the use of polychromatic x-rays is applicable, there is no other source which will permit such simple accompanying instrumentation and which will permit such rapid and highly precise measurements. Instantaneous meter readings may usually be made, and counting techniques are seldom necessary.

Factors in the Interpretation of X-ray Absorption Data. When an x-ray photon interacts with an atom of the sample, its entire energy may be transformed into kinetic energy of an electron which escapes from the atom. This fraction of energy subtracted from the incident beam is called photoelectric or "true" absorption. Instead of being photoelectrically absorbed the photon may also be scattered after colliding with the atom with either no loss of energy (coherent or Rayleigh scattering) or with some loss of energy (incoherent or Compton scattering). The scattering portion of the total absorption coefficient becomes significant only for elements lighter than iron, 26, and for wavelengths shorter than 0.5 Å.

The well-known equation for loss of intensity by absorption for a monochromatic beam, i.e., for a specific wavelength λ, is

$$I_\lambda = I_0^{-\mu\rho x} \tag{1}$$

for a mass absorption coefficient μ, density ρ, and path length x, where I_λ is the transmitted intensity and I_0 is the incident intensity.

For a sample whose composition is homogeneous, Eq. (1) may be rewritten as

$$2.303 \log (I_0/I_\lambda) = \mu_s\rho\, \Delta x = \mu_{sl}\, \Delta x \tag{2}$$

where Δx is the sample thickness, in centimeters, and μ_s is the mass absorption coefficient for the sample. The product $\mu\rho$ is sometimes replaced by μ_l, which is the linear absorption coefficient used in thickness measurements. The mass absorption coefficient of a sample μ_s may be written

$$\mu_s = W_1\mu_1 + W_2\mu_2 + \cdots + W_i\mu_i \tag{3}$$

where $W_1\mu_1$ is the weight fraction and mass absorption coefficient for one species of element and $W_2\mu_2$, etc., are corresponding terms for each other kind of element, either free or chemically combined, in the sample.

In the case of chemical analysis, the sample thickness is maintained at a constant specific value and the equation becomes

$$(2.303/\rho_s x) \log (I_0/I_\lambda) = W_a\mu_a + W_b\mu_b + \cdots + W_i\mu_i \tag{4}$$

where the subscript a refers to the element of interest and the remaining terms refer to all the other elements that make up the sample matrix.

With a polychromatic beam of x-rays, Eq. (4) becomes very complicated as follows:

$$\begin{aligned}(2.303/\rho_s X) \log (I_{0\lambda_1} + I_{0\lambda_2} + \cdots + I_{0\lambda_i}/I_{\lambda_1} + I_{\lambda_2} + \cdots + I_{\lambda_i}) \\ = W_a(\mu_a\lambda_1 + \mu_a\lambda_2 + \cdots + \mu_a\lambda_i) + W_b(\mu_b\lambda_1 + \mu_b\lambda_2 + \cdots + \mu_b\lambda_i) \\ + \cdots + W_i(\mu_i\lambda_1 + \mu_i\lambda_2 + \cdots + \mu_i\lambda_i)\end{aligned} \tag{5}$$

When using polychromatic x-rays, attempts to calculate absorption corrections for matrix elements and to calculate effects due to other factors are, for most applications, not only very complicated but not sufficiently accurate to be worth the effort. Published absorption coefficients are not yet accurate enough at most wavelengths.[1] But the main uncertainty is in knowing what wavelengths and corresponding intensities are involved. The usual practice is to determine empirical absorption coefficients and correction factors with the aid of a variety of standard samples. When the qualitative composition of the sample is known and when the matrix does not change very much from sample to sample, this technique can be rapid and accurate.

Although the usual calibrations with polychromatic x-rays are empirical, it is well to understand the several factors affecting x-ray absorption. For one thing, the intensity of each of the wavelengths in a polychromatic beam is not uniform over the entire area of the sample exposed to the x-rays. For another thing, with solid or liquid samples it is not unusual to have values as high as 10^3 or even 10^4 for the intensity ratio I_0/I. Detectors and associated electronic equipment are usually not linear over such wide ranges. Six other major factors are discussed in more detail.

Variation of Absorption with Atomic Number. Mass absorption coefficients would be greatly different for each element at any given wavelength if it were not for absorption edges, to be discussed later.

At a given wavelength, mass absorption coefficients increase with about the third to fourth power of the atomic number until an absorption edge is crossed. Coefficients start over then at much smaller values but increase rapidly again with atomic number until another absorption edge is crossed, when the process is repeated once more. Thus, there may be two or three elements at wide intervals throughout the periodic table which have similar absorption coefficients at some wavelength.

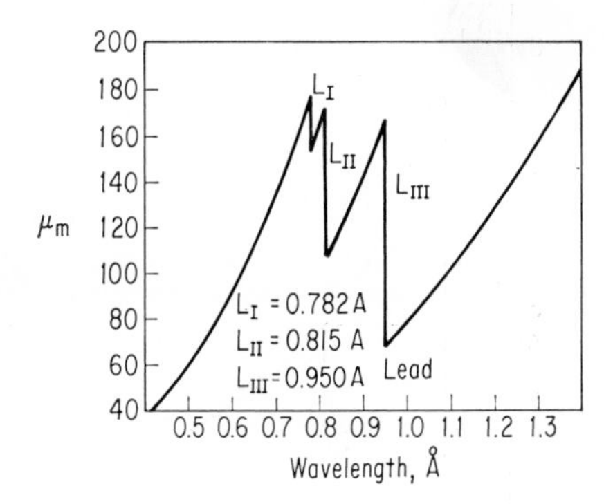

FIG. 1. Variation of the mass absorption coefficient for lead as a function of wavelength near the L edges.

Variation of Absorption with Wavelength. For each element, absorption coefficients are different at each wavelength in the x-ray beam. Mass absorption coefficients vary with wavelength, between energy levels, as shown in Fig. 1, according to the empirical equation

$$\mu = k\lambda^n \tag{6}$$

where the exponent n has the approximate value of 2.83 at wavelengths short of the K edge, 2.66 between K and L_I edges, and somewhat smaller values at wavelengths between the several M and N edges.

Absorption Edges. The above relationships between μ, Z, and λ are complicated by the presence of absorption edges, shown in Fig. 1. An x-ray beam made up of photons having just sufficient energy to eject a K, L, or M electron from an element will be much more strongly absorbed than a beam having slightly longer wavelengths. Therefore, there are abrupt discontinuities in the graph of absorption vs. wavelength for any given element. These discontinuities occur at shorter wavelengths for each heavier element. The relationship between atomic number and the wavelengths associated with K-absorption edges is symbolically indicated in Fig. 2.

Polychromatic x-ray beams generated in the range 25 to 75 kv involve "effective" wavelengths, to be described later, in the range of about 0.23 to 0.64 Å. Only those elements between atomic numbers 42 and 65 have absorption edges in this range of energies. Later discussion shows the anomalous behavior of this group of elements.

Energy Distribution in Polychromatic Beams vs. X-ray Voltage. The minimum wavelength and the distribution of energies in the continuous spectrum are characteristic of the voltage applied to the x-ray tube. Minimum wavelength is related to the accelerating voltage by the expression

$$\lambda = 12.396/\text{kv} \tag{7}$$

The continuous spectrum shifts toward shorter wavelengths and higher intensities with increase in voltage, as illustrated in Fig. 3. The spectrum has a bandwidth which may extend to some distance on each side of an absorption edge, as indicated in Fig. 4. As a result, the sharp discontinuities characteristic of absorption curves obtained with monochromatic x-rays of different wavelengths become smoothed over to a considerable extent.

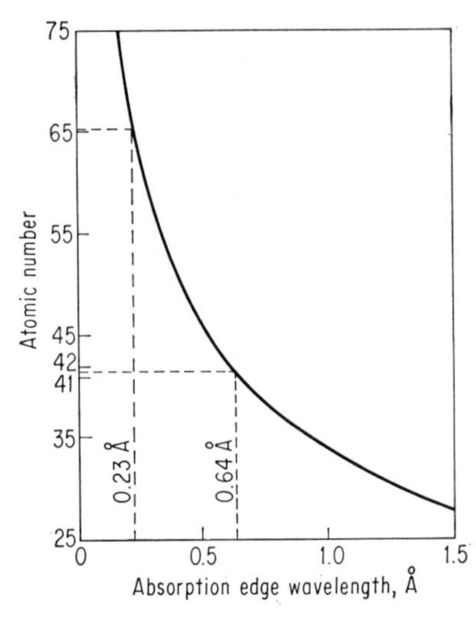

Fig. 2. Relationship between atomic number and K-absorption-edge wavelength.

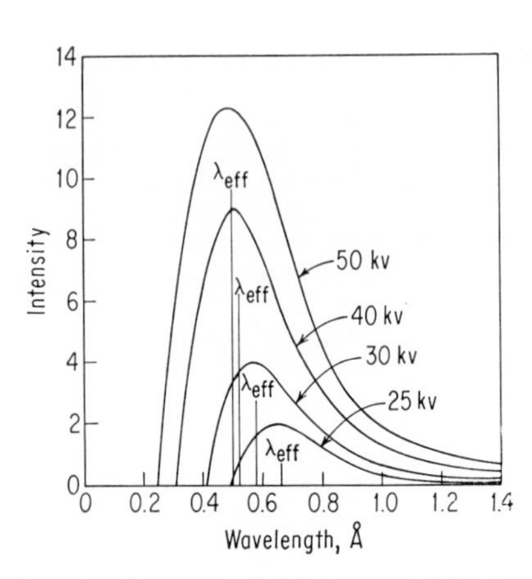

Fig. 3. Energy distribution and effective wavelengths at several x-ray voltages.

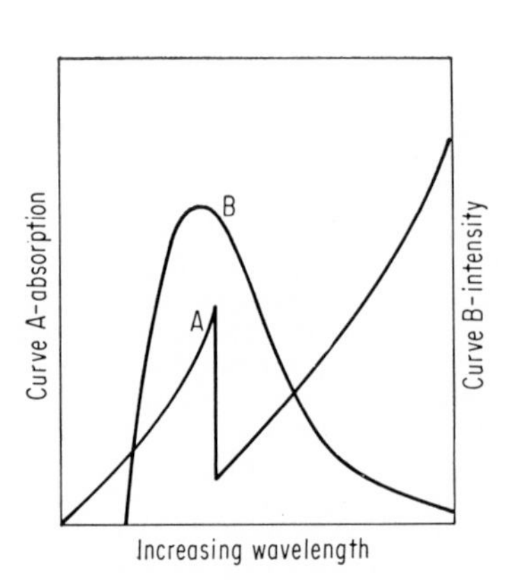

Fig. 4. Spectrum of x-ray continuum superimposed on a K-absorption edge.

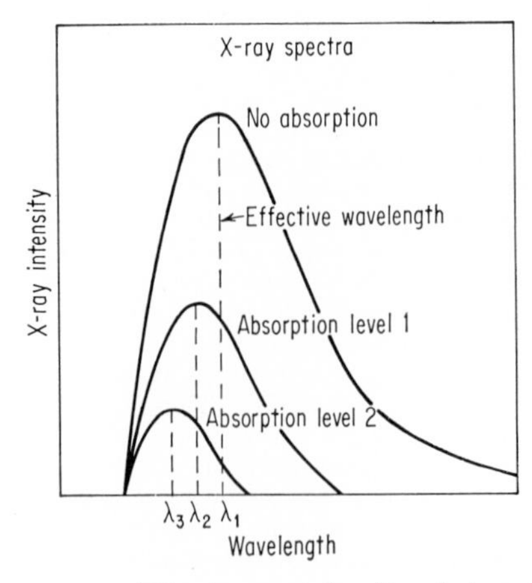

Fig. 5. Effective wavelength of transmitted x-rays as a function of absorption level.

Energy Distribution in Polychromatic Beams vs. Absorption Level. Figure 5 shows how x-ray energy associated with longer wavelengths is absorbed to a much higher relative degree than energy associated with the shorter wavelengths. Therefore, the effective wavelength of the spectrum continuously decreases as the x-ray beam traverses a sample. Furthermore, there is an additional shift of the transmitted spectrum toward shorter wavelengths with an increase in thickness of the sample and with an increase in concentration, especially of the heavy elements. This differential filtering effect by the sample continuously alters the energy distribution of the beam incident on each succeeding thickness increment of the sample. The relative filtering is also different for each sample composition.

Effective Wavelength. The effective wavelength of a polychromatic x-ray beam is defined as the wavelength of a monochromatic beam which has equivalent behavior in an absorption measurement. The effective wavelength can be determined by a method described by Liebhafsky.[2] It is useful in simplifying calculations since it requires that absorption coefficients at only one wavelength need be inserted in Eq. (5).

A polychromatic beam is never equivalent to a monochromatic beam in all respects, and it exhibits a particular effective wavelength only for a particular set of conditions. Because of the factors that have been described it is impossible to calculate accurately from mass absorption coefficients what the absorption of a sample, or the absorption of any particular element in the sample, will be. Coefficients of absorption of polychromatic x-rays by multicomponent materials are better determined empirically with the use of standard samples.

3. EQUIPMENT

Application of polychromatic x-rays to chemical analysis is not new, but it was only about 20 years ago that developments of photomultipliers and suitable phosphors made commercial photometers feasible.

Design of X-ray Photometers. The essential equipment requirements consist of:

1. A source of x-rays with accompanying filament and anode voltage transformers and voltage regulators
2. A shielded sample compartment which includes apertures or collimators to minimize divergence of the x-ray beam and to control its size, and sample cells or holders to position the samples reproducibly
3. One or two detectors which can transform x-ray energy into a proportional electric current
4. An amplifier and a read-out system such as a microammeter, a null-point meter, or a recorder

Single-beam Photometers. The direct method of measurement requires only a single x-ray beam and a single detector. The earliest instruments were of this kind. The initial beam intensity is adjusted to some standard value by altering the x-ray tube voltage or current until the desired detector current is obtained with a standard absorber, such as a block of aluminum, in the beam. Intensity measurements are then made with and without the sample in the beam.

Any laboratory which has x-ray diffraction equipment can use it as a single-beam photometer. The detector is positioned at zero degrees where it can receive the unfiltered and undiffracted beam directly. The only modification necessary is the addition of a device to support the specimens to be analyzed. Location of the specimen between the x-ray tube and the detector is not critical, so long as it is reproducible. If the diffraction instrument uses a Geiger counter, this detector should be replaced with a gas proportional counter. The proportional counter has a dead time several orders of magnitude shorter than a Geiger tube and can make linear measurements over a much wider range of intensities.

The intensity ratio I_0/I is too large, in the case of liquid and solid samples, for practical use. The usual procedure is to compare the attenuation of the x-ray beam by a liquid sample with that of the same weight of a solvent blank or with some other reference liquid in an identical cell. The detector current measurements are plotted on a logarithmic ordinate against concentration of the solute or component of interest (or sample thickness, etc.) as abscissa. Similarly, with solids the intensity of the beam transmitted through a piece of halogenated plastic, for example, is compared with that transmitted through a nonhalogenated or a standard plastic block of the same thickness.

Since the x-ray intensity of the incident beam varies as a large exponential power of the primary voltage, and since the gain of a proportional counter varies as about the fifth power of the applied voltage, it can be appreciated that the direct method with a single-beam instrument inherently lacks precision. One must use the best possible voltage regulation and then make repeated measurements alternately for the standard and unknown and compare average readings for each with one another in order to achieve reasonable analytical precision. The method is rapid, however, as 20 intensity measurements can be made in less than 5 min.

A recent instrument modification,[3] which obtains the same high precision as a double-beam photometer, utilizes two detectors in tandem with the sample between

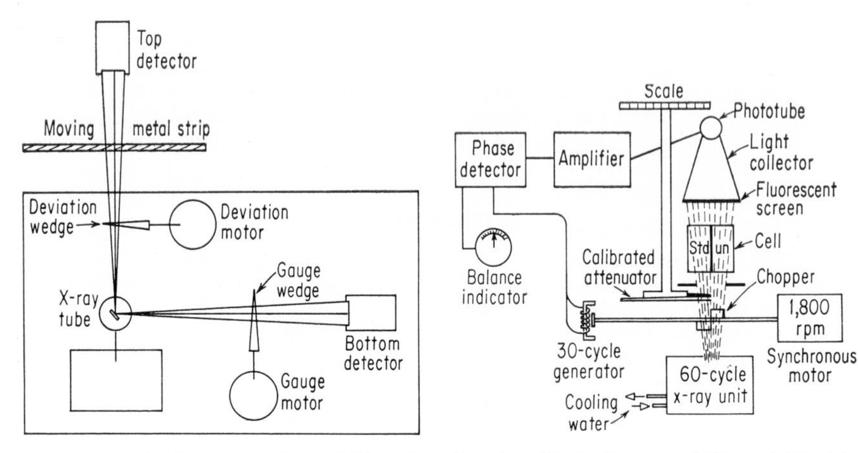

FIG. 6. Block diagram of General Electric x-ray thickness gauge. (*Courtesy of General Electric Company.*)

FIG. 7. Block diagram of General Electric x-ray photometer with chopper and split beam. (*Courtesy of General Electric Company.*)

them. The intensity of the incident beam is measured by one rate meter; that of the transmitted beam is measured simultaneously by another rate meter. Thus both components of the ratio I_0/I fluctuate to the same degree.

Double-beam Photometers. A double-beam or split-beam instrument permits the technique of comparison absorptiometry. The comparison method avoids deviations due both to voltage fluctuations and to changes in effective wavelengths by comparing simultaneously and continuously the detector output current obtained with a sample in one beam with the current obtained with a standard in the other beam. Since both beams come from the same x-ray tube, fluctuations in voltage affect the incident intensities of both beams and also their ratios I_0/I to the same degree. This eliminates the necessity for ultra-close regulation of x-ray anode and filament voltages, detector voltages, and amplifier gain, resulting in fewer components and greater reliability. Deviations due to differences in effective wavelength of the transmitted beams become negligible as the composition of the standard approaches that of the sample.

Commercial Photometers. Figure 6 shows a diagram of the General Electric x-ray thickness gauge,[4] used to control continuously the thickness of rolled steel strip and of aluminum foil. One x-ray beam passes through one wedge and up through the moving metal strip to one detector. The other beam passes through another calibrated aluminum wedge to a second detector. The signals from the two detectors are opposed and kept at the null point by a motor driving the tapered gauge wedge in or out of the reference beam. The difference in positions of the two wedges indicates the thickness of the metal strip. A servomechanism controls the mill rolls and the thickness of the metal strip automatically with finer and more frequent corrections than can be achieved manually.

Another comparison method was used in the first commercial x-ray photometer,[5] which the General Electric Company made available in 1946. A block diagram is shown in Fig. 7. This instrument used a single detector and split the x-ray beam from a single port into two parts by apertures. Half the beam passed through the sample; the other half passed through a tapered aluminum reference wedge. The transmitted x-ray beams struck a phosphor screen producing blue-violet light which was proportional to the x-ray beam intensities and which was measured by a photomultiplier tube. However, both beams did not strike the phosphor at the same time. Chopper blades between the 42-kvp x-ray source and the sample compartment provided synchronous commutation between sample and standard 30 times per second. When sample and standard had different absorbencies the unbalance was compensated manually by moving the aluminum wedge. The position of the wedge then measured the difference in absorbence between sample and standard. The very strong detector currents produced by the intense polychromatic x-rays made the instrument exceedingly sensitive to movement of the wedge. Very stable and reproducible readings could be obtained by unskilled operators in a matter of seconds.

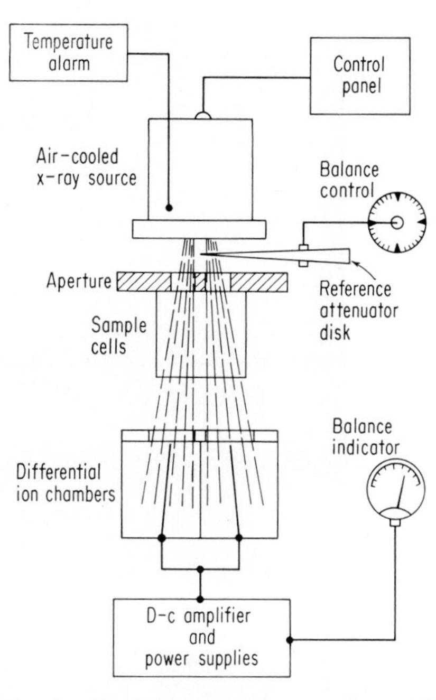

FIG. 8. Block diagram of improved general electric x-ray photometer. (*Courtesy of General Electric Company.*)

The aluminum wedge was made by machining the outer edge of a 10-in. disk into a smooth taper about 75 cm long and tapered from about 0.020 to 0.125 in. in thickness. A small section was cut out of the thin portion of the disk so that the x-ray beams could be balanced when there was no absorber in either one.

The amplifier was tuned to accept only the chopped signals from the alternate halves of the x-ray beam. These signals were opposed to each other in a null-balance circuit. Thus radioactive samples were successfully analyzed with this photometer because the steady signal produced in the phosphor-photomultiplier by gamma radiation was not amplified and had no effect on the null point.

The double-beam Sunbury x-ray photometer[6] operated on a similar principle. The reference and sample beams struck fluorescent screens in a light-tight box. A chopper was positioned between the phosphors and a single photomultiplier tube in order to obtain rapid comparison of standard and sample.

A more compact x-ray photometer was introduced by the General Electric Company in 1954. A block diagram of the smaller, revised instrument is shown in Fig. 8. There are five principal differences as compared with the earlier photometer. The 42-kvp x-ray head was replaced by a smaller 25-kvp source. The aluminum wedge was replaced by a tapered Lucite disk. The chopper was eliminated and a highly sensitive d-c amplifier and simpler balancing circuitry were used. The phosphor-photomultiplier detector was replaced by a more stable double ionization chamber. In this detector the polarity of the two collector plates was opposed so that when the currents generated in each half of the ionization chamber were added together only a difference current was amplified and a null point was obtained when absorption of both sample and reference beam was exactly matched. The lower-voltage x-rays were chosen because of their greater absorption by trace elements, and the Lucite wedge was chosen to more nearly match the absorption characteristics of petroleum products. Most commercial x-ray photometers have been designed principally for the petroleum industry for such determinations as tetraethyl lead in gasoline, sulfur, and metal additives in lubricants.

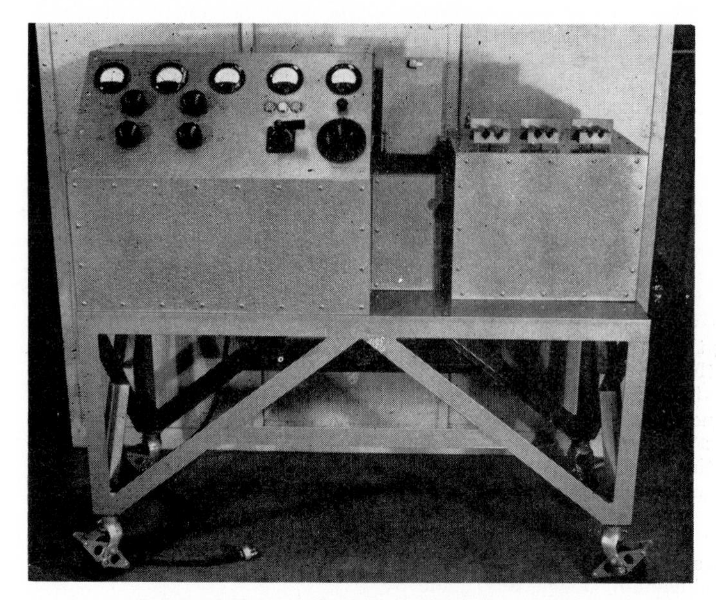

Fig. 9. Hanford x-ray photometer.

Fig. 10. Plug-in cell holders and apertures for different-sized cells.

Hanford X-ray Photometer. For light elements, such as hydrocarbons, relatively soft x-rays and deep, large-volume sample holders are required. At Hanford, where the interest was in determining heavy elements at higher concentrations, three of the original General Electric photometers were modified and two special photometers were built in 1954. A photograph of one of the Hanford photometers is shown in Fig. 9. In order to achieve higher intensities and greater penetrating power, an x-ray tube with a tungsten target was selected which could be operated up to 85 kvp and 20 ma. The attenuator disk was made of aluminum metal. The instrument was designed with horizontal optics in order to accommodate commercially available spectrophotometric cells of three diameters, with path lengths of 12 and 30 mm and glass windows 0.5 mm thick. Figure 10 illustrates the plug-in cell holders and their apertures. The smallest cell has a sample volume of only 1.25 ml.

The use of harder x-rays is essential in the analysis of concentrated aqueous solutions of heavy elements. Figure 11 shows that each side of an air-filled ionization chamber produced a current of 21.0×10^{-9} and 3.2×10^{-9} amp at 75 and 25 kvp, respectively, when there was no absorption of the beams. However, at an absorption level of 400 mils of aluminum, which is equivalent to about a 33 g/liter uranium solution in a 12-mm-path-length glass cell, the ion current was still as large as 1.27×10^{-9} amp at 75 kvp, but only 0.0046×10^{-9} amp for 25-kvp x-rays. From the data for I in Table 1 it can be calculated that the x-rays, after absorption by 400 mils of aluminum, produced an ion current in an air-filled chamber which was 276 times larger at the higher x-ray voltage. The corresponding detector current was 189 times larger in an argon-filled chamber.

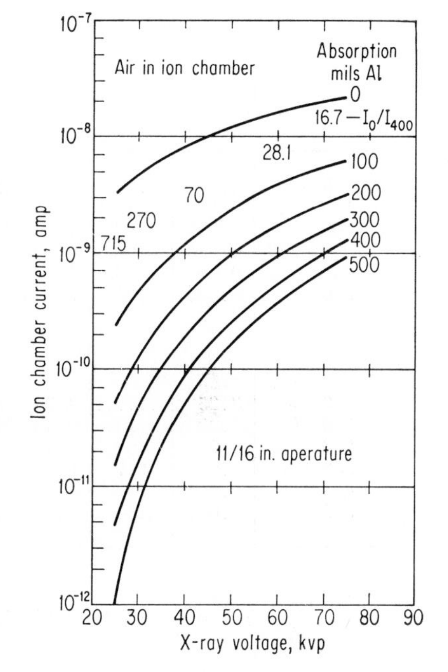

FIG. 11. Variation of detector current with x-ray voltage and absorption level.

The double-ionization-chamber detector in the Hanford photometer was filled with argon, which, because of its more complete absorption of the x-ray beam, provided signals approximately fifteen times larger than an air-filled detector.

Although there is no chopper used with the opposed-ionization-chamber detector, radioactive samples may be readily analyzed. Radioactive samples produce slightly more current in the sample ion chamber than in the reference side. However, this causes no problem since the x-ray beam intensity is many powers of 10 stronger than the sample radiation and the unbalance in ion currents can be nulled electrically before the x-rays are turned on.

At their peak usage at Hanford, five laboratories used x-ray photometers to make approximately 29,500 analyses annually. X-ray photometers were used principally for the determination of uranium and some plutonium concentrations in both aqeuous and organic process streams, at all concentrations exceeding a few grams per liter, and for accountability analyses of these elements where high precision was desired.

4. PROCEDURES

Sample Handling. X-ray absorptiometry is nondestructive to the sample after it is once prepared in a form suitable to present to the photometer. Little, if any, pretreatment is necessary for gas or liquid samples, but solids usually must be dissolved, pressed, or machined.

Solids. When thickness measurements are to be made of metals, alloys, plastics, or other solid sheets, the chemical composition of all the specimens must be constant. Surfaces must be smooth and they must be parallel to each other unless the x-ray beam is stopped down to a line that is narrow in the direction of any taper or undulations in the surfaces of a moving solid.

If chemical composition is to be determined, such as, for example, the weight per cent of uranium dioxide dispersed in a matrix of stainless steel, the thickness of the solid strip must be constant to a precision better than that desired in the analytical results.

Powder specimens should be very finely divided. An exact weight, the same weight

Table 1. Variation of I and of I_0/I with X-ray Voltage and Absorption Level
($1\frac{1}{16}$-in. apertures, 5-ma x-ray currents)

Absorption level, mils Al	Currents, amp × 10^9									
	25 kvp		30 kvp		42 kvp		60 kvp		75 kvp	
	I	I_0/I	I	I_0/I	I	I_0/I	I	I_0/I	I	I_0/I
Argon-filled Ion Chamber										
0	53.0	....	75.0	.....	135	.....	243	....	317	
100	4.10	12.9	7.90	9.5	22.2	6.1	58.5	4.2	90.0	3.5
200	0.880	60.2	2.14	35.0	7.90	17.1	25.8	9.4	46.0	6.9
300	0.265	200	0.720	104	3.63	37.2	14.3	17.0	26.5	12.0
400	0.090	589	0.30	250	1.90	71.1	8.5	28.6	17.0	18.6
500	0.030	1,770	0.135	556	1.09	124	5.5	44.2	11.6	27.3
Air-filled Ion Chamber										
0	3.25	....	4.70	.....	8.70	.....	15.8	....	21.0	
100	0.235	13.8	0.46	10.2	1.38	6.3	3.76	4.2	6.0	3.5
200	0.052	62.5	0.13	46.2	0.50	17.4	1.70	9.3	3.08	6.8
300	0.015	217	0.0475	99	0.232	37.5	0.90	17.6	1.88	11.2
400	0.0046	707	0.0212	222	0.116	75	0.56	28.5	1.27	16.5
500	0.0010	3,250	0.0070	671	0.0675	129	0.37	42.9	0.90	23.3

as used for other samples and standards, is distributed as uniformly as possible in a die and pressed into a wafer with flat, smooth surfaces and, hopefully, a uniform density.

Calibration standards should be similar in composition to the samples.

Liquids. Liquid samples are generally handled either in open-top cells or in cells of fixed path length with windows at both ends. Open-top cells may have a bottom window of thin aluminum metal or of plastic or other light-element material, but it must be rigid enough to remain flat when the weight of the sample is on it. It is best to weigh the samples in order to get reproducible masses. Pipetted volumes are satisfactory if the room temperature is controlled closely so that change of sample density due to expansion does not occur. Close temperature control is likewise required if samples of fixed path length are used. The latter cells are the most convenient to use as no exact volumes or weights are required.

Gases. Gases have very much smaller linear absorption coefficients than denser liquids and solids. Therefore, it is necessary to use highly transparent windows and long path lengths. Path lengths of 50 to 100 cm are not uncommon. Window material should be of the lightest possible elements. Typical window material would be hydrocarbons, such as polystyrene or polypropylene, 0.01 to 0.1 mm thick.

Because gases have small mass, x-rays of low energy with effective wavelengths exceeding 1.0 Å are used in order to obtain absorption measurements of reasonable magnitude. The filtering effect by the sample is greater the longer the wavelength. Therefore, it is especially difficult to calculate effective wavelengths or changes in them due to composition or density changes in the gas. Effective wavelengths are determined empirically by comparing the sample attenuation with the absorption properties of a known material, such as aluminum. But it takes no longer and is more accurate to make an empirical calibration of sample absorption against standard gases of known composition or pressure and avoid calculations based on uncertain absorption coefficients.

There is one other thing that is different with gas samples. Pressure and temperature measurements must also be made if it is required to calculate the sample mass from the gas laws.

Calibration. It is necessary to establish reproducible instrument conditions before measuring attenuation by each set of standards or samples.

The balance meter is zeroed electrically. Then the attenuator disk is rotated until the hole in the tapered edge is in front of the reference beam. The x-rays are turned on and with no absorbers in either beam the balance meter is again brought to the null point by moving a shadow bar with the aid of a vernier (on some photometers the beam apertures and sample supports are moved) so that it trims one or the other of the two x-ray beams just enough to produce equal ion currents in the two halves of the detector chamber. This ties the lower end of a calibration curve to a constant value.

Intensity measurements are affected by changes in x-ray voltage and current settings, and by changes in gain of the detector and amplifier. Therefore, these settings must all be reproduced as exactly as possible so that the slope of a calibration curve will not change. However, small changes in "trimming" or balancing the x-ray beams at a given absorption value may alter the slope of a curve slightly. Therefore, it is more accurate to tie absorption readings to the calibration curve at some point closer to the composition of the samples to be analyzed. To do this a standard absorber, such as a metal or plastic block or a standard solution in a sealed cell, which has a composition similar to, but with somewhat less absorption than, the samples to be analyzed, is placed in the reference beam plus a predetermined portion of the attenuator disk. With a standard sample in the sample beam the x-ray beams are trimmed to achieve a null balance at that particular absorption value.

If these instrument checks are made two or three times a day and standard solutions are not permitted to evaporate, or are replenished, a calibration curve will give reliable analytical results week after week.

Direct Calibration. In a direct calibration, absorption by the sample is matched entirely with the required thickness of aluminum metal (or with plastic gauge blocks plus a plastic attenuator wedge, depending on the kind of photometer). This technique requires the fewest number of standards for calibration over a wide range of concentrations (or thicknesses). Calibration curves usually possess appreciable curvature at absorption levels of less than about 175 mils of aluminum because of the unequal filtering of the various wavelengths by the sample and the aluminum (or plastic) reference material. At higher absorption levels effective wavelengths change only slightly and absorption curves are nearly straight lines. This technique is the least precise.

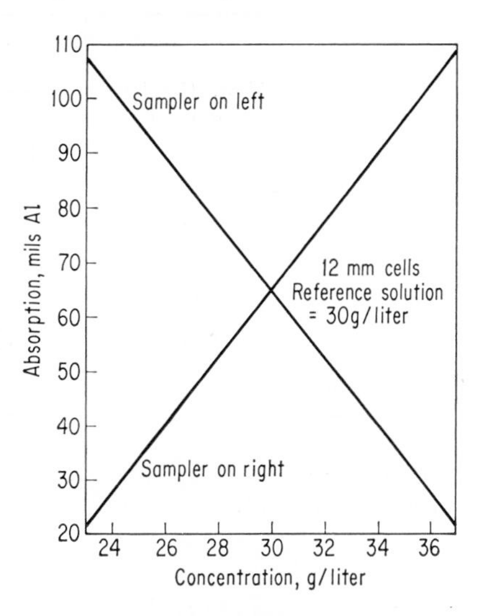

FIG. 12. Typical calibration curves for the "crisscross" technique.

Differential Calibration. Precision is improved by a differential technique in which the absorption of a sample is matched in large part by the absorption of a standard reference sample of similar composition, only a small thickness of the attenuator disk being required to complete the balance. Calibration curves cannot cover a wide range but they are straight lines. This technique is relatively free of errors due to voltage and temperature fluctuations because both x-ray beams traverse similar absorbents. Errors arising from incorrect adjustments of instrument controls are minimized since only a small difference between the absorptions of sample and standard is measured.

Crisscross Technique. Highest precision has been obtained with the crisscross differential technique. One reading is made with the sample in one of the x-ray beams and the reference solution or specimen in the other. A second measurement is made after switching positions of the two cells. Corrections for extraneous substances that may be present are subtracted from the reading obtained with the sample on the right side and added to the measurement taken with the sample in the reference beam. One curve has a positive slope, the other one a negative slope, whence comes the term "crisscross." See Fig. 12.

If an inaccurate adjustment of the controls causes high readings, the concentration read off the calibration curve will be high with the sample in the right-hand beam, and low by an equal amount when the positions of the sample and reference are switched. The average of the two results will contain a minimum of photometric error.

Precision. Although the balance meter responds with less sensitivity as absorption level increases, the ability to reproduce a measurement diminishes only slightly. Table 2 shows the 2σ precision of measurement by the direct and the crisscross techniques using 42-kvp x-rays. These values were obtained from measurements of standards covering the absorption range of 50 to 450 mils of aluminum over a 5-month period. Higher-energy x-rays produce stronger signals and still better precision, particularly at high absorption values.

Table 2. Photometric Precision as a Function of Absorption Level
(42 kvp)

Absorption level, mils Al	Precision of measurement,* mils Al	
	Normal technique	Crisscross technique
50	±0.41	±0.17
100	±0.50	±0.20
150	±0.61	±0.24
200	±0.72	±0.27
250	±0.83	±0.30
300	±0.95	±0.34
350	±1.07	±0.37
400	±1.20	±0.40
450	±1.33	±0.44

* All precision values given in terms of 95 per cent confidence intervals (1.96 times the standard deviations).

5. APPLICATIONS

Thickness Gauging. True thickness of solid homogeneous material is readily calibrated in terms of the amount of attenuation of an x-ray beam with the aid of Eq. (2). Completely automatic thickness control for tandem rolling of sheet metal has been in continuous use for several years.[4] This method gives highly stable and sensitive results in measuring metal thicknesses from 0.00045-in. aluminum foil to 0.125-in. steel plate. It provides more precise control than can be achieved manually, at rolling-mill speeds to 2,000 ft/min. The Denver Mint uses the absorption of x-rays to control the thickness of metals used for coins.[7] These include a variety of alloys and a thickness range of 0.038 to 0.196 in.

Examples of other applications are the measurement of wall thickness of aircraft propellers,[8] the selection of uniformly thin-walled glass bulbs for the diffusion of helium by exploration of the bulbs with a very small x-ray beam,[9] and the control of thickness and weight of inorganic coatings on paper.

Nondestructive Testing of Nuclear Fuel Elements. A determination of plutonium

Table 3. Variation of Core-thickness Sensitivity and Precision with X-ray Current
Al-14 wgt. % Pu cores, 75 kvp

Emission current, ma	Sensitivity, chart division/mil of core	Precision, ±mil of core
0.6	5.0	0.33
1.0	8.0	0.26
1.25	10.0	0.235
1.5	11.6	0.22
2.0	15.0	0.20

concentration and distribution in flat reactor fuel plates has been made by measuring variations of thickness of the heavy-element core inside a plate of constant total thickness.[10] A typical fuel element consisted of a 20-mil-thick core of 14 wgt. % plutonium-aluminum alloy sandwiched between two 20-mil-thick layers of aluminum cladding. These plates were rolled out from a 0.750-in.-thick biscuit, and the rolling process resulted in variations of core thickness all along the plate.

The x-ray photometric method proved to be far superior in sensitivity, precision, and speed to other nondestructive methods. Table 3 lists sensitivity and precision of the measurements as a function of x-ray current. To examine the degree of uniformity of fuel density in the plates, a small aperture, 0.05 by 0.25 in., was used. In spite of the small x-ray beam and a scanning rate of 12 in./min, the high intensity available with a polychromatic beam resulted in highly reproducible absorption curves, as shown in Fig. 13. This figure shows four scans of the same plate with the zero line displaced between each scan. Chemical analysis of ⅛-in. punchings agreed perfectly with the x-ray results.

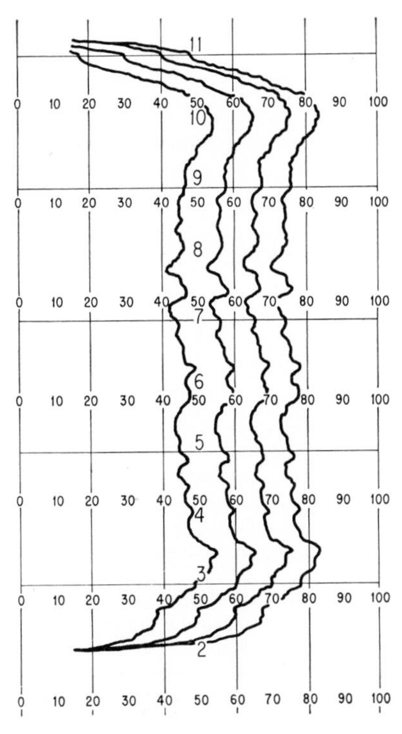

Fig. 13. X-ray photometric scans of MTR fuel plate with 14 wgt. % Pu-Al core. 75 kvp, 1 ma, 0.05-in. aperture, 12 in./min scanning speed.

Determination of Porosity. The porosity of a solid is the fractional volume of interstices or voids compared with the apparent volume, or

$$P = \frac{V_a - V_t}{V_a} = 1 - \frac{V_t}{V_a} \qquad (8)$$

where V_t and V_a are the true and apparent volumes of a solid. If X_t and X_a are true and apparent mass thicknesses, then

$$\frac{V_t}{V_a} = \frac{X_t}{X_a} \qquad (9)$$

and

$$P = 1 - \frac{X_t}{X_a} = 1 - \frac{2.303 \log (I_0/I)}{\mu\rho X_a} \qquad (10)$$

If the value of the absorption coefficient is known, it is possible to calculate porosity from measured values of I_0, I, and X_a. If the absorption coefficient cannot be determined accurately for a polychromatic x-ray beam, at least the porosity of a material can readily be compared with that of a standard of known porosity which has the same apparent thickness. This technique has been applied in industry to the determination of porosity in asbestos-cement pipes, various acoustic boards, papers, and pressed wood-pulp sheets. Related applications include the use of a differential thickness gauge to record voids as small as 0.0001 in.^{3} in filled artillery shells,[11] the determination of bed density profiles and the degree of fluidization of powders by gases,[12] and an x-ray absorption system which compensated for different-sized oranges and automatically sorted them, at the rate of 10 per second, into six different classifications, depending on their internal quality.[13] Porosity measurements have been made

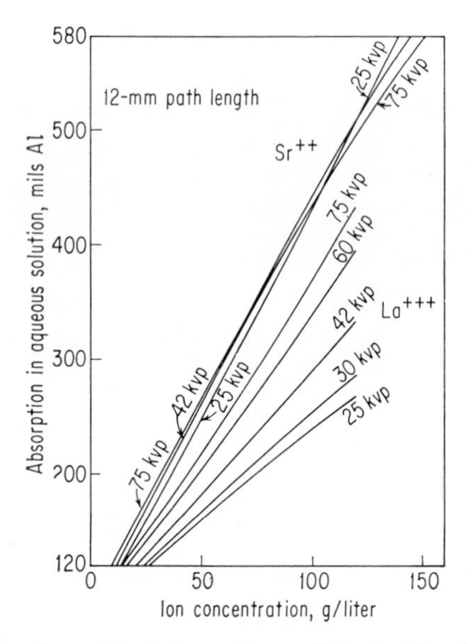

FIG. 14. Variation of empirical absorption coefficient with solute concentration.

of materials such as leather, textiles, lignin-filled rubber separators for storage batteries, hand-grenade fuses (at the rate of 4,000 per hour), and even sandstone from oil fields.

Other methods of measuring porosity involve long and difficult procedures. In some cases the determination results in destruction of the sample. Worst of all, the very small pores and pores that are not opened by fine grinding are not penetrated at all by these methods. X-ray absorption measurements, on the other hand, include all pores, whether the specimen is ground finely or not, and the method is simple and rapid.

Determination of Substances in Solution. The data reported in this section do not represent absolute absorption methods but rather involve the relative absorption of two continuously changing x-ray beams, one penetrating the sample and the other the reference material. In this case, aluminum metal serves as the attenuator wedge. Empirical absorption coefficients discussed in this section on solutions were calculated by dividing the difference in absorption between two solutions (in equivalent mils of aluminum) by the difference in concentration of the desired constituent. In other words, these empirical coefficients represent the average slopes of calibration curves. These slopes will change somewhat, as illustrated for two elements in Fig. 14, with changes in the (1) concentration of the heavy element, (2) sample thickness and composition, (3) primary x-ray voltage, and (4) material used for the attenuator wedge.

Figure 15 shows empirical coefficients of some of the ions studied as a function of x-ray voltage. Coefficients for ions were calculated from absorption measurements of corresponding compounds after subtracting the absorption due to all extraneous elements. Since these coefficients represent a ratio of absorption by aluminum and by the sample, they are normally not a linear function of voltage (or of wavelength). For highest accuracy, the absorption coefficient for a specific compound or element should be determined at concentrations near to those expected in the samples to be

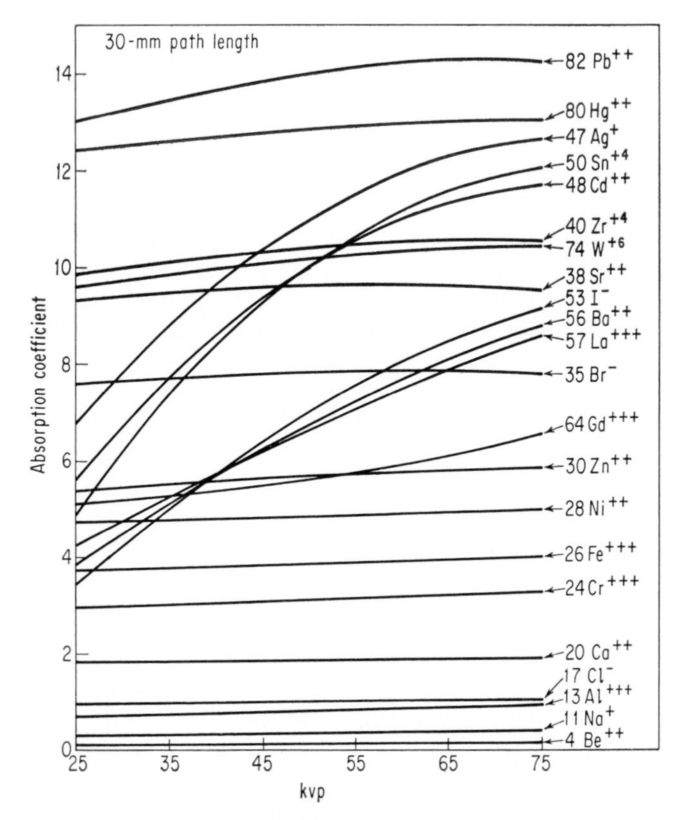

Fig. 15. Variation of empirical absorption coefficient with x-ray voltage.

analyzed. In most cases, as seen in Fig. 15, the coefficients remain nearly constant, but the anomalous behavior of atoms with absorption edges in the range of wavelengths involved, atoms having atomic numbers 42 to 65, is clearly evident.

As an example of the application of selective voltages in the x-ray photometric analysis of a mixture of two major absorbents, it is noted that a change from 75 to 25 kvp causes only a small change in the absorption by lead, whereas a large change in absorption is noted for cadmium as the voltage is decreased. Calibration curves in Fig. 16 show that selection of the lowest x-ray voltage, 25 kvp, gives a curve of sufficient slope to permit rapid determination of both lead and cadmium in samples of the binary alloy.

Empirical Coefficients for Materials in Solution. Table 4 lists just a few of the empirical absorption coefficients[14,15] to indicate relative values, in the last column, for elements of different atomic numbers. It can be seen that the determination of uranium in dilute nitric acid and aluminum nitrate solutions makes an ideal application of x-ray absorptiometry. Empirical coefficients calculated for the elements or ions are plotted against atomic number in Fig. 17 for 30-mm cells, and in Fig. 18 for a path length of

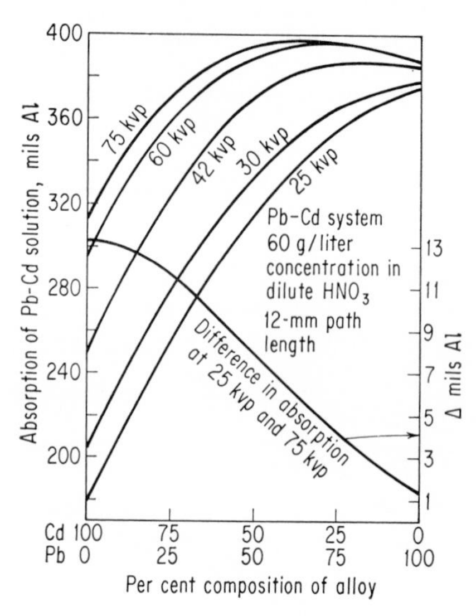

FIG. 16. Calibration curves for absorption by Pb-Cd alloy solution at several x-ray voltages.

Table 4. Empirical Absorption Coefficients and Relative Absorption for Several Elements and Compounds
(Normal technique—42 kv—12-mm path)

At. No.	Substance	Absorption coefficient, mils Al per g/liter	Relative absorption
94	Pu	7.39	100
92	U	7.00	94.8
82	Pb	5.14	69.6
57	La	2.11	28.6
30	Zn	2.12	28.7
	$KMnO_4$	0.576	7.8
	$Na_2Cr_2O_7$	0.471	6.4
	$Fe(NO_3)_3$	0.359	4.9
	H_2SO_4	0.135	1.8
	$Al(NO_3)_3$	0.056	0.76
	HNO_3	0.023	0.31

12 mm. These graphs portray the discontinuity for those elements in the atomic number range 42 to 65, resulting from the interaction of their absorption edges with the x-ray energies.

By interpolation, coefficients can be approximated for other voltages and path lengths. Empirical coefficients shown in these figures are useful (1) to select optimum voltages for absorptiometric analysis of various materials, (2) to determine the magnitude of absorption due to extraneous substances and the probable errors in their corrections, (3) to calculate the optimum concentration and path length, and (4) to calculate the probable accuracy for a given analytical application from the magnitude of absorption and known measurement precisions at various absorption levels. These empirical coefficients are applicable to substances in aqueous solutions or in organic solvents of low density. Their relative absorption values are also useful when considering the absorption of polychromatic x-rays by solids.

Purity of Compounds. A complete chemical analysis is usually necessary to establish the composition of an unknown material. However, a rapid comparison of the

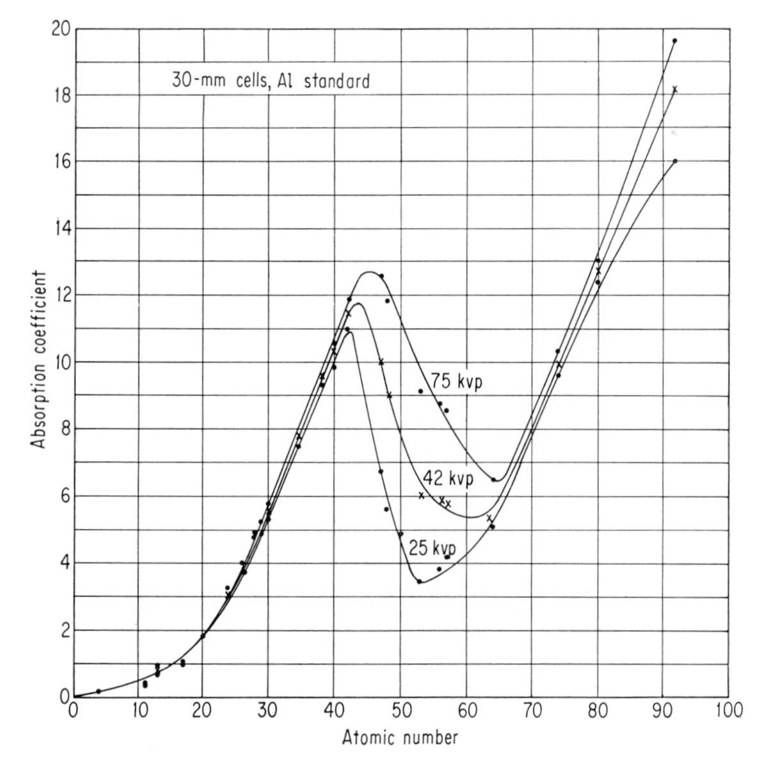

FIG. 17. Variation of empirical absorption coefficients for elements in solution with atomic number (30-mm path length).

sample's absorption of x-rays with that of the same thickness of a pure compound or of a synthetic mixture of known elemental composition will show either the probable identity of the two materials or that differences in elemental content exist.

Single Solutes: Control of Process Reagents. Table 5 illustrates the usefulness of x-ray absorptiometry for rapid control analyses of many reagent or process solutions containing only a single solute. Even substances having small atomic numbers may be satisfactory for x-ray photometric determination if their concentrations are high enough to give the desired accuracy. Sensitivity may be further increased over that shown in Table 5 with the selection of cells of longer path length.

Mixed Solutes. The usual materials to be analyzed are heterogeneous and contain several different elements or compounds. It is well to remember that this method measures total absorption of all solutes, solvents, and cell. However, if the element to be determined has sufficient absorptive power relative to that of the other sub-

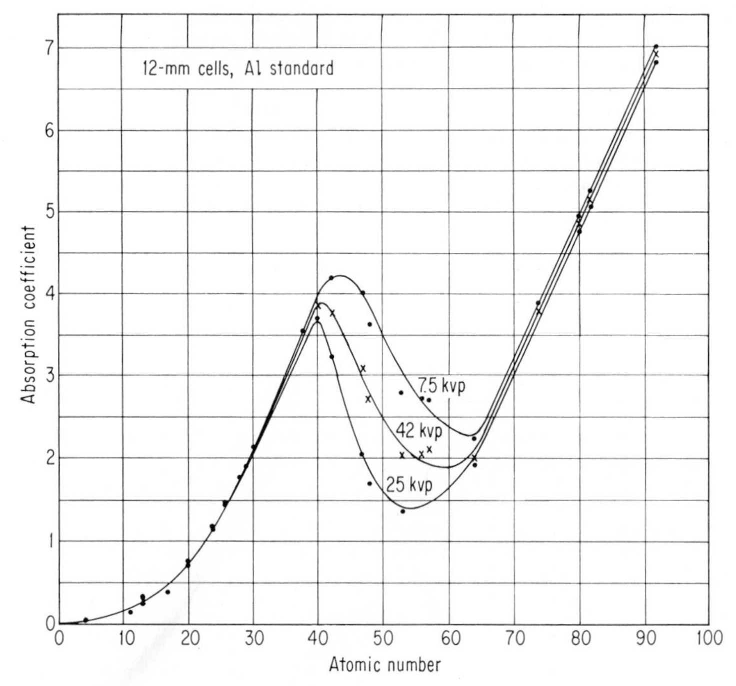

FIG. 18. Variation of empirical absorption coefficients for elements in solution with atomic number (12-mm path length).

Table 5. X-ray Photometric Analyses of Single-solute Systems
(Aqueous solutions—42 kvp—normal technique)

Reagent	Concentration, wgt./vol. %	Cell, mm	Absorption, mils Al	Slope of curve, mils Al/wgt. %	Absolute precision, wt. %	
					Normal technique	Crisscross technique
$Pb(NO_3)_2$.....	2	12	140	32.2	±0.018	±0.007
	2	30	338	85.6	±0.012	±0.004
$Zn(NO_3)_2$.....	5	12	113	7.46	±0.071	±0.028
	2	30	206	19.6	±0.037	±0.014
$KMnO_4$......	5	12	105	5.76	±0.089	±0.036
	2	30	197	15.1	±0.048	±0.018
$Na_2Cr_2O_7$.....	25	12	194	4.71	±0.15	±0.056
	5	30	233	12.3	±0.064	±0.024
H_2SO_4........	25	30	259	3.53	±0.24	±0.088
	5	30	189	3.53	±0.19	±0.074
NaOH........	25	30	238	2.27	±0.35	±0.13
	5	30	182	2.27	±0.30	±0.11
$Al(NO_3)_3$.....	25	30	211	1.58	±0.47	±0.18
	5	30	179	1.58	±0.42	±0.16

stances present, and if the concentrations of extraneous substances are comparatively low and are approximately known, the major absorbent may readily be determined by this method. It is usually possible to correct with reasonable accuracy for the absorption by extraneous substances. Absorption due to unit concentrations of interferences has been found to vary somewhat with the amount of the major absorbent. For highest accuracy it is best to determine specific coefficients for interferences with standard solutions containing the expected concentration of the major absorbent and different amounts of the interference.

In case the extraneous elements are relatively high in concentration or if some of them have large absorption coefficients, a chemical separation may be required prior to the determination. Separations can sometimes be quite rapid. A single contact with an organic extractant often affects the separation of the desired metal from an aqueous solution to a high and reproducible degree. The metal can then be determined in the organic phase. This technique has been used to determine uranium in a variety of materials[16] such as uranium oxide scrap, floor sweepings, chips from machining of uranium, pickling-acid sludge, centrifuge slurries, graphite from crucible linings, and fluxes, in which the uranium content varied from 0.1 to 100 per cent. The rapid single-extraction technique is also used to separate uranium from solutions too radioactive to be carried to the photometer.

The application of polychromatic x-ray absorptiometry to the rapid determination of uranium and of plutonium in various solutions has been tremendously successful. This is due in part to the very stable and reproducible measurements that are obtained with a split-beam instrument, and in part to careful empirical determination of absorption coefficients for extraneous substances. The method was even shown to be accurate for the analysis of waste streams containing only about 0.5 g/liter of uranium, in which the total absorption correction calculated for extraneous materials was about five times the net absorption due to the uranium.

Precision and Time of Analysis. Deviations of polychromatic x-ray absorption measurements, over a long period of time, are smaller than those normally experienced in wet chemical analyses. Typical laboratory precisions obtained in the analysis of plutonium solutions and alloys are shown in Table 6. Absorptiometric precisions as a function of concentration are illustrated in Table 7. All precision data in this chapter are expressed in terms of 2σ values (95 per cent confidence limits).

Once a sample is in solution and diluted to the desired range, only a few minutes is needed to complete the analysis. This results in an appreciable analytical economy.

In-line Analysis. Because high intensities of polychromatic beams result in instantaneous signals, an x-ray photometer may be readily converted to continuous in-line analysis as well as to the control of additive concentration. Cells of smaller path length may be used, to avoid dilution of concentrate streams, without an appreciable effect on precision. Although the absorption coefficient decreases with path length, a compensating increase in solute concentration maintains fairly constant relative precision, as indicated in Table 8 for measurements by the direct technique. Maximum usable absorption is determined by the x-ray tube voltage. Thicknesses of

Table 6. Comparison of X-ray and Chemical Determinations of Plutonium

	X-ray photometry	Chemical
No. of samples (Pu metal)	26	38
No. of reruns	6	20
No. of single determinations	62	182
Absolute precision (95% conf.), %:		
Reported results	±0.40	±0.37
Individual determinations	±0.54	±0.62
Bias (average deviation from 100% minus other component analyses), %	0.00	−0.14

Table 7. Absorptiometric Precision as a Function of Concentration ("Crisscross" Technique)

Pu concentration, g/liter aqueous solution	Path, mm	Approx. absorption, mils Al	Photometric precision, % (crisscross technique)	
			42 kv—5 ma	75 kv—3 ma
Water only	30	150		
1	30	168	±1.4	±0.91
5	30	240	±0.34	±0.28
10	30	330	±0.20	±0.15
15	30	420	±0.16	±0.125
Water only	12	50		
10	12	115	±0.32	±0.19
20	12	180	±0.20	±0.13
30	12	250	±0.15	±0.10
40	12	310	±0.13	±0.09
50	12	380	±0.12	±0.09

Table 8. Absorption Coefficients for Solutes and Photometric Precision as a Function of Path Length (Direct Technique)
(42 kvp)

Uranium concentration, g/liter	Path length, mm	Absorption coefficient, mils Al/(g/liter)	Precision	
			g/liter	%
12	30	18.1	±0.063	±0.53
40	12	7.00	±0.154	±0.39
50	10	5.72	±0.187	±0.37
100	5	2.83	±0.361	±0.36
250	2	1.14	±0.880	±0.35
500	1	0.58	±1.73	±0.35

Concentration of uranium chosen so that total absorption for all path lengths is between 320 and 380 mils.

aluminum absorbers giving the same signal-to-noise ratio were found to be 310 mils for x-rays at 25 kvp, 465 mils at 42 kvp, 775 mils at 60 kvp, and 1,075 mils of aluminum at 75 kvp.

Other Selected Applications. In order to emphasize the fact that polychromatic x-ray absorptiometry is useful in a great variety of analytical problems, several other selected applications will be mentioned.

Nondestructive Testing. An application similar to that of single-solute analysis is the use of x-ray photometry for the rapid point-to-point determination of the concentration of impregnator, such as lead chloride, barium fluoride, or molybdenum disulfide, in carbon brushes for high-altitude motors.[17] An x-ray photometer was designed at Hanford[10] with an x-ray source operable up to 140 kvp to provide greater penetrating power. This instrument, in addition to analyzing reactor fuel plates, can automatically scan graphite rods impregnated with plutonium and also plutonium- or uranium-aluminum alloy rods up to 1 in. in thickness. For a more complex fuel element containing uranium dioxide dispersed in a stainless-steel matrix, Plant[18] has made an interesting modification in a recording photometer utilizing a composite reference standard. The reference wedge consists of a uranium wedge and a stainless-steel wedge fastened together with their tapered ends overlapping. The uranium content of a fuel core of fixed thickness is determined from the position of the composite wedge that matches the absorption by the fuel element.

Determination of Heavy Elements in Organic Matrices. The absorption of polychromatic x-rays has been used extensively in the petroleum industry for the determination of constituents present in small amounts.[19,6] This is an ideal application because the hydrocarbon matrices have very low absorption coefficients and because these coefficients do not change appreciably with change in the hydrocarbon makeup of the matrix as absorption by hydrogen and by carbon is nearly the same at wavelengths near 0.5 Å. Tetraethyllead fluid in gasoline is determined with a precision better than ± 0.1 ml/gal; sulfur in oils is determined rapidly and reliably to ± 0.02 per cent; additives, such as metal soaps, are readily determined in lubricating oils; and the metal content of many metallo-organic preparations is determined by this method. Similar applications are the measurement of the ash content of coals and the heavy elements in ceramics, characterization of plastics, determination of chlorine in chlorinated hydrocarbons, and determination of heavy elements, such as barium, in paper coatings.

Study of Gases. The analysis of binary gas mixtures can be accomplished by measuring the absorption of polychromatic x-rays of long wavelength. Absorption of soft x-rays has also been used to measure the density of a gas during such transient conditions as exist in supersonic flow,[20] in shock and detonation waves,[21,22] in boundary layers,[23] and at high temperatures in flames.[24,25]

X-ray Microscopy and Histological Analysis (cf. Part 6 of this book). In projection x-ray microscopy[26] the x-rays from a pointlike source pass through the sample and produce a greatly enlarged shadow image on a photographic plate or fluorescent screen. Combined with optical enlargement, magnification up to 1,500 times is possible. Samples are examined in air, not in vacuum. This technique is adding much to the knowledge of the living cell and to the internal structure of matter on a microscale. It can be applied to thin sections of metals[27,28] as well as to biological specimens or tissues.[29,30,31] The great advantage of this method is its ability to compare adjacent sections of a sample which are only microns in width.

Two examples must suffice. Vose[32] has used the absorption of polychromatic x-rays for the rapid determination of the organic-to-inorganic ratio in bone tissue. The dry-ash method is difficult and time-consuming. Furthermore, large errors are possible if the ashing temperature is not closely controlled. Vose found the mean absorption coefficient for the organic material to be 1.30 at an effective wavelength of 0.413 Å, and the mean absorption coefficient for the inorganic material to be 14.8. The x-ray source was operated at 40 kvp, and at a constant effective wavelength the ratio of organic to inorganic matter is related to the per cent x-ray transmittance by an exponential function. Using 1.5-g samples of dried and powdered bone this ratio was accurately and rapidly determined with a precision of ± 1 per cent.

X-ray microscope techniques permit the dry weight of cytologic tissues to be determined in an area as small as 1 square micron. Results are expressed in terms of micromicrograms per square micron. Usefulness of such detailed information is apparent when one considers such a sample as striated muscle in which bands of high dry weight per unit area, and only 0.5 to 0.7 micron wide, alternate with bands of lighter dry weight. The analysis is done by the comparison method with soft polychromatic x-rays and with a reference step gauge of nitrocellulose foils.

High-resolution reflection x-ray microscopy, discussed by McGee,[33] also utilizes absorption of polychromatic x-rays in a conventional-type microscope in which x-rays are actually focused in the formation of the magnified images.

A technique that can weigh histological specimens whose cellular structures range from 10^{-12} to 10^{-14} g and can provide a greatly enlarged image of the internal structure of a cell or of a thin slice of an alloy or mineral is a powerful and useful tool to enlarge our knowledge of matter.

There are numerous other applications of polychromatic x-ray absorptiometry, not to mention the large field of industrial radiography which has contributed so much to our knowledge of metallurgy, metal fabrication, and the internal structure of other materials.

6. SUMMARY

Polychromatic x-ray absorptiometry is useful in a great variety of analytical problems, a few of which have been briefly described. The method is not specific for any element, and its application to chemical analysis is therefore limited. However, for any material which contains one component possessing high absorption compared with the remainder of the sample, the use of polychromatic x-rays is applicable and has the advantage of very great intensities. This permits highly reliable measurements at an enormous saving in time, with simple, stable, and easily maintained equipment.

REFERENCES CITED

1. G. L. Clark (ed.), *The Encyclopedia of X-rays and Gamma Rays*, pp. 9–15, New York, Reinhold Publishing Corporation, 1963.
2. H. A. Liebhafsky, H. G. Pfeiffer, E. H. Winslow, and P D. Zemany, *X-ray Absorption and Emission in Analytical Chemistry*, pp. 76–77, 88, John Wiley & Sons, Inc., New York, 1960.
3. J. P. Hansen, W. E. Flynt, and J. E. Dowdy, *Rev. Sci. Instr.*, **29**:1107 (1958).
4. S. Bernstein, *J. Soc. Nondestructive Testing*, **16**:305 (1958).
5. T. C. Michel and T. A. Rich, *Gen. Elec. Rev.*, **50**(2):45 (February, 1947).
6. R. W. Cranston, F. W. H. Matthews, and N. Evans, *J. Inst. Petrol.*, **40**:55 (1954).
7. *Elec. Eng.*, **77**:960 (1958).
8. H. A. Liebhafsky, *Anal. Chem.*, **25**:689 (1953).
9. F. J. Norton, *J. Am. Ceram. Soc.*, **36**:90 (1953).
10. M. C. Lambert, "Non-destructive Testing of MTR Type Fuel Plates by X-ray Absorption and Fluorescence Techniques," U.S. Atomic Energy Commission Rept. HW-57941, October, 1958, unclassified.
11. G. M. Ettinger, *Electronics*, **26**:142 (1953).
12. E. W. Grohse, *A.E.Ch.I.*, **1**:358 (1955).
13. *Electronics*, **23**:134 (1950).
14. M. C. Lambert, "Absorption of Polychromatic X-rays as a Function of Atomic Number and Source Voltage," U.S. Atomic Energy Commission Rept. HW-30190, December, 1953, unclassified.
15. M. C. Lambert, "Chemical Analysis by X-ray Photometry," U.S. Atomic Energy Commission Rept. HW-30634, January, 1954, unclassified.
16. M. C. Lambert and D. C. Bixby, "X-ray Photometric Determination of Uranium in Metal Oxides," U.S. Atomic Energy Commission Rept. HW-19300, November, 1950, unclassified.
17. A. C. Titus, *Power App. Systems*, no. 14: 1160 (1954).
18. W. R. Plant, *ASTM Spec. Tech. Publ.* **223**:358 (1958).
19. R. C. Vollmar, E. E. Petterson, and P. A. Petruzzelli, *Anal. Chem.*, **21**:1491 (1949).
20. E. M. Winkler, *J. Appl. Phys.*, **22**:201 (1951).
21. G. B. Kistiakowsky, *J. Chem. Phys.*, **19**:1611 (1951).
22. H. T. Knight and D. Venable, *Rev. Sci. Instr.*, **29**:92 (1958).
23. R. N. Weltmann and P. W. Kuhns, *NACA Tech. Note* 3098, 1954.
24. R. N. Weltmann and P. W. Kuhns, *NACA Tech. Note* 2580, 1951.
25. G. J. Mullaney, *Rev. Sci. Instr.*, **29**:87 (1958).
26. V. E. Cosslett and W. C. Nixon, *J. Appl. Phys.*, **24**:616 (1953).
27. S. E. Summers, "Recent Applications with the X-ray Microscope," in W. M. Mueller (ed.), *Advances in X-ray Analysis*, vol. 1, p. 483, Plenum Press, New York, 1960.
28. I. I. Bessen, "Selection of Spectra for X-ray Microscopy," in W. M. Mueller (ed.), *Advances in X-ray Analysis*, vol. 2, p. 79, Plenum Press, New York, 1960.
29. B. Lindstrom, Thesis, *Acta Radiol., Suppl.* 125, 1955.
30. B. L. Henke, B. Lundberg, and A. Engstrom, *X-ray Microscopy and Microradiography*, Academic Press Inc., New York, 1957.
31. B. L. Henke, "Microstructure, Mass and Chemical Analysis with 8 to 44 Angstrom X-radiation," in W. M. Mueller (ed.), *Advances in X-ray Analysis*, vol. 2, p. 117, Plenum Press, New York, 1960.
32. G. P. Vose, *Anal. Chem.*, **30**:1819 (1958).
33. J. F. McGee, "An Introduction to Total Reflection X-ray Microscopy," in W. M. Mueller (ed.), *Advances in X-ray Analysis*, vol. 3, p. 213, Plenum Press, New York, 1960.

Chapter 42

ABSORPTIOMETRY WITH MONOCHROMATIC X-RAYS

Charles G. Dodd

Owens-Illinois Glass Company Technical Center

1. INTRODUCTION

Monochromatic x-ray absorptiometry may be considered to include, for all practical purposes, only two types of spectroscopic procedures, simple absorptiometry and differential absorptiometry across an absorption edge. The former is of relatively little importance, except for simple chemical analytical procedures employing radioisotopes that produce monochromatic x-rays by K capture. By contrast, reported applications of the more powerful method of differential absorptiometry across an edge are found in the literature with increasing frequency. In this chapter we shall refer frequently to the differential method as "XAES" for "x-ray absorption-edge spectrometry."

XAES is characterized by certain unique advantages that justify its consideration over other spectrochemical methods for many chemical analytical applications. The most important advantages are the high degree of specificity, the marked freedom from sample matrix effects, and the relatively few interferences encountered. XAES is accurate and convenient to apply. On the other hand, the sensitivity attainable is somewhat less than that of some other spectral methods.

Glocker and Frohnmayer[1] are credited with the genesis of XAES in 1925, but its limited application to chemical analysis during the past 40 years has largely been the consequence of inadequate instrumentation. In 1946, Engström[2] described spectrographic applications of the principle, including chemical analyses of light elements such as carbon, nitrogen, and oxygen in living cells. Barieau[3] has developed procedures for the determination of molybdenum and zinc. Dunn[4] has discussed the pros and cons of XAES analysis and described procedures and instrumentation for precise determination of zirconium and other elements midway in the periodic table, utilizing a two-point measurement technique (rather than extrapolation to an edge). Hakkila has described methods using secondary fluorescent radiation from preselected targets, rather than white radiation monochromatized by a crystal, for the analysis of uranium and yttrium,[5] and the determination of cobalt in complex mixtures.[6]

2. THE ABSORPTION OF MONOCHROMATIC X-RAYS

Exponential Absorption Law. When a beam of *monochromatic* x-rays passes through a thin layer of matter, the fraction dI/I absorbed of the incident beam is proportional to the thickness of the layer dx. This is expressed by the equation

$$dI/I = -\mu\, dx \tag{1}$$

in which the proportionality constant μ is known as the "linear absorption coefficient." The negative sign indicates a decrease in the intensity of the transmitted beam. Integration of Eq. (1) may be accomplished if μ is truly constant to give

$$\ln (i/I) = -\mu x$$

or

$$i = I \exp (-\mu x) \tag{2}$$

in which I is the intensity when $x = 0$ and i the intensity of the transmitted beam. Examination of Eq. (2) indicates that μ has dimensions of reciprocal length; indeed, it is the fractional decrease in intensity per unit length of path through the absorbing medium. A more useful quantity for chemical analysis by x-rays is the "mass absorption coefficient" written as μ/ρ or μ_m (ρ is the density of matter traversed by the beam). Equation (2) then becomes

$$i = I \exp [(-\mu/\rho)x\rho]$$

or

$$i = I \exp [(-\mu/\rho)C] \tag{3}$$

in which C is the concentration of the element or compound expressed in grams per square centimeter. The mass absorption coefficient is a measure of the fraction of energy in the incident beam absorbed when a beam of unit cross section traverses unit mass of material. It is useful because it is characteristic of the chemical elements in the absorbing material essentially independent of their chemical or physical state. Mass absorption coefficients may be found in Table 5 on pages 1-26 to 1-29.

Equations (1) to (3) are valid only if the absorption coefficient is constant, but this is true only if the incident x-rays are monochromatic or homogeneous, i.e., of only one wavelength. If the incident beam is polychromatic, most of the "softer" rays of longer wavelength will be absorbed in the first layers of matter penetrated by the beam and the spectral distribution of energy in the transmitted beam will be shifted to shorter wavelengths. For a given element the mass absorption coefficient may be expressed empirically as a function of wavelength by an equation such as, for example,

$$\mu/\rho = A\lambda^n Z^m + b \tag{4}$$

in which A is a constant for a given element (over a limited wavelength range), λ is the wavelength, Z is the atomic number of the element, and b is an expression for the scattering (discussed below) and also a function of λ and Z; the exponent n may vary between 2.5 and 3.0, and m is approximately 4.

Absorption Mechanisms (cf. Chap. 1, Sec. 5). When x-rays traverse matter the predominant absorption mechanism is photoelectric in nature, with scattering making a minor contribution (except for elements of low atomic number and for wavelengths shorter than 0.5 Å). Secondary rays scattered from material traversed by the primary x-ray beam have essentially the same wavelength as the incident beam. They are generated by the acceleration of electrons in the irradiated material. According to electrodynamic theory, such an oscillating electric charge must radiate rays of essentially the same frequency. Simultaneously fluorescent rays are produced by a photoelectric mechanism. The primary x-ray beam ejects electrons from some of the atoms. This leaves these atoms in an ionized condition, and in returning to the normal state, energy is liberated when other electrons fall down to the energy level of the electrons that were ejected. The total mass absorption coefficient μ/ρ thus can be represented as the sum of two terms, the mass transformation coefficient (or fluorescent or photoelectric absorption coefficient) and the mass scattering coefficient:

$$\mu/\rho = \delta/\rho + \sigma/\rho \tag{5}$$

The mass transformation coefficient δ/ρ increases with both the wavelength of the radiation and the atomic number of the absorber. The value of the mass scattering coefficient σ/ρ (which includes both coherent and incoherent or Compton scattering) is small in comparison with δ/ρ and may be neglected in most applications concerned with chemical analysis by x-ray absorption, and the term b in Eq. (4) may likewise be dropped (unless wavelengths appreciably less than 0.5 Å are employed).

X-ray Photoelectric Absorption Edges. If the mass absorption coefficient of an element is determined as a function of wavelength, sharp discontinuities are observed at wavelengths characteristic of the element. These discontinuities are known as "absorption edges" or "absorption limits," and they are found to occur at wavelengths slightly shorter than the characteristic emission lines. For a given element, the K lines and edges occur at the shortest wavelengths (highest energies). At much longer wavelengths are found the three L-absorption edges with a similar relationship to the characteristic L lines, and M edges and lines occur at yet lower photon energies. At an absorption edge the magnitude of the sudden drop in mass absorption coefficient is referred to as the "absorption-edge jump," which we designate as $\Delta\mu_m$.

Although x-rays obey an absorption law [Eq. (1)] similar to that obeyed by light rays, the photoelectric mechanism accounting for most of the absorption of x-rays in matter results in the unique spectral properties described above. Characteristic K-emission lines of an element in an irradiated absorber are not excited unless the incident x-ray beam contains photons of high enough energy to eject electrons from the K shell completely outside the atom. The critical photon energy below which K absorption does not occur, W_K, is given by

$$W_K = h\nu_K = hc/\lambda_K \tag{6}$$

in which ν_K and λ_K are the frequency and wavelength, respectively, corresponding to the K-absorption edge. Similar relationships hold for L and M edges. Furthermore, the frequencies (or wavelengths) of the characteristic emission lines are simply related to the frequencies of the absorption limits. For example, the $K\alpha_1$ line is radiated when an electron at the L_{III} level in the L shell falls into the K shell, thus:

$$\nu_{K\alpha_1} = \nu_K - \nu_{L_{III}} \tag{7}$$

The absorption edge generally is considered to be a sharp discontinuity. This is not strictly true; the position and structure of the edge do depend on the chemical state of combination of an element and, probably, its physical state. These fine-structure effects are of a lesser order of magnitude, however, than those discussed in this chapter. When performing a chemical analysis by differential absorptiometry, or XAES, it is not usually possible to resolve details of the structure of an absorption edge with the instruments employed. Fine-structure absorption-edge spectroscopy is discussed in Chap. 43.

3. SIMPLE MONOCHROMATIC ABSORPTIOMETRY

In the case of simple monochromatic absorptiometry at one wavelength, the wavelength is selected close to the high-energy (short-wavelength) side of an absorption edge of the element being determined such that the greatest contrast in total absorption will be observed for differences in concentration of this element in the absorbing sample. Simple absorptiometry is generally not specific, although it may be designed to be much more sensitive for the determination of a particular element than polychromatic absorptiometry (see Chap. 41). The only advantage to be gained, however, in simple monochromatic absorptiometry is a somewhat higher degree of sensitivity to the desired element. Frequently the cost of this increased sensitivity is excessive, compared with polychromatic procedures, in terms of the cost of more elaborate equipment required, and lowered intensity of the x-ray beam with its consequent lowered precision, or longer time required for counting in order to obtain comparable precision. This may not be the case if a radioisotope (emitting x-radiation by K capture) is used as a monochromatic source (see Sec. 5, method IV). A much more useful type of monochromatic absorptiometry is differential absorptiometry across an edge, or XAES.

4. XAES, DIFFERENTIAL ABSORPTIOMETRY ACROSS AN EDGE

Principles of XAES. Equation (3) above describes the absorption of monochromatic x-radiation when the absorbing sample consists of one element. If several elements are present and monochromatic radiation is employed, the appropriate expression for the composite linear absorption coefficient is

$$\mu = \mu_m\rho + \sum_j (\mu_m\rho)_j \tag{8}$$

in which the summation of the right term is carried over all j chemical elements other than the element sought. Again, μ_m is the mass absorption coefficient, ρ the density of the element, and x the sample thickness or x-ray path length.

The peculiar virtue of the XAES method of chemical analysis is that it is possible, under the proper conditions, to determine the mass of one element in an absorbing sample in the presence of large amounts of other elements. The method is unique with respect to its high degree of specificity. In order to attain this specificity, together with sensitivity approaching microanalysis, it is necessary to measure absorption of monochromatized x-ray beams at selected wavelengths on each side of an absorption edge and, usually, to extrapolate the data to the edge.

If the K-absorption edge of an element sought lies at a known wavelength λ_K, select suitable wavelengths λ_1 and λ_2 on each side of the edge, where subscript 1 refers to the short-wavelength side of the edge and subscript 2 to the long-wavelength side ($\lambda_1 < \lambda_K < \lambda_2$), and define corresponding linear absorption coefficients on each side of the edge as

$$\begin{aligned} \mu_1 &= \mu_{m_1}\rho + \gamma_1 \\ \mu_2 &= \mu_{m_2}\rho + \gamma_2 \end{aligned} \tag{9}$$

In Eqs. (9), γ represents the right-hand summation term in Eq. (8). One may then combine Eqs. (9) with (3) to obtain (10).

$$\ln (I_1 i_2 / i_1 I_2) = (\mu_{m_1} - \mu_{m_2})\rho x + (\gamma_1 - \gamma_2)x \tag{10}$$

If λ_1 and λ_2 each approach λ_E, the wavelength corresponding to the center of the absorption edge of the element sought,

$$\lim_{\lambda \to \lambda_E} (\gamma_1 - \gamma_2) = 0$$

and

$$\lim_{\lambda \to \lambda_E} (\mu_{m_1} - \mu_{m_2}) = \Delta\mu_m$$

and Eq. (10) may be expressed as

$$\rho = [1/(x\,\Delta\mu_m)] \ln (I_1 i_2 / i_1 I_2) \tag{11}$$

in which I_1 represents incident-beam intensity at λ_1, i_1 represents transmitted-beam intensity at λ_1, etc., and ρ is defined as concentration in grams per cubic centimeter.

These relations are similar to those employed by Glocker and Frohnmayer[1] and by Engström.[2] In principle, if measurements are made essentially at an absorption edge, the above equations indicate that the chemical composition of the sample matrix has no effect on determination of the desired element.

Optimum Conditions for Chemical Analysis by XAES. The general problem of determining optimum absorber thickness to minimize statistical error in measurements involving the absorption or transmission of radiation has been discussed by Rainwater and Havens[7] and Rose and Shapiro.[8] The former authors considered the special case when the background is negligible and the cross-sectional area of the beam is fixed. Rose and Shapiro extended the analysis to the effects of background and variation of beam cross section within the absorber. Both these papers, however, deal only with simple absorptiometry.

In XAES, it is necessary to consider the consequences of the necessity to make measurements at wavelengths on each side of an absorption edge. Inasmuch as x-ray beams used in XAES generally are collimated, however, and because the entire beam cross section (except a negligible scattered fraction) passes through the sample and into the detector, it is not necessary to consider variations in beam cross section. Furthermore, under most experimental conditions, the background may be neglected in comparison with transmitted-beam intensity. An analysis of optimum conditions for chemical analysis by XAES has recently been completed by Dodd and Kaup.[9]

Derivation of Theoretical Conditions for Optimization. Refer to Eq. (11) and assume that the I's and i's are measured by collecting counts during specified timing intervals. The intensities on each side of an absorption edge then may be defined as

$$\begin{aligned} i_1 &= n_1/t_1 \\ I_1 &= N_1/T_1 \end{aligned} \quad \text{and} \quad \begin{aligned} i_2 &= n_2/t_2 \\ I_2 &= N_2/T_2 \end{aligned} \tag{12}$$

in which the n's and N's are numbers of counts collected during the corresponding counting times t and T, respectively. Equation (11) then may be expressed as

$$\rho = [1/(x\,\Delta\mu_m)] \ln (N_1 t_1 T_2 n_2 / T_1 n_1 N_2 t_2) \tag{13}$$

If it is assumed that the only errors considered are statistical counting errors, the law of propagation of errors as expressed by Birge[10] may be applied. Furthermore, in XAES one may elect to determine either ρ or $\Delta\mu_m$, but not both simultaneously. One of these quantities must be known with adequate precision. N, n, T, t, and x are directly measured quantities. The uncertainties in the timing periods T and t are at least an order of magnitude less than that associated with the quantitative detection of x-ray photons. Furthermore, it may be assumed that the uncertainty in the measurement of sample path length is negligible. If these assumptions are made, the concentration of the element sought may be considered solely as a function of the number of counts collected for the incident and transmitted beams on each side of an edge. Following this type of analysis, Liebhafsky et al.[11] have shown that x-ray emission is a random process whenever ideal operating conditions are attained. Under these conditions, x-ray photons reaching a detector fluctuate according to a unique Gaussian distribution, and the standard deviations are root-mean-square errors when a normal distribution is assumed and when the number of counts collected is high enough.

If τ is defined as the total time required to collect all counts,

$$\tau = T_1 + T_2 + t_1 + t_2 \tag{14}$$

Thus the individual counting times may be normalized for expression as timing ratios R and r (fractions of total counting time, $R_1 = T_1/\tau$, etc.). The numbers of counts collected N and n then may be expressed in terms of the incident-beam intensities, the timing ratios, the total time required to collect all counts, the absorption coefficients on each side of the edge μ_1 and μ_2, and the absorber thickness x.

To continue the analysis, the parameters α, β, and K may be defined as

$$\begin{aligned} \alpha &\equiv \mu_1 x \\ \beta &\equiv \mu_1/\mu_2 \\ K &\equiv I_1/I_2 \end{aligned} \tag{15}$$

and an expression for P^2, a term proportional to the expected error, expressed in terms of α, β, K, and the timing ratios. The type of analysis applied by Rose and Shapiro[8] for monochromatic absorptiometry then may be applied to derive a general expression for optimum path length and counting times. For practical considerations, however, there are three specific cases (B, C, and D below that involve selected restraints on the timing periods) that may profitably be considered.

The four cases are:

Case A: three R's independent (the general case)
Case B: $R_1 = R_2 = R$, and $r_1 = r_2 = r$
Case C: $R_1 = R_2 = r_2 = R$, and $r_1 = r$
Case D: $R_1 = R_2 = r_1 = r_2 = \frac{1}{4}$

The expression for P^2 may be derived by first combining Eq. (13) with the law of propagation of errors[10] to obtain

$$S_\rho^2 = [1/(x\ \Delta\mu_m)^2](1/N_1 + 1/n_1 + 1/N_2 + 1/n_2) \tag{16}$$

in which S_ρ is the standard deviation of the distribution of the measured value of ρ. Next, Eqs. (12) may be utilized with (2) (applied to each side of an absorption edge) and the definitions of the timing ratios given above to obtain the relations

$$\begin{aligned} N_1 &= I_1R_1\tau \\ n_1 &= I_1e^{-\mu_1 x}r_1\tau \end{aligned} \quad \text{and} \quad \begin{aligned} N_2 &= I_2R_2\tau \\ n_2 &= I_2e^{-\mu_2 x}r_2\tau \end{aligned} \tag{17}$$

Finally Eqs. (15), (16), and (17) may be combined with a definition of the term P^2,

$$P^2 \equiv I_1\tau(\Delta\mu_m/\mu_1)^2S_\rho^2 \tag{18}$$

to derive

$$P^2 = (1/\alpha^2)[1/R_1 + K^2/R_2 + e^\alpha/r_1 + K^2(e^{\alpha/\beta}/r_2)] \tag{19}$$

The above P^2 term defined by Eq. (18) is proportional to the p^2 term used by Rose and Shapiro.[8] Accordingly, optimization of P^2 can be considered either as optimizing S_ρ^2 for a given τ or as optimizing τ for a given S_ρ^2; and optimum conditions must correspond to a minimum P^2 for a given K and β. The differentiation of Eq. (19) and the requirement that $d(P^2) = 0$ then permit the development of a set of relations between the timing ratios and the parameters α, β, and K for each of the four cases.

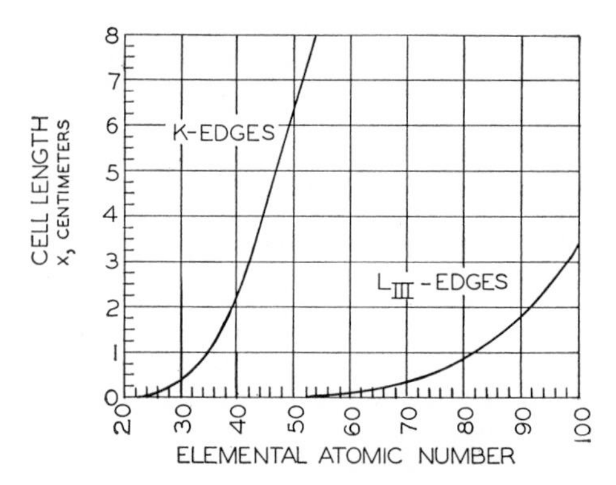

FIG. 1. Optimum path length x vs. elemental atomic number for dilute aqueous solutions (case D; cf. Sec. 4).

Optimum Sample Path Lengths in Practice. In practice, the optimum case to be employed for a given sample can be determined by using an arbitrary path length and measuring α or μ_1, β, and K. Curves of α, the timing ratios, and the relative expected error, computed by use of the above relations, are published elsewhere.[9] The maximum error resulting from application of case B, C, or D can be determined with the aid of these graphs, together with the corresponding quantity α, and the optimum case can be selected to yield the smallest error. The optimum path length can be computed by using the first of Eqs. (15).

The use of an optimum x-ray path length results frequently in a rather thick sample. For dilute solutions in water, for example (the special case D of the above-described analysis for which the timing ratios are equal to each other, and each equal to one-fourth the total time τ), it is found that the optimum sample path length varies, for K-absorption edges, from about 0.5 mm for titanium to about 9 cm for iodine, and from about 1 mm for cesium to about 2 cm for uranium if L_{III}-absorption edges are used. This variation is presented graphically in Fig. 1.

In general, it is advantageous to use reasonably thick samples for chemical analysis by XAES because the fine structure on each side of an absorption edge is thereby smeared out. (For fine-structure spectrometry, per se, the thinnest practical samples are used.) On the other hand, it is found that the use of relatively thick samples increases the effective width of an absorption edge. A consequence of this is that the apparent value of the absorption-edge jump $\Delta\mu_m$ will decrease with an increase in x or ρ for analytical procedures utilizing only one measurement on each side of an edge (such as that described by Dunn[4] or the fluorescent-source technique of Hakkila and Waterbury[6]). This situation emphasizes the desirability of measuring absorption at several wavelengths on each side of an edge and extrapolating to the edge.

5. THE GENERATION OF MONOCHROMATIC X-RAYS

Principles of Monochromatization. Monochromatic x-rays generally are obtained either from a beam of polychromatic or "white" x-rays or from a beam comprised of one or more characteristic x-ray emission lines superimposed on a white radiation background. In either case, monochromatization may be either partial or total. It should be emphasized that monochromatic x-ray beams never are strictly monochromatic, although single characteristic primary or secondary emission lines approach this criterion. Partial monochromatization is cheaper and simpler, and the loss of intensity is appreciably less than that lost by total monochromatization, although the generation of characteristic secondary radiation in a commercial spectrometer is relatively simple.

Various methods of obtaining monochromatic beams are summarized in the following outline:

I. Continuous primary white-radiation incident-beam source
   A. Partial monochromatization
      1. Absorption filters
      2. Electronic discrimination, including the use of single- and multichannel pulse-height analyzers
      3. Use of selective detector (as a Geiger counter with high relative sensititity for copper *K*-alpha radiation)
   B. Total monochromatization
      1. Ross balanced filters[12,13] (permits attainment of high intensities)
      2. Optical dispersion (monochromatization by diffraction from a single crystal, either flat or curved)
         a. Use of fixed single-crystal monochromator adjusted to diffract only one wavelength
         b. Single crystal mounted on x-ray diffractometer with detector adjusted to maintain an angle of incidence to initial beam twice that of analyzing crystal, x-ray line source, and detector slit on focusing circle (Bragg-Brentano parafocusing)
      3. Optical dispersion with single crystal on diffractometer, together with electronic discrimination, pulse-height analysis, and control of voltage applied to x-ray tube
      4. Two crystals in a double-crystal spectrometer
         a. First crystal in fixed position with second crystal adjustable (covering narrow-wavelength range)
         b. Both crystals rotate synchronously to adjust to any desired wavelength
II. Continuous primary incident-beam source with characteristic peak superimposed upon white-radiation background
   A. Partial monochromatization
      1. Use of beta-absorbing filter to suppress *K*-beta lines (filter of material whose *K*-absorption edge lies between the *K*-alpha and *K*-beta wavelengths of tube target material, the filter containing an element of atomic number one or two less than that of target material, as in x-ray diffraction procedures)

2. Use of beta-absorbing filter together with electronic discrimination and pulse-height analysis

B. Total monochromatization

1. Characteristic radiation from tube target together with fixed-crystal monochromator at angle to diffract characteristic wavelength
2. Suitable pair (or more) of characteristic emission lines, generated in tube, that bracket the absorption edge of the element sought for XAES, together with adjustable-crystal monochromator to permit selection of one line and then another

III. Characteristic secondary-emission radiation

A. Total monochromatization

1. One or more secondary-emission characteristic lines on each side of the pertinent absorption edge for XAES, from a selected fluorescing source, together with a fixed monochromatizing crystal, or a crystal mounted on a spectrometer adjustable to select the various characteristic emission lines (the *parallel* collimated beam resulting from use of Soller slits, and available on commercial spectrometers, is preferred for absorptiometry)

IV. Characteristic *K* x-rays emitted from a source containing a radioactive isotope that decays by *K* capture (conceivably, two sources might be selected to bracket an absorption edge, but this procedure is unknown to the writer)

In practice, methods I-*B*-2-*b*, I-*B*-3 and III-*A*-1 are the most effective and convenient for XAES. Probably the most convenient source for simple absorptiometry is method IV, as employed by Hughes and Wilczewski,[14] for example. These workers used a button containing 4 millicuries of iron-55 to determine sulfur in petroleum distillates.

Equipment. *X-ray Generating Equipment* (cf. Chap. 2, Sec. 3). The major requirements for x-ray generators used to supply a source of x-radiation for monochromatic absorptiometry are a high degree of x-ray source stability and a well-filtered constant-potential d-c power supply with a low ripple. This required degree of x-ray source stability is available in most modern x-ray generators designed for diffraction use. It is obtained by careful regulation of the electrical supply-line voltage together with x-ray tube current stabilization. Among the suppliers of well-regulated constant-potential x-ray sources in the United States are (in alphabetical order) General Electric Co., Philips Electronic Instruments, Picker X-ray Corp., and Siemens America, Inc. Instruments of the necessary high degree of regulation and with constant-potential d-c filters have become available only recently.

Precise regulation of the x-ray tube output is, actually, much more critical in polychromatic x-ray absorptiometry, but it is attained only by simultaneously monitoring the x-ray beam using a second detector. In monochromatic x-ray absorptiometry it generally is assumed that the incident x-ray beam is of constant intensity since relatively few instruments provide for simultaneous monitoring. One exception to this is Jarrell-Ash Company's x-ray diffraction generator as used with the diffractometer available from Hilger and Watts, Ltd. This unit employs a pumped gas tube. A monitoring device on the incident beam is available for precise diffraction work to guard against variation of x-ray intensity with gas pressure in the x-ray tube. This excellent x-ray source also is equipped with a constant-potential filter and a ratio recorder such that the recorded data at all times represent a ratio of transmitted-beam to incident-beam intensity.

X-ray Detection Equipment (see Chap. 3). The use of a direct-measurement type of detector is preferable to photographic registration, even if the film is scanned with a photometric device. A Geiger counter may be used as the detector in direct-measurement work, but it has the disadvantage of being limited to relatively low counting rates. In x-ray absorptiometry it generally is necessary to work with either high counting rates or long counting periods in order to collect enough counts to hold statistical errors to a desired low level. Experience has shown that it is preferable to use x-ray detectors having resolving times of 1 μsec or less together with associated electronic components with correspondingly short resolving times. Resolving times of this order of magnitude, together with long lives at high counting rates, are attainable in scintillation counters and gas-flow proportional counters. Proportional counters generally are considered superior with respect to their energy resolution. When the counter is combined with a single crystal mounted on a spectrometer, however, scintillation counters used together with pulse-height discrimination circuitry are eminently satisfactory. Scintillation counters are most efficient for harder x-rays with wavelengths up to approximately 1.5 Å. For longer wavelengths, xenon-filled proportional counters or gas-flow (usually argon-methane) proportional counters are more sensitive.

X-ray Tubes and Spectral Purity (cf. Chap. 2, Sec. 2). The incident x-ray beam spectrum in the range of interest should be free from characteristic emission lines resulting from target impurities or from fluorescence from windows, slits, or other instrumentation in the x-ray beam. For shorter wavelengths it generally is desirable to use a tungsten-target tube because higher intensities can be obtained and no excessive contamination of the target is observed during operation because the filament also is tungsten. On the other hand, it frequently becomes necessary during x-ray absorptiometry at wavelengths corresponding to absorption edges of the iron transition elements to use copper-target or chromium-target x-ray tubes because tungsten emission lines frequently interfere, but eventual contamination from hot tungsten filaments may cause trouble at x-ray tube lives over 200 hr. The above discussion refers only to sealed-off Coolidge-type tubes. Of course, these problems could be minimized by using the less convenient pumped and demountable gas tubes and replacing anodes frequently.

Secondary-emission Fluorescent Sources. When secondary-emission fluorescence sources are used, it is usually necessary to devise experimental arrangements compatible with available x-ray spectrometers. It seldom is necessary to make extensive alterations to commercial units. Reference may be made to Hakkila and Waterbury,[6] for example, who modified a Philips three-position-head spectrometer by removing the exit collimator and inserting a sample cell holder in a lead block having a ½-in.-diameter hole for passage of the beam. To determine cobalt (K-absorption edge at 1.608 Å) by the two-point XAES method, Hakkila used a coupon of a 50-50 alloy of copper and nickel ($K\alpha_1$ lines at 1.5405 Å and 1.658 Å, respectively) in the spectrometer sample holder.

Sample Holders or Cells. When samples are used in the form of acidic aqueous solutions, or other corrosive liquids, it is essential that the cell be constructed of inert materials. In any case it is essential that the sample holders be designed to permit precise alignment and repositioning at the same point in the x-ray beam and that the samples have precisely known and reproducible x-ray path lengths. Sample cells for liquids should have thin low-absorbance windows that do not expand under the pressure of a contained liquid. Many workers prefer thin rigid polystyrene, methyl methacrylate, or beryllium windows for this reason. Tightly stretched thin Mylar windows also are satisfactory.

When a crystal is employed with a spectrometer for x-ray monochromatization, the sample may be located either in the polychromatic beam before the crystal or, less satisfactorily, in the monochromatized beam between crystal and detector. The latter position may result in the loss of needed beam collimation if the Soller slit is removed and in the scattering of an excessive amount of undesired secondary fluorescent radiation into the detector if the sample is too close to the detector, especially without a collimator.

Typical Experimental Arrangements. Schematic sketches of experimental arrangements are shown in Figs. 2 and 3. Figure 4 shows equipment set up on a commercial diffractometer using incident white radiation, monochromatizing crystal in diffractometer sample holder, gas-flow proportional counter, and sample cell located between divergence slits and crystal, as in Fig. 2. The arrangement shown in Fig. 3 is an adaptation of a commercial spectrometer using a suitable fluorescing source in the spectrometer.

Application of XAES to Specific Elements. *Low-atomic-number Elements.* Using a gas-flow counter, the lightest element to which XAES may be applied with-

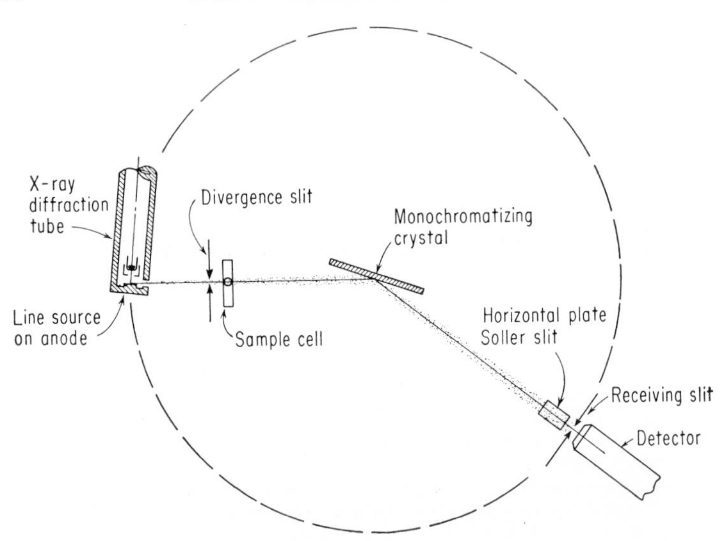

FIG. 2. Schematic and idealized optical diagram showing typical modification of commercial diffractometer for x-ray absorption-edge spectrometry using a "white" x-ray source (monochromatization by method I-*B*-2-*b* or I-*B*-3; cf. Sec. 5). A curved crystal is required for improved focusing of divergent beam.

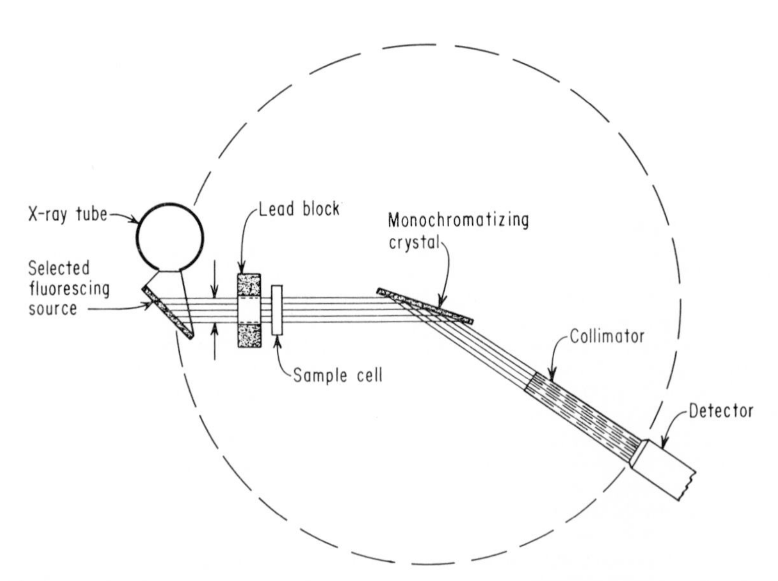

FIG. 3. Schematic optical diagram showing modification of commercial spectrometer for x-ray absorption-edge spectrometry using a fluorescent secondary x-ray source (monochromatization by method III-*A*-1; cf. Sec. 5).

out a helium tent or a vacuum x-ray path is titanium, element number 22 (but see Engström[2]). In addition to the difficulties encountered with the detection of soft x-rays at K edges of low-atomic-number elements, the corresponding path lengths required are so small that microtomes or similar instruments must be employed for sample preparation (as described by Engström[2]). It is difficult to determine chemical elements from 22 to about arsenic or selenium, 33 or 34, with a precision better than ± 1 per cent.

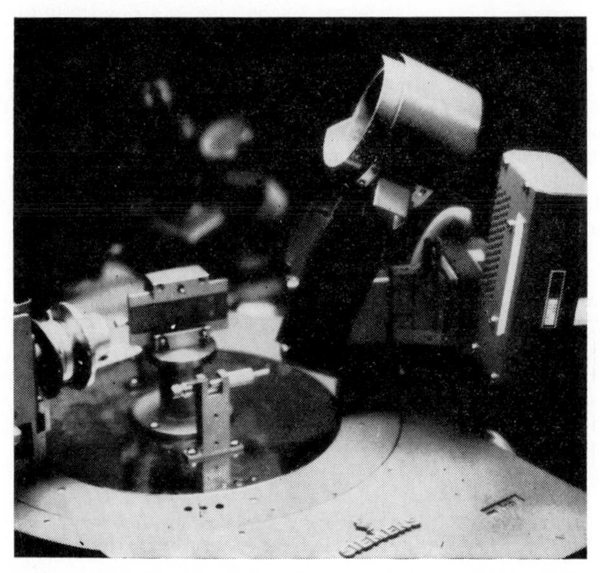

FIG. 4. Photograph of commercial diffractometer with sample cell, lithium fluoride monochromatizing crystal, and gas-flow proportional counter in place according to Fig. 2.

Elements in the Middle of the Periodic Table. Careful studies (unpublished) of the K edge of bromine (element 35) have demonstrated the possibility of determining this element with a precision of ± 3 parts per 1,000 and a sensitivity of 30 to 50 ppm. Analyses of this quality should be possible at the K edges of all elements from approximately bromine, element 35, to neodymium, 60, although the use of sodium iodide crystals in scintillation counters may tend to complicate the determination of iodine and reduce precision and sensitivity for this element. Another difficulty in this range is the need for longer path lengths for K edges of elements above barium, element 56 (see Fig. 1).

In about the middle of the rare-earth series of elements, above neodymium, the path lengths required for the use of K edges in XAES become inconveniently long and the high-voltage limitations of the majority of x-ray constant-potential generators do not permit the attainment of a continuous-beam output at the high energies of these K edges (the General Electric XRD-6 has a 75-kv generator). At this point it becomes necessary to shift over to L edges. The L_{III} edges are most satisfactory because they have the largest absorption-edge jumps.

High-atomic-number Elements. For elements from approximately neodymium, element 60, to dysprosium, 66, it is necessary to use L edges and gas-flow proportional counters. The resulting precision is about ± 1 per cent and the sensitivity about 100 ppm. From holmium, element 67, to the rare element lutetium, 71, the tungsten L edges interfere again and precision is reduced, as in the case with the K edge of nickel and other iron transition elements. From about hafnium, element 73, to gold, 79, a scintillation counter and copper-target x-ray tube may be used, but performance is about the same as with elements 60 to 66. From about mercury, element 80, to the highest-atomic-number elements the use of L_{III} edges results again in optimum performance with a precision of about 3 parts per 1,000 and a sensitivity of 30 to 50 ppm. A series of careful measurements of the L_{III} edge of lead have been completed by D. J. Kaup and the writer (unpublished) to determine this performance.

Absorption-edge Jumps. In order to apply XAES to the analysis of a specific element, it is necessary that the absorption-edge jump $\Delta\mu_m$ be determined with adequate precision. Glocker and Frohnmayer[1] first determined K-absorption-edge jumps for nine elements ranging from molybdenum to thorium, and L_I-edge jumps for thorium and uranium. A later survey of the magnitudes of absorption-edge jumps is presented for K, L_{III}, and M_V edges throughout the periodic table in the publication of Engström.[2] Recently D. J. Kaup and the writer have made similar measurements (unpublished) at the K edges of bromine, rubidium, and strontium and the L_{III} edge of lead. The results obtained are presented in column 5 of Table 1 as an example of the type of data required beforehand in order that XAES may be applied to a given element. It should be emphasized that these data are uniquely a function of the instrumental arrangement used. For highest precision, each edge jump should be determined under the same conditions used for analysis.

Table 1. Absorption-edge Jump and Extrapolation Data

Element	Ionic species (in aqueous solution)	Type of edge	Wave-length, Å	Absorption-edge jump $\Delta\mu_m$ (cm² g⁻¹ of element)	Spectral range free from fine structure and interference (degrees 2θ, LiF crystal)	Best least-squares fit of extrapolation data (log I/i vs. abscissas below)
Bromine......	Br^{+5} (and BrO_3^{-1})	K	0.9200	$135.6(1 \pm 3 \times 10^{-3})$	23.5–25.5 and 27.0–29.0	$\sin^3 \theta$
Lead.........	Pb^{+2}	L_{III}	0.9507	$95.20(1 \pm 2 \times 10^{-3})$	25.0–26.5 and 27.5–29.0	$\sin^3 \theta$
Rubidium.....	Rb^{+1}	K	0.8155	$114.1(1 \pm 3 \times 10^{-3})$	20.0–22.5 and 24.0–26.0	$\sin^5 \theta$
Strontium.....	Sr^{+2}	K	0.7697	$89.5(1 \pm 2 \times 10^{-2})$	21.0–22.7	$\sin^3 \theta$

Extrapolation of Absorption Data to Absorption-edge Wavelengths. If experimentally measured absorption edges were abruptly discontinuous, it would be possible to measure the sample attenuation of an essentially monochromatic beam precisely at wavelengths *just at* either side of an absorption edge and obtain data essentially independent of sample matrix effects. Experiment, on the other hand, indicates an appreciable finite width upon scanning an edge, and frequently an irregular variation in transmitted intensity on each side of the edge.

In practice it usually is difficult, if not impossible, to select spectrometer angular settings on both sides of an edge that are close enough to the edge to eliminate matrix effects entirely and, at the same time, free from the effects of artifacts such as unwanted spectral lines or edge fine structure. The problem may be solved by making empirical correction factors that are dependent to some extent upon sample composition. Dunn[4] has described such a procedure.

An alternative solution involves extrapolation of a linear plot of measured data to the generally accepted edge wavelength. From Eqs. (3) and (4) it is seen that straight lines on each side of an edge should be obtained by plotting log log (I/i) vs. log λ. We have found it more convenient, frequently, to plot log (I/i) vs. the crystal monochromator (diffractometer or spectrometer) angular setting in degrees 2θ. An example of such a plot is shown in Fig. 5. Better linear fits to absorption data often are obtained if the angular setting is raised to a power, usually a power of sin θ. In the last column of Table 1 are shown the abscissas [to be plotted vs. log (I/i) as ordinates] found to give the best least-squares fits of absorption data measured at bromine, lead, rubidium, and strontium edges.

Extrapolation procedures may be employed to avoid interferences of extraneous spectral lines or absorption-edge fine structure. Safe extrapolation ranges within which significant data can be taken should be determined beforehand. Representative extrapolation ranges are presented in column 6 of Table 1 for bromine, lead, rubidium, and strontium.

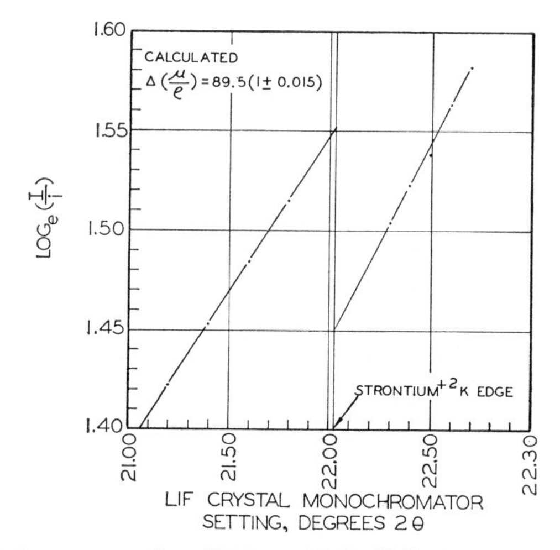

FIG. 5. Extrapolation at strontium K edge with ln (I/i) plotted vs. the lithium fluoride monochromatizing crystal setting in degrees 2θ (use of $\sin^3 \theta$, rather than 2θ, gives better least-squares fit to data; cf. Table 1).

Miscellaneous Procedural Requirements for XAES. In addition to the procedures outlined in the foregoing, a few additional operational precautions concerning limits of confidence on precision, x-ray tube operating voltages, the proper use of electronic discrimination, and precision and stability of equipment are outlined below.

Limitations on Confident Calculation of Probable Error. The need for a well-filtered constant-potential power supply with a low ripple has been emphasized above. In order to apply with confidence the indicated probable error calculated from the number of counts collected in a timing period, it is important that the x-ray tube be operated at a potential comfortably higher than the voltage corresponding to the absorption edge under study by the known percentage of ripple present. Furthermore, the effective counter resolving time should be 1 μsec or less, with correspondingly low resolving times for all components in associated electronic counting equipment, to permit confident calculation of probable error based on resolving time and statistical theory.

Proper Use of Electronic Discrimination Equipment (cf. Chap. 3). The absorption edges of elements in gases, crystals, and other materials used in the construction of counters must not interfere. This requirement may be satisfied by operation of the x-ray tube at potentials lower than such absorption edges or by proper pulse-height discrimination settings. Second harmonics of wavelengths diffracted by the monochromatizing crystal must be eliminated simultaneously by similar procedures. The pulses counted in counter escape peaks must also be eliminated by the same methods unless it is determined that escape peaks represent additional desired monochromatic-beam photons. Finally, K, L, and M edges of interfering elements must be eliminated by optical or electronic dispersion or the use of a different absorption edge of the same element that is free from such interferences.

ACKNOWLEDGMENTS

The support of the author's early work by the Atomic Energy Commission Division of Research is acknowledged with thanks. The invaluable assistance of David J. Kaup should be emphasized as a major factor in the original work reported in this chapter.

REFERENCES CITED

1. R. Glocker and W. Frohnmayer, *Ann. Physik*, **76**:369 (1925).
2. A. Engström, *Acta Radiol.*, Suppl. 63, 1946.
3. R. E. Barieau, *Anal. Chem.*, **29**:348 (1957).
4. H. W. Dunn, *Anal. Chem.*, **34**:116 (1962).
5. E. A. Hakkila, *Anal. Chem.*, **33**:1012 (1961).
6. E. A. Hakkila and G. R. Waterbury, *Advances in X-ray Analysis*, vol. 5, pp. 379–388, Proc. 10th Annual Conference on Applications of X-ray Analysis, Denver, 1961, W. M. Mueller (ed.), Plenum Press, Inc., New York, 1962.
7. J. Rainwater and W. W. Havens, *Phys. Rev.*, **70**:146 (1946).
8. M. E. Rose and M. M. Shapiro, *Phys. Rev.*, **74**:1853 (1948).
9. C. G. Dodd and D. J. Kaup, Optimum Conditions for Chemical Analysis by X-ray Absorption Edge Spectrometry, *Anal. Chem.*, **36**:2325 (1964).
10. R. T. Birge, *Am. Phys. Teacher*, **7**:351 (1939).
11. H. A. Liebhafsky, H. G. Pfeiffer, and P. D. Zemany, *Anal. Chem.*, **27**:1257 (1955).
12. P. A. Ross, *J. Opt. Soc. Am.*, **16**:433 (1928).
13. B. W. Roberts and W. Parish, "Filter and Crystal Monochromator Techniques," Sec. 2.3.2.2 in *International Tables for X-ray Crystallography*, vol. III, Physical and Chemical Tables, pp. 78–79, International Union of Crystallography, Kynoch Press, Birmingham, England, 1962.
14. H. K. Hughes and J. W. Wilczewski, *Anal. Chem.*, **26**:1889 (1954).

GENERAL REFERENCES

Bertin, E. P., R. J. Longobucco, and R. J. Carver, *Anal. Chem.*, **36**:641 (1964).
Cosslett, V. H., and W. C. Nixon: *X-ray Microscopy*, pp. 139–182, Cambridge University Press, New York, 1960.
Engström, A.: Quantitative Micro- and Histochemical Elementary Analysis by Roentgen Absorption Spectrography, *Acta Radiol.*, Suppl. 63, 1946.
Liebhafsky, H. A., H. G. Pfeiffer, E. H. Winslow, and P. D. Zemany: *X-ray Absorption and Emission in Analytical Chemistry*, pp. 136–145, John Wiley & Sons, Inc., New York, 1960 (contains references to earlier literature).
Liebhafsky, H. A., E. H. Winslow, and H. G. Pfeiffer: *Anal. Chem.*, **34**:282R (1962).*
Liebhafsky, H. A., E. H. Winslow, and H. Pfeiffer: *Anal. Chem.*, **32**:240R (1960).*
Liebhafsky, H. A., and E. H. Winslow: *Anal. Chem.*, **30**:580 (1958).*
Liebhafsky, H. A., and E. H. Winslow: *Anal. Chem.*, **28**:583 (1956).*
Lindström, B.: Roentgen Absorption Spectrophotometry in Quantitative Cytochemistry. *Acta Radiol.*, Suppl. 125, 1955.
Powers, M. C.: *X-ray Fluorescent Spectrometer Conversion Tables*, Philips Electronic Instruments, Mount Vernon, N.Y., 1957.
Sagel, K.: *Tabellen zur Röntgen-Emissions- und Absorptions-Analyse*, Springer-Verlag OHG, Berlin, 1959.
Sandström, A. E.: "Experimental Methods of X-ray Spectroscopy: Ordinary Wavelengths," in *Handbuch der Physik, Röntgenstrahlen*, vol. 30, pp. 78–245, Springer-Verlag OHG, Berlin, 1957.

* Biannual reviews of fundamental developments in analysis in *Analytical Chemistry*, X-ray Absorption and Emission.

Chapter 43

FINE STRUCTURE IN ABSORPTION-EDGE SPECTRA

R. A. Van Nordstrand

Sinclair Research, Inc.

1. INTRODUCTION

The x-ray absorption spectrum of a substance consists primarily of the absorption edges of the component elements. Associated with each edge is fine structure which is related to the chemical form of the corresponding element. Because of this relationship to chemistry, fine structure is useful in the study of complex solids, including catalysts, glasses, mixed oxides, minerals, and alloys.

Emphasis in this chapter is on the elements most readily studied, those with absorption edges between 2.5 and 1.0 Å (between 5 and 12 kev). This includes Ti^{22} through As^{33} on the basis of K edges and Cs^{55} through Hg^{80} on the basis of L_{III} edges. At shorter wavelengths resolving power is a serious limitation; at longer wavelengths transmission is a limitation. For the elements cited, significant fine structure is observed with a good one-crystal spectrometer. Additional detail close to the edge is obtained with a two-crystal spectrometer. A table of absorption edges and excitation potentials may be found in Chap. 1.

The basic experimental and theoretical work in fine-structure spectroscopy was done in the period 1920 to 1931. This work includes the studies of metals by Coster, the studies of a variety of chemical compounds by Hanawalt, and the theoretical developments by Kossel and Kronig. This period is reviewed by Compton and Allison[1] and by Sandström.[2]

2. PRINCIPLES

An absorption edge consists of an abrupt rise in the absorption coefficient at a photon energy just sufficient to liberate a specific inner electron from its atom. For photon energies greater than the value of the edge the absorption coefficient remains high and the freed electron accepts as kinetic energy all the excess energy of the photon.

Fine structure consists of the deviations of the actual absorption spectrum from the simple step function described above. It includes deviations both in the abrupt rise and in the flat portion on the high-energy side of the rise. The cause of this fine structure is not fully understood. Currently it is treated as if it had several causes, each contributing over a characteristic energy interval.

An absorption coefficient is treated as a product of three terms:

1. Density of initial electronic states
2. Density of final electronic states
3. Transition probability

For the x-ray case, only the second and third terms vary with energy. These variations may, in principle, be sensitive to chemical structure. The transition probability is the overlap integral of the product of the wave functions representing the initial and final electronic states. In the following discussion fine structure is accounted for alternately on the basis of these two factors, density of final states and transition probability.

Fermi-level Fine Structure. The first rise in absorption at the K edge of a metal is attributed to promotion of the $1s$ electron to the Fermi level in the conduction band. The energy value at the midpoint of this rise is the energy of the absorption edge. For metallic cobalt, shown in Fig. 1, the edge is at 7,709 ev.

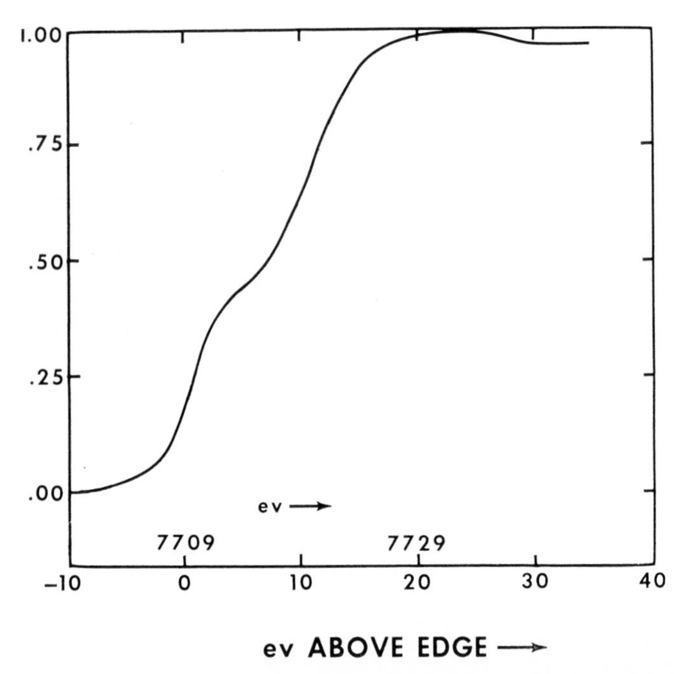

FIG. 1. Absorption spectrum of metallic cobalt in the vicinity of the K edge at 7709 ev The ordinate scale is the absorption coefficient arbitrarily set to zero below the edge and to unity for the maximum value. One energy scale is photon energy in ev, the other scale is ev above the edge. Data were obtained by R. O. Keeling, Jr., with a two-crystal spectrometer.

The value of this edge for the metal is used as the zero point of a new energy scale for that element in all its chemical states. This new scale represents the kinetic energy of the photoelectron. It provides an arbitrary basis for comparing fine structures at the edges of various elements, for example, at the chromium, manganese, and cobalt edges of the respective hexacyanide ions.

It is surprising that an energy scale zeroed at the absorption edge—or Fermi level—of a metal would be a suitable scale for compounds of the metal. Perhaps this zero is the Fermi level for both the metal and its compounds. Two types of evidence support this suggestion. First, there are no cases in which absorption begins at negative energy values. Second, in the case of nonmetallic compounds, which have no empty electron states within several electron volts of the Fermi level, the midpoint of the initial rise at the absorption edge is usually at 5 or 10 ev. Significant consequences of the use of this energy scale will be pointed out.

An important distinction between the absorption by an insulating compound and that by a metal has been discussed by Parratt.[3] In the insulator the absorbing atom loses a *1s* electron, exhibits an additional unit of positive charge, and serves as a stronger attracting center for the extracted electron. This changes the energy-level scheme of the insulating compound as seen by the ejected electron; the possibility of exciton states is introduced and the potential-energy base is changed. In the metal the conduction electrons collapse quickly around the hole being created during extraction of the 1*s* electron, and the latter electron may see the true energy levels of the metal.

A second rise is generally present at the absorption edge of a metal. At the cobalt *K* edge, seen in Fig. 1, this has a midpoint at 11 ev. This rise has been attributed to a corresponding rise in either the density of electronic states of the metal or the per cent *p* character of these states.

Kronig Structure or Extended Fine Structure. The low-amplitude long-period fluctuations in absorption coefficient which occur over the energy range from 50 or 100 ev up to several hundred electron volts above the edge are known as Kronig or extended fine structure. The absorption spectra of metallic cobalt and nickel[4] in Fig. 2 provide clear examples.

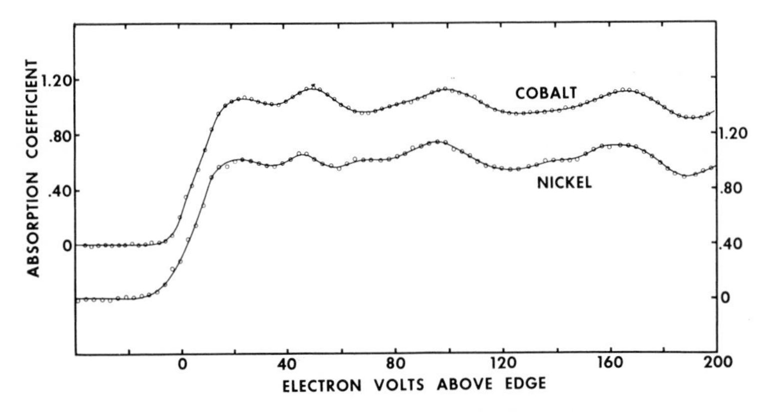

FIG. 2. Absorption-edge spectra for metallic nickel and cobalt, showing identity of extended fine structure. The ordinate scale on this and the following figures is the *K*-absorption coefficient, defined in Sec. 5.

The only absorbers giving fine structure beyond 100 ev are those with a high-symmetry crystal lattice, such as the cubic close-packed and the hexagonal close-packed crystals. This fine structure appears to be sensitive only to crystal system and to lattice constant. Thus nickel and cobalt, which are face-centered cubic with nearly identical lattice constants, have nearly identical Kronig structure. Most of the metals and many of the oxides give Kronig structure. Those which do not, such as alpha manganese and Mn_3O_4, have complex crystal structures.

The photoelectron in the Kronig theory is treated as a plane wave traveling in the periodic field of the crystal. Certain combinations of wavelength and direction are supposedly forbidden for a particular crystal structure, because these combinations produce Bragg diffraction rather than transmission. The wavelength of the photoelectron λ_e is given by the de Broglie equation

$$\lambda_e = \sqrt{150/E} \tag{1}$$

where E, in ev, is the kinetic energy of the electron. For wavelengths or energies at which a significant number of all possible directions are forbidden the absorption coefficient is expected to be low. Maxima are expected at wavelengths for which no directions are forbidden.

The Kronig theory has not been successful at predicting location and magnitude of fine-structure features. However, two relationships originally pointed out by

Kronig continue to provide the main support for his theory. The first of these relates change in fine structure to change in lattice parameter; the second relates it to change in temperature.

The first relationship applies to any pair of cubic crystals whose structures differ only in the value of the lattice parameters a_1 and a_2. Any pair of corresponding maxima or minima in the extended fine structure will occur at electron wavelengths λ_1 and λ_2, which are proportional to the lattice parameters

$$\lambda_1/\lambda_2 = a_1/a_2 \tag{2}$$

or at electron energy values E_1 and E_2 given by

$$E_1/E_2 = (a_2/a_1)^2 \tag{3}$$

Both these equations are dependent on—but not very sensitive to—the proper assignment of zero for the energy scale.

Table 1. Comparison of Experimental Values of Absorption Maxima (in Electron Volts) for Three Face-centered-cubic Metals

Cobalt*	Nickel*	Nickel†	Copper†	Copper‡
				15
24	22	27	21	23
50	47	49	45	45
	(67)§	. . .	. . .	(67)
100	96	98	89	92
				(111)
	(140)	. . .	. . .	(132)
168	163	167	153	152
				(165)
xx	xx	215	199	202
xx	xx	251	233	224

* One-crystal spectrometer.[4]
† Lytle.[5] At 78°K. One-crystal spectrometer.
‡ Krogstad.[6] Two-crystal spectrometer.
§ Very weak maxima are shown in parentheses.

Table 2. Test of Kronig Relation between Energy Values and Lattice Parameters

Metal	a	$(a_2/a_1)^2$	E_1/E_2 (avg)
Co.	3.55		
		1.02	1.03
Ni.	3.52		
		1.05	1.09
Cu.	3.61		

Energies for absorption maxima of cobalt, nickel, and copper are compared in Table 1. The data are taken from five spectra, obtained in three laboratories. The correspondence is remarkable. The small shifts of the maxima from one metal to another are related to lattice constants, as predicted by Eq. (3). The check of this equation is shown by the data in Table 2.

The second relationship referred to above concerns a pronounced temperature dependence, as found by Lytle,[5] in the extended fine structure of copper and nickel. At 9°K, fine structure extends to 900 ev; at room temperature, to only 400 ev. These results are compatible with the Debye-Waller theory for the temperature dependence of x-ray and electron diffraction, thus supporting a diffraction theory for fine structure.

The Kronig theory leads one to expect that a given crystalline material will give a specific extended fine-structure pattern, regardless of which absorption edge is examined. However, from Fig. 3 it is apparent that the spinel $Ni_3Mn_3O_8$ has two different fine structures, one associated with the Ni edge, one with the Mn edge. This distinction may be due to the different phase relationship of the photoelectrons with the lattice, depending on whether the electrons arise from nickel atoms in octahedral

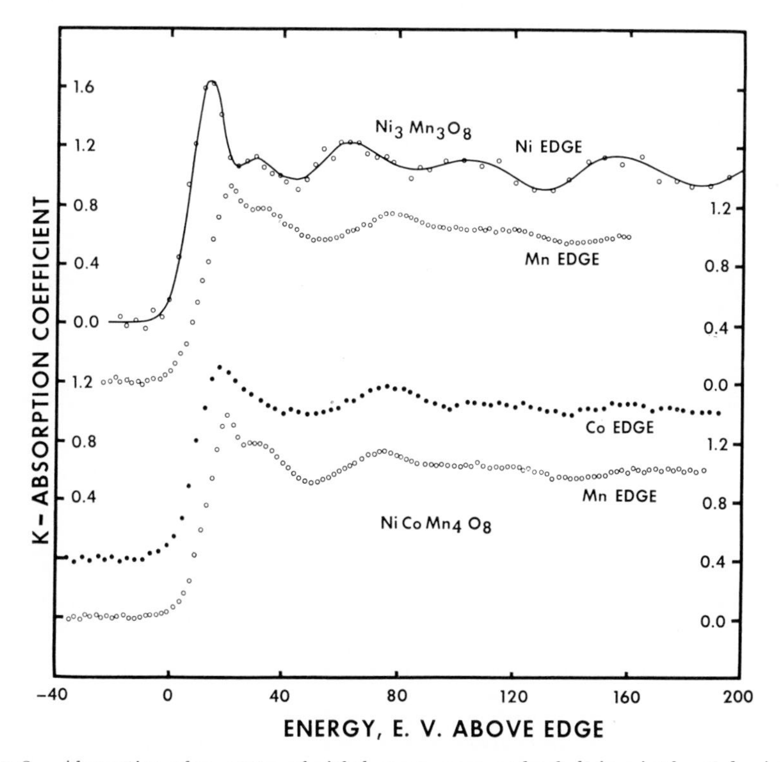

FIG. 3. Absorption-edge spectra of nickel, manganese, and cobalt in mixed-metal spinels

sites or from manganese atoms in both octahedral and tetrahedral sites.[7] The superposition of fine structures from manganese in both sites and of two or three valence states is probably the cause of the flatness of the extended fine structure associated with the manganese edge. Cobalt resembles manganese with regard to variability of both site and valence; this may account for the similarity of extended fine structure at the Co and Mn edges of the spinel $NiCoMn_4O_8$, shown also in Fig. 3.

The same problem arises in accounting for the pronounced differences in extended fine structure at the cobalt edge of two closely related spinels, Co_3O_4 with lattice parameter 8.084 Å and $CoAl_2O_4$ with parameter 8.103 Å. The spectra shown in Fig. 4 were obtained under identical experimental conditions. Again, from the Kronig theory one expects these extended fine structures to be very similar. Instead, much greater detail is apparent in the fine structure of the aluminate, which contains only divalent cobalt in tetrahedral sites. The fine structure of the cobalt oxide is much more diffuse, which may be due to superposition of fine structure from several cobalt types, varying in valence and lattice site.

It appears from the examples just cited that the Kronig theory of extended fine structure is incomplete if stated solely in terms of electronic states characteristic of a given crystal lattice; that it should include the phase relationship of the electron to the lattice, as established by the point of origin of the electron within the lattice; and that there may be a valence effect also which shifts the potential-energy base.

Several modifications of the Kronig theory have been proposed. These are discussed in some detail by Azaroff.[8] Each leads to Eqs. (2) and (3), but none has been successful in *predicting* fine-structure details.

Kossel Structure. Fine structure at the K edge of gaseous argon has become a landmark from both the experimental and theoretical viewpoints. The spectrum reproduced in Fig. 5 was obtained by Parratt[9] with a two-crystal spectrometer. Fine structure is confined to within 3 ev of the main edge; beyond this the absorption spectrum is flat.

The fine structure of argon gas is usually interpreted according to Kossel's suggestion that the maxima correspond to transitions of the electron to bound atomic states,

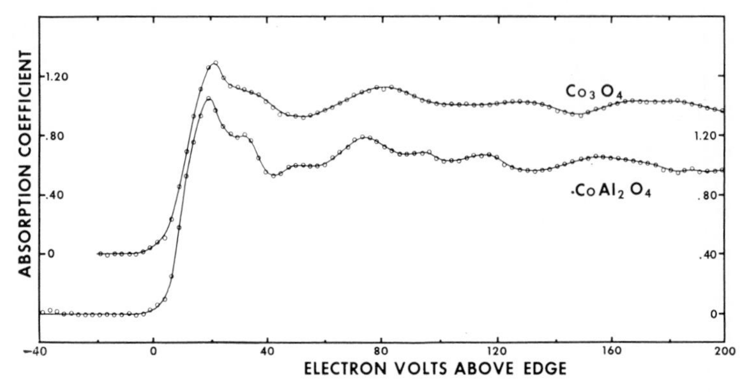

FIG. 4. Absorption-edge spectra of cobalt in the two spinels, Co_3O_4 and cobalt aluminate.

following the selection rules of spectroscopy. For argon these transitions are 1s to 4p, 1s to 5p, etc. The binding energy in the 4p case should be of the same magnitude as the electron affinity of the free potassium ion. The argon atom with a 1s electron missing is analogous to the potassium ion and should have the same energy levels with respect to addition of an electron.

Kossel's theory may apply rigorously only to monatomic gases. The only example studied is argon. Fine structure of solid argon already introduces grave problems, as it consists of a series of broad peaks extending for about 50 ev above the edge. Thus Kossel structure has been lost in the change from gas to the condensed state.

Sharp low-energy peaks, comparable with that at the argon gas absorption edge, are present at the absorption edge of gaseous chlorine,[10] many four-valent titanium compounds, and the chromate and permanganate ions.[11] Such peaks are ascribed to Kossel structure and are explained in terms of transitions of the electron to bound atomic states.

Beeman and Bearden[12] extended the Kossel theory to spectra with initial peaks 15 to 30 ev above the edge, thereby explaining spectra of the aqueous ions of nickel, copper, and zinc. The validity of this extension to condensed systems may be questioned, since the Kossel structure of argon gas is not recognizable in the fine structure of solid argon. Some of the p states invoked by Beeman and Bearden must already be involved in the bonding of water to the ion. The space needed for these p states is occupied by the water molecules. Several aspects of this problem have been discussed by Hanson.[13]

Intermediate Fine Structure. Condensed atomic systems, including polyatomic gases, aqueous solutions, and crystalline compounds, give rise to fine structure in the range 5 to 100 ev above the absorption edge. This fine structure is sensitive to short-range order and shows the influence of valence and of near-neighbor atoms.

Fine structure of four chemical forms of manganese is presented in Fig. 6, first to show the diversity of fine structure in this intermediate-energy range, and second to define the "types" used[11] for classifying a large number of spectra of titanium, chromium, manganese, cobalt, and nickel compounds. This classification of fine structure

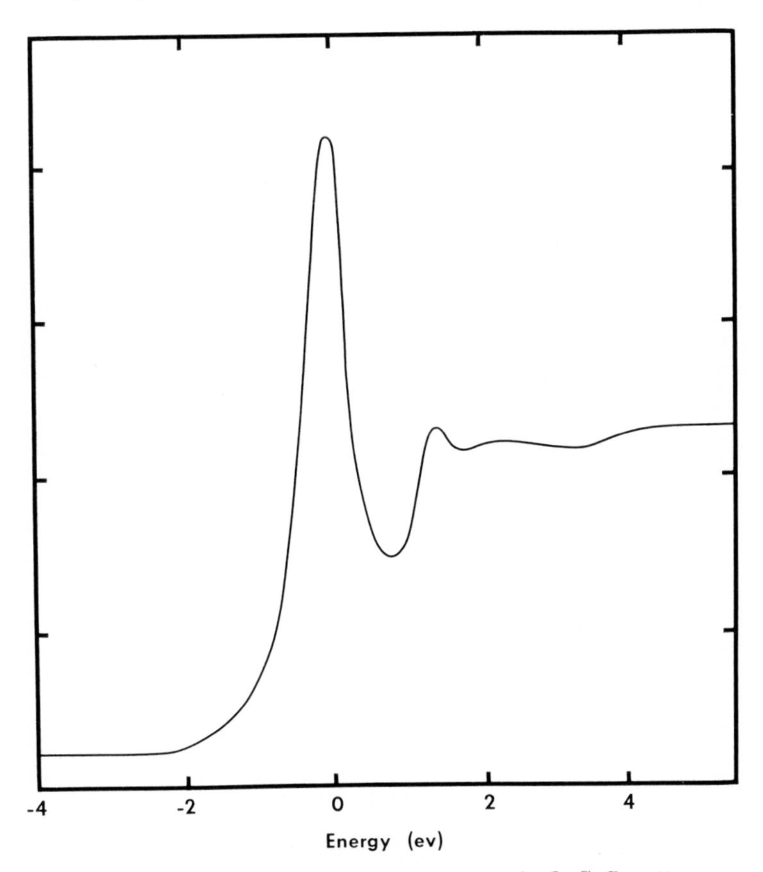

FIG. 5. Absorption-edge spectra of argon gas, by L. G. Parratt.

turns out to be very closely related to chemical structure, as seen in Table 3. Three of the types are established on the basis of congruence of the fine structure and one (type III) on the basis of amplitude of the fluctuations.

Fine structures at the absorption edges of different elements may be considered congruent only after they have been placed on a common energy scale with zero taken as the first absorption rise of the element in its metallic state. This basis for fixing zero, which appeared arbitrary, will here appear fortunate and perhaps vindicated.

The association of a specific fine-structure spectrum, type Ia, with common salts of divalent ions has long been recognized: Beeman and Bearden[12] for aqueous solutions of divalent nickel, copper, and zinc; Van Nordstrand[11] for crystalline salts and solutions of divalent manganese, cobalt, and nickel, their carbonates and their salts with organic acids. Analogous compounds of titanium and chromium are not available; and of the many compounds of titanium and chromium studied, none gave type Ia fine structure.

A closely related fine structure, type Ib, is associated with many of the complexes of trivalent chromium, manganese, and cobalt. Type Ib differs from Ia in having the maxima shifted to higher energies and broadened. The comparison is shown in Fig. 7.

Type II fine structure is associated with the hexacyanides of chromium, manganese, and cobalt and with chromium hexacarbonyl. According to Beeman,[14] it is also associated with both the ferrocyanide and ferricyanide ions. Type II fine structure

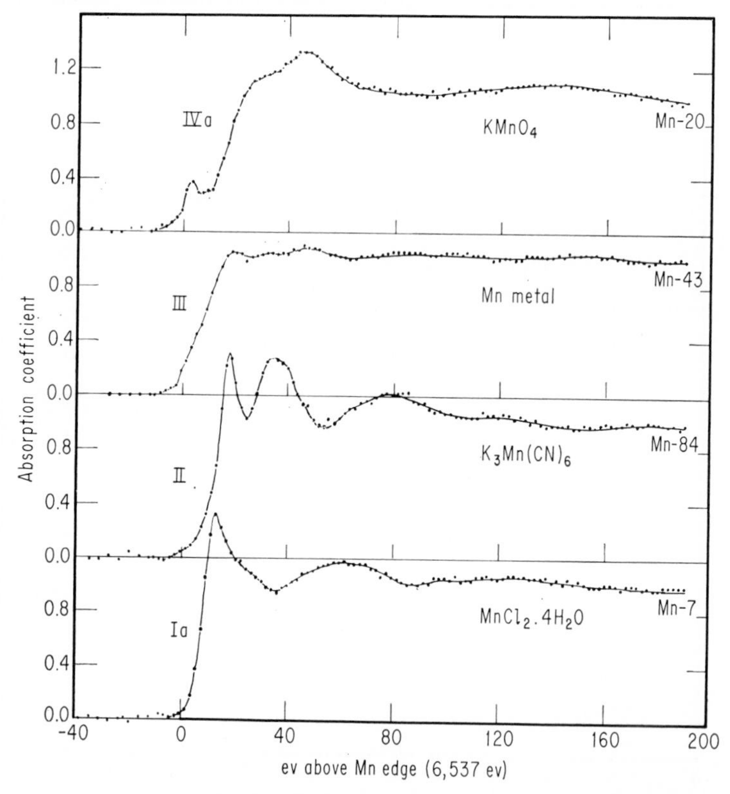

FIG. 6. Type spectra serving as the basis for classification of spectra of elements of the first transition series in various chemical forms.

is associated with a unique configuration in which the CO and CN ligands form linear arrays along the three orthogonal axes as N-C-Co-C-N. The formal valence of the metal atom does not appear to affect the fine structure.

Type III fine structure is defined on the basis of low-amplitude fluctuations in absorption coefficient. It is associated with materials of electronic conductivity or polarizability, including metals and sulfides.

Type IVa fine structure is associated with the isolated tetrahedral ions such as permanganate and chromate, either as crystalline salts or as aqueous solutions, and also with the paired tetrahedral ion, the dichromate. These tetrahedral ions contain the metal in its highest formal valence state, which has the electron configuration of argon. Type IVa fine structure is not observed when ions are in tetrahedral sites in spinel or zinc blende structures.

Type IVb fine structure is associated with the manganate ion, which is also tetrahedral. Types IVa and IVb are compared in Fig. 7. A comparison of these types (permanganate and manganate) over the first 15 ev is shown with much better resolution by Hanson and Beeman.[15]

The empirical grouping of compounds based upon these four (or six) types of intermediate fine structure includes only 70 per cent of the compounds studied. Additional types could be set up, but borderline cases would then become troublesome. A multiplicity of chemical criteria, including geometry of the coordination shell, valence, and electron mobility, seems to determine the types. In part this multiplicity is caused by the original designation of types based both on congruence of the fine-structure spectra and on amplitude of fluctuations.

There are three general theoretical approaches to fine structure in this 5- to 100-ev energy range:

1. As distinct from fine structure in other energy ranges
2. As an extension of the Kossel structure
3. As an extension of the Kronig structure

Hartree, Kronig, and Petersen[16] were the first to provide a theory treating this intermediate fine structure as distinct from the other two. They point out that the possibility of electron diffraction from the first coordination shell should influence the *transition probability,* and thereby influence the fine structure. The original Kronig theory, developed to explain fine structure in crystalline systems, points out that the

Table 3. Fine-structure Types

Type	Examples	Structural features
Ia $MnCl_2 \cdot 4H_2O$	Divalent Mn, Co, Ni salts, solutions	Octahedral coordination by oxygen
Ib	Complexes of trivalent Cr, Mn, Co	Octahedral coordination by ammonia, ethylene diamine, nitrite, acetate
II $K_3Mn(CN)_6$	$K_3Co(CN_6)$ (crystals and aqueous solutions), $K_3Cr(CN)_6$, $Cr(CO)_6$	Double octahedral coordination sphere, linear ligands
III Mn metal	Metals, carbides, sulfides, bromides	Electronic conductivity or polarizability
IVa $KMnO_4$	Permanganates, $KCrO_3Cl$, chromates, dichromates	Tetrahedral coordination, central atom with formal valence corresponding to its argon core
IVb	Manganate ion	Tetrahedral coordination

possibility of electron diffraction from the lattice creates a distinction between allowed and forbidden energy states, that the resulting variation in *density of states* should be sensitive to long-range order. The de Broglie wavelength of the photoelectron is an important parameter for both theories and must be considered in relation to either the lattice parameter or the radius of the first coordination shell.

According to the Hartree-Kronig-Petersen theory:

1. The amplitude of the fluctuations constituting the intermediate fine structure is proportional to the coordination number if the ligands are identical.

2. The energy values for the maxima and minima are determined by the radius of the coordination shell—as the radius decreases, all features of the fine structure shift to higher-energy values (shorter wavelengths).

The change in fine structure associated with an increase in ionic charge may thus be explained, at least qualitatively, as a result of shrinkage and increased polarization of the atoms of the first coordination shell. Changes of this type are shown in Fig. 7, which includes the shift from divalent to trivalent and the shift from manganate to permanganate.

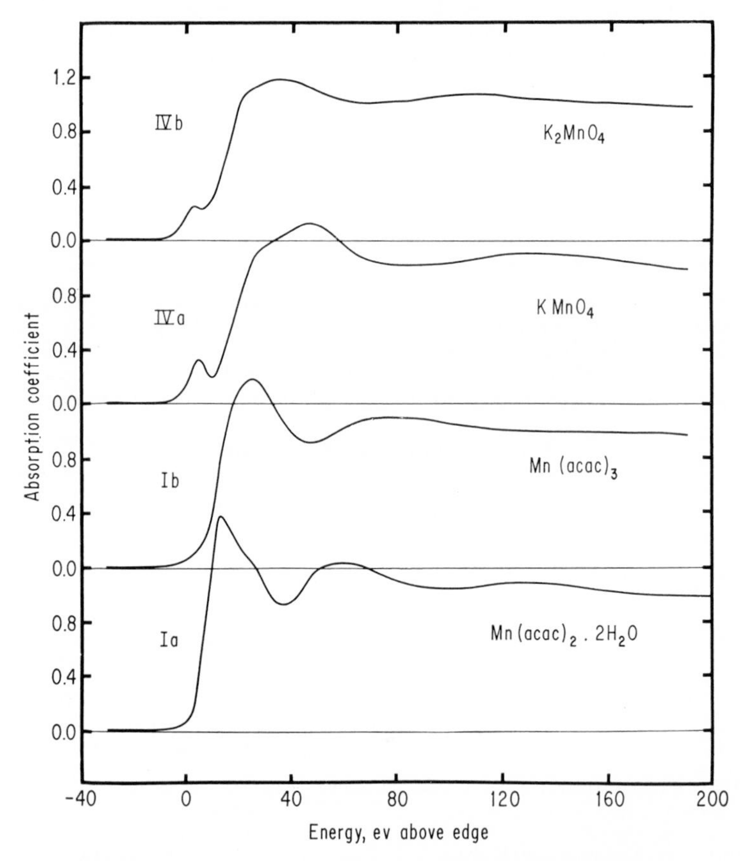

FIG. 7. Additional "type spectra" showing influence of valence.

Interesting support for this theory is seen in the data on three cuprous halides, shown in Table 4, from Beeman et al.[17] These compounds have the crystal structure of zinc sulfide, both types of atom being tetrahedrally coordinated. The wavelength of the

Table 4. Relationship of First Absorption Maxima to Bond Distances in Cuprous Halides

Compound	First absorption maximum E_1, ev	$\lambda_e = \sqrt{150/E_1}$, Å	Bond distance Cu–X, Å	Ratio Cu–X/λ_e
CuCl.........	7.1	4.60	2.34	0.51
CuBr.........	6.4	4.84	2.46	0.51
CuI..........	5.6	5.18	2.62	0.51

electrons emitted at the first absorption maximum, calculated from Eq. (1), is proportional to the copper-to-halogen bond distance. The proportionality constant is 0.51. However, this proportionality is predicted also by the Kronig theory and Eq. (2) because the copper-to-halogen distance is proportional to the lattice parameter.

Treatment of the intermediate fine structure as Kossel structure has been mentioned above.

Kostarev[18] attributes both intermediate and extended fine structure to the effect of the nearest neighbor atoms on the transition probability. This and other theories combining these two ranges of fine structure have been reviewed by Azaroff.[8]

3. SPECTROMETERS

Instrument requirements depend on the wavelength of the edge, the resolution desired, and the spectral span needed. Within the wavelength limits of this chapter, between 1.0 and 2.5 Å, three types of instruments are useful—the simple one-crystal spectrometer, the focusing bent-crystal spectrometer, and the precision two-crystal spectrometer. Resolution and spectral span provide the basis for comparing these spectrometers.

A commercial x-ray diffractometer without substantial modification may serve as a one-crystal spectrometer for x-ray absorption spectroscopy. An instrument based on the Norelco x-ray diffractometer has the following sequence of components:

Line-focus x-ray source of a copper- or tungsten-target tube
Set of parallel nickel foils as collimator
Divergence slit (1⁄12°)
Single crystal (quartz, d = 3.343 Å; silicon, d = 3.138 Å) mounted in place of diffraction sample
Absorption sample in holder
Receiving slit (0.003 in.)
Set of parallel nickel foils as collimator
Scatter slit (1⁄12°)
Geiger or proportional counter tube

The special components added for the absorption spectrometer are the single crystal and the absorption sample.

It is desirable to have a tube with an emission curve I_0 which is flat over the range from 10 ev below the edge to 200 ev above. Most tubes have targets contaminated with tungsten, copper, nickel, and iron, causing characteristic radiations which are a major nuisance. The $K\beta$ radiation of an element is immediately adjacent to the K edge of that element, making the definition of the edge difficult.

The crystals quartz and silicon provide about the same intensity. Silicon has somewhat greater dispersion and gives no second-order reflection. The latter feature of silicon permits one to operate the x-ray tube at a voltage just below three times the energy of the absorption edge without danger of including high-order reflections of more penetrating x-rays. With quartz the exciting voltage must be kept below twice the edge voltage.

The Geiger counter tube favors certain wavelengths depending on its window and filling. The proportional counter with discriminating circuits is much more selective and will eliminate most of the second- and third-order radiation. The voltage limitations cited above may often be ignored if a silicon crystal and a proportional-discriminating counter are used. The gain in intensity by use of higher voltage is sometimes important.

The resolving power of the one-crystal spectrometer with a silicon crystal is seen from a study of the 8,400-ev tungsten $L\alpha_1$ line (at spectrometer angle 27.21°). The full width at half maximum is 0.05°, which corresponds to 15 ev. This may be compared with the value 7 ev reported by Compton and Allison[1] for this same line using a calcite two-crystal spectrometer. In addition to half-width values the shape of the full curve should be considered. With the one-crystal spectrometer the tungsten line is symmetrical; the intensity readings above background, starting at the center and moving in angle increments of 0.01°, are 56, 51, 35, 19, 12, 7, 5, 3, 2, 2, 1, 1, 0. In this energy range it is apparent that angle increments less than 0.01° (3 ev) would not be justified.

An additional criterion of resolving power of the one-crystal spectrometer is seen in Fig. 8. The fine structures of $K_3Co(CN)_6$ obtained with a quartz crystal and with a silicon crystal are compared. This cobalticyanide ion provides a good check on resolving power because the 19-ev peak is sharp and far removed from the next peak (at 37 ev). From these spectra it is apparent that:

1. The silicon crystal is superior to the quartz in resolving power.
2. Increments as small as 0.01° are justified for both crystals; this increment corresponds to 2.6 ev for silicon, 2.8 ev for quartz.
3. The full half width of the 19-ev peak, assuming it is symmetrical, is 9 ev with silicon, 11 ev with quartz.
4. The drop from the maximum value to zero for the cobalticyanide absorption line requires 21 ev; the corresponding drop for the tungsten emission line requires 36 ev. Again, this emphasizes the sharpness of this absorption line.

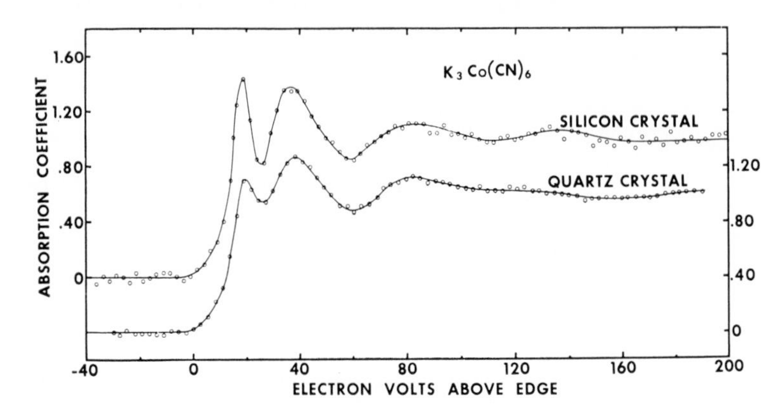

FIG. 8. Absorption-edge spectrum of Co in $K_3Co(CN)_6$ obtained with one-crystal spectrometer utilizing a quartz and a silicon crystal.

The very sharp absorption peak occurring at 4 ev in the permanganate spectrum has been studied by Hanson and Beeman[15] using a two-crystal spectrometer. They show this line to have a full half width of only 3 ev. This may be compared with the value of about 6 ev for the width of this peak in Fig. 6, determined with a quartz one-crystal spectrometer.

Figure 9 presents a comparison between data from one- and two-crystal spectrometers (both using silicon crystals) showing the absorption spectrum of $CoAl_2O_4$ close to the cobalt K edge.

From the preceding discussion it might appear that for many purposes the one-crystal spectrometer is adequate but that the two-crystal spectrometer is always superior. It should be emphasized that this applies to resolving power. The one-crystal instrument has certain important advantages.

The one-crystal spectrometer does not limit the spectral span. The two-crystal spectrometer, as used for absorption-edge studies, has one fixed crystal which diffracts a restricted range of wavelengths and a second crystal which serves as a monochromator for the mixture of radiation from the first. Because of requirements of intensity and of resolving power the span of the radiation corresponds to about 40 to 60 ev (in studies of elements of the first transition series). About 10 ev of this span is required below the edge, leaving only 30 to 50 ev above the edge. This restriction in energy span limits the value of the resultant data in three ways:

1. The fine-structure types, as shown in Figs. 6 and 7, are not readily recognized.
2. The possibility of normalizing the absorption coefficients is lost. This is an important aspect of fine-structure spectra which is discussed later.
3. Extended fine structure is missed altogether.

A second advantage of the one-crystal spectrometer is the reasonable time interval per reading. The high resolving power of the two-crystal instrument is achieved at considerable sacrifice of intensity. This requires a more stable x-ray source or necessitates measurement of the incident intensity before and after each reading of transmitted intensity. The latter alternative is normally used, which means that the absorbing sample must be lifted out of the beam and precisely replaced many times

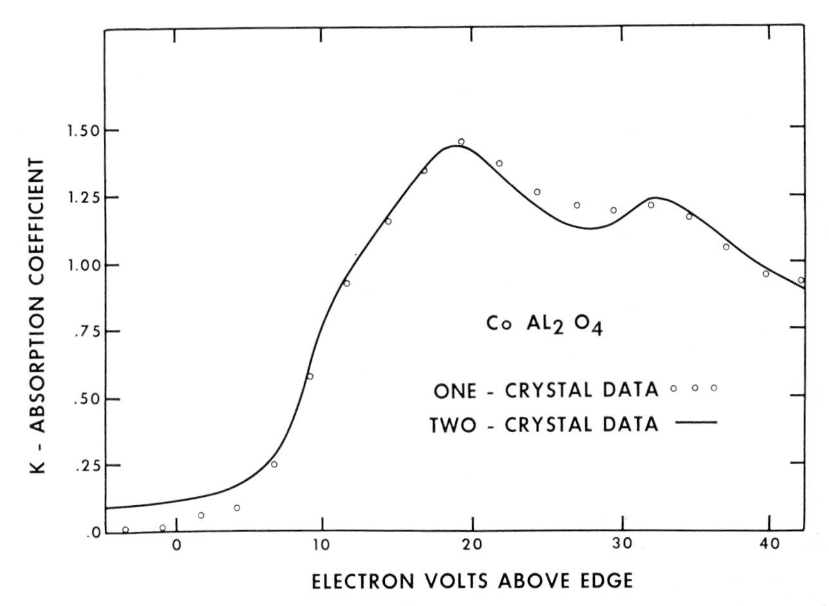

FIG. 9. Absorption-edge spectra for $CoAl_2O_4$ obtained by two types of spectrometer. The two-crystal data from R. O. Keeling, Jr., have been matched to the K-absorption coefficient defined herein.

during an experiment. With the one-crystal instrument incident-intensity values at all angles are measured once and are used for several absorption experiments. One experiment, lasting from 4 to 20 hr, does not involve serious intensity drift; from one point to the next the changes are indeed minor. The calculation procedure eliminates any effect of a proportionate change in incident intensity which occurs between experiments. This includes changes related to tube current.

The focusing bent-crystal spectrometer[2] is not compared here. Although it may be designed to give the same resolution as the two-crystal instrument, the monochromatic beam produced is accompanied by considerable white radiation.

Other details which should be emphasized are:

1. The importance of automatic programmed recording of data
2. The requirement of about 10,000 counts for each intensity determination
3. The hazards of making absorption measurements over the range where the incident radiation has a strong emission line

4. SAMPLE PREPARATION

The primary objectives in sample preparation are proper thickness and uniformity. Methods to achieve these depend on the sample.

The absorbing sample may be in many forms: metal foil, evaporated film, powder, or liquid. Metal foil may be rolled, etched, or electropolished to adjust thickness. Powder samples often must be separated on a size basis, using sieves, air elutriation, or sedimentation. The powder is packed as a self-supporting window, smeared onto a film of adhesive plastic tape, or made into a film using as binder cellulose acetate, wax, or viscous hydrocarbon. Liquid is held in a cell with mica windows or absorbed into porous paper.

An arbitrary definition of optimum sample thickness is suggested here. It is that thickness which will give a counting time of 1 min for 10,000 counts in the spectral range below the absorption edge and a counting time of 20 min at 100 ev above the edge. In practice the thickness is adjusted by successive trials to obtain this 1:20 ratio in counting times. Following this the incident intensity is varied to set the counting times at 1 and 20 min.

Frequently it is important to compute the optimum thickness for a sample. This requires knowing the elemental composition and density plus the mass absorption coefficients of the elements involved. The basic absorption equation is used.

Metallic cobalt, the first example, has a mass absorption coefficient which jumps from 47 to 400 cm^2/g across the edge. It has a density of 8.9. The optimum sample thickness is calculated as 10 microns.

A second example is an alloy consisting of 80 per cent gold, 20 per cent cobalt. The mass absorption coefficient of gold is 240 on both sides of the cobalt edge. Optimum sample thickness is calculated as 24 microns. This would require 2,700 times the incident intensity required for cobalt in the first example. A threefold increase is all that the x-ray source can provide. A compromise is reached as follows: The intensity is increased by the factor 3; a counting time of 20 min above the edge can then be achieved by cutting the sample thickness to 10 microns. This thickness will require a counting time of 6 min below the edge. Sensitivity is reduced by this compromise. The sample thickness must be accurately adjusted in a sample such as this.

A third example is an alloy consisting of 80 per cent aluminum, 20 per cent cobalt. The mass absorption coefficient of aluminum at the cobalt edge is 60. The optimum thickness is calculated to be 11 microns. This alloy presents no problems from the standpoint of incident intensity or of exact sample dimensions.

Uniformity of sample thickness is more important here than in most other branches of absorption spectroscopy. With powder samples this has been a major source of poor spectra. If particles are as large as or larger than the optimum sample thickness, the following difficulty arises: The sample may simulate optimum thickness but be so varied in thickness that fine structure is completely washed out.

A simple example of this washout is described here. The true value of the "K-absorption coefficient" (defined in Sec. 5) for the substance in this example rises from zero to a maximum value of 1.5 and then levels off at unity. These values will be obtained with a sample of uniform thickness, even if this thickness departs somewhat from the optimum. The substance here, however, is in the form of cubic particles whose edge is twice the calculated optimum thickness. The sample may be adjusted to "optimum thickness" using counting times, by making it one particle thick over 95 per cent of its area and zero thickness over the other 5 per cent. Measured values of the K-absorption coefficient again start at zero, again terminate at the value unity, but rise only to 1.015 at the maximum. Thus an absorption edge is obtained, but only 3 per cent of the fine structure persists.

A second example of nonuniformity consists of the same material but in the form of foil. Half of the exposed sample area is of single thickness, half of double thickness. In this case the spectrum would retain 84 per cent of its fine structure.

These examples show the difficulty caused by void space. They show also that a range in sample thickness from one value to twice that value will not cause difficulty.

Absorption samples made from powders should be of such thickness that the x-ray beam penetrates at least five particles on the average. If the sample thickness is to be adjusted to the optimum, the average particle size of the powder must be less than one-fifth of the optimum sample thickness.

5. COMPUTATIONS

A "K-absorption coefficient" μ_K, as defined below,[11] has been used throughout this chapter to facilitate comparisons of fine-structure spectra. This coefficient refers to absorption solely by the K electrons of the element under study. It has a value of zero below the edge and an average value of unity in the range 100 to 200 ev above the edge.

The total absorption coefficient of a sample is made up additively of absorption coefficients of the components and includes the various attenuation processes (coherent scattering and absorption) by each component. An alternative subdivision is significant in the vicinity of the K-absorption edge of an element. The absorption by the K electrons of this element may be considered as distinct from the "matrix absorption" which consists of all other attenuation caused by the sample. The K electrons do not absorb x-rays at spectral energies below the edge but absorb strongly above the edge. The matrix absorption is considered constant through the edge. Because of the additivity and this constancy, the value of the absorption coefficient below the edge (matrix absorption) may be subtracted from the total (matrix plus K) absorption coefficient beyond the edge. The resultant absorption coefficient may be attributed solely to absorption by the K electrons.

The final step in converting this latter coefficient to the K-absorption coefficient is to normalize it to the value unity in some range well above the edge. The range 100 to 200 ev was selected because the coefficient is reasonably constant beyond 100 ev. This normalization procedure is an effective means of correcting the spectrum to a standard number of atoms of the element in a unit area of the x-ray beam. For cobalt this corresponds to 3×10^{19} atoms/cm^2.

The detailed computation of the K-absorption coefficient across the absorption edge is based upon the set of experimental values of incident and transmitted intensities (I_0 and I) in the form $\log (I_0/I)$. Below the edge these values are low and usually constant, the matrix absorption. This constant is subtracted from the entire set of $\log (I_0/I)$ values. The resultant set of values is normalized by dividing by its average value over the spectral range 100 to 200 ev above the edge. This set of normalized values constitutes the K-absorption coefficients for the element in that sample.

For some samples the $\log (I_0/I)$ values below the edge decrease linearly with energy. In such a case this line is extrapolated through the edge to provide a suitable correction for matrix absorption. The data for K_2CrO_4 provide an example of this. The potassium-absorption coefficient contributes a pronounced slope to the matrix absorption in the vicinity of the K edge of chromium. In contrast, the matrix absorption of $(NH)_4)_2CrO_4$ is constant. The computation procedure outlined gives nearly identical K-absorption coefficients for chromium in these two chromates.

6. APPLICATIONS

Fine-structure spectra have been used as a tool in chemical physics, providing some information on the chemical bond[19,20] and on the electronic band structure of solids.[3] Although these applications will eventually be of great interest and value, substantial contributions to chemical physics must await a better understanding of the tool itself.

Applications to structural chemistry are based upon empirical associations such as those in Table 3. These may be used with caution to establish valence and coordination type.

Applications of these spectra in analytical chemistry are already of practical value. These depend on the classical and empirical aspects of the spectra. They include identification of compounds and of compound types and also the quantitative analysis of samples containing the absorbing element in two chemical forms.

The chemistry of heterogeneous catalysts has offered many interesting applications of fine-structure spectra. Reasons for this are:

1. Active components in a catalyst are usually highly dispersed, a condition ideally suited to fine structure.
2. Elements most readily studied by fine structure include those of the first transition series, which are of major significance in catalysis.
3. Fine structure permits the study of one specific element in a mixture such as mixed oxides.
4. X-rays penetrate catalyst supports, carbonaceous deposits, and certain types of reactor windows.
5. Quantitative analysis is feasible in certain cases.

Cobalt catalysts supported on silica and alumina have been examined by Keeling.[21] The supporting action of alumina, he finds, is due to the formation of a cobaltous

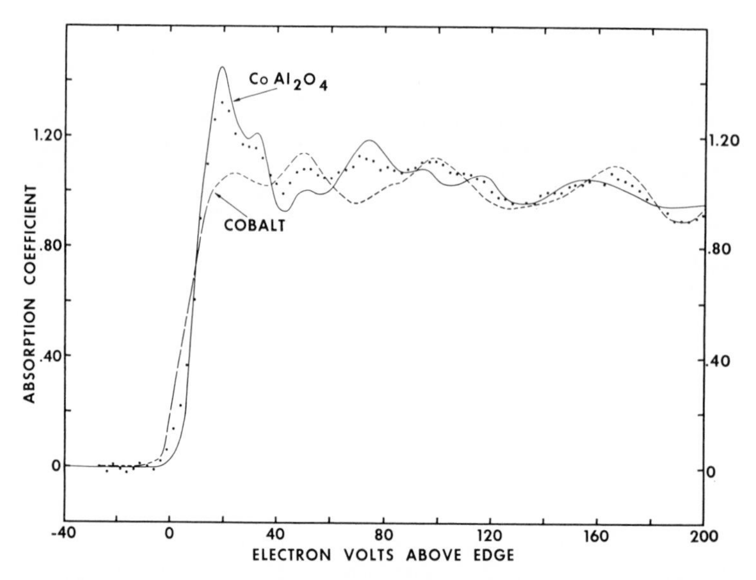

FIG. 10. Absorption-edge spectra of $CoAl_2O_4$, cobalt metal, and a mixture (dotted) containing 65 per cent of the cobalt as aluminate, 35 per cent as metal. Note that the dotted spectrum is everywhere between the two spectra of the components.

aluminate at the surface. Excess cobalt forms Co_3O_4. With the impregnation technique used, all the cobalt goes to Co_3O_4 on silica. Keeling also has pointed out a feature of the spectrum which may distinguish tetrahedral and octahedral cobalt. His method of obtaining quantitative results from his spectra may be invalid because of the method of normalization used.

Supported nickel and platinum catalysts have been studied by Lewis,[22] with the primary objectives of determining metal crystallite size and effects of monolayer adsorption of hydrogen and oxygen. To distinguish the subtle differences of his fine-structure spectra, confined to within 20 ev of the edge, he has developed a novel differential method of displaying his data. The study of platinum is based on an L_{III}-absorption edge, at 1.07 Å.

Many possibilities for qualitative use of these spectra were cited by Van Nordstrand[11] for catalysts of titanium, chromium, manganese, and cobalt.

An example of quantitative analysis is described[4] which is of significance in catalyst studies. A sample of cobalt aluminate, well crystallized, pigment grade, was partially reduced at high temperature in hydrogen. It became black and magnetic, showed an x-ray diffraction pattern of both cobalt aluminate and metal. The x-ray absorption-edge spectrum, shown in Fig. 10, was between those of the two components. Here it is obvious that the spectra must be normalized in a meaningful way, not merely by making the maximum peak height equal unity.

Various methods were used to determine from the spectra the fraction of the cobalt which was in the two forms. The final method was by machine computation. A correlation coefficient was computed between the "cobalt-metal" pattern produced by difference and the experimental pattern of cobalt-metal foil. The correlation coefficient was a maximum when 66 per cent of the cobalt was attributed to cobalt aluminate. Chemical analysis confirmed this, as two determinations showed 65 (± 0.5) per cent of the cobalt was in the form of cobalt aluminate.

The absorption-edge spectrum produced by difference from the mixture is unmistakably that of cobalt metal throughout the range 60 to 70 per cent. Thus a binary mixture may be examined by this method even if only one of the components is known. A succession of difference spectra is obtained, at 10 per cent intervals, for example. One of these difference patterns may be recognizable from the catalogue of spectra. If not, then perhaps some of the spectra obtained may be ruled out as impossible on the basis of experience. Composition limits on the one component may thus be established.

With regard to quantitative applications, the following points should be emphasized:

1. Components not containing the element under study do not influence the determination, except to reduce the accuracy of the individual points of the spectrum.
2. A component of a binary mixture should represent 10 per cent or more of the element under study.
3. Much depends on the identical resolving power in obtaining the spectrum of the mixtures and the reference spectra.
4. Spectra must all be normalized.

7. THE FUTURE

The strong interest in the use of fine-structure spectra for the solution of chemical problems may bring about important experimental and theoretical advances.

A commercial two-crystal spectrometer is needed which will have a wide energy range—as 300 ev. This will probably require synchronized crystals.

An x-ray tube is needed which gives white radiation without characteristic lines, over the range 1.0 to 2.5 Å. This may be a silver-target tube. It should be free of the current universal contaminants, tungsten, iron, nickel, and copper.

Improvement in understanding of the spectra is certainly needed. The empirical status of the relationship between intermediate fine structure and chemical structure should be both a guide and a challenge to the theoretical development. As long as the differences between the spectra for gaseous and solid argon are unexplained, little progress can be expected in the quest for electronic-band-structure information from these spectra.

REFERENCES CITED

1. A. H. Compton and S. K. Allison, *X-rays in Theory and Experiment*, pp. 662–669, 747, D. Van Nostrand Company, Inc., Princeton, N.J., 1935.
2. A. E. Sandström, in S. Flugge (ed.), *Handbuch der Physik*, vol. 30, pp. 208–222, Springer-Verlag OHG, Berlin, 1957.
3. L. G. Parratt, *Rev. Mod. Phys.*, **31**:616–645 (1959).
4. R. A. Van Nordstrand, unpublished results.
5. F. W. Lytle, in Ferraro and Ziomek (eds.), *Developments in Applied Spectroscopy*, vol. 2, pp. 285–296, Plenum Press, New York, 1963.
6. R. S. Krogstad, Ph.D. Thesis, Washington State College, 1955.
7. L. V. Azaroff, *Z. Krist.*, **112**:3–43 (1959).
8. L. V. Azaroff, *Rev. Mod. Phys.*, **35**:1012–1022 (1963).
9. L. G. Parratt, *Phys. Rev.*, **56**:295 (1939).
10. S. T. Stephenson, R. S. Krogstad, and W. F. Nelson, *Phys. Rev.*, **84**:806 (1951).

11. R. A. Van Nordstrand, in *Advances in Catalysis*, vol. 12, pp. 149–187, Academic Press Inc., New York, 1960.
12. W. W. Beeman and J. A. Bearden, *Phys. Rev.*, **61**:455–458 (1942).
13. H. P. Hanson, in Ferraro and Ziomek (eds.), *Developments in Applied Spectroscopy*, vol. 2, pp. 254–262, Plenum Press, New York, 1963.
14. W. W. Beeman, private communication. S. Yoshida, *Sci. Papers Inst. Phys. Chem. Res.* (*Tokyo*), **38**:272 (1941).
15. H. P. Hanson and W. W. Beeman, *Phys. Rev.*, **76**:118–121 (1949).
16. D. R. Hartree, R. de L. Kronig, and H. Petersen, *Physica*, **1**:895 (1934).
17. W. W. Beeman, J. Forss, and J. N. Humphrey, *Phys. Rev.*, **67**:217–222 (1945).
18. A. I. Kostarev, *Zh. Eksperim. i Teor. Fiz.*, **11**:60 (1941).
19. G. Mitchell and W. W. Beeman, *J. Chem. Phys.*, **20**:1298–1301 (1952).
20. F. A. Cotton and H. P. Hanson, *J. Chem. Phys.*, **26**:1758–1759 (1957); **25**:619–623 (1956); **28**:83–87 (1958).
21. R. O. Keeling, Jr., in Ferraro and Ziomek (eds.), *Developments in Applied Spectroscopy*, vol. 2, pp. 263–274, Plenum Press, New York, 1963.
22. P. H. Lewis, *J. Phys. Chem.*, **64**:1103 (1960); **66**:105 (1962); **67**:2151 (1963).

Chapter 44

MEASUREMENT OF FILM THICKNESS

William D. Johns

Washington University (St. Louis)

1. INTRODUCTION

The measurement of film thickness has become of increasing importance, and x-ray methods are being applied to an ever-increasing variety of systems. The classical case involves a thin film of metal lying on an x-ray opaque substrate of a different substance, for example, tin plate on steel. More and more, however, nonmetallic films are being scrutinized by x-ray methods. The techniques utilized for film thickness measurement are somewhat different from *thickness gauging* of homogeneous samples such as steel strip, described in Chap. 41. The opaque substrate prevents gauging the film thickness in the normal manner, but at the same time it serves as the source of diffracted or emitted fluorescent radiation to indirectly measure the thickness of the film resting on it.

In the usual experimental setup the x-ray source and detector are located on the same side of the sample, permitting the use of normal diffractometer or spectrometer optics. One exception, involving a transparent substrate and transmission optics, will be referred to later. Two basic experimental approaches are possible: (1) x-rays scattered or emitted by the *substrate* and attenuated by the film can be measured or (2) use can be made of the variation with thickness of the intensity of x-rays diffracted or emitted by the *film* itself. As already implied, the radiation to be monitored can be produced either by *diffraction*, when crystalline film and/or substrate are involved, or by *emission* of secondary fluorescent radiation when film and substrate are excited by primary radiation. In either case *absorption effects* are involved, which explains the inclusion of this chapter in Part 5 of this book.

2. THICKNESS MEASUREMENT BY DIFFRACTION METHODS

Diffraction from the Substrate. Soon after Clark, Pish, and Weeg[1] showed that characteristic diffraction patterns could be obtained from very thin films, Friedman and Birks[2] developed a method for determining the thickness of thin films on *crystalline substrates*, using a diffractometer. In this case the x-rays pass through the film and are diffracted by the crystalline substrate at some characteristic Bragg angle back to the detector. The intensity of the diffracted radiation is attenuated by absorption due to the double transmission through the film. In Fig. 1 a beam of monochromatic x-rays is incident on a coated specimen at a diffraction angle θ_{hkl} corresponding to a strong reflection from the substrate. The incident radiation is absorbed in penetrating the film before and after diffraction from the substrate. If

d is the film thickness and μ its mass absorption coefficient, the ratio of the diffracted intensity I from the coated specimen to I_0 from the uncoated substrate is

$$I/I_0 = \exp(-2\mu\rho d/\sin\theta) \tag{1}$$

Consideration of Eq. (1) and Fig. 1 suggests that in general soft radiation reflected at small angles should be used for thin films, and hard radiation at large angles for thick films.

I/I_0 is measured experimentally, and the film thickness computed from Eq. (1). To test the accuracy of the method, Friedman and Birks[2] prepared metallic foils of known thickness and applied the x-ray measurement using copper as a substrate. Table 1 lists the measurements obtained for comparison. This method was used in measuring the thickness of electroplated films and evaporated electrode coatings on piezoelectric crystals in the range 10^{-5} to 10^{-2} cm.

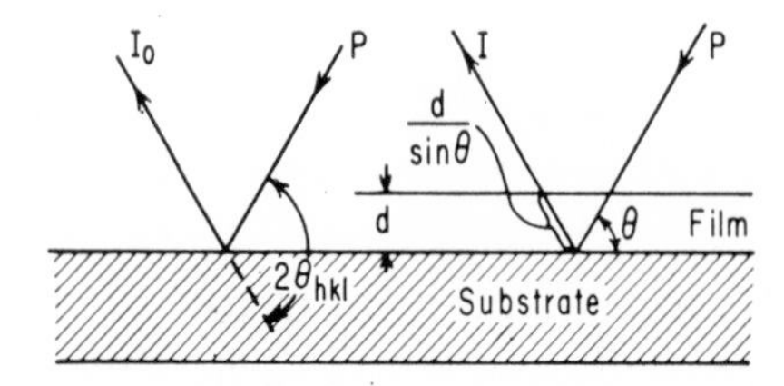

Fig. 1. Principle of thickness measurement by attenuation by a film of diffracted radiation from the substrate.

Table 1[2]

Film	X-ray reflection measurement, cm	Comparison measurement, cm
Al	0.00254	0.0025
Zn	0.00097	0.0010
		0.0013
Ag leaf	0.00016	0.00014
Au leaf	0.00010	0.00009

There are several attractive features of this diffraction procedure. Since one monochromatic wavelength is involved throughout, the absorption relations are simple, and film thicknesses can be computed without referring to standards. In addition it can be applied to systems in which the film and substrate contain the same element, as long as the crystalline phases containing this element are different in film and substrate. This is a shortcoming of the emission methods, although this situation can also be dealt with as we shall see later in discussing emission methods.

An important shortcoming of the Friedman and Birks method is that the procedure assumes a polycrystalline substrate with random orientation and small crystallite size. Only in such cases are diffraction intensities independent of specimen orientation. In many cases crystallites take on a preferred orientation, making diffraction intensities strongly dependent on specimen orientation with respect to the incident beam.

To eliminate these difficulties Keating and Kammerer[3] modified the previous method, eliminating unknown conditions of the substrate by measuring the intensity of a reflection using two different incident radiations. Consider again the situation depicted in Fig. 1, where the entire sample of area A_0 is bathed by the incident beam. The energy $P_{(\lambda)}$ reflected into the detector in scanning a reflection is expressed as

$$P_{(\lambda)} \sim I_0(\lambda) A_0 \frac{\lambda^3}{\mu_s(\lambda)} \cdot \frac{1 + \cos^2 2\theta_\lambda}{\sin 2\theta_\lambda} \cdot F_{hkl}{}^2 \bar{M}(\chi,\phi) \exp \frac{-2\mu_f(\lambda)t}{\sin \theta_\lambda} \tag{2}$$

where $I_0(\lambda)$ = incident beam intensity
$\mu_s(\lambda)$ = linear absorption coefficient of substrate for wavelength λ
$\mu_f(\lambda)$ = linear absorption coefficient of film for wavelength λ
θ_λ = Bragg angle for reflection (hkl) for wavelength λ
$F_{(hkl)}$ = structure factor for (hkl) reflection
t = film thickness
$\bar{M}_{(\chi,\phi)}$ = effective number of planes which, owing to crystal symmetry or preferred orientation, contribute to the reflecting beam; angles χ and ϕ represent polar angles between the diffraction vector $(\bar{S} - \bar{S}_0)/\lambda$ and a fixed coordinate system in the sample

Consider Eq. (2) for two incident wavelengths λ_1 and λ_2, and form the ratio of the two expressions $P(\lambda_1)/P(\lambda_2) = \mathbf{P}$. Then

$$\mathbf{P} = \frac{I_0(\lambda_1)\lambda_1{}^3(1 + \cos^2 2\theta_{\lambda_1})\mu_s(\lambda_2) \sin 2\theta_{\lambda_2}}{I_0(\lambda_2)\lambda_2{}^3(1 + \cos^2 2\theta_{\lambda_2})\mu_s(\lambda_1) \sin 2\theta_{\lambda_1}} \cdot \exp \left\{ -2t \left[\frac{\mu_f(\lambda_1)}{\sin \theta_{\lambda_1}} - \frac{\mu_f(\lambda_2)}{\sin \theta_{\lambda_2}} \right] \right\} \tag{3}$$

Let **R** be the multiplier of the exponential term. **R** is the ratio of the energies (intensities) reflected by the substrate without the film for the two different radiations and can be determined by direct measurement on a sample of substrate material. **P** is obviously the ratio of reflected intensities of the substrate plus film for the two different radiations. Thus Eq. (3) can be solved for film thickness as follows,

$$t = \frac{\ln(\mathbf{R}/\mathbf{P})}{2 \left[\frac{\mu_f(\lambda_1)}{\sin \theta_{\lambda_1}} - \frac{\mu_f(\lambda_2)}{\sin \theta_{\lambda_2}} \right]} \tag{4}$$

Keating and Kammerer[3] illustrated the applicability of this method for determining the thickness of a zirconium nitride film on a zirconium substrate, using filtered Cu $K\alpha$ and Cr $K\alpha$ radiation. The zirconium substrate exhibited considerable preferred orientation of the (201) reflection which was measured. From Eq. (4) a film thickness of 2.22 microns was determined, comparing favorably with an average value of 1.8 microns determined from a photomicrograph of a cross section through the specimen.

Diffraction from the Film. In principle, diffraction intensities from the film or coating itself should be related to film thickness. Starting with an infinitely thin film, the intensity of some characteristic diffraction maximum should increase as the film thickness increases. The rate of intensity increase will gradually diminish because of absorption until at some *critical thickness* a further increase has no effect on the diffraction intensity. Below this critical thickness, which varies inversely with the absorption coefficient of the film, diffracted intensities will vary directly with film thickness.

This method appears to have been used very little for film thickness measurements. Utilizing the conventional diffraction procedures, thin films of the order of a few microns thickness give very weak diffraction patterns. This is especially true if the polycrystalline film exhibits the random orientation normally deemed necessary for comparative measurements. The author, however, found this method suitable for obtaining very rapid and convenient estimates of clay coating thicknesses on paper. Kaolin clay crystallites, because of their platy character, orient preferably with their (001) surfaces parallel to the surface of the paper substrate. This preferred orientation is fairly reproducible and is in this case advantageous in that it strongly enhances the otherwise weak (001) diffraction maximum. The diffraction maxima for thin films can, therefore, be measured with considerable accuracy and calibrated under standardized conditions with film thicknesses determined by some independent method. The critical diffraction thickness for a kaolin coating on a paper substrate using filtered Cu $K\alpha$ radiation was 20 microns. Over the range 0 to 15 microns the correlation with diffracted (001) intensity was essentially linear. Kaolin film thicknesses could be determined to ± 0.5 micron over this range as compared to an accuracy of ± 0.2 micron as determined by a direct absorptiometric transmission method[4] to be discussed later.

Diffraction methods for film thickness measurement have been largely superseded by emission methods. This is largely because of the greater sensitivity and versatility of the latter. Except for special cases involving multiple films and those unique systems in which the same elements are present in both film and substrate, emission methods are now more widely utilized. There is no other recourse where noncrystalline and, therefore, nondiffracting phases are involved.

3. THICKNESS MEASUREMENT BY EMISSION METHODS

If the film and its substrate are radiated with sufficiently energetic primary radiation, elements in the film and substrate can be excited to produce characteristic

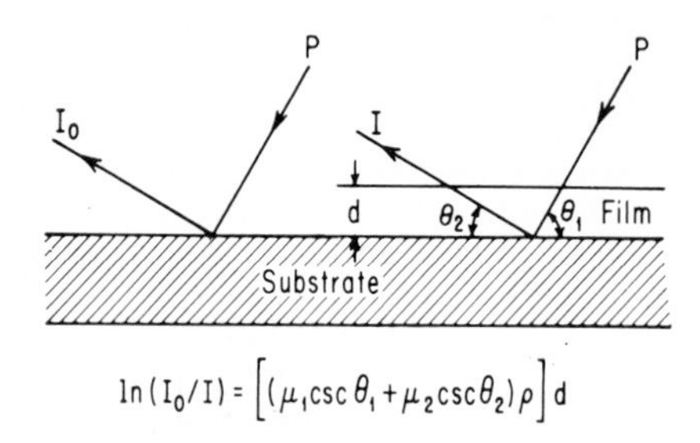

FIG. 2. Principle of thickness measurement by attenuation by the film of fluorescent radiation from the substrate.

secondary fluorescent radiation. This emitted radiation, if arising in the substrate, will be attenuated by the overlying film, or, if arising from the film, will vary in intensity depending upon the film thickness. Thus measurements of emitted radiation afford an indirect means of film thickness measurement.

The approach usually followed is to make appropriate measurements of emitted x-rays, utilizing films of known thickness, and to construct working curves from these with which to compare unknown systems. Applications of this approach can be considered in terms of three essentially different situations:

1. The emitted radiation stems from an element present in the substrate but absent in the overlying film.

2. The emitted radiation stems from an element present in the film but absent in the substrate.

3. The emitted radiation stems from an element present in both the substrate and overlying film.

We shall deal with each of these cases in this order.

Emission from the Substrate Only. The general situation which prevails is illustrated schematically in Fig. 2. A primary polychromatic x-ray beam incident upon the film and substrate at some angle θ_1 (not to be confused with a Bragg angle) excites the characteristic spectrum of an element in the substrate. Fluorescent radiation is emitted from the substrate in all directions. An emitted beam emerging at an angle θ_2 will have an intensity I depending upon the thickness d of the overlying film and the mass absorption coefficient μ_2 of the film for the characteristic wavelength under consideration. The polychromatic primary beam passing through the film before excitation will also be attenuated by the film to an extent depending on the film thickness, θ_1, and the mass absorption coefficient of the film μ_1. If I_0 is the intensity of the emitted radiation at angle θ_2 for the substrate alone and ρ is the density of the film, the following absorption law applies to this situation:

$$\ln (I_0/I) = [(\mu_1 \csc \theta_1 + \mu_2 \csc \theta_2)\rho]d \quad (5)$$

It is possible to utilize Eq. (5) to calculate directly the film thickness if one takes the trouble to determine experimentally the value μ_1 for the polychromatic source. Alternatively the entire multiplier term of d in Eq. (5), which is constant for any given experimental arrangement, can be determined experimentally. It is more convenient to experimentally determine I_0 and I for a particular system, utilizing films of known thickness. A plot of $\ln (I_0/I)$ versus d serves then as a working curve for further measurements. If this plot is linear, it is assumed that Beer's law is obeyed. Any nonlinear portions of the plot indicate the thickness range for which measurements are unsatisfactory.

There are two widely used and different experimental approaches to film thickness measurement involving analysis of characteristic emission from the substrate. These involve (1) attenuation by the film of an unresolved, polychromatic emitted beam and (2) attenuation by the film of a monochromatic emitted beam.

Attenuation of a Polychromatic Beam. With this method the characteristic spectral line from the substrate (Fig. 2) passes through the overlying film and is attenuated by it to an extent depending on the film thickness. The emitted beam is monitored directly by a detector placed at I. The spectral purity of the beam reaching the detector may be far from desirable with a resulting distortion of the data. The emerging beam may contain diffraction peaks from a crystalline substrate and/or film. These can be eliminated by situating the detector at an angle θ_2, different from the diffraction angles.

A more serious problem is the interference which may arise from fluorescence of elements in the film, which augment the substrate emission. If the substrate element being monitored is of lower atomic number than the interfering element in the overlying film, interference can be eliminated by appropriate adjustment of the primary x-ray potential. This was the approach used by Beeghly[5] in determining tin plating thickness on steel by this method. Using polychromatic Cu radiation, the K spectrum of Fe in the substrate was excited. A Mn filter was placed in the emergent beam primarily to eliminate the Fe $K\beta$ spectral line. Since the excitation potential for the Sn K spectrum is 29.2 kv while that of Fe K is 7.11 kv, interference by tin coating fluorescence could be eliminated by producing primary x-rays at 20 kv.

In those systems in which the film element is of lower atomic number than the substrate element being monitored, both film and substrate metal will be excited by the primary beam. Some other means must be provided to isolate the substrate fluorescence from that of the film.

Achey and Serfass[6] proposed a novel approach which is not dependent on atomic-number relationships between film and substrate elements and eliminates the necessity for crystal reflection procedures. They utilized a differential filter system, as first developed by Ross,[7] to isolate the substrate element fluorescence. They applied this procedure and tested it by using iron foils as films on zirconium and silver substrates. The two elements selected for filters are chosen so that their K absorption edges straddle the wavelength of the K radiation to be measured from the substrate. The details of filter preparation are described by Achey and Serfass.[6] The appropriate filters are balanced by adjusting their thickness so that they transmit the interfering film radiation equally. For their measurement of iron films on the silver and zirconium substrates, the filters used were based on data given in Table 2. In making measurements of a particular sample, the filters are alternately placed in the emergent beams consisting of fluorescent radiation from both the film and substrate. The difference in observed intensities from the balanced filters is due to the characteristic K radiation from the substrate, falling in the wavelength interval between the two filter absorption edges.

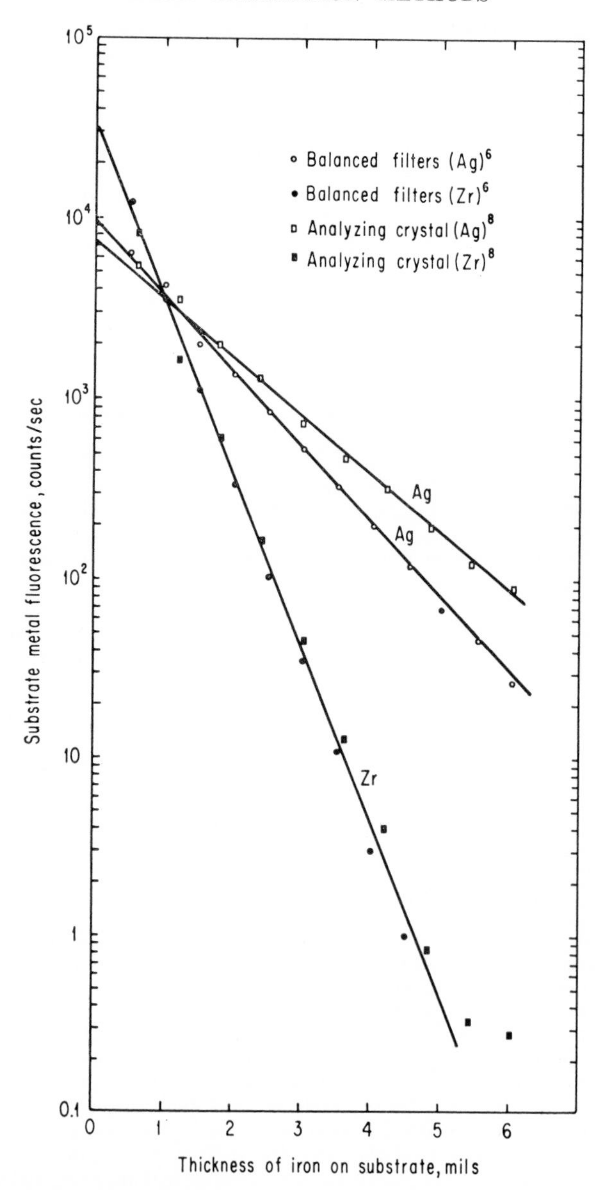

FIG. 3. Iron film thickness data for silver and zirconium substrates. Comparison of balanced filter[6] and crystal reflection[8] techniques, using attenuation of fluorescent substrate emission by the film.

Figure 3 is a plot of Achey and Serfass[6] data obtained in this manner. The linear relationships observed indicate adherence to the absorption laws. The measurements were made directly and did not involve corrections for background interference, which is also eliminated by the use of balanced filters. Also plotted in Fig. 3 are data obtained by Zemany and Liebhafsky[8] who studied the same system using an analyzing crystal reflection technique. The agreement is remarkable, especially for zirconium.

The advantage of thickness measurement by attenuation of an unresolved beam lies in its simplicity. Because of the simple optics, primary source and detector can be situated close to the sample, resulting in very high emitted beam intensity. As a result power requirements are modest. The method is conducive to commercial application and is indeed being applied extensively to monitoring tin plating on steel in many steel plants. It is likely that further commercial applications will evolve in the future.

Attenuation of a Monochromatic Beam. It is possible to modify the preceding method by adding an analyzing crystal to the system to monitor the emitted radiation from the substrate and thus eliminate interference from diffraction peaks or fluorescence from the overlying film. The loss in sensitivity due to reduction in intensity by monochromatization can be partially compensated by using increased primary

Table 2[6]

Filter	*K abs edge, Å*
Iron Film on Ag Substrate ($Ag\ K\alpha = 0.56$ Å)	
Mo	0.618
Rh	0.533
Iron Film on Zr Substrate ($Zr\ K\alpha = 0.78$ Å)	
Rb (as RbCl)	0.814
Sr (as $SrSO_4$)	0.768

x-ray voltages. This in turn is possible because interference from fluorescence of the overlying film is eliminated by the monochromating crystal. Zemany and Liebhafsky[8] tested this method using, like Achey and Serfass,[6] iron films on Zr and on Ag substrates. Their results were very much the same, after background corrections were made, so that Fig. 3 represents essentially also the results obtained by Zemany and Liebhafsky using attenuation of monochromatized radiation. Again the linear plot indicated adherence to Beer's law, even when with Zr the measured intensities varied over five orders of magnitude. Liebhafsky et al.[9] note that, since the thickness determination depends upon absorption by iron, results such as those plotted in Fig. 3 should be compatible with the known mass absorption coefficients for Fe. Equation (5) governs the absorption process here. If we replace μ_1 and μ_2 in Eq. (5) by an average mass absorption coefficient μ_{avg}, it follows that

$$\mu_{avg} = (\csc \theta_1 + \csc \theta_2)\rho \left[\frac{\ln (I_0/I)}{d}\right] \tag{6}$$

The multiplier of the ratio is constant and characteristic of the experimental arrangement. The last term is the negative slope of a curve such as that plotted in Fig. 3. Using this relationship for the Fe-Zr and Fe-Ag systems studied, Zemany and Liebhafsky[8] could show the following conformity of data.

Table 3[8]

Substrate	$\frac{\ln (I_0/I)}{d}$	μ_{avg}	$K\alpha$ substrate, Å	Known μ for Fe
Zr	0.944	34.7	0.79	38.5 at 0.71 Å
Ag	0.333	12.2	0.56	14.1 at 0.50 Å

Liebhafsky et al.[9] note that from Eq. (6) the thickness range for which this method is applicable depends largely on μ_{avg}. They noted, for example, that for a 0.6-mil Fe film on a Ni substrate, the Ni $K\alpha$ radiation is so strongly absorbed by Fe that the method is useless for this system. The mass absorption coefficient in this case is about 400, so that ln $[(I_0/I)/d]$ exceeds 10.

This method of film thickness determination has been widely used for a variety of systems. The conventional optics of the x-ray spectrograph are suitable without modification. Its widespread use reflects its versatility for a great variety of systems where fluorescent effects from the film require monochromatization.

Emission from the Film Only. Another method of thickness measurement involves emission from the film or coating, and has likewise been used frequently for a variety of film-substrate systems. Monitoring the fluorescent radiation from the film usually involves using an analyzing crystal as monochromator to eliminate interference from the substrate.

This procedure involves excitation of an element in the film by polychromatic primary radiation. If the film is sufficiently thin, it will not attenuate the incident beam, nor will the x-rays emitted by the film be absorbed by the film itself. In such infinitely thin films the intensity of the characteristic emission from the film would vary linearly with film thickness. As the film is increased in thickness, the film

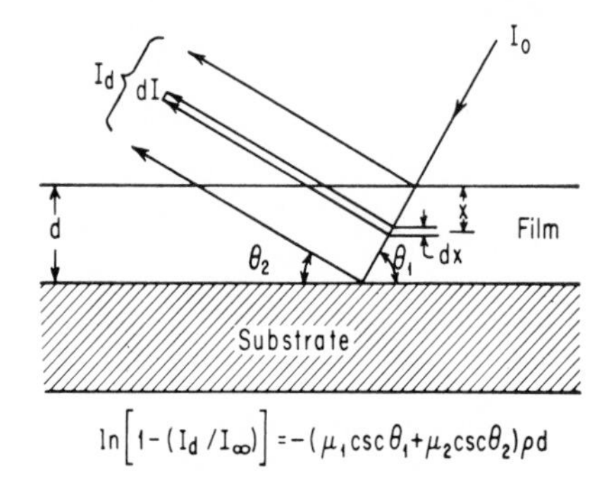

FIG. 4. Principle of thickness measurement by fluorescent emission from the film.

attenuates the incident beam. The intensity of the fluorescent radiation from the film increases with thickness at an ever-decreasing rate, until some *critical thickness* is reached above which there is no further increase in emitted radiation.

This situation is illustrated in Fig. 4. Here a film and its substrate are radiated by the primary beam. We shall assume that excitation of characteristic x-rays in the film by characteristic x-rays from the substrate does not occur. The theoretical treatment of this situation has been given by Liebhafsky and Zemany[10] as follows.

A beam of intensity I_0 is incident upon a film d cm thick and excites a characteristic spectral line of intensity I_d. The contribution to I_d of a volume element of constant area and thickness dx at depth x is

$$dI = kI_0 \exp\left[-(\mu_1 \csc\theta_1 + \mu_2 \csc\theta_2)\rho x\right] dx$$

where k is a constant related to absorption and conversion of incident to characteristic radiation, and all other terms have their usual significance. Integrating,

$$I_d = kI_0 \int_0^d e^{-ax}\, dx = \frac{kI_0(1 - e^{-ad})}{a} \tag{7}$$

where $a = (\mu_1 \csc\theta_1 + \mu_2 \csc\theta_2)\rho$. At infinite thickness ($d = \infty$)

$$I_\infty = kI_0/a \tag{8}$$

Therefore,

$$I_d/I_\infty = 1 - e^{-ad} \tag{9}$$

Since a film above the critical thickness is indistinguishable from one of infinite thickness, I_∞ can be measured experimentally from a film of greater than critical thickness. The critical thickness can be calculated from Eq. (9) by arbitrarily assigning a value of, say, 0.99 to the ratio I_d/I_∞.* From Eq. (9) it is apparent that

$$\ln (1 - I_d/I_\infty) = -ad \tag{10}$$

This method has been applied to a variety of film thickness determinations. An example is the determination by Kaelble and McEwan[11] of Si-bearing wax films on non-silicon-containing substrates. Figure 5 illustrates the working curve obtained for a series of such wax films of predetermined thickness. The linearity of the plot attests to the adherence to general absorption laws.

Emission from Film and Substrate. In all the preceding methods based on emission, it was assumed that the emitted radiation stemmed from an element in either the substrate or overlying film alone. Sometimes situations arise in which it is necessary to analyze the emitted radiation from an element present in both the film and substrate. This situation involving emission methods has not been dealt with in

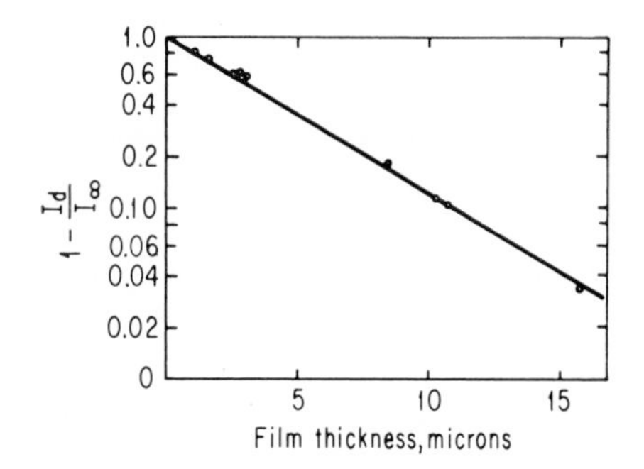

Fig. 5. Measurement of wax film thickness[11] using Si $K\alpha$ emission from the film.

the literature, although Keating and Kammerer[3] applied diffraction methods to measure the thickness of zirconium nitride on a zirconium substrate. Kaelble and McEwan[11] have determined silica-containing wax film thicknesses on Si-containing substrates utilizing monochromatic emission techniques. This case is really nothing more than a combination of the two cases illustrated previously in Figs. 2 and 4, utilizing an analyzing crystal to monochromatize the emergent radiation.

If $\mathbf{I}$ is the intensity of the characteristic radiation (Si $K\alpha$ in this case) emitted simultaneously from both film and substrate, I_1 the intensity from the substrate alone but with its film superimposed, and I_2 the intensity from the film alone, then

$$\mathbf{I} = I_1 + I_2$$

From Eq. (5)

$$I_1 = I_0 \exp(-ad) \tag{11}$$

where I_0 is the emitted intensity from the substrate without the overlying film. From Eq. (9)

$$I_2 = I_\infty - I_\infty \exp(-ad) \tag{12}$$

* Equation (9) is also applicable to critical thickness determinations for the characteristic radiation involved in diffraction procedures. The expression can be simplified in this case inasmuch as $a = (2\mu \csc \theta)\rho$, where θ is the Bragg angle. See Sec. 2 of this chapter.

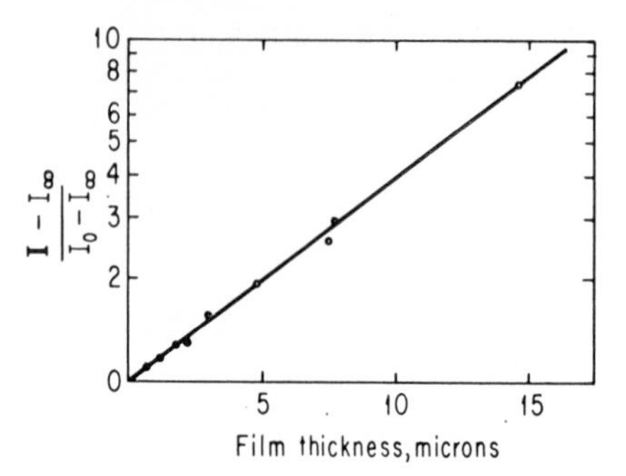

FIG. 6. Measurement of wax film thickness[11] using Si $K\alpha$ emission from both film and substrate.

where I_∞ is the emitted intensity from a film exceeding the critical thickness. Therefore

$$\mathbf{I} = I_0 \exp(-ad) - I_\infty \exp(-ad) + I_\infty$$
$$\mathbf{I} - I_\infty = (I_0 - I_\infty) \exp(-ad)$$
$$\ln \frac{\mathbf{I} - I_\infty}{I_0 - I_\infty} = -ad \tag{13}$$

Kaelble and McEwan[11] used this relationship in determining film thickness of SiO_2-bearing wax films on silicate-containing floor tiles. Figure 6, obtained from wax films on glass substrates, served as the working curve for the above application. The linearity of the plot shows conformity to the conventional absorption laws over the range of film thicknesses investigated.

4. FILM THICKNESS BY TRANSMISSION ABSORPTION

All the previous methods apply to thickness measurements involving x-ray opaque substrates, so that transmission methods are generally inapplicable. Occasionally situations arise when both film and substrate are transparent enough to warrant the

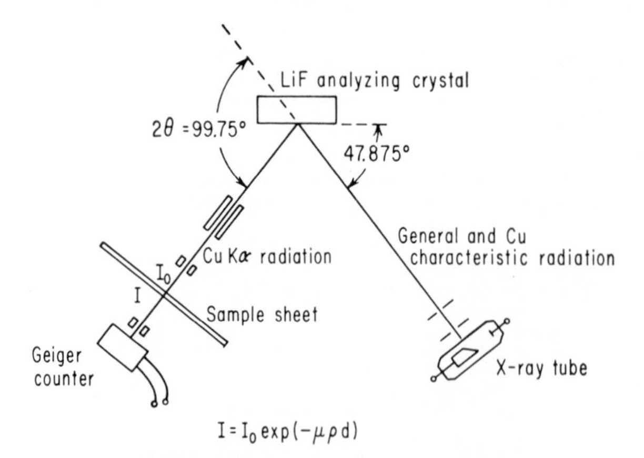

FIG. 7. Experimental arrangement for transmission-absorption measurement of film thickness.[4] (*Copyright, 1961, by Technical Association of the Pulp and Paper Industry, and reprinted by permission of the copyright owner.*)

use of simple transmission absorption for which the following relationship is valid,

$$I = I_0 \exp(-\mu\rho d) \tag{14}$$

Murray and Johns[4] determined the thickness of kaolin clay coatings on paper utilizing the experimental setup illustrated in Fig. 7. I_0 was determined after absorption by a sample of the uncoated paper substrate. Coating thicknesses for several clays were correlated with coat weight (expressed in pounds on a bookmaker's ream basis, 25 × 38 − 500), as shown in Fig. 8. Scatter of points could be attributed to nonuniformity of coating clay distribution, and coating thicknesses determined with an accuracy of ±0.2 micron.

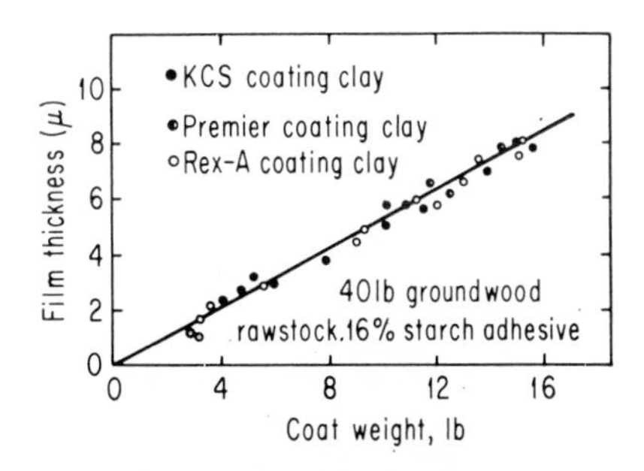

Fig. 8. Correlation of clay coating thickness and coating weight,[4] based on the transmission-absorption method. (*Copyright*, 1961, *by Technical Association of the Pulp and Paper Industry, and reprinted by permission of the copyright owner.*)

5. APPLICATIONS

The preceding discussion has already indicated something of the variations in applications possible. Although it is impossible to be fully comprehensive, a few additional examples merit mention. These include the study of tin and zinc coatings on steel,[10,12–15] cladding thicknesses of nuclear fuel elements,[16–19] plate metals on plated wires,[20,21] electrolytic silver,[22] iron-nickel films,[23,24] iron-nickel alloy films on glass,[25] and chromium plating on molybdenum.[26]

In conclusion mention should be made of the growing use of radioactive sources for film thickness measurement. Here also the established methods are used, involving attenuation by the film of characteristic emission from the substrate and characteristic *K* or *L* emission from the film. The radioactive source is utilized with a proportional or scintillation counter for resolution. Zemany[27] utilized iron-55 to measure the thickness of titanium on Kovar. Iron-55 emits essentially pure manganese *K* spectral lines, which in turn can only excite *K* spectra of elements lighter than manganese, and *L* spectra of elements lighter than Pr-61. The method is useful up to the critical thickness. Zemany[27] also suggests the use of iron-55 for Ti and for Ag, Sn, and Cd films utilizing their *L* spectra if air absorption can be minimized. Cook, Mellish, and Payne[28] utilized americium-241 to measure tin plate on iron and discussed the possible use of tungsten-181 and cesium-131 and tritium for copper films. The use of Sr-90, Pm-147, Am-141, Cs-131, and W-181 is further discussed in Refs. 20 and 28 to 32.

It appears likely that new developments using radioactive sources will continue to evolve and that in the future they may at least partially supplant x-ray spectrographic methods. Since the radioactive source can be placed close to the film, no spectrometer is needed. Interfering lines from other elements are not serious enough to require resolution by means of an analyzing crystal, a detector and pulse-height analyzer giving the required resolution. Thus intensity losses due to conventional monochromatization are avoided. For these reasons the future looks promising for the use of radioactive sources.

REFERENCES CITED

1. G. L. Clark, G. Pish, and L. E. Weeg, *J. Appl. Phys.*, **15**:193 (1944).
2. H. Friedman and L. S. Birks, *Rev. Sci. Instr.*, **17**:99 (1946).
3. D. T. Keating and O. F. Kammerer, *Rev. Sci. Instr.*, **29**:34 (1958).
4. H. H. Murray and W. D. Johns, *Tappi*, **44**:218 (1961).
5. H. F. Beeghly, *J. Electrochem. Soc.*, **97**:152 (1950).
6. F. A. Achey and E. J. Serfass, *J. Electrochem. Soc.*, **105**:204 (1958).
7. P. A. Ross, *Phys. Rev.*, **28**:425 (1926).
8. P. D. Zemany and H. A. Liebhafsky, *J. Electrochem. Soc.*, **103**:157 (1956).
9. H. A. Liebhafsky, H. G. Pfeiffer, W. H. Winslow, and P. D. Zemany, *X-ray Absorption and Emission in Analytical Chemistry*, Chap. 6, John Wiley and Sons, Inc., New York, 1960.
10. H. A. Liebhafsky and P. D. Zemany, *Anal. Chem.*, **28**:455 (1956).
11. E. F. Kaelble and G. J. McEwan, "X-ray Spectrographic Measurement of Wax Film Thickness," presented at 11th Annual Symposium on Spectroscopy, Society for Applied Spectroscopy, Chicago, 1960.
12. J. A. Dunne, Continuous Determination of Zinc Coating Weights on Steel by X-ray Fluorescence, in *Advances in X-ray Analysis*, vol. 6, pp. 345–351, W. M. Mueller and M. Fay (eds.), Plenum Press, Inc., New York, 1963.
13. G. E. Pellissier and E. E. Wicker, *Elect. Mfg.*, **49**:124 (1952).
14. A. Eisenstein, *J. Appl. Phys.*, **17**:874 (1946).
15. R. R. Webster, *Iron Steel Engr.*, **32**:65 (1955).
16. M. C. Lambert, X-ray Spectrographic Determination of Uranium and Plutonium in Aluminum and Other Reactor Fuel Materials, in *Advances in X-ray Analysis*, vol. 2, pp. 192–213, W. M. Mueller (ed.), Plenum Press, Inc., New York, 1960.
17. M. C. Lambert, *U.S. Atomic Energy Comm. Rept.* HW-57941 (1958).
18. B. J. Lowe, P. D. Sierer, Jr., and R. B. Ogilvie, Cladding Thickness of Fuel Elements by X-rays, in *Advances in X-ray Analysis*, vol. 2, pp. 275–281, W. M. Mueller (ed.), Plenum Press, Inc., New York, 1960.
19. P. Lublin, *Norelco Reptr.*, **6**:57 (1959).
20. J. F. Cameron and J. R. Rhodes, *Nucleonics*, **19**:53 (1961).
21. E. P. Bertin and R. J. Longobucco, *Anal. Chem.*, **34**:804 (1962).
22. P. P. Schreider, A. C. Ottolini, and J. L. Johnson, *Appl. Spectry.*, **17**:17 (1963).
23. K. Hirokawa, T. Shimanuki, and H. Goto, *Z. Anal. Chem.*, **190**:21 (1962).
24. R. R. Stone and K. T. Potts, *Norelco Reptr.*, **10**:94 (1963).
25. T. C. Loomis, *Spectrochim. Acta*, **13**:158 (1958).
26. T. N. Rhodin, *Anal. Chem.*, **27**:1857 (1955).
27. P. D. Zemany, *Rev. Sci. Instr.*, **30**:292 (1959).
28. G. B. Cook, C. E. Mellish, and J. A. Payne, *Anal. Chem.*, **32**:590 (1960).
29. J. F. Cameron and J. R. Rhodes, *Brit. J. Appl. Phys.*, **11**:49 (1960).
30. P. Lévêgue, R. Hours, P. Martinelli, S. May, J. Sandier, and J. Brilliant, *Proc. 2nd Intern. Conf. Peaceful Uses At. Energy*, Geneva, **19**:34 (1958).
31. P. Martinelli and G. Siebel, *Proc. 8th Intern. Spectry. Colloq.*, Lucerne, 307 (1959).
32. C. E. Mellish, *Research* (London), **12**:212 (1959).

GENERAL REFERENCES

Glocker, R., and W. Frohnmayer: *Ann. Physik*, **76**:369 (1925).

Klug, H. P., and L. E. Alexander: *X-ray Diffraction Procedures*, John Wiley and Sons, Inc., New York, 1954.

Liebhafsky, H. A., H. G. Pfeiffer, E. H. Winslow, and P. D. Zemany: *X-ray Absorption and Emission in Analytical Chemistry*, John Wiley and Sons, Inc., New York, 1960.

Powers, M. C.: *X-ray Fluorescent Spectrometer Conversion Tables*, Philips Electronic Instruments, Mount Vernon, N.Y., 1957.

Sagel, K.: *Tabellen zur Röntgen-Emissions- und Absorptions-Analyse*, Springer-Verlag OHG, Berlin, 1959.

Part 6

MICRORADIOGRAPHY AND X-RAY MICROSCOPY

Chapter 45

CONTACT MICRORADIOGRAPHY

Eugene P. Bertin

Radio Corporation of America

and

Rita Longobucco Samber

Formerly of Radio Corporation of America

1. INTRODUCTION

Literature. A comprehensive *bibliography* has been compiled of the very substantial literature of x-ray microradiography.[1] The original bibliography covers the literature up to about 1955, and a first supplement was issued in 1957. The bibliography and supplement were compiled by the Eastman Kodak Co., X-ray Division, and Kodak Research Laboratories.

A *review* of the whole field of x-ray microscopy, including the various forms of microradiography, has been published by Nixon.[2] *Books* on x-ray microscopy and microradiography[3–6] have appeared recently. Particularly *comprehensive papers* of great practical value in the area of x-ray contact microradiography have been published by Clark and Gross,[7] Maddigan,[8] Trillat,[9] the staff of Philips Electronics,[10] and the writers.[11] The use of *monochromatic radiation* has been described by Splettstosser and Seeman,[12] and considerations relating to obtaining monochromatic radiation by secondary ("fluorescence") emission by Rogers.[13] Woods and Cetrone[14] and Salkovitz[15] obtained results comparable with those obtained with monochromatic microradiography by use of a W-target tube operated at *specific potentials.* Stereomicroradiography has been described by Clark and Eyler.[16]

Features. The most favorable features of microradiography include the following: (1) It gives information about the entire sample body, showing diverse phases, segregations, inclusions, and internal microvoids. (2) By suitable choice of wavelength(s), the method is capable of identifying the element(s) in diverse phases, segregations, and inclusions. (3) The method is capable of showing the distribution of an element of interest throughout the sample. (4) It is applicable to stereo techniques. (5) Although the surface of a flat specimen must be plane and smooth, elaborate polishing and etching techniques are not required. (6) There is no problem of alteration of the sample by surface treatment because it is primarily the interior of the sample that is examined. (7) There is no problem of depth of focus. (8) Ordinary room vibrations are usually not troublesome because the sample and photographic emulsion are in contact. (9) The method is capable of permitting point-by-point quantitative analysis over the sample in certain cases.

Unfavorable features of the method include the following.

1. Many factors conspire to limit the resolution attainable in the microradiograph: (*a*) grain size and number of grains per unit volume in the photographic emulsion; (*b*) distance between the emulsion and the feature to be observed in the sample; (*c*) thickness of the emulsion; (*d*) collimation of the x-ray beam; (*e*) scattering of the x-ray beam in the sample and emulsion.
2. Very long exposures are required by the fine-grain photographic emulsions used and by the relatively low intensity of secondary ("fluorescence") monochromatic radiation sources.
3. The sample must be very thin, and many samples cannot be reduced sufficiently without destruction.
4. Both top and bottom surfaces of the sample must be prepared.

2. PRINCIPLES

The manner in which monochromatic microradiography is applied to identify elements and to establish their distribution throughout a sample merits detailed consideration.

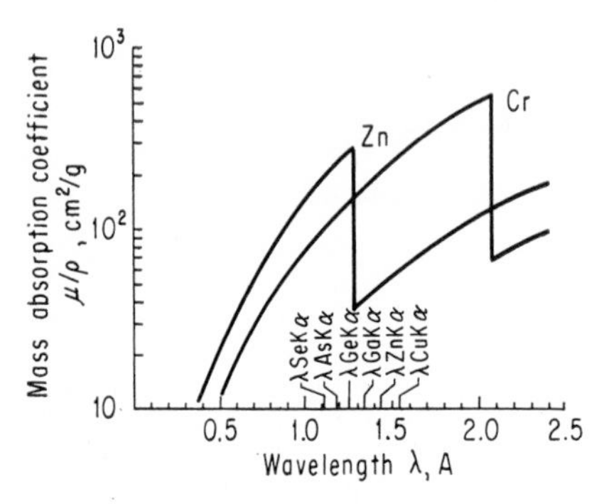

FIG. 1. Use of monochromatic x-rays to identify chemical elements.

Consider the x-ray absorption curve for Zn in Fig. 1. The $K\alpha$ spectral lines bracketing the Zn K-absorption edge are as follows:

$$\begin{aligned} \lambda\text{Ge } K\alpha &= 1.256 \text{ Å} \\ \lambda\text{Zn } K_{\text{abs}} &= 1.283 \text{ Å} \\ \lambda\text{Ga } K\alpha &= 1.341 \text{ Å} \end{aligned}$$

Now, if two microradiographs are made of a sample containing Zn segregations, one with Ge $K\alpha$, the other with Ga $K\alpha$ radiation, the Zn will appear lighter in the Ge and darker in the Ga microradiograph. However, in these two microradiographs, the photographic densities of other elements in the sample will be substantially the same for two such close wavelengths. For example, note the very slight difference in μ/ρ for Cr at λGe $K\alpha$ and λGa $K\alpha$ in Fig. 1. Thus an element may be identified by taking two microradiographs, one with each of the two $K\alpha$ lines bracketing its K-absorption edge. However, a standard 50-kv commercial x-ray unit cannot generate the $K\alpha$ spectral lines required for microradiography of elements of atomic number greater than 56 or 57 (Ba or La). Unless the unit is equipped for constant-potential operation, it generates only relatively inefficiently the $K\alpha$ lines required for elements of atomic number greater than 47 (Ag). Moreover, for these elements of higher atomic number, the K-absorption edges become progressively more closely spaced, so that more than one K-absorption edge may lie between the $K\alpha$ spectral lines of two adjacent elements. For these elements, identification may be based upon the L_{III}-absorption edges. However, $K\alpha$ spectral lines are still used for irradiation, because of the relatively low intensity of L lines.

If a sample is microradiographed using the $K\alpha$ spectral lines immediately adjacent to the K (or L_{III}) absorption edge of an element, the identification of that element is unequivocal, except in the following cases:

1. There are cases in which the K (or L_{III}) absorption edges of two consecutive elements A and B in the periodic system are bracketed by the $K\alpha$ lines of the *same* two consecutive elements C and D. This occurs in a few cases for the K edges of elements of atomic number less than 57 (La) (Table 1) and is the general rule for the L_{III} edges of elements of atomic number 47 to 92 (Ag to U) (Table 2).
2. It is possible for the L_{III} edge of a matrix element to lie between the two x-ray spectral lines being used to identify some other element using its K edge, and vice

versa. For example, the Hf L_{III} edge occurs at 1.297 Å, which is between the Ge $K\alpha$ and Ga $K\alpha$ lines used for identification of Zn in the example above.

Figure 1 also shows that the relative photographic densities of two elements may be reversed at various wavelengths. For example, Zn appears lighter than Cr for wavelengths less than λZn K_{abs}, Cr appears lighter between the Zn and Cr edges, and Zn appears lighter again at wavelengths greater than λCr K_{abs}.

3. USE OF POLYCHROMATIC X-RAYS

When the absorption coefficients of the detail and the matrix are very different, polychromatic x-rays may be used without any particular regard to effective wavelength. However, as these two absorption coefficients approach one another, choice of wavelength assumes increasing importance.

Woods and Cetrone[14] and Salkovitz,[15] using the direct beam from a tube having a tungsten target operated at specific potentials, obtained results comparable with those realized with monochromatic radiation. The wavelength required to establish the presence of the element of interest λ_E is selected in the same way as for monochromatic microradiography. The tungsten tube is operated at a potential at which the "effective wavelength" λ_{eff} of the direct beam approximates this wavelength. In general, λ_{eff} corresponds with the "hump" of the continuous spectrum, i.e., the wavelength at which the intensity is maximum $\lambda_{I_{max}}$, which occurs at $\sim$1.5 times the short-wavelength limit λ_0, which is dependent wholly upon the applied potential V. These relationships may be summarized as follows:

$$\lambda_E \sim \lambda_{eff} \sim \lambda_{I_{max}} \sim 1.5\lambda_0$$

$$\lambda_0 = 12.42/V_{kv} \quad (1)$$

$$\lambda_{eff} \sim 18.63/V_{kv} \quad (2)$$

These simple relationships enable selection of operating potential for the Woods-Cetrone method. The advantages of the method are its simplicity and the much greater intensity of the direct beam as compared with a secondary ("fluorescence") source. The simplified method is particularly suitable for cases where the inhomogeneity and matrix are of very different atomic number. However, it is to be emphasized that an *unequivocal* identification of an element, and optimum differentiation of it from the matrix, require monochromatic radiation.

4. USE OF MONOCHROMATIC X-RAYS

The principles involved in the choice of wavelength have already been discussed above.

Tables 1 and 2, compiled by the writers, serve as a guide to the selection of wavelengths suitable for monochromatic microradiography of elements of atomic number Z 20 to 92 (Ca to U). Elements of $Z < 20$ are not considered because more elaborate techniques are required in dealing with them. (Contact microradiography with ultrasoft x-rays is discussed in Chap. 46.) These tables enable selection of the secondary target element to be used in cameras of the types shown in Figs. 2*c* and 4*B*. The wavelength may be chosen to make the element of interest relatively transparent or opaque.

Table 1 is a guide to the selection of wavelengths suitable for monochromatic microradiography of elements E' using their *K-absorption edges*. It includes elements for which the K edges occur at wavelengths which (1) can be used in air-path cameras, such as those described elsewhere in this section, and (2) can be excited by irradiation of suitable secondary ("fluorescence") targets with the primary beam from an x-ray tube powered by a conventional 50-kv x-ray unit. On the basis of these criteria, Table 1 includes elements of Z 20 to 57 (Ca to La), except the following, which are not considered either as elements to be microradiographed E' or as elements for use as secondary targets E:36 (Kr), 43 (Tc), and 54 (Xe).

Table 1. Selection of $K\alpha$ Wavelengths for Monochromatic X-ray Microradiography. Elements for Which K-absorption Edges May Be Used (Z 20 to 57, Ca to La)

(Elements not considered in this table: Kr, Tc, Xe)

	Wavelengths absorbed Increasing absorption⟶ (E' appears light)			$Z'E'$ λK_{abs}	Wavelengths transmitted ⟵Increasing transmission (E' appears dark)		
Z, E........	23 V	22 Ti	21 Sc	**20 Ca**	20 Ca	19 K	17 Cl
$\lambda K\alpha$........	2.505	2.750	3.032	3.070	3.360	3.744	4.729
$(\mu/\rho)_{E'}$.....	630	795	970		120	190	400
Z, E........	24 Cr	23 V	22 Ti	**21 Sc**	21 Sc	20 Ca	19 K
$\lambda K\alpha$........	2.291	2.505	2.750	2.757	3.032	3.360	3.744
$(\mu/\rho)_{E'}$.....	545	725	895		150	205	275
Z, E........	26 Fe	25 Mn	24 Cr	**22 Ti**	23 V	22 Ti	21 Sc
$\lambda K\alpha$........	1.937	2.103	2.291	2.497	2.505	2.750	3.032
$(\mu/\rho)_{E'}$.....	377	475	603		110	150	195
Z, E........	27 Co	26 Fe	25 Mn	**23 V**	24 Cr	23 V	22 Ti
$\lambda K\alpha$........	1.791	1.937	2.103	2.269	2.291	2.505	2.750
$(\mu/\rho)_{E'}$.....	339	422	530		77.3	120	160
Z, E........	28 Ni	27 Co	26 Fe	**24 Cr**	25 Mn	24 Cr	23 V
$\lambda K\alpha$........	1.659	1.791	1.937	2.070	2.103	2.291	2.505
$(\mu/\rho)_{E'}$.....	316	392	490		70.5	89.9	138
Z, E........	29 Cu	28 Ni	27 Co	**25 Mn**	26 Fe	25 Mn	24 Cr
$\lambda K\alpha$........	1.542	1.659	1.791	1.896	1.937	2.103	2.291
$(\mu/\rho)_{E'}$.....	284	348	431		63.6	79.6	99.4
Z, E........	30 Zn	29 Cu	28 Ni	**26 Fe**	27 Co	26 Fe	25 Mn
$\lambda K\alpha$........	1.437	1.542	1.659	1.743	1.791	1.937	2.103
$(\mu/\rho)_{E'}$.....	270	324	397		59.5	72.8	90.9
Z, E........	31 Ga	30 Zn	29 Cu	**27 Co**	28 Ni	27 Co	26 Fe
$\lambda K\alpha$........	1.341	1.437	1.542	1.608	1.659	1.791	1.937
$(\mu/\rho)_{E'}$.....	270	292	354		54.4	65.9	80.6
Z, E........	32 Ge	31 Ga	30 Zn	**28 Ni**	29 Cu	28 Ni	27 Co
$\lambda K\alpha$........	1.256	1.341	1.437	1.488	1.542	1.659	1.791
$(\mu/\rho)_{E'}$.....	192	213	325		49.3	61.0	75.1
Z, E........	33 As	32 Ge	31 Ga	**29 Cu**	30 Zn	29 Cu	28 Ni
$\lambda K\alpha$........	1.177	1.256	1.341	1.380	1.437	1.542	1.659
$(\mu/\rho)_{E'}$.....	184	208	234		42.0	52.7	65.0
Z, E........	34 Se	33 As	32 Ge	**30 Zn**	31 Ga	30 Zn	29 Cu
$\lambda K\alpha$........	1.106	1.177	1.256	1.283	1.341	1.437	1.542
$(\mu/\rho)_{E'}$.....	169	183	209		32	49.3	59.0
Z, E........	35 Br	34 Se	33 As	**31 Ga**	32 Ge	31 Ga	30 Zn
$\lambda K\alpha$........	1.041	1.106	1.177	1.196	1.256	1.341	1.437
$(\mu/\rho)_{E'}$.....	153	170	192		10	23	52.4
Z, E........	37 Rb	35 Br	34 Se	**32 Ge**	33 As	32 Ge	31 Ga
$\lambda K\alpha$........	0.927	1.041	1.106	1.116	1.177	1.256	1.341
$(\mu/\rho)_{E'}$.....	143	182	205		13	25	37

Table 1. Selection of $K\alpha$ Wavelengths for Monochromatic X-ray Microradiography. Elements for Which K-absorption Edges May Be Used (Z 20 to 57, Ca to La) (*Continued*)

	Wavelengths absorbed Increasing absorption⟶ (E' appears light)			Z', E' λK_{abs}	Wavelengths transmitted ⟵Increasing transmission (E' appears dark)		
Z, E	38 Sr	37 Rb	35 Br	**33 As**	34 Se	33 As	32 Ge
$\lambda K\alpha$	0.877	0.927	1.041	1.045	1.106	1.177	1.256
$(\mu/\rho)_{E'}$	135	152	190		10	18	30
Z, E	40 Zr	39 Y	38 Sr	**34 Se**	35 Br	34 Se	33 As
$\lambda K\alpha$	0.788	0.831	0.877	0.980	1.041	1.106	1.177
$(\mu/\rho)_{E'}$	100	116	130		36	42	47
Z, E	40 Zr	39 Y	38 Sr	**35 Br**	37 Rb	35 Br	34 Se
$\lambda K\alpha$	0.788	0.831	0.877	0.920	0.927	1.041	1.106
$(\mu/\rho)_{E'}$	106	120	130		28	38	46
Z, E	42 Mo	41 Nb	40 Zr	**37 Rb**	39 Y	38 Sr	37 Rb
$\lambda K\alpha$	0.710	0.748	0.788	0.815	0.831	0.877	0.927
$(\mu/\rho)_{E'}$	94	102	112		20	25	32
Z, E	44 Ru	42 Mo	41 Nb	**38 Sr**	40 Zr	39 Y	38 Sr
$\lambda K\alpha$	0.644	0.710	0.748	0.770	0.788	0.831	0.877
$(\mu/\rho)_{E'}$	76	101	102		20	24	30
Z, E	45 Rh	44 Ru	42 Mo	**39 Y**	41 Nb	40 Zr	39 Y
$\lambda K\alpha$	0.614	0.644	0.710	0.728	0.748	0.788	0.831
$(\mu/\rho)_{E'}$	74	78	109		17	22	26
Z, E	46 Pd	45 Rh	44 Ru	**40 Zr**	42 Mo	41 Nb	40 Zr
$\lambda K\alpha$	0.587	0.614	0.644	0.689	0.710	0.748	0.788
$(\mu/\rho)_{E'}$	69	81	83		17	19	24
Z, E	46 Pd	45 Rh	44 Ru	**41 Nb**	42 Mo	41 Nb	42 Zr
$\lambda K\alpha$	0.587	0.614	0.644	0.653	0.710	0.748	0.788
$(\mu/\rho)_{E'}$	74	86	90		19	22	26
Z, E	47 Ag	46 Pd	45 Rh	**42 Mo**	44 Ru	42 Mo	41 Nb
$\lambda K\alpha$	0.561	0.587	0.614	0.620	0.644	0.710	0.748
$(\mu/\rho)_{E'}$	71	77	92		14	20	24
Z, E	50 Sn	49 In	48 Cd	**44 Ru**	46 Pd	45 Rh	44 Ru
$\lambda K\alpha$	0.492	0.514	0.536	*0.560*	0.587	0.614	0.644
$(\mu/\rho)_{E'}$	50	54	65		11	15	18
Z, E	51 Sb	50 Sn	49 In	**45 Rh**	48 Cd	47 Ag	46 Pd
$\lambda K\alpha$	0.472	0.492	0.514	0.534	0.536	0.561	0.587
$(\mu/\rho)_{E'}$	49	54	59		10	13	15
Z, E	52 Te	51 Sb	50 Sn	**46 Pd**	49 In	48 Cd	47 Ag
$\lambda K\alpha$	0.453	0.472	0.492	0.509	0.514	0.536	0.561
$(\mu/\rho)_{E'}$	47	50	55		10	11	14
Z, E	53 I	52 Te	51 Sb	**47 Ag**	50 Sn	49 In	48 Cd
$\lambda K\alpha$	0.435	0.453	0.472	0.486	0.492	0.514	0.536
$(\mu/\rho)_{E'}$	40	42	46		9	11	13

Table 1. Selection of $K\alpha$ Wavelengths for Monochromatic X-ray Microradiography. Elements for Which K-absorption Edges May Be Used (Z 20 to 57, Ca to La) (*Continued*)

	Wavelengths absorbed Increasing absorption⟶ (E' appears light)			$Z'E'$ λK_{abs}	Wavelengths transmitted ⟵Increasing transmission (E' appears dark)		
Z, E	55 Cs	53 I	52 Te	**48 Cd**	51 Sb	50 Sn	49 In
$\lambda K\alpha$	0.402	0.435	0.453	0.464	0.472	0.492	0.514
$(\mu/\rho)_{E'}$	28	32	34		8	10	12
Z, E	56 Ba	55 Cs	53 I	**49 In**	52 Te	51 Sb	50 Sn
$\lambda K\alpha$	0.387	0.402	0.435	0.444	0.453	0.472	0.492
$(\mu/\rho)_{E'}$	28	29	33		7	9	10
Z, E	57 La	56 Ba	55 Cs	**50 Sn**	53 I	52 Te	51 Sb
$\lambda K\alpha$	0.373	0.387	0.402	0.425	0.435	0.453	0.472
$(\mu/\rho)_{E'}$	28	30	31		6	7	9
Z, E	57 La	56 Ba	55 Cs	**51 Sb**	53 I	52 Te	51 Sb
$\lambda K\alpha$	0.373	0.387	0.402	0.407	0.435	0.453	0.472
$(\mu/\rho)_{E'}$	28	30	32		6	8	10
Z, E	58 Ce	57 La	56 Ba	**52 Te**	55 Cs	53 I	52 Te
$\lambda K\alpha$	0.359	0.373	0.387	0.390	0.402	0.435	0.453
$(\mu/\rho)_{E'}$	27	28	30		4	8	10
Z, E	60 Nd	59 Pr	58 Ce	**53 I**	56 Ba	55 Cs	53 I
$\lambda K\alpha$	0.334	0.346	0.359	*0.374*	0.387	0.402	0.435
$(\mu/\rho)_{E'}$	25	26	28		7	8	10
Z, E	63 Eu	62 Sm	60 Nd	**55 Cs**	58 Ce	57 La	56 Ba
$\lambda K\alpha$	0.301	0.311	0.334	*0.345*	0.359	0.373	0.387
$(\mu/\rho)_{E'}$	22	24	28		6	7	8
Z, E	64 Gd	63 Eu	62 Sm	**56 Ba**	60 Nd	59 Pr	58 Ce
$\lambda K\alpha$	0.291	0.301	0.311	0.331	0.334	0.346	0.359
$(\mu/\rho)_{E'}$	21	22	24		2	4	5
Z, E	64 Gd	63 Eu	62 Sm	**57 La**	60 Nd	59 Pr	58 Ce
$\lambda K\alpha$	0.291	0.301	0.311	0.318	0.334	0.346	0.359
$(\mu/\rho)_{E'}$	23	24	26		2	4	5

In Table 1, for each of the elements to be microradiographed E', the following information is given:

1. The central column gives the atomic number and symbol (in boldface type) of the element to be studied, and the wavelength of its K-absorption edge.

2. The three elements E having $K\alpha$ spectral lines which are most effectively *absorbed* by element E', i.e., having $K\alpha$ spectral lines to which element E' is most x-ray-opaque. These wavelengths tend to cause element E' to appear *light* on microradiographs. Data are given for these three elements as follows: (*a*) the atomic numbers Z and symbols E of the elements, arranged so that the closer the element is to the central (E') column, the more effectively is its $K\alpha$ line absorbed by E'; (*b*) the wavelengths of the $K\alpha$ lines (weighted average of the $K\alpha_1$-$K\alpha_2$ doublet); (*c*) the mass absorption coefficient μ/ρ of element E' for each of these wavelengths.

3. The three elements E having $K\alpha$ spectral lines which are most effectively *transmitted* by element E', i.e., having $K\alpha$ spectral lines to which element E' is most x-ray-transparent. These wavelengths tend to cause element E' to appear *dark* on

Table 2. Selection of $K\alpha$ Wavelengths for Monochromatic X-ray Microradiography. Elements for Which L_{III}-absorption Edges May Be Used (Z 47 to 92, Ag to U)
(Elements not considered in this table: Xe, Pm, Po, At, Rn, Fr, Ra, Ac, Pa)

	Wavelengths absorbed Increasing absorption⟶ (E' appears light)			$Z'E'$ $\lambda L_{III abs}$	Wavelengths transmitted ⟵Increasing transmission (E' appears dark)		
Z, E........	22 Ti	21 Sc	20 Ca	**47 Ag**	19 K	17 Cl	16 S
$\lambda K\alpha$........	2.750	3.032	3.360	3.698	3.744	4.729	5.373
$(\mu/\rho)_{E'}$.....	1030	1250	1520		340	780	1060
Z, E........	22 Ti	21 Sc	20 Ca	**48 Cd**	19 K	17 Cl	16 S
$\lambda K\alpha$........	2.750	3.032	3.360	3.504	3.744	4.729	5.373
$(\mu/\rho)_{E'}$.....	1120	1340	1660		380	840	1130
Z, E........	23 V	22 Ti	21 Sc	**49 In**	20 Ca	19 K	17 Cl
$\lambda K\alpha$........	2.505	2.750	3.032	3.324	3.360	3.744	4.729
$(\mu/\rho)_{E'}$.....	880	990	1120		215	400	870
Z, E........	23 V	22 Ti	21 Sc	**50 Sn**	20 Ca	19 K	17 Cl
$\lambda K\alpha$........	2.505	2.750	3.032	3.156	3.360	3.744	4.729
$(\mu/\rho)_{E'}$.....	940	......	775		215	400	920
Z, E........	24 Cr	23 V	22 Ti	**51 Sb**	21 Sc	20 Ca	19 K
$\lambda K\alpha$........	2.291	2.505	2.750	3.000	3.032	3.360	3.744
$(\mu/\rho)_{E'}$.....	727	1000	......		805	......	......
Z, E........	24 Cr	23 V	22 Ti	**52 Te**	21 Sc	20 Ca	19 K
$\lambda K\alpha$........	2.291	2.505	2.750	2.855	3.032	3.360	3.744
$(\mu/\rho)_{E'}$.....	742	1070	......		295	425	570
Z, E........	25 Mn	24 Cr	23 V	**53 I**	22 Ti	21 Sc	20 Ca
$\lambda K\alpha$........	2.103	2.291	2.505	2.719	2.750	3.032	3.360
$(\mu/\rho)_{E'}$.....	650	808	880		200	310	450
Z, E........	26 Fe	25 Mn	24 Cr	**55 Cs**	23 V	22 Ti	21 Sc
$\lambda K\alpha$........	1.937	2.103	2.291	2.474	2.505	2.750	3.032
$(\mu/\rho)_{E'}$.....	579	715	844		215	290	360
Z, E........	26 Fe	25 Mn	24 Cr	**56 Ba**	23 V	22 Ti	21 Sc
$\lambda K\alpha$........	1.937	2.103	2.291	2.363	2.505	2.750	3.032
$(\mu/\rho)_{E'}$.....	599	677	819		227	305	390
Z, E........	27 Co	26 Fe	25 Mn	**57 La**	24 Cr	23 V	22 Ti
$\lambda K\alpha$........	1.791	1.937	2.103	2.258	2.291	2.505	2.750
$(\mu/\rho)_{E'}$.....	320	632	......		218	240	330
Z, E........	27 Co	26 Fe	25 Mn	**58 Ce**	24 Cr	23 V	22 Ti
$\lambda K\alpha$........	1.791	1.937	2.103	2.164	2.291	2.505	2.750
$(\mu/\rho)_{E'}$.....	549	636	670		235	252	350
Z, E........	28 Ni	27 Co	26 Fe	**59 Pr**	25 Mn	24 Cr	23 V
$\lambda K\alpha$........	1.659	1.791	1.937	2.077	2.103	2.291	2.505
$(\mu/\rho)_{E'}$.....	493	......	624		......	251	267
Z, E........	28 Ni	27 Co	26 Fe	**60 Nd**	25 Mn	24 Cr	23 V
$\lambda K\alpha$........	1.659	1.791	1.937	1.995	2.103	2.291	2.505
$(\mu/\rho)_{E'}$.....	510	......	651		195	263	280

Table 2. Selection of $K\alpha$ Wavelengths for Monochromatic X-ray Microradiography. Elements for Which L_{III}-absorption Edges May Be Used (Z 47 to 92, Ag to U) (*Continued*)

	Wavelengths absorbed Increasing absorption⟶ (E' appears light)			$Z'E'$ λL_{IIIabs}	Wavelengths transmitted ⟵Increasing transmission (E' appears dark)		
Z, E........	29 Cu	28 Ni	27 Co	**62 Sm**	26 Fe	25 Mn	24 Cr
$\lambda K\alpha$........	1.542	1.659	1.791	1.844	1.937	2.103	2.291
$(\mu/\rho)_{E'}$.....	467	519	......		183	210	289
Z, E........	30 Zn	29 Cu	28 Ni	**63 Eu**	27 Co	26 Fe	25 Mn
$\lambda K\alpha$........	1.437	1.542	1.659	1.775	1.791	1.937	2.103
$(\mu/\rho)_{E'}$.....	420	461	498		115	193	215
Z, E........	30 Zn	29 Cu	28 Ni	**64 Gd**	27 Co	26 Fe	25 Mn
$\lambda K\alpha$........	1.437	1.542	1.659	1.709	1.791	1.937	2.103
$(\mu/\rho)_{E'}$.....	......	470	509		135	199	245
Z, E........	31 Ga	30 Zn	29 Cu	**65 Tb**	28 Ni	27 Co	26 Fe
$\lambda K\alpha$........	1.341	1.437	1.542	1.649	1.659	1.791	1.937
$(\mu/\rho)_{E'}$.....	......	......	435		140	135	211
Z, E........	31 Ga	30 Zn	29 Cu	**66 Dy**	28 Ni	27 Co	26 Fe
$\lambda K\alpha$........	1.341	1.437	1.542	1.579	1.659	1.791	1.937
$(\mu/\rho)_{E'}$.....	......	......	462		146	135	220
Z, E........	32 Ge	31 Ga	30 Zn	**67 Ho**	29 Cu	28 Ni	27 Co
$\lambda K\alpha$........	1.256	1.341	1.437	1.535	1.542	1.659	1.791
$(\mu/\rho)_{E'}$.....	......	......	(350)		128	153	155
Z, E........	32 Ge	31 Ga	30 Zn	**68 Er**	29 Cu	28 Ni	27 Co
$\lambda K\alpha$........	1.256	1.341	1.437	1.482	1.542	1.659	1.791
$(\mu/\rho)_{E'}$.....	......	......	......		133	159	......
Z, E........	33 As	32 Ge	31 Ga	**69 Tm**	30 Zn	29 Cu	28 Ni
$\lambda K\alpha$........	1.177	1.256	1.341	1.433	1.437	1.542	1.659
$(\mu/\rho)_{E'}$.....	......	......	......		......	139	168
Z, E........	33 As	32 Ge	31 Ga	**70 Yb**	30 Zn	29 Cu	28 Ni
$\lambda K\alpha$........	1.177	1.256	1.341	1.386	1.437	1.542	1.659
$(\mu/\rho)_{E'}$.....	......	......	......		......	144	174
Z, E........	34 Se	33 As	32 Ge	**71 Lu**	30 Zn	29 Cu	28 Ni
$\lambda K\alpha$........	1.106	1.177	1.256	*1.341*	1.437	1.542	1.659
$(\mu/\rho)_{E'}$.....	......	......	......		......	151	184
Z, E........	34 Se	33 As	32 Ge	**72 Hf**	31 Ga	30 Zn	29 Cu
$\lambda K\alpha$........	1.106	1.177	1.256	1.297	1.341	1.437	1.542
$(\mu/\rho)_{E'}$.....	......	......	......		90	130	157
Z, E........	35 Br	34 Se	33 As	**73 Ta**	31 Ga	30 Zn	29 Cu
$\lambda K\alpha$........	1.041	1.106	1.177	*1.255*	1.341	1.437	1.542
$(\mu/\rho)_{E'}$.....	229	......	......		......	136	164
Z, E........	35 Br	34 Se	33 As	**74 W**	32 Ge	31 Ga	30 Zn
$\lambda K\alpha$........	1.041	1.106	1.177	1.215	1.256	1.341	1.437
$(\mu/\rho)_{E'}$.....	239	......	......		30	60	143

Table 2. Selection of $K\alpha$ Wavelengths for Monochromatic X-ray Microradiography. Elements for Which L_{III}-absorption Edges May Be Used (Z 47 to 92, Ag to U) (*Continued*)

	Wavelengths absorbed Increasing absorption⟶ (E' appears light)			$Z'E'$ $\lambda L_{III abs}$	Wavelengths transmitted ⟵Increasing transmission (E' appears dark)		
Z, E	37 Rb	35 Br	34 Se	**75 Re**	32 Ge	31 Ga	30 Zn
$\lambda K\alpha$	0.927	1.041	1.106	*1.177*	1.256	1.341	1.437
$(\mu/\rho)_{E'}$	......	213	......		......	......	......
Z, E	37 Rb	35 Br	34 Se	**76 Os**	33 As	32 Ge	31 Ga
$\lambda K\alpha$	0.927	1.041	1.106	1.140	1.177	1.256	1.341
$(\mu/\rho)_{E'}$	......	222	......		......	......	......
Z, E	38 Sr	37 Rb	35 Br	**77 Ir**	33 As	32 Ge	31 Ga
$\lambda K\alpha$	0.877	0.927	1.041	*1.106*	1.177	1.256	1.341
$(\mu/\rho)_{E'}$	198	......	157		......	......	......
Z, E	38 Sr	37 Rb	35 Br	**78 Pt**	34 Se	33 As	32 Ge
$\lambda K\alpha$	0.877	0.927	1.041	1.072	1.106	1.177	1.256
$(\mu/\rho)_{E'}$	180	(130)	163		(99)	......	60
Z, E	39 Y	38 Sr	37 Rb	**79 Au**	34 Se	33 As	32 Ge
$\lambda K\alpha$	0.831	0.877	0.927	*1.040*	1.106	1.177	1.256
$(\mu/\rho)_{E'}$	(175)	(170)	(145)		(90)	(105)	(120)
Z, E	39 Y	38 Sr	37 Rb	**80 Hg**	35 Br	34 Se	33 As
$\lambda K\alpha$	0.831	0.877	0.927	1.009	1.041	1.106	1.177
$(\mu/\rho)_{E'}$	......	......	......		178	......	......
Z, E	39 Y	38 Sr	37 Rb	**81 Tl**	35 Br	34 Se	33 As
$\lambda K\alpha$	0.831	0.877	0.927	0.979	1.041	1.106	1.177
$(\mu/\rho)_{E'}$	......	......	......		72	105	130
Z, E	39 Y	38 Sr	37 Rb	**82 Pb**	35 Br	34 Se	33 As
$\lambda K\alpha$	0.831	0.877	0.927	0.950	1.041	1.106	1.177
$(\mu/\rho)_{E'}$	(120)	(135)	(160)		75	105	133
Z, E	40 Zr	39 Y	38 Sr	**83 Bi**	37 Rb	35 Br	34 Se
$\lambda K\alpha$	0.788	0.831	0.877	0.923	0.927	1.041	1.106
$(\mu/\rho)_{E'}$	......	121	139		......	77	110
Z, E	44 Ru	42 Mo	41 Nb	**90 Th**	40 Zr	39 Y	38 Sr
$\lambda K\alpha$	0.644	0.710	0.748	0.761	0.788	0.831	0.877
$(\mu/\rho)_{E'}$	......	143	......		......	58	68
Z, E	45 Rh	44 Ru	42 Mo	**92 U**	41 Nb	40 Zr	39 Y
$\lambda K\alpha$	0.614	0.644	0.710	0.722	0.748	0.788	0.831
$(\mu/\rho)_{E'}$	129	90	153		......	......	(61)

microradiographs. Data are given as follows: (*a*) the atomic numbers Z and symbols E of the elements, arranged so that the closer the element is to the central (E') column, the more effectively is its $K\alpha$ line transmitted by E'; (*b,c*) the wavelengths of the $K\alpha$ lines and mass absorption coefficient μ/ρ of element E' for each of these wavelengths are given, as above.

Table 2 is a guide to the selection of wavelengths suitable for monochromatic microradiography of elements using their L_{III}-*absorption edges*. It includes elements for which the K edges occur at wavelengths which cannot be excited or, at best, can be excited only inefficiently, by irradiation of suitable secondary ("fluorescence") targets with the direct beam from an x-ray tube powered by a conventional 50-kv x-ray unit. On the basis of this criterion, Table 2 includes elements of Z 47 to 92 (Ag to U), except the following, which are not considered either as elements to be microradiographed E' or as elements for use as secondary targets: 54(Xe), 61(Pm), 84 to 89(Po, At, Rn, Fr, Ra, Ac), and 91(Pa).

Whenever it is available, the same (or corresponding) data are given for these elements as for the elements in Table 1. However, absorption coefficients in the vicinity of L-absorption edges are available for only relatively few elements.

In Tables 1 and 2, three elements are given on each side of the absorption edges so that some latitude of choice is possible on the basis of availability, avoidance of absorption edges of other elements in the sample, etc. However, in general, the best choice of the elements on a given side of an absorption edge is the one for which the $K\alpha$ line is nearest to the edge.

There are several cases in Tables 1 and 2 in which the $K\alpha_1$-$K\alpha_2$ lines of one element lie on opposite sides of a K- or L_{III}-absorption edge of another. Such cases are marked in the tables by *asterisks* on both sides of the value of the wavelength of the E'-absorption edge in the central column. Such combinations are not suitable for monochromatic microradiography and are not listed in the tables.

Table 3. X-ray Diffraction Tubes as Sources for Monochromatic Microradiography

Target	Filter	$\lambda K\alpha$, Å
Cr	V	2.291
Fe	Mn	1.937
Co	Fe	1.791
Ni	Co	1.659
Cu	Ni	1.542
Mo	Nb or Zr	0.710
Ag	Pd	0.561

There are many cases in Tables 1 and 2 in which the same six elements E apply to both of two consecutive elements E'. There is one case in which the same six elements apply to three consecutive elements. Such cases are marked in the tables by *boxes*. In such cases, when the two consecutive elements E' occur in the same sample, they can possibly be distinguished by monochromatic microradiography by use of an L-emission line, or by crystal monochromatization.

Monochromatization. In practice, monochromatic x-radiation is obtained in one of four ways:

1. *Filtration* of the direct beams from diffraction tubes, in the manner commonly used in x-ray diffraction. Of course, the only wavelengths obtainable in this way are the $K\alpha$ spectral lines of target elements of diffraction tubes available commercially. At best, these target elements include only those listed in Table 3, and few laboratories have all these at hand.

2. *Excitation of primary emission* by irradiation of chemical elements on the target of a demountable x-ray tube. Approximate monochromatization of the $K\alpha$ emission is realized by filtration. Unfortunately, relatively few laboratories have demountable tubes.

3. *Excitation of secondary ("fluorescence") emission*[13] by irradiation of chemical elements with the direct beam of a high-intensity x-ray tube. In this way the $K\alpha$ spectral lines of all elements of atomic number equal to or less than ~56 (Ba) are obtainable from an x-ray tube operating at 50 kv. However, the $K\alpha$ lines of elements of atomic number greater than 47 (Ag) are excited with decreasing efficiency.

4. *Crystal monochromatization* of characteristic or continuous ("white") radiation. This method produces very pure monochromatic radiation of any wavelength present in the spectrum from the x-ray tube. However, unless a characteristic line is used, the intensity of any one wavelength is very low.

5. CAMERAS AND EQUIPMENT

Introduction. The microradiograph may be exposed in either of two basic ways: (1) With the primary beam from the x-ray tube, which may be either the tube in a diffraction unit or the excitation tube in a "fluorescence" spectrometer. The x-radiation may be used directly or roughly monochromatized with a filter. (2) With monochromatic secondary ("fluorescence") x-radiation excited by primary irradiation of a secondary target external to the x-ray tube.

The microradiograph may be recorded in either of two basic ways: (1) Direct—a single microradiograph is exposed with the film perpendicular to the direction of the x-radiation. (2) Stereo—two microradiographs are taken of the same sample with the incidence of the x-radiation at two different angles. The microradiographs are enlarged photographically and viewed with a stereo viewer. The technique permits perception of depth and spatial relationships of features of interest.

Microradiography without Cameras. Much useful microradiographic work can be done without any special camera equipment at all. The following technique has been used successfully for certain applications at the writers' laboratory for several years:

The back plate only of a flat-film x-ray diffraction camera is mounted on the camera track at one of the end-focus windows of the x-ray diffraction tube. The x-ray unit is operated at $\sim$20 kv, 7 ma, and the x-ray-illuminated area on the back plate is established by means of a fluorescent screen. The back plate is moved far enough away from the tube window so that this illuminated area is sufficient to cover the sample to be examined with radiation of uniform intensity.

The sample is placed directly on the emulsion of a piece of photographic film or plate, backed by a piece of sheet lead, and wrapped in 0.0005- to 0.002-in. aluminum foil, or in a double thickness of black photographic paper. Alternatively, the lead-film-sample assembly may be mounted in a small cardboard box. The package or box is affixed to the camera back plate by means of rubber bands or masking tape, and irradiated under suitable conditions. Precautions are taken to confine the scattered x-radiation.

For refinement and versatility beyond the limitations of this simple technique, more suitable equipment is required. The following section describes commercial equipment, as well as the construction and use of simple, yet very satisfactory equipment which was designed and built in the writers' laboratory.

Commercial Equipment. *Philips Electronics* manufactures the type CMR portable contact-microradiography unit.[17] This is a completely self-contained unit consisting of: (1) a 1- to 5-kv 0- to 5-ma power supply; (2) a specially designed x-ray tube having a Be window (50 microns thick), a focal spot 0.3 mm in diameter, and a focal-spot-to-window distance of 11 mm; and (3) a camera which uses a film [illegible]/8 in. in diameter and permits focal-spot-to-sample distances of 15 to 24 mm.

The tunnel between the x-ray tube window and camera can be evacuated for work at wavelengths >3 Å. Clearly, the unit is particularly suited to biological work but is useful for very thin sections of ceramics, and light metals.

Siemens has very versatile equipment for use on standard x-ray diffraction units as follows:

Camera for Stereomicroradiography (Fig. 2*a*). This camera enables taking four direct or two (i.e., two pairs) stereomicroradiographs of a sample on a single 5- by 2-cm film. The camera consists of a plate with studs for mounting on a Siemens camera carrier, film cassette, sample holder, and tweezers for manipulating the sample holder. The samples may be as large as 200 mm in diameter. The exposed area is 6 mm in diameter. For stereo work, the angle of incidence may be varied from 90 to 75°. The sample is loaded in a retractable holder and, when loading the camera, is advanced until it just contacts the film. Once the sample has thus engaged the film, the film cassette cannot be moved; thus damage to the emulsion and sample is avoided.

Extension Tube (Fig. 2*b*). The tube is 125 mm long, and when used with the camera, it increases the target-to-film distance and thereby enhances the resolution of the microradiograph. Two or more such tubes can be placed end to end.

Splettstosser Camera (Fig. 2*c*). The direct x-ray beam irradiates a secondary ("fluorescence") target of an element having $K\alpha$ spectral lines of appropriate wavelength. The secondary radiation illuminates an attached camera.

These instruments, which are designed for use with Siemens x-ray diffraction equipment, are also adaptable to Philips and General Electric equipment.

Laboratory-built Cameras. Figure 3*A* shows a simple general-purpose microradiography camera. A rectangular depression (1½ by ¾ by 3⁄16 in.) is machined in a rectangular brass plate (1¾ by 1 by ¼ in.). The "floor" (1⁄16 in. thick) of the depression is provided with a suitable *window* to admit x-radiation and with two

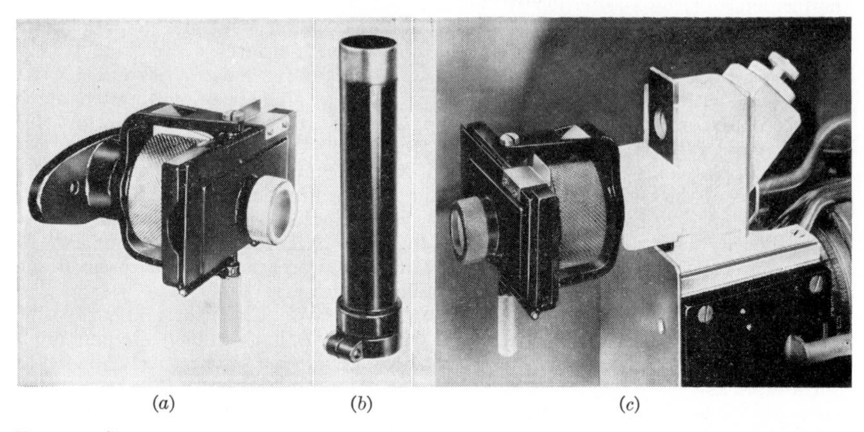

(*a*) (*b*) (*c*)

FIG. 2. Siemens cameras for contact microradiography. (*a*) Stereomicroradiography camera. (*b*) Extension tube. (*c*) Splettstosser camera.

⅝-in. 8-32 *threaded posts* to secure the cover. The *cover* consists of a rectangular brass plate ¼ in. thick and of length and width suitable to give a close fit in the depression of the main camera body. The cover is provided with two *holes* through which the two 8-32 threaded rods pass, a pad of *sponge rubber* 1⁄16 or ⅛ in. thick, and a short 8-32 round-head brass machine screw to serve as a *knob*. The cover is secured to the camera with two 8-32 *knurled nuts*. The *useful area* inside the camera, i.e., between the threaded rods and the side walls, is approximately 1 by ¾ in. Pieces of sample, foil, film, and plate must be of these dimensions or smaller. The cameras are adequately *lightproof* but should not be subjected to very bright light when loaded, e.g., by handling under a desk lamp.

Sherwood[18] has described a camera in which vacuum is used to ensure close contact between sample and plate.

Figure 3*B* shows an envelopelike holder for the cameras just described. Figure 3*C* shows a stereo-camera holder. The 1¾- by 1- by ¼-in. brass block has the same dimensions as the camera in Fig. 3*A*. A camera holder of the type shown in Fig. 3*B* is pivoted to the two extensions shown in Fig. 3*C* so that a camera inserted in the holder can be exposed at different angles.

Microradiography with Diffraction Units. Figure 4*A* shows an arrangement for microradiography with the direct beam from the x-ray tube on a diffraction unit. The device consists of a telescoping tube and a camera holder of the type shown in

Fig. 3*B*. The camera holder receives either a camera (Fig. 3*A*) or a stereo holder (Fig. 3*C*), which in turn receives a camera.

Figure 4*B* shows an arrangement for microradiography with the secondary ("fluorescence") beam excited by the primary x-ray beam from the x-ray tube in a diffraction unit. This accessory consists of a tube which seats in the camera mounting plate (see below). One inch from the seated end, a hole ⅜ in. in diameter is drilled in the tube, and the outside wall of the tube is machined flat for an area approximately

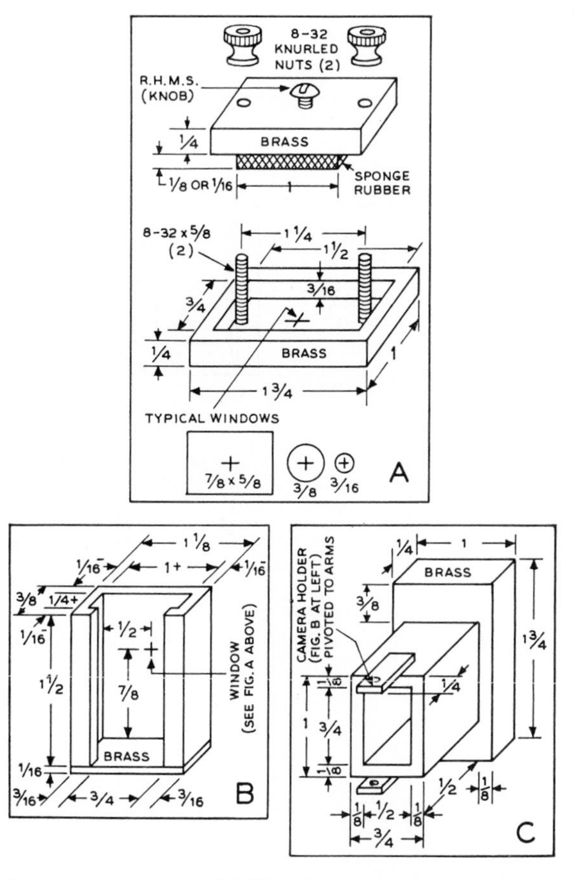

Fig. 3. General-purpose cameras and holders for x-ray contact microradiography. (*A*) Camera. (*B*) Camera holder. (*C*) Stereo-camera holder.

1⅛ in. long and approximately ¼ in. wide, with the hole at the center of the flattened area. A general-purpose camera holder (Fig. 3*B*), also provided with a ⅜-in. window, is brazed to the flattened area, with the two ⅜-in. apertures in register, as shown. The camera holder may receive either a camera (Fig. 3*A*) or a stereo holder (Fig. 3*C*) which in turn receives a camera. The other end of the tube is fitted with a removable assembly consisting of a bakelite probe fitted to a lead-backed brass insert. The end of the bakelite probe is beveled at 45°, and the beveled surface should be just inside of and face the ⅜-in. hole in the tube and camera holder.

The devices in Fig. 4*A* and 4*B* are mounted on the diffraction units by means of a suitable mounting plate. This consists of a brass plate for mounting microradiography camera holders at an end-focus port on General Electric type CA-7 diffraction tubes, Philips x-ray diffraction-tube housings, or Siemens camera carriers. The design of the plate will differ in each of these cases but must be provided with the following: (1) *mounting screws* for affixing the camera mounting plate to the diffraction tube (GE), diffraction-tube housing (Philips), or camera carrier (Siemens); (2) *leveling screws* for adjusting the tilt of the camera mounting plate for maximum uniform illumination of the microradiography camera; (3) *setscrews* for securing the camera holders to the camera mounting plate; (4) *x-ray port* (approximately ½ in. diameter)

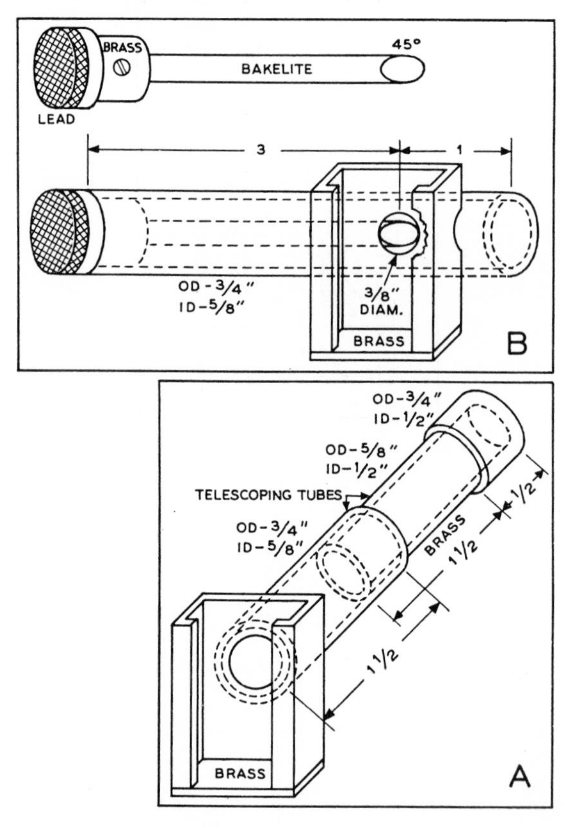

Fig. 4. Accessories for microradiography with commercial x-ray diffraction units. (*A*) Camera holder for microradiography with the primary x-ray beam. (*B*) Camera holder for microradiography with the secondary (fluorescence) x-ray beam.

for admitting x-radiation to the camera; (5) *counterbored recess*, concentric with the x-ray port, for seating the camera holders in the camera mounting plate; (6) a *groove* for a shutter-filter slide.

Microradiography with Spectrometer Units. Increased intensity, particularly for monochromatic microradiography with secondary ("fluorescence") radiation, is realized by use of an x-ray spectrometer sample compartment and x-ray tube. The accessories described in this section enable direct microradiography with commercial x-ray spectrometer units with the primary beam from the excitation tube, and both direct and stereomicroradiography with secondary x-radiation excited by the primary beam.

The sample drawers of General Electric, Philips, and Siemens spectrometers can be adapted to receive cameras of the type shown in Fig. 3*A*. The camera must be mounted in such a way that the sample and film planes are perpendicular to the direction of the primary x-ray beam.

Alternatively, a secondary target consisting of a chemical element having a $K\alpha$ spectral line of appropriate wavelength may be placed in the unmodified spectrometer sample drawer in the same manner as a sample for x-ray spectrometric analysis. The secondary radiation from this element illuminates a general-purpose camera or a stereo camera at the secondary-beam exit port, or at some other convenient place between the exit port and the analyzing-crystal stage. In fact, the cameras may be mounted in the analyzing-crystal stage.

For precise work, if very pure monochromatic radiation is required to illuminate the microradiographic sample, the camera may be placed beyond the analyzing crystal and the spectrometer set to the 2θ position appropriate to the particular $K\alpha$ wavelength used.

In any case, a suitable mounting bracket is required for mounting the cameras. Clearly, the modes of operation just described necessitate a certain degree of disarrangement of the spectrometer.

General Electric and Siemens x-ray spectrometers, in which the sample is mounted in a more or less spacious drawer, enable an alternative mode of operation. This mode requires no disarrangement of the spectrometer, only a modification of the sample drawer. The drawer may be modified so that the sample surface is inclined at the same angle, but tipped in the opposite direction, with the secondary beam directed away from the exit tunnel and toward the drawer face. The face is provided with a window and a camera holder (Fig. 3*B*) to receive cameras (Fig. 3*A*) or a stereo holder (Fig. 3*C*). Alternatively, a Siemens stereomicroradiography camera (Fig. 2*a*) can be mounted on the spectrometer sample drawer in the same manner.

Chemical elements used as secondary targets should preferably be in the form of elemental foil, sheet, bar, or disk. However, powdered element, oxide, or other stable compound may be pressed into pellets or packed into suitable dishes. A "library" of some 60 elements is kept in the writers' laboratory for this application.

6. SAMPLE PREPARATION

Some types of inorganic sample may be microradiographed without preparation. Among these are thin metal strip and foil, thin ceramic stock, paper, fabric, wires and fibers, and thin chips or flakes of metal, ceramic, or mineral. If the sample consists of small pieces, particles, wires, etc., they may be cemented with Duco cement to a small piece of 0.001- to 0.002-in. aluminum foil or Mylar; however, Mylar has the disadvantage that it attracts dust.

Usually a suitable sample must be prepared from bulk material by the following general procedure. A thin slice is sawed with a hack saw, band saw, water wheel, diamond saw, or wafering machine. The slice is made as thin and of as nearly uniform thickness as practical with the particular sample material and type of saw. The thickness is reduced further by rubbing both sides on progressively finer files, then progressively finer emery papers. Finally, the slice is polished on oiled 00 emery paper or chemically etched to remove grinding marks. The finished sample should be 0.5 to 0.01 mm thick, depending on the absorption coefficient of the material and the extent of overlapping detail.

Alternatively, the reduction in thickness may be made by mounting the saw-cut slice on a rigid block with thermoplastic wax and advancing it micrometrically into a grinding wheel. The sample is then reversed and the other side treated in the same way.

A still more refined, but also more elaborate, method is described by Maddigan.[8] The saw-cut slice is molded in bakelite and the exposed surface prepared by conventional metallographic techniques. At this stage the sample may be examined in a light microscope and areas of interest delineated with a scriber. The sample is then removed from the bakelite and broken up. The marked pieces are selected and remounted in lucite with the untreated surface outward. This surface is now prepared. A lathe, milling machine, or grinding wheel may be useful in rendering the surface parallel to the previously prepared one, and in reducing the thickness to the required value. The surface is then finished by metallographic techniques or in the manner mentioned above.

All reducing and polishing operations must be done in such a way as to avoid heating that may alter the structure. Chemical etching must be avoided or applied cautiously when preferential removal of certain constituents can occur.

7. PHOTOGRAPHY

The properties of some commercially available photographic emulsions suitable for contact microradiography are given in Table 4. Table 5 gives the nearest Gevaert equivalent[19-22] for most of the Kodak products in Table 4. A comprehensive line of photographic materials suitable for microradiography is also available from Ilford.[23]

Figure 5 shows photographic sensitometric curves for most of the photographic emulsions listed in Table 4. For Types M and D-2 X-ray Films, curves are given for both single and double emulsions. For 548-0 and 649-0 emulsions, curves are given for both film and plate. No curve is given for Gevaert 5E56 emulsion because no sample was available. However, it is reasonable to assume that the curves for this emulsion lie somewhere to the right of the curves for 649-0 emulsion. The experimental procedure by which these sensitometric curves were established is described in detail elsewhere.[11]

Anyone considering using photographic sensitometric curves for making calculations of the types described below should establish curves for the emulsions he plans to use. These curves should be established with the same development conditions that are to be used. Moreover, it would be wise to establish relative speeds by establishing curves at more than one wavelength.

The selection of the photographic film or plate to be used for a particular application is based upon the following considerations:

Kodak Type M is the fastest film which is of any real value in microradiography. It may be used for examination of relatively large features. The film is also useful for trial exposures from which to estimate exposure times for the very slow, fine-grain emulsions, in the manner to be described in the next sections.

Gevaert Type D-2 requires only slightly longer exposure than Kodak Type M and has finer grain. It is preferable to Type M for the applications given above.

Panatomic-X, Contrast Process Ortho, and High Contrast Copy Film are single-emulsion light films of substantially higher resolution than Types M and D-2, yet are still very fast. They are suitable for much practical microradiographic work. They have the disadvantages that they must be loaded and developed in total darkness and that they are available only as film.

Kodak Lantern Slide Plates are excellent for general practical microradiography, except where very high resolution is required.

Kodak High Resolution Plates, 649-0 *emulsions* are excellent general-purpose emulsions for microradiography. They give very high resolution and contrast without special precautions. The High Resolution Plates have the advantage of being much faster than the 649-0, while still having resolution and contrast more than adequate for most work.

Gevaert Scientia 5E56 has the highest resolution of any emulsion available commercially. However, it is very slow, and unless care is taken in its use, optimum performance will not be realized.

In general, for a given emulsion, plates are preferable to film, even though film usually has a thinner emulsion and, consequently, a higher resolving power. Plates, having a thicker emulsion, are faster, give better contact with the sample, and do not curl and shift when examined under the microscope.

The most convenient plate size for microradiographic work is 1 by 3 in. These plates are readily *cut to proper size* by scoring the glass side heavily with a diamond-point pencil or glass cutter, moistening the scratch, and breaking the plate by bending away from the scratch.

Table 4. Photographic Films and Plates Suitable for Contact Microradiography

Emulsion[a]	Description	Form	Darkroom illumination[c] Wratten filter series No. and color[29]	Kodak developer[d] [30]	Development time at 68° F, min	Resolution,[e] lines/mm	Gamma or gradient[f]	Exposure time,[g] sec	Relative exposure time[h]	References
Kodak Industrial X-ray Film, Type M, double emulsion	An extra-fine-grain high-contrast x-ray film	Film	6B, amber	X-ray	5	......	3.6	3	1	24
Kodak Industrial X-ray Film, Type M, single emulsion[b]		Film	6B, amber	X-ray	5	......	3.4	5.5	1.8	24
Gevaert Structurix X-ray Film, Type D-2, double emulsion	The finest-grain highest-contrast x-ray film available commercially	Film	6B, amber	X-ray	5	......	3.0	13	4.3	19, 20
Gevaert Structurix X-ray Film, Type D-2, single emulsion		Film	6B, amber	X-ray	5	......	3.9	23	7.8	19, 20
Kodak Lantern Slide Plates, Medium	A fine-grain plate for making transparencies for projection	Plate	1, ruby	Dektol(1:2)	3	90	3.4	15	5	25
Kodak Lantern Slide Plates, Contrast		Plate	1, ruby	Dektol(1:2)	3	120	...	....	....	25
Kodak Panatomic-X Film...	A fine-grain film of moderate speed and contrast capable of substantial enlargement	Film	Total darkness 3, dark green	DK-60a	4.5	100	2.5	4.5	1.5	26
Kodak Fine Grain Positive Film	A slow positive-type emulsion for printing positive transparencies for projection	Film	1A, light red	Dektol(1:2) D-11	4.5 7	120	...	....	....	26
Kokak Contrast Process Ortho Film	A fine-grain very-high-contrast, orthochromatic film for copy work	Film	1, ruby	D-11	5	125	3.7	7	2.3	26
Kodak Spectroscopic Plates, Type V-0	A very-fine-grain high-contrast spectroscopic plate; a finer-grain, but slower plate than Kodak Lantern Slide Plates	Plate	0A, greenish yellow	D-19 X-ray	3 5	160	3.0	23	7.8	27, 28
Kodak High Contrast Copy Film (formerly Kodak Micro-file Film)	A very-fine-grain slow panchromatic film for making greatly reduced (10× or more) copies of books, drawings, etc.	Film	Total darkness 3, dark green	D-11	5	175	3.6	36	12	26
Kodak Spectroscopic Plate and Film, Type 649-0	An extremely fine-grain emulsion said to have higher resolving power than any known lens system can utilize fully	Plate	0A, greenish yellow	X-ray	5	~1,000	5.7	2,800	930	27, 28
		Film	0A, greenish yellow	X-ray	5	~1,000	5.4	7,600	2,500	27, 28

Table 4. Photographic Films and Plates Suitable for Contact Microradiography *(Continued)*

Emulsion[a]	Description	Form	Darkroom illumination[c] Wratten filter series No. and color[29]	Kodak developer[d] [30]	Develop-ment time at 68° F, min	Reso-lution,[e] lines/mm	Gamma or gradient[f]	Exposure time,[g] sec	Relative exposure time[h]	Refer-ences
Kodak High Resolution Plate.	Kodak's finest-grain highest-contrast emulsion; for use in making reticles for optical instruments	Plate	0A, greenish yellow	D-19	5	>1,000	3.5	660	220	
Gevaert Scientia Type 5E56 (Lippmann) Film and Plate	Probably the finest-grain emulsion available commercially	Film Plate	1, ruby 1, ruby	....	... ...	2,200 2,400	...	....	....	22

[a] Table 5 gives the Gevaert equivalent for most of the Kodak films and plates listed here.

[b] Type M emulsion is also available in the form of Kodak M Metallographic Plates.

[c] Safelights should be provided with 15-watt lamps and mounted 4 ft from the work area where film and plate are to be handled. Emulsions may be exposed to 0A, 1, 1A, and 6B safelights for any reasonable time. Emulsions requiring total darkness should be exposed for only a few seconds under the series 3 safelight.

[d] The numbers in parentheses indicate dilution of stock developer solution prepared as specified on the package; e.g., (1:3) indicates 1 volume of stock solution to 3 volumes of water. Where no such number is given, the stock solution is used without dilution.

[e] These are the values claimed by the manufacturer for optimum exposure to light, 30:1 subject contrast, and the recommended development conditions.

[f] The values were taken from the sensitometric curves in Fig. 5 and the equation $\gamma = D/\log_{10} E$, where D is photographic density and E is photographic exposure. For curves having linear portions, γ is the tangent of the slope. For curves not having linear portions, the gradient was derived from the same equation from the tangent drawn to the curve at the point where $D = 1.0$.

[g] The values were taken from the curves in Fig. 5 and represent the exposure times required to give $D = 1.0$ at 100 cm from an x-ray tube having a Cu target operating at 40 kv, 20 ma, and filtered with 0.0004 in. of nickel.

[h] The values in the preceding column are reduced to terms of the exposure time for double-emulsion Type M film (3 sec) = 1.0.

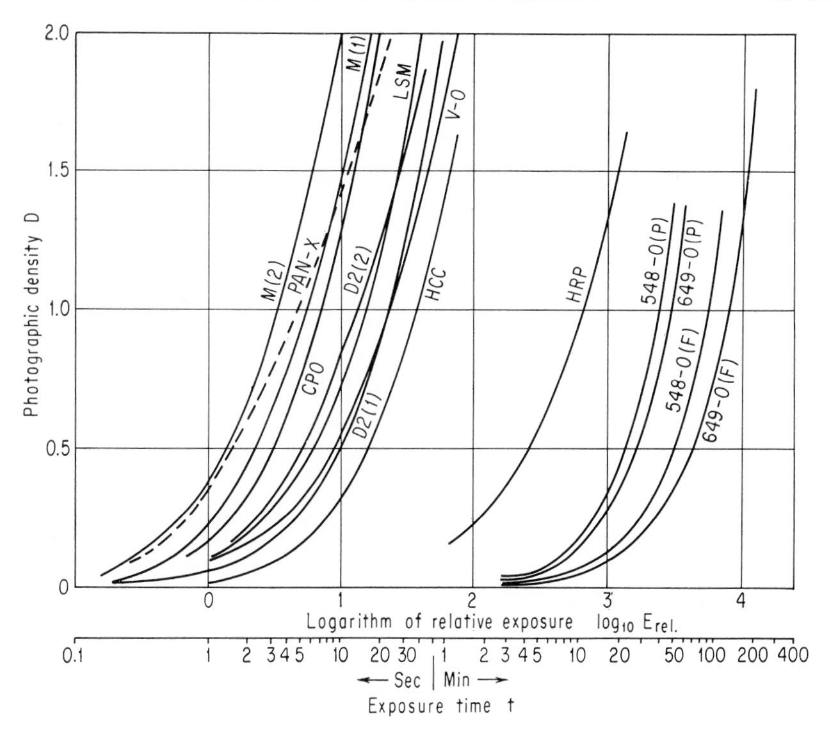

FIG. 5. Sensitometric curves for photographic films and plates suitable for x-ray contact microradiography.

M(2)............	Kodak Industrial X-ray Film, Type M, double emulsion
M(1)............	Kodak Industrial X-ray Film, Type M, single emulsion
PAN-X.........	Kodak Panatomic-X Film
CPO............	Kodak Contrast Process Ortho Film
D2(2)...........	Gevaert Structurix X-ray Film, Type D-2, double emulsion
D2(1)...........	Gevaert Structurix X-ray Film, Type D-2, single emulsion
LSM............	Kodak Lantern Slide Plates, medium
V-0.............	Kodak Spectroscopic Plates, Type V-0
HCC............	Kodak High Contrast Copy Film
HRP............	Kodak High Resolution Plate
548-0(P).........	Kodak Spectroscopic Plate, Type 548-0
548-0(F).........	Kodak Spectroscopic Film, Type 548-0
649-0(P).........	Kodak Spectroscopic Plate, Type 649-0
649-0(F).........	Kodak Spectroscopic Film, Type 649-0

The numbers along the bottom edge (below the logarithm of relative exposure scale) are exposure times for the following conditions: Cu $K\alpha$ x-radiation (0.0004-in. Ni filter); 40 kv, 20 ma; 100-cm target-emulsion distance.

The *emulsion side* is established in one of several ways. For sheet film, the emulsion side is readily established by notching, feel, or appearance. When the notching is held in the upper right corner, the emulsion side is up. The back side of the film has a glassy feel. If a safelight may be used, the emulsion side has a dull or milky appearance; the back side is shiny. For roll film (e.g., 35-mm 649-0 or High Contrast Copy Films), the emulsion side is in, and when the film is cut, it curls with the emulsion on the concave side. For very high resolution films (e.g., 649-0, 5E56), the emulsion side may be recognized under a safelight by its somewhat milky appearance. However, it is quite impossible to recognize the emulsion side of very high resolution plates by any of these methods. For these, a corner of the plate is placed between the slightly moistened lips. The emulsion side "sticks" to the lip.

For *processing* the exposed microradiograph, fresh, clean, filtered developer and fixer solutions should be used in small porcelain dishes. The progress of the *development* should be observed under the safelight if permissible, and such observation is facilitated by the white porcelain. (High Resolution, 649-0, and 5E56 Plates are completely transparent in the developer until the image begins to appear.) For most work, Kodak Rapid X-ray *Developer and Fixer* are satisfactory, but for optimum results, the developers recommended in Table 4 should be used. Type M, Panatomic X, and High Contrast Copy Films should be fixed the usual "twice the clearing time." The High Resolution, 649-0, and 5E56 emulsions are extremely thin, and fixing for 3 to 5 min is adequate. The microradiographs are *washed* 15 to 20 min in running water, *rinsed* with distilled water, and allowed to *dry* in a dust-free place.

Table 5. Gevaert Photographic Materials for Microradiography*

Kodak product	*Gevaert product which is most nearly equivalent*
Industrial X-ray Film, Type M	Structurix X-ray Film, Type D-4 (available with double and single emulsion)
(No Kodak equivalent)	Structurix X-ray Film, Type D-2 (available with double and single emulsion)
Lantern Slide Plate, Medium	Diapositive Normal Plate
Lantern Slide Plate, Contrast	Diapositive Contrast Plate
Panatomic-X Film	Gevapan-27 Film
Fine Grain Positive Film	Positive Fine Grain T.561 Cine Film
Contrast Process Ortho Film	Graphic Film and Plate 053
Spectroscopic Plate, Type V-0	Scientia Type 23D50 Plate
High Contrast Copy Film	Duplo Film
Spectroscopic Film and Plate, Type 548-0	Scientia Type 9E56 Film and Plate (slightly lower resolution)
Spectroscopic Film and Plate, Type 649-0	(No Gevaert equivalent)
High Resolution Plate	(No Gevaert equivalent)
(No Kodak equivalent)	Scientia Type 5E56 (Lippmann) Film and Plate

* Personal communication from D. D. Storing, Manager, Industrial Sales Div., Gevaert Co. of America, 321 W. 54th St., New York 19, N.Y.

Because the emulsion is easily *marred*, great care should be taken in handling and processing the films and plates. During processing, the emulsion side should be kept up.

For very fine work, dust must be excluded at all times, and a small safelighted *dry box* is to be recommended for cutting film or plate, loading cameras, and processing and drying the microradiograph.

A convenient way to *mount* microradiographs is as follows: A few very small "dabs" of Pliobond (available in tube or applicator jar at automobile supply stores) are applied near the edge of the microradiograph on the side away from the emulsion, and it is then placed on a microscope slide, emulsion up. If it is intended to view the microradiograph only with low-power microscopes, the emulsion may be down, in which case the Pliobond is applied to the edge of the emulsion side. It takes about 1 hr for the Pliobond to set securely; during this time, film microradiographs must be pressed with a suitable weight. A piece of paper is placed between the emulsion and the weight. The slides are *stored* in a microscope slide-file box.

8. CALCULATIONS

Exposure Time. "Correct exposure time" may be defined as that time which, for a given sample at a given set of conditions, gives a microradiograph which is satisfactory to the operator. For any given equipment, wavelength, excitation conditions, target-sample-film geometry, and photographic emulsion and development, the correct exposure time t_c for a sample having absorption coefficient μ and thickness x is given by

$$t_c = k \exp(\mu x_{\text{cm}}) = k \exp(2.54\ \mu x_{\text{in.}}) \tag{3}$$

From these equations, one can calculate the correct exposure time t_c for the microradiography of a sample of *any* substance if the linear absorption coefficient μ, the thickness x, and the value of k are known, and if the same conditions are used.

k may be evaluated as follows: Trial microradiographs are made of a sample of the substance of interest of known thickness x, at a certain wavelength, operating conditions (kv, ma), target-sample-film geometry, and photographic emulsion and development. For example, suppose that by trial it is found that correct exposure is obtained for a sample of Cu 0.003 in. thick in 15 min, using a certain microradiography

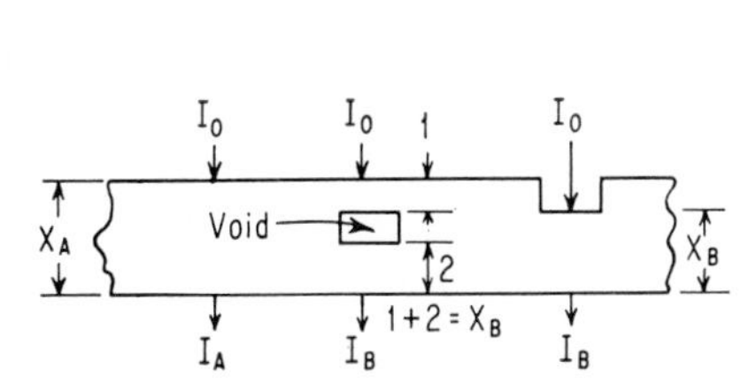

FIG. 6. Intensity relationships for microradiography of voids and variations in thickness.

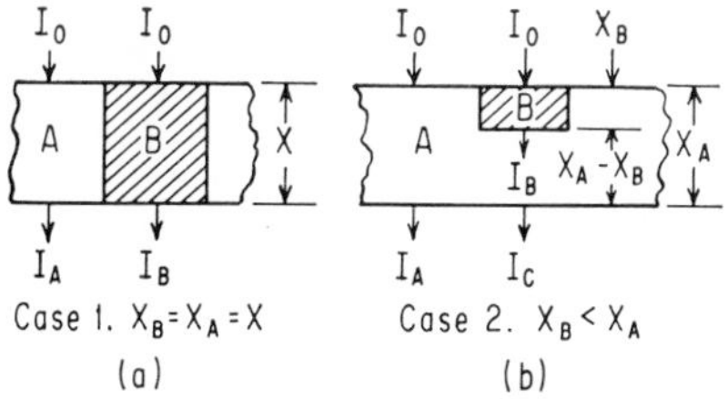

FIG. 7. Intensity relationships for microradiography of inclusions.

camera on a certain diffraction unit, with Cu $K\alpha$ radiation from a tube operating at 40 kv, 18 ma. Then,

$x_{\text{in.}} = 0.003$ in.
$t_c = 15$ min
$\mu = (\mu/\rho)$ for Cu at λCu $K\alpha \times \rho_{\text{Cu}}$; both these values are found in tables: (52.7 cm²/g) (8.96 g/cm³) $= 472\ \text{cm}^{-1} = \mu$

Then,

$$k = t_c/\exp(2.54\ \mu x_{\text{in.}}) = t_c \exp(-2.54\ \mu x_{\text{in.}}) \tag{4}$$

In the present case,

$$k = 15 \exp -[(2.54)(472)(0.003)] = 0.476$$

Then, in all subsequent cases, when making microradiographs under the conditions assumed above for the example given, correct exposure time for a sample of any substance of linear absorption coefficient μ and thickness x is given by

$$t_c = 0.476 \exp 2.54\ \mu x_{\text{in.}}$$

The value of k must be determined for each wavelength to be used.

In practice, k is calculated as above for the *matrix* element of a sample. Then various phases, inclusions, segregations, etc., having higher μ will be underexposed, while those having lower μ, including microvoids, will be overexposed. In either case, such features will be distinguishable from the matrix.

Voids and Variations in Thickness. Figure 6 shows a void and a depression in a sample of substance of density ρ and mass absorption coefficient μ/ρ for the particular wavelength used. Consider two x-ray beams passing through the sample, one of intensity I_A through the full thickness x_A, the other of intensity I_B through a part of the sample of reduced total thickness x_B because of a void or depression.

$$I_B/I_A = \exp(\mu/\rho)\rho(x_A - x_B) \tag{5}$$

Inclusions. Figure 7 shows an inclusion or segregation of substance B, having mass absorption coefficient $(\mu/\rho)_B$ and density ρ_B, occurring in a matrix of substance A

having mass absorption coefficient $(\mu/\rho)_A$ and density ρ_A. In Fig. 7*a*, the inclusion and matrix are of equal thickness x, which is also the thickness of the sample. In Fig. 7*b*, the inclusion is of thickness x_B, smaller than that of the sample matrix x_A.

Case 1. $x_B = x_A = x$ (Fig. 7*a*)

$$I_B/I_A = \exp x[(\mu/\rho)_A\rho_A - (\mu/\rho)_B\rho_B] \tag{6}$$

Case 2. $x_B < x_A$ (Fig. 7*b*)

$$I_C/I_A = \exp x_B[(\mu/\rho)_A\rho_A - (\mu/\rho)_B\rho_B] \tag{7}$$

Note that I_C/I_A is a function of $(\mu/\rho)_A$, $(\mu/\rho)_B$, and x_B but is not a function of x_A. Since $(\mu/\rho)_A$ and $(\mu/\rho)_B$ depend upon wavelength, the wavelength is chosen so as to give the greatest difference in these coefficients.

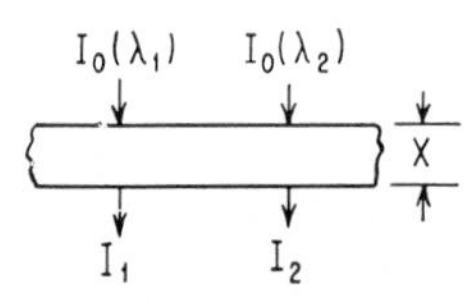

FIG. 8. Intensity relationships for microradiography with two wavelengths.

Multiple-wavelength Microradiography. In Fig. 8, two microradiographs are made of a substance of thickness x and density ρ. One of these is made with x-radiation of wavelength λ_1 for which the mass absorption coefficient of the substance is $(\mu/\rho)_1$, the other with λ_2 for which the coefficient is $(\mu/\rho)_2$.

Assuming $I_0(\lambda_1) = I_0(\lambda_2)$,

$$I_1/I_2 = \exp \rho x[(\mu/\rho)_2 - (\mu/\rho)_1] \tag{8}$$

Absorption Coefficients of Compounds and Mixtures. If the value of μ/ρ of a compound or mixture is not available, an approximate value may be calculated from the weight per cents or the weight fractions of the constituent elements A, B, . . . , N, as follows:

$$(\mu/\rho)_{AB\cdots N} = (\%A/100)\,(\mu/\rho)_A + (\%B/100)\,(\mu/\rho)_B + \cdots + (\%N/100)\,(\mu/\rho)_N \tag{9}$$

If one or more of the constituents A, B, etc., of a mixture are compounds, the values of μ/ρ of these compounds are calculated by the same equation, and then used in the calculation for the overall mixture.

If the value of the density ρ (in g/cm^3) is not available, an approximate value may be calculated in a similar manner:

$$\rho_{AB\cdots N} = (\%A/100)\rho_A + (\%B/100)\rho_B + \cdots + (\%N/100)\rho_N \tag{10}$$

Excitation-Exposure Relationships. Neglecting reciprocity and intermittency effects, photographic exposure E may be defined simply in terms of intensity I and exposure time t as follows:

$$E = It \tag{11}$$

There are three convenient means for varying intensity at the microradiography camera: x-ray tube target potential kv, x-ray tube current ma, and focal spot–film distance L. These variables, and the exposure time t, are related to exposure E as follows:

$$E \propto t \qquad E_1/E_2 = t_1/t_2 \tag{12}$$
$$E \propto \text{ma} \qquad E_1/E_2 = \text{ma}_1/\text{ma}_2 \tag{13}$$
$$E \propto 1/L^2 \qquad E_1/E_2 = L_2^2/L_1^2 \tag{14}$$

The relationship between E and kv is not so simple but may be approximated as follows:

For continuous ("white") x-radiation,

$$E \propto \text{kv}^{1.7} \tag{15}$$
$$E_1/E_2 = (\text{kv}_1/\text{kv}_2)^{1.7} \tag{16}$$

For target $K\alpha$ radiation,

$$E \propto (\text{kv} - \text{kv}_{\text{exc}})^{1.7} \tag{17}$$

$$\frac{E_1}{E_2} = \left(\frac{\text{kv}_1 - \text{kv}_{\text{exc}}}{\text{kv}_2 - \text{kv}_{\text{exc}}}\right)^{1.7} \tag{18}$$

where kv, kv_1, and kv_2 are operating potentials, and kv_{exc} is the K excitation potential of the target element.

When the x-ray tube is being used to excite secondary ("fluorescence") radiation, the tube must usually be operated at or near its maximum kv limit, and kv ceases to be a useful variable.

Application of these relations may be illustrated as follows: Suppose that an exposure time of 60 min is required to give a photographic density of 1.0 for Kodak 649-0 Plates exposed and developed as follows:

X-radiation: Cu $K\alpha$ (0.0004-in. Ni filter)
Excitation: 40 kv, 8 ma
Target-film distance: 75 cm
Development: Kodak Rapid X-ray Developer, 65° F, 5 min

Although such exposure times are not uncommon in microradiography, in this case the time can be reduced substantially:

1. Increasing the x-ray tube current from 8 to 20 ma increases the exposure by a factor of 2.5.
2. Decreasing the distance from 75 to 25 cm increases the exposure by a factor of 3^2 or 9.

Combining these measures results in an increase in exposure of 22.5, so that a photographic density of 1.0 is realized in only $60/22.5 \sim 2.7$ min.

Application of the Sensitometric Curves. Application of the sensitometric curves in Fig. 5 may be illustrated by three examples:

Example 1. *Calculating Correct Exposure from a Trial Exposure.* Suppose that a trial microradiograph recorded on Kodak Type M Film (double emulsion) at an exposure of 100 ma-sec has a photographic density in an area of interest of 0.5. It is desired to increase this density to 1.0, where the contrast is greater and the density-exposure curve more nearly linear. Referring to the sensitometric curve for double-emulsion Type M Film (Fig. 5),

$$\begin{aligned} \log_{10} E \text{ (for } D = 1.0) &= 0.50 \\ \log_{10} E \text{ (for } D = 0.5) &= 0.13 \\ \Delta \log_{10} E &= 0.37 \\ \text{antilog } \Delta \log_{10} E &= 2.35 \end{aligned}$$

Hence the original exposure (100 ma-sec) should be increased by a factor of 2.35 to 235 ma-sec.

Example 2. *Calculation of Correct Exposure Time for Very Slow, High-resolution Emulsions from a Trial Exposure on a Fast Emulsion.* Suppose that it is now decided to record the microradiograph in Example 1 at density 1.0 on Kodak 649-0 Plates, in order to realize greater contrast and resolution. Referring to the example above, and to the sensitometric curve for 649-0 Plates (Fig. 5),

$$\begin{aligned} \log_{10} E \text{ (for } D = 1.0 \text{ on 649-0 Plates)} &= 3.47 \\ \log_{10} E \text{ (for } D = 1.0 \text{ on Kodak M Film)} &= 0.50 \\ \Delta \log_{10} E &= 2.97 \\ \text{antilog } \Delta \log_{10} E &= 934 \end{aligned}$$

Hence the original exposure (235 ma-sec) should be increased by a factor of 934. If the original microradiograph was recorded at, say, 10 ma for 23.5 sec, the new exposure would be 10 ma for 21,949 sec, or $\sim$6 hr. However, increasing the tube current to 20 ma reduces this time to $\sim$3 hr, and if target-film distance can be decreased, even more reduction can be realized.

Using the procedure outlined in this example, one can make a quick trial exposure using a fast film (e.g., Kodak Type M) and, from this, estimate the exposure time for the very slow, very fine-grain emulsions (Kodak 649-0 or High Resolution). Substantially the same estimate can be arrived at with less calculation by referring to Table 4 and noting that for photographic density $D = 1.0$, the relative exposures for Kodak M double emulsion and 649-0 Plates are 1:930.

Example 3. Application of Eqs. (5), (6), (7), *and* (8). Suppose that by use of Eq. (7) it is calculated that the ratio of intensities I_C/I_A of x-ray beams, one I_C through an inclusion, the other I_A through homogeneous sample matrix, is 1.25. If a microradiograph is made on Kodak 649-0 Plates under exposure conditions such that the photographic density of the sample matrix is 1.0, what will be the density of the inclusion?

Since the inclusion and the matrix are exposed for the same time, the exposure ratio E_C/E_A = the intensity ratio $I_C I_A = 1.25/1.00$.

$$\begin{aligned} \log_{10} E_C &= \log_{10} 1.25 = 0.097 \\ \log_{10} E_A &= \log_{10} 1.00 = 0.000 \\ \Delta \log_{10} E &= 0.097 \end{aligned}$$

This interval in logarithm of relative exposure $\Delta \log_{10} E$ may be applied anywhere along the $\log_{10}$ relative-exposure axis to any curve in Fig. 5, and the corresponding interval in photographic density derived. For example, referring to the sensitometric curve for 649-0 Plates, and recalling that it is intended to have the density of the matrix be 1.0,

$$\log_{10} E_A \text{ (for } D = 1.0 \text{ for 649-0 Plates)} = 3.47$$

Then, for the inclusion,

$$\begin{aligned} \log_{10} E_C &= \log_{10} E_A + \Delta \log_{10} E \\ &= 3.47 + 0.097 \\ &= 3.57 \end{aligned}$$

Applying 3.57 to the curve gives $D_C = 1.33$, so that $\Delta D = 1.33 - 1.00 = 0.33$, a very substantial degree of contrast.

Using the procedure outlined in this example, one can calculate whether an intensity ratio predicted from Eqs. (5), (6), (7), and (8) gives sufficient difference in density to warrant making the microradiographic investigation. $\Delta D \sim 0.01 - 0.02$ is considered perceptible to the normal eye under good viewing conditions.

9. SPECIAL TECHNIQUES

There are many variations of the basic technique of x-ray contact microradiography.

Semimicroradiography. This is the technique of conventional radiography applied to very small objects such as insects or transistors, or to sections ~1 mm thick. The radiographs are recorded on fine-grain x-ray or light film and observed either with the unaided eye or with a 5 to 25× magnifier.

X-ray Optical Microradiography.[31,32] The x-rays are focused optically through the sample and on the photographic plate or film.

Pinhole-projection Microradiography. The sample, having the same form as for contact microradiography, is placed between a photographic film or plate and a pinhole source of x-radiation. The direct beam from the x-ray tube is intercepted by a thin metal diaphragm perforated with a circular aperture 10 to 125 microns in diameter. Although the pinhole is a simple way to obtain a virtual x-ray point source, the intensity is very low, and the exposure times very long. A much better way to effect projection microradiography is to use a true point source of x-rays obtained by electron-optic means.[33] This method is described in Chap. 47.

Topographic Microradiography.[34] Richards has reviewed several of these techniques as follows: (1) A radiolucent sample may be wiped with x-ray-opaque liquid to fill surface microtopography or impregnated with it to fill internal microvoids. (2) Thin radiolucent samples, such as leaves or insect wings, may be sandwiched between two cellulose acetate sheets; and x-ray opaque liquid may be used to fill the interstice between either sample surface and its adjacent plastic sheet or between both surfaces and their respective adjacent sheets. The entire sandwich is then microradiographed. The microradiograph reveals the topography of either or both surfaces, depending upon how the sandwich was prepared. (3) A mold may be made of thin radio-opaque samples, such as coins, and from the mold a radiolucent wax or plastic replica is made. This replica is treated in the same way as a radiolucent sample, as already described. (4) A replica may be made by pressing a thin layer of thermoplastic wax on a glass slide against the surface of the sample. The replica is later stripped from the glass and treated in the same way as radiolucent samples.

X-ray Diffraction Micrography (Berg-Barrett Technique).[35] A slit-collimated beam of x-radiation passes over the surface of the sample at a small glancing angle. A fine-grain photographic emulsion is mounted a short distance above the sample. The x-radiation is scattered by crystallites in the sample surface which happen to be oriented at the Bragg angle for the x-ray wavelength used. Scattered beams directed upward are intercepted by the photographic plate. Variations of this method[36–38] have enabled revelation of dislocations and other defects in single crystals. The Berg-Barrett technique is the x-ray analog of dark-field light microscopy.

X-ray Photoelectron Reflection Microradiography.[39,40] A high-energy (>100 kv) x-ray beam passes *through* the very fine grain photographic emulsion and strikes the sample, which is in contact with the emulsion on the side opposite the x-ray source. The x-radiation causes x-ray photoelectron emission from the sample surface. The photoelectrons are much more efficient in exposing the photographic emulsion than is the high-energy x-radiation, and give a satisfactory exposure before the x-radiation builds up an objectionable background. Since the chemical elements differ in their x-ray photoemissivity, it is possible to observe the distribution of an element over the sample surface.

X-ray Emission Micrography (X-ray Emission Spectroscopy).[41] The sample surface is irradiated by the primary beam from an x-ray tube, causing the chemical elements on the sample surface to emit characteristic secondary ("fluorescence") x-radiation. Cylindrically curved crystals are used to produce true monochromatic images of the sample surface on a fine-grain photographic plate. The crystals may be set to the appropriate position to image the characteristic radiation of any element of interest. In this way, it is possible to perform "topographical analysis," i.e., "chemical mapping" of the concentration of any element of interest on the sample surface.

The last three methods described, unlike the others, permit examination of the sample surface.

Direct-view X-ray Contact Microscopy.[42] Engström describes a technique in which the photographic film or plate is replaced by a fine-grain calcium tungstate fluorescent screen or a thin plate of uranium glass. The fluorescent images may be observed directly with a microscope at magnifications of 50× or more.

REFERENCES CITED

1. Eastman Kodak Co., X-ray Div. and Kodak Research Labs., *Bibliography: Microradiography and Soft X-ray Radiography,* 31 pp., 1955; Supplement no. 1, 12 pp., 1957.
2. W. C. Nixon, X-ray Microscopy, *Research,* **8**:473–483 (1955).
3. V. E. Cosslett and W. C. Nixon, *X-ray Microscopy,* Cambridge University Press, New York, 406 pp., 1960.
4. V. E. Cosslett, A. Engström, and H. H. Pattee (eds.), *X-ray Microscopy and Microradiography;* Proceedings of a Symposium held at Cambridge, England, 1956, Academic Press, Inc., New York, 645 pp., 1957.
5. A. Engström, V. E. Cosslett, and H. H. Pattee (eds.), *X-ray Microscopy and X-ray Microanalysis;* Proceedings of the Second International Symposium, Stockholm, 1960, Elsevier Publishing Company, New York, 542 pp., 1960.
6. J. J. Trillat (translated from French by F. W. Kent), *Exploring the Structure of Matter,* pp. 19–50, Interscience Publishers, Inc., New York, 1959.
7. G. L. Clark and S. T. Gross, Technique and Applications of Industrial Microradiography, *Ind. Eng. Chem., Anal. Ed.,* **14**:676–683 (1942).
8. S. E. Maddigan, The Technique of Microradiography, *J. Appl. Phys.,* **15**:43–54 (1944).
9. J. J. Trillat, Metallurgical Aspects of Microradiography, *Met. Rev.,* **1**:3–30 (1956).
10. Principles of Microradiography, *Norelco Reptr.,* **4**:125–129, 140 (1957).

11. E. P. Bertin and R. J. Longobucco, Practical X-ray Contact Microradiography, *RCA Sci. Instr. News*, **5**(3): 4–16 (1960); **6**(1):1–13, 24 (1961).
12. H. R. Splettstosser and H. E. Seeman, Application of Fluorescence X-rays to Metallurgical Microradiography, *J. Appl. Phys.*, **23**:1217–1222 (1952).
13. T. H. Rogers, Production of Monochromatic X-radiation for Microradiography by Excitation of Fluorescent Characteristic Radiation, *J. Appl. Phys.*, **23**:881–887 (1952).
14. R. C. Woods and V. C. Cetrone, Microradiography of Alloys, *Metals and Alloys*, **18**:1320–1325 (1943).
15. E. I. Salkovitz, Microradiography with Routine X-ray Equipment, *Metal Progr.*, **50**:1091–1096 (1946).
16. G. L. Clark and R. W. Eyler, Camera for Stereoscopic Microradiography, *Rev. Sci. Instr.*, **14**:277–278 (1943).
17. B. Combee and A. Recourt, Simple Apparatus for Contact Microradiography between 1.5 and 5 kv, *Philips Tech. Rev.*, **19**:221–233 (1957–1958).
18. H. F. Sherwood, Vacuum Exposure Holder for Microradiography, *Rev. Sci. Instr.*, **18**:80–83 (1947).
19. Gevaert Photo-Producten, N. V., D-2 [Structurix Type D-2 X-ray Film], *Bull.* 210.928(859).
20. Gevaert Photo-Producten, N. V., Gevaert Industrial X-ray Films, *Bull.* 991(257).
21. Gevaert Photo-Producten, N. V., Gevaert Scientia Films-Plates, *Bull.* 210.937(1259).
22. Gevaert Photo-Producten, N. V., Gevaert Scientia 5E56 Film or Plate (Lippmann type), *Bull.* MS/250-4.
23. Ilford, Ltd., Ilford Plates for Electron Micrography, *Bull.* G-45, Ilford, Inc., New York.
24. Eastman Kodak Co., X-ray Div., *Radiography in Modern Industry*, 2d ed., 130 pp., 1957; Supplement no. 2, 24 pp., 1959.
25. Eastman Kodak Co., *Kodak Data Book on Slides*, 4th ed., 49 pp., 1954.
26. Eastman Kodak Co., *Kodak Films*, 7th ed., 69 pp., 1954.
27. Eastman Kodak Co., *Kodak Materials for Spectrum Analysis*, 2d ed., 40 pp., 1954.
28. Eastman Kodak Co., *Kodak Photographic Films and Plates for Scientific and Technical Use*, 8th ed., 40 pp., 1960.
29. Eastman Kodak Co., *Kodak Wratten Filters for Scientific and Technical Use*, 20th ed., 81 pp., 1960.
30. Eastman Kodak Co., *Kodak Processing Formulas* and *Chemicals*, 5th ed., 68 pp., 1954.
31. P. Kirkpatrick and A. V. Baez, Formation of Optical Images by X-rays, *J. Opt. Soc. Am.*, **38**:766–774 (1948).
32. C. M. Lucht and D. Harker, An X-ray Microscope Using Mirrors of Adjustable Curvature, *Rev. Sci. Instr.*, **22**:392–395 (1951).
33. V. E. Cosslett and W. C. Nixon, The X-ray Shadow Microscope, *J. Appl. Phys.*, **24**: 616–623 (1953).
34. A. G. Richards, Methods for Radiographic Molds and Replicas of Surfaces, *Med. Radiography Phot.*, **32**(1): 24–29 (1956).
35. C. S. Barrett, A New Microscopy and Its Potentialities, *Trans. AIME*, **161**:15–64 (1945).
36. A. R. Lang, Direct Observation of Individual Dislocations by X-ray Diffraction, *J. Appl. Phys.*, **29**:597–598 (1958).
37. A. R. Lang, Studies of Individual Dislocations in Crystals by X-ray Diffraction Microradiography, *J. Appl. Phys.*, **30**:1748–1755 (1959).
38. J. B. Newkirk, Method for the Detection of Dislocations in Silicon by X-ray Extinction Contrast, *Phys. Rev.*, **110**:1465–1466 (1958).
39. A. I. Berman, Electron Radiography, *U.S. Atomic Energy Comm. Rept.*, AECU-1853, 48 pp., 1950.
40. J. J. Trillat, Electronic Radiography and Microradiography, *J. Appl. Phys.*, **19**:844–852 (1948).
41. L. von Hamos, X-ray Microanalyzer Camera, *Trans. Roy. Inst. Technol. Stockholm*, **68**:3–67 (1953).
42. A. Engström, Quantitative Microchemical Analysis by Microradiography with Fluorescent Screen, *Experientia*, **3**:208–209 (1947).

Chapter 46

CONTACT MICRORADIOGRAPHY WITH ULTRASOFT X-RAYS

Arne Engström

Karolinska Institute

1. INTRODUCTION

The simple laws which govern the interaction between x-rays and matter and the specific changes of x-ray emission, absorption, and diffraction with wavelength and material make x-ray microanalytical procedures very reliable methods for chemical analysis on the ultramicroscale. As an example, it can be mentioned that amounts of substance in the order of 10^{-12} to 10^{-14} g can be quantitatively determined with an error of only a few per cent by x-ray microabsorptiometry.

In general, the linear resolution of the x-ray microscopic procedures is approximately the same as the maximum resolution of the optical microscope. The value of microradiography, which is one form of x-ray microscopy, is therefore not its eventually high resolution but its ability to yield chemical information on samples of microscopic sizes.

The classification of the x-ray energies utilized in x-ray microscopy and x-ray microanalysis is now agreed to adhere to the following scheme:

Ultrahard →	← hard →	← soft →	← ultrasoft
0.1 Å	1.0 Å	10 Å	

In the wavelength region 1 to 100 Å the associated range of x-ray absorption coefficients varies by a factor of 10^5.

In contact microradiography, the basis for contrast is the simple law

$$I = I_0 \exp(-\mu_m m)$$

where I and I_0 are the transmitted and incident x-ray intensities, m the mass of specimen per unit area, and μ_m the mass absorption coefficient.

The soft and ultrasoft x-ray regions are mainly used when examining, at as high resolution as possible, specimens exerting a low x-ray stopping power. As a consequence ultrasoft x-ray micrography is mainly used for the examination and analysis of organic samples. Also inorganic specimens composed of elements of very low atomic numbers are often advantageously examined with x-rays of such unconventional wavelengths.

Another reason for using soft and ultrasoft x-rays for microscopy is that when high resolution is desired the thickness of the specimen must be reduced, because the "focal depth" in the microradiographic procedures is practically infinitely large, with a superimposed image as a result. Therefore, in order to secure enough contrast in the x-ray image of such necessarily thin specimens, x-rays with low energies must be used.

2. ABSORPTION OF SOFT AND ULTRASOFT X-RAYS

General. There is relatively little information on the absolute values of the x-ray constants in the ultrasoft x-ray region, and many of the numerical values now listed in handbooks were obtained in the days of classical x-ray physics.

Henke and collaborators[1] have recently considered the problem of the numerical values of x-ray absorption coefficients and put forward a semiempirical method to determine the x-ray mass absorption coefficients. In Table 1 there are grouped mass absorption coefficients for some elements at specific wavelengths which are often used.

Table 1. Mass Absorption Coefficients in the Ultrasoft X-ray Region

Absorber	Atomic No.	Al $K\alpha_{1,2}$ 8.34 Å	Cu $L\alpha_{1,2}$ 13.3 Å	Fe $L\alpha_{1,2}$ 17.6 Å	Cr $L\alpha_{1,2}$ 21.7 Å	O $K\alpha_{1,2}$ 23.7 Å	Ti $L\alpha_{1,2}$ 27.4 Å	C $K\alpha_{1,2}$ 44 Å
H	1	7.5	30	70	130	170	260	1,100
He	2	30	120	275	500	660	1,000	4,300
Li	3	78	280	640	1,200	1,450	2,300	9,400
Be	4	152	581	1,288	2,292	2,965	4,532	17,430
B	5	324	1,233	2,711	4,784	6,130	9,200	32,540
C	6	605	2,290	4,912	8,440	10,730	15,760	
N	7	1,047	3,795	7,910	13,120	16,270	22,590	3,647
O	8	1,560	5,430	10,740	16,610	983	1,473	5,470
F	9	1,913	6,340	11,600	1,015	1,301	1,949	7,280
Ne	10	2,763	8,240	1,079	1,863	2,379	3,575	13,180
Na	11	3,129	661	1,402	2,429	3,100	4,651	16,650
Mg	12	3,797	981	2,085	3,601	4,592	6,830	22,850
Al	13	323	1,146	2,441	4,189	5,310	7,840	24,910
Si	14	510	1,813	3,812	6,420	8,040	11,510	33,840
P	15	640	2,259	4,661	7,670	9,470	13,280	38,610
S	16	814	2,839	5,710	9,160	11,190	15,520	45,230
Cl	17	990	3,364	6,530	10,210	12,450	17,330	50,100
A	18	1,163	3,795	7,110	11,070	13,540	18,820	
K	19	1,429	4,504	8,310	12,960	15,820	22,030	
Ca	20	1,706	5,150	9,450	14,800	18,030	24,910	
Zapon	...	998	3,571	7,270	11,690	6,500	9,470	
Parlodion	...	1,177	4,167	8,390	13,320	5,450	7,870	
Animal proteins	...	854	3,095	6,391	10,480	8,719	12,584	
H_2O	...	1,388	4,830	9,554	14,779	893	1,338	4,984

The photoelectric absorption coefficient is the overall dominating component of the composite mass absorption coefficient in the ultrasoft x-ray region.

A large set of x-ray transmission data in the ultrasoft x-ray region for a series of specimens have been programmed and calculated on a computer, and some conditions of interest are reproduced in Fig. 1.

The Absorption Discontinuities. The K-absorption edges of elements with atomic numbers below that of aluminum are situated in the ultrasoft x-ray region, and Table 2 gives the wavelengths of these discontinuities together with the emission lines. It must be remembered that the exact position in the spectrum and the relative size of the discontinuities as well as their fine structures have not been determined in detail by modern precision techniques. Therefore, the values quoted can only be used to compute an approximately optimal condition for a specific experiment. When it comes to the analytical use of the absorption differential produced by an absorption discontinuity, model experiments must be performed or a standard included in the measurements. Because of the difficulties of obtaining monochromatic x-rays of high intensity and suitable wavelengths in the ultrasoft region, one is often forced to use a part (band) of the continuous x-ray spectrum, and the permissible bandwidth must be properly chosen for each experiment. It depends on several factors such as the signal-to-noise ratio with regard to the size of the absorption differential. Elementary analysis by estimation of the specific absorption differential produced by the absorption discontinuities in the x-ray region beyond 10 Å has been relatively little explored and mainly used in analysis of organic material but should have considerable applications in the examination of organic and biological specimens of minute size. Dichromatic contact microradiography has been much used in the soft x-ray region, that is, below 10 Å, for elementary analysis.

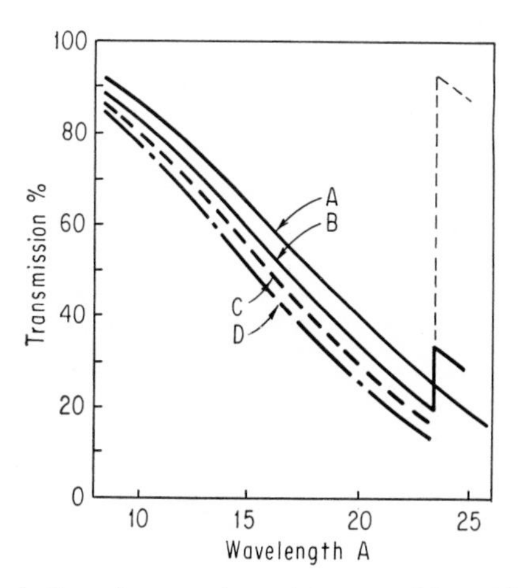

FIG. 1. Transmission of ultrasoft x-rays in various materials. (*A*) 1 micron aluminum. (*B*) 1 micron dried protein. (*C*) 1 micron water. (*D*) 1 mm air.

Resolution and Optimum Contrast. Several factors determine the linear resolution possible in contact microradiography. As thin specimens are used it is easy to arrange the experiment in such a way that the blurring due to geometrical factors is kept far below 0.5 micron. The Fresnel-diffraction fringes become a disturbing factor only when the resolution is aimed at values below 0.1 micron. The limit of resolution is usually set by the photographic recording material, but grainless recording materials such as certain plastics may help to overcome this difficulty.

Table 2. Wavelengths of Some Absorption Discontinuities and Emission Lines in Angstroms

Element	Atomic No.	*K*-absorption edge	$K\alpha_{1,2}$ emission	L_{III} edge	$L\alpha_1$ emission
C..........	6	43	44		
N..........	7	31	31.2		
O..........	8	23	23.7		
Na..........	11	11.5	11.9		
Al..........	13	7.95	8.34	172	
P..........	15	5.79	6.16	96	
Ca..........	20	3.07	3.36	35.6	36
Cu..........	29	1.38	1.54	13.1	17.6
I..........	53	0.373	0.43	2.72	3.15

The exposure times for such recording materials are considerably longer than for photographic emulsions, and as there is always a great need for intensity in all ultrasoft x-ray work, these special recording materials have found little use in ultrasoft contact microradiography. Proper handling of presently available fine-grained photographic emulsions exposed with ultrasoft x-rays makes it possible to resolve several thousand lines per millimeter. Hence the limiting factor in the ultimate resolution is the optical system used to inspect the contact microradiogram, that is, the optical microscope. Therefore, for practical purposes and properly designed experiments, the maximal resolution in ultrasoft contact microradiography can be set at ¼ micron, the limit of resolution in the optical microscope.

When microradiography is applied to produce an image of a specimen, as soft x-rays as possible should be used in order to differentiate between two adjacent structures. Assume two neighboring structures have the same thickness t but slightly varying linear absorption coefficients μ_1 and μ_2. The difference between the transmitted intensities I_2 and I_1 is

$$I_2 - I_1 = I_0(\exp \mu_1 t - \exp \mu_2 t)$$

and this function has no maximum. That is, maximum contrast is obtained when the difference between μ_1 and μ_2 is as large as possible, which occurs with increasing wavelength as μ increases with λ^n, where n has a value between 2 and 3. The exposure time is the practical limit in this case, when the transmission reaches very low values.

When the transmission in points in a specimen is to be measured in order to calculate certain chemical information from absorption data, the thickness of the specimen must be chosen in such a way that a minimum of errors occur when the intensities of the incident and transmitted radiations are compared. In this case it can be shown that the thickness of the specimen should be $1/\mu$ where μ is the linear absorption coefficient, and in such a specimen the transmission is 37 per cent. If the radiation not passing through the specimen, that is, the incident radiation I_0, is stopped in a known way, one can permit a lower transmission in the specimen and still have the same high accuracy in the measurement of the quotient I_0/I. The conditions are in this case equivalent to the principles for precision measurements in optical absorptiometry.

3. PRODUCTION OF SOFT AND ULTRASOFT X-RAYS

General. There are mainly two technical difficulties which present themselves when generating ultrasoft x-rays, namely, the relatively low production efficiency and the high absorption of ultrasoft x-rays even in thin layers of material. For these reasons the x-ray tube and microradiographic camera are usually built together into a compact unit with simultaneous evacuation.

Because of the low intensities involved, the photographic emulsions must be placed as close as possible to the target. This means that there must be a lighttight filter to prevent the visible radiation emitted by the filament from reaching the photographic film. Such light filters have to be very thin in order to transmit ultrasoft x-rays. Figure 2 shows the half-value layers (a layer which transmits 50 per cent of the incident radiation) of some materials for soft and ultrasoft x-rays, and the diagram can be used to design proper thicknesses of, for example, the aluminum filter separating the x-ray tube from the camera. In the x-ray tube shown in cross section in Fig. 3 the camera is evacuated simultaneously with the x-ray tube, and the approximately 1,000 Å thick Al or Be foil protects the film from the light emitted by the filament. Such a foil is fragile and must therefore be arranged so that, when the camera and x-ray tube are evacuated, no pressure is acting on this foil. In order to secure as good resolution as possible with a short target-to-specimen-film distance the size of the focal spot should be in the order of 0.1 mm.

Other types of soft x-ray sources have been constructed by Henke[2] among others, and Fig. 4 shows one of his x-ray sources suitable for the generation of high fluxes of ultrasoft x-rays.

Defining the Wavelengths. For many types of microradiographic studies it is sufficient to define the x-rays by the voltage, that is, the short-wavelength limit

$\lambda_0 = 12{,}400/V$, where V is measured in volts. The shape of the continuous spectrum in the soft and ultrasoft regions is defined by

$$I_\lambda = \frac{CZ}{\lambda^5}\left(\frac{1}{\lambda_0} - \frac{1}{\lambda}\right)$$

where Z is the atomic number of the target, I_λ the intensity of x-rays at wavelength

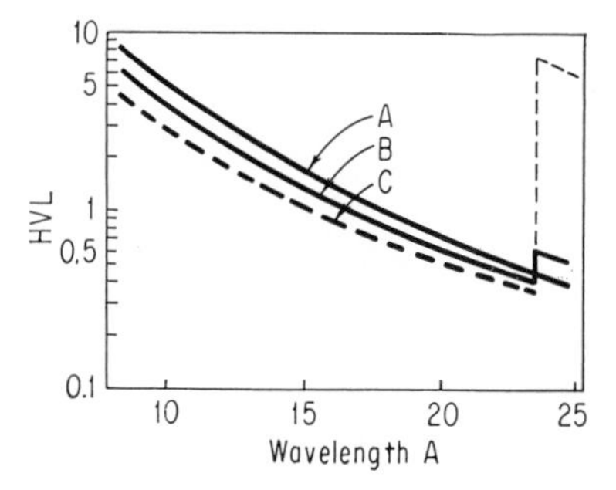

FIG. 2. Half-value layers in microns for (A) aluminum, (B) dried protein, and (C) water.

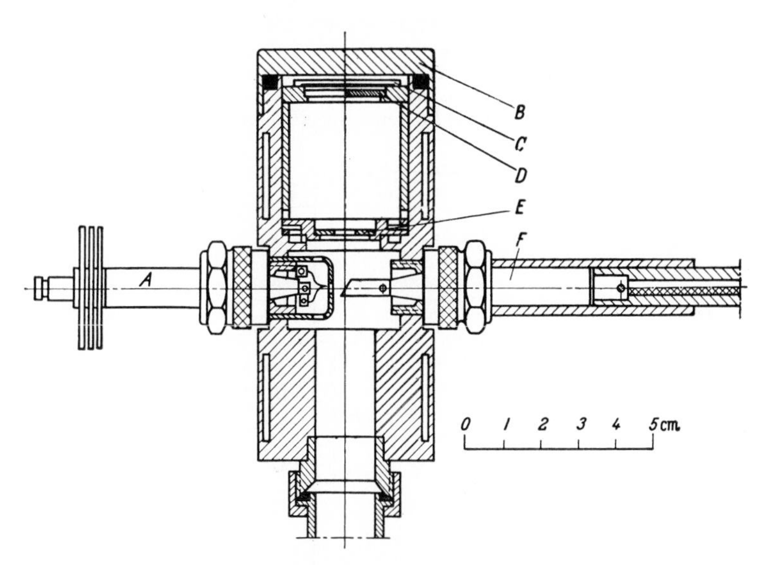

FIG. 3. Ultrasoft x-ray microradiographic equipment. (A) Cathode. (B) Removable lid for loading camera. (C) Photographic film. (D) Specimen. (E) Light filter. (F) Anode. The tube is evacuated at bottom.

λ, and C a constant. It should be noted that this equation gives a somewhat sharper peak to the continuous spectrum than the classical formula used to compute the shape of the continuous spectrum for hard x-rays. If the target is properly chosen and the voltage low enough the spectrum is almost entirely composed of the continuous white radiation. A single or a balanced filter might serve to narrow the range of wavelengths in the spectrum.

When more intensity is required, the voltage of the tube can be increased and the

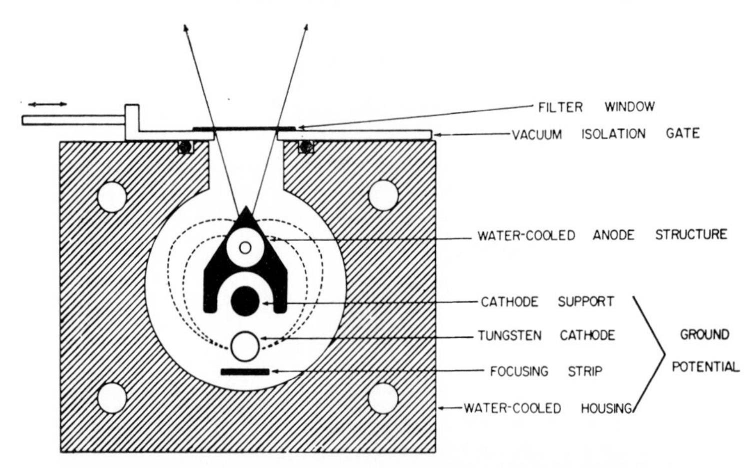

FIG. 4. High-intensity ultrasoft x-ray source designed by Henke.

hard portions of the spectrum removed by total reflection. Figure 5 shows the principle of the construction of such an x-ray tube, which was developed by Henke[2] and is based on gaseous discharge. This tube is particularly useful when isolating long-wavelength emission lines, as the x-rays are collected at an angle 180° from the incident electrons, in which direction the white (continuous) radiation has a minimum intensity.

Strictly monochromatic radiation is obtained after reflection by a crystal with a large spacing or a ruled grating, and often a specific emission line is isolated. Such

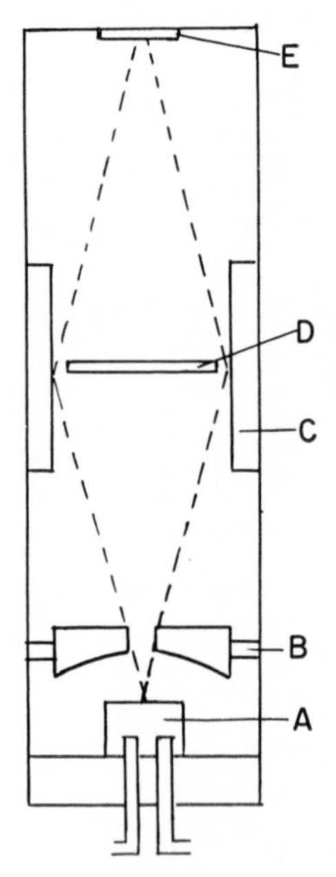

FIG. 5. Gas-discharge ultrasoft x-ray source. (*A*) Water-cooled anode. (*B*) Cathode. (*C*) Cylindrical glass mirror for total reflection. (*D*) Central stop. (*E*) Sample film.

devices by necessity have a low reflection intensity. In Fig. 6 is shown an x-ray spectrograph for microradiography with monochromatic soft and ultrasoft x-rays. The x-ray tube and spectrometer are evacuated simultaneously, and both photographic and direct recordings of the x-ray absorption are possible.

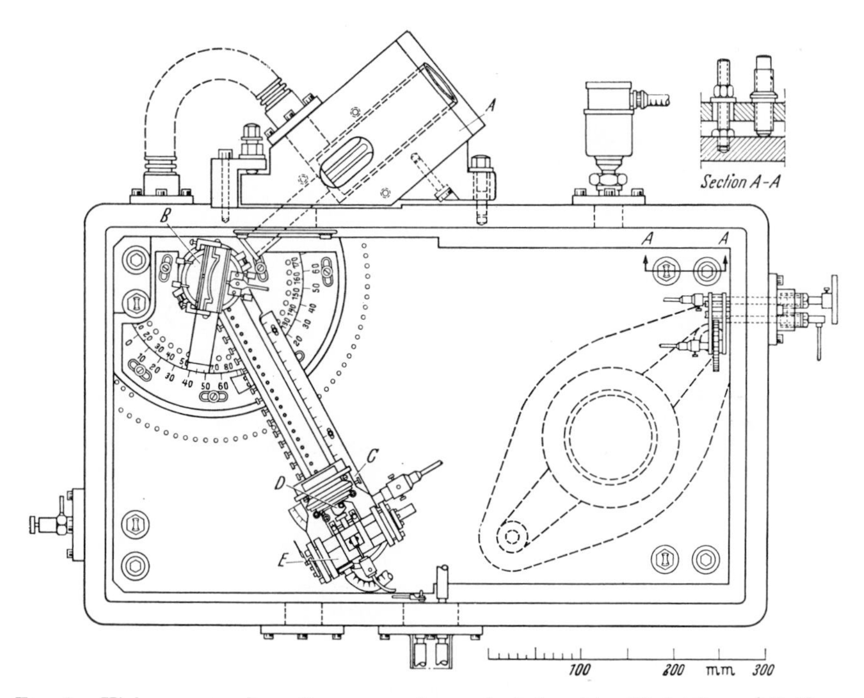

FIG. 6. High-vacuum ultrasoft x-ray spectrograph designed by Lindström. (*A*) X-ray tube. (*B*) Monochromator. (*C*) Sample. (*D*) Photographic film (or *E*, proportional counter).

4. RECORDING MATERIALS

The fine-grained photographic emulsions utilized in conventional microradiography can also be used with advantage for the recording of microradiograms in the ultrasoft x-region. Such emulsions are, for example, the Lippmann emulsion manufactured by Gevaert, Antwerp, Belgium; Eastman Kodak spectroscopic plates 548 or 649; or Kodak high-resolution plates. The diffusion of ultrasoft x-rays in these fine-grained emulsions is very low. Therefore, high-resolution images can be obtained even in relatively thick emulsion layers. The penetration of ultrasoft x-rays in the silver halide–gelatin layer is only a fraction of a micron, and the blurring due to the geometrical factor when the x-rays penetrate the emulsion is therefore below the resolution of the optical microscope in a conventional experiment.

The microradiographic image is viewed in a high-power optical microscope or its distribution of densities is recorded in a microdensitometer. For pictorial recording the microradiogram should be given a heavy exposure in order to obtain a clear and well-defined image. The microradiogram intended for the subsequent photometry should have less density in order to avoid photometric errors due to neighboring effects, Schwarzschild-Villiger effects, etc. Therefore, it is advisable to record two microradiograms of a specimen, one for visual inspection (heavily exposed) and one for photometry (less exposed).

5. WEIGHING BIOLOGICAL SPECIMENS BY ULTRASOFT X-RAY MICROGRAPHY

As an example of quantitative contact microradiography by ultrasoft x-rays the method for weighing cellular structures will be briefly described. Figure 7 illustrates the principle. A section of a biological tissue or a smear of cells is microradiographed together with a small reference system made up of thin strips of parlodion, for example. The theoretical basis for this procedure is that the majority of the x-ray absorption in

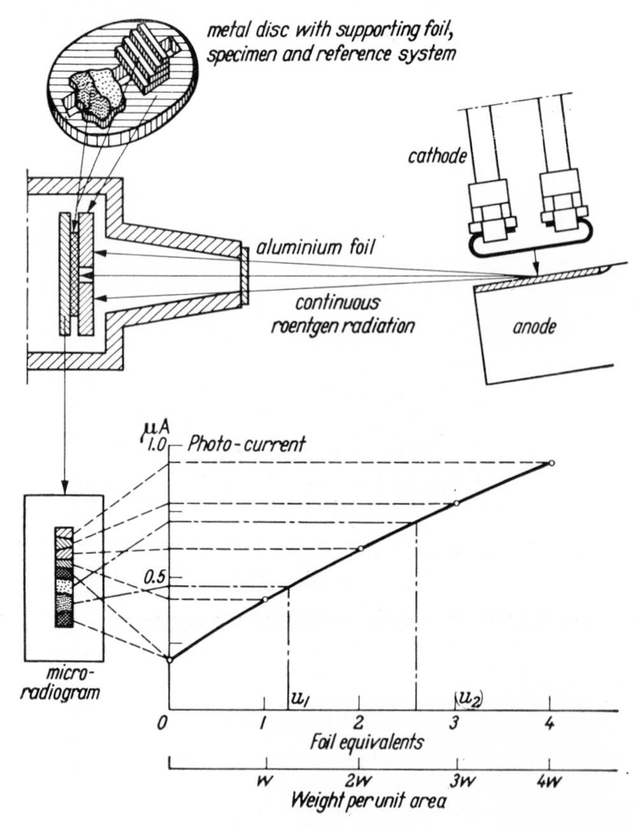

FIG. 7. Principle for quantitative microradiography for weighing biological specimens.

a dehydrated soft tissue is caused by carbon, nitrogen, and oxygen having the proportions occurring in protein. But soft biological tissues also contain traces of elements with higher atomic numbers and a considerable fraction of hydrogen. It appears, however, that the mass absorption coefficients of the elements with atomic numbers higher than 8 in the ultrasoft x-ray region are greatly reduced as the radiation is situated beyond the wavelengths of their K-absorption edges. For certain elements in the region of atomic numbers 20 to 30 the mass absorption coefficients with respect to ultrasoft x-rays are actually lower than those for carbon, nitrogen, and oxygen. Extensive computations have shown that, for wavelengths beyond the K-absorption edge of phosphorus, that is, wavelengths longer than ~ 6 Å and below the wavelength for the K-absorption edge of oxygen (~ 23 Å), a mass absorption coefficient representing a carbon, nitrogen, and oxygen mixture in the proportions occurring in protein can represent the total mass absorption coefficient for a soft biological tissue. There is one factor, however, which must be corrected for and which introduces a negative error, and that arises from hydrogen. This error can be compensated by proper choice of material in the reference system. The latter is therefore usually made up of parlodion or of nitrocellulose foils. Referring to Fig. 7, the weight per unit area of biological object can be calculated from the expression

$$\frac{m_\alpha}{K_{\mathrm{H}p}} = \frac{K_{\mathrm{Href}}}{K_{\mathrm{H}p}} m_{\mathrm{ref}} \frac{(\mu/\rho)_{\mathrm{CNOref}}}{(\mu/\rho)_{\mathrm{CNO}p}}$$

where m_α = weight per unit area of biological structure
m_{ref} = weight per unit area of reference system with same x-ray transmission as biological structure
$K_{\mathrm{H}p}$ = correction factor for hydrogen in proteins
K_{Href} = correction factor for hydrogen in reference system
$(\mu/\rho)_{\mathrm{CNO}p}$ = mass absorption coefficient of a CNO mixture with same proportions as in proteins
$(\mu/\rho)_{\mathrm{CNOref}}$ = mass absorption coefficient of CNO mixture in reference system at same wavelength

The complete theory for this procedure has been published elsewhere;[3] also numerical values for a great number of mass absorption coefficients are given. The reader is also referred to this paper for the interaction of ultrasoft x-rays with material with regard to photoelectron and Auger electron production as well as the eventual excitation of radiation of other wavelengths.

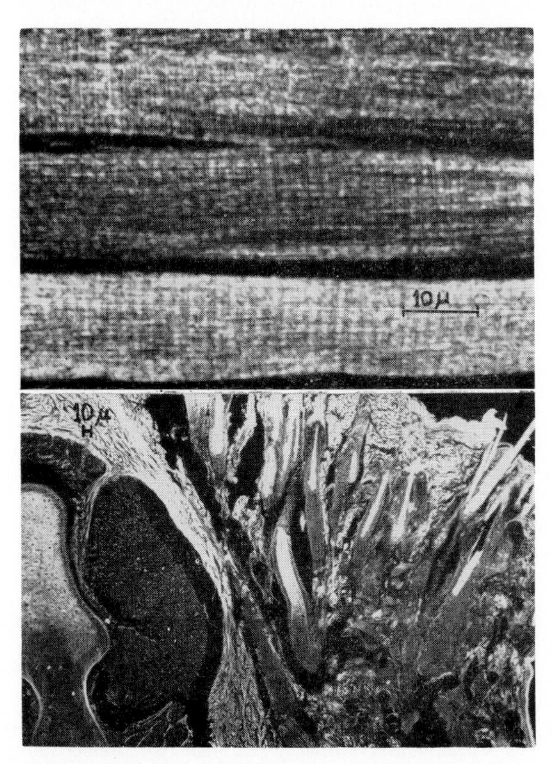

FIG. 8. Ultrasoft microradiograms of thin sections of biological tissues showing distribution of mass. (*Top*) Section of muscle fiber, magnification 2,400×. (*Bottom*) Section of skin, magnification 200×.

In practice, the weighing is performed in the following way: A dehydrated section of a biological tissue a few microns thick is placed across one end of a slit in a holder. Across the other end of the slit is placed a number of thin foils making up a step wedge. Usually about five steps are used, and the middle step should have approximately the same weight per unit as the average weight of the biological specimen. After the microradiogram is processed, a microphotometer is employed to read the transmission of light in the image of a particular structure and to compare it with the transmission of light in the microradiographic image of the step wedge. In such a way the mass of each structure can be expressed in foil equivalents of the step wedge. If we know the weight per unit area of the sheet from which the small step wedge was built, the absolute weight of the structure under investigation can be calculated.

With the present resolution of the microradiographic and microphotometric procedures the weight of as little as 1 cu micron of material in a cell or tissue can be determined with an error not exceeding 5 per cent. Thus the weights determined are in the order of 10^{-12} to 10^{-13} g sensitivity of the method is in the order of 10^{-15} g.

Many more examples of quantitative contact microradiography with ultrasoft x-rays could be given, but the example mentioned may give an idea of how flexible the x-ray microradiographic procedure is. It can be adapted to a variety of problems, and a significant feature of the method is that it is possible to calculate in advance optimal conditions for a specific experiment and to examine also in advance what kind of information can be obtained. Figure 8 shows two microradiograms recorded with ultrasoft x-rays and demonstrates the distribution of total mass (dry weight) in various structures. The linear resolution is better than 0.5 micron and the "chemical" or dry-weight resolution is in the order of 10^{-14} g/sq micron.

6. CONCLUSION

Contact microradiography with ultrasoft x-rays, that is, x-rays with wavelengths longer than 10 Å, has until now found most of its applications in quantitative cell chemistry and for the analysis of small amounts of organic material. The optimal linear resolution is the same as the maximal resolution in the light microscope. It is true that it has been possible to examine thin sections of the photographic contact microradiographic images in the electron microscope with still higher resolution, but because of the difficulties of making thin sections of the photographic image this extension of resolution has found little practical use. The greatest value of contact microradiography lies not in its resolution but in its possibilities as a tool for chemical analysis of very minute amounts of substance.

REFERENCES CITED

1. B. L. Henke, R. White, and B. Lundberg, Semiempirical Determination of Mass Absorption Coefficients for the 5 to 50 Angström X-ray Region, *J. Appl. Phys.*, **28**(1):98–105 (1957).
2. B. L. Henke, Microanalysis with Ultrasoft X-radiations, *Tech. Rept. AFDSR*-1995, 1962.
3. F. C. Hoh and B. Lindström, On the Theory of Quantitative Microradiography in Biology, *J. Ultrastruct. Res.*, **2**:512 (1959).

GENERAL REFERENCES

Cosslett, V. E., and W. C. Nixon: *X-ray Microscopy*, Cambridge University Press, New York, 1961.

Cosslett, V. E., A. Engström, and H. H. Pattee: *X-ray Microscopy and Microradiography*, Academic Press, Inc., New York, 1957.

Engström, A., V. E. Cosslett, and H. H. Pattee: *X-ray Microscopy and X-ray Microanalysis*, Elsevier Publishing Company, Amsterdam, 1960.

Pattee, H. H., A. Engström, and V. E. Cosslett: *X-ray Optics and X-ray Microanalysis*, Academic Press, Inc., New York, 1963.

Engström, A.: *X-ray Microanalysis in Biology and Medicine*, Elsevier Publishing Company, Amsterdam, 1962.

Lindström, B.: Roentgen Absorption Spectrophotometry in Quantitative Cytochemistry, *Acta Radiol. Suppl.* 125, 1955.

Chapter 47

X-RAY PROJECTION MICROSCOPY

Poen Sing Ong

Philips Electronic Instruments

1. INTRODUCTION

Principle. A very small x-ray source, generally 1 to 0.1 micron in diameter, is used to project an enlarged image of a specimen onto a fluorescent screen or film.

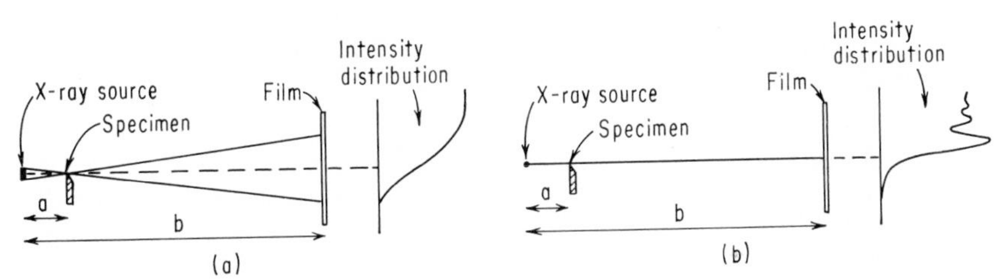

FIG. 1. (*a*) Resolution limitation due to the finite size of the x-ray source. (*b*) Resolution limitation due to Fresnel diffraction.

The magnification equals the ratio of the source-to-screen and source-to-specimen distance, i.e. (see Fig. 1),

$$M = b/a \tag{1}$$

Resolution. The resolution is limited by either the diameter of the x-ray source or the width of the diffraction fringe, whichever is the larger (Fig. 1*a* and 1*b*). For a specimen consisting of particles which completely absorb the x-rays,

$$\delta \approx d \quad \text{(determined by the source diameter)} \tag{2}$$

or

$$\delta \approx \sqrt{a\lambda} \quad \text{(determined by diffraction phenomena)} \tag{3}$$

in which δ is the resolution, d the source diameter, a the source-to-specimen distance, and λ the wavelength. The following approximate values are typical for an experimental setup: $d \approx 0.1$ micron $= 10^3$ Å, $\lambda = 3$ Å, $a = 40$ microns, $\sqrt{a\lambda} = 1.1 \times 10^3$ Å, $b = 10$ mm, $M = 250\times$. The film can be magnified $10\times$, giving a final magnification of $2{,}500\times$.

2. CONSTRUCTION OF THE PROJECTION MICROSCOPE

The Essential Parts. The x-ray projection microscope consists basically of a vacuum tube comprising an electron gun, an electron lens system, and a thin transmission-type target (Fig. 2). This type of target makes it possible to place the specimen very close to the target, as is required to reduce the width of the diffraction fringe. In most cases, the target functions at the same time as a vacuum-tight window. Thus the specimen can remain in air. The electron lens system is used to focus a

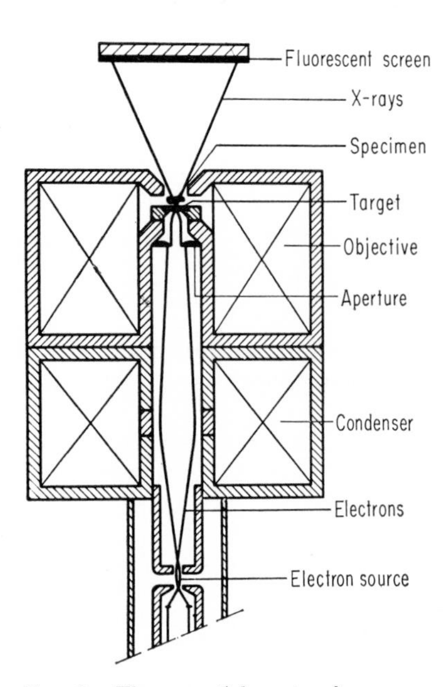

FIG. 2. The essential parts of an x-ray projection microscope.

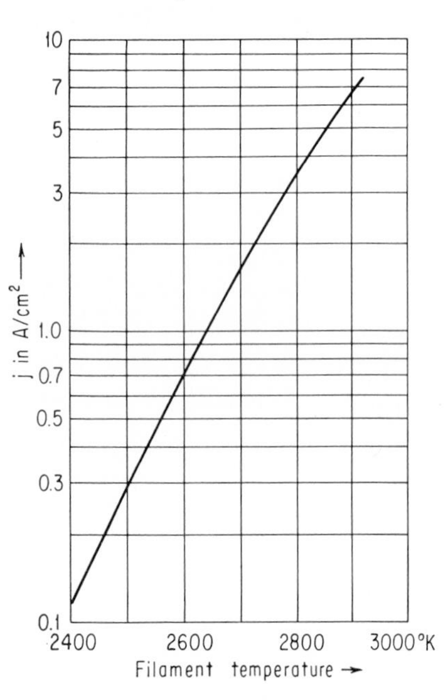

FIG. 3. The specific emission j of a tungsten filament as a function of the temperature. (*From Manfred von Ardenne, Tabellen der Elektronenphysik, Ionenphysik und Uebermikroskopie, vol.* I, *p.* 79, *VEB Deutscher Verlag der Wissenschaften, Berlin,* 1956.)

greatly reduced image of the source onto the target. X-rays are generated at essentially the focus area.

The enlarged x-ray shadow image of the specimen is projected onto a fluorescent screen which can be viewed with the aid of a low-power optical microscope with 5 to 20× magnification. The filament and the target have a limited lifetime. Thus both components are made replaceable. This requires that the microscope be constructed as a demountable unit, which should be continuously pumped down to maintain the required vacuum.

The Electron Gun. The electron gun consists of a tungsten-hairpin-type cathode carefully centered within the hole of an enclosing cap (the Wehnelt cylinder) and an accelerating electrode, the anode. The Wehnelt cylinder is kept at a lower potential than the filament so that only the uppermost tip of the filament emits electrons. The filament, cap, and anode form an immersion-type electron lens which gives a crossover somewhere between the cap and the anode. This crossover is the disk of least confusion and is used as the electron source. Its diameter is approximately

25 microns for 50 kv[1] and is inversely proportional to the square root of the anode voltage (Ref. 2, p. 130).

The brightness of the electron source is defined as the electron current density per unit solid angle. This magnitude is invariant throughout any optical system. An expression for the brightness is given by Langmuir:[3]

$$B^* = jeV/\pi kT \tag{4}$$

in which B is the brightness, j the specific emission of the cathode, e the charge on an electron, V the anode voltage, k Boltzmann's constant = 1/11,600 ev/°K, and T the cathode temperature in °K.

The specific emission j depends largely on the temperature of the cathode. Figure 3 shows that relationship. Figure 4 shows the specific emission as a function of the lifetime expectancy.

The current density at the focal spot is proportional to the brightness of the electron source and to the solid angle subtended by the objective aperture. If the semiangular aperture is $\gamma = h/f$ (h is the radius of the aperture stop and f the focal length of the objective) and $\gamma \ll 1$, then the solid angle amounts to $\pi\gamma^2$.

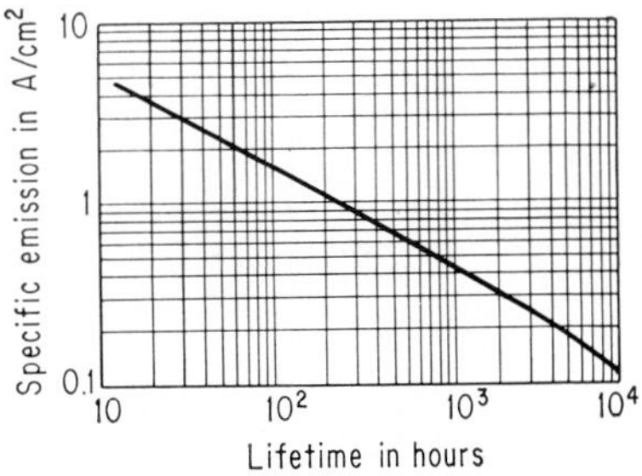

Fig. 4. The specific emission j of a 100-micron tungsten filament as a function of the lifetime expectancy. (*From Manfred von Ardenne, Tabellen der Elektronenphysik, Ionenphysik und Uebermikroscopie, vol. I, p. 79, VEB Deutscher Verlag der Wissenschaften, Berlin,* 1956.)

The Electron Lens System. The electron lens system forms a greatly reduced image of the electron source on the target. It consists of two lenses, which usually are referred to as the objective lens and the condenser lens.

The objective lens is a strong lens which forms the final point focus. It should have small aberrations.

The condenser lens is a weak lens. Its purpose is to control the rate of demagnification. A variable reduction factor is necessary, as the intensity of the x-ray source is proportional to the 8/3 power of the diameter of the focus. The condenser makes it possible to increase the intensity at the expense of the resolution and vice versa.

The focal properties of magnetic electron lenses are given in Fig. 5. For weak lenses $[(ni)^2/V_r \leq 100]$ we can use the formula of Van Ments and Le Poole, which is accurate to within 10 per cent[4] for pole pieces of any conventional shape:

$$f = 3.6\sqrt{S^2 + D^2}\,(10/K + 0.04) \tag{5}$$

in which S = length of pole-piece gap, D = pole-piece bore diameter, $K = (ni)^2/V_r$, ni = ampere-turns, V_r = relativistically corrected anode voltage.

Figures 6 and 7 show the focal properties of electrostatic lenses.

The electron lens has aberrations which should be kept small in comparison with the desired spot size. The most important ones are:

1. The spherical aberration. In conventional, rotationally symmetrical lenses, the spherical aberration cannot be corrected. The disk of least confusion d_{sf} is given by (Fig. 8)

$$d_{sf} \approx \tfrac{1}{2}C_s\gamma^3 \tag{6}$$

in which C_s is the spherical-aberration constant and γ the semiangular aperture.

The spherical-aberration constant C_s depends on the field distribution and on the

* This value assumes an initial electron velocity corresponding to the peak value of a Maxwellian distribution.

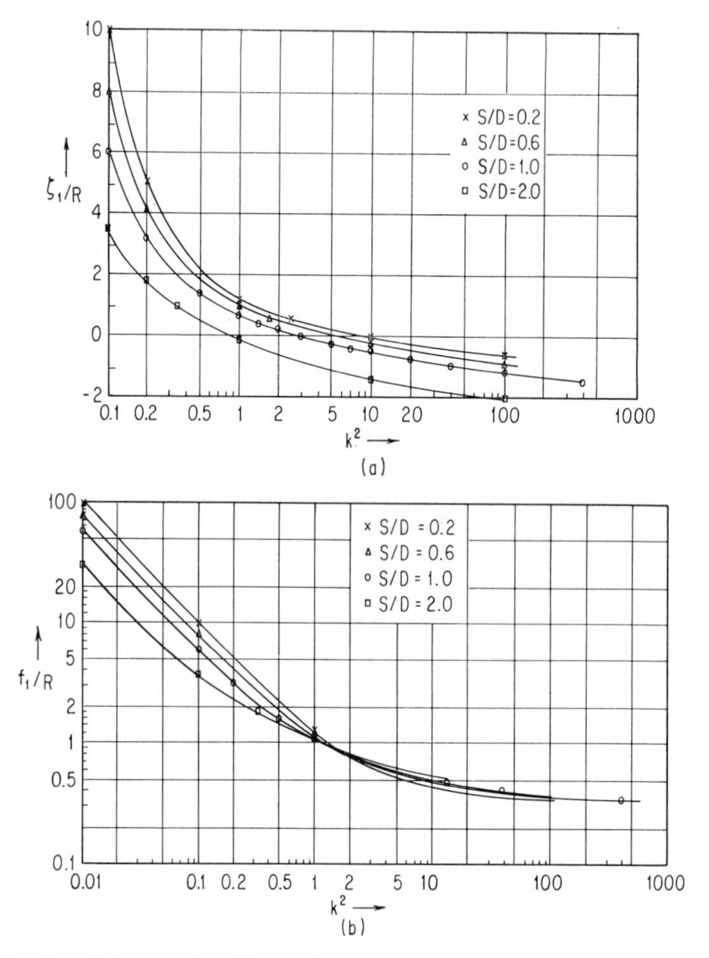

FIG. 5. Focal properties of symmetrical magnetic lenses. (*a*) The relative focal distance ζ_1/R as function of the excitation parameter k^2. (*b*) The relative focal length f_1/R as function of the excitation parameter k^2. $k^2 = \beta(ni)^2/V_r$ with the following values of β: For $S/D = 0.2, 0.6, 1, 2$, $\beta = 0.0154, 0.0101, 0.060, 0.0020$, respectively. S is the pole-piece gap width, $D = 2R$ = pole-piece bore diameter, ni is the ampere-turns, V_r is the relativistically corrected accelerating voltage, $V_r \approx V(1 + 10^{-6}V)$. (*From G. Liebmann, Characteristics of Symmetrical Magnetic Electron Lenses, Electron Physics, Proceedings of the NBS Semicentennial Symposium on Electron Physics, held at the NBS, Nov. 5–7, 1951, Natl. Bur. Std. Circ.* 527, *Mar.* 17, 1959.)

excitation of the lens. For weak magnetic lenses the value of C_s is given by[4]

$$C_s \approx 2.4f^3/(S^2 + D^2) \tag{7}$$

For strong lenses the value of C_s as a function of the excitation parameter is plotted in Fig. 9.

Thus it is favorable to use a strong lens as an objective. As the angular aperture of the condenser is usually much smaller than that of the objective lens the spherical-aberration constant of the condenser lens is less important. A strong lens requires,

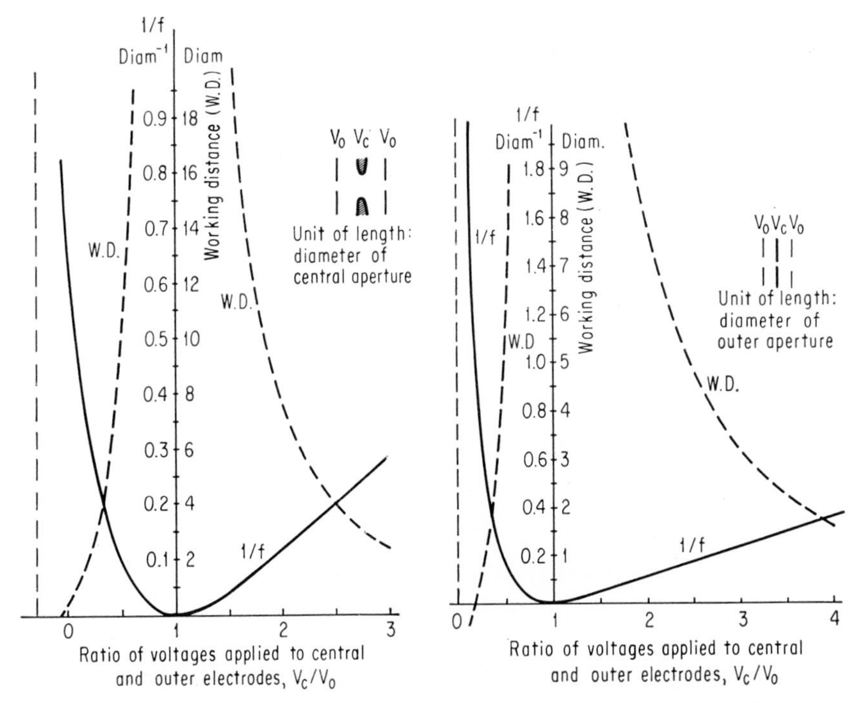

FIG. 6. The refractive power and the working distance as functions of the ratio of applied voltages for the electrostatic lens shown. (*From Zworykin, Morton, Ramberg, Hillier, and Vance, Electron Optics and the Electron Microscope, p.* 438, *Fig.* 13.11, *John Wiley & Sons, Inc., New York,* 1948.)

FIG. 7. The refractive power and the work ing distance as functions of the ratio o applied voltages for the electrostatic len shown. (*From Zworykin, Morton, Ramberg Hillier, and Vance, Electron Optics and the Electron Microscope, p.* 439, *Fig.* 13.12, *John Wiley & Sons, Inc., New York,* 1948.)

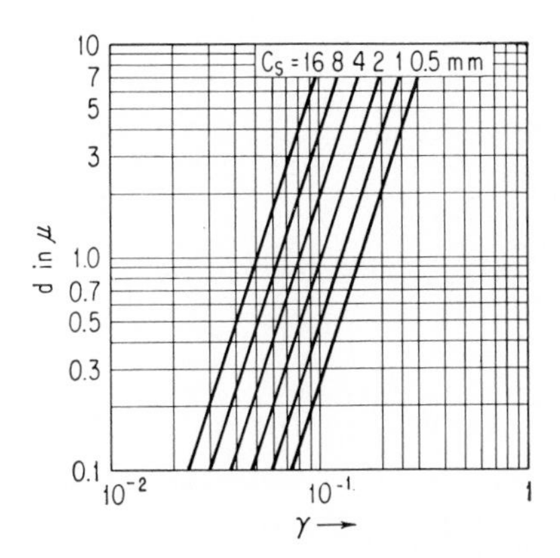

FIG. 8. The spot size d as a function of the semiangular aperture γ for different values of the spherical-aberration constant. Diameter of least confusion due to spherical aberration $d = \frac{1}{2}C_s\gamma^3$.

however, that the specimen be placed in the active region of the lens field. As a result, such a system cannot be used for ferromagnetic specimens.

2. Chromatic aberration. We shall confine ourselves here to the errors caused by fluctuations in lens current and high voltage. The diameter of the disk of confusion

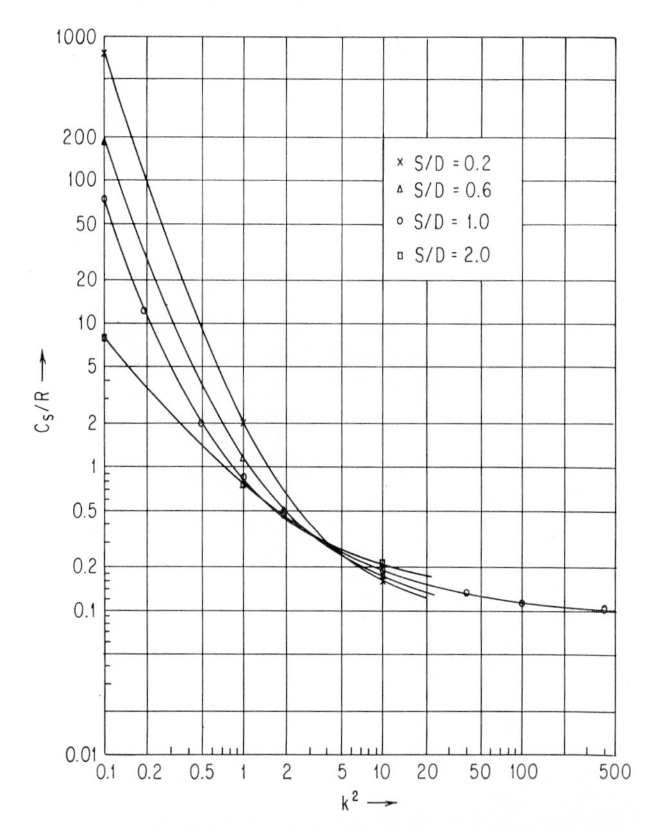

FIG. 9. The relative spherical-aberration constant C_s/R as a function of the lens excitation parameter k^2 for symmetrical magnetic lenses; cf. Fig. 5. (*From G. Liebmann, Characteristics of Symmetrical Magnetic Electron Lenses, Electron Physics, Proceedings of the NBS Semicentennial Symposium on Electron Physics, held at the NBS, Nov.* 5–7, 1951, *Natl. Bur. Std. Circ.* 527, *Mar.* 17, 1959.)

due to this error d_c is given by (Ref. 2, pp. 206, 213)

$$d_c = \Delta f \, \gamma = (\Delta f/f) f\gamma \tag{8}$$

while for magnetic lenses

$$\Delta f/f = C_c[(\Delta V/V) - 2(\Delta i/i)] \tag{9}$$

In the case of a strong magnetic lens C_c (the chromatic-aberration constant) = 0.7, increasing to unity for very weak lenses.[4]

As d_c is proportional to the focal length f, it is favorable to use a lens with a short focal length.

If in an electrostatic lens the center electrode is directly connected to the cathode, the permissible fluctuations in the high voltage are determined by the relativistic aberration. The diameter of confusion due to this error d_r amounts to

$$d_r = C_r \, \Delta V \, f\gamma \tag{10}$$

in which $C_r = 6.55 \times 10^{-7}/V$ for a weak lens and $2.47 \times 10^{-7}/V$ for a strong lens. If the center electrode is fed through a voltage divider, the constancy of the voltage ratio should be some five times better than is the case with the anode voltage of a magnetic lens (Ref. 2, p. 215).

3. Astigmatism. Deviations from completely rotational symmetry of the lens field and asymmetrical electric fields caused by electron charges result in astigmatism. The net result is the same as if the lens has different focal lengths f_1 and f_2 in two mutual perpendicular planes, the difference in focal length $f_1 - f_2 = \Delta f$ being a measure of the degree of astigmatism. A point on the optical axis will then be focused

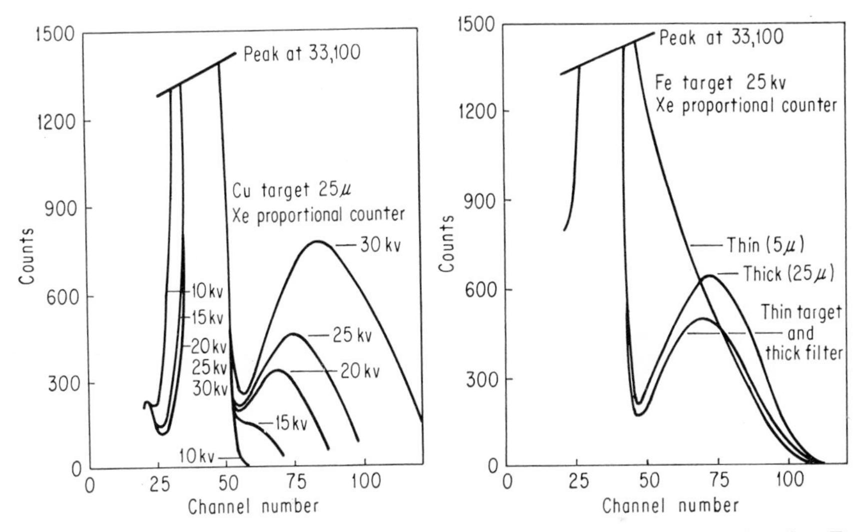

FIG. 10. Pulse-height distributions of a Cu target. The peak appears at channel 40. Philips Xe proportional counter, R.C.L. 128-channel analyzer.

FIG. 11. Pulse-height distribution of an Fe target. The peak appears at channel 33. Philips Xe proportional counter, R.C.L. 128-channel analyzer.

into two mutually perpendicular lines separated by a distance Δf. The diameter of the circle of least confusion d_a is

$$d_a = \Delta f \, \gamma = C_a \gamma \tag{11}$$

in which $C_a = \Delta f$ is the astigmatism constant and γ the semiangular aperture. Correction of this type of aberration can easily be done by introducing correcting cylindrical lenses (lenses which focus in one direction only). In a projection microscope, however, astigmatism correction has not yet been practically realized because of the impossibility of doing this visually. The intensity is so low that the effect of astigmatism cannot be seen on the fluorescent image. The forward-scattering method of Nixon (see Focusing Aids) may make astigmatism correction feasible. Careful machining of the lens pole pieces and keeping the microscope column, especially the small apertures, extremely clean will reduce astigmatism.

The X-ray Target. 1. The x-ray spectra. The target material, target thickness, and anode voltage determine the spectral distribution of the x-ray source. By a correct choice of the parameters and by using a β filter, the radiation can be made fairly monochromatic ($K\alpha$ line). The spectra of a copper target at various voltages are shown in Fig. 10. Figure 11 shows the effect of self-filtering of the target. For detecting an element by its absorption edge it is necessary to use two monochromatic radiations with wavelengths on both sides of such an edge. Thus it is necessary to change the target without interrupting the vacuum. At least three commercial instruments are provided with such possibilities.

For normal morphological examination, the "white radiation" can successfully be utilized. It is favorable, in this case, to use an element with a high atomic number as a target, as the total x-ray energy is proportional to the atomic number of the target material.

$$I_x = 1.4(10^{-9})ZiV^2 \tag{12}$$

in which I_x is the total x-ray energy of the "white radiation," i the target current, Z the atomic number, and V the anode voltage.

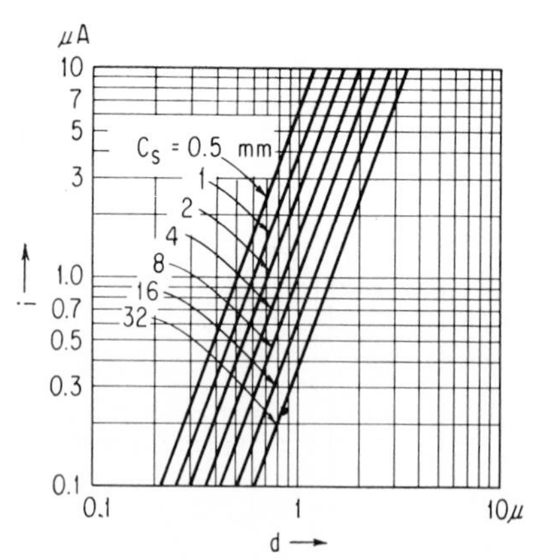

FIG. 13. Target current as function of the focus diameter for several values of the spherical-aberration constant.

$$i = \pi jeVd^{8/3}/4kT(\tfrac{1}{2}C_s)^{2/3}$$

assuming $j = 0.7$ Å/cm²
$T = 2600$ °K
$V = 10$ kv
$k = 1/11{,}600$ ev/°K

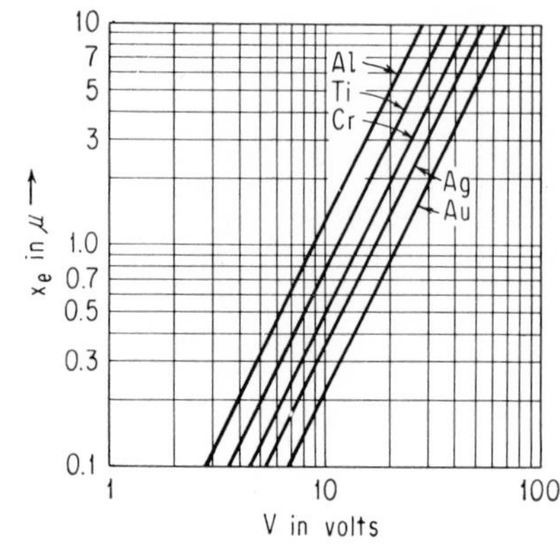

FIG. 12. The Thomson-Whiddington equation plotted for several elements.

2. Electron scattering within the target. The high-energy electrons penetrate and diffuse within a finite depth of the target before losing all their energy. As a result, the x-rays can be excited within a sphere with the depth of penetration as its approximate diameter. The depth of penetration of electrons can be calculated from the Thomson-Whiddington equation[5] (see Fig. 12)

$$x_e = AV^2/CZm \tag{13}$$

in which x_e is the depth of penetration, A the atomic weight, V the anode voltage, Z the atomic number, C a constant $\approx 6 \times 10^{11}$ (volt, cm, g), and m the mass density. Because at small depth the scattering angles are very small, it is possible to reduce the source-broadening effect by using a very thin target. In this case a resolution equal to the target thickness can be obtained.[6] As the electrons lose their energy gradually, characteristic radiation can be excited only within a depth less than that calculated by the Thomson-Whiddington equation. Hink[7] calculated, using data of Castaing,[8] that at 29 kv, 70 per cent of the characteristic radiation is excited within one-third of the depth of penetration.

3. Target load. The brightness of the electron source [Eq. (4)] multiplied by the solid angle as is determined by the objective aperture [Eq. (6)] gives the current density of the focal spot:

$$\rho = 11{,}600jVd^{2/3}/T(\tfrac{1}{2}C_s)^{2/3} \tag{14}$$

The total current i amounts to (see Fig. 13)

$$i = 2{,}900\pi j V d^{8/3} / T(\tfrac{1}{2}C_s)^{2/3} \tag{15}$$

The total power $W = iV$ is almost completely dissipated as heat. In conventional x-ray tubes with a focal-spot diameter of the order of millimeters, heat transport becomes a problem and target temperature becomes a limiting factor of the admissible load. For a round focus and a target which is thick compared with the spot diameter, the maximum specific load is given by[9]

$$E = 17C_T(T - T_0)/\pi d \tag{16}$$

in which E is the specific load (watts/mm^2), C_T the thermal conductivity, T the melting point of the target, T_0 the ambient temperature, and d the diameter of the focal spot. For a thin target like that used in projection microscopy a correction factor should be added which depends on the ratio of spot size and target thickness,[10] but still the proportionality of the specific load to the inverse value of the spot diameter holds. Thus extremely high specific loading can be tolerated at spot sizes of the order of microns or less. As the current density at the target is less than proportional to the spot size [see Eq. (14)], the maximum specific load at the target is limited by the electron optics.

Viewing Systems. Although the x-ray projection microscope is not suitable for visual observations, it should be supplied with a viewing system for positioning the specimen and for focusing the electron beam. A considerable gain in fluorescent-image brightness can be obtained with the aid of a magnifying optical system. If the magnification of such a system is M, the fluorescent screen can be placed M times closer to the x-ray source to yield the same overall magnification. The brightness of the fluorescent image, however, increases with a factor M^2. If the exit pupil of the optical system is adapted to the eye pupil, the full brightness gain can be utilized. In practice, the value of M is limited to approximately 20× because of the graininess of the screen and the construction of the optical system.

By sacrificing some of the initial magnification, a further increase in brightness can be obtained for viewing the specimen.

During focusing a considerable gain can be obtained at the expense of the field of view. In this case the specimen can be placed very close to the x-ray source, and the screen can be placed proportionally closer. The very limited field of view during focusing is not serious since we look only at the edge of a highly absorbing particle.

Focusing Aids. The electron spot must be focused on the target, which usually is done before the micrograph is made. For this purpose the specimen is replaced by a highly absorbing fine-mesh grid, or alternatively, a part of such a grid can be placed near the edge of a specimen holder.

An indirect way of focusing is to use the electrons which are scattered either backward or forward by the target.

1. The backward-scattered electron-focusing aid.[11] The electrons which are elastically backward-scattered at the target are used to make an enlarged image of the focus at the electron-source level. As these electrons possess the same energy as the primary ones, no additional electron lens is needed (see Fig. 14). A transverse magnetic field or simply a slight tilt of one of the magnetic lenses causes the back-scattered electrons to be separated from the primary beam and cast on a fluorescent screen. The symmetry of the arrangement ensures a sharp focus when the spot on this screen is at its smallest. An additional feature of this focusing method is the possibility of using it as an aligning aid because the back-scattered image will be exactly at the electron gun when the microscope is aligned. For the sake of clearness, Fig. 14 shows the position of the fluorescent screen and electron gun at quite a large angle from the optical axis. In practice the screen can be just above the anode with a small hole for the passage of the primary electrons. Thus the necessary tilt of the lens can be kept to a minimum. The effect of astigmatism can be seen on the back-scattered image, but attempts to correct this aberration have up to now failed because the direction as well as the magnitude of this error is different for the primary and the return beams.

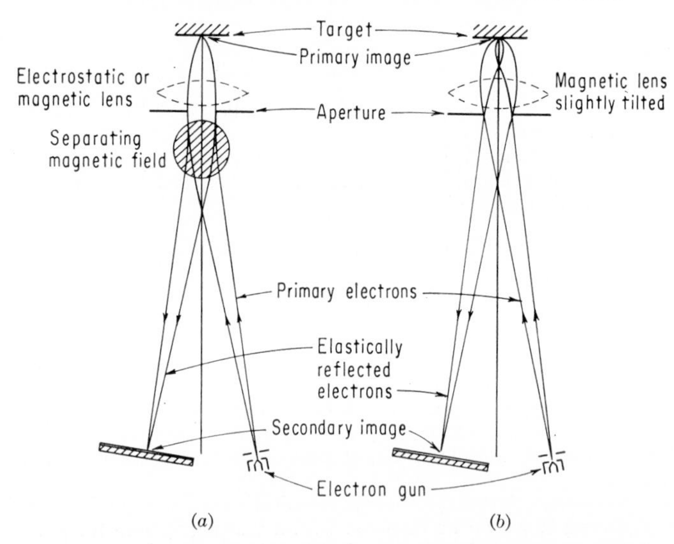

Fig. 14. Principle of the backward-scattered electron-focusing method. Beam separation can be obtained by using a transverse magnetic field (*a*) or by slightly tilting the magnetic lens (*b*).

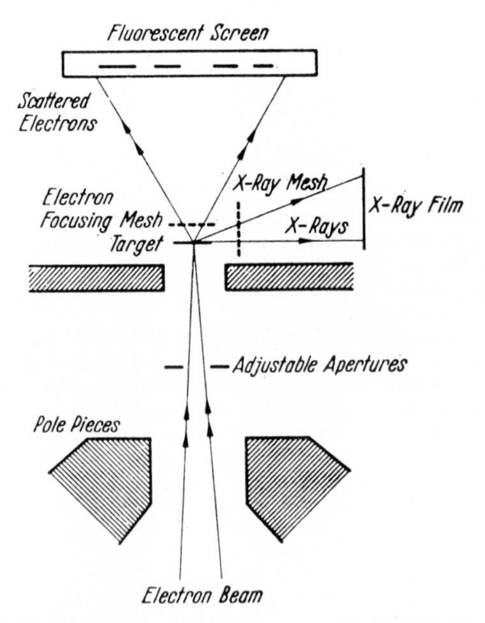

Fig. 15. Principle of the forward-scattered electron-focusing method. [*From W. C. Nixon, X-ray Microscopy Using Point Sources, Fourth International Conference on Electron Microscopy, p.* 249, *Berlin, Sept.* 10–17, 1958, *G. Möllenstedt, H. Niehrs, and E. Ruska* (*eds.*), *Springer-Verlag OHG, Berlin,* 1960.]

FIG. 16. X-ray projection microscope manufactured by the Canal Industrial Corporation (Canalco). (*Courtesy of Canal Industrial Corporation, Bethesda, Md.*)

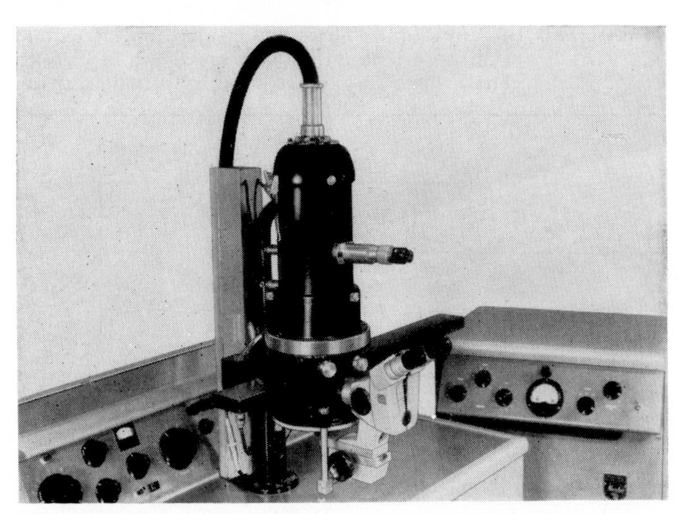

FIG. 17. X-ray projection microscope manufactured by Philips Electronic Instruments (Norelco). This instrument is a conversion of the EM75 electron microscope. Backward-scattered electron-focusing-aid attachment is optional. (*Courtesy of Philips Electronic Instruments, Mount Vernon, N.Y.*)

2. The forward-scattered electron-focusing aid.[12] If a thin target is used, the electrons which are scattered in the forward direction can be used to form an enlarged projection image of a grid on a fluorescent screen (see Fig. 15). A disadvantage of this method is that the target must be extremely thin, the specimen must be in vacuum, and the x-rays must be picked up at an angle. A direct advantage is the possibility of correcting astigmatisms. The electron projection image can be viewed with good brightness and adequate magnification.

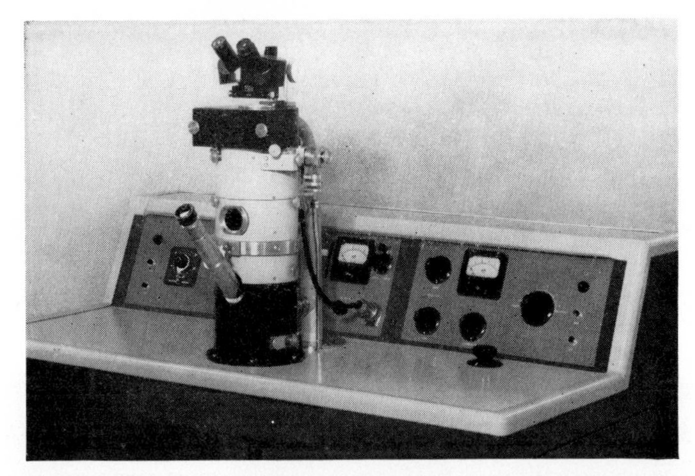

FIG. 18. X-ray projection microscope manufactured by the Electron Microscopy Division of the Technical Physics Department, T.N.O. and Technological University of Delft. The backward-scattered electron image is viewed with a reflective objective. (*Courtesy of Electron Microscopy Division of the Technical Physics Department, T.N.O. and T.H., Delft, Holland.*)

Some Commercial Instruments. Three commercial projection microscopes, the Canalco, the Philips, and the T.P.D. microscope, are shown in Figs. 16, 17, and 18, respectively. The technical specifications are listed in the following table.

	Instrument		
	Canalco	Philips	T.P.D.
Types of lens	Magnetic	Magnetic	Magnetic
Focal length (objective), mm	3	4.6	1.8
Spherical-aberration constant (objective), mm	3.5	4.1	1.5
Voltage range, kv	5–30 in 32 steps	0–50 continuous	5–20 in 4 steps
Resolution, microns	1	1	0.5
Film	3 exposures, 1-in. field	4–6 exposures on 2- by 10-in. plate	20 exposures on 35-mm film
Focusing aid	None	Electron back scattering	Electron back scattering
Specimen chamber	Vacuum/air	Vacuum/air	Vacuum only
Maximum magnification (on film)	100 ×	70 ×	150 ×
Viewer	Monocular 10 ×	Binocular 20 ×	Binocular 20 ×
Specimen viewed by same viewer	No	Yes	Yes
Calibrated specimen movement	No	Yes	Yes

3. ADDITIONAL METHODS OF PRODUCING POINT X-RAY SOURCES

The Pinhole Camera (Camera Obscura).[13] Instead of focusing the electron beam into a fine spot, we can use a very fine aperture (pinhole) to limit the size of a conventional x-ray source. In the same way as was discussed before, the resolution will then be determined either by the size of the aperture or by diffraction phenomena. If the aperture cannot be located exactly at the x-ray source, for instance, if a solid target is used, then this method conforms in principle with the well-known pinhole camera. In such an arrangement, emission- as well as transmission-type microradiographs can be obtained. The emission of an x-ray target is usually not uniform over the whole field. Therefore, the camera is rotated around its optical axis during exposure (see Fig. 19). Because focusing is not necessary, pictures can be taken at extremely low intensities. Thus soft and ultrasoft x-ray pictures can be made. So far, the resolution which has been obtained is around 1 micron. The aperture is made of 20- to 30-

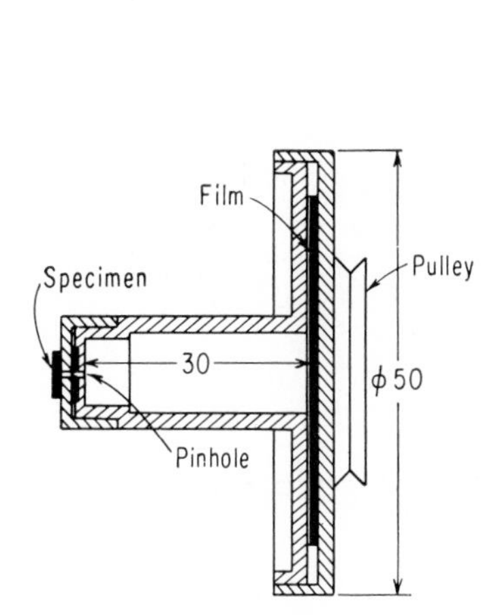

FIG. 19. Cross section of the camera obscura with an aperture less than 1 micron in diameter for point-projection x-ray microscopy. [*From B. M. Rovinsky and V. G. Lutsau, Point Projection X-ray Microscopy with the Aid of a Camera Obscura, X-ray Microscopy and Microradiography, Proceedings of a symposium held at the Cavendish Laboratory, Cambridge*, p. 129, *V. E. Cosslett, A. Engström, and H. H. Pattee* (*eds.*), *Academic Press Inc., New York*, 1956.]

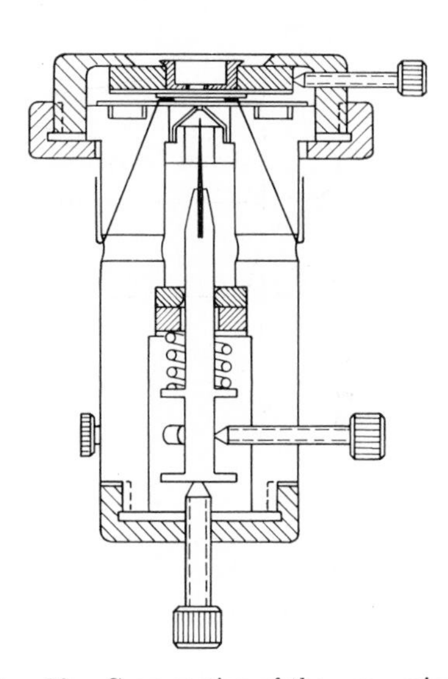

FIG. 20. Cross section of the x-ray microprojector. [*From B. M. Rovinsky, V. G. Lutsau, and A. I. Avdeyenko, Miniature Point X-ray Sources for Point Projection Microscopy and Diffraction Studies, X-ray Microscopy and X-ray Microanalysis, Proceedings of the Second International Symposium held in Stockholm, p.* 111, *A. Engström, V. E. Cosslett, and H. H. Pattee, Jr.* (*eds.*), *Elsevier Publishing Company, Amsterdam*, 1960.]

micron thick gold sheet, which has been annealed at 500 to 600° C. The hole is punched with a steel needle.

The Microprojector.[14] The microprojector uses the extreme tip of a sharp needle as a target. To achieve this, the needle tip has a radius of around 0.1 micron and is enclosed in an insulated focusing cap (see Fig. 20) provided with a small hole. Electrons passing this hole will charge the cap and contribute to focusing the electron beam onto the tip of the needle. The effective source diameter is around 0.2 micron usable at voltages between 1 and 12 kv. The anode current is 1 to 5 μa. Targets are made by electrolytically etching W or Mo wire. It is reported that targets of Ni, Co, Fe, and Cr can also be made.

4. TECHNIQUES IN PROJECTION MICROSCOPY

Stereomicroscopy (cf. Chap. 45, Sec. 5). A unique feature of the projection microscope is the large depth of field and the perfect perspective of the image. This makes ideal stereomicroscopy feasible. It can be shown that the projection-type microscopes (including the micropinhole camera) (cf. Chap. 45, Sec. 9) are the only ones which satisfy all geometrical requirements for perfect stereography at high magnification. An important contribution to the often striking results obtained with the projection x-ray microscope is the absence of disturbing reflection, refraction, and scattering.

In microstereography it is our desire to see the specimen in the right spatial proportion but on an M times larger scale. The geometrical conditions to achieve this

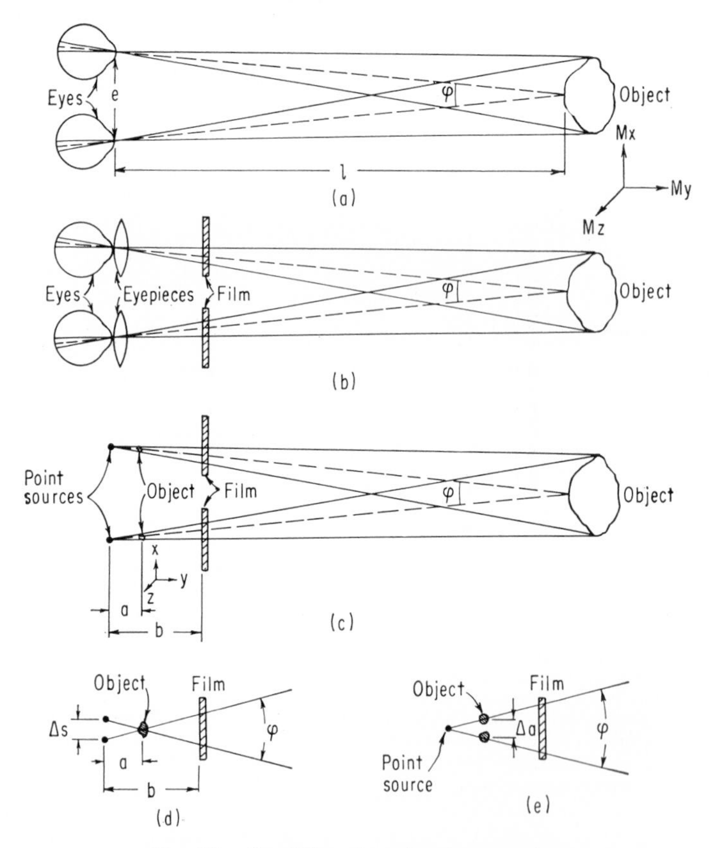

FIG. 21. Conditions for microstereography.

can be deduced from Fig. 21. Assume that the M times magnified specimen is placed at a distance l from the observer (Fig. 21a). Let the maximum angle of convergence be φ. Thus $\tan \varphi = e/2l$, in which e is the interocular distance. In Fig. 21b, the specimen can be thought of as being replaced by two film images, obtained by projecting the various points with each of the eye pupils as a projecting center. Figure 21c shows that the same images can also be the projection of two equal objects which are M times smaller (and thus have the dimension of the real specimen). As the two objects are identical, the two film images are the projection of one object, with the projection center shifted over a distance Δs (Fig. 21d). Figure 21e shows that, instead of moving the projection center, the specimen itself may be displaced over a distance $\Delta a = \Delta s$. The geometrical condition for making stereographs will thus be

$$\Delta s = \Delta a = ae/l \tag{17}$$

in which a is the source-to-specimen distance. In general the value of a is difficult to determine, especially for high magnification. The source-to-film distance b, however, is in most cases an instrumental constant. Thus by introducing the magnification $M = b/a$ we can rewrite Eq. (17) as

$$M \, \Delta s = M \, \Delta a = be/l \tag{18}$$

in which the second term is a constant. To satisfy this condition neither the magnification nor the specimen displacement need be known. If we know the displacement Δa (for instance, by using a calibrated movement), the magnification can be determined.

Determination of the Magnification. Three ways of determining the magnification will be described. It should be noticed here that, especially at high magnification and with a thick object, the value of the magnification may change considerably over the various points.

1. By taking a picture of a reference object in the same field of view, or by comparing the specimen with the dimension of the specimen carrier, magnification can be determined. A fine-mesh silver grid is often used as a reference object (1,500 meshes/in.) and a copper grid with well-defined dimension (75 meshes/in.) as a specimen carrier.
2. Another way is to measure the specimen or parts of it with the aid of an optical microscope. If the irradiated part cannot be localized it is often difficult to find the corresponding structure with the light microscope because the light image may differ completely from the x-ray image.
3. A third method is from the known displacement of the specimen between stereo exposures. If stereo exposures have been made, the magnification of thick specimens can also be given. At a specimen displacement of Δa, the various image points are displaced over a distance $M \, \Delta a$, in which M is the magnification. If Δa is known, the magnification can be determined. The distance $M \, \Delta a$ can be measured by superimposing the two negatives with coinciding boundaries.

Preparation Techniques. To reveal one particular feature of the specimen, it is sometimes necessary to prepare the specimen so that it becomes more suitable for study with the x-ray microscope. These preparation techniques can be similar to or modifications of existing techniques which are used in light and electron microscopy. For instance:

1. Shadowing with a heavy element. This reveals the surface structure superimposed on the absorption image of the specimen.
2. Selective staining with an agent which causes a particular element to be deposited or chemically bound by certain chemical compounds. For example, OsO_4 will be reduced by fatty acids.
3. Injecting a radio-opaque solution into blood vessels or feeding living insects with food containing radio-opaque material.
4. Drying, freeze drying, embedding, and sectioning.

Chemical Analysis. *Absorption Technique.* Chemical analysis by absorption is possible because each element has one or more absorption edges, the wavelength of which is characteristic for that element. Thus the presence of a particular element can be detected by measuring the absorption coefficient on both sides of its absorption edge. For accurate measurement of the concentration, highly monochromatic radiation is required, and use of a crystal monochromator is imperative (see Fig. 22). Analysis on small selected areas[15] is possible because of the high brilliance of the point source.

Analysis can also be carried out on the microradiographs obtained with the projection microscope. The principle is that of subtracting the two pictures taken with wavelengths slightly smaller and slightly larger than that of the absorption edge of the element sought. The general change in contrast due to this small wavelength change can be corrected with a well-controlled photographic process. Thus, when the two images are subtracted (superposition of positive and negative prints) only those parts which have a change due to an absorption edge will remain: the other parts cancel out. The accuracy and sensitivity are not high because of the presence of the "white spectrum" in the radiation. It gives, however, the two-dimensional distribution of

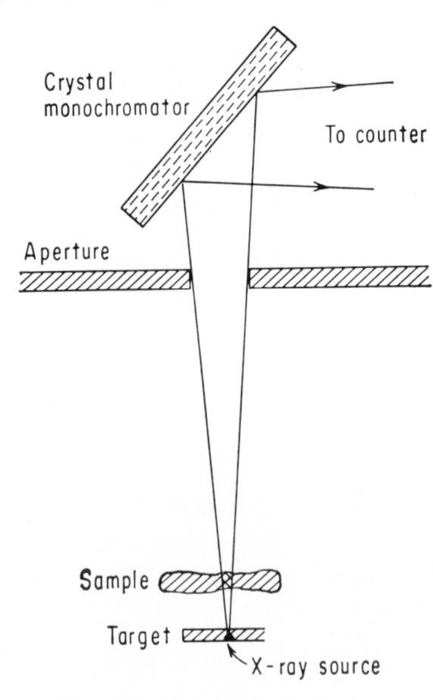

FIG. 22. Principle of microanalysis by absorption.

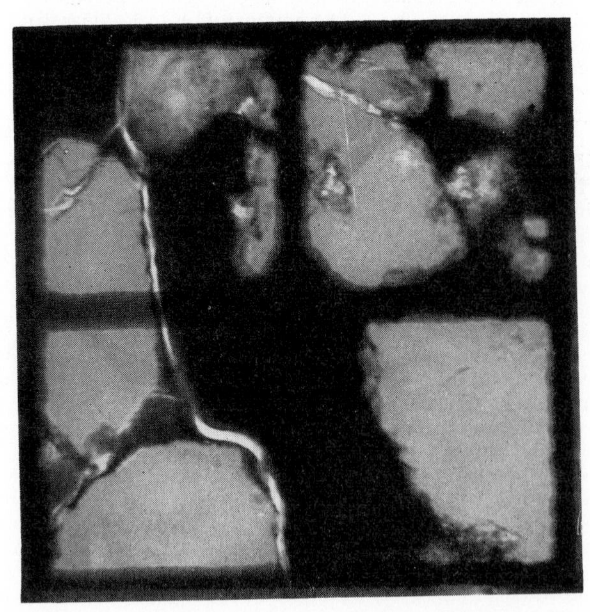

FIG. 23. 50-micron rock section (sandstone) mounted on 75 mesh/in. copper grid. Cu target, 25 kv. (*Specimen courtesy of Dr. A. K. Baird, Pomona College, Seaver Laboratory, Claremont, Calif.*)

the selected element directly in an image on an intensity or density scale. This technique has been described in detail.[16] An example of the results of such an analysis is shown in Figs. 23 to 25. To make such an analysis feasible the instrument must have:

1. A choice of different target material which can be used in succession without breaking the vacuum
2. An exact and reproducible location of target, specimen, and film for the two exposures

Changes in the location of one or more of the components mentioned result in a change of the viewing angle, magnification, and perspective. The error in magnification accumulates from the center toward the periphery. The result will be that the two pictures do not match. Thus the possibility of comparing corresponding points of the two pictures simultaneously is restricted to a narrow field.

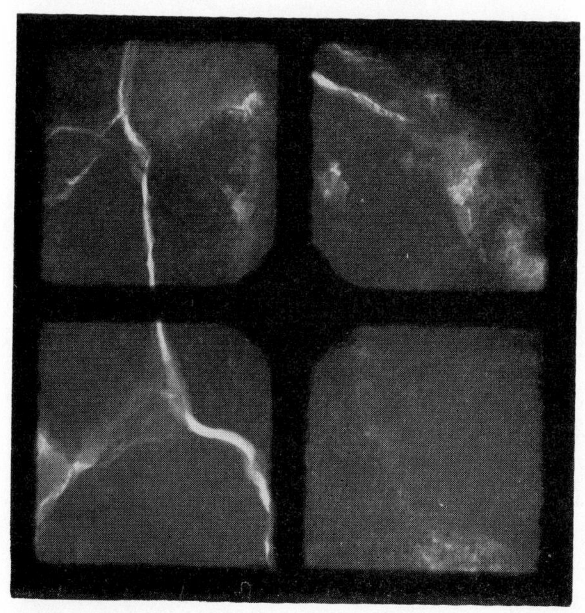

FIG. 24. The same as Fig. 23. Fe target, 25 kv. Change in contrast is due to iron.

Fluorescence Technique. The high brilliance of the fine-focus tube also makes microfluorescence feasible.[15,17] The primary x-ray beam is stopped down to illuminate only a small area of the specimen, and the fluorescence radiation is picked up at an angle (see Fig. 26). To take full advantage of the high brilliance of the x-ray source, the specimen should be placed as close to the source as possible. The shortest distance is limited by the thickness of the aperture. The problems associated with this method arise from the difficulties of making the small apertures, from the x-ray scattering at and fluorescence of the aperture, and from the instability of the x-ray source.

Divergent-beam Diffraction. Divergent-beam diffraction occurs whenever a single crystal is illuminated by a divergent x-ray beam, emerging from a small source. No apertures are needed to limit the angular range of the incident radiation: on the contrary, the full cone of radiation may be utilized. Diffraction occurs at angles determined by Bragg's condition

$$n\lambda = 2d \sin \theta \tag{19}$$

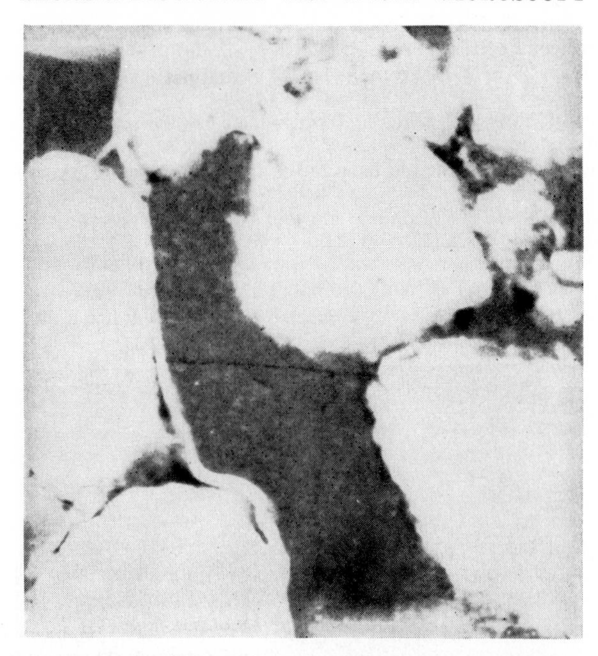

Fig. 25. Iron distribution isolated from the radiographs shown in Figs. 23 and 24.

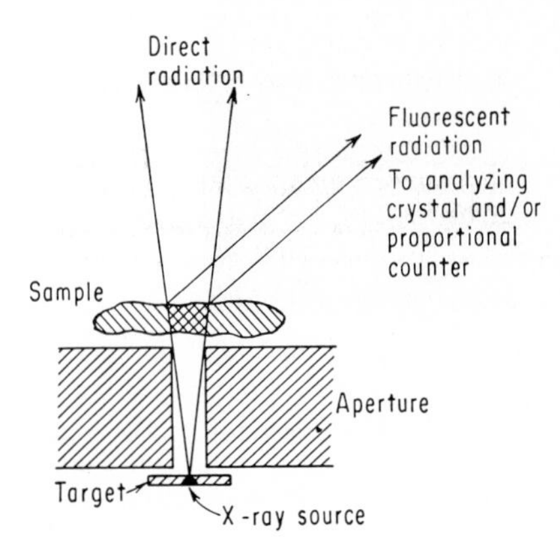

Fig. 26. Principle of microanalysis by fluorescence.

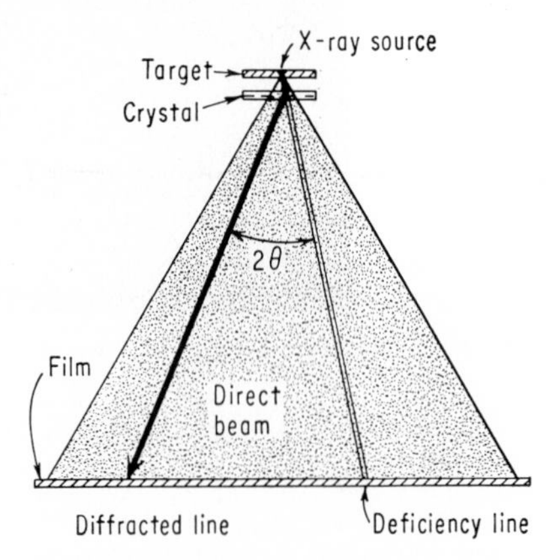

Fig. 27. A single crystal irradiated by a monochromatic divergent beam will show diffracted lines and deficiency lines (Kossel lines) superimposed on a background of the direct radiation.

in which n is an integer (the order of diffraction), λ the wavelength, d the spacing of the crystallographic planes, and θ the angle of incidence. The locus of all the rays coming from the point source and making the angle θ with a crystallographic plane lies in a cone. Thus diffraction will occur at intersections of such cones and the surface plane of the crystal, which is not necessarily the crystallographic plane under study. Divergent-beam diffraction may be used in the forward as well as in the backward direction.

Kossel Lines. Kossel lines have been intensively studied by Lonsdale.[18] The crystal is placed very close to the monochromatic x-ray source (see Fig. 27), and light (diffracted) and dark (deficiency) lines superimposed on the direct radiation appear on the film. The contrast of the lines depends very much on the transmission of the crystal and the degree of crystallographic perfection. Lattice parameters can be measured to a high degree of accuracy. The target itself may, on many occasions, give Kossel lines (see Fig. 28). After a long period of high-intensity electron bombardment the target recrystallizes. The larger crystals thus give patterns similar to that shown in Fig. 28 superimposed on the microradiographs.

FIG. 28. Kossel-line pattern formed by divergent-beam diffraction within the target itself. Cu target 25 microns thick and 6-micron Ni filter.

The contrast of the lines is usually poor because of the direct radiation. Thus the intensities of the lines are difficult to measure. By shielding half of the crystal we can obtain the diffracted lines separated from the direct radiation (see Fig. 29). The radiations which illuminate the crystal are absorbed by a lead shield to prevent them from reaching the film. In a second exposure the other half of the crystal and film are exposed. It is obvious that some of the lines which fall within the area of the direct radiation are lost. The contrast can be very high, but there remains a background due to scattering and fluorescence at the exposed part of the crystal. Figure 30 shows the reflected lines of mica in an arrangement as shown in Fig. 29. In this exposure the lower shield was located somewhere between the upper shield and the film. The target was Cu.

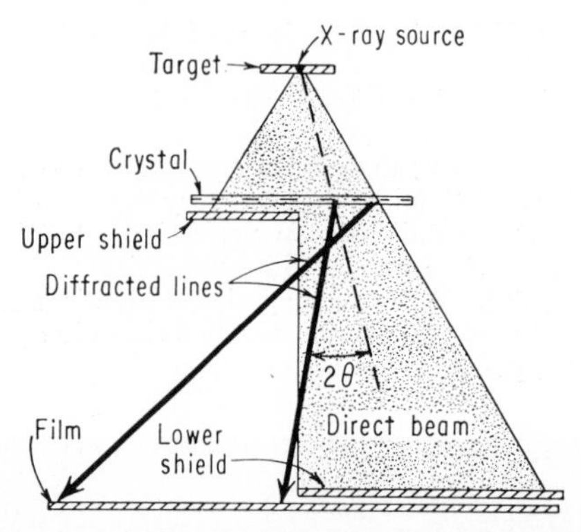

FIG. 29. The background caused by direct radiation can be eliminated by taking two consecutive pictures, each with one half of the crystal and film exposed. Only the lines which are diffracted out of the direct beam, however, can be recorded.

FIG. 30. Diffraction lines obtained with the arrangement shown in Fig. 29. Mica crystal and Cu target without filter.

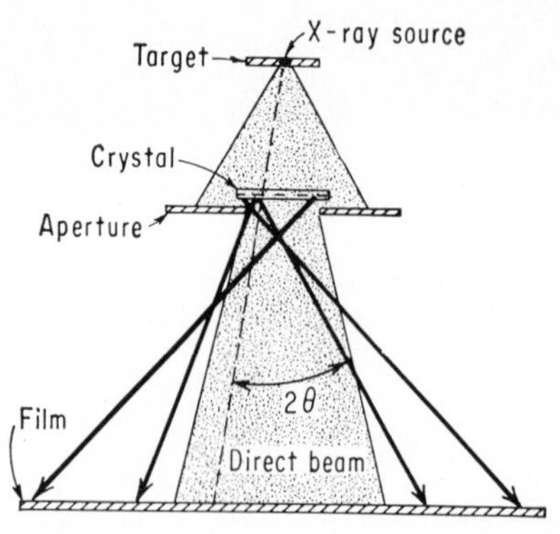

FIG. 31. Symmetrical arrangement for divergent-beam diffraction. The relative intensities of the lines as well as the crystal orientation, symmetry, etc., can be determined from such pictures. See Fig. 32.

Where a symmetrical arrangement is desirable we may use the setup shown in Fig. 31. An exposure taken with such an arrangement is shown in Fig. 32. In this picture, the reflection lines are broken on several points. This is due to the crosshairs

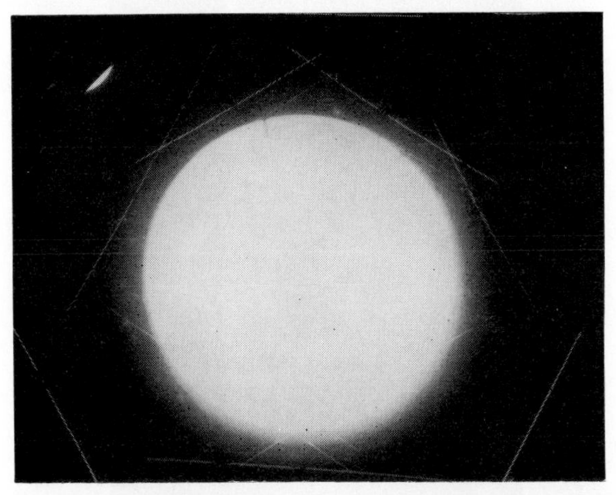

FIG. 32. Diffraction lines obtained with the arrangement shown in Fig. 31. Mica crystal, Cu target. The crystallographic axis is determined with respect to the crosshairs (vaguely visible) which have been mounted on the crystal. The various lines are broken because of the crosshairs. Thus the location of the lines where the beam has been diffracted can be traced.

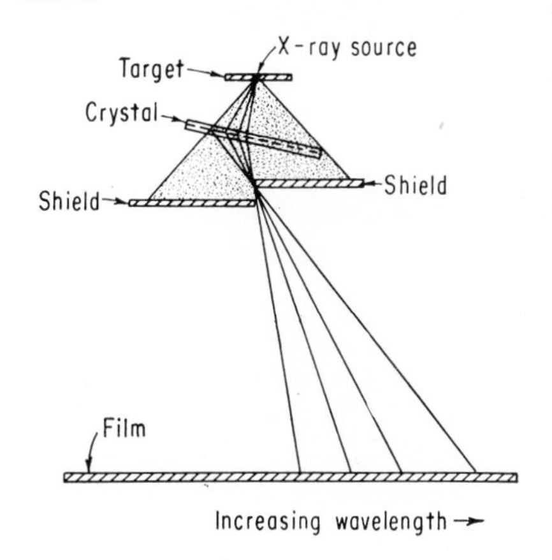

FIG. 33. Divergent-beam transmission spectrograph. In this arrangement the crystal acts as a spectrograph and casts a certain region of the spectrum simultaneously on the film.

FIG. 34. Spectrum of a Ni target (6 microns) obtained with an arrangement similar to that shown in Fig. 33. The white spectrum forms an enlarged "image" of the irradiated area of the crystal. Co and Fe impurities are seen. The crystal was mica.

(tungsten) which were fixed on the crystal as reference lines. Thus each reflected line can be traced back to the crystal surface where the reflection occurs.

Divergent-beam Spectroscopy. A divergent-beam spectrograph can be made based on the same principle described above. A wide beam of polychromatic x-rays is thrown on a thin sheet of a crystal. Diffraction occurs for the various wavelengths,

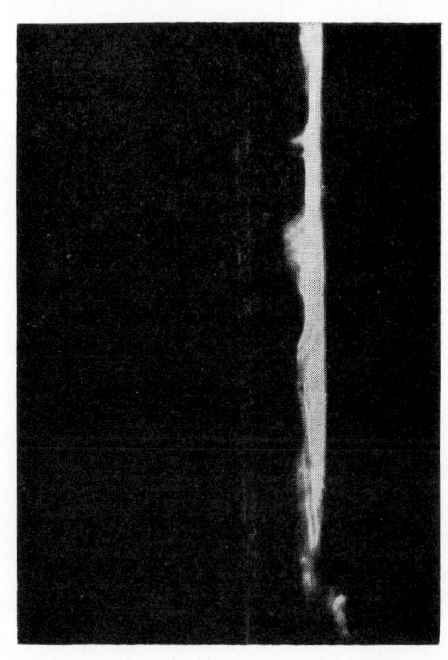

Fig. 35. Spectrum of Cu target obtained with an arrangement similar to that shown in Fig. 33. NaCl crystal. Cf. Figs. 34 and 37.

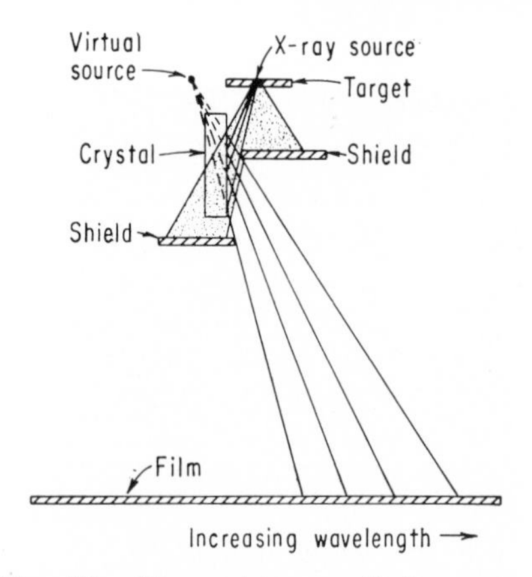

Fig. 36. Divergent-beam reflection spectrograph.

Fig. 37. Spectrum of a Cu target obtained with an arrangement similar to that shown in Fig. 36. The crystal was calcite; the $K\alpha_1$ and $K\alpha_2$ are clearly resolved. Cf. Fig. 35.

the angles of incidence and the wavelength being governed by Bragg's equation. In the plane of the drawing (Fig. 33) all the beams diffracted by one particular set of planes converge into a narrow spot. This spot resembles a true focus for the diffracting planes which are perpendicular to the crystal surface. This holds, of course, only for rays lying in the plane perpendicular to the diffracting planes and going through the x-ray source. With an aperture slit, all the radiation can be shielded off except for that diffracted by one selected set of crystallographic planes. The sharpness of the lines shown in the previous pictures (Figs. 30 and 32) ensures a good spectroscopic resolution with a short source-to-film distance. If white radiation is used, we can obtain a "reflection image" of the crystal. Thus crystal imperfections become visible. Figure 34 shows the "reflection image" of a mica crystal: a thin (6-micron) Ni target was used. With such a target, the white radiation is still considerable. The line radiations visible in this picture (Ni with impurities of Co and Fe) mark the places where the reflection occurs. The cleanness of the lines indicates the high degree of perfection of the mica crystal in contrast to that of NaCl, shown in Fig. 35. This picture shows the mosaic structure which causes reflection to occur in a broad region rather than in a well-defined line.

The principle of the divergent-beam spectrograph by reflection is shown in Fig. 36. Because the beam diverges from the crystal it is not possible to place a narrow aperture as is the case with the transmission type shown in Fig. 33.

As a result, each point on the film "sees" the whole crystal and the background due to the fluorescence, and scattered radiation is more serious. An example of the reflection on a calcite crystal is shown in Fig. 37.

5. SUMMARY

The x-ray projection microscope is basically a microfocus x-ray tube. An enlarged absorption x-ray image is obtained by using the "point source" as a projection center. To obtain good resolution the source must be as small as practical. This is done by focusing a narrow electron beam onto the x-ray target. In contrast to conventional x-ray tubes, the target is used in transmission and thus acts as a high-transparency filter for its characteristic radiation. By an appropriate choice of electron energy, target material, and target thickness, it is possible to obtain quite monochromatic radiation: the wavelength is determined by the target material. The field of application for this type of instrument is determined by its inherent features, i.e.,

1. Large depth of field (stereomicroscopy)
2. Large penetrating power of the radiation (thick, opaque specimen)
3. Wide choice of monochromatic radiation (chemical analysis by absorption)
4. High brilliance of the source (microdiffraction, microfluorescence)
5. Small size of the spot (high-resolution microradiography, divergent-beam diffraction on single crystals)

A great drawback is the low total x-ray output for high-resolution work and when long-wavelength radiation is used.

REFERENCES CITED

1. M. E. Haine and P. A. Einstein, *Brit. J. Appl. Phys.*, **3**:40 (1952).
2. Zworykin, Morton, Ramberg, Hillier, and Vance, *Electron Optics and the Electron Microscope*, 3d ed., John Wiley & Sons, Inc., New York, 1948.
3. D. B. Langmuir, *Proc. IRE*, **25**:977 (1937).
4. M. van Ments and J. B. Le Poole, *Appl. Sci. Res.*, **B1**:3 (1947).
5. R. Whiddington, *Proc. Roy. Soc.* (*London*), **A89**:554 (1914).
6. W. Nixon, *Proc. Roy. Soc.* (*London*), **A232**: 475 (1955).
7. W. Hink, in *X-ray Microscopy and X-ray Microanalysis*, p. 83, A. Engström, V. Cosslett, and H. Pattee (eds.), Elsevier Publishing Company, Amsterdam, 1960.
8. R. Castaing, *Proc. Intern. Conf. Electron Microscopy* (*London*, 1954), p. 300, Royal Microscopical Society, London, 1956.
9. A. Müller, *Proc. Roy. Soc.* (*London*), **A132**:646 (1931).
10. W. J. Oosterkamp, *Phil. Tech. Rept.*, **3**:58, 303 (1948).
11. Poen Sing Ong and J. B. Le Poole, *Appl. Sci. Res.*, **B7**:233 (1958).
12. W. C. Nixon, *Proc. 4th Intern. Conf. Electron Microscopy, Berlin*, 1958, p. 249, Springer-Verlag OHG, Berlin, 1960.
13. B. M. Rovinsky and V. G. Lutsau, Point Projection X-ray Microscopy with the Aid of a Camera Obscura, in *X-ray Microscopy and Microradiography*, p. 128, V. E. Cosslett, Arne Engström, and H. H. Pattee (eds.), Academic Press, Inc., New York, 1957.

14. B. M. Rovinsky, V. G. Lutsau, and A. I. Avdeyenko, Miniature Point X-ray Sources for Point-projection Microscopy and Diffraction Studies, in *X-ray Microscopy and X-ray Microanalysis*, p. 110, Arne Engström, V. Cosslett, and H. Pattee (eds.), Elsevier Publishing Company, Amsterdam, 1960. See also X-ray Microprojector, in *X-ray Microscopy and Microradiography*, p. 269, Cosslett, Engström, and Pattee (eds.), Academic Press Inc., New York, 1957.
15. J. V. P. Long and V. E. Cosslett, Some Methods of X-ray Microchemical Analysis, in *X-ray Microscopy and Microradiography*, p. 435, V. E. Cosslett, A. Engström, and H. H. Pattee (eds.), Academic Press, Inc., New York, 1957.
16. Poen Sing Ong, *Norelco Reptr.*, **VIII**:3 (1961).
17. L. Zeitz, Thesis, Stanford University, Stanford, Calif., *B. L. Rept.* 67, April, 1962.
18. K. Lonsdale, *Phil. Trans. Roy. Soc. London,* **240**:219 (1947).

GENERAL REFERENCES

Cosslett, V. E., A. Engström, and H. H. Pattee (eds.): *X-ray Microscopy and Microradiography*, Academic Press Inc., New York, 1957.
Cosslett, V. E., and W. C. Nixon: *X-ray Microscopy*, Cambridge University Press, New York, 1961.
Ely, R. V.: *Micro X-radiography and Analysis*, Bibliography (1913–1962), Guilford, England.
Engström, A., V. E. Cosslett, and H. H. Pattee (eds.): *X-ray Microscopy and X-ray Microanalysis*, Elsevier Publishing Company, Amsterdam, 1960.
Ong Sing Poen: *Microprojection with X-rays*, Martinus Nyhoff, The Hague, Holland, 1959.
Pattee, H. H., V. E. Cosslett, and Arne Engström (eds.): *X-ray Optics and X-ray Microanalysis*, Academic Press, Inc., New York, 1963.

Chapter 48

REFLECTION MICROSCOPY

Paul Kirkpatrick

Stanford University

1. INTRODUCTION AND PRINCIPLES

In the visible region of the spectrum, microscopy is invariably conducted by using lenses to form enlarged optical images. Roentgen reported in his earliest papers that lenses produced no such effects upon x-rays, and though we now know that there is a slight refractive effect when x-rays impinge upon any matter, no x-ray lens has been made and none seems probable. Accordingly the inspection of small structures by x-rays has depended upon other methods of magnification such as geometric projection and the enlargement of photographic images (cf. Chaps, 45, 46, and 47).

There remains the intriguing possibility of producing real enlarged optical images not by refraction but by reflection. Mirrors have of course been used with success in the microscopy of the ultraviolet where the nature of the radiation made lenses

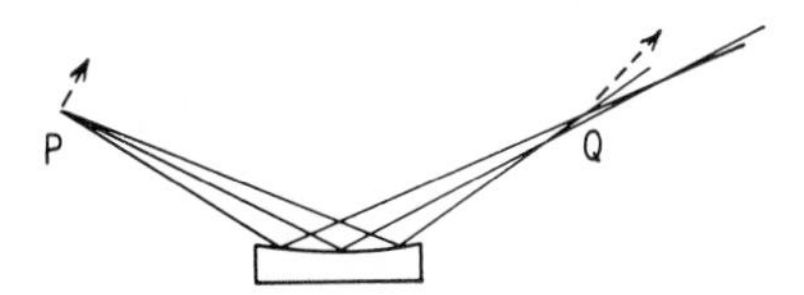

Fig. 1. Aberrant image formation by a mirror of circular section irradiated at grazing incidence.

impractical. X-ray reflection microscopy may be thought of as an extension of this ultraviolet usage, but one immediately finds that this step, involving a frequency shift of some two orders of magnitude, involves the experimenter in new difficulties never before faced by microscopists and not at this writing satisfactorily solved. Reflection x-ray microscopy has not yet taken its place as a practical tool of the applied scientist, but the fact that it is the only known x-ray method permitting primary optical magnification preserves its interesting position in the general area of x-ray microscopy.

A smooth solid surface can reflect x-rays efficiently only if the incident beam makes a small acute angle with the surface. With a glass surface and radiation 1 Å in wavelength this angle must be less than 1°. With longer waves and denser mirrors the angle (critical angle) may be somewhat greater, but it never approaches anything like the 90° angle which is preferred for reflecting telescopes and other optical instruments requiring the formation of good images by curved mirrors. If x-rays are directed at a concave spherical mirror from a point source as shown in Fig. 1, the reflected rays will intersect in the region Q, though not in a perfect point image of the source point P. Rays lying in the plane of the drawing will meet along a caustic; their failure to meet in a point is simply the defect of spherical aberration, common with spherical surfaces under even the best conditions but exaggerated when incidence must be grazing, as in the x-ray cases.

A more drastic fault of the image at Q is that it extends behind and in front of the drawing in a linear locus. The spherical mirror, in other words, is exceedingly astigmatic when illuminated at grazing incidence. Now the image of a point, though a basic matter, is of little satisfaction to the microscopist; an array of points constituting an extended object must be properly imaged to serve his needs. But if the point object P is moved in the direction of the small arrow its image moves in the approximate direction shown by the longer arrow at Q. The image then is seriously inclined. A further obstacle to good reflection microscopy is the great difficulty of forming sufficiently well polished mirror surfaces.

It is easily shown that the focal length of a reflector is

$$f = (r/2) \sin i \tag{1}$$

where r is the radius of the spherical curvature and i is the angle between the narrow incident pencil of rays and the tangent to the mirror surface at the point of incidence. This is the focal length only for rays lying in a plane such as that of the drawing (Fig. 1). Rays in planes normal to the figure are very weakly deflected and their focal length may ordinarily be considered infinite. To secure equal focal powers for the two sets of rays it would be necessary to abandon the spherical figure and utilize a barrel-shaped reflector with the object and image points on its axis. This form, however, possesses the aberration of coma in an extreme degree. Design expedients for counteracting the special difficulties of grazing-incidence optics will be presented in later paragraphs.

The desired attributes of a microscope or microscopic technique are magnification, resolution, differentiation, fidelity, field, convenience, and economy. We may not with confidence arrange these qualities in a unique order of desirability, for the sequence would vary with the user and with the contemplated application. Among the existing and proposed methods of x-ray microscopy the reflection variety has, up to now, demonstrated no characteristic superiority over projection microscopy or microradiography with respect to any of the listed desiderata. Its strongest hope is in its theoretical possibility of a superior resolving power, but realization of this awaits the practical achievement of the required near-perfect optical surfaces. Lacking this advantage the present use of reflection microscopy would be indicated only in special circumstances where its particular combination of characteristics might offer advantage. While on the subject of *relative* virtues this writer would say that in spite of his special interest in reflection microscopy he feels that in the *overall* comparison, microradiography, the earliest of the techniques under consideration, has not yet been displaced from the position of preference.

2. DESIGN OF REFLECTION MICROSCOPES

It is desirable to secure as large an angle as possible between the reflecting surface and the rays of the incident bundle, for as this angle is decreased aberrations all increase, field diminishes, and resolution declines. An approximate expression of the cutoff angle (critical angle) in radian measure is

$$\theta_c = 1.6 \times 10^5 \lambda \sqrt{\rho} \tag{2}$$

where λ is the wavelength in centimeters and ρ is the density of the reflector surface in g/cm^3. Clearly a microscope designed for use with long waves should perform better than one restricted to higher frequencies, and this expectation is borne out in practice. This is a fortunate circumstance because short-wave (high-frequency) x-radiation is of little use in microscopy anyway since thin specimens of almost anything will be nearly uniformly transparent to it, and hence differentiation will be lacking in the resulting record. The most likely application of any x-ray microscopy is in work with biological materials, and here atomic numbers are low and radiation stopping power correspondingly slight; so long waves are preferred on all counts. The first reflection microscopes were tested with metal screens as objects and with radiation of the spectral region below 1 Å in wavelength, but the later and best yet images were obtained with aluminum K radiation ($\lambda = 8.32$ Å).

The effect of mirror density is less compelling than that of wavelength, both because of the radical sign and because the cutoff angle is far from sharp. With high values of ρ the larger values of θ_c made possible are exacted at the price of less efficient reflection throughout the band of useful incidence angles between θ_c and zero. High values of ρ can of course be obtained by applying metal coats to polished surfaces of glass, but this never results in a smoother reflecting surface than that of the clean glass, and with most heavy metals it results in a rougher one.

The grossest aberration of a single concave reflector working at grazing incidence is astigmatism. The first proposal for its alleviation was the obvious one of crossing two astigmatic mirrors (see Fig. 2). This works well enough but with some unwelcome reduction in the power of the delivered beam. The mirrors employed are, for convenience of figuring, spherical, but they perform practically as cylinders when illuminated at the unavoidable grazing angles. Replacement of the two mirrors by a single aspheric reflector has often been suggested, but the requisite figure is most unattractive to optical workers.

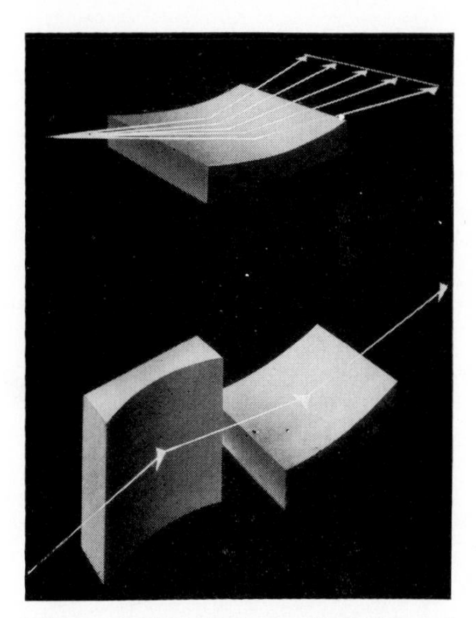

FIG. 2. Astigmatic image formation and correction by two crossed units.

Ignoring astigmatism we return to two-dimensional ray diagrams and note that the several incident rays (Fig. 1) necessarily meet the reflecting surface at differing angles i and therefore, by Eq. (1), are characterized by different focal lengths. This difference is such that a spherical mirror operated at grazing incidence can never produce a point image of a point object, but only a caustic. Some relief is gained by utilizing a mirror of *elliptical* profile; this shape effects a point image of an object point in one specific location, i.e., at a geometrical focus of the ellipse. Our solution is useful if we are content with imaging a single point, as we might be in the design of a sharp, probing x-ray beam, but microscopy requires concurrent imaging of the multiplicity of points constituting an extended object, and this turns out to be beyond the power of any single reflecting surface of elliptical or any other form. We are dealing here with the aberration known as coma.

Optical systems, whether of one element or more, are free from coma only if they conform to the so-called sine condition first presented by Abbe and readily looked up under his name in any science library. The special fulfillment of the sine condition in a grazing-incidence microscope was first treated by Wolter.[1] See also Pattee[2,3] on this and other points of reflection-microscope theory. It is found that coma may be eliminated by two successive reflections of the image-forming beam from suitably designed grazing-incidence mirrors. These mirrors possess a common plane of incidence and are not to be confused with the pair of crossed mirrors mentioned above as one method of dealing with astigmatism. Some of the more elegant of proposed solutions of the coma problem are shown in Fig. 3. The surfaces of these mirrors have the curvature of conic sections, but the more easily prepared circular approximations should be acceptable substitutes.

Returning now to the correction of astigmatism, we see that the designs of Fig. 3 may be used in two ways. In the first place two systems like that of Fig. 3*a* might be crossed, yielding the result shown in Fig. 4. The curvatures of these mirrors in directions crosswise to the general direction of propagation of the beams are of the same order as that which performs the focusing, but the precise shapes of these normal profiles is of no importance, for their focusing effects are negligible. Except for the difficulties of production we should probably specify that all these reflectors should be sections of cylinders, elliptical, parabolic, or hyperbolic as the case might be.

Alternatively astigmatism might be corrected by rotating the curves of Fig. 3 about their axis of figure as proposed by Wolter. In such a system each ray would be reflected only twice instead of four times as in the system of the preceding paragraph.

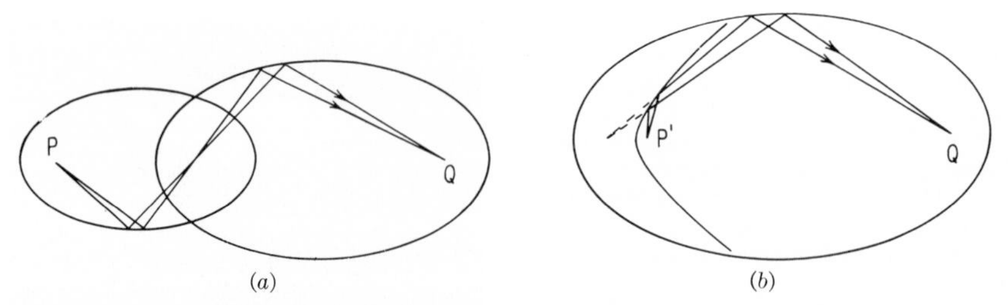

FIG. 3. Systems for reduction of coma by two successive reflections. An object point at P is imaged at Q by (*a*) two mirrors of elliptic section, and (*b*) mirrors with hyperbolic and elliptic sections. The point P' is the virtual image of P as formed by the hyperbolic reflector alone. In practice only small areas of the extended conic sections shown here would be employed.

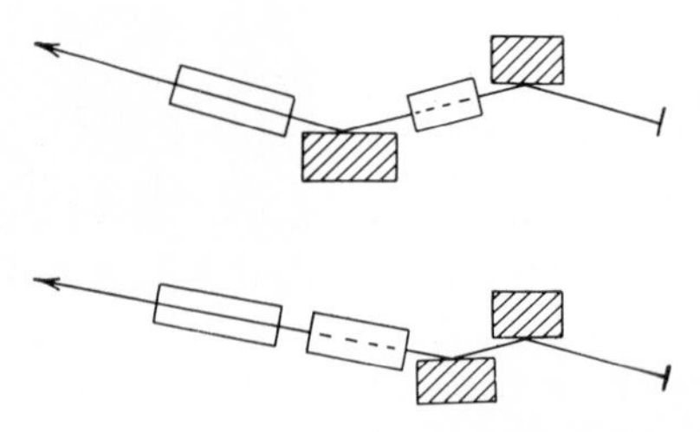

FIG. 4. Four concave mirrors in two dispositions capable of correcting both astigmatism and coma.

Probably no reflection microscope embodying these rational designs for abatement of both astigmatism and coma has as yet been constructed. The fact that none has been found in the literature accents the difficulties found in the production of the optical surfaces. It may certainly be said that theory is in advance of experimental and technical practice in the construction of reflection microscopes. Not only do we ask for small parts with precisely figured internal surfaces without precedent, but the more conventional shapes of Fig. 2 require a perfection of surface polish beyond that which suffices in the best commercial practice.

There are other image defects to be reckoned with. Spherical optical surfaces are widely used in optical instruments, not because their shapes are the best but because they are the easiest to make. If we seek to do reflection microscopy with spherical mirrors we must expect spherical aberration to limit the size of the well-defined field. We shall not discuss this image damage quantitatively, as has been done in the relevant literature, but suggest that rejection of spherical forms is a sure cure for spherical aberration.

The optical systems of Figs. 1 and 2 have no axis of symmetry; so it is perhaps no surprise to find that the image plane is obliquely disposed to the bundle of intersecting rays. Unless the aperture angles are greatly restricted this obliquity of the focal surface limits the useful field. Fortunately this defect may be corrected in considerable measure, at the cost of restricted speed, by proper placement of an aperture stop.

3. A SIMPLE REFLECTION MICROSCOPE

The simplicity ascribed above is not that of structure but of basic theory. There follows a description of a reflection microscope consisting of two crossed spherical mirrors designed to use the K radiation of aluminum as illuminant. The wavelength of this radiation (8.32 Å) is in the range appropriate for biological applications. Because the instrument does not utilize the special means described for control of either coma or spherical aberration its useful field is small, but it is the most successful reflection x-ray microscope known to have been constructed as yet. The instrument was designed, in part constructed, tested, and employed by Dr. James F. McGee.[4,5] In the present context its description is intended to illustrate the advantages and limitations of reflection microscopy, the problems of design and construction in this

Fig. 5. Two-mirror x-ray microscope utilizing principally the soft aluminum K radiation. Working parts are necessarily concealed in the helium-filled envelope. Radiation source is at the left and the film holder at the right.

field, techniques of utilization, and possibilities for the future. The assembly presented is strictly a research and development instrument, quite lacking in the refinements of appearance and operation which one expects in apparatus for the public.

In Fig. 5 we see distributed from left to right along the optical bench the following essential components: x-ray source, specimen holder, mirror cell, helium tube, and photographic-plate compartment. The essential parts are invisible in this external view because of the housing required for containment of the helium atmosphere in which the ray system is propagated throughout its course from the x-ray source window to the photographic emulsion. The soft radiation employed would be almost completely extinguished by an air path even a tenth as long as the 50-cm-long system pictured. Several of the component units of the instrument will now be further examined.

The x-rays are generated in a disk of aluminum 0.003 in. thick which is bombarded by electrons accelerated through 35 kv. It is important that the source spot be big enough so that its rays upon passing through any point of the specimen should be able to illuminate the entire useful area of the mirrors, since otherwise areas of the object under observation would be incompletely represented in the recorded image. But it is also important not to have the focal spot larger than this usefully defined size, for not only would the excess areas be wasteful of power and filament current but the useless target heating thus incurred would interfere with the conduction cooling of the essential central focal area. The specific loading (watts/mm^2) which a target may sustain without melting is known to be a sensitive function of the bombarded area. The electron control in the present instance was accordingly worked out with some care using an electrostatic focusing system employing two coaxial cylindrical electrode structures, but any of a number of other known and commercially employed systems might have served. The attained object here was to produce a circular focus, uniform in current density and a little less than a millimeter in diameter. It was calculated that such a spot should be able to operate at a power input of 2.7 kw without melting, but to avoid pitting it was actually operated at lower loads.

The radiation principally desired from this source was the K lines of aluminum at a wavelength of 8.32 Å. Earlier reflection microscopes had always used the convenient higher-frequency rays available from commercial x-ray tubes, but while this radiation penetrates the air and so makes the helium path unnecessary it restricts the grazing-incidence angles to undesirable small values and penetrates thin specimens of biological materials altogether too well to permit the registration of any contrasting structures. A spectrum analysis of the emission from the aluminum target, performed with a crystal spectrograph in helium, showed the K lines prominently against a background of continuous x-rays extending to a short-wave limit determined by the bombardment voltage. This continuous radiation adds a little to the useful flux and does no harm since its higher-frequency portion is absorbed by the reflectors.

The necessary window between the high vacuum of the x-ray source and the adjacent helium at approximately atmospheric pressure is composed of Mylar of the thinnest commercial gauge, which was 0.00025 in. This material passes the aluminum radiation more completely than does an aluminum window of equal blowout resistance, and has the further advantage of transparency, a property useful in some line-up procedures. Experience has shown that a thinner Mylar window would be desirable.

The carriage at the extreme left end of the optical bench carries the specimen stage, connected to the radiation source by a short length of rubber pressure tubing. The specimen is carried at the center of a small, paddle-shaped mount with a ⅛-in. hole through its disk portion for the passage of the rays. Several methods of specimen mounting have been used. It may be placed directly on a conventional electron-microscope support grid, in which case the grid network appearing in the final picture provides a convenient scale of measurement. If it is feared that the grid may cover up interesting detail the specimen may be stuck to a thin collodion or plastic film attached to the specimen mount. A third mounting technique, useful with biological materials, is to embed the specimen in collodion and section it with a microtome. The complete section is then applied to the specimen mount.

The metal paddle, carrying its specimen, is inserted into the specimen stage, which retains it positively in a carrier which is subject to orthogonal positioning adjustments by screwdriver. Ports for inserting and adjusting the specimen mount are covered with plastic sealing tape to keep the system gastight, but with the contained helium kept at a pressure slightly above atmospheric the ports may be uncovered as may be necessary for operation, without admission of air.

Connected to the specimen mount by a black rubber tube stands the mirror cell, a cylinder of metal carried by two vertical metal rings. This unit, the heart of the instrument, is shown separately in Fig. 6. The two concave spherical reflectors, cut from a silica mirror of good optical quality having a radius of curvature of 8.5 m, are disposed in the relative positions shown in Fig. 2. The lengths of mirror surface in the direction of the rays, however, are only a few millimeters, and each mirror is carried as an inset in a steel disk as shown in Fig. 6, where one sees also a beam-limiting knife-edge which may be advanced toward the reflecting surface to stop rays not so directed as to become incident upon the mirror.

The several parts shown in Fig. 7 are explained in the figure caption. In use they are all combined into the steel tube which is then mounted in the complete mirror-cell assembly shown in Fig. 6, where it is the innermost of the three visible coaxial cylinders. This inner cylinder is on a gimbal mounting and under control by the two micrometers, which independently tilt the mirror tube so as to vary the angles between the reflecting faces and their incident rays. The slitlike stops carried by the two disks shown in the lower left corner of Fig. 7 are critical limiters of the reflected beams, necessary for minimization of aberrations. Their positions are determined by the length of the spacing cylinder shown, and the widths of their apertures are subject to screwdriver adjustment. For the full theory of these stops, the McGee dissertation[4] should be consulted.

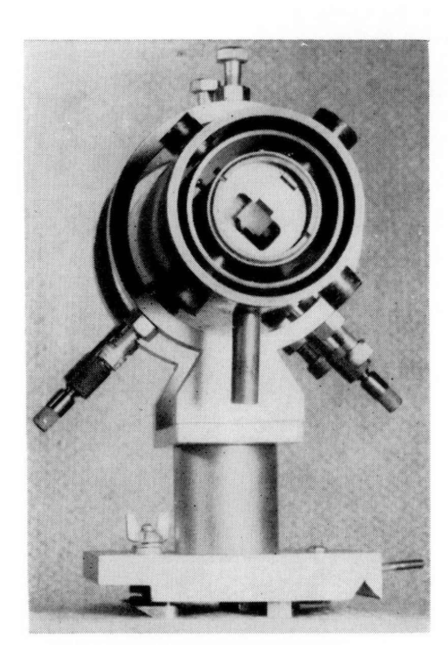

FIG. 6. Mirror assembly for the microscope of Fig. 5. A mirror may be seen near the axis of the three concentric tubes. The micrometers control the angular adjustment of the mirrors.

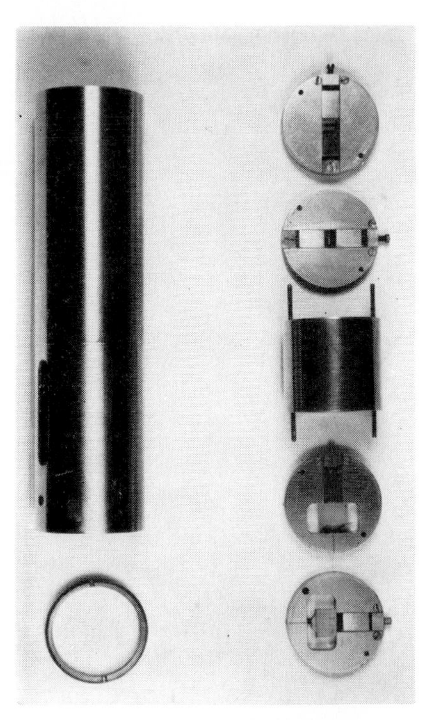

FIG. 7. Internal parts of the mirror and stop assembly of Fig. 6. Disk-shaped mirror holders are at the lower right. Adjustable stops limiting the reflected beam are shown at the upper right.

To the right of the mirror cell (Fig. 5) and joined to it by a section of thin rubber tube comes a brass tube for the exclusion of light and the inclusion of helium. The length of this tube depends upon the magnification to be recorded, since high magnification requires large distance between mirrors and final image. As shown in the illustration the direct magnification is about 17 diameters; micrographs on following pages have been further enlarged by photographic processing.

At the right end of the bench (Fig. 5) is seen the film or plate compartment, accommodating a standard 2¼- by 3¼-in. plate holder. For alignment of parts the plate holder is removed and x-rays are observed with a magnifying fluoroscope at the aperture of the tube extension visible at the extreme right side of the picture.

Obtainable image quality is indicated by Fig. 8, which is a micrograph of a silver-mesh screen having 1,500 bars/lin in. At the center of the field the resolution seems to be limited more by photographic graininess than by optical aberration. The bars were approximately 3 microns wide and their spacing was about 17 microns. The x-ray magnification in this case was 7×. Outside a central area about 0.007 in. in diameter at the object the image fidelity declines rapidly, thus setting a limit on the useful field of the instrument. The extent of this field is a few hundred times the

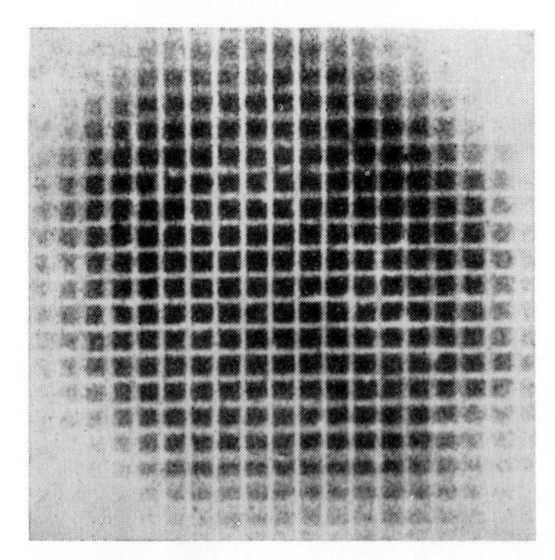

Fig. 8. Test micrograph showing image quality and field limitations. The object was a silver screen with 1,500 bars/lin in. Grid bars were 3 microns in width. The resolution in the center of the field approaches the limiting quality permitted by diffraction.

Fig. 9. X-ray micrograph of a section of earthworm gut 7 microns thick. Original x-ray magnification was 7× and total magnification is 230×.

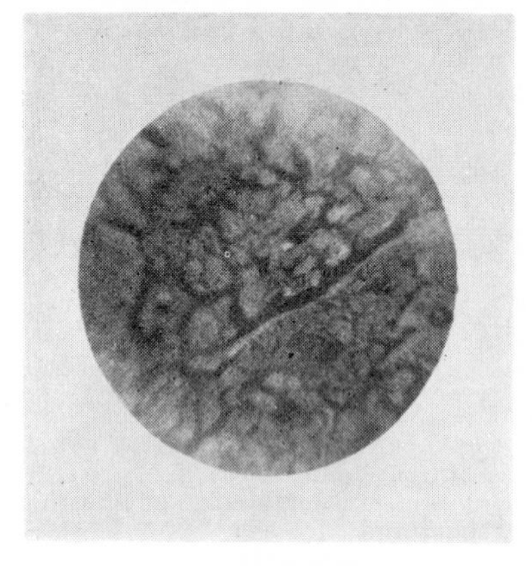

Fig. 10. X-ray micrograph of salamander kidney. The 7-micron section had been stained with osmic acid. X-ray magnification is 7× and total magnification as reproduced here is 230×.

minimum resolvable distance but is far less than the fields of microradiographic methods.

In Fig. 9 is shown one of the first reflection x-ray microscope pictures ever taken of a histological specimen. The subject was a 7-micron section of earthworm gut. This thickness gives good contrast with the characteristic aluminum radiation. The specimen, originally prepared for student use in an elementary biological laboratory, had been stained with haematoxylin and embedded in paraffin. It was prepared for x-ray observation by removal of the paraffin with xylene. For this exposure the

McGee microscope was equipped with fused-quartz mirrors with curvature radii of 8.5 m. The initial microphotograph with magnification 7× was copied at a magnification of 4× onto a medium lantern-slide plate by use of a light microscope. Subsequent processing steps have brought the illustration here to a total magnification of 230×.

The x-ray micrograph of Fig. 10 was made from a 7-micron section of salamander kidney which had been stained with osmic acid. The magnifications are the same as in Fig. 9. The limited resolution of the McGee microscope confines its usefulness to the examination of fairly coarse biological organisms such as plant and animal cells, red-blood cells, and muscle fiber, subjects whose gross aspects show dimensions greater than 1 micron.

4. MICROSCOPY BY CRYSTAL REFLECTION

Mention should be made of an alternative form of x-ray reflection microscopy which has been occasionally discussed but as yet only a little pursued by experimenters. This microscopy would make use of Bragg reflection from crystals rather than total reflection from optical surfaces. Crystal reflections obey the geometrical law of reflection (as well as the chromatic restrictions of Bragg's law); so there is no doubt of the theoretical possibility of image-forming reflectors; doubts may arise over the practicality of producing the theoretically indicated crystal shapes and concerning the quality of the resulting images. This latter concern has much to do with the possible perfection of crystal structure, any departure from which would coarsen optical imagery, as poor figuring and polishing impair glass mirror images.

A difficulty for this microscopy is the low reflecting power of crystals, leading to optically slow imaging systems. The fact that a Laue spot pattern can be photographed in a few minutes, or even seconds, justifies little optimism, for in such photography one is not concerned with image formation of high precision and hence welcomes geometrical crudities which could not be tolerated in microscopy, where point-to-point image formation (rather than hole-to-spot) is the aim of the designer. In ideal microscopy every ray from an object point should strike the mirror at a point where crystal structure and crystal orientation permit the fullfillment of Bragg's law, but surface orientation has already been committed by the requirements of mirror-image formation. This may mean that only some one or some few wavelengths of the incident radiation chance to be reflectible. It would seem necessary then to work with a continuous spectrum of x-rays and be resigned to the wastage of nearly all of it.

Image quality demands crystals without appreciable mosaic structure, since structural irregularities will scatter reflected rays about the desired point of convergence. It is also to be desired that diffraction spreading shall be small. It is probable that these conditions can be met to the extent that other image afflictions will more seriously damage the performance of the instrument. These other afflictions include the expected technical errors of figure and the ordinary optical aberrations of image formation, some of which may not be so severe as in total-reflection microscopy because with crystals the grazing angles of incidence need not be so minute.

The errors of figure present formidable problems since it does not suffice to cut the reflectors from crystal blocks; they must be bent into shapes of the requisite curvature. It is simple to bend a flat crystal plate to a cylindrical shape, circular or otherwise, but focusing mirrors require compound (nondevelopable) curvature, and crystals do not have sufficient plasticity for much of such deformation. It has been shown possible[6] to secure such curvature (of rather long radius) by a program of bending, machining, and rebending, but the microscopic quality of products of this process has not as yet been established.

Ramachandran and Thathachari[7] successfully strained a slip of mica in an approximately spherical concave curvature by differential air pressures, as shown in Fig. 11. The mirror is stressed by a pressure difference of about half an atmosphere and takes up a curvature with radius as small as 15 cm. The object at O receives radiation from the x-ray tube X and transmits it to the mirror by way of the lead stop L. With this primitive prototype instrument magnifications of 4 and 6 required exposures of 30 min and 6 hr, respectively. The published micrograph of a fine metal grid seems to show a resolving distance exceeding 1 micron, but it seems reasonable to expect that this figure may be brought well below a micron. At the present writing the crystal reflection microscope has demonstrated no superiorities over any of the several other instruments in the field, but it has not as yet been the focus of enough research and development to warrant conclusive pronouncements.

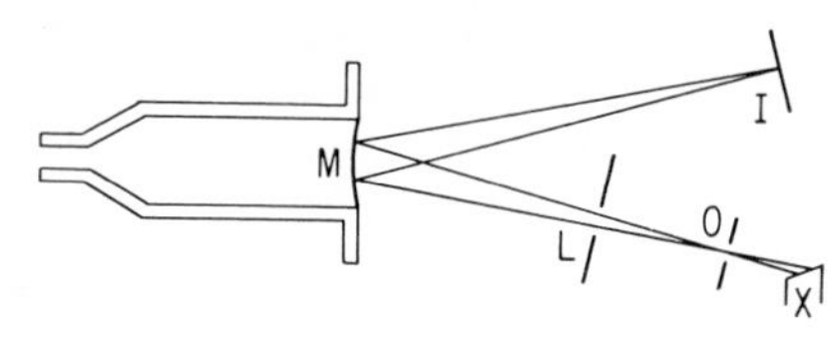

Fig. 11. Image formation by Bragg reflection from a thin mica crystal *M*, strained to concave form by atmospheric pressure. The space at the left of the reflector is maintained at reduced pressure. Radiation from the x-ray source *X* passes through the object at *O* and the limiting lead stop at *L*. After reflection at *M* it converges to the image at *I*.

5. RESOLUTION

The inverse dependence of resolving power upon wavelength is well known and leads the optimistic to presume that well-made x-ray microscopes of whatever sort should be expected to achieve resolution in the same range with electron microscopy. Unfortunately the diffraction equation which expresses the limiting resolution of an optical instrument is permissive only and cannot give assurance that the conditions for its application will be met in a particular case. Actually, a variety of frustrations may intervene, keeping the minimum resolvable distances of all x-ray microscopic processes at a hundred to a thousand times the employed wavelength. Pattee[3] has calculated expected performance of a particular aplanatic reflection microscope employing four mirrors and has found, under the assumption of practically perfect surfaces, that a resolving distance of 500 Å should be obtained over a field some 10 microns wide. In these calculations a wavelength of 2 Å was considered. Wolter[1] investigated the aberrations of a system composed of a pair of axially symmetric mirrors resembling the section shown in Fig. 3. He predicts that for an x-ray wavelength of 20 Å a resolution of 250 Å should be achieved over a field 40 microns wide.

As far as direct magnification is concerned there are no important theoretical or practical problems. Systems magnifying up to about 100× have been operated, but photographic images of large area call for proportionately long exposure times; so it is economical to run up the magnification only to the point where photographic graininess is no longer impairing definition.

REFERENCES CITED

1. H. Wolter, *Ann. Physik*, **10**:94 (1952).
2. H. H. Pattee, Dissertation, Stanford University, 1953. Available in microfilm or Xerox from University Microfilms, Inc., Ann Arbor, Mich.
3. H. H. Pattee, The Compound, Four-mirror, Reflection X-ray Microscope, in *X-ray Microscopy and Microradiography*, p. 135, V. E. Cosslett, Arne Engström, and H. H. Pattee (eds.), Academic Press Inc., New York, 1957.
4. J. F. McGee, Dissertation, Stanford University, 1956. Available in microfilm or Xerox from University Microfilms, Inc., Ann Arbor, Mich.
5. J. F. McGee, A Long-wavelength X-ray Reflection Microscope, in *X-ray Microscopy and Microradiography*, p. 164, V. E. Cosslett, Arne Engström, and H. H. Pattee (eds.), Academic Press Inc., New York, 1957.
6. D. W. Berreman, J. W. M. DuMond, and P. E. Marmier, *Rev. Sci. Instr.*, **25**:1219 (1954).
7. G. N. Ramachandran and Y. T. Thathachari, *J. Indian Inst. Sci.*, **34**:67 (1952).

INDEX